Contents

G000254755

Hello

Welcome to the 2008 edition of Creative Handbook published by Creative Review.

CR became the proud owner of Creative Handbook during last year and we hope you like the innovations that we have introduced for the 2008 edition.

Our goals were to emphasise the relationship with CR, hence the change in format and layout, both of which also now provide a more visually pleasing showcase for the advertisers' work, and an easier-to-use product for you, the reader.

We've also created two new sets of listings: Design & Advertising Contacts, (which lists some useful addresses and contact details for advertising agencies and design consultancies) and Models & Casting.

This new-look Creative Handbook also has some additional reference material from Creative Review and Design Week which we also hope will give you more reasons to keep the book within arm's reach. However, if you find that someone else has decided to 'borrow' your copy, we have launched a new website that contains all the contacts listed in this book plus additional portfolio material.

You can find us at creativehandbook.co.uk

Centaur Media PLC
50 Poland Street, London W1F 7AX
United Kingdom

Sales
☎ +44 (0) 20 7970 6267
📠 +44 (0) 20 7970 6713
✉ advertising@creativehandbook.co.uk

Production
☎ +44 (0) 20 7970 4764
✉ production@creativehandbook.co.uk

Publisher
Jessica Macdermot

Editor
Patrick Burgoyne

Project Manager
Emma Nicolle

Production Manager
Neil Ayres

Display Sales
Dave Harvey

Online Sales
Russell Jamieson

Website
creativehandbook.co.uk

Designer
James Melaugh

Illustrators
peepshow.org.uk

© Centaur Media PLC 2008 All rights reserved. No Part of this publication may be reproduced or used in any term or by any means whether graphic, electronic or mechanical, including, photocopying, recording, taping or information storage and retrieval systems without the permission of the publisher. The publication–in whole or part–may not be used to prepare or compile other directories or mailing lists, without the prior written permission of the publisher.

The use of cuttings taken from this directory in connection with solicitation of insertions or advertisements in other publications is expressly forbidden. Measures have been adopted during the preparation of this publication that will assist the publisher to protect its copyright.

Any unauthorised use of this data will result in immediate legal proceedings.

All advertising copy appearing in the book is the choice of the individual advertiser, not the publisher, and copyright remains with the advertiser or other copyright owner. No responsibility is accepted by the publisher for any infringement of copyright or otherwise arising out of the publication thereof.

All reasonable measures are taken to ensure accuracy of the information in this edition but the publisher cannot accept responsibility for any errors or omissions or any liability resulting from the use or misuse of any such information.

ISBN: 978-1-871783-43-8

Printed by: Asia Pacific Offset
Reprographics by:
PH Media 01726 891111

Editor's letter

Every day, the contributors to the Creative Handbook are producing the work that goes on to fill the pages of Creative Review magazine. So we thought we would return the favour. On the following pages you will find a selection of articles that were published over the past year either in Creative Review, on our website, CR Blog, or in our sister magazine, Design Week. They give you a small taster of what we are all about and will perhaps provide some food for thought when you come to embark on your next project.

Patrick Burgoyne
Editor

The Gunn Report

For the first time, this year's Gunn Report has included interactive work in its calculations of the most-awarded advertising of the past twelve months. What does it tell us about the state of the industry?

Each year, the Gunn gathers together the results of all the major advertising awards schemes around the world, weights them according to relative importance and produces a set of league tables to work out who won the most amusingly-shaped statuettes. This year it has bowed to the inevitable and included 'interactive' work in its calculations (for which, read 'websites'). Leading the way is R/GA's Nike+ project, which picked up a host of major prizes including a D&AD Gold. Although the site works beautifully, it's the overall idea that excites, bringing Apple and Nike together to create something that is novel, powerful and genuinely useful.

For many creatives, Nike+ points the way to a future in which their companies become not ad agencies but, genuinely, creative agencies. It's a product idea, not just an advertising execution and certainly not one that is dependant on a clever copyline or a neat visual pun. This is the territory that many of what are currently termed 'advertising agencies' want to be in – developing product ideas with clients for which they can (ideally) share the intellectual property rights. And if they can't get a share of that particular pie, they can at least create something that is engaging in the manner of some of the other top-performing interactive work. Gunn, for instance, rates Forsman & Bodenfors' Come Into The Closet microsite as the second most-awarded interactive ad last year. In third place was Crispin Porter's Golf GTI Features site for VW, while the brilliant Nike Chain from Framfab in Copenhagen (to my mind easily the best marketing activity around the 2006 World Cup) took fourth.

Note that these are all based around websites and are not "digital advertising" in the sense of banners or skyscrapers. Gunn is yet to embrace that field, sharing the general sniffyness in the ad world about the latter's

quality, perhaps. Gunn may also have made a good call in terms of identifying the bias of future activity. Media owners have, to their immense relief been able to offset the fall in print and TV advertising by pulling in handsome revenues from banners etc on their websites. But for advertisers surely the better model is to cut out the middleman and create their own sites that consumers will choose to spend time with and go directly to, without clicking through expensive ads on third party sites. Hopefully, and I say this as the editor of a magazine that very much welcomes advertising on its website, consumers will still need help in getting to these advertiser sites, which is where the banner will continue to have a role.

After all the excitement of the interactive section, good old TV suffers slightly – we know how this stuff works, we've been watching it for years. But it still does work, even if its role now is often to point viewers to a website or, as with the most-awarded commercial of last year, Sony Paint, it relies heavily on the net for distribution.

And what about print? Top of the tree was a campaign for Clima Bicycle Locks by Leo Burnett Bangkok, followed by Marmite Squeezy from DDB London and, in joint third place, the 42 Below Vodka and Stuffit Deluxe ads from Saatchi NY. Note that the Misereor campaign that, in the year's quirkiest bit of judging, took a Gold at D&AD, comes in at 45th in Gunn's list.

One other quirk is that the year's most talked about ad, Dove Evolution, doesn't top any of the tables (it made 7th spot in TV & Cinema and 6th in Interactive). Presumably this is due to the fact that juries didn't really know how to categorise it: a film that was viewed almost exclusively on the web and yet had no interactive element. It did produce some great spoofs though.

The most awarded commercials in the world in 2007

			AD POINTS
01	Sony Bravia LCD TV	Paint Fallon (London)	24
02	Ariston Aqualis Washing Machine	Underwater World Leo Burnett Italia (Milan)	23
03	Coca-Cola	Happiness Factory Wieden+Kennedy (Amsterdam)	20
04	Skittles	Beard/Trade/Leak* TBWA\Chiat\Day (New York)	19
05	Combos	Grace / Heart-to-Heart / Fever / Videogame* TBWA\Chiat\Day (New York)	17
06	Toyota Cars	Humanity* Hakuhodo (Tokyo)	16
07	Dove Self Esteem Fund	Evolution Ogilvy & Mather (Toronto)	15
08	Coca-Cola	Videogame Wieden+Kennedy (Portland, OR)	14
09	Axe 3 Body Spray	Crashes VegaOlmosPonce (Buenos Aires)	14
10	Happy Dent Teeth Whitening Gum	Palace McCann Erickson (Mumbai)	13

The most awarded print ads & campaigns in the world in 2007

			AD POINTS
01	Clima Bicycle Locks	Barriercycle / Polecycle / Railcycle Leo Burnett (Bangkok)	20
02	Marmite Squeezy	Love Or Hate campaign DDB London (London)	19
03	42	Below Vodka Bareback Mt / Transvestite & campaign Saatchi & Saatchi (New York)	15
04	Stuffit Deluxe	China / Tourist / Divorce Saatchi & Saatchi (New York)	15
05	East Timor Tourism	Chickens / Nuns / Turtles & campaign Ogilvy & Mather (Singapore)	13
06	Singapore Hospice Council	Ogilvy & Mather (Singapore) Death / Lung Cancer / The End & campaign	12
07	Penline Art Pens	Black / Blue / Red McCann-Erickson (Kuala Lumpur)	11
08	Harvey Nichols	Balloon / Ice / Moth DDB London (London)	11
09	Amnesty International	Not Here But Now campaign Walker (Zurich)	11
10	Axe Body Spray	Get A Girlfriend campaign Lowe Bull (Johannesburg)	11

The most awarded interactive in the world in 2007

			AD POINTS
01	Nike	Nike+ R/GA (New York)	18
02	Ikea	Come Into The Closet Forsman & Bodenfors (Gothenburg)	14
03	Volkswagen GTI	GTI Features Crispin Porter & Bogusky (Miami)	14
04	Nike	The Chain Framfab (Copenhagen)	12
05	Visit Sweden Tourism	Stockholm The Musical Farfar (Stockholm)	11
06	Dove Self Esteem Fund	Evolution Ogilvy & Mather (Toronto)	10
07	Diesel Underwear	Heidies 15mb Of Fame Farfar (Stockholm)	10
08	Microsoft XBOX 360	Big Shadow GT (Tokyo)	10
09	Philips Norelco Bodygroom Shaver	Philips Bodygroom Tribal DDB New York (New York)	10
10	Volvo XC90	The Hunt Euro RSCG 4D (Amsterdam)	10

The most awarded countries in the world in 2007

		WINNERS PTS TV	WINNER PTS PRINT	WINNERS PTS INTERACTIVE	TOTAL
01	USA (2)	150	62	93	305
02	Great Britain (1)	119	45	54	218
03	Argentina (3=)	088	25	03	116
04	Brazil (6)	022	27	41	090
05	Japan (9=)	053	03	32	088
06	Spain (9=)	023	28	25	076
07	Germany (7)	026	22	26	074
08	Thailand (5)	047	25	00	072
09	Sweden (23)	006	03	60	069
10	Singapore (14)	001	54	09	064

The most awarded advertisers in the world in 2007

		WINNER PTS TV	WINNER PTS PRINT	WINNER PTS INTERACTIVE	TOTAL
01	Nike (3)	24	14	25	63
02	Volkswagen (1)	18	05	19	42
03	Sony (2)	22	16	01	39
04	Coca-Cola (7)	32	00	01	33
05	Axe/Lynx (21=)	15	08	02	25
06	Adidas (5)	11	07	06	24
07	WWF	02	15	06	23
08	MTV (11=)	14	04	04	22
09	Toyota (21=)	17	01	01	19
10	Greenpeace(–)	03	07	06	16

The most awarded directors in the world in 2007

		WINNER PTS
01	Thanonchai Sornsrivichai (Thailand) (1)	40
02=	Tom Kuntz (USA) (–)	19
	Ivan Zacharias (Great Britain, USA) (4=)	19
04=	Andy Fogwill (Argentina) (2)	13
	Dario Piana (Italy) (-)	13
06=	Jonathan Glazer (Great Britain) (12)	12
	Martin Granger (USA) (23=)	12
08=	Danny Kleinman (Great Britain) (3)	11
	Todd Mueller/Klyie Matulick (USA) (–)	11
10	Nicolai Gufslig (Great Britain, USA) (9)	10

The most awarded agencies in the world in 2007

		WINNER PTS TV	WINNER PTS PRINT	TOTAL
01	TBWA\Chiat\Day (NY)/TBWA\Media Arts (LA) (43=)	28	05	33
02	Saatchi & Saatchi (New York, Los Angeles) (26=)	05	27	32
03	DDB London (1)	09	22	31
04=	Dentsu (Tokyo, Osaka, Fukuoka) (3=)	23	01	24
	Fallon (London) (11)	20	04	24
06=	Ogilvy & Mather (Singapore) (45=)	00	22	22
	TBWA\Paris (Boulogne-Billancourt) (2)	12	10	22
08=	BBDO (New York) (26=)	15	05	20
	Wieden+Kennedy (Amsterdam) (–)	20	00	20
10=	Santo (Buenos Aires) (35=)	18	00	18
	VegaOlmosPonce (Buenos Aires) (45=)	18	00	18
	Wieden+Kennedy (London) (6)	12	06	18
13=	AlmapBBDO (Sao Paulo) (8)	04	13	17
	Saatchi & Saatchi (Singapore) (21=)	00	17	17
15=	Creative Juice\G1 (Bangkok) (9)	16	00	16
	Hakuhodo (Tokyo, Osaka) (-)	16	00	16
	Leo Burnett (Chicago) (35=)	06	10	16
18	Abbott Mead Vickers.BBDO (London) (3=)	14	01	15
19=	Jung von Matt (Hamburg, Berlin, Stuttgart) (-) 9	05	14	
	Leo Burnett Italia (Milan) (-)	13	01	14
	Wieden+Kennedy (Portland, OR) (35=)	13	01	14
22=	Bartle Bogle Hegarty (New York) (-)	12	01	13
	McCann Erickson (Mumbai) (-)	13	00	13
	Saatchi & Saatchi (London) (-)	12	01	13
25=	Crispin Porter + Bogusky (Miami) (3=)	12	00	12
	Del Campo Nazca Saatchi & Saatchi (Bs As) (18=)	08	04	12
	F/Nazca Saatchi & Saatchi (Sao Paulo) (-)	09	03	12
	JEH United (Bangkok) (18=)	12	00	12
	Madre (Buenos Aires) (-)	12	00	12

The Design Week Creative Survey

The Creative Survey listings are based on awards success. Those included in the charts are the design consultancies and in-house teams that have earned the most points through awards wins over the past 12 months.

The awards schemes covered are those with a strong reputation on the international stage for honouring creativity. Most are long-standing, but where appropriate we have added new awards into the mix.

Disciplines included cover the main interests of the majority of Design Week readers – graphics, branding, digital design, packaging, product design, interiors and exhibition design.

We do not include architecture or fashion. We have awarded points for wins and placings according to the system we have used over the past six surveys – see the table below for full details.

The charts are compiled from data supplied by the organisers of the various awards schemes, rather than by design consultancies, and rankings are based on points accrued over the past three years. There are two main listings. The All Awards chart below takes account of performance in prominent awards, whether international, discipline-led or relating to a particular geographic location. It also includes personal awards such as the D&AD President's Award and the Prince Philip Prize. The UK chart ranks consultancies and inhouse teams according to their success in the UK's two most prestigious schemes for design: the Design Week Awards and the D&AD Awards.

DW Awards, Benchmarks
Best of show: 25
Best of show runner up: 15
Category win:10
Commended: 05
Shortlisted: 03
D&AD Awards
Gold award:25
Silver award: 10
Silver nomination: 03
In book: 01
New York Festivals
Clio Awards,
New York Art Directors Club
Grand award: 25
Gold: 10
Silver: 08
Bronze: 06
Finalist/Shortlisted: 03
Mobius, Roses Design Awards, Promax Awards, Scottish Design Awards,British Council for Offices Awards, Fresh Awards,Innovation and Design Excellence Awards, Cream Awards, Red Dot Award
Best of Show: 05
Gold/Winner/Certificate: 03
Silver/Commendation: 02
Finalist/ Bronze: 01
The Rest (includes Bimas, Starpack and Fab)
Winner: 01
Personal Awards
D&AD President's Medal, Prince Philip Designers Prize, BCO President's Awards: 25

Disciplines Key
A: Interiors
B: Exhibitions
C: Branding/ packaging
D: Print
E: Corporate identity
F: Product
G: Digital media
H: Other

Reproduced with the permission of Design Week designweek.co.uk

2007	COMPANY	AWARD PTS	DISCIPLINES
01	Williams Murray Hamm (1)	245	CDE
02	Apple Design Group (2)	136	F
03	Hat Trick Design (4)	125	CDEG
04	The Chase (3)	122	BCDEG
05	The Partners (10)	120	DE
06	True North (6)	115	CDEG
07	Taxi Studio (12)	108	BCDEGH
08	Love Creative (21)	107	D
09	GBH (31)	096	CDEG
10	Pearlfisher (11)	090	C
11	Johnson Banks (5)	079	BDEGH
12	Elmwood (8)	074	CDEGH
13	Radley Yeldar (13)	069	CDEGH
14	Red Bee Media (7)	067	DGH
15	NB Studio (23)	066	CD
16	Channel Four/E4/Filmfour (16)	063	G
17	Foster & Partners (9)	059	AF
18	Like A River (15)	058	CDE
19	Airside (27)	056	DGH
20	Wolff Olins (20)	055	ACDEG
21	Stand (24)	054	DEG
22	SAS	051	DEH
23=32	All Of Us	046	G

2007	COMPANY	AWARD PTS	DISCIPLINES
23=	Coley Porter Bell	46	CEF
23=14	Design Bridge	46	CEG
26	Pentagram (29)	44	ABCDEFH
27	Land Design Studio (17)	43	AB
28	Thomas Heatherwick Studio(18)	41	H
29=	Fallon London	40	CDEFGH
29=39	Mark Studio	40	CD
40	Poke (41)	31	G
41	Navy Blue	30	ABCDEFGH
42=	AKQA	28	G
42=44	Philippe Starck	28	AF
44=	Cake	27	G
44=36	Pemberton & Whiteford	27	C
46=	Draft Co	26	D
46=47	Omnific Studios	26	DH
46=	Propaganda	26	CDEFG
49=49	Emap Design	25	DG
49=	HMKM	25	ACDEG
49=	John Brown Publishing	25	DG
49= 49	L&Co Design	25	CDEG
49=	Radford Wallis	25	BCDEG
49=30	Turner Duckworth	25	CEG
49=39	Virgin Atlantic	25	AF

April 07:
The "It's about
time we did
something
about the
environment"
issue

With thanks to:
Sion Whellens at Calverts,
Phil Sudwell at Park Lane
Press, Richard Owers at
Beacon Press, Clare Taylor
Consultancy

How to be Green(er)

We asked graphic designer Caroline Clark, co-founder of online resource Twig, to give us her recommendations for how you can work in a more environmentally sustainable way.

As graphic designers, we care passionately about how our designs look, the paper they're printed on and the quality of the print, but there's one thing we don't usually consider – how our designs impact on the environment.

Graphic designers are involved in the destruction of forests, we're fuelling the need for oil, and we're increasing air pollution by choosing petroleum-based inks. What's more, we create much of the 12.5 million tonnes of paper and cardboard that gets thrown into landfill every year in the UK. However, by following this guide you can, at the very least, reduce the impact of your designs.

Caroline Clark's new website for designers is at www.lovelyasatree.com

DESIGNING FOR LOW IMPACT

Tips for format:
_ Does your project need to be this size or can it be smaller? A reduced format could save paper, ink, water, carbon emissions in distribution and it may even save money on postage costs.
_ Check paper size availability and press size with your printer and paper supplier before designing your product. Many materials are available in a limited range of sizes which will limit the options for waste- and cost-effective formats.
_ The most waste- and cost-effective formats are A sizes, as all materials and printing presses are based around these.
_ If your product is likely to be around for some time, design it to be updateable.
_ Window envelopes cannot currently be recycled in the UK. Unless the windows have been cut/torn out, the envelopes will be removed from the waste paper when it is sorted. However, cellulose film for window envelopes is now available and, although this is not recyclable, at least it will biodegrade in landfills. Eventually.
_ Don't print more copies than you need just because it's not going to cost much more.
_ Make sure that the job has been proofed extremely carefully. This reduces the risk of a re-print or a job being pulled off the press halfway through.

Think about the timings, and try to plan as far in advance as possible:
_ Book time with your printer, and try to get quantities and paper agreed well in advance to stop emergency transportation of materials, especially if buying special order recycled paper.
_ Plan well for grouped, low cost deliveries.

Binding:
The binding you choose can make your product pretty toxic and can also affect the recyclability of your design.
_ The most environmentally friendly method is wire stitching as staples can be easily removed during the recycling process and then recycled themselves. Singer sewing is not as good due to the cotton thread being more difficult to remove. The same goes for comb and wire-o bindings.
_ Glue is really bad news for recycling and can be pretty toxic, usually containing VOC-releasing solvents (see glossary).

CHOOSING THE MOST ENVIRONMENTALLY FRIENDLY PAPER FOR YOUR JOB

There are so many different types of paper, all produced in such different ways, that it is difficult to summarise the overall environmental impact. However, if you follow this checklist, you won't go too far wrong.

Look for:
_ 100% post-consumer waste (PCW, see glossary on p38)) or at least the highest possible percentage for your job.
_ Off-white or "downshade" – this means that the paper will have undergone less intensive processing.

Unbleached recycled paper undergoes fewer processes than other recycled or virgin fibre, and therefore uses fewer chemicals and less energy. However, any degree of recycled content, whether post- or pre-consumer and regardless of colour, is better than none.

If none of the above suit your job, then look for:
_ FSC certified – if you're buying virgin paper, then you can make sure that it really is from sustainable forestry by buying paper certified 100% FSC only. Paper that is certified FSC Mixed Sources may include pulp that is from non-FSC certified sources, although those sources are still required to meet certain standards eg no illegal logging. Treat anything that claims to be from sustainable forestry with caution.

If your paper originates from the UK or Europe, not only will you be minimising transport, but you can be sure that the paper won't have been bleached using chlorine bleach and will be either ECF, PCF or TCF (see glossary).

Tip:
Can you use lighter paper for your job? Avoid specifying heavier paper than is necessary.

See www.lovelyasatree.com for lists of good recycled and FSC certified papers.

In April 2007 we devoted an issue to discussing the creative industries' role and responsibilities concerning sustainability and the environment. We calculated our own carbon footprint, looked at the impact of publishing magazines and even removed the cover in order to save resources. But as well as highlighting problems, we also wanted to offer solutions, which is where this piece came in. Drawing on a wide range of experts, Caroline Clark put together a comprehensive guide to being a greener designer

Foil blocking: Some say that this should be avoided due to the heavy metals involved (see glossary). However, if you're covering only a very small area in foil, the effects on the environment are negligible.

Lamination: this renders a product unrecyclable and un-biodegradable and the lamination process emits high levels of VOCs. Use cellulose (wood based) alternatives.

UV varnishes: UV varnishes are mineral-oil based, they contain solvents, the process uses a lot of energy, and as if that wasn't enough, they cause problems for the recycling process. If you still want to use a varnish, go for aqueous (water based) coatings instead. They come in matt and gloss finishes – the gloss is pretty shiny although not as shiny as UV varnish.

Vegetable-oil based inks: Conventional mineral-oil based inks (see glossary) emit low levels of VOCs as they dry and can result in environmental and worker health hazards. They also come from non-renewable resources – the main oils in non-vegetable based inks are petroleum-based.

Ask for 100% vegetable-oil based inks as many printers will be using only a percentage of vegetable mixed with conventional inks (typically 60% vegetable).

Some inks go one step further by reducing the levels of environmentally damaging drying catalysts such as cobalt. However, this means that they dry more slowly than conventional inks.

Fluorescent colours: Unfortunately these are not available as vegetable-oil based inks.

Metallics: Metallics are also not available as vegetable-oil based inks and contain heavy metals that impact on the environment (see glossary).

Screen printing: the inks used in screen printing contain a higher percentage of solvents than conventional litho inks as they need to be more liquid. As a result, they emit more VOCs.

Tips:
- Avoid lamination
- Water-based coatings are less harmful than UV varnish
- Ask for vegetable-oil based inks

There's little point in worrying about foil blocking if your printer is delivering the product in an old fume-belching lorry to the other end of the country. Here's a checklist of what to consider when choosing a printer:

- Do they have EMAS, ISO14001, FSC or Greenmark certification?* (see glossary)
- Do they use waterless or low-alcohol printing processes?
- Do they measure their carbon footprint?**
- Do they use renewable energy?
- Choose a printer with a press that can run enough inks for your job on one press pass. This avoids multiple passes involving more 'make-ready' waste, more clearing up, more energy and more chemicals.
- Do they use vegetable/water-based inks?
- Are they local?

* Please note that environmental performance will vary even amongst printers with the same environmental accreditations due to the fact that some have been working at reducing their environmental impact for longer and will have made more progress.
** Be aware that carbon neutral status is not always a good indication of environmental performance. There is currently no regulation in this area and so carbon neutral status can simply be bought through offsetting schemes. Please ask your printer and paper suppliers what they have done to reduce their carbon footprint.

See lovelyasatree.com for a comprehensive list of environmentally accredited printers.

Digital

There are some huge environmental advantages to printing digitally:
- you can run a job as and when needed
- re-printing costs no extra, so there is no need to print 5000 extra copies in case you run out
- no make ready waste

Downsides:
- Digital inks are currently difficult to remove in the recycling process.
- Ink cartridges are often sent to landfill (as well as adding to our over-crowded landfill sites, the ink residue will leach out).
- The choice of paper can be limited to approved papers, which are rarely recycled or FSC certified.

See lovelyasatree.com for more about print and the environment.

Waterless printing

What is it?
Waterless printing is basically sheet-fed litho printing using different printing plates and a method of transferring the image to the paper without using water.

Removing water from the process means that you also eliminate the problem of achieving the correct balance of ink and water on press. It also eliminates the need for IPA (see glossary).

At present only a few printers have tried waterless, all are listed in www.lovelyasatree.com

Benefits of Waterless Printing:
- Improved colour consistency throughout the press run
- Greater colour saturation
- Lower dot gain, therefore higher screen rulings can be used and more detail can be printed
- Better results on uncoated paper than with conventional litho printing
- Faster make-ready time meaning less paper and ink is wasted
- Improved registration
- No VOCs (see glossary)
- Conserves water
- More environmentally friendly

Most benefit gained when printing:
- Flat colours
- Long print runs
- On uncoated and stocks
- Corporate identity work (as colour consistency can be maintained across different stocks).
- Fine and very detailed print

Downsides:
- It can be more expensive than conventional litho printing
- Some say that the same effects can be achieved by stochastic printing
- Others say that clients will not notice the difference and that conventional printing is good enough

WATER RESISTANT

VIVOBAREFOOT TECHNOLOGY

VEGETABLE TANNED

TURN SHOE

SIDE STITCH

SACHETTO

RECYCLED

E-LEATHER

MOCCASIN

MINIMUM GLUE

LOCALLY SOURCED

LIGHT WEIGHT

LATEX

HAND MADE

FLEX

CLIMATE CARE

CHROME FREE

CANASTA

BLAKE STITCH

STITCH DOWN

1. UK-based footwear company Terra Plana uses this system of icons (designed in-house by Matt Delahunt) to give consumers easily-digestible information about its products. Its Worn Again range (2&3) is a collaboration with Anti-Apathy, a non-profit social and environmental awareness organisation. Launched in 2005, the unisex trainers are made from 99% recycled material such as prison blankets, T-shirts and coffee bags. Part of the profits generated help to support Anti-Apathy's public outreach work. And 17 pence from the sale of every pair of Worn Again products goes to Climate Care to offset carbon emissions from the manufacture and transport of the shoes

Companies whose stories are real, compelling and smartly designed are starting to shine. Sarah Rich of World Changing explains how Creative Review's readers can help genuinely green businesses to thrive

Towards Creative Activism

Conscious consumers in the modern marketplace rarely face an either/or proposition. Gone are the days of choosing between pleasure and principle. Gone is the sacrifice of flavour, colour and style in the name of environmental responsibility. With the likely exception of toilet paper (which it seems still cannot be made both recycled and soft), many of our everyday items can now be found in a luxurious shade of green.

Savvy advocates of sustainability know that business is not the enemy of the good. In fact, it can be a vehicle for doing better in the world, and making a comfortable living with a guilt-free conscience. But in an increasingly crowded green business sphere, knowing who's authentic presents a challenge. The responsibility for giving not-so-sustainable products a green face – as well as for making truly green products as desirable as their counterparts – lies entirely in the hands of designers, as the make-up artists and storytellers for brands. In a consumer culture teeming with excess and endlessly driving our desire for more stuff, designers become responsible, too, for reconsidering how we engage with products, and how we might transform the consumers' motivation from quantity to quality, and from singular to whole systems thinking.

There are three primary categories into which green-oriented brands fall. The best of them don't craft their identity around sustainability. Their social and environmental characteristics tend to show up as if they are a given in the bigger picture of a current, cutting-edge brand; because the reality is that a lack of awareness around these issues equates to a lack of viability in the twenty-first century. A second category comprises campaigns that do direct their messaging squarely on green, but intentionally incorporate an urban edge and a modern aesthetic in order to combat the stereotype of something four decades too tired. Finally, there are those brands that aggressively present an "eco" image as a way to capitalise on the green consumer movement without matching their practices to their pretence. This "greenwashing" trend has fairly well permeated the industry and it's now up to consumers to develop a radar for spotting duplicitous brands. As a New York Times article on greenwashing put it, "When a trend starts to show success, it's a design pile-up...[But] merely dressing up the package is not enough. There is value in telling a story, but it must be true." Companies whose story is real, compelling, and smartly designed are the ones who are starting to shine.

Then there is another category, which transcends or stands peripheral to the others, and may represent the direction green consumption is headed. It's design for the elimination of excess – dematerialisation – in which user experience takes precedence over acquiring more things. Product service systems, or service designs, reconceive goods as functions and permit users to obtain access to the outcome yielded by a product without actually owning it, meaning each of us needs to consume less in order to get the same result. The concept has taken hold well in the UK – perhaps better than anywhere else in the world – where sharing of commodities such as cars, office space and power tools has become relatively commonplace. An inventive group of students ▶

Creative Review
April 2007

25

Also from April 07, we asked Sarah Rich of the World Changing organisation to suggest ways in which CR readers could help green businesses to thrive

4&5. Nau is an outdoor apparel company from Portland Oregon with a novel retail model. Each of its stores stocks just one piece in each style and each size. Customers try the clothes on, then order their purchases to be delivered to their homes using kiosks or via the website shown. This cuts down on wasted deliveries of clothing stock that may never be sold on to customers.

6. Arlene Birt's Background Story on Green & Black's chocolate. Birt's concept features a detailed graphic telling the story of how the chocolate is produced, including information on the company's fair trade policies. She proposes that the company could feature this information on the inside of its packaging, thus providing accessible information for consumers who would like to indulge without feeling guilty. For more information on the project, see www.back groundstories.com

◀ from Cologne recently developed an even deeper interpretation of the system, called Wir Hier Service Group. After researching what kinds of things consumers generally take for granted, Wir Hier's designers ascertained that a successful service system would approach "mind redesign" by offering interlinked sets of services rather than discreet programmes. Wir Hier already has around 30 service systems in place. The systems themselves serve as a marketing tool for the company, which brands its programmes heavily, allowing the meme to spread virally as a result of the enhanced community interaction the services foster. For example, their "Tea-4-Two" programme dropped branded tea bags in community mailboxes, with a location, date and time printed on them. At the designated meeting place, neighbours would share tea and get to know one another. This kind of branded service preserves the value and profitability of the entity that creates it, while fundamentally transforming what the users seek, and what they gain by engaging with the product. Wir Hier dematerialises the structure for consumption, and strips it down to pure experience.

Somewhere in between the material and immaterial product lies a new niche that straddles the gap. One player emerging at that junction is Nau, an apparel company out of Portland, Oregon, whose updated take on classically "crunchy" outdoor clothing merges urban cuts with a socially and environmentally conscious corporate mission. The apparel collections themselves do push gently on the envelope of outdoor style, but where Nau has really innovated is on the design of their retail space, which they don't call a "store", but rather a Webfront.

At a Nau Webfront, one sample of every piece in the collection and every available size hangs ready for visiting customers to try on. But the company encourages shoppers to use the Webfront just as a testing platform for the clothes, and to then make their purchases online at computer kiosks located on-site, then take delivery at home. By running retail this way, Nau dramatically decreases the regular inventory required at its multiple physical locations, thereby reducing the impacts of freight and lengthy supply chains. In order to help this experimental model fly, they've applied design strategy to strengthening their web presence, which will be a key component of any Webfront success. Nau has run several innovative multi-media online campaigns, including a low-budget web documentary about a woman living in a compact, off-grid mobile dwelling, crossing rural, suburban and urban divides and sharing her observations. The video had a feverish viral run on the net, reaching half a million eyes in a single day.

But it can't all disappear. Nau may encourage customers to buy fewer, more versatile and longer-lasting clothes, but they still sell clothes. And we will always need clothes, just as we'll need toilet paper and food, shoes and vehicles, and plenty of other furnishings for our comfort and wellbeing. So the question every green company and designer now aims to answer is, "Can we have our cake and eat it, too?" And the answer is yes.

Take Terra Plana, the British footwear company that makes trainers out of recycled uniforms, sport jackets, rubber tires and used denim. The shoes have a distinct design that pinpoints all the characteristics of a hip, young, urban target market, and like the best of these emerging green companies, Terra Plana's product would be desirable on style alone, even if it lacked an ecological agenda. But its value escalates on account of the company's commitment to sustainable materials and social responsibility. They've designed a series of icons that communicate the various details of the shoe and its production process. A similar effort was undertaken by Timberland, the less stylish but much bigger footwear company that recently began printing "nutrition labels" on their shoe boxes, which provide calculations of the energy required to manufacture the shoes, the materials they contain, and other impact-related information. While it may be more of a brand-beautifying gesture than a truly useful display, it represents their attention to shifting consumer priorities.

But how do we distinguish between gestures towards responsibility and practical transformation? How does a designer know if they are just painting a face on an idealistic idea, or applying aesthetics to a substantive and sincere brand? There's no easy answer, but there are designers out there who've made it their business to learn the back story of well-branded companies, and subsequently developed compelling campaigns from what they've learned.

Background Stories emerged from designer Arlene Birt's research at Design Academy Eindhoven in the Netherlands. It's an early concept using graphic design to tell the story of chocolate production for a variety of different brands. The theory Birt addresses is "context connection" – a fairly self-explanatory name for the process of helping consumers establish an understanding of the bigger picture from which their products come. By using well-designed, brand-aligned graphics on the inside of the packaging, the education arrives in the consumer's hand in a simple, digestible form. To deepen the mini-lesson on the wrapper, an affiliated website provides clickable pop-up details on each element of the illustration that will link you even further, to resource pages on drying and fermentation processes, and even the websites of the shipping and trucking companies who transport the ingredients to the factory. So far Birt has designed concept labels for Dagoba, Green & Black, and Hershey's. Dagoba, which is branded (and began) as a small, chocolatier with a conscience, is actually owned by Hershey; and Green & Black, which has a similar identity as a high-end, fair-trade brand, was acquired by Cadbury Schweppes several years ago. But Birt doesn't use her skills to expose or defame corporations; this is constructive design activism. Through visual storytelling and extensive resource offerings, Birt builds an accessible education for the skyrocketing population of consumers who want to indulge without feeling guilty. What better launch pad than chocolate for demonstrating that decadence and diligence can go hand in hand?

Brands can design all manner of slick packaging and alluring ads, but in order to achieve credibility, they have to deliver transparency with every product and interaction. The conscious consumer wants to know what's in her cake before she eats it. Creatives and designers face the challenge of telling the true story behind a brand in a way that's sincere, engaging and reassuring so that green business can thrive and the bar can keep rising on what sustainability means in the market. ◼

Sarah Rich is a writer and editor working where sustainability intersects with design, branding and consumer culture. She is the managing editor of Worldchanging.com, and co-editor/co-author of Worldchanging: A User's Guide for the 21st Century (Abrams)

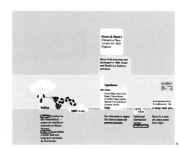

Volume 27
Number 04
April 2007

1-3. Tony de Marco's remarkable photographs capture the moment when São Paulo's unique Clean City laws came into force. April 1 was the deadline for the removal of not just posters, but all forms of advertising from the city's streets. Left behind were hundreds of skeletons: the structures that had housed the giant billboards previously such a feature of Brazil's second city. "In the weeks before my birthday," de Marco says, "my visual enemies began to disappear like the happy end of a motion picture. To see my city clean was my best birthday present: my photos were the record of the feast."
4. One of the principal reasons for the introduction of the law was to curb the unregulated siteing of billboards. Impoverished citizens gladly accepted money from outdoor media companies, even if it meant obscuring their homes in the process. Now, a forgotten city is emerging from behind the ads

The Naked City

São Paulo: the city that said no to advertising.
By Patrick Burgoyne. Photographs: Tony de Marco

A city stripped of advertising. No Posters. No flyers. No ads on buses. No ads on trains. No Adshels, no 48-sheets, no nothing.

It sounds like an Adbusters editorial: an activist's dream. But in São Paulo, Brazil, the dream has become a reality.

In September last year, the city's populist right-wing mayor, Gilberto Kassab, passed the so-called Clean City laws. Fed up with the "visual pollution" caused by the city's 8,000 billboard sites, many of them erected illegally, Kassab proposed a law banning all outdoor advertising. The skyscraper-sized hoardings that lined the city's streets would be wiped away at a stroke. And it was not just billboards that attracted his wrath: all forms of outdoor advertising were to be prohibited, including ads on taxis, on buses – even shopfronts were to be restricted, their signs limited to 1.5 metres for every 10 metres of frontage. "It is hard in a city of 11 million people to find enough equipment and personnel to determine what is and isn't legal," reasoned Kassab, "so we have decided to go all the way."

The law was hailed by writer Roberto Pompeu de Toledo as "a rare victory of the public interest over private, of order over ▶

1

In April last year, the city of São Paulo in Brazil brought in its Clean City laws, banning all forms of outdoor advertising and severely restricting signage and shopfronts. With specially commissioned photographs from a local designer, we reported on the laws' impact

5. Although opinion is divided over the Clean City laws, one group of Paulistanos is unequivocably in favour: the city's scrap dealers who are busy removing the structures that once held up 8000 billboards.

6-18. More of de Marco's photographs. See his flickr set at www.flickr.com/ photos/tonydemarco

◄ disorder, aesthetics over ugliness, of cleanliness over trash… For once, all that is accustomed to coming out on top in Brazil has lost."

Border, the Brazilian Association of Advertisers, was up in arms over the move. In a statement released on 2 October, the date on which law PL 379/06 was formally approved by the city council, Border called the new laws "unreal, ineffective and fascist". It pointed to the tens of thousands of small businesses that would have to bear the burden of altering their shopfronts under regulations "unknown in their virulence in any other city in the world". A prediction of US\$133 million in lost advertising revenue for the city surfaced in the press, while the São Paulo outdoor media owners' association, Sepex, warned that 20,000 people would lose their jobs.

Others predicted that the city would look even worse with the ads removed, a bland concrete jungle replacing the chaos of the present. North Korea and communist Eastern Europe were cited as indicative of what was to come. "I think this city will become a sadder, duller place," Dalton Silvano, the only city councillor to vote against the laws and (not entirely coincidentally) an ad executive, was quoted as saying in the International Herald Tribune. "Advertising is both an art form and, when you're in your car, or alone on foot, a form of entertainment that helps relieve solitude and boredom," he claimed.

There was also much questioning of whether there weren't, in fact, far greater eyesores in the city – such as the thousands of homeless people, the poor condition of the roads and the notorious favelas: wouldn't Kassab's time be better spent removing these problems than persecuting taxi drivers and shop owners? Legal challenges followed while, in an almost comical scenario, advertising executives followed marches by the city's students and its bin men by driving their cars up and down in front of city hall in protest.

Nevertheless, the council pressed ahead. "What we are aiming for is a complete change of culture," its president Roberto Tripoli said. "Yes, some people are going to have to pay a price but things were out of hand and the population has made it clear that it wants this."

Originally, the law was to be introduced last autumn with immediate effect but it was first delayed until December and then finally introduced in January 2007 with a 90-day compliance period, supposedly giving everyone time to take down any posters or signs that did not meet the new regulations or face a fine of up to US\$4,500 per day. Throughout that period, the city's workmen

were busy dismantling around 100 sites per day, occasionally supervised personally by Kassab, a man with an obvious eye for a photo opportunity.

In theory, 1 April was the first day of São Paulo's re-birth as a Clean City. So what does it feel like?

"I can't tell you what it's like to live in a city without ads yet," says Gustavo Piqueira, who runs the studio Rex Design in São Paulo, "because in a lot of places they still haven't been removed. In Brazil, every time that some new law comes in, everybody waits a little to see if it will really be applied and seriously controlled, or if it's just something to fill the newspapers for a week or two."

In a lot of places, Piqueira says, this has led to the removal of posters but not the structures on which they were displayed. "It's a kind of 'billboard cemetery'. I guess they're waiting to see if the law will really last. If the mayor keeps the law for a year or so, people will start to remove them and the city will, finally, start to look better."

Photographer and typographer Tony de Marco has been out documenting this strange hiatus in a sequence of images published on Flickr and used to illustrate this piece. The city, he says, is starting to feel more "serene".

Already the law has led to some strange discoveries. Because the siteing of billboards was unregulated, many poor people readily accepted cash to have a poster site in their gardens or even in front of their homes. With their removal, a new city is emerging: "Last week, on my way to work, I 'discovered' a house," says Piqueira. "It had been covered by a big billboard for years so I never even knew what it looked like." The removal of the posters has "revealed an architecture that we must learn to be proud of, instead of hiding," says de Marco.

But there are downsides – Piqueira worries that much of the "vernacular" lettering and signage from small businesses – "an important part of the city's history and culture" – will be lost. The organisers of the São Paulo carnival have also expressed concerns about the long-term future of their event now that sponsors will not be allowed to advertise along the route. The city authorities for their part have made it clear that certain public information and cultural works will be exempted from the rules.

After a period of zero tolerance, Piqueira believes that advertising, albeit in a far more regulated form, will start to creep back into the city, either as a result of legal challenges, a change in administration, or compromises between media owners and the city. Already, the council has stated that it would like to see

the introduction of approved street furniture such as bus stops, which may well carry ads. As these will no doubt be for the major brands that can afford such lucrative positions, a more sterile, bland visual environment may replace the vibrant, if chaotic streets of the past. Flyposters, hand-lettered signs and club flyers will remain banned while international ad campaigns for global brands on city-approved poster sites will return.

For de Marco, though, "the low quality of the letters and the images on those immense pieces of propaganda" were always a concern, as was "the misuse and occupation of public space. In the weeks before my birthday," he says, "my visual enemies begin to disappear like the happy end of a motion picture. To see my city clean was my best birthday present and my photos were the record of the feast."

Meanwhile, according to Augusto Moya, creative director of ad agency DDB Brasil, the ban is forcing agencies to be more inventive. "As a creative, I think that there is one good thing the ban has brought: we must now use more traditional outdoor media (like bus stops and all kinds of urban fittings) in a more creative way," he says. "People at all the agencies are thinking about how to develop outdoor media that do not interfere so much in the physical structure of the city."

Moya takes an enlightened view of the law. "As a citizen, I think that future generations will thank the current city administration for this ban," he says. "There's still a lot to be done in terms of pollution – air pollution, river pollution, street pollution and so on. São Paulo is still one of the most polluted cities in the world. But I believe this law is the first step for a better future."

And even if some Paulistanos remain unconvinced, there is at least one group who are certainly not complaining – the city's scrap dealers, who are set to make a killing from recovering all the old signs and structures. ◼

Volume 27
Number 06
June 2007

This is Advertising

The most coveted awards at Cannes this year
went not to posters or commercials, but to
computer games, fragrances, tap water and
widgets for your Facebook page. Eliza Williams
reports on the changing face of advertising

The advertising industry is going through a
period of enormous change and disruption. It
is no longer about just commercials and print
ads. Now an ad can be a computer game, a
widget, or even a fragrance.

6-8. BBDO Argentina is behind Barrio Bonito, a football neighbourhood created in Buenos Aires and inspired by Nike's global Jogo Bonito campaign. Barrio Bonito is located in the La Boca district and contains artworks developed by local artists. It

is now listed as a "must visit" attraction by tour guides in the city.
9. The UK has so far been slow to adapt to these new styles of advertising, but some of the smaller interactive agencies are beginning to make strides. AKQA's integrated

campaign for Yell.com included print, TV and cinema ads, alongside interactive information screens placed in bus shelters (shown). The bus shelters contain unique information, which changes depending on whether it is day or night.

10&11. Agency Republic's Musicubes website for BBC Radio 1 allows users to assemble towers of their favourite genres of music and then leads them to radio programmes that specialise in their preferred sound. The towers can then be pasted into blogs

◀ such as Graham Coxon and The Chemical Brothers were asked to create a track inspired by a piece of art at the Tate, which was then made available on listening posts for visitors to the gallery; BBDO Argentina took home a Lion for Barrio Bonito, a football neighbourhood created in Buenos Aires and inspired by the Nike Jogo Bonito campaign; and Clemenger BBDO, Wellington, won for its campaign for the World Press Photo Exhibition, which reiterated the importance of the exhibition for promoting awareness of war and politics by inviting world leaders to attend it and then displaying their negative responses around the city alongside the words, "See the exhibition they should be seeing".

"It's at the tipping point now, it isn't a novelty anymore for sure," claims Alex Bogusky, founder of CP&B and President of the Titanium and Integrated juries this year at Cannes. "I think people are maybe realising that you have to offer some kind of tool or service. It's good news for consumers, but it's hard for advertisers – rather than interrupting, you have to put out a point of contact that people are drawn to. The [advertising] landscape just fractures, every new idea makes our job harder, it creates more options for advertisers and more options for consumers."

Perhaps because of the new skills that these non-traditional campaigns demand, some of the regions that are enjoying the most success in this area so far are those less established in the more traditional forms of advertising. Bogusky points to Argentina and Latin America generally as leading the way – "they are very free in their thinking, and very accepting to new media... they are not so burdened by their past success in other areas," he comments – while others have suggested other less-dominant ad regions, such as Japan, Korea and China, as places to watch.

This in part may explain the UK's lack of impact in this arena so far. While some smaller interactive agencies, such as Agency Republic, who created the Radio 1 Musicubes site, and AKQA, who were behind the interactive Yell.Com campaign, are making in-roads, many of the larger agencies are still concentrating on what the UK ad industry does best: beautiful film campaigns. The suggestion is that this may be about to change, however, as agencies realise that, alongside their skills in creating traditional ad messages, they need to offer something more.

"I think the internet has heightened everyone's expectations of all media," says JWT Worldwide CCO, Craig Davis. "People expect choice, control and the ability to contribute. There are wonderful opportunities in all this for brands in the creation and curation of content, services and utility. But the bar is, and should be, very high. My view is that communication will continue to be very important, but that a brand's communication and behaviour will need to be genuinely entertaining, involving and, quite possibly, useful going forward."

Rather than coming from within the industry, many of these changes are being foisted on the ad industry by consumers, who are increasingly demanding more from brands. "What's happening in the real world is not being driven by clients or agencies, it's being driven by consumers – real people with a remote, a mouse and a mobile," continues Davis. "In response to that, agencies and clients are looking for new ways to make marketing work harder. With that comes a growing appetite for exploration, experimentation and risk-taking."

And these changes rely, of course, on risk-taking clients, as well as agencies. "Great clients make for great advertising,"

agrees Bogusky. "Some agencies are reaching that spot with their clients where they think strategically, they are thinking about the product. Sometimes you can't separate the marketing from the product – when that happens business really changes, the results are amazing and agencies get invited even earlier to the table. Now we get briefed on product with BK, which is great, but some agencies won't want to do it, as it will mean big changes."

All this may suggest that a paradigm shift is occurring in advertising, although with nearly 5000 Film entries at Cannes compared to under 350 Titanium and Integrated ones, it is one that is still in its infancy. Perhaps it is important not to see these non-traditional campaigns as a replacement to film and print commercials, but a necessary addition. "I still think film has a lot of momentum," says Bogusky. "I don't see it changing for the next five years but other models are starting to establish themselves. I don't see film going away though."

"Whatever you do, you end up transmitting a message," agrees Juan Cabral, creative director at Fallon London on the Tate Tracks work. "The important thing is to leave people with something: a feeling, a bit of content or even get them involved and let them be part of it. As long as it feels like a gift, rather than an intrusion, I think it's okay." ▣

1&2. Crispin Porter & Bogusky's Xbox King Games campaign saw the agency take the Titanium Grand Prix at this year's Cannes advertising festival. The campaign partnered Burger King with Microsoft to create three new Xbox games that were then sold by the fast food chain. 3. Vegaolmosponce in Buenos Aires won the Integrated Grand Prix for its Axe 3 campaign, a new scent for the deodorant brand created by mixing two established fragrances. The winning combination was decided by votes from users. Stills from the TV ad promoting the campaign, directed by Lynn Fox at Blink Productions, shown. 4. R/GA in New York created the Nike+ concept, a running shoe that communicates with an Apple iPod Nano, which can then be synched to a computer to record runners' progress (website shown). 5. Droga5's Tap Project sold tap water across New York to raise money for UNICEF. 6. Tate Tracks by Fallon London commissioned musicians to create tracks inspired by their favourite Tate artworks

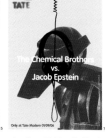

In years to come, we may look back at this year's Cannes Lions International Advertising Festival as a tipping point. This was the year that the change that has been gathering pace in the industry really became explicit.

Up until now, the big prize at Cannes was always the Film Grand Prix, given to the best commercial. It was the grand finale of the week and reflected the realities of the industry – TV commercials were what everybody measured their creative worth by, then came print and poster ads, then everything else. But this year came a change in priorities mirrored by the industry itself. This year, the prize to win was the Titanium Lion. And if you couldn't win that, the next best thing was an Integrated award.

"The rules for entry state that 'Titanium stands for breakthrough ideas. It's an award for work that is provocative and points to a new direction. It's for work that causes the industry to stop in its tracks and reconsider the way forward.' For this reason alone I think there is more kudos to winning a Titanium Lion than a Film Lion," says Gavin Gordon-Rogers, creative director of interactive agency Agency Republic.

The Titanium award was introduced in 2003 but has had a difficult time becoming established as entrants struggled to understand what it was for. Originally, it was simply for "breakthrough ideas" which could be in any medium. Now it is seen more as an award for ideas that don't fit into the strict categories of TV commercials, posters or press ads – in other words, for the kind of work that most believe represents the ad industry's future. "Obviously that's where we should be going and that's where we are going… some day there will be just one category in Cannes – I don't know what it will be called but it will

be for the best idea," agrees Bob Scarpelli, DDB Worldwide chairman and chief creative officer, and Film Lions President at the awards festival this year.

The priority for agencies now is not to demonstrate that they can make a beautifully crafted TV spot – clients know that. What is far more valuable to them as a business is to show they have a grasp of the kind of big, cross-media, projects that clients are increasingly demanding.

The Titanium Grand Prix winner this year was Crispin, Porter & Bogusky's Xbox King Games campaign, which saw Burger King partner with Microsoft to develop three new Xbox games featuring characters and products from the burger chain's advertising. The games were then sold in store for $3.99 each when a BK Value Meal was purchased. The promotion, which included online trailers, TV and print executions, led to 2.4 million copies of the games sold in just five weeks.

"The Titanium Grand Prix winner from Crispin Porter & Bogusky is a truly outstanding example of a creative agency leading a brave client into unexplored territory," continues Gavin Gordon-Rogers. "The key word here is 'brave'. The creatives, the agency chiefs, and most importantly the client have had the guts to go with something new, something they haven't seen done before. Of course, Burger King is by no means the first brand to embrace gaming. Nestle did it with Smarties Meltdown for the PS2, for example. Lego has been at it since back in 1997. And film studios have long recognised the merchandising opportunity of video game spin-offs. But with the King games, CP&B actually created a new revenue stream, and it's the fact that this campaign actually turned a profit for Burger King that makes it

extraordinary. I doubt any Film Lion winners can claim that."

The Integrated Grand Prix winner was no less innovative, with Buenos Aires-based agency Vegaolmosponce proposing a new fragrance for deodorant brand Axe, created by mixing two already established scents in the Axe range. "To communicate the concept of 'mixable fragrances' we came up with a simple, straightforward and 100 per cent Axe media neutral idea: mixable Axe fragrances would give guys mixable women," claimed the agency. "The campaign was based on this simple concept, showing guys in every form of media available that it is good to mix, and even better to mix different kinds of gorgeous women." Okay, so it's not exactly a politically correct premise, but the campaign, which allowed consumers to vote for their favourite combinations online or by using mobile phones, proved phenomenally successful.

And the Lion winners in the Titanium and Integrated categories go even further to demonstrate the diversity of work that these categories accommodate. Titanium Lions went to Droga5 for its Tap Project for UNICEF, which saw restaurants in New York sell tap water for a dollar, generating funding for a year's worth of clean drinking water in the Third World in just one day; to Leo Burnett Sydney for its elaborate promotion of Earth Hour, where residents of Sydney turned off their lights for one hour to save energy; and to R/GA, New York for the Nike+ concept, a Nike running shoe that communicates with an Apple iPod Nano and uses a bespoke website to track and record runners' progress.

In Integrated, the Lion winners were equally varied. Fallon in London won for its Tate Tracks campaign, where musicians ▶

1. Wolff Olins' logo for the 2012 Olympics, was, says creative director Patrick Cox, designed to be deliberately provocative: "it doesn't ask to be liked very much," he told the press.
2&3. A major influence on the logo appears to have been the New Rave style created by Super Super magazine. Co-founder Namalee (seen here on the cover and an inside spread from the April 2007 issue) defines the style as "maxi-maximalism" – a kind of everything-but-the-kitchen-sink approach that translates in the magazine as cramming as much content as possible onto every page.
4. Super Super creative director Steve Slocombe cites this spread, featuring drag queen agony aunt Jodie Harsh, as epitomising his approach. "Because there are bright colours people think it looks cheap and just dashed off, but it's still very structured and considered," he insists.
5. The cover of Super Super's first issue, from February 2006

Stretched type, day-glo colours and a flagrant disregard for the rules: are we witnessing a knee-jerk reaction to the slick sameness of so much design or a genuine cultural shift? asks Patrick Burgoyne

The New Ugly

In the early 90s, the mother of all rows blew up between, on the one hand, the traditionalist school of American designers led by Massimo Vignelli and, in defiant opposition, the avant garde of Emigre and the Cranbrook Academy of Art. The catalyst was an essay in Eye magazine by Steven Heller entitled Cult of the Ugly, in which the world's most prolific design writer took Cranbrook and its students to task over, as he saw it, their gratuitously ugly output. Well now, it seems, ugly is back.

Exhibit A: Wolff Olins' 2012 Olympics logo. When finally wheeled out to confront an ever-more-hostile national press, Wolff Olins creative director Patrick Cox claimed that "Its design is intentionally raw, it doesn't… ask to be liked very much. It was meant to provoke a response, like the little thorn in the chair that gets you to breathe in, sit up and take notice."

In addition, Wolff Olins' chairman Brian Boylan claimed success for having "created something original in a world where it is increasingly difficult to make something different". In other words, when we are surrounded by logos created to a slick, if mediocre, aesthetic standard, the only way to stand out is deliberately to reject those standards.

Which brings us to Exhibit B: the magazine that seemingly influenced Wolff Olins' thinking – style magazine and New Rave progenitor, Super Super. Launched early last year, its art direction has been likened to "a clown being sick". Its wilfully distorted ▶

6&7. Mike Meiré's recent redesign of German cultural magazine 032c was, he admits, a deliberate provocation. "We wanted [to create] a truthful, intelligent independent magazine with a touch of the underground," he says

September 07:
The New Ugly

"An architect is a foreigner.
A strange person.
A person that thinks that buildings are alive.
A child in disguise."

— **Mark Wigley**

"The stretched typography makes you look twice – in our eye-candy, lifestyle magazine world it looks like an accident"

Mike Meiré, art director, 032c

8. The type "was actually the hardest job to get right," says Meiré of his 032c redesign. "My assistant, Tim Giesen, was stretching types like hell. Aesthetically, we had to recondition our minds while we were working on the magazine. After a while,

everything commercial looked so boring…"

See more of Meiré's work at www.meireundmeire.de

◀ typography, day glo colours and total rejection of the holy tenets of magazine design are enough to give more mature art directors a fit of the vapours. It's MySpace made flesh, with all the clashing cacophony that concept brings to mind.

And yet, according to its creative director, Steve Slocombe, what underlines the magazine is "harmony". "There is nothing in Super Super that is empty or frivolous," he insists, "everything is there for a reason."

When it comes to style magazines, Slocombe has form, having previously been editor of Sleazenation. His last issue there (May 2003 which, incidentally, got him the sack) introduced the freeform approach that Super Super has taken to such troubling extremes. But, he says, it was a period working for photographer Wolfgang Tillmans that most influenced his approach. A fine art graduate from St Martins, Slocombe's role included helping Tillmans install his shows – a process that was, in itself, an artistic exercise. "We'd get a plan of the space and we'd turn up with work in all kinds of different sizes and respond to the space, arranging the work accordingly: it was an organic process about what work would sit best in certain situations," he explains.

This, then, is the approach that he brings to designing Super Super. There is no predefined grid: Slocombe starts with the images (which may or may not be in focus) and arranges them so as to maximise the space, just as he and Tillmans would on the gallery wall. There are some rules: copy is set in blocks either 90mm or 40mm wide, at 10 point on 12 point leading or eight on 10, using either Helvetica or Times. But word and image rarely line up: "Things feel a lot more human if they are a fraction out," Slocombe claims, "it's about a sense of harmony and rhythm." It's what sets Super Super apart: "Magazines had become very machine-like, very impersonal. Super Super is very human. It speaks to the reader very directly, removes the barriers. The values of the magazine are to be fun, to be positive, to say 'have a go, you can do this'."

While other magazines may seek to manipulate pace by contrasting full-bleed images with more detailed spreads, Super Super tries to cram in as much as possible onto every available inch of space. The reason, according to Slocombe, is that its readers (typically aged between 14 and 24) are part of the "ADD Generation". Their alarmingly short attention spans mean that they cannot be guaranteed to look at more than one spread in any particular issue, he claims, so each one has to embody all the values of the magazine. And, he says, they have a completely different idea about colour. If you are 30-plus, white may embody sophistication and expense, but to the Super Super "reader" it is colour that does this – bright colours and lots of them.

The magazine is not, Slocombe insists, anti-design. "That whole argument that you have to be either a follower of David Carson or of the Swiss School is not the debate we have now – I'll take the best of both and anything else that's around. The old way of things was movement followed by anti-movement, now the culture swallows the past and moves on instead of defining itself against what has gone before," he argues. "I'm not against what may have gone before, I just think this is more appropriate for here and now. At the core of the Swiss ideal is efficient communication – well, this is the most appropriate way to communicate to our audience."

The charitable view would be that Slocombe's lack of formal design training has left him unencumbered by the profession's history and therefore more able to seek out new forms of expression: the uncharitable view would be that Super Super is simply a mess, created for young kids who will move on to no more sophisticated tastes as they mature. And yet the magazine's core concerns – of seeking to inject some quirky humanity into a slickly homogenised magazine market, of being true to a vision deemed appropriate to the readership – are shared by a designer with a far more "establishment" pedigree. Which brings us to Exhibit C: Mike Meiré's recent redesign of German cultural magazine 032c.

Meiré is renowned in magazine circles for his art direction of Brand Eins, a German business magazine that mixed beautiful photography with classic typography and lots of white space. That was in 1999: since then, Meiré says he's been waiting for an alternative approach to emerge, but to no avail. "There are so many magazines out there which pretend to be cool, sophisticated or even culturally relevant. They all look the same," he says. "I became a bit tired of all these look-a-like magazines," which, through Brand Eins, he helped create. "They're all made very professionally but I was looking for something more

charismatic. I wanted to search for an interesting look that was beyond the mainstream."

The result is a magazine that, wrote designer Jeremy Leslie on his blog MagCulture, "uses typography and layouts that are hard to describe as anything but ugly. The pages feel thrown together. When I expressed my confusion about the redesign to the magazine's founder/editor Joerg Koch," continued Leslie, "I received a surprising reply. 'Thanks for your message which made me incredibly happy! This is exactly what we wanted to achieve, this sort of engagement with a magazine where you question yourself if it makes sense, if it is really brilliant or simply daft.'"

Meiré readily admits that "Yes, I did deliberately set out to break rules with this and yes, it is a provocation – but in the first place to myself! If every magazine or every building or every brand or everybody tries to look appealing by using the same idea of being modern, it becomes interesting to go in the opposite direction, because life has different kinds of beauty to present. If people feel confused by it, it is because we are all so used to this kind of efficient, streamlined, correctness."

In his original essay, Heller slammed those using ugliness as a knee-jerk reaction to the status quo. "Ugliness as its own virtue diminishes all design," he said. All three projects cited here could be accused of such a crime. However, Heller also argued that ugliness "is not a problem when it is a result of form following function". Though none of Wolff Olins, Slocombe or Meiré may feel comfortable with describing their work as ugly, they all lay claim to their pursuit of the latter.

"Making a magazine is about finding the right look for its content, its attitude," Meiré argues. "To me it's the only way to create a unique identity. [In doing so] maybe you don't please the [mainstream] anymore – but you become who you are, authentic in your own way."

This, it would seem, is the crux of the matter. If all three of these projects, and other contemporary works in the same vein, are merely an attempt to zig while the world zags, to be different for difference's sake, then they need not detain us for long. If, however, they are the honest result of form following function and thereby represent the visual expression of a genuine cultural shift, then that becomes something altogether more interesting.

Take colour, for instance. Both the Olympics logo and Super Super propose a new relationship between colour and quality. That bright no longer necessarily equals trashy. That a younger generation is inverting the chromatic scale as it relates to notions of quality and class. Super Super claims to address the impact of changing patterns of media consumption on design. This, it says, is what happens when your "readers" are not readers at all but mere "scanners" of content who are as likely to start at page 46 as page one. And all three claim to be fired by a desire to involve their audiences rather than simply presenting themselves to them. Inevitably this would seem to require a move away from the slick and the forbidding, toward, as Slocombe describes it, something more "human".

There is more than empty styling at work here. Something like Super Super can easily be dismissed as just a few kids messing about, but, as a recent piece on New Rave in The Sunday Times Style magazine noted, that's pretty much how all trends start. All three projects are well-intentioned attempts to respond to and engage with a shifting cultural landscape. If this is the future, it may not be a pretty sight. ▦

Volume 27
Number 09
Sept. 2007

20

PEEPSHOW.ORG.UK

Photography

Advertising showcase:
Photography
01.

Mutton Bones	Henry Arden	Sharon Brandman/Richard Seymour	Piers Golden
Jo Talbot and Sue Young	Julian Cotton	James Callaghan Photography	Frank Adam Photography
Pixelate Imaging	Tim Brightmore	Bill Charles London	MBP
Peter Mason	Basement Photographic	Richard Bradbury	Jesse Seaward
Gusto Images	Howard Kingsnorth	Ben Fisher	Metcalfe Lancaster
Wendy Jackson	edsonwilliams	Derek Seaward	Andrew Hobbs
Ray Massey	Esser Associates	Ashley Cameron	Gandee Vasan
Paul Webster	Julian Deghy	David Parfitt	Kulbir Thandie
Marcus Lyon	Richard Pullar	Agent Orange	The Angela Woods Agency
Chris Biggs & Associates	Xavier Harcq	Lisa Pritchard Agency (LPA)	
Julian Calverley	Sharon Brandman/Jeremy Hudson	Dave Brown	
Paul Hartley	Sharon Brandman/Marie Louise Avery	Jamie Stephen Represents	
Ray Massey	Sharon Brandman/Ian Boddy	Alun Callender	
Andy Seymour	Sharon Brandman/Paul Bussell	Process	

CREATIVE REVIEW PRESENTS CREATIVEHANDBOOK.CO.UK

Creative Review presents the launch of the Creative Handbook website. Featuring regularly updated portfolios from leading imagemakers and unique editorial by the Creative Review team, it's an invaluable tool for finding creative suppliers and resources across the UK.

GET LISTED

If you're a photographer, illustrator, designer, agency, or if you work in any of the related creative service industries, then it's not too late to make sure your details are included on the website: For a FREE listing, which provides basic contact details, go to: creativehandbook.co.uk

and click on Get Listed. From here you can provide details of your company and your work.

Alternatively, we are offering a limited number of suppliers the chance to post up a full portfolio of their work, (12 images or video clips which can be updated as many times as you like) full

contact details including a link to your own website, details of your current work in progress and award nominations. All for a special price of £300.

To take advantage of this offer call:
Emma Nicolle: 020 7970 6267
Dave Harvey: 020 7970 6455
Russell Jamieson: 020 7970 8020

mutton bones

Photographers' Agent

E hello@muttonbones.co.uk
T +44 (0) 20 7723 8244

www.muttonbones.co.uk

mutton
bones

Helen McArdle

mutton bones

mutton
bones

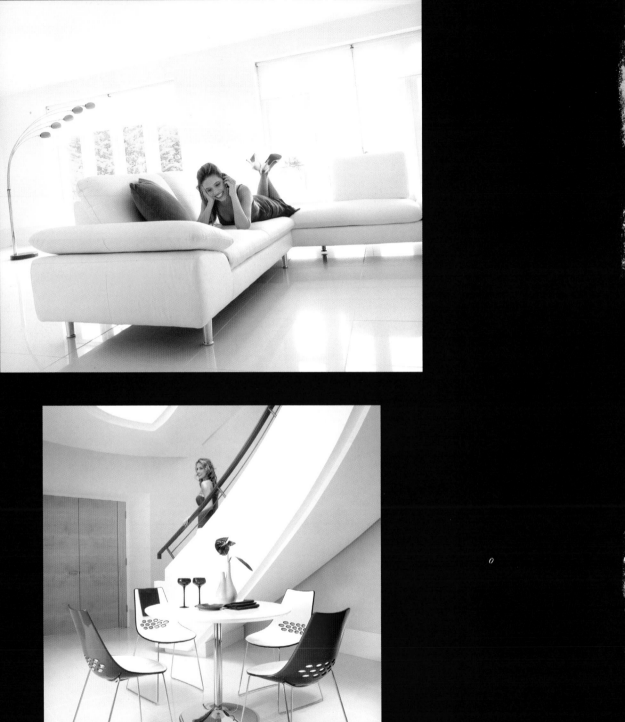

mutton
bones

**mutton
bones**

mutton
bones

Michael Prince

mutton
bones

Douglas Fisher

mutton bones

PETER DENCH

LUC BEZIAT

KELVIN MURRAY

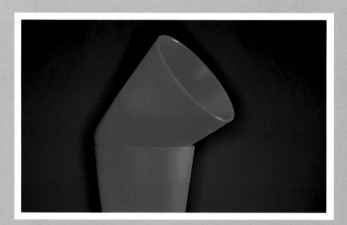

KEVIN MALLETT

ROLPH GOBITS

STUART HAMILTON

RAY BARRETT

DEAN BELCHER

JAMES MURPHY

MAX OPPENHEIM

ADRIAN HOUSTON

DEAN MARSH

BARRY LEWIS

MIKE CARSLEY

TALBOT YOUNG

TEL: 02072620189

WWW.TALBOTYOUNG.COM

8 Flitcroft St London WC2H 8D

Digital Photography and Image Manipulation

www.pixelate.biz
020 72409808

Peter Mason : Photography   www.petermason.biz   +44 (0)20 7738 9955

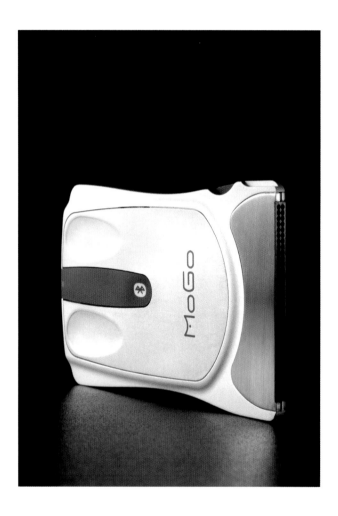

ARTEMI KYRIACOU | FOOD & STILL LIFE PHOTOGRAPHER

HUGH TURVEY | X-RAY & SPECIALIST PHOTOGRAPHER

Tag: Creative

PEAR TREE STUDIOS

Creative studio offering digital photography and retouching
www.peartree-studios.com

smoke&mirrors

Offering the very best in cgi creation and high end retouching
www.smoke-mirrors.com

WENDY JACKSON

Representing freelance photographers
www.wendyjackson.co.uk

Representing freelance photographers and illustrators
www.kariburton.com

Offering visualizing, storyboards and animatics
pmitchell@tagworldwide.com

Smoke & Mirrors
57-59 Beak St
London
W1F 9SJ
t +44 (0) 20 7468 1000

Pear Tree Studios
44 Pear Tree St
London
EC1V 3SF
t +44 (0) 20 7251 4571

For further information contact: mgrosvenor@tagcreative.com

www.raymassey.com

T: +44(0)207 267 9550 E: ray@raymassey.com
Camden Park Studios, The Church Hall CamdenPark Road, London, NW1 9AY

Paul Webster Photography

Waitrose fruit tarte packaging for The Park Consultancy

Paul Webster Photography

http://www.paulsnap.com   020 8748 5786

THE
GLASS
WORKS

Chris Biggs and associates
represents

Chris Biggs

www.chrisbiggs.co.uk

℡:020 7323 6606

Chris Biggs and associates represents

Sarah Leggett

t: +44 (0)1462 441251   m: +44 (0)7971 272815
julian@juliancalverley.com   **www.juliancalverley.com**

JULIAN CALVERLEY

Paul Hartley

Photography of jewellery, watches, diamonds, pens, gifts, cosmetics.
Tel: 020 7731 0244   enquiries@hartleystudios.com   www.hartleystudios.com

SOPLICA

Wódka

SZLACHETNA POLSKA

www.raymassey.com

T: +44(0)207 267 9550 E: ray@raymassey.com
Camden Park Studios, The Church Hall CamdenPark Road, London, NW1 9AY

Andy Seymour   020 7221 2021

Andy Seymour   www.andyseymour.co.uk/

HENRY ARDEN   PHOTOGRAPHER

+44 (0) 7860 384 633

HENRY@HENRYARDEN.COM

WWW.HENRYARDEN.COM

telephone: 020 7723 3100
mobile: 07932 151 999

e-mail: info@juliancotton.co.uk
web: www.juliancotton.co.uk

julian cotton
photographers agent

graeme ainscough
roomsets

telephone: 020 7723 3100
mobile: 07932 151 999

e-mail: info@juliancotton.co.uk
web: www.juliancotton.co.uk

richard booth
shoots people

paul cordwell
machines, industry and architecture

telephone: 020 7723 3100
mobile: 07932 151 999

e-mail: info@juliancotton.co.uk
web: www.juliancotton.co.uk

laurence davis
still life, drinks

leo mason
sports

paul fosbury
fashion

telephone: 020 7723 3100
mobile: 07932 151 999

e-mail: info@juliancotton.co.uk
web: www.juliancotton.co.uk

adam lawrence
people, celebrities

julian cotton
photographers agent

graham precey
food & drink

simon plant
automotive for cgi, location

TIM **B**RIGHTMORE

020 7278 4747   w w w . t i m b r i g h t m o r e . c o . u k

of course I'm a professional...

www.basementphoto.com

www.howardkingsnorth.com   020 7739 8655

tom watson

www.edsonwilliams.com info@edsonwilliams.com +44(0)2073752077

VALENTINO

L'ORÉAL PARIS

BODY-EXPERTISE

CONTRE LA CELLULITE INSTALLÉE
1. Pétrissez 2. Désincrustez
Constatez les résultats dès 15 jours.

PERFECTSLIM
PRO

NOUVEAU

GESTE 1
Massage pétrisseur préparateur,
inspiré des techniques professionnelles.

GESTE 2
Concentré amincissant, désincrustant
à la Co-caféine Cx™.

EFFICACITÉ PROUVÉE
PAR UN TEST CLINIQUE.

DES RÉSULTATS VISIBLES
DÈS 15 JOURS
MESURÉS SUR 102 FEMMES
PAR UN MEDECIN.

· Taille - 0,75 cm
· Hanches - 0,7cm
· Cuisse - 0,9 cm

PARCE QUE VOUS LE VALEZ BIEN.

Diagnostic cellulite
personnalisé
sur www.lorealbody.com

"Plus besoin d'attendre un mois pour voir les résultats !"
Doutzen Kroes

N°1 DE L'ANTI-CELLULITE*

* Source : panels distributeurs, total des ventes en valeur dans 29 pays, cumul à septembre 2000.

L'ORÉAL
PARIS

andrea klarin

www.edsonwilliams.com   info@edsonwilliams.com   +44(0)2073752077

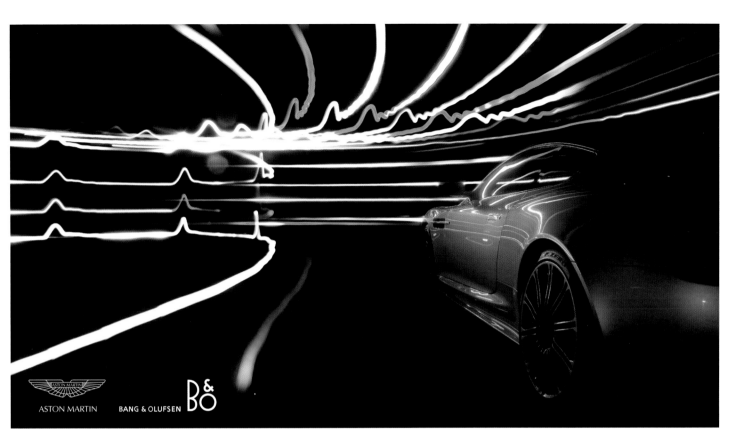

alex p

www.edsonwilliams.com   info@edsonwilliams.com   +44(0)2073752077

ESSER ASSOCIATES

REPRESENTING

ASHLEY CAMERON

JULIAN ABRAMS

DAVID BURGESS

ED LEE

DOM MOWBRAY

DANIEL SMITH

T +44 (0)20 8547 3177   M +44 (0)7778 980 101   ROB.ESSER@VIRGIN.NET   WWW.ESSERASSOCIATES.COM

Julian Deghy

020 7267 7635   julian@deghy.com   www.deghy.com

XAVIER HARCQ

www.sharonbrandman.com

sharon@sharonbrandman.com

sba

+44 (0)844 800 9003

jeremy hudson

www.sharonbrandman.com

sharon@sharonbrandman.com

+44 (0)844 800 9003

sba

marie louise | avery

www.sharonbrandman.com

sharonbrandman.com

+44 (0)844 800 9003

ian boddy

www.sharonbrandman.com

sharon@sharonbrandman.com

sba

+44 (0)844 800 9003

paul bussell

www.sharonbrandman.com

sba

richard seymour

James Callaghan Photography

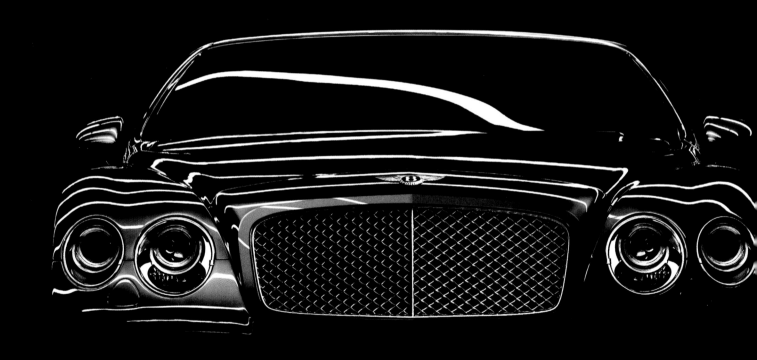

Bill Charles London

Sasha Bezzubov, Fiorenzo Borghi
Oliver Chanarin, Leon Chew
Mitch Epstein, Alesia Exum
Stuart Franklin, Kyoko Hamada
Simen Johan, Nadav Kander
Antonin Kratochvil, Peter Marlow
John Midgley, Bill Owens, Martin
Matthu Placek, Mark Power
Stephan Schacher, Stephen
Alec Soth, Anthony Suau, Larry

Nadav Kander Europe and UK excluding France
Gilles Peress excluding editorial, Europe

Adam Broomberg and Tom Craig. Julian Dufort. Larry Fink. Richard Foster. Frederike Helwig. Jean-Pierre Khazem. Jeff Mermelstein. Parr. Gilles Peress* Joseph Rodriguez. Shore. Sage Sohier. Sultan. Massimo Vitali.

Bill Charles Represents

New York
t +1.212.965.1465
f +1.212.965.9235
mailbox@billcharles.com

London
t +44.20.7033.9284
f +44.20.7033.9285
london@billcharles.com

www.billcharles.com

Photography & image manipulation by ▣ **Richard Bradbury**

U.K. London Studio : +44 (0)7768 352100   U.S.A. Agent : 626 583 1442   www.rbradbury.com

ben fisher © 2008
www.benfisherphotography.com +44 (0) 20 7613 1623 mobile +44 (0) 7976 659 605

Derek Seaward

tel: +44 (0)20 7531 4393 mob:+44 (0)7785 323 819
www.derekseaward.com derek@derekseaward.com
USA Carolyn Potts: 001 312 560 6400

12 Empress Mews
Kenbury Street
London SE5 9BT

T: + 44 (0) 20 7737 0666
F: + 44 (0) 20 7737 4321

studio@ashleycameron.com
www.ashleycameron.com

Ashley Cameron photography

davidparfitt

www.**davidparfitt**.com

T 020 7251 1427
3 LEVER STREET, LONDON EC1V 3QU

WILL SANDERS   ROB PAYNE   BEN STOCKLEY   GARRY OWENS   JASON HINDLEY

JULIA FULLERTON-BATTEN   SPIROS POLITIS   GIBLIN & JAMES   FRANK HERHOLDT

AGENTORANGE

+44 (0)20 7226 0440   10½ SWAN YARD LONDON N1 1SD   www.agentorange.co.uk

IAIN CROCKART

JOSEPH FORD

IGOR EMMERICH

JOHN ROSS

NICK DALY

JOHN RENSTEN

NICK DAVID

MICHAEL HEFFERNAN

NANCY HONEY

LISA
PRITCHARD
AGENCY/

3RD FLOOR
BLOCK A
MORELANDS
5–23 OLD STREET
LONDON EC1V 9HL

TELEPHONE
+44 (0) 20 7250 1362
FACSIMILE
+44 (0) 20 7250 1357
LISAPRITCHARD.COM

LISA
PRITCHARD
AGENCY/

LISAPRITCHARD.
COM

Dave Brown

tel: 020 7404 9888 fax: 020 7404 9800
web: www.davebrownstudio.co.uk email: dave@davebrownstudio.co.uk
agent: Sarah Whitelock tel: 020 7497 0635 web: www.sarah-whitelock.co.uk

John Bennett / Martin Hooper / Sandrine Dulermo and Michael Labica / Alex Macro / Jez Matthews / Stelianour Sani / Ian Scigliuzzi / Michael Sugrue / Colin Thomas / Graham Westmoreland / Andy Whale / Grey Zisser

T +44 (0) 845 373 3510   www.jamiestephen.com

alun Callender
+44(0)7850678085
mail@aluncallender.com
www.aluncallender.com

process
+44 (0)20 7277 8400
processphotography.com
bill robinson
dylan collard
gareth sambidge
louisa parry
rainer elstermann
tim morris

camel market, al ain, united arab emirates, 2006

piers golden photography

website   www.goldenphoto.com
email   info@goldenphoto.com

studio   +44 [0] 208 442 4240
mobile   +44 [0] 795 853 3510

www.frankadam.co.uk

www.mbp2.co.uk
0170 624 2900
studio@mbp2.co.uk
manchester, uk

lifestyle | roomsets | interiors | still life | food

JESSE
07970 266 907

WWW.JESSESEAWARD.CO.UK

JUSTIN DE DENEY
REPRESENTED BY
METCALFELANCASTER.COM
020 7580 8875

Metcalfe
Lancaster

CARL WARNER
REPRESENTED BY
METCALFELANCASTER.COM
020 7580 8875

SARAH LOUISE RAMSAY
REPRESENTED BY
METCALFELANCASTER.COM
020 7580 8875

Metcalfe
Lancaster

ANDREW WILLIAMS
REPRESENTED BY
METCALFELANCASTER.COM
020 7580 8875

DAVID LIDBETTER
REPRESENTED BY
METCALFELANCASTER.COM
020 7580 8875

Metcalfe
Lancaster

Photography
Andrew G. Hobbs

Telephone
+44(0)7973 146 119

Email
andrew@andrewghobbs.com

Internet
www.andrewghobbs.com

Model
Claudia Merikula for Harpers Bazaar

The Dogs' Bollocks

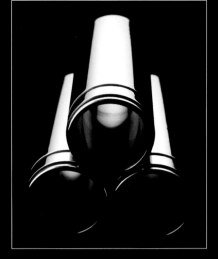

KULBIR THANDI

WWW.KULBIRTHANDI.COM

Represented in London by David & Rose Lambert +44 (0) 20 7352 0033

Tara Moore

Steve Hoskins

John Mac

Adrian Samson

www.angelawoods.com

IMPORTANT.

Angela Woods
Photographer's Agent
represents

THE YOUTH'S COMPANION.

Nick Cronin - www.eastwing.co.uk

PHOTOGRAPHERS GENERAL

1st Option Representation 64 West Yard, Camden Lock Place, London, NW1 8AF, United Kingdom
📞 (020) 7284 2345/ 📠 (020) 7284 2456
✉ mail@1st-option.com
🖳 www.1st-option.com

2Can Productions PO Box 668, Cardiff, CF11 1EZ
📞 0845 0545096/ 📠 0845 0545097
✉ info@2canproductions.com
🖳 www.2canproductions.com

360 Spin@Inspired Reflection 28 Dayton Grove, Peckham, London, SE15 2NX, United Kingdom
📞 (0870) 9193587/(07040) 402770 📠 (0870) 9193588
✉ deborah@inspiredreflection.com
🖳 www.inspiredreflection.com

3rd Eye Studio 12 Waterside, 44-48 Wharf Road, London, N1 7SF, United Kingdom
📞 (020) 7490 8787/(07702) 233721 📠 (020) 7490 1009
✉ mail@markharwood.plus.com
🖳 www.markharwoodstudio.co.uk

4photo Fernleigh, Sherburn Road, Durham, DH1 2JW, United Kingdom
📞 (07890) 022356
✉ shaun@4photo.co.uk
🖳 www.shaunmcmanus.com

8ball Multimedia Unit L, The Eurocentre, North River Rd, Great Yarmouth, Norfolk, NR30 1TE, United Kingdom
📞 (01493) 857473
✉ joseph@8ballmultimedia.com
🖳 www.8ballmedia.com

A & R Photographic 16A Crane Grove, London, N7 8LE, United Kingdom
📞 (020) 7607 3030/ 📠 (020) 7607 2190
✉ info@aandrphotographic.co.uk
🖳 www.aandrphotographic.co.uk

A B Digital 32 Church End Avenue, Runwell, Wickford, Essex, SS11 7JD, United Kingdom
📞 (01268) 573840/07860 603 451
✉ ab@digitalpackshots.co.uk
🖳 www.digitalpackshots.co.uk

A B P 2 Hollins Walk, Reading, London, RG30 2BU, United Kingdom
📞 (07760) 406273
✉ info@anthonybryson.com
🖳 www.anthonybryson.com

A Beautiful World Flat 55, Greenhill, Prince Arthur Rd, London, NW3 5UA, United Kingdom
📞 (020) 7794 2166
✉ jgoldcrown@gmail.com
🖳 www.abeautifulworld.co.uk

A C P S Inc 12555 Biscayne Boulevard 865, Miami, 33181, United States of America
📞 00 1 305 582 4978
✉ eugeneb@hotmail.com
🖳 www.eugenebreaux.com

A C Photography 5 Cryselco Close, Kempston, Bedford, MK42 7TJ, United Kingdom
📞 (01234) 300316/07836 684434 📠 (01234) 402266
✉ a.c.cook@ntlworld.com

A G P Social Photography@A G P Corporate Photography 3 Granville Square, Scarborough, North Yorkshire, YO11 2QZ, United Kingdom
📞 01723 376257/(07969) 156044
✉ ag@agphoto.co.uk
🖳 www.agphoto.co.uk

A J Hedgecock 4 Dean Garden Rise, High Wycombe, Buckinghamshire, HP11 1RE, United Kingdom
📞 (07810) 402325
✉ alan@ajhconcepts.com
🖳 www.ajhconcepts.com

A.C. Cooper (Colour) Ltd 2nd Floor, 104 New Bond St, London, W1S 1SU, United Kingdom
📞 (020) 7629 7585/ 📠 (020) 7409 3449
✉ info@accooper.com
🖳 www.accooper.com

A&J Photography 12 Emlyn Walk, Kingsway Centre, Newport, Gwent, NP20 1EW, United Kingdom
📞 (01633) 253625
✉ aj@ajphotography.co.uk
🖳 www.ajphotography.co.uk

Aardvark Photography Flat 6, 36 The Chase, London, SW4 0NH, United Kingdom
📞 (020) 7627 6116/(07973) 213840
✉ pdurell@talk21.com

Abbas@Magnum Photos 63 Gee Street, London, EC1V 3RS, United Kingdom
📞 (020) 7490 1771/ 📠 (020) 7608 0020
✉ magnum@magnumphotos.co.uk
🖳 www.magnumphotos.com

Accolade Photography No 1 The Studio, Slack Lane Works, Swinton, Manchester, M27 8QU, United Kingdom
📞 (01539) 567030/ 📠 (01539) 567030
✉ ian@accolade-photography.com
🖳 www.accolade-photography.com

Ad Rotam 105 Cranley Gardens, London, N10 3AD, United Kingdom
📞 (020) 8444 7916/ 📠 (020) 8372 6158
✉ adrotam@blueyonder.co.uk
🖳 www.adrotam.com

Ad@Opt 66 High Street, Hemel Hempstead, Hertfordshire, HP1 3AQ, United Kingdom
📞 (01442) 216324
✉ peter-grainger@btclick.com
🖳 www.peter-grainger.co.uk

Adam Barnes@WildeHague Ltd Suite 4, The Swan centre, Fishers Lane, London, W4 1RX, United Kingdom
📞 (020) 8747 9988/ 📠 (020) 8747 8228
✉ info@wildehague.com
🖳 www.wildehague.com

Adam Broomberg & Oliver Chanarin@Bill Charles London Ltd. Unit 3E1, Zetland House, 5-25 Scrutton Street, London, EC2A 4HJ, United Kingdom
📞 020 7033 9284/020 2033 9285
✉ london@billcharles.com
🖳 www.billcharles.com

Adam Dawe Hangar 9, Perserverance Works, 38 Kingsland Road, London, E2 8DD, United Kingdom
📞 (020) 7613 3262/ 📠 (020) 7613 2152
✉ mail@adamdawe.com
🖳 www.adamdawe.com

     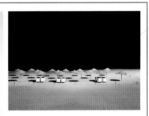

Paul O'Connor · People, Lifestyle & Portraiture
Dan Jones · Food
David Oxberry · Exteriors, Interiors, People & Still life
Rooney · Reportage Still life & Locations
David Sykes · Still life
Edgar Martins · Contemporary landscape

swerve photography

www.swervephotography.com +44 (0) 7967 628 769 lucy@swervephotography.com

Adam Hinton The White House, 26 Mortomer Street, London, W1W 7RB, United Kingdom
(020) 7580 7570/(07973) 131618 (020) 7580 7578
theoffice@wyattclarkejones.com
www.adamhinton.net

Adam Hurlin Photography Randlay, Telford, Shropshire, TF3 2NN, United Kingdom
(01952) 596211
phot@adamhurlin.co.uk
www.adamhurlin.co.uk

Adam Lawrence@Wilde Representation 314 Mare St, London, E8 1HA, United Kingdom
(020) 8653 4466/(07810) 795036 (01424) 201070
sian@wilderepresentation.com
www.wilderepresentation.com

Adam Tolner 10A Printing House Yard, Hackney Road, London, E2 7PR, United Kingdom
(020) 7739 6329/ (020) 7739 6213
at@adamtolner.com
www.adamtolner.com

Adam Woolfitt 31 Church Crescent, London, N10 3NA, United Kingdom
(020) 8444 6516/(07768) 613312
adampix@dircon.co.uk
www.adampix.com

Adolfo Crespo 9 Lansdell House, Tulse Hill, London, SW2 2ER, United Kingdom
(020) 8671 2461/(07768) 071019 (020) 8671 2461
contact@crespo.co.uk
www.adolfocrespo.com

Adrenalin Management Temple Works, Brett Passage, London, E8 1JR, United Kingdom
(020) 8986 3939/ (020) 8986 3665
info@adrenalinmanagement.com
www.adrenalinmanagement.com

Adri Berger 45 Mitchell Street, London, EC1V 3QZ, United Kingdom
(020) 7490 3595
info@adriberger.com
www.adriberger.com

Adrian Arbib 35 Warnborough Road, Oxford, OX2 6JA, United Kingdom
(01865) 454600/(07711) 090544
photo@arbib.org
www.arbib.org

Adrian Brown Studio, 81 Tachbrook Street, Pimlico, London, SW1V 2QP, United Kingdom
(020) 7828 1800
adrian@adrianbrown.com
www.adrianbrown.com

Adrian Burke 23 Hartismere Road, London, SW6 7UB, United Kingdom
(020) 7386 8299/(07973) 874924
adrianburke@btconnect.com
www.adrianburke.co.uk

Adrian Gale 44 Highgate Place, Highgate, Birmingham, B12 0DD, United Kingdom
0121-440 0502/(07768) 180719
adrian@adriangale.co.uk
www.adriangale.co.uk

Adrian Green@Shoot Production Ltd 23 Glebe Road, London, N8 7DA, United Kingdom
(020) 8442 9171/ (020) 8348 7404
adele@shootgroup.com
www.shootgroup.com

Adrian Houston Amberley Studio, 32A Goldney Road, London, W9 2AX, United Kingdom
(020) 7289 1419/(07850) 475105 (020) 7289 1419
adrian@adrianhouston.co.uk
www.adrianhouston.co.uk

Adrian Lyon, London, United Kingdom
(07973) 358220
mail@adrianlyon.com
www.adrianlyon.com

Adrian Mott Photography 81 Rivington Street, London, EC2A 3AY, United Kingdom
(07831) 229489
amott@onetel.com

Adrian Myers@Mutton Bones Ground Floor, 51 Balcombe Street, London, NW1 6HD, United Kingdom
(020) 7723 8244/ (020) 7723 2770
hello@muttonbones.co.uk
www.muttonbones.co.uk

Adrian Samson@Angela Woods 4 The Carlton Tavern, 73 Grafton Road, London, NW5 4BB, United Kingdom
(020) 7284 3417/(07850) 263077 (020) 7482 2466
angela@angelawoods.com
www.angelawoods.com

Adrian Taylor 3 Ravenscroft Street, London, E2 7SH, United Kingdom
(020) 7739 7776/(07796) 431659
acoletaylor@btconnect.com

Adrian Turner Unit 1-2, 29-42 Windsor Street, Brighton, BN1 1RJ, United Kingdom
(01273) 821840
mail@adrianturner.co.uk
www.adrianturner.co.uk

Adrian Wroth Brand Photography The Old Fire Station, Church Street, Burnham, Slough, SL1 7HX, United Kingdom
(01628) 669099/(07976) 352959 (01628) 669105
studio@adrianwroth.com
www.professionalphotography.co.uk

Aernout Overbeeke@Freddie Brazil 211 Abercairn Road, London, SW16 5AJ, United Kingdom
(020) 8764 2801/(07711) 753072 (020) 8764 2801
frederick.brazil@btconnect.com
www.freddiebrazil.com

Aerotechnical Tayvallich House, Silver Street, Minety, Malmesbury, Wiltshire, SN16 9QU, United Kingdom
/(07801) 802812 (01666) 860333
bryony.duncan@aerialphotographers.com
www.aerialphotographers.com

Agent Orange 10 Swan Yard, London, N1 1SD, United Kingdom
(020) 7226 0440/ (020) 7226 1613
annika@agentorange.co.uk
www.agentorange.co.uk
See ad in showcase

Agent Pandora 12 Stonells Road, London, SW11 6HQ, United Kingdom
(07966) 181825
pandora@agentpandora.com
www.agentpandora.com

Aidan McCarthy 2 Harcourt Road, London, SW19 1LS, United Kingdom
(07798) 830957
aidanmccarthy@onetel.net.uk
www.aidanmccarthy.net

Airshots 10 Bladden Drive, Rushmear St Andrew, Ipswich, IP4 5UG, United Kingdom
(01473) 716838/(07836) 710226 (01473) 716838
mike@airshots.co.uk
www.airshots.co.uk

Akehurst Creative Management Ltd, London, United Kingdom
(020) 7624 2366
na@nickyakehurst.com
www.akehurstcreativemanagement.com

Alan Clarke@Pearce Stoner Associates 12B Links Yard, Spelman Street, London, E1 5LX, United Kingdom
(020) 7247 7100/ (020) 7247 7144
info@pearcestoner.com
www.pearcestoner.com

Alan Hampson Foulis Cottage, Great Ayton, Middlesbrough, Cleveland, TS9 6LL, United Kingdom
(01642) 722711/(07831) 694248
alan@ahampson.freeserve.co.uk
www.alanhampson.com

Alan Kitching@Début Art & The Coningsby Gallery 30 Tottenham Street, London, W1T 4RJ, United Kingdom
(020) 7636 1064/ (020) 7580 7017
info@debutart.com
www.debutart.com

Alan Mahon@Horton-Stephens Photographers' Agent 14 Peacock Yard, Iliffe Street, London, SE17 3LH, United Kingdom
(020) 7252 7979/ (020) 7252 6409
us@horton-stephens.com
www.horton-stephens.com

Alan Marsh 325 Borough High Street, London, SE1 1JH, United Kingdom
(020) 7407 1751
info@alanmarsh.com
www.alanmarsh.com

Alan Newnham 18A Bromells Road, London, SW4 0BG, United Kingdom
(020) 7498 2399/ (020) 7498 2238
alan@newnhamphoto.co.uk
www.newnhamphoto.co.uk

Alan Peebles@Cormack Creative Management Ltd Suite 208, 95 Morrison Street, Glasgow, G5 8BE, United Kingdom
0141-429 6810/(07778) 323169 0141-429 2603
susie@cormackcreativemanagement.co.uk
www.cormackcreativemanagement.co.uk

Alan Powdrill@Vue Units 1 & 2 Elm Court, 1 Royal Oak Yard, London, SE1 3TP, United Kingdom
(020) 7403 5555/ (020) 7403 2005
production@vue-us.com
www.vue-us.com

Alan Randall Canonbury Studio, 36A Canonbury Square, London, N1 2AN, United Kingdom
(020) 7226 1642

Alan Scrymgeour@Ellison Lee 17 Quadrant Business Centre, 135 Salusbury Road, London, NW6 6RJ, United Kingdom
(020) 7624 2345/ (020) 7624 1100
info@ellisonlee.com
www.ellisonlee.com

Alan Simpson@Cormack Creative Management Ltd Suite 208, 95 Morrison Street, Glasgow, G5 8BE, United Kingdom
0141-429 6810/(07778) 323169 0141-429 2603
susie@cormackcreativemanagement.co.uk
www.cormackcreativemanagement.co.uk

Alan Weintraub@Arcaid Picture Library Parc House, 25-37 Cowleaze Road, Kingston upon Thames, Surrey, KT2 6DZ, United Kingdom
(020) 8546 4352/ (020) 8541 5230
arcaid@arcaid.co.uk
www.arcaid.co.uk

Alan Wickes 135 Downton Avenue, London, SW2 3TX, United Kingdom
(020) 8674 2242/(07774) 259352
a.wickes@btinternet.com
www.alanwickes.com

Alan Williams@Axiom Photographic Agency The Pall Mall Deposit, 124-128 Barlby Road, London, W10 6BL, United Kingdom
(020) 8964 9970/ (020) 8964 8440
info@axiomphotographic.com
www.axiomphotographic.com

Alasdair McLellan@MAP 72 Rochester Place, London, NW1 9JX, United Kingdom
(020) 7424 9144/ (020) 7284 3274
info@mapltd.com
www.mapltd.com

Alasdair Ogilvie The Old School, Daglingworth, Cirencester, Gloucestershire, GL7 7AQ, United Kingdom
(01285) 650339/(07932) 182237 (01285) 650339
alasdair@mortalfilms.co.uk
www.tintabernacles.com

Alastair Hood@The White Agency 60 Epirus Road, Fulham, London, SW6 7UH, United Kingdom
(020) 7381 2004/(07970) 619277 (020) 7386 8479
annabel@thewhiteagency.com
www.thewhiteagency.com

Alastair Laidlaw, London, United Kingdom
(020) 7242 0625/(07711) 762464
laidlaw1@mac.com
web.mac.com/laidlaw1

Alastair Thain@Bonakdar Cleary 35 Charles Square, London, N1 6HT, United Kingdom
(020) 7490 1155
bc@bonakdarcleary.com
www.bonakdarcleary.com

Alberto Arzoz@Axiom Photographic Agency The Pall Mall Deposit, 124-128 Barlby Road, London, W10 6BL, United Kingdom
(020) 8964 9970/ (020) 8964 8440
info@axiomphotographic.com
www.axiomphotographic.com

Alberto Piovano@Arcaid Picture Library Parc House, 25-37 Cowleaze Road, Kingston upon Thames, Surrey, KT2 6DZ, United Kingdom
(020) 8546 4352/ (020) 8541 5230
arcaid@arcaid.co.uk
www.arcaid.co.uk

Alec Soth@Magnum Photos 63 Gee Street, London, EC1V 3RS, United Kingdom
(020) 7490 1771/ (020) 7608 0020
magnum@magnumphotos.co.uk
www.magnumphotos.com

Alesia Exum@Bill Charles London Ltd. Unit 3E1, Zetland House, 5-25 Scrutton Street, London, EC2A 4HJ, United Kingdom
📞 020 7033 9284/020 2033 9285
✏ london@billcharles.com
🖥 www.billcharles.com

Alessandra Benedetti Via dei Giornalisti 64, Rome, 135, Italy
📞 00 39 333 219 2725
✏ alessandrabenedetti@mac.com
🖥 homepage.mac.com/alessandrabenedetti

Alex Macro 1 Ada Road, London, SE5 7RW, United Kingdom
📞 (07973) 324379
✏ studio@alexmacro.com
🖥 www.alexmacro.com

Alex Majoli@Magnum Photos 63 Gee Street, London, EC1V 3RS, United Kingdom
📞 (020) 7490 1771/ (020) 7608 0020
✏ magnum@magnumphotos.co.uk
🖥 www.magnumphotos.com

Alex Orrow Photographer 38 Bavent Road, London, SE5 9RY, United Kingdom
📞 (07768) 152 787
✏ alex@alexorrow.co.uk
🖥 www.alexorrow.co.uk

Alex P@edsonwilliams photography consultancy 52 Brushfield Street, London, E1 6AJ, United Kingdom
📞 (020) 7375 2077/(07867) 517777 (020) 7375 3077
✏ info@edsonwilliams.com
🖥 www.edsonwilliams.com

Alex Reilly@Creative Talent (UK) Limited 78 York Street, London, W1H 1DP, United Kingdom
📞 (020) 7439 1877/ (020) 7434 1144
✏ info@creativetalentlimited.com
🖥 www.creativetalentlimited.com

Alex Smith Photography 60 Mayfield Close, Uxbridge, Middlesex, UB10 0DU, United Kingdom
📞 (01895) 234415/(07720) 350735 (01895) 234415
✏ alexsmithphoto@aol.com
🖥 www.alexsmithphotography.co.uk
See ad in showcase

Alex Telfer Photography Kingsland Church Studios, Priory Green, Newcastle upon Tyne, NE6 2DW, United Kingdom
📞 0191-265 7384/ 0191-276 7778
✏ peter@telfer-photography.com
🖥 www.alextelferphotography.com

Alex Trebus@Defrance 47 Rethelstrasse, Deusseldorf, 40237, Germany
📞 00 49 211 87 67 89/ 00 49 211 87 67 89
✏ defrance@defrance.de
🖥 www.defrance.de

Alex Vaughan 59 Lambeth Walk, London, SE11 6DX, United Kingdom
📞 (020) 7735 6623/(07775) 630137
✏ me@alexvaughan.com
🖥 www.alexvaughan.com

Alex Webb@Magnum Photos 63 Gee Street, London, EC1V 3RS, United Kingdom
📞 (020) 7490 1771/ (020) 7608 0020
✏ magnum@magnumphotos.co.uk
🖥 www.magnumphotos.com

Alex Williamson@Début Art & The Coningsby Gallery 30 Tottenham Street, London, W1T 4RJ, United Kingdom
📞 (020) 7636 1064/ (020) 7580 7017
✏ info@debutart.com
🖥 www.debutart.com

Alex Wilson 1K Woodstock Studios, 36 Woodstock Grove, London, W12 8LE, United Kingdom
📞 (020) 8749 9552/ (028) 7749 9777
✏ alex@viewfolio.com
🖥 www.viewfolio.com

Alexander Kent@Andrea Walji Agency 6 Brewer Street, London, W1F 0SB, United Kingdom
📞 (020) 7439 4144/(07789) 871871 (020) 7439 4133
✏ andrea@andreawalji.com
🖥 www.andreawalji.com

Alexandra Studio 30 St Marys Street, Eynesbury, St. Neots, Cambridgeshire, PE19 2TA, United Kingdom
📞 (01480) 213314
✏ enquiries.alexandrastudio@ntlworld.com
🖥 www.alexandrastudio.co.uk

Alexandra Von Ziechmann Flat 1, 90 Sutherland Avenue, London, W9 2QR, United Kingdom
📞 (020) 7289 4248/(07962) 082691
🖥 www.alexandravz.com

Alexandre Weinberger@T Photographic 1 Heathgate Place, 75-83 Agincourt Road, London, London, NW3 2NU, United Kingdom
📞 (020) 7428 6070/ (020) 7428 6079
✏ peter@tphotographic.com
🖥 www.tphotographic.com

Ali Pellatt@Début Art & The Coningsby Gallery 30 Tottenham Street, London, W1T 4RJ, United Kingdom
📞 (020) 7636 1064/ (020) 7580 7017
✏ info@debutart.com
🖥 www.debutart.com

Alina Kisina Flat 8/10 Salamander Court, Edinburgh, EH6 7JP, United Kingdom
📞 (07919) 234997
✏ info@alinakisina.co.uk
🖥 www.alinakisina.co.uk

Alistair Berg@Ellison Lee 17 Quadrant Business Centre, 135 Salusbury Road, London, NW6 6RJ, United Kingdom
📞 (020) 7624 2345/ (020) 7624 1100
✏ info@ellisonlee.com
🖥 www.ellisonlee.com

Alistair Hughes Vyner Street Studios, 23 Vyner Street, London, E2 9DG, United Kingdom
📞 (020) 8980 1224/(07966) 422868
✏ alistair@alistairhughes.co.uk
🖥 www.alistairhughes.co.uk

Alister Thorpe@Esser Assocs 2nd Floor North, 6 Buckingham Street, London, WC2N 6BU, United Kingdom
📞 (020) 7976 2915/(07778) 149149 (01372) 464326
✏ rob.esser@virgin.net
🖥 www.davidesser.com

Alive Digital Media 83 Riversdale Road, London, N5 2ST, United Kingdom
✏ info@areyoualive.com
🖥 www.areyoualive.com

ALEX SMITH PHOTOGRAPHY

Alex shoots architecture in its widest context, from large scale projects to individual newly designed houses and stately homes.

Also room sets in studios and location houses. Shooting a wide range of architectural related subjects ensures continued inspiration. Alex is equally inspired by depicting furniture in the studio and by recording great architecture on location.

60 Mayfield Close Uxbridge UB10 0DU
+44 7720 350 735 +44 1895 234 415
www.alexsmithphotography.co.uk

Allan Baxter 188 Goswell Road, London, EC1V 7DT, United Kingdom
📞 (07958) 729884
✏ agb@allanbaxter.org.uk
🖥 www.allanbaxter.org.uk

Allan Grainger@Andrea Walji Agency 6 Brewer Street, London, W1F 0SB, United Kingdom
📞 (020) 7439 4144/(07789) 871871 (020) 7439 4133
✏ andrea@andreawalji.com
🖥 www.andreawalji.com

Allan Jones 1A Chance Street, London, E1 6JT, United Kingdom
📞 (020) 7739 0873/(07899) 925580
✏ allan@omnimage.co.uk

Allan McPhail@David Lambert 108 Oakley Street, London, SW3 5NR, United Kingdom
📞 (020) 7352 0033/(07747) 032 299 (020) 7352 5553
✏ david@davidlambert.com
🖥 www.davidlambert.com

Allun Callender 33 Totland Road, Brighton, East Sussex, BN2 3EP
📞 07850 678085/ ✏ alun@aluncallender.com
🖥 www.aluncallender.com
See ad in showcase

Allure Photography, London, United Kingdom
📞 (020) 8909 2258/(07879) 498578
✏ sharna44@hotmail.com

ALPS Photography Lee Lane, Pinkneys Green, Maidenhead, Berkshire, SL6, United Kingdom
📞 (07779) 572360
✏ info@photo-wall.com
🖥 www.photo-wall.com

Altered TV 166a Lancaster Road, London, W11 1QU, United Kingdom
📞 (07974) 070990
✏ leer@edgy.co.uk
🖥 www.altered.tv

Alternative Portraits 14 Witchbrae, Dunfermline, Fife, KY12 0LG, United Kingdom
📞 (01383) 844610/ (01383) 844610
✏ callummcphail@aol.com
🖥 www.freewebs.com/callummcphail12/

Alternative Weddings 22 Green Street, Birmingham, B12 0NB, United Kingdom
📞 (07739) 689316
✏ kristin@sillypix.com
🖥 www.sillypix.com

Alun Crockford 51 Calthorpe Street, London, WC1X 0HH, United Kingdom
📞 (020) 7837 8338/ (020) 7833 1950
✏ alun@aluncrockford.com
🖥 www.aluncrockford.com

Alver Bernadine 23 Exbury House, Ferndale Road, London, SW9 8AZ, United Kingdom
📞 (020) 7326 4277
✏ alver@alverbernadine.com
🖥 www.alverbernadine.com

Alwyn Coates, London, United Kingdom
📞 (020) 8979 5454/(07850) 881927 (07802) 259736
✏ info@alwyn-coates.com
🖥 www.alwyn-coates.com

Amanda Bibby@Shirley Hart Creative Consultants 19 Ulundi Road, London, SE3 7UQ, United Kingdom
- (020) 8853 2987/(07867) 806250
- shirleyhart@btinternet.com
- www.shirleyhart.com

Amber Gray Photography 213 E. 21 St, New York, 10010, United States of America
- 00 1 212 375 9449
- julian@ambergrayphotography.com
- www.ambergray.net

Amit & Naroop - Photography 7 Upper Sutton Lane, Hounslow, TW5 0PR, United Kingdom
- (07949) 780192
- info@amitandnaroop.com
- www.amitandnaroop.com

Amos Schliack Unit 8, 220 Kingsland Road, London, E2 8DF, United Kingdom
- (020) 7033 9972/(07906) 449 776
- amos@london.com
- www.amosschliack.com

Ana Yao@Private View Artists Agency 17A Swan Hill, Shrewsbury, SY1 1NL, United Kingdom
- (01743) 350355/ (01743) 233923
- create@pvuk.com
- www.pvuk.com

Ancient Egypt Picture Library 6 Branden Drive, Knutsford, Cheshire, WA16 8EJ, United Kingdom
- (01565) 633106/ (01565) 633106
- bobegyptpl@aol.com

Anders Hald@Alan Wickes 135 Downton Avenue, London, SW2 3TX, United Kingdom
- (020) 8674 2242/(07774) 259352
- a.wickes@btinternet.com
- www.alanwickes.com

Anders Overgaard@M & M Management Studio B, 11 Edith Grove, London, SW10 0JZ, United Kingdom
- (020) 7823 3723/ (020) 7351 3714
- admin@mmmanagement.com
- www.mmmanagement.com

Anderson & Low@Alan Wickes 135 Downton Avenue, London, SW2 3TX, United Kingdom
- (020) 8674 2242/(07774) 259352
- a.wickes@btinternet.com
- www.alanwickes.com

Andrea Klarin@edsonwilliams photography consultancy 52 Brushfield Street, London, E1 6AJ, United Kingdom
- (020) 7375 2077/(07867) 517777 / (020) 7375 3077
- info@edsonwilliams.com
- www.edsonwilliams.com

Andrea Walji Agency 6 Brewer Street, London, W1F 0SB, United Kingdom
- (020) 7439 4144/(07789) 871871 / (020) 7439 4133
- andrea@andreawalji.com
- www.andreawalji.com

Andreas Einsiedel 72-80 Leather Lane, London, EC1N 7TR, United Kingdom
- (020) 7242 7674/(07973) 137690 / (020) 7831 3712
- andreas@einsiedel.com
- www.einsiedel.com

Andreas Heumann Productions The Old Vicarage, 42 Broad Lane, Evenley, Brackley, Northamptonshire, NN13 5SF, United Kingdom
- (01280) 703472/(07785) 392729 / (01280) 706278
- pictures@andreas-heumann.com
- www.andreas-heumann.com

Andrew Atkinson Photography Ltd Unit 209 Belgravia Works, 157-163 Marlborough Road, London, N19 4NF, United Kingdom
- (020) 7281 3737
- andy@andrew-atkinson.com
- www.andrew-atkinson.com

Andrew Bettles@MAP 72 Rochester Place, London, NW1 9JX, United Kingdom
- (020) 7424 9144/ (020) 7284 3274
- info@mapltd.com
- www.mapltd.com

Andrew Bret Wallis Photography Studio 2, Rodley House, Coal Hill Lane, Leeds, LS13 1DJ, United Kingdom
- 0113-236 2223/(07850) 712028 / 0113-236 2223
- email@abw.co.uk
- www.abw.co.uk

Andrew Cameron Studio 31, 25-27 Bickerton Road, London, N19 5JT, United Kingdom
- (020) 7561 0256/(07768) 097010
- andy.cameron@btconnect.com
- www.andycameron.co.uk

Andrew Catterall 37 St. Lukes Road, Old Windsor, Windsor, Berkshire, SL4 2QL, United Kingdom
- (01753) 854411/(07774) 796281
- info@andycatterall.com
- www.andycatterall.com

Andrew Cockrill 448 New Cross Road, London, SE14 6TY, United Kingdom
- (020) 8692 2784
- photography.40@tiscali.co.uk

Andrew Dunn@Creative Talent (UK) Limited 78 York Street, London, W1H 1DP, United Kingdom
- (020) 7439 1877/ (020) 7434 1144
- info@creativetalentlimited.com
- www.creativetalentlimited.com

Andrew Dunn (BSC) Poole House, Castle Street, Nether Stowey, Bridgwater, Somerset, TA5 1LN, United Kingdom
- (01278) 733194/ (01278) 733086
- awdphoto@cs.com

Andrew Errington 14 Nottingham Road, SW17 7EA, United Kingdom
- (020) 8672 9764/(07768) 635710
- mail@andrewerrington.com
- www.andrewerrington.com

Andrew Houston 8 Marshall Road, Cambridge, CB1 7TY, United Kingdom
- (01223) 213232/(07973) 670107 / (01223) 213232
- mail@andrewhouston.com
- www.andrewhouston.com

Andrew Kingsbury 57 Kenwood Gardens, Gants Hill, Ilford, Essex, IG2 6YQ, United Kingdom
- (07836) 766319
- andrewkingsbury@freeuk.com

Andrew Kolesnikow The Old Barn, 13-15 Canfield Place, London, NW6 3BT, United Kingdom
- (01923) 842 238/(07860) 719937 / (020) 7328 1529
- a.kolesnikow@btinternet.com
- www.andrewkolesnikow.com

Andrew Lawson Photography Noahs Ark, Market Street, Charlbury, Oxfordshire, OX7 3PL, United Kingdom
- (01608) 810654/ (01608) 811251
- photos@andrewlawson.com
- www.andrewlawson.com

Andrew Llewellyn Kelmscott House, The Leys, Wightwick Bank, Wolverhampton, WV6 8EA, United Kingdom
- (01902) 762998/(07956) 825601
- info@design-photo.fsnet.co.uk
- www.design-photo.fsnet.co.uk

Andrew McArthur Church Farm, 117 Church Street, Langford, Biggleswade, Bedfordshire, SG18 9NX, United Kingdom
- (01462) 700124/(07973) 735471 / (01462) 700800
- andrew@mcarthur.co.uk
- www.mcarthur.co.uk

Andrew Meredith Photography 17 Chatsfiled Place, London, W5 2GD, United Kingdom
- (07968) 780927
- info@meredithphoto.com
- www.meredithphoto.com

Andrew Newton-Cox 5 Poulton Cottages, Tinpit, Marlborough, Wiltshire, SN8 1BQ, United Kingdom
- (01672) 511973/(07976) 819638 / (01672) 516531
- andrewnewton-cox@eclipse.co.uk

Andrew Olney 180 Victoria Road, London, N22 7XQ, United Kingdom
- (020) 8374 2382/(07768) 198934
- andrew@andrewolney.com
- www.andrewolney.com

Andrew Pendlebury Wallett Street, Nottingham, NG2 3EL, United Kingdom
- 0115-985 0680/(07775) 932544 / 0115-985 0681
- andrewpendlebury@hotmail.com
- www.pendleburystudios.com

Andrew Putler 46 Highbury Hill, London, N5 1AP, United Kingdom
- (020) 7226 9911/(07836) 283284 / (020) 7354 8503
- mail@andrewputler.co.uk
- www.andrewputler.com

Andrew Sydenham 1 The Old Laundry, Alexander Studios, London, SW11 1YF, United Kingdom
- (020) 7207 1957/(07831) 756866 / (020) 7207 1958
- sydphoto@mac.com
- www.andrewsydenham.co.uk

Andrew Thomas La Douelle, rue de Bourg, Dirac, 16410, France
- 00 33 54 562 0741/00 33 68 659 2008
- andrewsimages@aol.com
- www.andrew-thomas.com

Andrew Waffinden@S Management 15 Rocks Lane, London, SW13 0BD, United Kingdom
- (020) 8487 9655/ (020) 8487 9541
- fiona@smanagement.co.uk
- www.smanagement.co.uk

Andrew Weekes Brunswick House, 34 St. Catherines, Lincoln, LN5 8LY, United Kingdom
- (01522) 804144/(07836) 566295 / (01522) 804145
- andrew.weekes@ntlworld.com
- www.contact-ne.net/andrewweekes

Andrew Whittuck 12 Middleton Grove, London, N7 9LS, United Kingdom
- (020) 7607 7373/ (020) 7609 7893
- andrew@whittuck.demon.co.uk

Andrew Wiard 15 Pembroke Road, London, N10 2HR, United Kingdom
- (07973) 219201
- andrew@reportphotos.com
- www.wiard.co.uk

Andy Baker@Début Art & The Coningsby Gallery 30 Tottenham Street, London, W1T 4RJ, United Kingdom
- (020) 7636 1064/ (020) 7580 7017
- info@debutart.com
- www.debutart.com

Andy Barter 6 Warner House, Warner Street, London, EC1R 5ER, United Kingdom
- (020) 7278 8181/(07976) 659172
- andy@andybarter.com
- www.andybarter.com

Andy Chittock Ivydene, Llwyncelyn, Aberaeron, Dyfed, SA46 0HF, United Kingdom
- (01545) 580882/(07774) 652850 / (01545) 580882
- chittockac@aol.com
- www.andychittock.com

Andy Earl Flat 2, 26 Craven Street, London, WC2N 5NT, United Kingdom
- (020) 7403 1156/ (020) 7403 1157
- andyearlphoto@yahoo.co.uk
- www.andyearl.com

Andy Eaves, London, United Kingdom
- (020) 7359 6174/(07966) 278963
- www.andyeaves.com

Andy Flack 12 Waterside Studios, 44-48 Wharf Road, London, N1 7SF, United Kingdom
- (020) 8244 4155/(07831) 651867 / (020) 7253 3203
- www.andyflack-photography.co.uk

Andy Gallacher The Coach House, 10 Causeway Head Road, Sheffield, S17 3DT, United Kingdom
- 0114-262 0032/(07775) 688774 / 0114-262 1691
- andy@gallacher.co.uk
- www.gallacher.co.uk

Andy Glass@Wyatt-Clarke & Jones 26 Mortimer Street, London, W1W 7RB, United Kingdom
- (020) 7580 7570/(07958) 712658 / (020) 7903 5330
- office@wyattclarkejones.com
- www.wyattclarkejones.com

Andy Green@Annabelle Dalton 20 Glebe Street, London, W4 2BG, United Kingdom
- (020) 8742 1883/(07973) 392625 / (020) 8742 1856
- daltphotogr@aol.com
- www.annabelledalton.com

Andy Grimshaw 6 Cameron House, 12 Castlehaven Road, London, NW1 8QW, United Kingdom
- (020) 7267 7600
- andy@andygrimshaw.com

Andy Kruczek Photography 405 The Custard Factory, Gibb Street, Birmingham, B9 4AA, United Kingdom
- (07956) 991786
- andy@kruczek.co.uk
- www.kruczek.co.uk

Andy Lane 62 Bassein Park Road, London, W12 9RZ, United Kingdom
- (020) 8740 9445/(07973) 414257 / (020) 8740 9445
- andy@andylane.com
- www.andylane.com

Andy Mac@Renate Decker-Berry- Europe Unlimited 59 Lambeth Walk, London, SE11 6DX, United Kingdom
- (020) 7735 6623/(07768) 251626 / (0707) 5009648
- renate@europeunlimited.com
- www.europeunlimited.com

Andy Rudak@Mark Gibson 250 York Road, London, SW11 3SJ, United Kingdom
(020) 7228 9085/(07768) 696227
mark@markgibsonphotography.com
www.markgibsonphotography.com

Andy Seymour 82 Princedale Road, Holland Park, London, W11 4NL, United Kingdom
(020) 7221 2021/ (020) 7792 0702
andy@andyseymour.co.uk
www.andyseymour.co.uk
See ad in showcase

Andy Shennan 111 The Fairway, Ruislip, Middlesex, HA4 0SW, United Kingdom
(020) 8842 0108/(07860) 739990
info@andyshennan.com
www.andyshennan.com

Andy Snaith St Michaels Hall, Bennett Road, Leeds, LS6 3HN, United Kingdom
0113-274 9474/(07718) 782440
andy@snakey.net
www.snakey.net

Andy Stevens Photography 31 Redland Grove, Bristol, BS6 6PR, United Kingdom
0117-942 5279/ 0117-942 5289
andrew@andystevensphoto.demon.co.uk
www.andystevensphotography.co.uk

Andy Stewart@Jo Talbot & Sue Young 6M Hyde Park Mansions, Cabbell Street, London, NW1 5BJ, United Kingdom
(020) 7262 0189/(07850) 353468 / (020) 7262 2160
joandsue@btconnect.com
www.joandsue.com

Andy Sutcliffe Photography Sunnycrest, Webbs Terrace, Halifax, West Yorkshire, HX3 6AY, United Kingdom
(01422) 382004/ (01422) 382004
andy@andysutcliffephotography.com
www.andysutcliffephotography.com

Andy Tommo 7 Burgess Hill, West Hampstead, London, NW2 2BY, United Kingdom
(020) 7681 9460/(07976) 760385

Andy Whale 16-24 Underwood Street, London, N1 7JQ, United Kingdom
(020) 7608 3743/(07774) 190023 / (020) 7608 3743
andy@andywhale.com
www.andywhale.com

Andy White 19 Ashbridge Road, Leytonstone, London, E11 1NH, United Kingdom
(020) 8518 8350/(07973) 178613
f@tfish.co.uk
www.tfish.co.uk

The Angela Woods Agency 4 The Carlton Tavern, 73 Grafton Road, London, NW5 4BB, United Kingdom
(020) 7284 3417/(07850) 263077 / (020) 7482 2466
angela@angelawoods.com
www.angelawoods.com

Angus Fraser@Noelle Pickford 27 Britton Street, London, EC1M 5UD, United Kingdom
(020) 7336 6773/ (020) 7336 7043
info@noellerepresents.com
www.noellerepresents.com

Angus Leadley-Brown Studio 11, Debra House, Retreat Place, London, E9 6RJ, United Kingdom
(020) 8986 4093/(07956) 370263
angus@albphoto.com
www.albphoto.com

Anita Corbin 11 Wellesley Park, Wellington, Somerset, TA21 8PT, United Kingdom
(01823) 662329/(07802) 613911 / (01823) 660913
anita.corbin@virgin.net
www.anitacorbin.co.uk

Ann & Bury Peerless 22 Kings Avenue, Minnis Bay, Birchington, Kent, CT7 9QL, United Kingdom
(01843) 841428/ (01843) 848321
ann@peerlessmail.com

Ann Johansson Photography 1254 9th Street #9, Santa Monica, 90401, United States of America
00 1 310 393 2708
ann@annjohansson.com
www.annjohansson.com

Anna Kari Unit 303, Mare Street Studios, 203 Mare Street, London, E8 3QE, United Kingdom
(07944) 357 963
anna@documentography.com
www.annakari.com

Annabelle Dalton 20 Glebe Street, London, W4 2BG, United Kingdom
(020) 8742 1883/(07973) 392625 / (020) 8742 1856
daltphotog@aol.com
www.annabelledalton.com

Anne Dokter@Adrenalin Management Temple Works, Brett Passage, London, E8 1JR, United Kingdom
(020) 8986 3939/ (020) 8986 3665
info@adrenalinmanagement.com
www.adrenalinmanagement.com

Annie Collinge, London, United Kingdom
(07980) 258386
annie@anniecollinge.com
www.anniecollinge.com

Anthea Bowen Willow Tree Cottage, Cloghams Green, Leaden Roding, Dunmow, Essex, CM6 1WG, United Kingdom
(01279) 876640/(07860) 389352
anthea@antheabowen.com
www.antheabowen.com

Anthony Atkins Photography 33 Station Road, Aldridge, Walsall, WS9 0BL, United Kingdom
0121 441 3673
aka_foto@yahoo.co.uk

Anthony Bradshaw 11 The Courtyard, Alexander Studios, London, SW11 1YF, United Kingdom
(020) 8870 6532/(07932) 062001
images@brad.uk.com

Anthony Bryson Bakrac Sokak 1/7, Cihangir, Istanbul, 80060, Turkey
(07760) 406273
info@anthonybryson.com
www.anthonybryson.com

Anthony Bryson Photography 17 Gilpin Green, Harpenden, Hertfordshire, AL5 5NP, United Kingdom
(07760) 406273
info@anthonybryson.com
www.anthonybryson.com

Anthony Cake 3 Georgian Court, Gleneldon Road, London, SW16 2BN, United Kingdom
(020) 8677 5469/(07860) 214031 / (020) 8769 1068
info@anthonycake.com
www.anthonycake.co.uk

Anthony Cotsifas@MAP 72 Rochester Place, London, NW1 9JX, United Kingdom
(020) 7424 9144/ (020) 7284 3274
info@mapltd.com
www.mapltd.com

Anthony Dawton Studio 12, 69 Courtfield Gardens, London, SW5 0NJ, United Kingdom
(020) 7370 1966/(07715) 047381
anthony@dawton.com
www.dawton.com

Anthony Dickenson@Stem Agency Top Floor, 23 Charlotte Road, London, EC2A 3PB, United Kingdom
(07790) 026628
will@stemagency.com
www.stemagency.com

Anthony McArdle (LBIPP) Bigcheese, 10 Windle Court, Neston, CH64 3UH, United Kingdom
0151-336 8882/(07774) 832083 / 0151-336 8371
photography@bigcheese.co.uk
www.bigcheese.co.uk

Anthony Pickhaver Poplar Farm, Duck End, Stebbing, Dunmow, Essex, CM6 3BS, United Kingdom
(01371) 856370
info@pickhaver.com
www.pickhaver.com

Anthony Suau@Bill Charles London Ltd. Unit 3E1, Zetland House, 5-25 Scrutton Street, London, EC2A 4HJ, United Kingdom
020 7033 9284/020 2033 9285
london@billcharles.com
www.billcharles.com

Antoine D'Agata@Magnum Photos 63 Gee Street, London, EC1V 3RS, United Kingdom
(020) 7490 1771/ (020) 7608 0020
magnum@magnumphotos.co.uk
www.magnumphotos.co.uk

Anton Watts@Catherine Collins The Power Station, Coronet Street, London, N1 6HD, United Kingdom
(020) 7739 8678/(07785) 571187 / (020) 7739 8489
catherine@catherinecollins.co.uk
www.catherinecollins.co.uk

Antonia Reeve Photography 11 Grosvenor Crescent, Edinburgh, EH12 5EL, United Kingdom
(07808) 474926/ 0131-337 4640
antoniareevephoto@blueyonder.co.uk

Antonin Kratochvil@Bill Charles London Ltd. Unit 3E1, Zetland House, 5-25 Scrutton Street, London, EC2A 4HJ, United Kingdom
020 7033 9284/020 2033 9285
london@billcharles.com
www.billcharles.com

Antony Crolla@Izzy King 22 Alder Lodge, 73 Stevenage Road, London, SW6 6NP, United Kingdom
(07961) 168086/ (020) 7381 9726
izzy@izzyking.co.uk
www.izzyking.co.uk

Apricot Packshots Depot 14, Parsons Green Depot, Parsons Green, London, SW6 4HH, United Kingdom
(020) 7736 9933
studio@apricotphotography.com
www.apricotphotography.com

Apricot Virtual Support Ltd Unit 14 Parsons Green Depot, Parsons Green lane, London, SW6 4HH, United Kingdom
(0845) 009 3070
support@apricotvs.com
www.apricotvs.com

Aquaviolet Ltd 8 Hartley Close, Lymm, Cheshire, WA13 0JJ, United Kingdom
(01925) 756193/07881 633 192 / (08700) 548785
aquaviolet1@mac.com
www.aquaviolet.com

Archie Miles Photographer Hill House Farm, Stoke Lacy, Bromyard, Herefordshire, HR7 4RE, United Kingdom
(01432) 820588/07891 513045
archiemiles@btinternet.com
www.archiemiles.co.uk

Archie Miles Photography Hill House Farm, Stoke Lacy, Bromyard, Herefordshire, HR7 4RE, United Kingdom
(01432) 820588/ (01432) 520588
hfdarchiemiles@aol.com
www.archiemiles.co.uk

Archimage, London, United Kingdom
(01582) 872179/(07831) 622140
anthony.weller@archimage.co.uk
www.archimage.co.uk

Architek Ltd St. Margaret, Checkendon, Reading, RG8 0TE, United Kingdom
(07973) 165360
paul@architek.co.uk
www.architecturalimages.co.uk

Arden Studios Shepley Lane, Hawk Green, Marple, Stockport, Cheshire, SK6 7JW, United Kingdom
0161-449 6607/ 0161- 449 9436
info@ardenstudios.co.uk
www.ardenstudios.co.uk

Areia London Studio1, 42 Theobalds Road, London, WC1X 8NW, United Kingdom
(020) 7404 8600/ (020) 7404 8601
info@areia.com
www.areia.com

Ariel van Straten 90 Portnall Road, London, W9 3BE, United Kingdom
(07768) 344210
ariel@arielvanstraten.com
www.arielvanstraten.com

Armand Attard@Alexandra Von Ziechmann Flat 1, 90 Sutherland Avenue, London, W9 2QR, United Kingdom
(020) 7289 4248/(07962) 082691
www.alexandravz.com

Armet Francis, London, W10 5ZH, United Kingdom
(020) 8968 7069/ (020) 8968 7069

Armitage Online Solutions 1 Tall Trees, Lancaster, Lancashire, LA1 2LD,
0845 094 3795/ 0845 094 3795
andrew@armitage-online.co.uk
www.armitage-online.co.uk

Aroomwithviews The Barn, Duncastle Farm, Main Road, Alvington, Lydney, Gloucestershire, GL15 6AT, United Kingdom
(01594) 529111/(07836) 216909
steph@molyneuxassociates.com
www.molyneuxassociates.com

Art & Management Studio C19, 71 Warriner Gardens, London, SW11 4XW, United Kingdom
- (020) 7978 1759/ (0870) 4205024
- lisa@artandmanagement.co.uk
- www.artandmanagement.co.uk

Artemi Kyriacou @Gusto 25 Meadway, Barnet, Hertfordshire, EN5 5LG, United Kingdom
- (0845) 2002746/(07785) 723352
- artemi@gustoimages.com
- www.gustoimages.com

Artseens Images The Hub, 123 Star Lane, London, E16 4PZ, United Kingdom
- (020) 7055 0005/ (020) 7055 0005
- info@artseens.co.uk
- www.artseens.com

Ash Photography Church Farm, Ashchurch, Tewkesbury, Gloucestershire, GL20 8JU, United Kingdom
- (01684) 291200/(07885) 670032 (01684) 291201
- info@ashphotography.co.uk
- www.ashphotography.co.uk

Ashley Cameron 12 Empress Mews, Kenbury Street, London, SE5 9BT, United Kingdom
- **(020) 7737 0666/ (020) 7737 4321**
- **ashley@ashleycameron.com**
- **www.ashleycameron.com**
- **See ad in showcase**

Ashton Keiditsch@Joyce Morris, London, SW3 5TQ, United Kingdom
- (020) 7823 3238/(07850) 064222 (020) 7376 7787
- joyce@joycemorris.co.uk
- www.joycemorris.co.uk

Association of Photographers 81 Leonard Street, London, EC2A 4QS, United Kingdom
- (020) 7739 6669/ (020) 7739 8707
- general@aophoto.co.uk
- www.the-aop.org

AtomicSupersonic MCA Studios, Hanger 10, Perseverance Works, 25-27 Hackney Road, London, E2 7NX, United Kingdom
- (020) 7749 5902/ (020) 7749 5909
- info@atomicsupersonic.com
- www.atomicsupersonic.com

Attic 160 Main Street, Bushmills, County Antrim, BT57 8QE, United Kingdom
- (028) 2073 1788
- arthurward@yahoo.com
- www.artwardphotography.com

Avid Photography 4 Churchfield Road, Cheshire, WA6 6RD, United Kingdom
- (07803) 513098
- darren@avidphotography.co.uk
- lisa.avidphotography.co.uk

Aviemore Photographic Edelweiss, Feshie Bridge, Kingussie, Inverness-Shire, PH21 1NG, United Kingdom
- (01540) 651322/(07010) 041338 (01540) 561513
- pavel@aviemorephotographic.com
- www.aviemorephotographic.com

Axel Hoedt 45 Tuder Road, Unit 8, London, E9 7SN, United Kingdom
- (07899) 908 667
- axel.hoedt@btinternet.com
- wwwaxelhoedt.com

Axel Michel 44 Oakington Road, London, W9 2DH, United Kingdom
- (020) 7286 4681/ (020) 7286 4681
- axelm@btinternet.com
- www.axelmichel.com

Axiom Photographic Agency The Pall Mall Deposit, 124-128 Barlby Road, London, W10 6BL, United Kingdom
- (020) 8964 9970/ (020) 8964 8440
- info@axiomphotographic.com
- www.axiomphotographic.com

Axl Jansen@Upper Orange Nostitzstrasse 15, Berlin, 10961, Germany
- 49 178 6121661/ 49 30 6121661
- mail@upperorange.com
- www.upperorange.de

Aylesbury Studios The Merlin Centre, Gatehouse Close, Aylesbury, Buckinghamshire, HP19 8DP, United Kingdom
- (01296) 431707/ (01296) 431707
- sales@aylesburystudios.com

B A Photography Sodens Avenue, Ryton on Dunsmore, Coventry, CV8 3FE, United Kingdom
- (024) 7630 2980
- lee.wilkins2@btopenworld.com

B J P Photography Unit 19, Jubilee Trade Centre, Letchworth Garden City, Hertfordshire, SG6 1SP, United Kingdom
- (01462) 679325
- brian@bjpphotography.co.uk
- www.bjpphotography.co.uk

B M Totterdell Photography (Volleyball) Constable Cottage, Burlings Lane, Knockholt, Sevenoaks, Kent, TN14 7PE, United Kingdom
- (01959) 532001/ (01959) 532001
- btrial@btinternet.com
- www.whatvolleyball.co.uk

B R D Associates 4 The Berries, Hawkinge, Folkestone, Kent, CT18 7PY, United Kingdom
- (01303) 893341/(07768) 510930 (01303) 893341
- brian@brd.uk.com
- www.brd.uk.com

B.E. Gold Photography 1 Salisbury Road, Hove, East Sussex, BN3 3AB, United Kingdom
- (01273) 720042/ (01273) 202533
- mrben.gold@btopenworld.com
- www.bengold.co.uk

Baboo Roberts 62 Ashworth Mansions, Elgin Avenue, London, W9 1LW, United Kingdom
- (020) 7286 1260/(07879) 635537

Bagalue Bonieventure 131 Rendlesham Road, London, E5 8PA, United Kingdom
- (020) 8986 7462/(07956) 665073 (020) 8986 7462
- bonieventure@mac.com
- www.bonphoto.co.uk

Balcony Jump Management 61 Bayham Place, London, NW1 0ET, United Kingdom
- (020) 7121 6380/ (020) 7121 6382
- tim@balconyjump.co.uk
- www.balconyjump.co.uk

Bank House Studio 5 Hewitt Crescent, Werrington, Stoke-on-Trent, ST9 0LQ, United Kingdom
- (01782) 305599/(07005) 948421 (01782) 305599
- info@bankhousestudio.co.uk
- www.bankhousestudio.co.uk

Barbara Bellingham@Début Art & The Coningsby Gallery 30 Tottenham Street, London, W1T 4RJ, United Kingdom
- (020) 7636 1064/ (020) 7580 7017
- info@debutart.com
- www.debutart.com

Barbara Donninelli, London, United Kingdom
- (07801) 698794
- mail@barbaradonninelli.com
- www.barbaradonninelli.com

Barnaby Roper@Ellison Lee 17 Quadrant Business Centre, 135 Salusbury Road, London, NW6 6RJ, United Kingdom
- (020) 7624 2345/ (020) 7624 1100
- info@ellisonlee.com
- www.ellisonlee.com

Barrett-Forster 126 Shoreditch High Street, London, E1 6JE, United Kingdom
- (020) 7739 9300/ (020) 7729 7749
- b-f@barrett-forster.com
- www.barrett-forster.com

Barrie Downie Photography The Stables, Westlands Lane, Birdham, Chichester, West Sussex, PO20 7HH, United Kingdom
- 01243) 514194
- barrie@barriedownie.com
- www.barriedownie.com

Barrie Smith 26A Denbigh Place, London, SW1V 2HA, United Kingdom
- (020) 7834 3007
- barrie@frenchpix.com
- www.frenchpix.com

Barrie Thompson Brooklea Barn, Tabley Lane, Higher Bartle, Preston, PR4 0LH, United Kingdom
- (07894) 278692
- info@barriethompson.com
- www.barriethompson.com

Barrie Watts Photographer Gelli Studio, Crafnant Road, Trefriw, Conwy, LL27 0JZ, United Kingdom
- (01492) 642264
- barrie@barriewatts.co.uk
- www.barriewatts.co.uk

Barry Bullough The Oaks, Millersford, Wood Green Road, Fordingbridge, Hampshire, SP6 2LP, United Kingdom
- (01425) 653405/ (01425) 654800
- b.s.b@btinternet.com

Barry Herman 14 Grosvenor Road, Muswell Hill, London, N10 2DS, United Kingdom
- (020) 8442 1391/(07860) 331060 (020) 8444 6299
- baz@barryherman.co.uk
- www.barryherman.co.uk

Barry Jell Bishops Hall, 8 Ayres Street, London, SE1 1ES, United Kingdom
- (020) 7407 2158/(07775) 658010 (020) 7407 2158
- studio@jell.co.uk

Barry Lategan@Creative Talent (UK) Limited 78 York Street, London, W1H 1DP, United Kingdom
- (020) 7439 1877/ (020) 7434 1144
- info@creativetalentlimited.com
- www.creativetalentlimited.com

Barry Lewis@Jo Talbot & Sue Young 6M Hyde Park Mansions, Cabbell Street, London, NW1 5BJ, United Kingdom
- (020) 7262 0189/(07850) 353468 (020) 7262 2160
- joandsue@btconnect.com
- www.joandsue.com

Barry Marsden 48 Avenue Road, Witham, Essex, CM8 2DP, United Kingdom
- (01376) 516569/(07860) 499706 (01376) 516569
- barrymarsden@btopenworld.com

Barry Pickthall Bookers Yard, The Street, Walberton, Arundel, West Sussex, BN18 0PF, United Kingdom
- (01243) 555561/(07768) 395719 (01243) 555562
- ppl@mistral.co.uk
- www.pplmedia.com

Barry Willis 29 Eversley Road, London, SE19 3PY, United Kingdom
- (020) 8916 1195/ (020) 8916 1195
- barry@barrywillis.com
- www.barrywillis.com

Basement Photographic Unit 22, Soho Mills, Wooburn Green, High Wycombe, Buckinghamshire, HP10 0PF, United Kingdom
- **(01628) 529900/ (01628) 851039**
- **studio@basementphoto.com**
- **www.basementphoto.com**
- **See ad in showcase**

Bay Hippisley@Martin Roper Photographer's Agent 158a Chamberlayne Road, London, NW10 3JS, United Kingdom
- (020) 8964 4780/(0779) 9410942
- martin.roper@btinternet.com
- www.martinroper.com

Beanshoot 24 Ferdinand House, Ferdinand Place, London, NW1 8EB, United Kingdom
- (07903) 502323
- annebv@gmail.com
- www.beanshoot.co.uk

Beasley Photography 2370 Hendon Avenue, St Paul, 55108-1453, United States of America
- 00 1 651 644 1400/ 00 1 651 644 2122
- info@beasleyphotography.com
- www.beasleyphotography.com

Beaver Photography East Mead House, Mis House Road, Lavant, Chichester, West Sussex, PO18 0BB, United Kingdom
- 01243 780616/ 01243 785149
- admin@bvrprint.co.uk
- www.bvrprint.co.uk

Becky Nixon 47 Heathfield Square, London, SW18 3HZ, United Kingdom
- (07881) 825374
- pictures@beckynixon.co.uk
- www.beckynixon.co.uk

Becky Seager@Victoria Lees Management (VLM) 2 Fairview Gardens, Woodford Green, Essex, IG8 7DJ, United Kingdom
- (07710) 287220/ (020) 8504 8125
- victoria@victorialeesmanagement.co.uk
- www.victorialeesmanagement.co.uk

Beken Ltd 16 Birmingham Road, Cowes, Isle of Wight, PO31 7BH, United Kingdom
- (01983) 297311/ (01983) 291059
- beken@beken.co.uk
- www.beken.co.uk

Bellwood Photography 6/8 Barlow Road, Sheffield, S6 5HR, United Kingdom
0114-234 4746/ 0114-285 5667
bellphoto@aol.com
www.bellwood.co.uk

Ben Edwards@Hungry Tiger Unit 16, The Piper Building, Peterborough Road, London, SW6 3EF, United Kingdom
(020) 7751 8600/ (020) 7751 8618
studio@hungrytiger.co.uk
www.hungrytiger.co.uk

Ben Fisher Photography 45-46 Charlotte Road, London, EC2A 3PD, United Kingdom
(020) 7613 1623/(07976) 659605 / (020) 7613 1623
contact@benfisherphotography.com
www.benfisherphotography.com
See ad in showcase

Ben Fitchett B/21 Phipp Street, London, EC2A 4NP, United Kingdom
(07977) 490106/ (020) 7033 9446
ben@parallax.fsnet.co.uk
www.benfitchett.com

Ben Hassett@Blunt Management The Courtyard Studio 2, Old Grammarphone Works, London, W10 5BZ, United Kingdom
(020) 8960 2041/(07979) 900068 / (020) 8960 2039
info@bluntlondon.com
www.bluntlondon.com

Ben Jennings Photography Studio-D, 86 Greenfield Road, London, E1 1EJ, United Kingdom
(020) 7247 9842/ (020) 7247 9843
info@studio-d.co.uk

Ben Monk 1 Darlington Street, London, EC1Z 0EH, United Kingdom
0207 553 7744
ben@benmonk.com
www.benmonk.com

Ben Morris Photography Pleasant Studio, Number 21 (Second Floor), Roseberry Avenue, Clerkenwell, London, EC1R 4SP, United Kingdom
(020) 7833 0940/(07720) 827752
ben@benmorrisphotography.co.uk
www.benmorrisphotography.co.uk

Ben Rector Photography 38 Longfield Road, Wickford, Essex, SS11 8PU, United Kingdom
(07770) 467791
ben@benrector.com
www.benrector.com

Ben Rice 1 Rushworth Studios, 63 Webber Street, London, SE1 0QW, United Kingdom
(020) 7261 9753/ (020) 7401 2206
ben@benrice.com
www.benrice.com

Ben Shaul@Adrenalin Management Temple Works, Brett Passage, London, E8 1JR, United Kingdom
(020) 8986 3939/ (020) 8986 3665
info@adrenalinmanagement.com
www.adrenalinmanagement.com

Ben Stockley@Agent Orange 10 Swan Yard, London, N1 1SD, United Kingdom
(020) 7226 0440/ (020) 7226 1613
annika@agentorange.co.uk
www.agentorange.co.uk

Benedict Campbell@Début Art & The Coningsby Gallery 30 Tottenham Street, London, W1T 4RJ, United Kingdom
(020) 7636 1064/ (020) 7580 7017
info@debutart.com
www.debutart.com

Benedict Luxmoore@Arcaid Picture Library Parc House, 25-37 Cowleaze Road, Kingston upon Thames, Surrey, KT2 6DZ, United Kingdom
(020) 8546 4352/ (020) 8541 5230
arcaid@arcaid.co.uk
www.arcaid.co.uk

Benjamin Kaufmann@S Management 15 Rocks Lane, London, SW13 0BD, United Kingdom
(020) 8487 9655/ (020) 8487 9541
fiona@smanagement.co.uk
www.smanagement.co.uk

Benjamin Kaufmann Photography 5a Hugo Road, Garden Flat, London, N19 5EU, United Kingdom
(020) 7619 9009/ (07950) 452 109
mail@benjaminkaufmann.com
www.benjaminkaufmann.com

Benoit Ltd Flat 5, Grove House, 16 Tudor Grove, London, E9 7QP, United Kingdom
(020) 8985 9343/ (020) 8985 9343
studio@benoitaudureau.com
www.benoitaudureau.com

Berkowitz Photography Whithou, Market Square, Coldstream, Berwickshire, TD12 4BG, United Kingdom
(01890) 883756/(07831) 761067
bb@berkowitzphotography.com
www.berkowitzphotography.com

Bernard Bleach Photography Barrington House, Barrington Road, Horsham, West Sussex, RH13 5SN, United Kingdom
(01403) 270888
info@bernardbleachphotography.com
www.bernardbleachphotography.com

Bernard Levy@Adrenalin Management Temple Works, Brett Passage, London, E8 1JR, United Kingdom
(020) 8986 3939/ (020) 8986 3665
info@adrenalinmanagement.com
www.adrenalinmanagement.com

Bernd Eberle Photographer Heideckstr 12, Munich, 80637, Germany
00 49 89 547 79849
mail@berndeberle.com
www.berndeberle.com

Bernie Martins@Jo Talbot & Sue Young 6M Hyde Park Mansions, Cabbell Street, London, NW1 5BJ, United Kingdom
(020) 7262 0189/(07850) 353468 / (020) 7262 2160
joandsue@btconnect.com
www.joandsue.com

Berry Bingel c/o David Hall, 197 Boston Manor Road, Brentford, Middlesex, TW8 9LE, United Kingdom
(0871) 2102013/(07768) 077254 / (020) 8400 7574
info@photohall.co.uk
www.berrybingel.co.uk

Beth Coyne Agency, London, NW6 1GF, United Kingdom
(020) 7431 8981/ (020) 7813 9750
info@bethcoyne.com
www.bethcoyne.com

Beth Evans@Tattersall Love 40 Langham Street, London, W1W 7AS, United Kingdom
(020) 7637 5737/ (020) 7637 5747
mail@tattersall-love.com
www.tattersall-love.com

Beth Wightman Represents Studio, 42 Theobalds Road, London, WC1X 8NW, United Kingdom
(020) 7404 9003/ (020) 7430 1771
beth@bethwightman.com
www.bethwightman.com

Beyond Design UK Ltd Stubbings House, Henley Road, Maidenhead, Berkshire, SL6 6QL, United Kingdom
(01628) 823007
mail@beyond-design.co.uk
www.beyond-design.co.uk

Big Active Ltd Unit 6.01, The Tea Building, 56 Shoreditch High Street, London, E16 JJ, United Kingdom
(020) 7739 5601/ (020) 7739 7479
contact@bigactive.com
www.bigactive.com

Bigcheese 10 Windle Court, Clayhill, Neston, CH64 3UH, United Kingdom
0151-336 8882/(07774) 944943 / 0151-336 8371
photography@bigcheese.co.uk
www.bigcheese.co.uk

Bill Batten 67 Brixton Water Lane, London, SW2 1PH, United Kingdom
(020) 7274 7555/ (020) 7738 7183
bill.rbatten@virgin.net

Bill Burnett 2 Bleedingheart Yard, London, EC1N 8SJ, United Kingdom
(020) 7242 7031

Bill Halford Saint Vincent School, Greenside Street, Manchester, M11 2EX, United Kingdom
0161-223 9666/ 0161-223 9686
bill@billhalfordphoto.com
www.billhalfordphoto.com

Bill Kaye@Blowup 146 Amyand Park Road, St. Margaret's, Twickenham, TW1 3HY, United Kingdom
(020) 8744 0210/ (020) 8892 2521
orders@blowup.net
www.blowup.net

Bill Kingston@Re:fresh Suit 4, The Swans Centre, Fishers Lane, London, W4 1RX, United Kingdom
(020) 8747 8080/ (020) 8747 8228
info@refresh-agency.com
www.refresh-agency.com

Bill McConkey@Début Art & The Coningsby Gallery 30 Tottenham Street, London, W1T 4RJ, United Kingdom
(020) 7636 1064/ (020) 7580 7017
info@debutart.com
www.debutart.com

Bill Morton, London, EC1A 1LB, United Kingdom
(01635) 529943/(07831) 880075 / (01635) 529943
billmorton@btconnect.com
www.billmortonphotography.com

Bill Owens@Bill Charles London Ltd. Unit 3E1, Zetland House, 5-25 Scrutton Street, London, EC2A 4HJ, United Kingdom
020 7033 9284/020 2033 9285
london@billcharles.com
www.billcharles.com

Bill Prentice@Photographic Techniques Ltd 1b Montague Road, Wimbledon Broadway, London, SW19 1TB, United Kingdom
(020) 8542 2444/ (020) 8542 3444
images@phototech.co.uk
www.phototech.co.uk

Bill Robinson@Process 5 Choumert Mews, Choumert Road, London, SE15 4BD, United Kingdom
(020) 7277 8400/(07950) 311425 / (020) 7277 7223
info@processphotography.com
www.processphotography.com

Birgir.org Engihjalli 5, Kopavogur, IS-200, Iceland
00 354 8214600
birgir@birgir.org
www.birgir.org

Black & Ginger 14 Colquitt Street, Liverpool, L1 4DE, United Kingdom
(07782) 201620
alex@blackandginger.com
www.blackandginger.com

Black Paw Ink 6 Woodhayes Road, Wimbledon, London, SW19 4RJ, United Kingdom
(020) 8946 6038/ (020) 8944 8171
blackpaw_ink@hotmail.com
www.carew-hunt.com

Black Sheep Display 141/149 Upper Newtownards Road, Belfast, BT4 3HX, United Kingdom
(028) 9065 7404/ (028) 9065 7919
info@blacksheepni.com
www.blacksheepdisplay.com

Blerim Racaj 9 George Mews, London, NW1 2EU, United Kingdom
(07792) 959732
info@blerimracaj.com
www.blerimracaj.com

Blink Photographic Ltd Studio House, 142 Merton Hall Road, Wimbledon, London, SW19 3PZ, United Kingdom
(020) 8543 3855
sales@blinkphotographic.co.uk
www.blink photographic.co.uk

Blinkk@Webber Represents Ltd 25 Lexington Street, Soho, London, W1F 9AG, United Kingdom
(020) 7439 0678/ (020) 7439 0543
london@webberrepresents.com
www.webberrepresents.com

Blokford Ltd Basement, 12-14 Whitfield Street, London, W1T 2RF,
4.47948E+11
joakim@joakimblockstrom.com
www.joakimblockstrom.com

Blowup 146 Amyand Park Road, St. Margaret's, Twickenham, TW1 3HY, United Kingdom
(020) 8744 0210/ (020) 8892 2521
orders@blowup.net
www.blowup.net

Blue Chapter Havelock Studio, 2 Havelock Terrace, London, SW8 4AR, United Kingdom
(07768) 708288
maryrose@whitcomb.co.uk
www.bluechapter.co.uk

Blueskystudio Bluebell Cottage, Steeple Lane, St. Ives, Cornwall, TR26 2GY, United Kingdom
(01736) 793740
kerry@blueskystudio.co.uk
www.blueskystudio.co.uk

Blunt Management The Courtyard Studio 2, Old Grammarphone Works, London, W10 5BZ, United Kingdom
(020) 8960 2041/(07979) 900068 (020) 8960 2039
info@bluntlondon.com
www.bluntlondon.com

Bob Aird 23 Glen View, Cumbernauld, Glasgow, G67 2DA, United Kingdom
(01236) 731770/(07831) 875478 (01236) 731770
bob@airdfoto.co.uk
www.airdfoto.co.uk

Bob Cramp Southwest Photographic The Buttery, Oare, Lynton, Devon, EX35 6NU, United Kingdom
(01598) 741106/(07099) 723183 (01598) 741196
bobcramp1@btinternet.com

Bob Elsdale@Yara Gremoli Photographers Agent Studio 210, Canalot Studios, 222 Kensal Road, London, W10 5BN, United Kingdom
(0870) 8501209/(07880) 627413 (0870) 8501209
yara@sbmanagement.org
www.yaragremoli.com

Bob Fyffe 4 The Courtyard, Alexander Studios, Haydon Way, London, SW11 1YF, United Kingdom
(020) 7207 8778/(07831) 455754 (020) 7207 8787
info@mansfieldfyffe.co.uk
www.mansfieldfyffe.co.uk

Bob Harris 26 Albany Park Road, Kingston upon Thames, Surrey, KT2 5SW, United Kingdom
(020) 8546 4018/(07802) 457940 (020) 8546 4018

Bob Komar 12 Cranford Close, London, SW20 0DP, United Kingdom
(020) 8946 9353/(07860) 217638
bob@komarpix.com
www.komarpix.com

Bob Miller 22 Gerard Road, London, SW13 9RG, United Kingdom
(020) 8748 7133
lensmiller@btopenworld.com

Bob Norris@Mark Gibson 250 York Road, London, SW11 3SJ, United Kingdom
(020) 7228 9085/(07768) 696227
mark@markgibsonphotography.com
www.markgibsonphotography.com

Bob Turner 57 Burdon Lane, Cheam, Surrey, SM2 7BY, United Kingdom
(020) 8642 3593/ (020) 8395 7230
images@artdirectors.co.uk
www.artdirectors.co.uk

Bobby Fisher@MAP 72 Rochester Place, London, NW1 9JX, United Kingdom
(020) 7424 9144/ (020) 7284 3274
info@mapltd.com
www.mapltd.com

Bocek Production Cubuklu cad.agaclik mesire yeri, d+e burunbahce, beykoz, Istanbul, 34805,
00 9 02166801058
selma@bocekyapim.com.tr
www.bocekyapim.com.tr

Bombshell Ent Inc 6588 Wellington Avenue, West Vancouver, V7W 2H9, Canada
00 1 800 921 9882/ 00 1 604 921 6654
cbenge@shaw.ca
info@chrisb.com

Bonakdar Cleary 35 Charles Square, London, N1 6HT, United Kingdom
(020) 7490 1155
bc@bonakdarcleary.com
www.bonakdarcleary.com

Branka Jukic 67A Saint Margaret's Road, Twickenham, TW1 2LL, United Kingdom
(020) 8744 1070/ (020) 8287 1374
bj@brankajukic.com

Brendon MacNeill 34 Jane Street, Edinburgh, EH6 5HD, United Kingdom
0131-555 1118/(07774) 806608
brendan@macneill.co.uk
www.macneill.co.uk

Brian Bradbury Rose Mount Cottage, St. Johns Road, Wroxall, Ventnor, Isle of Wight, PO38 3EE, United Kingdom
(01983) 854646/(07974) 476774 (01983) 854646
brian.bradburyphotographer@virgin.net
www.brianbradburyphotographer.com

Brian Evans 457 North End Road, Fulham, London, SW6 1NZ, United Kingdom
(020) 7385 9600/ (020) 7385 9600
bripix@hotmail.com

Brian Galloway 77 Peterborough Road, London, SW6 3BT, United Kingdom
(07973) 386904
brian@gallowayphoto.co.uk
www.gallowayphoto.co.uk

Brian Nash 36 St Stephen's Gardens, Bayswater, London, W2 5NJ, United Kingdom
(020) 7727 2626
brnnsh@aol.com

Brian Nice@,Brian Seaward 106 Tollington Park, London, N4 3RB, United Kingdom
/(07941) 158810
brian@brianseaward.co.uk
www.brianseaward.co.uk

Bridlington Colour Labs Ltd 95 Kingsgate, Bridlington, East Yorkshire, YO15 3NQ, United Kingdom
(01262) 673400/(07932) 141129
david@callme.go-plus.net
www.davidowenphotography.com

Brightline Imaging Lodge Farm Studios, Tilford Road, Farnham, Surrey, GU9 8HU, United Kingdom
/(07776) 425474 (01252) 719223
mail@brightline.co.uk
www.brightline.co.uk

Broad Daylight Ltd 18a Albany Street, Edinburgh, EH1 3QB, United Kingdom
0131-477 9571
info@broaddaylightltd.co.uk
www.broaddaylightltd.co.uk

Brooke's Photography The Barn, 2 Sidney Road, Beckenham, Kent, BR3 4QA, United Kingdom
(020) 8658 0989/(07774) 859717 (020) 8650 0259
g.brooke@btconnect.com

Browns Photography Ltd 34 Rokeby Drive, Gosforth, Newcastle upon Tyne, NE3 4JY, United Kingdom
0191-285 7004
info@brownsphotography.com
www.brownsphotography.com

Bruce Anderson Photography 126 Shoreditch High Street, London, E1 6JE, United Kingdom
(020) 7729 2299/(07930) 406668
bruce@bruceanderson.co.uk
www.bruceanderson.co.uk

Bruce Davidson@Magnum Photos 63 Gee Street, London, EC1V 3RS, United Kingdom
(020) 7490 1771/ (020) 7608 0020
magnum@magnumphotos.co.uk
www.magnumphotos.com

Bruce Fleming 60 Wimpole Street, London, W1G 8AG, United Kingdom
(020) 7486 4001/ (020) 7486 4001
mail@brucefleming.com
www.brucefleming.com

Bruce Gilden@Magnum Photos 63 Gee Street, London, EC1V 3RS, United Kingdom
(020) 7490 1771/ (020) 7608 0020
magnum@magnumphotos.co.uk
www.magnumphotos.com

Bruce Head Photographer The Studio, 1 Avenue Approach, Bury St. Edmunds, Suffolk, IP32 6BA, United Kingdom
(01284) 760159/(07885) 370980
bruce@brucehead.com
www.fabfoodphotography.com

Bruce Hemming Lloyds Cottage, Wallcrouch, Wadhurst, East Sussex, TN5 7JL, United Kingdom
(01580) 200277/(07974) 918414
bruce@bhphoto.biz
www.bhphoto.biz

Bruce Mackie 4th Floor, 37-42 Compton Street, London, EC1V 0AP, United Kingdom
(020) 7608 2888/(07831) 230090 (020) 7608 2889
bruce@mackie.co.uk
www.mackie.co.uk

Bruce Smith, Liverpool, United Kingdom
0151-284 9052/(07958) 231761
b.s@mac.com
www.brucesmithphoto.com

Bruno Barbey@Magnum Photos 63 Gee Street, London, EC1V 3RS, United Kingdom
(020) 7490 1771/ (020) 7608 0020
magnum@magnumphotos.co.uk
www.magnumphotos.com

Bruno Fabbris@S Management 15 Rocks Lane, London, SW13 0BD, United Kingdom
(020) 8487 9655/ (020) 8487 9541
fiona@smanagement.co.uk
www.smanagement.co.uk

Bryan James Brophy Photography 51 Knocklyon Road, Templeogue, Dublin 16, Ireland, Republic of
00 353 1 493 9947/00 353 87 246 9221 00 353 1 493 9947
bryan@bjbphotography.com
www.bjbphotography.com

Buchanan Davey 7 Orleston Road, London, N7 8LH, United Kingdom
(020) 7619 9943
info@buchanandavey.com
www.buchanandavey.com

Bullock Partners Poplars Farm, Knightcote, Southam, Warwickshire, CV47 2SF, United Kingdom
(01926) 815154/(07836) 510082

Bullock Partners Photography Poplars Farm, Knightcote, Southam, Warwickshire, CV47 2SF, United Kingdom
(07710) 295956
jax@bullockpartners.co.uk
www.bullockpartners.com

Burnham Niker Unit 8, Canonbury Business Centre, 190A New North Road, London, N1 7BJ, United Kingdom
(020) 7704 6565/ (020) 7704 8383
enquiries@burnham-niker.com
www.burnham-niker.com

Burt Glinn@Magnum Photos 63 Gee Street, London, EC1V 3RS, United Kingdom
(020) 7490 1771/ (020) 7608 0020
magnum@magnumphotos.co.uk
www.magnumphotos.com

C B A 11 The Paddock, Hambridge Road, Newbury, Berkshire, RG14 5TQ, United Kingdom
(01635) 32259
cbaphotography@btconnect.com

C G S Photographers The Studio, 102 Ewell Bypass, Ewell, Epsom, Surrey, KT17 2PP, United Kingdom
(020) 8394 0010
info@cgs-photographers.co.uk
www.cgs-photographers.co.uk

C J B Photography 39 Central Road, Portchester, Fareham, Hampshire, PO16 9AG, United Kingdom
(023) 9232 4591/(07836) 795584
chris@cjbphotography.co.uk
www.cjbphotography.co.uk

C L M Top Floor, 19 All Saints Road, London, W11 1HE, United Kingdom
(020) 7750 2999/ (020) 7792 8507
clm@clmuk.com
www.clmuk.com

C M E Images Flat 1, 59 Westwood Hill, London, SE26 6NS, United Kingdom
(07990) 543031/ (020) 8659 5872
chris.edwards@cmeimages.co.uk
www.cmeimages.co.uk

C S B Management 40 Bowling Green Lane, London, EC1R 0NE, United Kingdom
(020) 7415 7051/ (020) 7415 7059
susie@csbmanagement.com
www.csbmanagement.com

C W A Studios Ltd 10 Treadaway Technical Centre, Treadaway Hill, Loudwater, High Wycombe, Buckinghamshire, HP10 9RS, United Kingdom
(01628) 530676/ (01628) 810085
info@cwa-studios.com
www.cwa-studios.com

Cafe du Monde Rectory Road, London, SW13, United Kingdom
(07092) 301146
creative@cafedumonde.net
www.cafedumonde.net

Calvert Studios Ltd Enterprise Way, Grovebury Road, Leighton Buzzard, Bedfordshire, LU7 4SZ, United Kingdom
(01525) 853700/(07831) 562152 (01525) 852111
kevin@calvertstudios.com
www.calvertstudios.com

Calvey Taylor-Haw Studios 46 Hill Drive, Hove, East Sussex, BN3 6QL, United Kingdom
📞 (01273) 565999/(07802) 206887 📠 (01273) 565999
✉ calvey@calvey-studios.co.uk
🖥 www.calvey-studios.com

Cameo Photography Cameo House, 1072 High Road, London, N20 0QP, United Kingdom
📞 (020) 8446 4477/ 📠 (020) 8446 8181
✉ info@cameophoto.co.uk
🖥 www.cameophoto.co.uk

Cameo Photography Ltd Harding Way, Somersham Road, St. Ives, Cambridgeshire, PE27 3WR, United Kingdom
📞 (01480) 467708/ 📠 (01480) 465830
✉ cameophotography@btinternet.com
🖥 www.cameostudios.co.uk

Camera Crew Heywood, Best Lane, Oxenhope, Keighley, West Yorkshire, BD22 9NA, United Kingdom
📞 (01535) 647439/(07703) 360858
✉ ccrew@btconnect.com
🖥 www.cameracrewdigital.co.uk

Camera Press 21 Queen Elizabeth Street, London, SE1 2PD, United Kingdom
📞 (020) 7378 1300/ 📠 (020) 7278 5126
✉ info@camerapress.com
🖥 www.camerapress.com

Cameron Watt@Mark Gibson 250 York Road, London, SW11 3SJ, United Kingdom
📞 (020) 7228 9085/(07768) 696227
✉ mark@markgibsonphotography.com
🖥 www.markgibsonphotography.com

Campos & Davis Photos 6 Cranbourne Road, London, N10 2BT, United Kingdom
📞 (020) 8883 8638/ 📠 (020) 8815 0070
✉ photos@campos-davis.com
🖥 www.campos-davis.com

Candice@Traffic Unit P102, 23 - 28 Penn Street, London, N1 7DL, United Kingdom
📞 020 7739 6090
✉ rebecca@rebeccavalentine.com
🖥 www.trafficphotographic.com

Candice Photography Ltd The Studio, 1 Sunnyhill Road, London, SW16 2UG, United Kingdom
📞 (020) 7787 9396/(07778) 616990 📠 (020) 7787 9896
✉ info@candice.co.uk
🖥 www.candice.co.uk

Car Photo Library 28 Fernside Road, Talbot Park, Bournemouth, BH9 2LB, United Kingdom
📞 (01202) 528849/(07785) 537928
✉ davidkimber@carphoto.co.uk
🖥 www.carphoto.co.uk

Caramel Photography 5 Pingate Drive, Cheadle Hulme, Cheadle, Cheshire, SK8 6NL, United Kingdom
📞 0161-485 2318/(07712) 863864
✉ info@caramelphoto.com
🖥 www.caramelphoto.com

Carisma-Photographers Rue Langeveld 12, Brussels, B-1180, Belgium
📞 00 32 23 754 415/47 333 4150
✉ martin@carisma-photographers.com
🖥 www.carisma-photographers.com

Carl Cori Lyttle 14A Dufours Place, London, W1V 1FE, United Kingdom
📞 (020) 7287 0884/(07850) 390611 📠 (020) 7734 8792
✉ carl@carllyttle.com
🖥 www.carllyttle.com

Carl de Keyzer@Magnum Photos 63 Gee Street, London, EC1V 3RS, United Kingdom
📞 (020) 7490 1771/ 📠 (020) 7608 0020
✉ magnum@magnumphotos.co.uk
🖥 www.magnumphotos.com

Carl Lyttle@Noelle Pickford 27 Britton Street, London, EC1M 5UD, United Kingdom
📞 (020) 7336 6773/ 📠 (020) 7336 7043
✉ info@noellerepresents.com
🖥 www.noellerepresents.com

Carl Sanders Photography Tower Studios, London, NW5 4PU, United Kingdom
📞 (020) 7485 9585
✉ carl@newmedia.demon.co.uk
🖥 www.newmedia.demon.co.uk

Carl Warner Photography No 1 The Printworks, 230 Long Lane, London, SE1 4QB, United Kingdom
📞 (020) 7357 6353/ 📠 (020) 7357 6373
✉ carl@carlwarner.com
🖥 www.carlwarner.com

Carl Wilson Ltd The Old Bakery, Rear Of, 695 Blandford Road, Poole, Dorset, BH16 5ET, United Kingdom
📞 (01202) 620824/(07850) 877654
✉ carl@carlwilson.com
🖥 www.carlwilson.com

Carlo Miari Fulcis@Sharon Brandman Agency No 2 Milner Court, Bridgewater Way, Bushey, WD23 4UB, United Kingdom
📞 020 8950 9213/07973 305575 📠 020 8950 7990
✉ sharon@sharonbrandman.com
🖥 www.sharonbrandman.com

Carlos Dominguez Unit 6A, 9 Park Hill, London, SW4 9NS, United Kingdom
📞 (020) 7622 2255/078 36 717861 📠 (020) 7622 2255
✉ cadaphoto@easynet.co.uk
🖥 www.dominguez.co.uk

Carlton Davis@C L M Top Floor, 19 All Saints Road, London, W11 1HE, United Kingdom
📞 (020) 7750 2999/ 📠 (020) 7792 8507
✉ clm@clmuk.com
🖥 www.clmuk.com

Carnegie & Conway Photography, London, United Kingdom
📞 (020) 8444 2985/(07884) 376686
✉ info@carnegieconway.com
🖥 www.carnegieconway.com

Carnival of Souls Photography 158 Platt Lane, Manchester, M14 7PY, United Kingdom
📞 (07792) 953930
✉ carnival-of-souls@lycos.co.uk
🖥 www.carnival-of-souls.co.uk

Carol Fulton Photography 32 Bridge Street, Wye, Ashford, Kent, TN25 5EA, United Kingdom
📞 (07754) 877333
✉ images@carolfulton.com
🖥 www.carolfulton.com

liz artindale
photographer

architecture
interiors
people
landscapes
travel

www.lizartindale.co.uk

9

Carol kwok 41b Fairholme Road, London, W14 9JZ, United Kingdom
- (020) 7385 9222
- carol@carolkwok.com
- www.carolkwok.com

Carol Sharp 71 Leonard Street, London, EC2A 4QU, United Kingdom
- (020) 7729 8040/ (020) 7729 7909
- carol@carolsharp.co.uk
- www.carolsharp.co.uk

Carolina Ambida 20 South Villas, Camden Square, London, NW1 9BS, United Kingdom
- (020) 7424 0102/(07956) 264321

Caroline Arber@Creative Talent (UK) Limited 78 York Street, London, W1H 1DP, United Kingdom
- (020) 7439 1877/ (020) 7434 1144
- info@creativetalentlimited.com
- www.creativetalentlimited.com

Caroline Bamber Photographic Management 72 Harberton Road, London, N19 3JP, United Kingdom
- (07968) 946752
- caroline@carolinebamber.com
- www.carolinebamber.com

Caroline Binch 1-2 Bojewyan Stennack, Pendeen, Penzance, Cornwall, TR19 7TN, United Kingdom
- (01736) 786100
- ceebee.info@carolinebinch.co.uk
- www.carolinebinch.co.uk

Caroline Ryan@Germaine Walker Photographers' Agent Crayford House, 49A Tabley Road, London, N7 0NA, United Kingdom
- (020) 7697 8291/(07867) 780272/ (020) 7619 9051
- germaine@germaine.co.uk
- www.germaine.co.uk

Carolyn Trayler Photographers Agent Unit 566, 56 Gloucester Road, London, SW7 4UB, United Kingdom
- (020) 7370 0712/ (020) 7370 0765
- carolyn@trayler.co.uk
- www.trayler.co.uk

Carsten Flieger 417 Dumbarton Road, Glasgow, G11 6DD, United Kingdom
- 0141-334 6254/(07958) 550333
- carsten@carstenflieger.com
- www.carstenflieger.com

Cassandra Photography 38 Moorland View, Crownhill, Plymouth, PL6 6AN, United Kingdom
- (07786) 075125
- cassandra_horsley@hotmail.com
- www.cassandra-photography.com

Cat Stevens, London, E2 7ST, United Kingdom
- (07714) 098734
- catstevens1@gmail.com
- www.catstevensphotography.co.uk

Catherine Ashmoore 4B Moore Park Road, London, SW6 2JT, United Kingdom
- (020) 7381 0007/ (020) 7381 0008
- dominicphoto@catherineashmoore.co.uk

Catherine Collins The Power Station, Coronet Street, London, N1 6HD, United Kingdom
- (020) 7739 8678/(07785) 571187/ (020) 7739 8489
- catherine@catherinecollins.co.uk
- www.catherinecollins.co.uk

Central Photography 10 Victoria Park, Dover, Kent, CT16 1QR, United Kingdom
- (01304) 215938/(07974) 746766 (01303) 779734
- info@centralphotography.com
- www.centralphotography.com

CG Photography 4 Sumpter Pathway, Chester, Cheshire, CH2 3JF,
- 7830114054/ 1244463319
- crawlergraphic@postmaser.co.uk
- www.crawlergraphic.co.uk

Chapman Brown Partnership 133 Norton Road, Stockton-on-Tees, Cleveland, TS18 2BG, United Kingdom
- (01642) 679333/(07831) 819922 (01642) 679333
- chapmanbrown@boxbrownie.co.uk
- www.boxbrownie.co.uk

Charles Best 1 Cumberland Gardens, London, WC1X 9AF, United Kingdom
- (020) 7837 3271/(07860) 281633
- charlie@charlesbest.co.uk
- www.charlesbest.co.uk

Charles Dragazis Photography Unit 301 Kings Wharf, 297-301 Kingsland Road, London, E8 4DS, United Kingdom
- /(07973) 540834
- charles@dragazis.com
- www.dragazis.com

Charles Tait Photographic Ltd Kelton, St. Ola, Kirkwall, Orkney, KW15 1TR, United Kingdom
- (01856) 873738/(07785) 220269 (01856) 875313
- charles.tait@zetnet.co.uk
- www.charles-tait.co.uk

Charles Ward Photography Farm Studios, London End, Earls Barton, Northampton, NN6 0EZ, United Kingdom
- (01604) 812465/ (01604) 812778
- craig@charlesward.com
- www.charlesward.com

Charlie Fawell 40 Ondine Road, East Dulwich, London, SE15 4EB, United Kingdom
- (020) 8299 8299/(07802) 820408
- info@charliefawell.com
- www.charliefawell.com

Charlie Gray Manhattan Building, The Bow Quarter, Fairfield Road, London, E3 2UQ, United Kingdom
- (07909) 988866
- studio@charlie-gray.com
- www.charlie-gray.com

Charlie Hopkinson Photographer, London, United Kingdom
- (07976) 402891
- charlie@charliehopkinson.com
- www.charliehopkinson.com

Charlie Kemp Flat 8, Bronwen Court, Grove End Road, London, NW8 9HH, United Kingdom
- (020) 7286 5878/ (020) 7286 5878

Charlie Magee 13 Chertsey Road, London, E11 4DG, United Kingdom
- (020) 8539 1507/(07831) 093730 (020) 8923 1192
- charlie@charliemagee.com
- www.charliemagee.com

Charlie Phillips@Akehurst Creative Management Ltd London, United Kingdom
- (020) 7624 2366
- na@nickyakehurst.com
- www.akehurstcreativemanagement.com

Charlie Surbey Studio 3H, Leyroy House, 436 Essex Road, London, N1 3QD, United Kingdom
- (020) 7226 8799/ (020) 7704 5252
- charlie@surbey.com
- www.csurbey.com

Charlie Varley North Cottage, Upper Sheriff Farmhouse, Hammingden Lane, Ardingly, Haywards Heath, West Sussex, RH17 6SR, United Kingdom
- (01444) 891340/(07836) 322227
- charlie.varley@tiscali.co.uk

Charlie Waite@Rosie Beckett 102 Cole Park Road, Twickenham, TW1 1JA, United Kingdom
- (020) 8255 1574/(07973) 193071
- rosiebeckett@mac.com

Charlotte Krag Ground Floor Studio, 10-11 Bishop's Terrace, London, SE11 4UE, United Kingdom
- (020) 7735 5353/ (020) 7735 9944
- charlottephoto@lineone.net
- www.charlottekrag.com

Charnock Photography South Lodge Studio, Chorley Road, Wigan, Lancashire, WN1 2XN, United Kingdom
- (01257) 427447/(07957) 996382 (01257) 427447
- phil@charnockphotography.co.uk
- www.charnockphotography.co.uk

Cheryl Maeder@Jo Clark 2nd Floor, 202B Camden Lock, London, NW1 8AF, United Kingdom
- (020) 7267 7267/ (020) 7267 7495
- jo@joclark.com
- www.joclark.com

Chiara Romagnoli@Sarah Kaye Representation Ltd 38 Queen's Gate, London, SW7 5HR, United Kingdom
- (020) 7225 5005/ (020) 7225 0109
- sarah@sarahkaye.com
- www.sarahkaye.com

Chien-Chi Chang@Magnum Photos 63 Gee Street, London, EC1V 3RS, United Kingdom
- (020) 7490 1771/ (020) 7608 0020
- magnum@magnumphotos.co.uk
- www.magnumphotos.com

Chippy Tiffany Perseverance Works, Kingsland Road, London, E2 8DD, United Kingdom
- (07850) 540701
- www.chippy.co.uk

Chris Bailey@Carolyn Trayler Photographers Agent Unit 566, 56 Gloucester Road, London, SW7 4UB, United Kingdom
- (020) 7370 0712/ (020) 7370 0765
- carolyn@trayler.co.uk
- www.trayler.co.uk

Chris Bell Photography Unit 8, Cedar Way, Camley Street, London, NW1 0PD, United Kingdom
- (020) 7388 4500/(07850) 652911 (020) 7388 4119
- contact@chrisbell.co.uk
- www.chrisbell.co.uk

Chris Biggs & Associates 167-169 Great Portland Street, London, W1W 5PF, United Kingdom
- **(020) 7323 6606/ (020) 7636 6606**
- **laura@chrisbiggs.co.uk**
- **www.chrisbiggs.co.uk**
- **See ad in showcase**

Chris Blott@Sarah Kaye Representation Ltd 38 Queen's Gate, London, SW7 5HR, United Kingdom
- (020) 7225 5005/ (020) 7225 0109
- sarah@sarahkaye.com
- www.sarahkaye.com

Chris Caldicott@Axiom Photographic Agency The Pall Mall Deposit, 124-128 Barlby Road, London, W10 6BL, United Kingdom
- (020) 8964 9970/ (020) 8964 8440
- info@axiomphotographic.com
- www.axiomphotographic.com

Chris Close, London, N4 4RR, United Kingdom
- (020) 8341 9880/(07740) 870579 (020) 8341 9880
- cc@chrisclose.co.uk
- www.chrisclose.co.uk

Chris Close Photography 21 Kirkhill Road, Edinburgh, EH16 5DE, United Kingdom
- 0131-662 9999/(07740) 870579 0131-662 9999
- cc@chrisclose.co.uk
- www.chrisclose.co.uk

Chris Coe 20 Yew Tree Courtyard, Framlingham Road, Earl Soham, Woodbridge, Suffolk, IP13 7SG, United Kingdom
- (01728) 669 185/(07941) 111 430 (01728) 669 185
- email@chriscoe.com
- www.chriscoe.com

Chris Coles 37 Fitzjohn Avenue, Barnet, Hertfordshire, EN5 2HH, United Kingdom
- (020) 8440 4415/(07831) 687089
- cjkcoles@hotmail.com

Chris Cypert Photography Sloane Avenue Mansions, Sloane Avenue, Flat 85, London, SW3 3JF, United Kingdom
- (07795) 345543
- mail@chriscypert.com
- www.chriscypert.com

Chris Everard@Sarah Kaye Representation Ltd 38 Queen's Gate, London, SW7 5HR, United Kingdom
- (020) 7225 5005/ (020) 7225 0109
- sarah@sarahkaye.com
- www.sarahkaye.com

Chris Frazer Smith 5B Blackstock Mews, London, N4 2BT, United Kingdom
- (020) 7359 4961
- chris@chrisfrazersmith.com
- www.chrisfrazersmith.com

Chris Frazer-Smith@Wyatt-Clarke & Jones 26 Mortimer Street, London, W1W 7RB, United Kingdom
- (020) 7580 7570/(07958) 712658 (020) 7903 5330
- office@wyattclarkejones.com
- www.wyattclarkejones.com

Chris Harrison Akersbakken 10, Oslo, 172, Norway
- 22 64 99 46/48 13 45 55
- chris@chrisharrison.no
- www.chrisharrison.no

Chris Holland 75 Thurleigh Road, London, SW12 8TZ, United Kingdom
- (020) 8673 6909/ (020) 8673 6935
- chris@hollandfoto.demon.co.uk
- chrishollandfoto.com

Chris Honeywell, United Kingdom
- (07831) 843338
- chris@working-images.co.uk
- www.working-images.co.uk

Chris Laurens Photography, Whitstable, Kent, CT5, United Kingdom
- (01227) 282253/(07973) 620518
- chris@phot2002.fsnet.co.uk
- www.laurensphotos.com

Chris Leah 52C Sunny Bank Mill, Leeds LS28 5UJ, United Kingdom
(07956) 591675
chris@chrisleah.com
www.chrisleah.com

Chris Lomas Apartment 8, Coburg Wharf, 3 Coburg Street, Edinburgh, EH6 6ET, United Kingdom
(07860) 121916
info@chrislomas.demon.co.uk
www.chrislomas.com

Chris Martin@Axiom Photographic Agency The Pall Mall Deposit, 124-128 Barlby Road, London, W10 6BL, United Kingdom
(020) 8964 9970/ (020) 8964 8440
info@axiomphotographic.com
www.axiomphotographic.com

Chris Middlebrook@Picture Workshop 45 Highgate Place, Highgate, Birmingham, B12 0DD, United Kingdom
0121-440 2342/(07768) 937739 0121-440 2844
chris@pictureworkshop.co.uk
www.pictureworkshop.co.uk

Chris Morris Tan House, Longhope, Gloucestershire, GL17 0LA, United Kingdom
(01452) 830911/(07801) 388194
cmorris@beeb.net
www.tannersyardpress.co.uk

Chris Nurse@Début Art & The Coningsby Gallery 30 Tottenham Street, London, W1T 4RJ, United Kingdom
(020) 7636 1064/ (020) 7580 7017
info@debutart.com
www.debutart.com

Chris Overton, London, United Kingdom
(07860) 418921
chris@chrisoverton.com
www.chrisoverton.com

Chris Owens 39 Bunning Way, London, N7, United Kingdom
(07814) 028714
owens_photo@hotmail.com

Chris Parker@Axiom Photographic Agency The Pall Mall Deposit, 124-128 Barlby Road, London, W10 6BL, United Kingdom
(020) 8964 9970/ (020) 8964 8440
info@axiomphotographic.com
www.axiomphotographic.com

Chris Price Designs 121 Engleheart Road, Catford, London, SE6 2EU,
2081230016
info@chrispricedesigns.com
www.chrispricedesigns.com

Chris Ryan@Rosie Beckett 102 Cole Park Road, Twickenham, TW1 1JA, United Kingdom
(020) 8255 1574/(07973) 193071
rosiebeckett@mac.com

Chris Sattlberger 30 Tannery House, 6 Deal Street, London, E1 5AG, United Kingdom
(020) 7247 0071/(07775) 561104 (020) 7247 0071
www.sattlberger.com

Chris Steele-Perkins@Magnum Photos 63 Gee Street, London, EC1V 3RS, United Kingdom
(020) 7490 1771/ (020) 7608 0020
magnum@magnumphotos.co.uk
www.magnumphotos.com

Chris Tribelhorn@T Photographic 1 Heathgate Place, 75-83 Agincourt Road, London, London, NW3 2NU, United Kingdom
(020) 7428 6070/ (020) 7428 6079
peter@tphotographic.com
www.tphotographic.com

Chris Turner Photography 8-9 Pratt Mews, London, NW1 0AD, United Kingdom
(020) 7383 3666/ (020) 7383 4777
info@christurnerphotography.co.uk
www.christurnerphotography.co.uk

Chris Turner Photography Ltd 8-9 Pratt Mews, Camden Town, London, NW1 0AD, United Kingdom
(020) 7383 3666/(07941) 675308 (020) 7383 4777
gael@christurnerphotography.co.uk
www.christurnerphotography.co.uk

Chris Whitehead 9 Chiltern Road, Hitchin, Hertfordshire, SG4 9PL, United Kingdom
(07850) 509995
chrisw@chriswhitehead.com
www.chriswhitehead.com

Chris Windsor 75 Bedford Avenue, Barnet, Hertfordshire, EN5 2ES, United Kingdom
(020) 8449 9495/(07831) 858350 (020) 8440 2007
chris@chriswindsor.com
www.chriswindsor.com

Christian Keenan 1st Floor, 50 Don Street, St Helier, Jersey, JE2 4TR, United Kingdom
(01534) 888752
christiankeenan@mac.com
www.christiankeenan.com

Christian McGowan Photography 9 Sherwoofd House, 70 New North Road, Huddersfield, HD1 5NE, United Kingdom
(0870) 9905138/(07979) 690629 (0870) 9905139
chris@mcgowan.tv
www.mcgowan.tv

Christine Donnier-Valentin Ground Floor Studio, 10-11 Bishop's Terrace, London, SE11 4UE, United Kingdom
(020) 7735 5454/(07850) 025254 (020) 7735 9944
cdval@tiscali.co.uk
www.cdvphotography.com

Christine Hanscomb@Agent Pandora 12 Stonells Road, London, SW11 6HQ, United Kingdom
(07966) 181825
pandora@agentpandora.com
www.agentpandora.com

Christine Hanscomb@The Producers 11 Perseverance Works, 38 Kingsland Road, London, E2 8DD, United Kingdom
(020) 7739 0132/(07050) 039992 (020) 7729 7066
mail@christinehanscomb.co.uk
www.christinehanscomb.co.uk

Christine Voge Long Ridge, Loudwater Lane, Rickmansworth, Hertfordshire, WD3 4AW, United Kingdom
(01923) 772932
c.voge@btinternet.com

Christoph Grothgar 11a Hansard Mews, London, W14 8BJ, United Kingdom
(020) 7603 6611/ (020) 7603 6622
info@jackiegibbs.com
www.jackiegibbs.com

Christoph Jouany@Christoph Morlinghaus@Valeriehersleven Boundary House (3rd Floor), 91-93 Charterhouse Street, London, EC1M 6HR, United Kingdom
(07775) 717474
me@valeriehersleven.com
www.valeriehersleven.com

Christophe Jouany@N M P Photo 211 Westbourne Park Road, London, W11 1EA, United Kingdom
(020) 7243 0074
info@nmpphoto.co.uk
www.nmpphoto.co.uk

Christophe Rihet@C L M Top Floor, 19 All Saints Road, London, W11 1HE, United Kingdom
(020) 7750 2999/ (020) 7792 8507
clm@clmuk.com
www.clmuk.com

Christopher Drake 63 Kings Road, Kingston upon Thames, Surrey, KT2 5HS, United Kingdom
(020) 8287 7748/ (020) 8287 7748
drakephoto@btinternet.com

Christopher Hill Photographic Library 17 Clarence Street, Belfast, BT2 8DY, United Kingdom
(028) 9024 5038/(07836) 361916 (028) 9023 1942
chrishillphotographic@btclick.com
www.scenicireland.com

Christopher Hopper 60 St. Stephens Gardens, London, W2 5NJ, United Kingdom
(020) 8891 1937/(07973) 737794 (020) 8891 1937
chris@chrishopper.demon.co.uk
www.chrishopper.com

Christopher Liddington Photography 14 Lewes Road, London, N12 9NL, United Kingdom
(07740) 336676
info@christopherliddington.com
www.christopherliddington.com

Christopher McMurray Photography The Design Foundry, Smith Way, Ossett, West Yorkshire, WF5 9JZ, United Kingdom
(01924) 884400/(07774) 182078 (01924) 884420
cmcmurray@thedesignfoundry.co.uk
www.mcphoto.co.uk

Christopher Rudquist@Z Photographic The Mezzanine, 5 Dryden Street, Covent Garden, London, WC2E 9NW, United Kingdom
(020) 7829 8455/(07917) 302 491 (020) 7240 5600
zuk@zphotographic.com
www.zphotographic.com

Christopher Sturman@East Photographic Ltd 8 Iron Bridge House, 3 Bridge Approach, London, NW1 8BD, United Kingdom
(020) 7722 3444/ (020) 7722 3544
roger@eastphotographic.com
www.eastphotographic.com

Chuck Ealovega@Esser Assocs 2nd Floor North, 6 Buckingham Street, London, WC2N 6BU, United Kingdom
(020) 7976 2915/(07778) 149149 (01372) 464326
rob.esser@virgin.net
www.davidesser.com

Chuck Elliott@Alan Wickes 135 Downton Avenue, London, SW2 3TX, United Kingdom
(020) 8674 2242/(07774) 259352
a.wickes@btinternet.com
www.alanwickes.com

Cinebuild Ltd Studio House, 34 Rita Road, London, SW8 1JU, United Kingdom
(020) 7582 8750/(07836) 220441 (020) 7793 0467
cinebuild@btclick.com
www.cinebuild.com

Claire Harrison Photography 3 Gladstone Road, Kingston upon Thames, Surrey, KT1 3HD, United Kingdom
(07793) 764003
claire_red_123@hotmail.com
www.claireharrisonphotography.com

Claire Wood Photography, Huddersfield, West Yorkshire, United Kingdom
(01484) 512484/(07946) 543566
mail@clairewood.com
www.clairewood.com

Claire-Jessica Photography 7a Bellevew Road, London, SW17 7EG, United Kingdom
(07887) 907348
info@clairejessica.co.uk
www.clairejessica.co.uk

Claudia Dulak Stoke Newington, London, N16 7BH, United Kingdom
(07956) 544046
claudia@claudiadulak.com
www.claudiadulak.com

Claudia Leisinger Photographer 65b Kingsmede Road, London, SW2 3HZ, United Kingdom
(07768) 547700
claudia@singer-leisinger.com
www.singer-leisinger.com

Clay Perry, London, United Kingdom
(020) 8834 4747
clay@clayperry.co.uk
www.clayperry.co.uk

CLB Photo 8 Highbury Hill, Lower Ground, London, N5 1AL,
7733206857
www.lopzphoto.co.uk

Cleve Severin 5 Mattison Road, London, N4 1BG, United Kingdom
(020) 8348 0131/(07931) 779010
mail@cleve-severin.co.uk
www.cleve-severin.co.uk

Clifford Studios 283-291 Wandsworth Road, London, SW8 2ND, United Kingdom
(020) 7622 5425/ (020) 7622 5426
cliffordstudios@btclick.com

Clifton-Gould Photography 38 Watery Lane, Wimbledon, London, SW20 9AD, United Kingdom
(07958) 515421
jcg@jcgphoto.com
www.jcgphoto.com

Clint Eley 208 East Ferry Road, London, E14 3AY, United Kingdom
(020) 7538 9372
clint@allangles.co.uk
www.allangles.co.uk

Cliona O'Flaherty 43 Lorcan Drive, Santry, Dublin 9, Ireland, Republic of
00 353 87 958 1048
info@clionaoflaherty.com
www.clionaoflaherty.com

Clive Barda Photography 48 Manor Court Road, London, W7 3EL, United Kingdom
(020) 8579 5202/(07973) 226474 (020) 8840 1083
clivebarda@pobox.com
www.clivebarda.com

Clive Boursnell 5A Borneo Street, London, SW15 1QQ, United Kingdom
(020) 8789 8956/(07831) 647244 (020) 8785 1110
cliveb@ndo.co.uk

Clive Bozzard-Hill Photograhpy, Twickenham, Middlesex, United Kingdom
(020) 8744 1714/(07966) 161619
clive@bozza-uk.com
www.bozza-uk.com

Clive Bozzard-Hill Photography, Twickenham, United Kingdom
(020) 8744 1714
clive@bozza-uk.com

Clive Coote 31 Elm Park Court, Pinner, Middlesex, HA5 3LJ, United Kingdom
(020) 8868 1169/ (01430) 422156

Clive Frost Little Garde, Crowborough Road, Nutley, East Sussex, TN22 3HU, United Kingdom
(07710) 019847
cf@clivefrost.com
www.clivefrost.com

Clive Helm 48 Cephas Avenue, London, E1 4AT, United Kingdom
(020) 7265 9160/(07952) 162759
clivehelm@yahoo.co.uk

Clive Johnson 3 Norman House, Hardwick Mount, Buxton, Derbyshire, SK17 6PP, United Kingdom
(01298) 25405/(07950) 760962 (01298) 25405
clive@clive-johnson.com
www.clive-johnson.com

Clive Nichols Garden Pictures Rickyard Barn, Castle Farm, Chacombe, Banbury, Oxfordshire, OX17 2EN, United Kingdom
(01295) 712288/ (01295) 713672
enquiries@clivenichols.com
www.clivenichols.com

Clive Sawyer 6 Linnet Lane, Camber Sands, East Sussex, TN31 7SL, United Kingdom
(01797) 222213/(07738) 715354
clive@clivephotographer.com
www.clivephotographer.com

Clive Shalice@T Photographic 1 Heathgate Place, 75-83 Agincourt Road, London, London, NW3 2NU, United Kingdom
(020) 7428 6070/ (020) 7428 6079
peter@tphotographic.com
www.tphotographic.com

Clockwork Craven House, 121 Kings Way, London, WC2B 6PA, United Kingdom
(020) 7436 9696/ (020) 7953 8083
admin@clockwork.tm

Cloud Nine Photography 3 Beech Drive, Horssorth, Leeds, LS18 4LD, United Kingdom
(0700) 0256839/(07970) 816920
jt@cloud9leeds.co.uk
www.cloud9leeds.co.uk

Cocken Photography 274-276 Queenstown Road, Battersea, London, SW8 4LP, United Kingdom
(020) 7498 9074/(07771) 691023
paul@paulcocken.co.uk
www.paulcocken.co.uk

Cody Burridge@The White Agency 60 Epirus Road, Fulham, London, SW6 7UH, United Kingdom
(020) 7381 2004/(07970) 619277 (020) 7386 8479
annabel@thewhiteagency.com
www.thewhiteagency.com

Colchester Photographic Brunel Way, Severalls Park, Colchester, CO4 4QX, United Kingdom
(01206) 843700/ (01206) 844401
photo@cpw.uk.com
www.cpw.uk.com

Colin Beer 177 High Street, Tonbridge, Kent, TN9 1BX, United Kingdom
(01732) 352160/ (01732) 352160
allwork@lineone.net

Colin Bell Photography Unit E, Purdon Street, Glasgow, G11 6AF, United Kingdom
0141-334 8008/(07787) 573155 0141-334 8008
colin@colinbellphotography.com
www.colinbellphotography.com

Colin Campbell 23-28 Penn Street, London, N1 5DL, United Kingdom
(020) 7729 3740/ (020) 7729 9410
colin.studio@virgin.net
www.colincampbell-photo.com

Colin Crisford 11a Greenwich South Street, London, SE10 8NJ, United Kingdom
(020) 8858 5008/(07956) 142077 (020) 8858 2128
studio@colincrisford.co.uk
www.colincrisford.co.uk

Colin Curwood Photography Ltd 9 Beche Road, Cambridge, CB5 8HX, United Kingdom
(01223) 328188/07836 701764
colin@colincurwood.com
www.colincurwood.com

Colin Dixon 77 The Link, Hexham, Northumberland, NE46 3AL, United Kingdom
(01434) 602467

Colin Gray 1 Beaumont Gate, Glasgow, G12 9EE, United Kingdom
0141 334 4020/(07901) 826254 0141-334 4020
c.gray@strath.ac.uk
www.colingray.net

Colin Jones 15 Cleveland Gardens, London, SW13 0AE, United Kingdom
(020) 8876 8842/(07901) 563257
www.colinjonesphotography.com

Colin Lane@Blunt Management The Courtyard Studio 2, Old Grammarphone Works, London, W10 5BZ, United Kingdom
(020) 8960 2041/(07979) 900068 (020) 8960 2039
info@bluntlondon.com
www.bluntlondon.com

Colin Peacock Photographic The Rectory, Berwick Lane, Compton Greenfield, Bristol, BS35 5RU, United Kingdom
(01454) 633545/ (01454) 633575
cpeacock@dircon.co.uk
www.colinpeacockphotographer.com

Colin Prior 3 Wren Court, Strathclyde Business Park, Bellshill, Lanarkshire, ML4 3NQ, United Kingdom
(01698) 844430/ (01698) 844428
info@colinprior.co.uk
www.colinprior.co.uk

Colin Streater 2 Caldercott Way, London, London, E5 0DA, United Kingdom
(020) 7682 0070/(07780) 705303
studio@colinstreater.com
www.colinstreater.com

Colin Thomas@Jamie Stephen Represents 9 Upper Wimpole Street, London, W1G 6LJ, United Kingdom
(0845) 3733510/(07957) 784810 (020) 7681 1027
jamie@jamiestephen.com
www.jamiestephen.com

Colin Thomas Photography 6 Burlington Lodge Studios, Rigault Road, London, SW6 4JJ, United Kingdom
(020) 7736 0060/ (020) 7736 0069
colin@colinthomas.com
www.colinthomas.com

Colin Varndell The Happy Return, Whitecross, Bridport, Dorset, DT6 5NH, United Kingdom
(01308) 488341/(07779) 941844
colin_varndell@hotmail.com

Colonial Studios Unit 10, Brassmill Enterprise Centre, Bath, BA1 3JN, United Kingdom
(01225) 469121/ (01225) 469121
colonialstudios@tiscali.co.uk
www.colonialstudios.com

Con Putbrace The Old School, Lawn Lane, Market Drayton, Shropshire, TF9 2RN, United Kingdom
(01630) 661588/ (01630) 661588
info@conputbrace.co.uk
www.conputbrace.co.uk

Coneyl Jay Po Box 65, Llandysul, Dyfed, SA44 5WS, United Kingdom
(01239) 654 550
coneyl@coneyljay.com
www.coneyljay.com

Confetti Shots 3 Townsend Cottages, Coldharbour Road, Pyrford, Woking, Surrey, GU22 8SN, United Kingdom
(07711) 526987
julie@confettishots.co.uk
www.confettishots.co.uk

Conor Caffrey@Axiom Photographic Agency The Pall Mall Deposit, 124-128 Barlby Road, London, W10 6BL, United Kingdom
(020) 8964 9970/ (020) 8964 8440
info@axiomphotographic.com
www.axiomphotographic.com

Conor Masterson@Catherine Collins The Power Station, Coronet Street, London, N1 6HD, United Kingdom
(020) 7739 8678/(07785) 571187 (020) 7739 8489
catherine@catherinecollins.co.uk
www.catherinecollins.co.uk

Constantine Manos@Magnum Photos 63 Gee Street, London, EC1V 3RS, United Kingdom
(020) 7490 1771/ (020) 7608 0020
magnum@magnumphotos.co.uk
www.magnumphotos.com

Construction Photography 2 Whitacre Mews, 26-34 Stannary Street, London, SE11 4AB, United Kingdom
(020) 7820 6200/(07946) 705650
lucy@constructionphotography.com
www.constructionphotography.com

Contrast Photography Whitney Road, Daneshill East, Basingstoke, Hampshire, RG24 8NS, United Kingdom
(01256) 840676
david@contrastphotography.co.uk
www.contrastphotography.co.uk

Coochie Management 26 Harcourt Street, Marylebone, London, W1H 4HW, United Kingdom
(020) 7724 9700/(07802) 795620 (020) 7724 2598
amanda@coochie-management.com
www.coochie-management.com

Cooper Photography 10 Headon Gardens, Exeter, EX2 6LE, United Kingdom
(01392) 426640/(07763) 367639 1392209080
peter@cooperphotography.co.uk
www.cooperphotography.co.uk

Coopers 207-209 Regent Street, London, W1B 4ND, United Kingdom
(020) 7491 2273/ (020) 7493 4489
ac.coopers@virgin.net
www.ac-cooper.com

Corinne Turner 87 Lynton Road, London, SE1 5QT, United Kingdom
(020) 7231 5111

Cornell C. Capa@Magnum Photos 63 Gee Street, London, EC1V 3RS, United Kingdom
(020) 7490 1771/ (020) 7608 0020
magnum@magnumphotos.co.uk
www.magnumphotos.com

Craig Alexander Wilson@Cormack Creative Management Ltd Suite 208, 95 Morrison Street, Glasgow, G5 8BE, United Kingdom
0141-429 6810/(07778) 323169 0141-429 2603
susie@cormackcreativemanagement.co.uk
www.cormackcreativemanagement.co.uk

Craig Dunsmuir Photography 49 Dunsmure Road, London, N16 5PT, United Kingdom
(020) 7502 0622/(07747) 032114
craigdunsmuir@hotmail.com
www.craigdunsmuir.com

Craig Easton@David Edmunds Represents Unit 105, 54-58 Kingsland Road, London, E2 8DP, United Kingdom
(020) 7739 1166/(07785) 580024
info@davidedmundsrepresents.com
www.davidedmundsrepresents.com

Craig Eccleston Unit 317, Jubilee Trade Centre, Birmingham, B5 6ND, United Kingdom
0121-693 0736/(07850) 808665
craig@craigeccleston.co.uk

Craig Fordham@Sarah Kaye Representation Ltd 38 Queen's Gate, London, SW7 5HR, United Kingdom
(020) 7225 5005/ (020) 7225 0109
sarah@sarahkaye.com
www.sarahkaye.com

Craig Knowles@Creative Talent (UK) Limited 78 York Street, London, W1H 1DP, United Kingdom
(020) 7439 1877/ (020) 7434 1144
info@creativetalentlimited.com
www.creativetalentlimited.com

Craig Lynn 39 Casselden Road, London, NW10 8QR, United Kingdom
(020) 8838 2410/(07767) 456059 (020) 8838 2410
www.craiglynn.com

Craig Shuttlewood@Début Art & The Coningsby Gallery 30 Tottenham Street, London, W1T 4RJ, United Kingdom
(020) 7636 1064/ (020) 7580 7017
info@debutart.com
www.debutart.com

Crash Media Group 1 Silverstone Innovation Centre, Silverstone Circuit, Towcester, Northamptonshire, NN12 8GX, United Kingdom
(0870) 3505044/ (01327) 856001
info@crash.net
www.crash.net

CRE8 Photography Ltd 2nd Flr, 145-157 St. John St, London, EC1V 4PY, United Kingdom
(07909) 975144
info@cre8photo.com
www.cre8photo.com

Creative Camera The Stables, Heddings Farm, Wyboston, Bedford, MK44 3AS, United Kingdom
(01480) 472888/ (01480) 472722
photodance@aol.com.

Creative Glamour Cumbria Court, Sycamore Park, Farnborough, Hampshire, GU14 6TB, United Kingdom
(01252) 660701
creativeglamour.co.uk
www.creativeglamour.co.uk

Creative ID Ltd Unit 2 W2, Scotts Yard, Ber Street, Norwich, NR1 3HA, United Kingdom
(07909) 647314
alanreid2003@aol.com
www.photo-canvas.co.uk

Creative Photography 32 Ambleside Road, Manchester, M41 6PH, United Kingdom
0161-748 6262
paulsweeney@btconnect.com

Creative Talent (UK) Limited 78 York Street, London, W1H 1DP, United Kingdom
(020) 7439 1877/ (020) 7434 1144
info@creativetalentlimited.com
www.creativetalentlimited.com

Creative Talent UK Ltd 78 York Street, London, W1H 1DP, United Kingdom
(020) 7439 1877/ (020) 7434 1144
info@creativetalentlimited.com
www.creativetalentlimited.com

Creative Workshop The Old Wheel Cottage, Eastern Road, Wivelsfield Green, Haywards Heath, West Sussex, RH17 7QH, United Kingdom
(01444) 471364/(07802) 293766
studio@jamesbeaton.com
www.jamesbeaton.com

Crena Watson@WildeHague Ltd Suite 4, The Swan Ctre, Fishers Lane, London, W4 1RX, United Kingdom
(020) 8747 9988/ (020) 8747 8228
info@wildehague.com
www.wildehague.com

D B L Cromwell House, 68 Calvin Road, Bournemouth, BH9 1LN, United Kingdom
(01202) 532366/ (01202) 535650
info@dbl-imaging.co.uk
www.dbl-imaging.co.uk

D J C Design 7 Glenfield Road, Liverpool, L15 5BJ, United Kingdom
0151-735 1641
david@djcdesign.co.uk
www.djcdesign.co.uk

D+V Management 1 Lonsdale Road, London, NW6 6RA, United Kingdom
(020) 7372 2555/ (020) 7372 2123
kenny@dandvmanagement.com
www.dandvmanagement.com

Dale Durfee 1 Westfield, 89 Epson Road, Guildford, Surrey, GU1 3PA, United Kingdom
(01483) 576012/(07889) 966991
durfee@dircon.co.uk
www.daledurfee.com

Damian Gillie 1 Barton Close, Cambridge, CB3 9LQ, United Kingdom
(01223) 366619/(07770) 630131
dg@gilliepixels.com
www.damiangillie.com

Dan Burn-Forti@Mark George 5 St. George's Court, 131 Putney Bridge Road, Putney, London, SW15 2PA, United Kingdom
(020) 8877 9922/(07771) 595 999 (020) 8870 5533
mg@markgeorge.com
www.markgeorge.com

Dan Duchars 7 Lockhurst Street, London, E5 0AP, United Kingdom
(07976) 750827
dan@danduchars.com
www.danduchars.com

Dan Hallman@Pearson Lyle Management 3rd Floor, 40 Bowling Green Lane, London, EC1R 0NE, United Kingdom
(020) 7415 7061/ (020) 7415 7059
contact@pearsonlyle.co.uk
www.pearsonlyle.co.uk

Dan Holdsworth@MAP 72 Rochester Place, London, NW1 9JX, United Kingdom
(020) 7424 9144/ (020) 7284 3274
info@mapltd.com
www.mapltd.com

Dan Jones 8 Enfield Road, Brentford, Middlesex, TW8 9NX, United Kingdom
(07947) 700046
danjonesphoto@mac.com
www.danjonesphoto.co.uk

Dan Sims@Alexandra Von Ziechmann Flat 1, 90 Sutherland Avenue, London, W9 2QR, United Kingdom
(020) 7289 4248(07962) 082691
www.alexandravz.com

Dan Stevens 29 Cell Studios, 80-84 Wallis Road, London, E9 5LW, United Kingdom
(020) 8986 6900/(07973) 416937
ds@danstevens.com
www.danstevens.co.uk

Dan Tobin-Smith@The Katy Barker Agency Ltd 11 Mason's Arms Mews, Maddox Street, London, W1S 1NX, United Kingdom
(020) 7493 3933/ (020) 7493 3311
catherine@katybarker.com
www.katybarker.com

PearsonLyle

Photographers
Jan Baldwin
Jonathan Gregson
Dan Hallman
Emma Lee
Tom Leighton

Art Director/Stylist
Lesley Dilcock

Art Director/
Food & Prop Stylist

Pearson Lyle Management Ltd.
3rd Floor, 40 Bowling Green Lane, London EC1R 0NE
Telephone 020 7415 7061 Facsimile 020 7415 7059
contact@pearsonlyle.co.uk www.pearsonlyle.co.uk

Daniel Allan@Metcalfe Lancaster 20 Hanson Street, London, W1W 6UF, United Kingdom
(020) 7580 8875/(07778) 331771 / (020) 7580 8689
julie@metcalfelancaster.com
www.metcalfelancaster.com

Daniel Allen 188 Goswell Road, London, EC1V 7DT, United Kingdom
(020) 7490 5515
www.danielallen.com

Daniel Farmer@Sarah Kaye Representation Ltd 38 Queen's Gate, London, SW7 5HR, United Kingdom
(020) 7225 5005/ (020) 7225 0109
sarah@sarahkaye.com
www.sarahkaye.com

Daniel Mayer Photography Tuerkenstrasse 37, Munich, 80799, Germany
89 2865 9361/17 1854 7472
dm@danielmayer.com
www.danielmayer.com

Daniel Pangbourne Ltd 1 Park Hill, London, SW4 9NS, United Kingdom
(020) 7498 2222/ (020) 7498 7555
daniel@danielpangbourne.com
www.danielpangbourne.com

Daniel Ward@T Photographic 1 Heathgate Place, 75-83 Agincourt Road, London, London, NW3 2NU, United Kingdom
(020) 7428 6070/ (020) 7428 6079
peter@tphotographic.com
www.tphotographic.com

Daniela Federici@T Photographic 1 Heathgate Place, 75-83 Agincourt Road, London, London, NW3 2NU, United Kingdom
(020) 7428 6070/ (020) 7428 6079
peter@tphotographic.com
www.tphotographic.com

Danilo Giuliani@John Parkinson Photographic Agent Unit 17, 1-10 Summer's Street, London, EC1R 5BD, United Kingdom
(020) 7278 6882/ (020) 7278 1251
johnparkinsonagency@btinternet.com
www.johnparkinsonagency.co.uk

Dano Battista 3D Ltd 9-10 Charlotte Mews, London, W1T 4EF, United Kingdom
(07958) 735069/ (020) 7636 2455
enquiries@danobattista.com
www.danobattista.com

Daren Wilding Photographer 17 Faraday Road, Ipswich, IP4 1PU, United Kingdom
(07855) 764970/ (01473) 425672
info@darenwilding.co.uk
hppt:/www.darenwilding.co.uk

Dario Mitidieri@David Lambert 108 Oakley Street, London, SW3 5NR, United Kingdom
(020) 7352 0033/(07747) 032 299 / (020) 7352 5553
david@davidlambert.com
www.davidlambert.com

Darius Photography 171 Brighton Road, Coulsdon, Surrey, CR5 2NH, United Kingdom
(020) 8668 3232/ (020) 8668 2954
dariusphoto@btconnect.com
www.dariusorganisation.co.uk

Darrell Russell 59 Gayford Road, London, W12 9BY, United Kingdom
(07831) 653643/ (020) 8743 1382
darrell@cdni.co.uk
www.darrellrussell.co.uk

Darren Hopes@Début Art & The Coningsby Gallery 30 Tottenham Street, London, W1T 4RJ, United Kingdom
(020) 7636 1064/ (020) 7580 7017
info@debutart.com
www.debutart.com

Darren Lennon@SK Creative Management 23 New Mount Street, Manchester, M4 4DE, United Kingdom
0161-953 4032/ (0870) 486 1940
info@skcreativemanagement.com
www.skcreativemanagement.com

Darren Whear Flat 4 1518 King Street West, Toronto, M6K 1J5, Canada
00 1 416 668 5477
darrenwhear@aim.com
www.darrenwhearphoto.com

Darrin Jenkins Chapel Studio, 158 High Street, Codicote, Hertfordshire, SG4 8UB, United Kingdom
(01438) 820530
djenkins@dj-photo.com
www.dj-photo.com

darrochdonald.com Moulin, St. Abbs Road, Coldingham, Eyemouth, Berwickshire, TD14 5NR, United Kingdom
(01890) 771895
darrochd@hotmail.com
www.darrochdonald.com

DasUnit Zwiestader Strasse 5, Berlin, 12055, Germany
00 49 30 6822 4763/00 49 17 2785 4254
info@das-unit.com
www.das-unit.com

Dave Bentley 234 Proxted Road, London, SE24 9DG, United Kingdom
(07977) 050 201
dave@davebentley.com
www.davebentley.com

Dave Brown 55 Farringdon Road, London, EC1M 3JB, United Kingdom
(020) 7404 9888/ (020) 7404 9800
dave@davebrownstudio.co.uk
www.davebrownstudio.co.uk
See ad in showcase

Dave Daggers Albany Road, Cardiff, CF24 3RW, United Kingdom
(029) 2048 2096
dave@davedaggers.com
www.davedaggers.com

Dave Harriman@Mark Gibson 250 York Road, London, SW11 3SJ, United Kingdom
(020) 7228 9085/(07768) 696227
mark@markgibsonphotography.com
www.markgibsonphotography.com

Dave King 2 Willow Way, Sunbury-on-Thames, Middlesex, TW16 6BT, United Kingdom
(0870) 7540901/(07801) 492641
mail@davekingsstudio.co.uk
www.davekingsstudio.co.uk

Dave Page Photography 23 Walnut Tree Lane, Longwick, Princes Risborough, Buckinghamshire, HP27 9SJ, United Kingdom
(01844) 273889/ (01844) 273195
dave@davepage.co.uk
www.davepage.co.uk

Dave Tyler Associates 8 Portland Mews, London, W1V 3FJ, United Kingdom
(07071) 202470/(07860) 364225 / (01438) 871680
dave@davetyler.com
www.davetyler.com

Dave Wilcox Photography 56-58 Sugar Lane, Rainow, Macclesfield, Cheshire, SK10 5UJ, United Kingdom
(01625) 560500/(07887) 555065 / (01625) 576182
dave@davewilcoxphotography.com
www.davewilcoxphotography.co.uk

Dave Young@Axiom Photographic Agency The Pall Mall Deposit, 124-128 Barlby Road, London, W10 6BL, United Kingdom
(020) 8964 9970/ (020) 8964 8440
info@axiomphotographic.com
www.axiomphotographic.com

David & Bobby Appleby High House, East Compton, Shepton Mallet, Somerset, BA4 4NR, United Kingdom
(01749) 344662/(07778) 934154 / (01749) 344662
DvAppleb@aol.com

David Alan Harvey@Magnum Photos 63 Gee Street, London, EC1V 3RS, United Kingdom
(020) 7490 1771/ (020) 7608 0020
magnum@magnumphotos.co.uk
www.magnumphotos.com

David Appleby@Blowup 146 Amyand Park Road, St. Margaret's, Twickenham, TW1 3HY, United Kingdom
(020) 8744 0210/ (020) 8892 2521
orders@blowup.net
www.blowup.net

David Austin Photography 76 Woodson Road, London, NW5 1RZ, United Kingdom
(020) 7482 1306/(07866) 802229
info@davidaustinphotography.net
www.davidaustinphotography.net

David Bailey@The Katy Barker Agency Ltd 11 Mason's Arms Mews, Maddox Street, London, W1S 1NX, United Kingdom
(020) 7493 3933/ (020) 7493 3311
catherine@katybarker.com
www.katybarker.com

David Banks 81 Engadine Street, London, SW18 5DU, United Kingdom
(020) 8874 3247
david@dbanks.co.uk
www.davidbanks.co.uk

David Barnes Photographer, Cardiff, United Kingdom
(07974) 050079
info@davidbarnesphotographer.com
www.davidbarnesphotographer.com

David Body, Colchester, CO4 9TQ, United Kingdom
07860 376903
bigmanbod@aol.com

David Boughton 8 Chippendale Street, Hackney, London, E5 0BB, United Kingdom
(020) 8525 9717/(07932) 767699
david@davidjboughton.com
www.davidjboughton.com

David Bramley 5 Willoughby Street, London, WC1A 1JD, United Kingdom
(020) 7636 1676/(07798 8144109 / (020) 7813 2083
david@davidbramley.com
www.davidbramley.com

David Burgess@Esser Assocs 2nd Floor North, 6 Buckingham Street, London, WC2N 6BU, United Kingdom
(020) 7976 2915/(07778) 149149 / (01372) 464326
rob.esser@virgin.net
www.davidesser.com

David Burton Photography@ Picture Library 23 Old Grove Court, Norwich, NR3 3NL, United Kingdom
(01603) 411222/(07774) 843573 / (01603) 411234
sales@dbphoto.co.uk
www.dbphoto.co.uk

David Calvert Photography 1 Hillhead, Perry Green, Much Hadham, Hertfordshire, SG10 6DU, United Kingdom
(01279) 843050
enquiries@calvert.biz
www.calvert.biz

David Carpenter Helensbourne, 34 East St. Helens Street, Abingdon, Oxfordshire, OX14 5EB, United Kingdom
(01235) 530200/(07885) 537090 / (01235) 201573
david.carpenter40@ntlworld.com

David Churchill@Arcaid Picture Library Parc House, 25-37 Cowleaze Road, Kingston upon Thames, Surrey, KT2 6DZ, United Kingdom
(020) 8546 4352/ (020) 8541 5230
arcaid@arcaid.co.uk
www.arcaid.co.uk

David Cockroft 10 Madrid Road, Barnes, London, SW13 9PD, United Kingdom
(020) 8748 5117/(07836) 368636

David Constantine@Axiom Photographic Agency The Pall Mall Deposit, 124-128 Barlby Road, London, W10 6BL, United Kingdom
(020) 8964 9970/ (020) 8964 8440
info@axiomphotographic.com
www.axiomphotographic.com

David Cotsworth Photography 192a High Street, Egham, Surrey, TW20 9ED, United Kingdom
(07713) 255348
david@cotsworth.com
david.cotsworth.com

David Denny Flat1, 3a Park Road, London, N8 TE, United Kingdom
(07973) 739090
d@david-denny.com
www.david-denny.com

David Deveson Via del Moro 33, Rome, 153, Italy
00 39 65 833 1154
davidbd@fastwebnet.it
www.daviddeveson.com

David Drebin@Coochie Management 26 Harcourt Street, Marylebone, London, W1H 4HW, United Kingdom
(020) 7724 9700/(07802) 795620 / (020) 7724 2598
amanda@coochie-management.com
www.coochie-management.com

David Edmunds Represents Unit 105, 54-58 Kingsland Road, London, E2 8DP, United Kingdom
(020) 7739 1166/(07785) 580024
info@davidedmundsrepresents.com
www.davidedmundsrepresents.com

David Ellis@Terri Manduca The Basement, 11 Elvaston Place, London, SW7 5QG, United Kingdom
(020) 7581 5844/ (020) 7581 5822
terri@terrimanduca.co.uk
www.terrimanduca.co.uk

Esser Assocs 2nd Floor North, 6 Buckingham Street, London, WC2N 6BU, United Kingdom
(020) 7976 2915/(07778) 149149/ (01372) 464326
rob.esser@virgin.net
www.davidesser.com

David Gamble 16 Quadrant Grove, London, NW5 4JN, United Kingdom
/07836 634111 / (020) 7284 0757

David Garcia@M & M Management Studio B, 11 Edith Grove, London, SW10 0JZ, United Kingdom
(020) 7823 3723/ (020) 7351 3714
admin@mmmanagement.com
www.mmmanagement.com

David George@Wendy Jackson Tag Creative, 29 Clerkenwell Road, London, EC1M 5TA, United Kingdom
(020) 3217 2241/(07711) 084801 / (020) 7439 1971
wjackson@tagworldwide.com
www.wendyjackson.co.uk

David Gill, London, SE1, United Kingdom
(020) 7401 3704/ (020) 7401 3726
studio@dgill.com
www.dgill.com

David Hall 6 Cambridge Yard, Hanwell, London, W7 3UP, United Kingdom
(07768) 077254/ (020) 8400 7574
info@photohall.com
www.photohall.com

David Hardy 66B Haydn Park Road, London, W12, United Kingdom
07887 572 580
contactme@davidhardy.co.uk
www.davidhardy.co.uk

David Hares, London, United Kingdom
(07956) 902509
mail@davidhares.co.uk
www.davidhares.co.uk

David Hautzig@Dave Tyler Associates 8 Portland Mews, London, W1V 3FJ, United Kingdom
(07071) 202470/(07860) 364225 / (01438) 871680
dave@davetyler.com
www.davetyler.com

David Helsby 43 Westley Grange, off Chartwell Drive, Leicester, LE1 2FL, United Kingdom
0116-288 2255
david.helsby@virgin.net
www.heliosphotography.co.uk

David Hiscock@Creative Talent (UK) Limited 78 York Street, London, W1H 1DP, United Kingdom
(020) 7439 1877/ (020) 7434 1144
info@creativetalentlimited.com
www.creativetalentlimited.com

David Hurn@Magnum Photos 63 Gee Street, EC1V 3RS, United Kingdom
(020) 7490 1771/ (020) 7608 0020
magnum@magnumphotos.co.uk
www.magnumphotos.com

David Jacobs 168 West End Lane, London, NW6 1SD, United Kingdom
(020) 7794 7858/ (020) 7435 1945
steve@colourdivision.com

David Kelly 19 Lonsdale Road, London, NW6 6RA, United Kingdom
(07977) 235694
david@kellypartnership.co.uk
www.kellypartnership.co.uk

David Kimber 28 Fernside Road, Talbot Park, Bournemouth, BH9 2LB, United Kingdom
(01202) 528849/(07785) 537928
davidkimber@carphoto.co.uk
www.carphoto.co.uk

David Lambert 108 Oakley Street, London, SW3 5NR, United Kingdom
(020) 7352 0033/(07747) 032 299 / (020) 7352 5553
david@davidlambert.com
www.davidlambert.com

David Levenson Ashley House, Heathside Crescent, Woking, Surrey, GU22 7AQ, United Kingdom
(01483) 772341
mail@davidlevenson.com
www.davidlevenson.com

David Lloyd Roberts 44 Murray Mews, London, NW1 9RJ, United Kingdom
(020) 7267 9658/ (020) 7267 4590

David M. Grossman 211 E 7th Street, Brooklyn, 11218, United States of America
00 1 718 438 5021/ 00 1 718 438 5060
david@grossmanphotos.com
www.grossmanphotos.com

David Martin Photography 254 Southport Road, Lydiate, Liverpool, L31 4EG, United Kingdom
0151-283 0808
james@topsnapper.com
www.topsnapper.com

David Modell@Bonakdar Cleary 35 Charles Square, London, N1 6HT, United Kingdom
(020) 7490 1155
bc@bonakdarcleary.com
www.bonakdarcleary.com

David Montgomery@M & M Management Studio B, 11 Edith Grove, London, SW10 0JZ, United Kingdom
(020) 7823 3723/ (020) 7351 3714
admin@mmmanagement.com
www.mmmanagement.com

David Moore Photography Ltd Mission House, Biddulph Common Road, Biddulph, Stoke-On-Trent, ST8 7SR, United Kingdom
(01782) 515588
david@moorephoto.co.uk
www.moorephoto.co.uk

David Murphey Photography 63 Wood Lane, London, W12 7DP, United Kingdom
(020) 8740 1953
davo.murphey@virgin.net

David Muscroft 16 Broadfield Road, Heeley, Sheffield, S8 0XJ, United Kingdom
(07770) 384831/ 0114-255 0113
dave@glamourintl.demon.co.uk

David Newton@Début Art & The Coningsby Gallery 30 Tottenham Street, London, W1T 4RJ, United Kingdom
(020) 7636 1064/ (020) 7580 7017
info@debutart.com
www.debutart.com

David Noton Photography Clark House, Higher Kingsbury, Sherborne, Dorset, DT9 5EB, United Kingdom
(01963) 250061/(07968) 850960
info@davidnoton.com
www.davidnoton.com

David Oliver 12 Billers Chase, Chelmsford, CM1 6BD, United Kingdom
(01245) 450045/(07850) 656909
david@davidoliver.co.uk
www.davidoliver.co.uk

David Owen 95 Kingsgate, Bridlington, East Yorkshire, YO15 3NQ, United Kingdom
(01262) 673400/ (01262) 673400
weddings@callme.go-plus.net
www.davidowenphotography.com

David Oxberry@Swerve Photography 29-31 Saffron Hill, London, EC1N 8SW, United Kingdom
/(07967) 628769
info@swervephotography.com
www.swervephotography.com

David Parfitt@N M P Photo 211 Westbourne Park Road, London, W11 1EA, United Kingdom
(020) 7243 0074
info@nmpphoto.co.uk
www.nmpphoto.co.uk

David Parfitt Photography 3 Lever Street, London, EC1V 3QU, United Kingdom
(020) 7251 1427/ (020) 7608 0628
david@davidparfitt.com
www.davidparfitt.com
See ad in showcase

David Parmiter 27 Lottage Road, Aldbourne, Marlborough, Wiltshire, SN8 2EB, United Kingdom
(01672) 540949/(07973) 205275 / (01672) 540949
david@davidparmiter.co.uk
www.davidparmiter.co.uk

David Partner Conigre House, Conigre, Frome, Somerset, BA11 3AA, United Kingdom
(01225) 816216/(07976) 737337 / (01225) 816209
mail@davidpartner.co.uk
www.davidpartner.co.uk

David Peters Studios Unit 14, Fordhouse Road Industrial Estate, Wolverhampton, WV10 9XB, United Kingdom
(01902) 397739/ (01902) 397001
dp@davidpeters.co.uk
www.davidpeters.co.uk

David Preutz 40 Bassingham Road, London, SW18 3AG, United Kingdom
(020) 8874 3369/(07831) 350725
studio@preutz.com
www.preutz.com

David Purdie@Mutton Bones Ground Floor, 51 Balcombe Street, London, NW1 6HD, United Kingdom
(020) 7723 8244/ (020) 7723 2770
hello@muttonbones.co.uk
www.muttonbones.co.uk

David Rees Photography 33 Kirkwood Road, London, SE15 3XT, United Kingdom
(020) 7639 3896/(07889) 379946 / (020) 7639 3896
mail@davidreesphotography.com
www.davidreesphotography.com

David Rendell 17 Ridgeway Close, Paulsgrove, Portsmouth, PO6 4LT, United Kingdom
(023) 9238 2547/(07803) 888073
davidrendellphoto@tiscali.co.uk

David Richards 34 Rosaline Road, London, SW6 7QT, United Kingdom
(020) 7386 7439/07776 180900
drphoto@onetel.net.uk
www.richardsphoto.freeserve.co.uk

David Robinson@WildeHague Ltd Suite 4, The Swan centre, Fishers Lane, London, W4 1RX, United Kingdom
(020) 8747 9988/ (020) 8747 8228
info@wildehague.com
www.wildehague.com

David Scheinmann 70-71 Wells Street, London, W1T 3QE, United Kingdom
(020) 7636 2202/(07785) 236875
d.scheinmann@virgin.net
www.davidscheinmann.com

David Seymour@Magnum Photos 63 Gee Street, London, EC1V 3RS, United Kingdom
(020) 7490 1771/ (020) 7608 0020
magnum@magnumphotos.co.uk
www.magnumphotos.com

David Sheppard Church House, Simpson, Milton Keynes, MK6 3AD, United Kingdom
(01908) 664714
david@sheppards.eclipse.co.uk

David Short 18 Kirk Street, Sheffield, S4 7JX, United Kingdom
0114 281 6179/(07973) 249454 / 0114 275 1066
david@davidshort-photography.co.uk
www.davidshort-photography.co.uk

David Slijper@C L M Top Floor, 19 All Saints Road, London, W11 1HE, United Kingdom
(020) 7750 2999/ (020) 7792 8507
clm@clmuk.com
www.clmuk.com

David Soulsby@Arcaid Picture Library Parc House, 25-37 Cowleaze Road, Kingston upon Thames, Surrey, KT2 6DZ, United Kingdom
(020) 8546 4352/ (020) 8541 5230
arcaid@arcaid.co.uk
www.arcaid.co.uk

David Stewart@Noelle Pickford 27 Britton Street, London, EC1M 5UD, United Kingdom
(020) 7336 6773/ (020) 7336 7043
info@noellerepresents.com
www.noellerepresents.com

David Sykes@Swerve Photography 29-31 Saffron Hill, London, EC1N 8SW, United Kingdom
/(07967) 628769
info@swervephotography.com
www.swervephotography.com

David Thompson@N M P Photo 211 Westbourne Park Road, London, W11 1EA, United Kingdom
(020) 7243 0074
info@nmpphoto.co.uk
www.nmpphoto.co.uk

David Tipling 9 Eccles Road, Holt, Norfolk, NR25 6HJ, United Kingdom
(07973) 181375
dt@windrushphotos.demon.co.uk
www.davidtipling.com

David Ward Rowley Cottage, Westhope, Hereford, HR4 8BU, United Kingdom
(01432) 830781/(07889) 296797 / (01432) 839112
dw@davidwardphoto.co.uk
www.davidwardphoto.co.uk

Daydream Linton House, 164-180 Union Street, London, SE1 0LH,
+44 (0) 20 7096 1471/+44 (0) 20 7117 1636
ralph@daydream.co.uk
www.daydream.co.uk

Dazeley The Studios, 5 Heathmans Road, Parsons Green, London, SW6 4TJ, United Kingdom
(020) 7736 3171/ (020) 7371 8876
studio@peterdazeley.com
www.peterdazeley.com

DAZphoto 101a Newington Green Road, Islington, London, N1 4QY, United Kingdom
(020) 7503 7514
david@davidzanes.com
www.davidzanes.com

Dean Belcher Studio 3, 231-233 Stoke Newington Church Street, London, N16 9HP, United Kingdom
(020) 7241 4070/(07711) 199334
dean@deanbelcherphotography.com
www.deanbelcherphotography.com

Dean Chalkley@Shoot Production Ltd 23 Glebe Road, London, N8 7DA, United Kingdom
(020) 8442 9171/ (020) 8348 7404
adele@shootgroup.com
www.shootgroup.com

Dean Dorat@Shirley Hart Creative Consultants 19 Ulundi Road, London, SE3 7UQ, United Kingdom
(020) 8853 2987/(07867) 806250
shirleyhart@btinternet.com
www.shirleyhart.com

Dean Freeman@Terri Manduca The Basement, 11 Elvaston Place, London, SW7 5QG, United Kingdom
(020) 7581 5844/ (020) 7581 5822
terri@terrimanduca.co.uk
www.terrimanduca.co.uk

Dean Marsh@Jo Talbot & Sue Young 6M Hyde Park Mansions, Cabbell Street, London, NW1 5BJ, United Kingdom
(020) 7262 0189/(07850) 353468/ (020) 7262 2160
joandsue@btconnect.com
www.joandsue.com

Dean Northcott@Andrea Walji Agency 6 Brewer Street, London, W1F 0SB, United Kingdom
(020) 7439 4144/(07789) 871871/ (020) 7439 4133
andrea@andreawalji.com
www.andreawalji.com

Debbie Bragg C/o Everynight Images, Top Floor Studio, 127 Strathleven Road, London, SW2 5JS, United Kingdom
(020) 7738 7297/ (020) 7738 7297
info@everynight.co.uk
www.everynight.co.uk

Debbie Rowe, London, United Kingdom
(020) 8947 1813/(07831) 607038
debbie@debbierowe.com
www.debbierowe.com

Debi Treloar 14 Mount Pleasant Road, London, NW10 3EL, United Kingdom
(020) 8930 6463/(07881) 528512
mail@debitreloar.com
www.debitreloar.com

Deena Beverley 5 Poulton Cottages, Tinpit, Marlborough, Wiltshire, SN8 1BQ, United Kingdom
(01672) 511973/(07976) 958699/ (01672) 516531
deenabeverley@eclipse.co.uk
www.deenabeverley.co.uk

Defrance 47 Rethelstrasse, Deusseldorf, 40237, Germany
00 49 211 87 67 89/ 00 49 211 87 67 89
defrance@defrance.de
www.defrance.de

Deft Studios 27-29 Millstone Lane, Leicester, LE1 5JN, United Kingdom
0116-251 7068/ 0116-251 7068
nick@deftstudios.co.uk
www.deftstudios.co.uk

Delta Design Studio@Cathy Robert Studio 2, 14-16 Meredith Street, London, EC1R 0AE, United Kingdom
(020) 7837 7557/ (020) 7837 9878
info@cathyrobert.com
www.cathyrobert.com

Demon Agency Top Floor, 23 Charlotte Road, London, EC2A 3PB, United Kingdom
(020) 7739 9697/ (020) 7729 8258
info@demonagency.com
www.demonagency.com

Demon Imaging 8C Raleigh Gardens, London, SW2 1AD, United Kingdom
(020) 8674 9548
info@demonagency.com
www.demonagency.com

Denis Firman Photographic 5 Oxford Road, Middlesbrough, Cleveland, TS5 5DY, United Kingdom
(01642) 823802
denis@denisfirman.co.uk
www.denisfirman.co.uk

Dennis Coutts 165 Commercial Street, Lerwick, Shetland, ZE1 0EX, United Kingdom
(01595) 693765/ (01595) 696649
j.coutts@btconnect.com

Dennis Pedersen 4-5 Academy Buildings, Fanshaw Street, London, N1 6LQ, United Kingdom
(020) 7613 0603/(07774) 990857
dp@dennispedersen.com
www.dennispedersen.com

Dennis Stock@Magnum Photos 63 Gee Street, London, EC1V 3RS, United Kingdom
(020) 7490 1771/ (020) 7608 0020
magnum@magnumphotos.co.uk
www.magnumphotos.com

Derek Askem Lodge Barn, Aylburton, Lydney, Gloucestershire, GL15 6DH, United Kingdom
(01594) 841390/(07775) 785645
da.photo@pgen.net

Derek Brown Photography Annandale Road, Greenwich, London, SE10 0DB, United Kingdom
(020) 8488 6856
chb@derekbrown.co.uk
www.derekbrown.co.uk

Derek Grace 3 Pinders Farm, Pinders Lane, Holme, Carnforth, Lancashire, LA6 1PW, United Kingdom
(01524) 782844/(07831) 430074
dig.photo@derekgrace.com
www.derekgrace.com

Derek Hillier 211B Kentish Town Road, London, NW5 2JU, United Kingdom
(020) 7267 3326/(07831) 819372
derek@derekhillier.com
www.derekhillier.com

Derek Lomas Unit 45, Abey Business Centre, Ingat Place, London, SW8 3NS, United Kingdom
(020) 7622 0123/ (020) 7720 8357
derek.lomas@btopenworl.com
www.dereklomas.com

Derek Pratt Waterways Photo Library, 39 Manor Court Road, Hanwell, London, W7 3EJ, United Kingdom
(020) 8840 1659/(07721) 329950/ (020) 8567 0605
watphot39@aol.com
www.waterwaysphotolibrary.com

Derek Seaward 23 Mercury Court, Homer Drive, London, E14 3UF
020 7531 4393/07785 323 819
derek@derekseaward.com
www.derekseaward.com
See ad in showcase

Derry Brabbs Mulberry Manor, Nidd, Harrogate, North Yorkshire, HG3 3BL, United Kingdom
(01423) 771332/ 772514
derry.brabbs@virgin.net
www.derrybrabbs.com

Derry Robinson Little Gayles, Gayles, Friston, Eastbourne, East Sussex, BN20 0BA, United Kingdom
(01323) 422043/(07721) 023845/ (01323) 422043
info@derryrobinson.com
www.derryrobinson.co.uk

Des Fildes Unit 4A, George Leigh Street, Manchester, M4 6BD, United Kingdom
0161-203 5942/(07733) 113 135/ 0161-203 5872
info@desfildes.com
www.desfildes.com

Designer Photography Kelmscott House, The Leys, Wightwick Bank, Wolverhampton, WV6 8EA, United Kingdom
(01902) 762998/(07956) 825601
info@design-photo.fsnet.co.uk
www.design-photo.fsnet.co.uk

Desiree Dolron@edsonwilliams photography consultancy 52 Brushfield Street, London, E1 6AJ, United Kingdom
(020) 7375 2077/(07867) 517777/ (020) 7375 3077
info@edsonwilliams.com
www.edsonwilliams.com

Desktop Pictures 49 Collyer Avenue, Croydon, CR0 4QY, United Kingdom
(020) 8686 7220/ (020) 8688 5397
info@desktoppictures.co.uk
www.desktoppictures.co.uk

Desmond Burdon Studio 4, 38 St. Oswald's Place, London, SE11 5JE, United Kingdom
(020) 8882 8646/(07836) 575051
desmond@dburdon.com
www.desmondburdon.com

Desperate Frog Flat 3, 17 York Terrace East, London, NW1 4PT, United Kingdom
(07815) 797 906
contact@karlblanchet.com
www.desperatefrog.com

Di Lewis 3 Manor Farm Cottages, Etchilhampton, Devizes, Wiltshire, SN10 3JR, United Kingdom
(01380) 860542
dilewisportfolio@aol.com
www.dilewisportfolio.com

Diana Miller@Horton-Stephens Photographers' Agent 14 Peacock Yard, Iliffe Street, London, SE17 3LH, United Kingdom
(020) 7252 7979/ (020) 7252 6409
us@horton-stephens.com
www.horton-stephens.com

Dianna Bonner Photography 184 Ellerdine Road, Hounslow, TW3 2PX, United Kingdom
(020) 8580 1652/(07718) 881768
dianna.bonner@talk21.com
www.worldvisionphotos.co.uk

Dick Makin Imaging Manvers Studios, 12 Ollerton Rd, Tuxford, Newark, Nottinghamshire, NG22 0LF, United Kingdom
(01777) 870166/(07771) 961217/ (01777) 871739
dick@dmimaging.co.uk
www.dmimaging.co.uk

Dick Marsh 16 Norfolk Mansions, Prince of Wales Drive, London, SW11 4HL, United Kingdom
(020) 7603 9021

Diego Merino@T Photographic 1 Heathgate Place, 75-83 Agincourt Road, London, London, NW3 2NU, United Kingdom
(020) 7428 6070/ (020) 7428 6079
peter@tphotographic.com
www.tphotographic.com

Digital Evolution 13 Clapham Common South Side, London, SW4 7AA, United Kingdom
(07906) 029589
frankmedranos@yahoo.co.uk

Digital-Photo Ltd 62 Rosebery Avenue, London, EC1R 4RR, United Kingdom
(020) 7833 9911/ (020) 7689 3404
admin@digital-photo.co.uk
www.digital-photo.co.uk

Dinesh Khanna@Axiom Photographic Agency The Pall Mall Deposit, 124-128 Barlby Road, London, W10 6BL, United Kingdom
(020) 8964 9970/ (020) 8964 8440
info@axiomphotographic.com
www.axiomphotographic.com

Dirk Karsten@Glo London 32 Stratford Road, London, W8 6QF, United Kingdom
(020) 7938 1330/ (020) 7938 3120
kate@glolondon.com
www.glolondon.com

Dirk Seiden Schwan@Ellison Lee 17 Quadrant Business Centre, 135 Salusbury Road, London, NW6 6RJ, United Kingdom
(020) 7624 2345/ (020) 7624 1100
info@ellisonlee.com
www.ellisonlee.com

Ditte Isager@Gina Phillips Represents Ltd 6 Leverton Place, London, NW5 2PL, United Kingdom
(020) 7284 2022/ (020) 7424 0272
info@ginaphillips.com
www.ginaphillips.co.uk

DL Design Associates Limited 38a Duke Street, Chelmsford, CM1 1HY,
01245 299047/ 01245 299047
darren@dl-design.co.uk
www.dl-design.com

Dobson Agency.co.uk 20 Seafield Avenue, Osgodby, Scarborough, North Yorkshire, YO11 3QG, United Kingdom
(01723) 585141/ (0871) 433 8973
pix@dobsonagency.co.uk
www.dobsonagency.co.uk

Dom Mowbray Photography 18 Petersham Place, London, SW7 5PX, United Kingdom
(020) 7823 9597
mail@dominicmowbray.com
www.dominicmowbray.com

Dominic Blackmore Ltd 9 Cadogan Road, Surbiton, Surrey, KT6 4DQ, United Kingdom
(020) 8715 6995/(07798) 626246 / (020) 8399 1702
drb@dominicblackmore.com
www.dominicblackmore.com

Dominic Harris@Martin Roper Photographer's Agent 158a Chamberlayne Road, London, NW10 3JS, United Kingdom
(020) 8964 4780/(0779) 9410942
martin.roper@btinternet.com
www.martinroper.com

Dominic Mowbray@Esser Assocs 2nd Floor North, 6 Buckingham Street, London, WC2N 6BU, United Kingdom
(020) 7976 2915/(07778) 149149 / (01372) 464326
rob.esser@virgin.net
www.davidesser.com

Dominique Davoust 43 Avenue du Stade, Rueil-Malmaison, 92500, France
00 33 14 751 0842/6 80 07 47 77 / 00 33 14 751 5615
davoust@club-internet.fr
www.davoust.com

Don Cunningham Via Fabio Filzi, Milan, 201232, Italy
00 39 2 670 1021
doncunningham@mac.com
www.homepage.mac/doncunningham/

Don McCullin@Mark George 5 St. George's Court, 131 Putney Bridge Road, Putney, London, SW15 2PA, United Kingdom
(020) 8877 9922/(07771) 595 999 / (020) 8870 5533
mg@markgeorge.com
www.markgeorge.com

Don Wales Photography 11 Weston Avenue, Addlestone, Surrey, KT15 1UW, United Kingdom
(01932) 882823/(07860) 859779
bluebirdsr@aol.com
www.donwales.co.uk

Don Wood 16 Bisham Gardens, London, N6 6DD, United Kingdom
(07973) 545757
donwoodphotographer@btinternet.com
www.donwoodimages.com

Don Wood Photographer 22 Brookfield Park, Parliament Hill Fields, London, NW5 1ER, United Kingdom
(020) 7485 5224/ (020) 7485 5224
donwoodphotographer@btinternet.com
www.donwoodimages.com

Donaghue Photography 280A Cowley Road, Oxford, OX4 1UR, United Kingdom
(01865) 251996/ (01865) 251767
chris@oxford-photo-library.co.uk
www.oxford-photo-library.co.uk

Donald Christie@East Photographic Ltd 8 Iron Bridge House, 3 Bridge Approach, London, NW1 8BD, United Kingdom
(020) 7722 3444/ (020) 7722 3544
roger@eastphotographic.com
www.eastphotographic.com

Donald MacLellan 14 Addison Road, Banbury, Oxfordshire, OX16 9DH, United Kingdom
(01295) 258807/(07850) 947284 / (01295) 258807
donald.maclellan@btinternet.com
www.donny-bygosh.com

Donna Eaves@Donovan Wylie@Magnum Photos 63 Gee Street, London, EC1V 3RS, United Kingdom
(020) 7490 1771/ (020) 7608 0020
magnum@magnumphotos.co.uk
www.magnumphotos.com

Dorchester Ledbetter Photographers Ltd The Studio, 54 North Street, Leeds, LS2 7PN, United Kingdom
0113-245 1718/ 0113-245 0737
info@dorchesterledbetter.co.uk
www.dorchesterledbetter.co.uk

Dorian Shaw@Axiom Photographic Agency The Pall Mall Deposit, 124-128 Barlby Road, London, W10 6BL, United Kingdom
(020) 8964 9970/ (020) 8964 8440
info@axiomphotographic.com
www.axiomphotographic.com

Double Red Photographic The Old School, Thorn Lane, Goxhill, Barrow-upon-Humber, North Lincolnshire, DN19 7JE, United Kingdom
(01469) 531416/ (01469) 531888
s.ward@doublered.co.uk
www.doublered.co.uk

Doug Currie 6 Cape Mills, Coal Hill Lane, Leeds, LS28 5NA, United Kingdom
0113-255 6140/(07774) 946349 / 0113-255 8335
doug@dougcurrie.co.uk
www.dougcurrie.co.uk

Doug McKinlay@Axiom Photographic Agency The Pall Mall Deposit, 124-128 Barlby Road, London, W10 6BL, United Kingdom
(020) 8964 9970/ (020) 8964 8440
info@axiomphotographic.com
www.axiomphotographic.com

Douglas Cape Flat 1, 45 Hilldrop Crescent, London, N7 0JD, United Kingdom
(020) 7609 3445/(07973) 747523
douglas@z360.com
www.z360.com

Douglas Corrance 9 Lonsdale Terrace, Edinburgh, EH3 9HN, United Kingdom
0131-228 1528/(07774) 158727 / 0131-228 1528
dcorrance@blueyonder.co.uk

Douglas Fisher@Mutton Bones Ground Floor, 51 Balcombe Street, London, NW1 6HD, United Kingdom
(020) 7723 8244/ (020) 7723 2770
hello@muttonbones.co.uk
www.muttonbones.co.uk

Douglas Robertson Photography 42 Royal Park Terrace, Edinburgh, EH8 8JA, United Kingdom
0131-467 7028/(07930) 433834
douglasinscotland@blueyonder.co.uk
www.douglasinscotland.co.uk

Duncan Caratacus Clark 43a Gunter Grove, London, SW10 0UN, United Kingdom
(020) 7376 5843/ (020) 7751 5845
duncan@fotografique.com
www.fotografique.com

Duncan Davis The Clock Mill, Capheaton, Newcastle upon Tyne, NE19 2AF, United Kingdom
(01830) 530371/ (01830) 530380
duncan@picturedisc.co.uk
www.duncandavies.com

Duncan MacQueen, United Kingdom
(07973) 542346
studio2@duncanmacqueen.com
www.duncanmacqueen.com

Duncan McKenzie@van Hauen Moore 14 Powis Mews, Notting Hill, London, W11 1JN, United Kingdom
(020) 7792 0022/ (020) 7792 8636
email@vanhauenmoore.com
www.vanhauenmoore.com

Duncan McNicol The Studio, Treyford, Midhurst, West Sussex, GU29 0LD, United Kingdom
(01730) 825100/(07973) 386520
info@duncanmcnicol.com
www.duncanmcnicol.com

Duncan Smith 12 Mallow Street, London, EC1Y 8RQ, United Kingdom
(020) 7490 0070/ (020) 7490 3370
www.duncansmith.net

Duncan Soar Photography 15 Kimberley Road, London, SW9 9DQ, United Kingdom
(07940) 547135
duncan@duncansoar.com
www.duncansoar.com

DunningPhotographic 38 Southfields, Bridgerule, Holsworthy, Devon, EX22 7DX, United Kingdom
(01288) 381 589
hdphotographic@btinternet.com

Dylan Collard@Process 5 Choumert Mews, Choumert Road, London, SE15 4BD, United Kingdom
(020) 7277 8400/(07950) 311425 / (020) 7277 7223
info@processphotography.com
www.processphotography.com

Dylan Garcia Photography 22 Tennyson Road, Cowes, Isle of Wight, PO31 7QA, United Kingdom
(07973) 427794
dylanphotolight@yahoo.com
www.dylan-garcia.co.uk

E J M Photography 56A Clerkenwell Road, London, EC1M 5PX, United Kingdom
(020) 7608 2341/(07774) 422120 / (020) 7608 2138
jtickner@lineone.net

E P C Photography Unit 6, Trafalgar Mews, London, E9 5JG, United Kingdom
(07956) 194599
epcphotography@aol.com
www.epcphotography.co.uk

E S P Agency 1st Floor, 63 Charlotte Street, London, W1T 4PG, United Kingdom
(020) 7209 1626/ (020) 7209 1627
info@esp-agency.com
www.esp-agency.com

E T H O S Represents 23 Albert Square, London, SW8 1BS, United Kingdom
(020) 7735 7006/ (020) 7735 7009
ethosrepresents@btconect.com

E T R I Unit 5, 7 Long Street, London, E2 8HN, United Kingdom
(020) 7033 9134
info@etri.org.uk
www.etri.org.uk

Eamonn McGoldrick Photography 3 Mount Hooly Crescent, North Queensferry, Inverkeithing, Fife, KY11 1JW, United Kingdom
(01383) 419987/(07810) 482491
contact@eamonnmcgoldrick.com
www.eamonnmcgoldrick.com

Earl Carter@Mark George 5 St. George's Court, 131 Putney Bridge Road, Putney, London, SW15 2PA, United Kingdom
(020) 8877 9922/(07771) 595 999 / (020) 8870 5533
mg@markgeorge.com
www.markgeorge.com

East Photographic Ltd 8 Iron Bridge House, 3 Bridge Approach, London, NW1 8BD, United Kingdom
(020) 7722 3444/ (020) 7722 3544
roger@eastphotographic.com
www.eastphotographic.com

Eclipse Studios Old Tye Place, 3 London Road South, Merstham, Redhill, RH1 3AZ, United Kingdom
(01737) 642020/(07973) 354576 / (01737) 642020
eclipsestudios@btinternet.com
www.eclipsephotostudios.co.uk

Ed Baxter Photography Bank House Studio, 95a Drumlanrig Street, Thornhill, Dumfriesshire, DG3 5LU, United Kingdom
(07932) 918205
ed@ed-baxter-photography.co.uk
www.ed-baxter-photography.co.uk

Ed Davis 14 Faraday Road, Acton, London, W3 6JB, United Kingdom
(020) 8896 3226/(07831) 474342 / (020) 8896 3226
info@ed-davis-photography.co.uk
www.ed-davis-photography.co.uk

Ed Ironside Galleon House, 3 Fore Street, Calstock, Cornwall, PL18 9RN, United Kingdom
(01822) 832574/(07973) 335509
ed@bremweb.co.uk
www.bremweb.co.uk

Ed Lee@Esser Assocs 2nd Floor North, 6 Buckingham Street, London, WC2N 6BU, United Kingdom
(020) 7976 2915/(07778) 149149 / (01372) 464326
rob.esser@virgin.net
www.davidesser.com

Ed Pritchard 43 Museum Street, London, WC1A 1LY, United Kingdom
(020) 7404 9640

Eddie Macdonald 66 Vassall Road, London, SW9 6HY, United Kingdom
(07932) 624225/ (020) 8643 0437
edmacphoto@btinternet.com
www.edmacphoto.co.uk

Edgar Martins@Swerve Photography 29-31 Saffron Hill, London, EC1N 8SW, United Kingdom
/(07967) 628769
info@swervephotography.com
www.swervephotography.com

edsonwilliams Creative Consultancy
52 Brushfield Street, London, E1 6AG, United Kingdom
020 7375 2077/020 7375 3077 info@edsonwilliams.com
www.edsonwilliams.com
See ad in showcase

Education Photos 8 Whitemore Road, Guildford, Surrey, GU1 1QT, United Kingdom
(01483) 511 666
johnwalmsley@educationphotos.co.uk
www.educationphotos.co.uk

Edward Beierle@Upper Orange Nostitzstrasse 15, Berlin, 10961, Germany
49 178 6121661/ 49 30 6121661
mail@upperorange.de
www.upperorange.de

Edward Edwards Jewellery Photographer 16 The Vale, London, W3 7SB, United Kingdom
(020) 8749 8887/ (020) 8749 8884
studio@edwardsphotography.co.uk
www.edwardsphotography.co.uk

Edward James Allwright G4 Panther House, 38 Mount Pleasant, London, WC1X 0AN, United Kingdom
(020) 7837 7375/(07930) 563033
eallwright@hotmail.com
www.edwardallwright.co.uk

Edward Moss Photography Oaklands Avenue, Birmingham, B17 9TU, United Kingdom
0121-426 5201/(07766) 250970 0121-426 5201
info@edwardmoss.co.uk
www.edwardmoss.co.uk

Edward Shaw Photography 132 Station Road, Kings Heath, Birmingham, B14 7TD, United Kingdom
0121-443 1741/(07904) 919223
info@edwardshaw.co.uk
www.edwardshaw.co.uk

Edward Sykes 61 Plimsoll Road, London, N4 2EN, United Kingdom
(020) 7226 5329/ (020) 7226 5329
edsykesphotographer@tesco.net

Edward Webb 1A Chance Street, London, E1 6JT, United Kingdom
(020) 7739 6789/(07774) 236272
edward@ewebb.co.uk
www.ewebb.co.uk

Elaine Constantine@Marco Santucci Photography 85 Essex Road, London, N1 2SF, United Kingdom
(020) 7226 7705/ (020) 7226 9563
email@marcosantucci.com
www.marcosantucci.com

Electra Studios 11a Seaway Drive, Seaway Parade Industrial Estate, Port Talbot, West Glamorgan, SA12 7BR, United Kingdom
(01639) 820840/ (01639) 820840
mike@photographer-uk.com
www.photographer-uk.com

Electric Images, London, United Kingdom
(07989) 412179
electr1c@mac.com
www.electricimages.com

Electric Pictures Ltd The Old Fire Station, Church Street, Burnham, Slough, SL1 7HX, United Kingdom
(01628) 669000/(07764) 687316 (01628) 669105
sales@electric-pictures.co.uk
www.electric-pictures.co.uk

Eleni Leoussi 57 Oakfield Road, London, N4 4LD, United Kingdom
(020) 8341 1369/(07976) 741160
eleni.leoussi@ukonline.co.uk

Eli Reed@Magnum Photos 63 Gee Street, London, EC1V 3RS, United Kingdom
(020) 7490 1771/ (020) 7608 0020
magnum@magnumphotos.co.uk
www.magnumphotos.com

Elina Simonen@Wilde Representation 314 Mare Street, London, E8 1HA, United Kingdom
(020) 8653 4466/(07810) 795036 (01424) 201070
sian@wilderepresentation.com
www.wilderepresentation.com

Elise Dumontet Photography Unit 3, Wilmer Industrial Estate, Wilmer Place, London, N16 0LW, United Kingdom
(07989) 989840
info@elisedumontet.com
www.elisedumontet.com

Elizabeth Furth 11 Holdernesse Road, London, SW17 7RG, United Kingdom
(07956) 100548
ehef@talktalk.net

Elizabeth Zeschin@Alexandra Von Ziechmann Flat 1, 90 Sutherland Avenue, London, W9 2QR, United Kingdom
(020) 7289 4248/(07962) 082691
www.alexandravz.com

Ellen Rooney@Axiom Photographic Agency The Pall Mall Deposit, 124-128 Barlby Road, London, W10 6BL, United Kingdom
(020) 8964 9970/ (020) 8964 8440
info@axiomphotographic.com
www.axiomphotographic.com

Elliott Erwitt@Magnum Photos 63 Gee Street, London, EC1V 3RS, United Kingdom
(020) 7490 1771/ (020) 7608 0020
magnum@magnumphotos.co.uk
www.magnumphotos.com

Ellis Photography 122 Risca Road, Newport, Gwent, NP20 3SA, United Kingdom
(01633) 267580/ (01633) 265894
info@ellisphotography.com
www.ellisphotography.com

Ellison Lee 17 Quadrant Business Centre, 135 Salusbury Road, London, NW6 6RJ, United Kingdom
(020) 7624 2345/ (020) 7624 1100
info@ellisonlee.com
www.ellisonlee.com

Ellyart Photography 95 Crookham Road, Church Crookham, Fleet, Hampshire, GU51 5NP, United Kingdom
(07710) 433454
elly@ukonline.co.uk
www.ellyart.co.uk

Emby Images 15 Alexander Close, Sandwich, Kent, CT13 0EY, United Kingdom
(01304) 612989/(07812) 133071
steve@embyimages.com
www.embyimages.com

Emily Andersen 42 Chepstow Place, London, W2 4TA, United Kingdom
(020) 7229 8307/(07774) 164607 (020) 7229 8770
emilyandersen@onetel.com
www.andersenphotographic.org

Emily Bowling Photography, London, United Kingdom
(07710) 493833
contact@emilybowling.com
www.emilybowling.com

Emily Skinner@Graham-Cameron Illustration The Studio, 23 Holt Road, Sheringham, Norfolk, NR26 8NB, United Kingdom
(01263) 821333/ (01263) 821334
enquiry@graham-cameron-illustration.com
www.graham-cameron-illustration.com

Emli Bendixen 77B Rectory Road, London, N16 7PP,
4.47801E+11
emli@emli.dk
www.emli.dk

Emma Hardy@East Photographic Ltd 8 Iron Bridge House, 3 Bridge Approach, London, NW1 8BD, United Kingdom
(020) 7722 3444/ (020) 7722 3544
roger@eastphotographic.com
www.eastphotographic.com

Emma Hughes 120 Latchmere Road, Kingston upon Thames, Surrey, KT2 5TT, United Kingdom
(020) 8546 7199/(07971) 957596
emma@lesandemma.co.uk

Emma Lee@Pearson Lyle Management 3rd Floor, 40 Bowling Green Lane, London, EC1R 0NE, United Kingdom
(020) 7415 7061/ (020) 7415 7059
contact@pearsonlyle.co.uk
www.pearsonlyle.co.uk

Emma Summerton, United Kingdom
es@emmasummerton.com
www.emmasummerton.com

Enrico Sachetti@Victoria Lees Management (VLM) 2 Fairview Gardens, Woodford Green, Essex, IG8 7DJ, United Kingdom
(07710) 287220/ (020) 8504 8125
victoria@victorialeesmanagement.co.uk
www.victorialeesmanagement.co.uk

ERA Management Ltd 120 The Beaux Arts Building, 10-18 Manor Gardens, London, N7 6JT, United Kingdom
(020) 7281 5996/ (020) 7281 6202
kate@eramanagement.com
www.eramanagement.com

Eric Crichton Longthorns, Blandford Forum, Dorset, DT11 0HT, United Kingdom
(01258) 837990/ (01258) 837996
eric@ecrichton.fsnet.co.uk

Eric Hayman 32 Beaumont Road, London, W4 5AP, United Kingdom
(020) 8994 5199
e-c-hayman@fsmail.net

Eric Swayne 34C Princess Road, London, NW1 8JL, United Kingdom
(020) 7586 3731/(07966) 131920

Eric Whitehead, Kendal, Cumbria, LA9 4SU, United Kingdom
(01539) 448894/(07768) 808249 (01539) 448294
eric@snookerimages.co.uk
www.snookerimages.co.uk

Eric Whitehead Photography 10 Brow Close, Windermere, Cumbria, LA23 2HA, United Kingdom
(01539) 448894/(07768) 808249 (01539) 448294
snooker@snookerimages.co.uk
www.snookerimages.co.uk

Erich Hartmann@Magnum Photos 63 Gee Street, London, EC1V 3RS, United Kingdom
(020) 7490 1771/ (020) 7608 0020
magnum@magnumphotos.co.uk
www.magnumphotos.com

Erik Hijweege@Freddie Brazil 211 Abercairn Road, London, SW16 5AJ, United Kingdom
(020) 8764 2801/(07711) 753072 (020) 8764 2801
frederick.brazil@btconnect.com
www.freddiebrazil.com

Erin Levy Photography Eclipse Building, 26 Laycock Street, London, N1 1AH, United Kingdom
(07974) 362109
erin.levy@gmail.com
www.erinlevy.com

Ernst Fischer@Mark George 5 St. George's Court, 131 Putney Bridge Road, Putney, London, SW15 2PA, United Kingdom
(020) 8877 9922/(07711) 595 999 (020) 8870 5533
mg@markgeorge.com
www.markgeorge.com

Erwan Frotin@Big Active Ltd Unit 6.01, The Tea Building, 56 Shoreditch High Street, London, E16 JJ, United Kingdom
(020) 7739 5601/ (020) 7739 7479
contact@bigactive.com
www.bigactive.com

Erwin Olaf Ijselstraat 26-28, Amsterdam, 1078 CJ, Netherlands
20 692 3438/ 20 694 1291
info@erwinolaf.com
www.erwinolaf.com

Estelle Rancurel@Valeriehersleven Boundary House (3rd Floor), 91-93 Charterhouse Street, London, EC1M 6HR, United Kingdom
(07775) 717474
me@valeriehersleven.com
www.valeriehersleven.com

Ethel Davies P O Box 48687, London, NW8 1AY, United Kingdom
(020) 7724 8563/(07801) 636057
fishpot@earthlink.net
www.fishphot.com

Etienne Bol 2 Colville Terrace, London, W11 2BE, United Kingdom
(07836) 361821
e.bol@virgin.net

Euan Myles Norton House, 54 Easter Road, Edinburgh, EH7 5RQ, United Kingdom
0131-659 5445/(07768) 471930 0131-659 5446
www.euanmyles.co.uk

Eugene W. Smith@Magnum Photos 63 Gee Street, London, EC1V 3RS, United Kingdom
(020) 7490 1771/ (020) 7608 0020
magnum@magnumphotos.co.uk
www.magnumphotos.com

Eugenio Franchi@Horton-Stephens Photographers' Agent 14 Peacock Yard, Iliffe Street, London, SE17 3LH, United Kingdom
(020) 7252 7979/ (020) 7252 6409
us@horton-stephens.com
www.horton-stephens.com

Eva Mueller@WildeHague Ltd Suite 4, The Swan centre, Fishers Lane, London, W4 1RX, United Kingdom
(020) 8747 9988/ (020) 8747 8228
info@wildehague.com
www.wildehague.com

Eva Vermandel@Bonakdar Cleary 35 Charles Square, London, N1 6HT, United Kingdom
(020) 7490 1155
bc@bonakdarcleary.com
www.bonakdarcleary.com

Eve Arnold@Magnum Photos 63 Gee Street, London, EC1V 3RS, United Kingdom
(020) 7490 1771/ (020) 7608 0020
magnum@magnumphotos.co.uk
www.magnumphotos.com

Everard Smith Photography Shimpling Place, Diss, Norfolk, IP21 4UB, United Kingdom
(01379) 740404/(07778) 281228
info@photosmithuk.com
www.photosmithuk.com

Ewan Fraser@Début Art & The Coningsby Gallery 30 Tottenham Street, London, W1T 4RJ, United Kingdom
(020) 7636 1064/ (020) 7580 7017
info@debutart.com
www.debutart.com

Ewen Spencer@Marco Santucci Photography 85 Essex Road, London, N1 2SF, United Kingdom
(020) 7226 7705/ (020) 7226 9563
email@marcosantucci.com
www.marcosantucci.com

Exile Images 1 Mill Row, West Hill Road, Brighton, BN1 3SU, United Kingdom
(01273) 208741
pics@exileimages.co.uk
www.exileimages.co.uk

Fabrice Robin@Gina Phillips Represents Ltd 6 Leverton Place, London, NW5 2PL, United Kingdom
(020) 7284 2022/ (020) 7424 0272
info@ginaphillips.co.uk
www.ginaphillips.co.uk

Fabrizio Valenzano Photography Studio J101, Tower Bridge Business Complex, 100 Clements Road, London, SE16 4DG, United Kingdom
(07903) 302264
mail@fabrizio Valenzano
www.fabriziovalenzano.com

Farringdon Photo Studio Hire 2 Bleeding Heart Yard, Greville Street, London, EC1N 8SJ,
020 7242 7031
bill@billburnett.co.uk
www.billburnett.co.uk

Farrow D P P Unit 1A Savile Bridge Mills, Savile Road, Dewsbury, West Yorkshire, WF12 9AF, United Kingdom
(01924) 461077/(07940) 704366 / (01924) 461077
john@farrowdpp.com
www.farrowdpp.com

Farrow Photographers The Cottage, Main Road, East Keal, Spilsby, Lincolnshire, PE23 4BA, United Kingdom
(07973) 131341
eddie.maples@ukonline.co.uk

Fashion Executives Via Monte, Di Pieta, Milan, Italy, 20121,
7717366567/ 8700625674
riz@fashionexecutives.com
www.fashionexecutives.com

Ferdinando Scianna@Magnum Photos 63 Gee Street, London, EC1V 3RS, United Kingdom
(020) 7490 1771/ (020) 7608 0020
magnum@magnumphotos.co.uk
www.magnumphotos.com

Fernando Milani@Horton-Stephens Photographers' Agent 14 Peacock Yard, Iliffe Street, London, SE17 3LH, United Kingdom
(020) 7252 7979/ (020) 7252 6409
us@horton-stephens.com
www.horton-stephens.com

Ffoto Fictions 8 Wells Street, Riverside, Cardiff, CF11 6DW, United Kingdom
(029) 2022 8367
www.Ffotofictions.com

Ffotograff 10 Kyveilog Street, Cardiff, CF11 9JA, United Kingdom
(029) 2023 6879
ffotograff@easynet.co.uk
www.ffotograff.com

Fi McGhee Unit G2, The Glasshouse, 3 Royal Oak Yard, Bermondsey Street, London, SE1 3GD, United Kingdom
(020) 7739 2210/(07860) 519444 / (020) 7490 4968
fi@northdesign.co.uk
www.northdesign.co.uk

Fin Serck-Hanssen@Beth Coyne Agency, London, NW6 1GF, United Kingdom
(020) 7431 8981/ (020) 7813 9750
info@bethcoyne.com
www.bethcoyne.com

Finlay MacKay@Marco Santucci Photography 85 Essex Road, London, N1 2SF, United Kingdom
(020) 7226 7705/ (020) 7226 9563
email@marcosantucci.com
www.marcosantucci.com

Fiorenzo Borghi@Bill Charles London Ltd. Unit 3E1, Zetland House, 5-25 Scrutton Street, London, EC2A 4HJ, United Kingdom
020 7033 9284/020 2033 9285
london@billcharles.com
www.billcharles.com

First Image 205 Ladbroke Grove, London, W10 6HQ, United Kingdom
(020) 8969 7492
firstimage@onetel.com

Firth Photo 18a Yonge Park, Islington, London, N4 3NT, United Kingdom
(07803) 726767
andrew@firthphoto.co.uk
www.firthphoto.co.uk

Flair Photography 11 Langholme, Sparrows Herne, Bushey, WD23 1AR, United Kingdom
(020) 8950 0097/ (020) 8950 0097

Flare 30 Hillbury Road, London, SW17 8JT, United Kingdom
(07951) 717722
info@flare.uk.com
www.flare.uk.com

Fleur Olby@C S B Management 40 Bowling Green Lane, London, EC1R 0NE, United Kingdom
(020) 7415 7051/ (020) 7415 7059
susie@csbmanagement.com
www.csbmanagement.com

Florian Geiss@Horton-Stephens Photographers' Agent 14 Peacock Yard, Iliffe Street, London, SE17 3LH, United Kingdom
(020) 7252 7979/ (020) 7252 6409
us@horton-stephens.com
www.horton-stephens.com

Florian Seidel@Upper Orange Nostitzstrasse 15, Berlin, 10961, Germany
49 178 6121661/ 49 30 6121661
mail@upperorange.com
www.upperorange.de

Focusing Ltd Unit 6, New Milton Bus. Center, Wick Drive, New Milton, Hampshire, BH25 6RQ,
01425 617800
info@focusingltd.com
www.focusingltd.com

Forth Photography Unit 1, Leith Citadel, 15 East Cromwell Street, Edinburgh, EH6 6HD, United Kingdom
0131-553 2178/ 0131-553 7499
johns@almondtds.com
www.almondtds.com

Forum Photography 154-156 London Road, Leicester, LE2 1NN, United Kingdom
0116-247 3044/ 0116-255 0556
chris.a@forumphotography.co.uk
www.forumphotography.co.uk

Foto Theme Digital Ltd 70-71 Wells Street, London, W1T 3QE, United Kingdom
(020) 7255 1277
info@fotothemedigital.co.uk
www.fotothemedigital.co.uk

Fotoformula Via A. Milesi, 1, Milano, 20133, Italy
00 39 2 7010 6775/00 39 33 5634 4879 / 00 39 2 7010 6775
alessandro@fotoformula.com
www.fotoformula.com

Fotografikus 59 Roundhill Crescent, Brighton, BN2 3FQ, United Kingdom
(07786) 515793
info@fotografikus.com
www.fotografikus.com

Fourninety Limited Robeson Way, Manchester, M22 4SX, United Kingdom
(0845) 490 4901/ (0845) 490 4902
info@fourninety.com
www.fourninety.com

Fox-Waterman Photography Ltd 24 Edward Road, Bromley, BR1 3NQ, United Kingdom
(020) 8466 5330/ (020) 8464 1372

Fran Banbury Photography Beech Way, Twickenham, TW2 5JT, United Kingdom
(020) 8408 3000
info@franbanbury.com
www.franbanbury.com

Francesca Yorke@Axiom Photographic Agency The Pall Mall Deposit, 124-128 Barlby Road, London, W10 6BL, United Kingdom
(020) 8964 9970/ (020) 8964 8440
info@axiomphotographic.com
www.axiomphotographic.com

Francis Loney Unit One, 315 Kingsland Road, London, E8 4DL, United Kingdom
(020) 7254 1199/(07753) 634443 / (020) 7254 8399
francisloney@talktalk.net
www.francisloney.co.uk

Franck Malithiery@T Photographic 1 Heathgate Place, 75-83 Agincourt Road, London, London, NW3 2NU, United Kingdom
(020) 7428 6070/ (020) 7428 6079
peter@tphotographic.com
www.tphotographic.com

Francois Gillet@Annabelle Dalton 20 Glebe Street, London, W4 2BG, United Kingdom
(020) 8742 1883/(07973) 392625 / (020) 8742 1856
daltphotog@aol.com
www.annabelledalton.com

Frank Adam Photography 4 Empress Mews, Kenbury Street, London, SE5 9BT
020 7738 6901/ frank@frankadamphoto.com
www.frankadamphoto.com
See ad in showcase

Frank Connor@Blowup 146 Amyand Park Road, St. Margaret's, Twickenham, TW1 3HY, United Kingdom
(020) 8744 0210/ (020) 8892 2521
orders@blowup.net
www.blowup.net

Frank Herfort@Defrance 47 Rethelstrasse, Deusseldorf, 40237, Germany
00 49 211 87 67 89/ 00 49 211 87 67 89
defrance@defrance.de
www.defrance.de

Frank Herholdt@Agent Orange 10 Swan Yard, London, N1 1SD, United Kingdom
(020) 7226 0440/ (020) 7226 1613
annika@agentorange.co.uk
www.agentorange.co.uk

Fraser Jones Studios 54 Russell Road, Newbury, Berkshire, RG14 5LA, United Kingdom
(01635) 36602/(07719) 510467
fraserjones@btconnect.com

Freddie Brazil 211 Abercairn Road, SW16 5AJ, United Kingdom
(020) 8764 2801/(07711) 753072 / (020) 8764 2801
frederick.brazil@btconnect.com
www.freddiebrazil.com

Frederic Auerbach@Ellison Lee 17 Quadrant Business Centre, 135 Salusbury Road, London, NW6 6RJ, United Kingdom
(020) 7624 2345/ (020) 7624 1100
info@ellisonlee.com
www.ellisonlee.com

Frederike Helwig@Bill Charles London Ltd. Unit 3E1, Zetland House, 5-25 Scrutton Street, London, EC2A 4HJ, United Kingdom
020 7033 9284/020 2033 9285
london@billcharles.com
www.billcharles.com

Frost Studio Ltd 8 Shambles, York, YO1 7LZ, United Kingdom
(01904) 623895/ (01759) 303065
gtam@froststudio.co.uk
www.froststudio.co.uk

Fuji Photo Film (U.K.) Ltd 125 Finchley Road, London, NW3 6HY, United Kingdom
(020) 7586 5900/ (020) 7722 4259
www.fujifilm.co.uk

Fujifilm Motion Picture Fujifilm Hse, 125 Finchley Rd, London, NW3 6HY, United Kingdom
(020) 7465 5766/ (020) 7483 1419
movingimage@fuji.co.uk
www.fujifilm.co.uk/motion

19

Fusako Akimoto@Début Art & The Coningsby Gallery 30 Tottenham Street, London, W1T 4RJ, United Kingdom
☎ (020) 7636 1064/📠 (020) 7580 7017
✉ info@debutart.com
🖳 www.debutart.com

Fyfephoto 76 Milton Grove, London, N16 8QY, United Kingdom
☎ (020) 7241 0502/📠 (0788) 455 9229
✉ alastair@fyfephoto.com
🖳 www.fyfephoto.co.uk

G G S Photo Graphics Ltd 1 White Lodge Business Park, Hall Road, Norwich, NR4 6DG, United Kingdom
☎ (01603) 622500/📠 (01603) 633876
✉ enquir@ggs.co.uk
🖳 www.ggs.co.uk

G S Abroad 90 Devonport Road, London, W12 8NU, United Kingdom
☎ (020) 8749 1631
✉ gisela@gsabroad.com
🖳 www.gsabroad.com

G S R Studios 20 Buchanan Close, Northampton, NN4 8RA, United Kingdom
☎ (07787) 158562/📠 (01604) 707833
✉ geoff.rowe@gsrstudios.com
🖳 www.gsrstudios.com

Gael McDougall@Cormack Creative Management Ltd Suite 208, 95 Morrison Street, Glasgow, G5 8BE, United Kingdom
☎ 0141-429 6810/(07778) 323169 📠 0141-429 2603
✉ susie@cormackcreativemanagement.co.uk
🖳 www.cormackcreativemanagement.co.uk

Gandee Vasan 65 Marlborough Road, London, SW19 2HF, United Kingdom
☎ (020) 8287 8378/📠 (020) 8287 7617
✉ gandee@blueyonder.co.uk
🖳 www.gandeevasan.com

Gareth Boden 65 The Avenue, Hertford, SG14 3DT, United Kingdom
☎ (01920) 486482/(07774) 806502 📠 (01920) 486483
✉ gareth@imageexpress.co.uk
🖳 www.contact-me.net/garethboden

Gareth Morgans Photography 93A Brownlow Road, London, N11 2BN, United Kingdom
☎ (07775) 582185/ 📠 (0870) 1372443
✉ info@garethmorgans.com
🖳 www.garethmorgans.com
See ad

Gareth Munden Photography 93a North View Road, London, N8 7LR, United Kingdom
☎ (020) 8347 9907/📠 (020) 8347 9907
✉ info@garethmunden.freeserve.co.uk
🖳 www.garethmunden.co.uk

Gareth Sambidge@Process 5 Choumert Mews, Choumert Road, London, SE15 4BD, United Kingdom
☎ (020) 7277 8400/(07950) 311425 📠 (020) 7277 7223
✉ info@processphotography.com
🖳 www.processphotography.com

Gareth Trevor 47 Lancaster Mews, London, W2 3QQ, United Kingdom
☎ (020) 7262 3848/(07956) 364342
✉ gareth@garethtrevor.com
🖳 www.garethtrevor.com

Garrard Martin@Shirley Hart Creative Consultants 19 Ulundi Road, London, SE3 7UQ, United Kingdom
☎ (020) 8853 2987/(07867) 806250
✉ shirleyhart@btinternet.com
🖳 www.shirleyhart.com

Garry Owens@Agent Orange 10 Swan Yard, London, N1 1SD, United Kingdom
☎ (020) 7226 0440/ 📠 (020) 7226 1613
✉ annika@agentorange.co.uk
🖳 www.agentorange.co.uk

Garry Simpson@Vue Units 1 & 2 Elm Court, 1 Royal Oak Yard, London, SE1 3TP, United Kingdom
☎ (020) 7403 5555/📠 (020) 7403 2005
✉ production@vue-us.com
🖳 www.vue-us.com

Garry Stevenson@Carolyn Trayler Photographers Agent Unit 566, 56 Gloucester Road, London, SW7 4UB, United Kingdom
☎ (020) 7370 0712/📠 (020) 7370 0765
✉ carolyn@trayler.co.uk
🖳 www.trayler.co.uk

Garth Dale Studios 2 Phoenix Court, Finch Close, Nottingham, NG7 2PU, United Kingdom
☎ 0115-952 7107/(07889) 924038 📠 0115-952 7107
✉ talk2us@garth.co.uk
🖳 www.garth.co.uk

Garth Dawson Studio 6 Bridge Street, Accrington, Lancashire, BB5 1HL, United Kingdom
☎ (01254) 231802/ 📠 (01254) 386577
✉ reg@garthdawsonstudio.co.uk
🖳 www.garthdawsonstudio.co.uk

Gary Bates@Début Art & The Coningsby Gallery 30 Tottenham Street, London, W1T 4RJ, United Kingdom
☎ (020) 7636 1064/📠 (020) 7580 7017
✉ info@debutart.com
🖳 www.debutart.com

Gary Bryan@Jo Clark 2nd Floor, 202B Camden Lock, London, NW1 8AF, United Kingdom
☎ (020) 7267 7267/📠 (020) 7267 7495
✉ jo@joclark.com
🖳 www.joclark.com

Gary Bryan Photography Limited Holborn Studios, 49-50 Eagle Wharf Road, London, N1 7ED,
☎ 7973825574
✉ gary@garybryanphotography.com
🖳 www.garybryanphotography.com

Gary Childs@Agent Pandora 12 Stonells Road, London, SW11 6HQ, United Kingdom
☎ (07966) 181825
✉ pandora@agentpandora.com
🖳 www.agentpandora.com

Gary Hind Photography The Boathouse, Church Lane, Northampton, NN14 4ED, United Kingdom
☎ (07785) 777145
✉ garyhindltd@aol.com
🖳 www.garyhind.com

Gary Latham 15 Pennant Terrace, London, E17 5BD, United Kingdom
☎ (020) 8928 0372/(07958) 302161
✉ info@garylatham.co.uk
🖳 www.garylatham.co.uk

Gareth Morgans Photography M +44(0)7775 582185 E info@garethmorgans.com W www.garethmorgans.com

Gary Ledden 41 Elmwood Drive, Stoneleigh, Epsom, Surrey, KT17 2NL, United Kingdom
☎ (020) 8873 2084/(07778) 553086
✉ garyledden@aol.com

Gary Ombler 10 Swan Court, Oxfordshire, OX28 6EA,
☎ 1993771468
✉ gary@garyombler.com
🖥 www.garyombler.com

Gary Salter@Horton-Stephens Photographers' Agent 14 Peacock Yard, Iliffe Street, London, SE17 3LH, United Kingdom
☎ (020) 7252 7979/(020) 7252 6409
✉ us@horton-stephens.com
🖥 www.horton-stephens.com

Gary Taylor Travel Photographers 3 Scrutton Street, London, EC2A 4HF, United Kingdom
☎ (020) 7613 5881/(07956) 449528 (020) 7729 4323
✉ mail@gary-taylor.net

Gary Wallis 10 Bell Road, East Molesey, Surrey, KT8 0SS, United Kingdom
☎ (07976) 310043
✉ wallis@bigsmilepictures.com

Gavin Bond@John Parkinson Photographic Agent Unit 17, 1-10 Summer's Street, London, EC1R 5BD, United Kingdom
☎ (020) 7278 6882/(020) 7278 1251
✉ johnparkinsonagency@btinternet.com
🖥 www.johnparkinsonagency.co.uk

Gavin Cottrell 16 Elizabeth Mews, London, NW3 4UH, United Kingdom
☎ (020) 7586 8625/(07961) 409022
✉ studio@gavin-cottrell.com
🖥 www.gavin-cottrell.com

Gavin Harrison@Victoria Lees Management (VLM) 2 Fairview Gardens, Woodford Green, Essex, IG8 7DJ, United Kingdom
☎ (07710) 287220/(020) 8504 8125
✉ victoria@victorialeesmanagement.co.uk
🖥 www.victorialeesmanagement.co.uk

Gavin O'Neill@Milc Studio 7, Zeus House, 16-30 Provost Street, London, N1 7NG, United Kingdom
☎ (020) 7278 8838/(0870) 0941564
✉ gemma@milc.co.uk
🖥 www.milc.co.uk

Genesis Imaging (Chelsea) Unit D2, The Depot, 2 Michael Road, London, SW6 2AD, United Kingdom
☎ (020) 7731 2227/(020) 7731 8778
✉ chelsea@genesisimaging.co.uk
🖥 www.genesisimaging.co.uk

Genesis Imaging (City) The Depo, 2 Michael Road, Fulham, London, SW6 2AD, United Kingdom
☎ (020) 7731 2227/(020) 7731 8778
✉ city@genesisimaging.co.uk
🖥 www.genesisimaging.co.uk

Geof Kern@Izzy King 22 Alder Lodge, 73 Stevenage Road, London, SW6 6NP, United Kingdom
☎ (07961) 168086/(020) 7381 9726
✉ izzy@izzyking.co.uk
🖥 www.izzyking.co.uk

Geoff Brightling 92 Ridge Road, London, N8 9NR, United Kingdom
☎ (07974) 188102
✉ geoff@brightlingphoto.com
🖥 www.brightlingphoto.com

Geoff Causton 34 Druid Stoke Avenue, Bristol, BS9 1DQ, United Kingdom
☎ 0117-968 0949/ 0117-914 1322
✉ geoff@caustonphotography.co.uk
🖥 www.caustonphotography.co.uk

Geoff Dann Photographer 164 Whitecross Street, London, EC1Y 8QN, United Kingdom
☎ (020) 7251 2873/(07785) 755652
✉ gd@geoffdann.com
🖥 www.geoffdann.com

Geoff Howard 92 Vallance Road, London, N22 7UG, United Kingdom
☎ (020) 8365 7053/(07773) 521630 (020) 8889 8072
✉ geoffahoward@hotmail.com

Geoff Langan 38 Oldville Avenue, Clevedon, Avon, BS21 6HG, United Kingdom
☎ (07850) 754471
✉ geoff@geofflangan.com
🖥 www.geofflangan.com

Geoff Senior 19 Chippenham Mews, London, W9 2AN, United Kingdom
☎ (020) 7286 3688/(07767) 860504 (020) 7266 3920

Geoff Smith 1 Bradbrook House, Studio Place, London, SW1X 8EL, United Kingdom
☎ (020) 7823 1345/(07785) 280218 (020) 7823 1292
✉ geoff@geoffsmith.com
🖥 www.geoffsmith.com

Geoff Williamson Photography Panta Ponsa, Mallorca, Spain
☎ 00 34 971 691308/ 00 34 971 693418
✉ gw@ccr.es
🖥 www.geoffwilliamson.com

Geoffrey Benson 1 Pickering Street, Leeds, LS12 2QG, United Kingdom
☎ 0113-263 7706/ 0113-263 7706

Geoffrey Frosh 87 Lynton Road, London, SE1 5QT, United Kingdom
☎ (020) 7231 5111
✉ geoffrey@geoffreyfrosh.com

Geoffrey Pass Photography 58 St Augustines Avenue, Grimsby, Lincolnshire, DN32 0LD, United Kingdom
☎ (01472) 750033/(07836) 640635 (01472) 593829
✉ stephen.almond@ntlworld.com
🖥 www.geoffreypass.com

Geoffrey Pieters Hillside Farm, Freckenham, Bury St. Edmunds, Suffolk, IP28 8JA, United Kingdom
☎ (01638) 720986/(07778) 753078
✉ geoffrey@pieters.fsworld.co.uk

Georg Fischer@George & Glenys Dawber Associates 159 Dialstone Lane, Offerton, Stockport, Cheshire, SK2 6AU, United Kingdom
☎ 0161-483 3114/ 0161-483 6063
✉ george@dawberphoto.co.uk
🖥 www.georgeandglenysdawber.com

George Bamford@N M P Photo 211 Westbourne Park Road, London, W11 1EA, United Kingdom
☎ (020) 7243 0074
✉ info@nmpphoto.co.uk
🖥 www.nmpphoto.co.uk

George Brooks 16 Pages Hill, Muswell Hill, London, N10 1QA, United Kingdom
☎ (020) 8374 7304/(07831) 815281 (020) 8374 7304
✉ hotdog@georgebrooks.net
🖥 www.georgebrooks.net

George Kavanagh@Noelle Pickford 27 Britton Street, London, EC1M 5UD, United Kingdom
☎ (020) 7336 6773/ (020) 7336 7043
✉ info@noellerepresents.com
🖥 www.noellerepresents.com

George Logan 29 Waterside, 44-48 Wharf Road, London, N1 7UX, United Kingdom
☎ (020) 7490 5813/(07775) 744850 (020) 7490 3798
✉ info@georgelogan.co.uk
🖥 www.georgelogan.co.uk

George Ong Studio 7, Canal Building, 135 Shepherdess Walk, London, N1 7RR, United Kingdom
☎ (020) 7490 1727/(07930) 441690 (020) 7490 1828
✉ info@georgeong.co.uk
🖥 www.georgeong.co.uk

George Rodger@Magnum Photos 63 Gee Street, London, EC1V 3RS, United Kingdom
☎ (020) 7490 1771/ (020) 7608 0020
✉ magnum@magnumphotos.co.uk
🖥 www.magnumphotos.com

George Taylor Rear Building, 1st Floor, 150 Curtain Road, London, EC2A 3AT, United Kingdom
☎ (020) 7613 0901/(07831) 340372 (020) 7613 3013

George Wright@Axiom Photographic Agency The Pall Mall Deposit, 124-128 Barlby Road, London, W10 6BL, United Kingdom
☎ (020) 8964 9970/ (020) 8964 8440
✉ info@axiomphotographic.com
🖥 www.axiomphotographic.com

Geraint Lewis 5 Bishops Meadow, Stonesfield, Witney, Oxfordshire, OX29 8LS, United Kingdom
☎ (01993) 898804/(07831) 413452
✉ geraint@geraintlewis.com
🖥 www.geraintlewis.com

Gerald Wortman 29 Flanders Mansions, Flanders Road, London, W4 1NE, United Kingdom
☎ (020) 8995 6056/ (020) 8987 7339
✉ gerald@geraldwortman.co.uk
🖥 www.geraldwortman.co.uk

Gerard Brown 42 Hamilton Road, Brentford, Middlesex, TW8 0QF, United Kingdom
☎ (07973) 422983
✉ kam14@dial.pipex.com
🖥 www.gerardbrown.co.uk

Gerhard Linnekogel@C S B Management 40 Bowling Green Lane, London, EC1R 0NE, United Kingdom
☎ (020) 7415 7051/ (020) 7415 7059
✉ susie@csbmanagement.com
🖥 www.csbmanagement.com

Germaine Walker Photographers' Agent Crayford House, 49A Tabley Road, London, N7 0NA, United Kingdom
☎ (020) 7697 8291/(07867) 780272 (020) 7619 9051
✉ germaine@germaine.co.uk
🖥 www.germaine.co.uk

Gerrit Buntrock Unit 1, Warple Muse, Off Warple Way, London, W3 0RF, United Kingdom
☎ (020) 8749 1797/(07973) 548346 (020) 8742 9873
✉ info@gerritbuntrock.com
🖥 www.gerritbuntrock.com

Gerry Clist Photography 235 Webheath, Netherwood Street, Kilburn, London, NW6 2JX, United Kingdom
☎ (020) 7691 3200/(07798) 838839
✉ gerryclist@onetel.com
🖥 www.gerryclist.biz

Gianluigi Siragusa Photo 18 rue Caroline, Paris, 75017, France
☎ 00 33 1 42 28 34 77/00 33 6 12 47 25 23
✉ mail@giannisiragusa.com
🖥 www.giannisiragusa.com

Giblin & James@Agent Orange 10 Swan Yard, London, N1 1SD, United Kingdom
☎ (020) 7226 0440/ (020) 7226 1613
✉ annika@agentorange.co.uk
🖥 www.agentorange.co.uk

Giles Angel Vision Architects, The Studio, 2 Vera Road, London, SW6 6RN, United Kingdom
☎ (020) 7384 3523/(07879) 480681 (020) 7384 2992
✉ giles@angelphoto.co.uk
🖥 www.angelphoto.com

Giles Heather Photography Greystone, Colmore Lane, Kingwood, Henley-on-Thames, Oxfordshire, RG9 5NA, United Kingdom
☎ (01491) 628972
✉ image@giles-heather.com
🖥 www.gilesheather.com

Giles Keyte 30 Spinney Gardens, London, SE19 1LL, United Kingdom
☎ (07958) 616727/ (020) 8670 7848
✉ giles.keyte@lineone.net
🖥 www.gileskeyte.co.uk

Giles Revell@Stella Pye The Basement, 22 Castellain Road, London, W9 1EZ, United Kingdom
☎ (020) 7286 8200/(07956) 501977 (020) 7286 8400
✉ stella@stellapye.com
🖥 www.stellapye.com

Gill Orsman 1 The Old Church Hall, 15 Ditchling Rise, Brighton, BN1 4QL, United Kingdom
☎ (01273) 887627/(07831) 855324 (0870) 3502761
✉ info@gillorsman.com
🖥 www.gillorsman.com
See ad in showcase

Gill Turner Photogrpaher's Agent The Power Station, Coronet Street, London, N1 6HD, United Kingdom
☎ (020) 7033 2800/ (020) 7033 2801
✉ gill@gillturner.com
🖥 www.gillturner.com

Gilles Peress@Magnum Photos 63 Gee Street, London, EC1V 3RS, United Kingdom
☎ (020) 7490 1771/ (020) 7608 0020
✉ magnum@magnumphotos.co.uk
🖥 www.magnumphotos.com

Gina Harris 64 Station Road, Birmingham, B17 9LX, United Kingdom
☎ 0121-427 4316/(07973) 427549

Gina Phillips Represents Ltd 6 Leverton Place, London, NW5 2PL, United Kingdom
☎ (020) 7284 2022/ (020) 7424 0272
✉ info@ginaphillips.co.uk
🖥 www.ginaphillips.co.uk

Gino Sprio, London, United Kingdom
☎ (020) 8941 4320/(07973) 114063
✉ gino@gsprio.demon.co.uk
🖥 www.ginosprio.com

Giulio Mazzarini@Yara Gremoli Photographers Agent Studio 210, Canalot Studios, 222 Kensal Road, London, W10 5BN, United Kingdom
☎ (0870) 8501209/(07880) 627413 (0870) 8501209
✉ yara@sbmanagement.org
🖥 www.yaragremoli.com

Glen Burrows@Milc Studio 7, Zeus House, 16-30 Provost Street, London, N1 7NG, United Kingdom
(020) 7278 8838/ (0870) 0941564
gemma@milc.co.uk
www.milc.co.uk

Glen Garner@Joyce Morris, London, SW3 5TQ, United Kingdom
(020) 7823 3238/(07850) 064222 (020) 7376 7787
joyce@joycemorris.co.uk
www.joycemorris.co.uk

Glo London 32 Stratford Road, London, W8 6QF, United Kingdom
(020) 7938 1330/ (020) 7938 3120
kate@glolondon.com
www.glolondon.com

Glyn Barney Pigtails, Boyton End, Stoke-by-Clare, Sudbury, Suffolk, CO10 8TB, United Kingdom
(01440) 763502/(07774) 110465 (01440) 763502
glyn.barney@btopenworld.com

Goodwin Studio 15 Northcross Street, Gosport, Hampshire, PO12 1BE, United Kingdom
(023) 9252 0252
thegoodwinstudio@btconnect.com
www.the-goodwin-studio.co.uk

Gooseloft Ltd The Spire, Leeds Road, Halifax, West Yorkshire, HX3 8NU, United Kingdom
(01422) 200788/ (01422) 200788
peter@gooseloft.com
www.gooseloft.com

Gordon Singer Top Flat, 25 Lidyard Road, London, N19 5NR, United Kingdom
(020) 7281 2571/077 78 810517 (020) 7281 2571

Gordon Welters Flat 71, Orwell Court, Pownall Road, London, E8 4PR, United Kingdom
(01708) 346683
gordon@welters.ws
www.gordon.welters.ws

Gore & Ball Photography C15 Hilton Trading Estate, Hilton Road, Wolverhampton, WV4 6DW, United Kingdom
(01902) 353999/ (01902) 353555
info@goreandball.com
www.goreandball.com

Grabshot 55 Hampden Close, North Weald, Epping, Essex, CM16 6JX, United Kingdom
(07974) 010393
info@grabshot.com
www.grabshot.com

Graciela Preece Images 1 Golden Lion Lane, Harwich, Essex, CO12 3NG, United Kingdom
(01255) 551443/(07818) 461833
photo@graciela.info
www.gracielapreeceimages.com

Graeme Ainscough Europa Studios, Studio 17, Victoria Road, London, NW10 6ND, United Kingdom
(020) 8961 9718/(07831) 199251 (020) 8961 4991
graeme@graemeainscough.co.uk
www.graemeainscough.co.uk

Graeme Cooper Rosebank Cottage, 67 Lees Road, Mossley, Lancashire, OL5 0PQ, United Kingdom
(07973) 333791
graemecooper@bungalow-zen.com
www.bungalow-zen.com

Graeme Montgomery 4 Roberts Place, Off Bowling Green Lane, London, EC1R 0BB, United Kingdom
(020) 7253 0853/ (020) 7253 0852
graeme@graememontgomery.com
www.graememontgomery.com

Graeme Oliver The Thruff, Dipton Mill, Hexham, Northumberland, NE46 2JU, United Kingdom
(01434) 600679
info@omgphotography.co.uk
www.omgphotography.co.uk

Graeme Stuart@Burnham Niker Unit 8, Canonbury Business Centre, 190A New North Road, London, N1 7BJ, United Kingdom
(020) 7704 6565/ (020) 7704 8383
enquiries@burnham-niker.com
www.burnham-niker.com

Grafic House 6 Parkview Terrace, Sketty, Swansea, SA2 9AN, United Kingdom
(07903) 809884
pictures@grafichouse.co.uk
www.grafichouse.co.uk

Graham Atkins Hughes@ERA Management Ltd 120 The Beaux Arts Building, 10-18 Manor Gardens, London, N7 6JT, United Kingdom
(020) 7281 5996/ (020) 7281 6202
kate@eramanagement.com
www.eramanagement.com

Graham Dale 154 Lower High Street, Stourbridge, West Midlands, DY8 1TS, United Kingdom
(01384) 444886/(07710) 445732
info@grahamdale.co.uk
www.grahamdale.co.uk

Graham Ford Unit 3, Perseverance Works, London, E2 8DD, United Kingdom
(020) 7739 6898/ (020) 7739 0546
gford@easynet.co.uk

Graham Fox 19 North View Terrace, East Morton, Keighley, West Yorkshire, BD20 5SY, United Kingdom
(01274) 510312/(07831) 626796
info@foxphotos.co.uk
www.foxphotos.com

Graham Hughes 24 Kingsway, London, SW14 7HS, United Kingdom
(020) 8876 5041/(07860) 541291 (020) 8876 5041

Graham Kirk Photography Oast Studio, Forge Farm House, Goudhurst, Cranbrook, Kent, TN17 2QZ, United Kingdom
(01580) 212288/ (01580) 212255
www.contact-me.net/grahamkirk

Graham Kuhn@The White Agency 60 Epirus Road, Fulham, London, SW6 7UH, United Kingdom
(020) 7381 2004/(07970) 619277 (020) 7386 8479
annabel@thewhiteagency.com
www.thewhiteagency.com

Graham Lawrence Photography Studio 466, 2 Old Brompton Road, London, SW7 3DQ, United Kingdom
(07973) 166172
fotolawrence@onetel.com
www.fotolawrence.com

Graham Lees 180 Sauchiehall Lane, Glasgow, G2 4JD, United Kingdom
0141-332 8323/ 0141-331 1492
graham@grahamlees.com
www.grahamlees.com

Graham Lowe Montage Gallery, 12 Church Street, Castleton, Whitby, North Yorkshire, YO21 2EQ, United Kingdom
(01287) 660159
glowpix@ntlworld.com
www.grahamlowe.co.uk

Graham Precey Photography Ltd Studio 4, Sun Studios, 30 Warple Way, London, W3 0RX, United Kingdom
(020) 8740 6610/ (020) 8762 9994
info@foodanddrinkphotos.com
www.foodanddrinkphotots.com

Graham Pym@Hungry Tiger Unit 16, The Piper Building, Peterborough Road, London, SW6 3EF, United Kingdom
(020) 7751 8600/ (020) 7751 8618
studio@hungrytiger.co.uk
www.hungrytiger.co.uk

Graham Rae, London, United Kingdom
(020) 7608 0066/(07775) 620108
info@graham-rae.co.uk
www.graham-rae.co.uk

Graham Seager Photography 100b Cazenove Road, London, N16 6AD, United Kingdom
(020) 8806 7358
graham@gseager.plus.com
www.grahamseager.co.uk

Graham Shearer@East Photographic Ltd 8 Iron Bridge House, 3 Bridge Approach, London, NW1 8BD, United Kingdom
(020) 7722 3444/ (020) 7722 3544
roger@eastphotographic.com
www.eastphotographic.com

Graham Tooby@Horton-Stephens Photographers' Agent 14 Peacock Yard, Iliffe Street, London, SE17 3LH, United Kingdom
(020) 7252 7979/ (020) 7252 6409
us@horton-stephens.com
www.horton-stephens.com

Graham Turnill (ARPS) 45 Longton Grove, Upper Sydenham, London, SE26 6QQ, United Kingdom
(020) 8778 0014/(07812) 789238 (020) 8778 0014

Graham Vasey Photographic 20 Cromarty Close, Darlington, County Durham, DL1 3RE, United Kingdom
(07788) 411297
grahamvasey@hotmail.com
www.grahamvasey.co.uk

Graham Westmoreland@Traffic Unit P102, 23 - 28 Penn Street, London, N1 7DL, United Kingdom
020 7739 6090
rebecca@rebeccavalentine.com
www.trafficphotographic.com

Graham Young@Freddie Brazil 211 Abercairn Road, London, SW16 5AJ, United Kingdom
(020) 8764 2801/(07711) 753072 (020) 8764 2801
frederick.brazil@btconnect.com
www.freddiebrazil.com

Grant Sainsbury@M & M Management Studio B, 11 Edith Grove, London, SW10 0JZ, United Kingdom
(020) 7823 3723/ (020) 7351 3714
admin@mmmanagement.com
www.mmmanagement.com

Grant Smith 34 Queen Anne Road, London, E9 7AH, United Kingdom
(020) 8985 1101
grant@grant-smith.com
www.grant-smith.com

Grantly S. Lynch 31 Third Avenue, Havant, Hampshire, PO9 2QR, United Kingdom
(023) 9247 8188/(07831) 366136 (01705) 345969
www.photoswamp.com

Granville Davies Photography 23 Colebrooke Industrial Estate, Tunbridge Wells, Kent, TN2 3DG, United Kingdom
(01892) 725533/(07887) 918291
gd@gdphoto.co.uk
www.gdphoto-architecture.co.uk

Graphic Eye Ltd Shire House, Monk Sherborne Road, Ramsdell, Basingstoke, Hampshire, RG26 5PR, United Kingdom
(01256) 851210/ (01256) 850484
graphiceye@compuserve.com
www.graphiceyeltd.com

GreatPortraits.co.uk Arle Court, Hatherley Lane, Cheltenham, Gloucestershire, GL51 6PN, United Kingdom
(01242) 255000
sqw@c2000.com
www.greatportraits.co.uk

Greaves Photographers 6 & 7 Union Bank Yard, New Street, Huddersfield, HD1 2BP, United Kingdom
(01484) 420775/ (01484) 421393
info@greavesphotographers.com
www.greavesphotographers.com

Greenproject@Carolyn Trayler Photographers Agent Unit 566, 56 Gloucester Road, London, SW7 4UB, United Kingdom
(020) 7370 0712/ (020) 7370 0765
carolyn@trayler.co.uk
www.trayler.co.uk

Grey Zisser@Jamie Stephen Represents 9 Upper Wimpole Street, London, W1G 6LJ, United Kingdom
(0845) 3733510/(07957) 784810 (020) 7681 1027
jamie@jamiestephen.com
www.jamiestephen.com

Gueorgui Pinkhassov@Magnum Photos 63 Gee Street, London, EC1V 3RS, United Kingdom
(020) 7490 1771/ (020) 7608 0020
magnum@magnumphotos.co.uk
www.magnumphotos.com

Gullachsen Productions 9 Wimpstone, Stratford-upon-Avon, Warwickshire, CV37 8NS, United Kingdom
(01789) 450080/ (01789) 450098
lorentz@gullachsen.com
www.gullachsen.com

Gus Campbell Photography 23 Avondale Road, Rayleigh, Essex, SS6 8NJ, United Kingdom
(01268) 778519/(07860) 722671
mail@guspix.com
www.guspix.com

Gus York Unit 1, Sheeplands Farm, Twyford Road, Wargrave, RG10 8DL, United Kingdom
0118- 940 6553/(07767) 835659 0118- 940 6219
gus@gusyork.co.uk
www.gusyork.co.uk

Gustavo Papaleo@A & R Photographic 16A Crane Grove, London, N7 8LE, United Kingdom
(020) 7607 3030/ (020) 7607 2190
info@aandrphotographic.co.uk
www.aandrphotographic.co.uk

Gustoimages Ltd 25 Meadway, New Barnet, Barnet, Hertfordshire, EN5 5LG, United Kingdom
☎ (0845) 2002746/ (020) 8442 1499
✎ info@gustoimages.com
🖳 www.gustoimages.com
See ad in showcase

Guy Drayton, London, United Kingdom
☎ (07976) 919053
✎ guy@guydrayton.com
🖳 www.guydrayton.com

Guy Farrow Photography The Old School, Low Lane, Kirkgate, Birstall, Leeds, West Yorkshire, WF17 9HE, United Kingdom
☎ (01924) 444774/(07740) 513996
✎ info@guy-farrow.co.uk
🖳 www.guy-farrow.co.uk

Guy Le Querrec@Magnum Photos 63 Gee Street, London, EC1V 3RS, United Kingdom
☎ (020) 7490 1771/ (020) 7608 0020
✎ magnum@magnumphotos.co.uk
🖳 www.magnumphotos.com

Guy Woodland (LBIPP) 4 Warren Park, 85 Grove Road, Wallasey, Merseyside, CH45 3HG, United Kingdom
☎ 0151-639 0960/(07968) 742165
✎ guy@liverpoolphotos.com
🖳 www.liverpoolphotos.com

Gwyndows Photographic Services 1 Collyberry Road, Woodmancote, Cheltenham, Gloucestershire, GL52 9HH, United Kingdom
☎ (0845) 057 3268
✎ gwyn@gwyndowsphotographic.co.uk
🖳 www.gwyndowsphotographic.co.uk

Haddon Davies Photography Barnside Studios, Spelsbury Road, Charlbury, Oxfordshire, OX7 3LR, United Kingdom
☎ (01608) 811595/ (01608) 811595
✎ haddon@haddondavies.co.uk
🖳 www.haddondavies.com

Hag 33 Park Street, Chatteris, Cambridgeshire, PE16 6AB, United Kingdom
☎ (01354) 696291/(07711) 618382
✎ hag.is@virgin.net
🖳 www.hagsphotography.com

Hamilton Photographic Services Unit 1, Lisle Road, High Wycombe, Buckinghamshire, HP13 5SH, United Kingdom
☎ (01494) 533959/ (01494) 769025
✎ hamilton.photo@btconnect.com
🖳 www.tonyslade.com

Hamish Brown@Blunt Management The Courtyard Studio 2, Old Grammarphone Works, London, W10 5BZ, United Kingdom
☎ (020) 8960 2041/(07979) 900068 (020) 8960 2039
✎ info@bluntlondon.com
🖳 www.bluntlondon.com

Hampton Hill Studios 73 High Street, Hampton Hill, Middlesex, TW12 1NH, United Kingdom
☎ (020) 8979 9484/(07966) 518310 (020) 8979 4942
✎ paul@hamptonhillstudios.co.uk
🖳 www.hamptonhillstudios.co.uk

Hand Colouring Helena Zakrzewska-Rucinska Invicta Works, 8 Graces Mews, London, SE5 8JF, United Kingdom
☎ (020) 7701 4865/7920042865
✎ helena@helenazr.com
🖳 www.helenazr.com

Hands on Pictures Studio 7, Dickson House, 3 Grove Road, Richmond, Surrey, TW10 6SP, United Kingdom
☎ (020) 8940 4848
✎ terryaking@aol.com
🖳 www.hands-on-pictures.com

Hannes.co.uk 46-48 Bromley Market, London, E8 4QJ, United Kingdom
☎ (07880) 628932
✎ gudmundsson@hannes.co.uk
🖳 www.hannes.co.uk

Hanspeter Schneider@Terri Manduca The Basement, 11 Elvaston Place, London, SW7 5QG, United Kingdom
☎ (020) 7581 5844/ (020) 7581 5822
✎ terri@terrimanduca.co.uk
🖳 www.terrimanduca.co.uk

Happy Pigs Productions 20 Felstead Street, Unit 3E, London, E9 5LG, United Kingdom
☎ (07808) 403932
✎ happypigs.lilly@virgin.net
🖳 www.happypigs.net

Haris Artemis Photography 19 Hunter Lodge, Admiral Walk, London, W9 3TQ, United Kingdom
☎ (07960) 932197/ (020) 7266 7603
✎ photography@harisartemis.com
🖳 www.harisartemis.com

Harry Borden@Bonakdar Cleary 35 Charles Square, London, N1 6HT, United Kingdom
☎ (020) 7490 1155
✎ bc@bonakdarcleary.com
🖳 www.bonakdarcleary.com

Harry Dillon 25a Berrymead Gardens, London, W3 8AA, United Kingdom
☎ (07941) 503166
✎ harrydillon30@hotmail.com
🖳 www.harrydillon.com

Harry Gruyaert@Magnum Photos 63 Gee Street, London, EC1V 3RS, United Kingdom
☎ (020) 7490 1771/ (020) 7608 0020
✎ magnum@magnumphotos.co.uk
🖳 www.magnumphotos.com

Hartley Studios 23 Hurlingham Studios, Ranelagh Gardens, Fulham, London, SW6 3PA, United Kingdom
☎ (020) 7731 0244
✎ info@hartleystudios.com
🖳 www.hartleystudios.com

Harvey Wood Photographer Clachtoll, Croft Road, West Linton, Peeblesshire, EH46 7DZ, United Kingdom
☎ (01968) 660619/ (01968) 660619
✎ harvey@photoscotland.com
🖳 www.photoscotland.com

Hastings Photography 12 Seaward Walk, Caister-on-Sea, Great Yarmouth, Norfolk, NR30 5NS, United Kingdom
☎ (01493) 720822/ (01493) 720822
✎ emmahastings@hotmail.com
🖳 www.hastingsphotography.biz

Have Camel Eill Travel Flat 3, 9 Oakhill Avenue, London, NW3 7RD, United Kingdom
☎ (020) 7794 4436
✎ l.frieda@4castweb.com
🖳 www.havecamelwilltravel.com

Victoria Blackie

photography

www.victoriablackie.co.uk

07831 423 177

Hayley Lehmann Ltd The Den, 2 Dingle Close, Arkley, Hertfordshire, EN5 3EL, United Kingdom
(020) 8447 0728
info@hayleylehmann.co.uk
www.hayleylehmann.co.uk

Heini Schneebeli 10 York Rise, London, NW5 1SS, United Kingdom
(020) 7482 6568/(07801) 263880
heinischneebeli@hotmail.com

Helen Fickling Photography 14 Stratford Grove, London, SW15 1NU, United Kingdom
(07976) 946536
helen@helenfickling.com
www.helenfickling.com

Helen Kitto Photography The Little White Studio, Clockview Cottage, Green Road, Horsmonden, Tonbridge, Kent, TN12 8JS, United Kingdom
(07712) 222192
helen@helenkitto.com
www.helenkitto.com

Helen Miller@Beth Coyne Agency, London, NW6 1GF, United Kingdom
(020) 7431 8981/ (020) 7813 9750
info@bethcoyne.com
www.bethcoyne.com

Helena Kouzeleas@Sarah Kaye Representation Ltd 38 Queen's Gate, London, SW7 5HR, United Kingdom
(020) 7225 5005/ (020) 7225 0109
sarah@sarahkaye.com
www.sarahkaye.com

Helene Rogers 57 Burdon Lane, Cheam, Surrey, SM2 7BY, United Kingdom
(020) 8642 3593/ (020) 8395 7230
images@artdirectors.co.uk
www.artdirectors.co.uk

Henning Marstrand@Axiom Photographic Agency The Pall Mall Deposit, 124-128 Barlby Road, London, W10 6BL, United Kingdom
(020) 8964 9970/ (020) 8964 8440
info@axiomphotographic.com
www.axiomphotographic.com

Henri Cartier-Bresson@Magnum Photos 63 Gee Street, London, EC1V 3RS, United Kingdom
(020) 7490 1771/ (020) 7608 0020
magnum@magnumphotos.co.uk
www.magnumphotos.com

Henrik Bulow@A & R Photographic 16A Crane Grove, London, N7 8LE, United Kingdom
(020) 7607 3030/ (020) 7607 2190
info@aandrphotographic.co.uk
www.aandrphotographic.co.uk

Henrik Knudsen@Burnham Niker Unit 8, Canonbury Business Centre, 190A New North Road, London, N1 7BJ, United Kingdom
(020) 7704 6565/ (020) 7704 8383
enquiries@burnham-niker.com
www.burnham-niker.com

Henrik Thorup Knudsen 8.1 The Ziggurat, 60-66 Saffron Hill, London, EC1N 8QX, United Kingdom
(020) 7831 6361/(07774) 863698 (020) 7831 6374
henrik@henrikknudsen.com
www.henrikknudsen.com

Henry Arden Photography 7 The Old Laundry, Haydon Way, London, SW11 1YF, United Kingdom
(020) 8871 1274/07860 384633 020 7207 1965
henry@henryarden.com
www.henryarden.com
See ad in showcase

Henry Baddour Photographer 8 Rue Dupleix, Paris, 75015, France
00 33 6 14 53 62 12/ 00 33 1 53 01 06 82
studio@henrybaddour.com
www.henrybaddour.com

Henry Bourne@C L M Top Floor, 19 All Saints Road, London, W11 1HE, United Kingdom
(020) 7750 2999/ (020) 7792 8507
clm@clmuk.com
www.clmuk.com

Herb Schmitz 17 Willow Street, London, EC2A 4BH, United Kingdom
/(07831) 774146
herbschmitz@btopenworld.com
www.herbschmitz.com

Herbert List@Magnum Photos 63 Gee Street, London, EC1V 3RS, United Kingdom
(020) 7490 1771/ (020) 7608 0020
magnum@magnumphotos.co.uk
www.magnumphotos.com

Heribert Schindler@Defrance 47 Rethelstrasse, Deusseldorf, 40237, Germany
00 49 211 87 67 89/ 00 49 211 87 67 89
defrance@defrance.de
www.defrance.de

Heseltine Archive The Old Mill Studio, Frogmarsh Mills, South Woodchester, Stroud, Gloucestershire, GL5 5ET, United Kingdom
(01453) 873792/(07932) 160664
john@heseltine.co.uk
www.heseltine.co.uk

Hewson Pictures St James House, 150 London Road, East Grinstead, West Sussex, RH19 1HB, United Kingdom
/ (01342) 332037
phewson@reedinfo.co.uk
www.kftv.com

Hilary Moore Westminster Business Square, Unit E309, London, SE11 5JH, United Kingdom
(020) 7735 9595/(07836) 362506 (020) 7735 5559
info@hilarymoorephoto.com
www.hilarymoorephoto.com

Hilary Shedel c/o Arena Pal, Lambert House, 55 Southwark Street, London, SE1 1RU, United Kingdom
(01332) 694525
hilary@hilaryshedel.com
www.hilaryshedel.com

Hilde Vanderplancke@Gina Phillips Represents Ltd 6 Leverton Place, London, NW5 2PL, United Kingdom
(020) 7284 2022/ (020) 7424 0272
info@ginaphillips.co.uk
www.ginaphillips.co.uk

Hiroji Kubota@Magnum Photos 63 Gee Street, London, EC1V 3RS, United Kingdom
(020) 7490 1771/ (020) 7608 0020
magnum@magnumphotos.co.uk
www.magnumphotos.com

Holly Kuper 5522 Anita Street, Dallas, 75206, United States of America
00 1 214 827 4494/ 00 1 214 827 4495
photo@hollykuper.com
www.hollykuper.com

Horst Kolo 60 Hamilton Road, London, NW11 9EJ, United Kingdom
(020) 8458 6364/ (020) 7435 3873
horst@horstkolo.co.uk
www.horstkolo.co.uk

Horst Neumann@Mark Gibson 250 York Road, London, SW11 3SJ, United Kingdom
(020) 7228 9085/(07768) 696227
mark@markgibsonphotography.com
www.markgibsonphotography.com

Horton-Stephens Photographers' Agent 14 Peacock Yard, Iliffe Street, London, SE17 3LH, United Kingdom
(020) 7252 7979/ (020) 7252 6409
us@horton-stephens.com
www.horton-stephens.com

Howard Bartrop 45 Lewes Road, London, N12 9NH, United Kingdom
(020) 8445 3160/(07956) 864572 (020) 8445 3160
hbartrop@aol.com
www.howardbartrop.com

Howard Grey 1 Studio Place, Kinnerton Street, London, SW1X 8EW, United Kingdom
(020) 7235 4001/(07860) 414022
howard@howardgrey.com
www.howardgrey.com

Howard Kemp 7 Gladeside Court, Succombs Hill, Warlingham, Surrey, CR6 9JG, United Kingdom
(01883) 622171

Howard Kingsnorth 1A Chance Street, London, E1 6JT, United Kingdom
(020) 7739 8655/ (020) 7739 8656
info@howardkingsnorth.com
www.howardkingsnorth.com
See ad in showcase

Howard McAlpine@Germaine Walker Photographers' Agent Crayford House, 49A Tabley Road, London, N7 0NA, United Kingdom
(020) 7697 8291/(07867) 780272 (020) 7619 9051
germaine@germaine.co.uk
www.germaine.co.uk

Howard Phillips 1B Old Brewery Yard, Penzance, Cornwall, TR18 2SL, United Kingdom
(01736) 366567/(07720) 885967
info@howardphillips.co.uk
www.howardphillips.co.uk

Howard Winter 2 Washington Road, London, SW13 9BE, United Kingdom
(020) 8563 1879/(07767) 226391 (020) 8563 1879
mail@howard-winter.co.uk
www.howard-winter.co.uk

howellphoto.com 6 Eastbridge Avenue, Stoke-on-Trent, ST1 6DQ, United Kingdom
(07968) 817272
info@howellphoto.com
www.howellphoto.com

Huger Foote@Maconochie Photography 4 Meard Street, Soho, London, W1F 0EF, United Kingdom
(020) 7439 3159/ (020) 7439 2552
info@macphoto.co.uk
www.macphoto.co.uk

Hugh Burden Photographer Cooks Folly Road, Avon, Bristol, BS9 1PL, United Kingdom
0117-968 7111/(07788) 746797
hugh@hughburden.com
www.hughburden.com

Hugh Gilbert Photography Studio Six, 125 Battersea High Street, London, SW11 3HY, United Kingdom
(07973) 142729
hugh@hughgilbert.com
www.hughgilbert.com

Hugh Johnson@Mark Gibson 250 York Road, London, SW11 3SJ, United Kingdom
(020) 7228 9085/(07768) 696227
mark@markgibsonphotography.com
www.markgibsonphotography.com

Hugh McKnight The Swan House, 1 Priory Terrace, St. Neots, Cambridgeshire, PE19 2PY, United Kingdom
(01480) 407440/077 13 402423

Hugh Threlfall RoseOak House, Colwood Lane, Warninglid, Haywards Heath, West Sussex, RH17 5UQ, United Kingdom
(01444) 461676/(07941) 686791
hugh@hughthrelfall.co.uk
www.hughthrelfall.co.uk

Hugh Turvey @Gusto 25 Meadway, New Barnet, Barnet, Hertfordshire, EN5 5LG, United Kingdom
(0845) 2002746/ (020) 8441 5712
hugh@gustoimages.com
www.gustoimages.com

Hungry Tiger Unit 16, The Piper Building, Peterborough Road, London, SW6 3EF, United Kingdom
(020) 7751 8600/ (020) 7751 8618
studio@hungrytiger.co.uk
www.hungrytiger.co.uk

Hylton Photography The Studio, Rocom Building, Wetherby, Leeds, LS23 7RR, United Kingdom
(01937) 847460/ (01937) 844545
simon@hyltonphotography.co.uk
www.hyltonphotography.co.uk

I C S Photography The Studios, Dolcliffe Road, Mexborough, South Yorkshire, S64 9AZ, United Kingdom
(01709) 570966/(07836) 724229 (01709) 570966
roy@icsphotography.co.uk
www.icsphotography.co.uk

Iain Bagwell Photography 110 Wing Mill Road, Atlanta, 30350, United States of America
00 1 404 642 8919/(07990) 591923
foodphotos@bellsouth.net
www.iainbagwell.com

Iain Crockart@L P A (Lisa Pritchard Agency) 3rd Floor, Block A, Morelands, 5-23 Old Street, London, EC1V 9HL, United Kingdom
(020) 7250 1362/ (020) 7250 1357
info@lisapritchard.com
www.lisapritchard.com

Iain Gibbs@Mutton Bones Ground Floor, 51 Balcombe Street, London, NW1 6HD, United Kingdom
(020) 7723 8244/ (020) 7723 2770
hello@muttonbones.co.uk
www.muttonbones.co.uk

Iain Richardson Photogrpahy 362 Leeds Road, Lofthouse, Wakefield, West Yorkshire, WF3 3QF, United Kingdom
(07712)384995
iainrichardson@hotmail.co.uk
www.iainrichardson.co.uk

Ian Atkinson Studio 502, 417 Wick Lane, London, E3 2JG, United Kingdom
(07971) 821107/ (020) 8980 9678
ian@isaphoto.co.uk
www.isaphoto.co.uk

Ian Berry@Magnum Photos 63 Gee Street, London, EC1V 3RS, United Kingdom
(020) 7490 1771/ (020) 7608 0020
magnum@magnumphotos.co.uk
www.magnumphotos.com

Ian Boddy @ Sharon Brandman Agency, No 2 Elmhurst Close, Bushey, WD23 2QB
0844 800 9003/ sharon@sharonbrandman.com
www.sharonbrandman.com
See ad in showcase

Ian Bruce Houldsworth Business & Arts Centre, 3rd Floor, Houldsworth Street, Stockport, Cheshire, SK5 6DA, United Kingdom
0161-975 6020/ 0161-975 6030
clickon@ianbrucephoto.com
www.ianbrucephoto.com

Ian Cartwright's Caramel Photography 5 Pingate Drive, Cheadle Hulme, Cheadle, Cheshire, SK8 6NL, United Kingdom
0161-485 2318/(07712) 863864
enquiry@caramelphoto.com
www.caramelphoto.com

Ian Cook@Axiom Photographic Agency The Pall Mall Deposit, 124-128 Barlby Road, London, W10 6BL, United Kingdom
(020) 8964 9970/ (020) 8964 8440
info@axiomphotographic.com
www.axiomphotographic.com

Ian Copping 33 Moss Lane, Alderley Edge, Cheshire, SK9 7HP, United Kingdom
(07778) 524944
ian@coppingphotography.com
www.coppingphotography.co.uk

Ian Cumming@Axiom Photographic Agency The Pall Mall Deposit, 124-128 Barlby Road, London, W10 6BL, United Kingdom
(020) 8964 9970/ (020) 8964 8440
info@axiomphotographic.com
www.axiomphotographic.com

Ian Derry@ERA Management Ltd 120 The Beaux Arts Building, 10-18 Manor Gardens, London, N7 6JT, United Kingdom
(020) 7281 5996/ (020) 7281 6202
kate@eramanagement.com
www.eramanagement.com

Ian Goodrick 34 Parrock Avenue, Gravesend, Kent, DA12 1QQ, United Kingdom
(01474) 333066/(07860) 362322
ian@goodrick-photo.com
www.goodrick-photo.com

Ian Hessenberg 60 Westbourne Park Villas, London, W2 5EB, United Kingdom
(020) 7727 3834
ian@hessenberg.com
www.hessenberg.com

Ian Hooton Spaced Studios, 90 The De Beauvoir Road, London, N1 4EN, United Kingdom
(020) 7249 2288
www.ianhooton.com

Ian Lambot@Arcaid Picture Library Parc House, 25-37 Cowleaze Road, Kingston upon Thames, Surrey, KT2 6DZ, United Kingdom
(020) 8546 4352/ (020) 8541 5230
arcaid@arcaid.co.uk
www.arcaid.co.uk

Ian Macdonald@SK Creative Management 23 New Mount Street, Manchester, M4 4DE, United Kingdom
0161-953 4032/ (0870) 486 1940
info@skcreativemanagement.com
www.skcreativemanagement.com

Ian Meeson Photography 25 Ayr Avenue, The Chase, Catterick Garrison, Richmond, North Yorkshire, DL9 4GE, United Kingdom
(01748) 831309/(07939) 565505 (01748) 831309
info@ianmeesonphotography.com
www.ianmeesonphotography.com

Ian Nolan Photographer Hangar 9, Perseverance Works, 38 Kingsland Road, London, E2 8DD, United Kingdom
(020) 7613 3362/(07973) 824745

Ian Phillips-McLaren Orchard End, Watling Lane, Thaxted, Dunmow, Essex, CM6 2QY, United Kingdom
(01371) 831910/(07889) 861654
ian@ianphillips-mclaren.com
www.ianphillips-mclaren.com

Ian Pilbeam 11 Bank Street, Castletown, Isle of Man, IM9 1AT, United Kingdom
(01624) 825789/ (01624) 8255779
creative@manx.net
www.ianpilbeam.com

iD2 Country House, Sea End Road, Benington, Boston, Lincolnshire, PE22 0DQ, United Kingdom
(01205) 761793/(07801) 766863
vincentwakerley@btinternet.com
www.id2-studio.com

Idem 98 Avenue Kléber, Paris, 75116, France
00 33 1 47 04 28 74
gabrielle.veyrinforrer@wanadoo.fr
www.gabrielle-veyrinforrer.com

Igor Emmerich@L P A (Lisa Pritchard Agency) 3rd Floor, Block A, Morelands, 5-23 Old Street, London, EC1V 9HL, United Kingdom
(020) 7250 1362/ (020) 7250 1357
info@lisapritchard.com
www.lisapritchard.com

Ilan Godfrey - Photographer 8 Violet Hill, London, NW8 9EB, United Kingdom
(07796) 405788
ilangodfrey@btinternet.com
www.ilangodfrey.com

Ilkka Uimonen@Magnum Photos 63 Gee Street, London, EC1V 3RS, United Kingdom
(020) 7490 1771/ (020) 7608 0020
magnum@magnumphotos.co.uk
www.magnumphotos.com

Image Depot The Old Exchange, Wellington Court, Belper, Derbyshire, DE56 1UP, United Kingdom
(01773) 827610
adrian@image-depot.co.uk
www.image-depot.co.uk

Imagen 5, Becklands Park Industrial Estate, York Road, Market Weighton, York, YO43 3GA, United Kingdom
(01430) 871971/ (01430) 803300
enquiry@imagenphotography.co.uk
www.imagenphotography.co.uk

Imageri Haverhill, Church Street, Whitchurch, Hampshire, RG28 7AS, United Kingdom
(01256) 895600
info@imageri.com
www.imageri.com

Images 23 Castle Street, Bishop's Stortford, Hertfordshire, CM23 3TG, United Kingdom
(01279) 654723/(07836) 282453
imagesuk@btconnect.com
www.imagesphotographers.com

Imagesmith Studios Unit 46, Micro Business Park, 46-50 Greatorex Street, London, E1 5NP, United Kingdom
(020) 7247 8544
kath@imagesmith.co.uk
www.imagesmith.co.uk

Immersive Media Ltd 56 Frederick Road, Sutton, Surrey, SM1 2HU, United Kingdom
020 84011278
seo@immersivemedia.co.uk
www.immersivemedia.co.uk

Ina Senftleben Flat 4, Broadstone, Agar Place, London, NW1 0RH, United Kingdom
(07901) 641036
senftlebenina@hotmail.com
www.ina-senftleben.com

Indira Cesarine@John Parkinson Photographic Agent Unit 17, 1-10 Summer's Street, London, EC1R 5BD, United Kingdom
(020) 7278 6882/ (020) 7278 1251
johnparkinsonagency@btinternet.com
www.johnparkinsonagency.co.uk

Indira Flack@Creative Talent (UK) Limited 78 York Street, London, W1H 1DP, United Kingdom
(020) 7439 1877/ (020) 7434 1144
info@creativetalentlimited.com
www.creativetalentlimited.com

Industrial Image 168 Leahurst Road, London, SE13 5NL, United Kingdom
(020) 8297 8080/(07860) 652735 (020) 8297 8181
jimwheeler@industrialimage.co.uk
www.industrialimage.co.uk

Infidels (Creative Representation) Suite 131, Victoria Junction, Gate 4 Prestwhich Street, Green Point, Cape Town, South Africa
00 27 21 425 7878/ 00 27 21 425 6915
bz@infidels.co.za
www.infidels.co.za

Infocus Photography 106 Holyhead Road, Ketley, Telford, Shropshire, TF1 5DJ, United Kingdom
(01952) 618986
michael@infocus-photography.co.uk
www.infocus-photography.co.uk

Inge Morath@Magnum Photos 63 Gee Street, London, EC1V 3RS, United Kingdom
(020) 7490 1771/ (020) 7608 0020
magnum@magnumphotos.co.uk
www.magnumphotos.com

Inigo Bujedo Aguirre@Arcaid Picture Library Parc House, 25-37 Cowleaze Road, Kingston upon Thames, Surrey, KT2 6DZ, United Kingdom
(020) 8546 4352/ (020) 8541 5230
arcaid@arcaid.co.uk
www.arcaid.co.uk

Ink & Colors Ltd 27 Old Gloucester Street, London, WC1N 3XX, United Kingdom
(020) 7558 8374
info@inkandcolors.com
www.inkandcolors.com

Innovision Photography Ford Street, New Basford, Nottingham, NG7 7BE, United Kingdom
0115-970 2612/(07970) 160622 0115-978 3791
colin@vivaimaging.co.uk
www.vivaimaging.co.uk

Inoya Photography Flat 23, Key House, Bowling Green Street, London, SE11 5TT, United Kingdom
(07888) 723 197
admin@inoya.co.uk
www.inoya.co.uk

Inpho 15a Lower Baggot Street, Dublin, Ireland, Republic of
00 33 1 676 4604/ 00 33 1 661 0552
www.inpho.ie

Inspired Reflection 28 Dayton Grove, Peckham, London, SE15 2NX, United Kingdom
(0870) 9193587/(07040) 402770 (0870) 9193588
deborah@inspiredreflection.com
www.inspiredreflection.com

Intersport Photographic 58 South Avenue, Egham, Surrey, TW20 8HQ, United Kingdom
(07973) 819551
images@intersport-images.com
www.intersport-images.com

Iris Brosch@A & R Photographic 16A Crane Grove, London, N7 8LE, United Kingdom
(020) 7607 3030/ (020) 7607 2190
info@aandrphotographic.co.uk
www.aandrphotographic.co.uk

Isabelle Blondiau 39 Truro Road, London, N22 8EH, United Kingdom
(020) 8889 8898

Ivan Bjerkhamn Daneville Road, London, SE5 8SE, United Kingdom
(07790) 702693
mail@ivanbjerkhamn.com
www.ivanbjerkhamn.com

Ivor Innes Ltd 11-13 The Square, Hessle, East Yorkshire, HU13 0AF, United Kingdom
(01482) 649271/ (01482) 647189
info@innes.co.uk
www.smile@.innes.co.uk

Izzy King 22 Alder Lodge, 73 Stevenage Road, London, SW6 6NP, United Kingdom
(07961) 168086/ (020) 7381 9726
izzy@izzyking.co.uk
www.izzyking.co.uk

J Y Photography Frodingham Road, Scunthorpe, North Lincolnshire, DN15 7NS, United Kingdom
(01724) 864 287
jerome@jy-photo.co.uk
www.jy-photo.co.uk

Jaap Buitendijk@Blowup 146 Amyand Park Road, St. Margaret's, Twickenham, TW1 3HY, United Kingdom
(020) 8744 0210/ (020) 8892 2521
orders@blowup.net
www.blowup.net

Jaap Photo Ltd 77 Dublin Street, Edinburgh, EH3 6NS, United Kingdom
✆ (07790) 909561/☎ 0131-477 1102
✉ jaap@jaapphoto.com
🖥 www.jaapphoto.com

Jack Webb@MAP 72 Rochester Place, London, NW1 9JX, United Kingdom
✆ (020) 7424 9144/☎ (020) 7284 3274
✉ info@mapltd.com
🖥 www.mapltd.com

Jackie Gibbs PMP 11a Hansard Mews, London, W14 8BJ, United Kingdom
✆ (020) 7603 6611/☎ (020) 7603 6622
✉ simon@jackiegibbs.com
🖥 www.jackiegibbs.com

Jacopo Pandolfi Photography 2nd Floor, 145-157 St John Street, London, EC1V 4PY, United Kingdom
✆ (020) 7274 2569/(07946) 860678 ☎ (020) 7274 2569
✉ info@jacopopandolfi.com
🖥 www.jacopopandolfi.com

Jacqui Hurst 66 Richford Street, London, W6 7HP, United Kingdom
✆ (020) 8743 2315/(07970) 781336
✉ jacquihurst@yahoo.co.uk
🖥 www.jacquihurstphotography.co.uk

Jaidcreative 5/12/27, Shirokane, Minato-Ku, Tokyo, 108-0072, Japan
✆ 00 81 3 5423 6855/☎ 00 81 3 5423 0071
✉ justin@jaidcreative.com
🖥 www.jaidcreative.com

Jake Curtis@Re:fresh Suit 4, The Swans Centre, Fishers Lane, London, W4 1RX, United Kingdom
✆ (020) 8747 8080/☎ (020) 8747 8228
✉ info@refresh-agency.com
🖥 www.refresh-agency.com

Jake Walters@Pearce Stoner Associates 12B Links Yard, Spelman Street, London, E1 5LX, United Kingdom
✆ (020) 7247 7100/☎ (020) 7247 7144
✉ info@pearcestoner.com
🖥 www.pearcestoner.com

James Abelson 19 Bispham Road, London, NW10 7HB, United Kingdom
✆ (020) 8998 6868/(07768) 296296 ☎ (020) 8998 5956
✉ james@jamesabelson.co.uk
🖥 www.jamesabelson.co.uk

James Bareham@edsonwilliams photography consultancy 52 Brushfield Street, London, E1 6AJ, United Kingdom
✆ (020) 7375 2077/(07867) 517777 ☎ (020) 7375 3077
✉ info@edsonwilliams.com
🖥 www.edsonwilliams.com

James Barlow Photography 63 King Street, Whalley, Clitheroe, Lancashire, BB7 9SW, United Kingdom
✆ (01254) 824386
✉ info@jamesbarlow.net
🖥 www.jamesbarlow.net

James Bedford Photography Marne Street, London, W10 4JF, United Kingdom
✆ (020) 8960 8822
✉ james@jamesbedford.com
🖥 www.jamesbedford.com

James Bunch 80 Ribblesdale Road, London, SW16 6SE, United Kingdom
✆ (07808) 401435
✉ jambun@aol.com

James Callaghan@Beth Coyne Agency, London, NW6 1GF, United Kingdom
✆ (020) 7431 8981/☎ (020) 7813 9750
✉ info@bethcoyne.com
🖥 www.bethcoyne.com

James Callaghan Photography 51 Avenue Road, Leamington Spa, Warickshire, CV31 3PF
✆ **07740 411 124/01926 313 623** ☎ **jim.c@btinternet.com**
✉ **www.jamescallaghan.co.uk**
See ad in showcase

James Cotier c/o Daphna Stone, 30 Tudor Close, Belsize Park, London, NW3 4AG, United Kingdom
✆ (020) 7794 0214/(07950) 151139
✉ jamescotier@yahoo.it
🖥 www.jamescotier.com

James D Ross 70 Fletching Road, London, E5 9QR, United Kingdom
✆ (07976) 657112
✉ james@jamesrossphotography.com
🖥 www.jamesrossphotography.com

James Day@Siobhan Squire 111 Shoreditch High Street, London, E1 6JN, United Kingdom
✆ (020) 7739 8985/☎ (020) 7729 5125
✉ siobhan@siobhansquire.com
🖥 www.siobhansquire.com

James Duncan Unit 4, Cranleigh Mews, London, SW11 2QL, United Kingdom
✆ (020) 7924 5585/☎ (020) 7924 5595
✉ james@jduncan.co.uk
🖥 www.jduncan.co.uk

James Galloway@Areia London Studio1, 42 Theobalds Road, London, WC1X 8NW, United Kingdom
✆ (020) 7404 8600/☎ (020) 7404 8601
✉ info@areia.com
🖥 www.areia.com

James Harris@Axiom Photographic Agency The Pall Mall Deposit, 124-128 Barlby Road, London, W10 6BL, United Kingdom
✆ (020) 8964 9970/☎ (020) 8964 8440
✉ info@axiomphotographic.com
🖥 www.axiomphotographic.com

James J Johnson 15a Prospect Road, Ossett, Wakefield, West Yorkshire, WF5 8AN, United Kingdom
✆ (01924) 279777
✉ jamesjjohnson@virgin.net
🖥 www.james-johnson.com

James Jordan N1 Studio, 6-8 Vestry Street, London, N1 7RE, United Kingdom
✆ (07836) 747200/☎ (020) 7490 2392
✉ jamesjordan@btinternet.com
🖥 www.jamesjordanphotography.co.uk

James Kelly Flat 801C, Londonderry House, 2 Newton Street, Birmingham, B4 7LN, United Kingdom
✆ (07974) 838004
✉ jamiekelly@gmail.com
🖥 www.nuozek.com

James King Photographer Unit 19c Barton Hill trad est, Maze Street, Bristol, BS5 9BD,
✆ 1179350839
✉ james@jameskingphotographer.co.uk
🖥 www.jameskingphotographer.co.uk

James Merrell@C S B Management 40 Bowling Green Lane, London, EC1R 0NE, United Kingdom
✆ (020) 7415 7051/☎ (020) 7415 7059
✉ susie@csbmanagement.com
🖥 www.csbmanagement.com

James Murphy@Jo Talbot & Sue Young 6M Hyde Park Mansions, Cabbell Street, London, NW1 5BJ, United Kingdom
✆ (020) 7262 0189/(07850) 353468 ☎ (020) 7262 2160
✉ joandsue@btconnect.com
🖥 www.joandsue.com

James Russell Cant@Germaine Walker Photographers' Agent Crayford House, 49A Tabley Road, London, N7 0NA, United Kingdom
✆ (020) 7697 8291/(07867) 780272 ☎ (020) 7619 9051
✉ germaine@germaine.co.uk
🖥 www.germaine.co.uk

James Sparshatt@Axiom Photographic Agency The Pall Mall Deposit, 124-128 Barlby Road, London, W10 6BL, United Kingdom
✆ (020) 8964 9970/☎ (020) 8964 8440
✉ info@axiomphotographic.com
🖥 www.axiomphotographic.com

James Starr@Début Art & The Coningsby Gallery 30 Tottenham Street, London, W1T 4RJ, United Kingdom
✆ (020) 7636 1064/☎ (020) 7580 7017
✉ info@debutart.com
🖥 www.debutart.com

James Wedge 1 Ruston Mews, London, W11 1RB, United Kingdom
✆ (020) 7221 9922/☎ (020) 7221 9933

James Williamson Studio 3h, Leyroy House, 436 Essex Road, London, N1 3QD, United Kingdom
✆ (020) 7704 5252/☎ (020) 7704 5252
✉ james@jameswilliamson.co.uk
🖥 www.jameswilliamson.co.uk

Jamie Hodgson@Akehurst Creative Management Ltd, London, United Kingdom
✆ (020) 7624 2366
✉ na@nickyakehurst.com
🖥 www.akehurstcreativemanagement.com

Jamie King@Creative Talent (UK) Limited 78 York Street, London, W1H 1DP, United Kingdom
✆ (020) 7439 1877/☎ (020) 7434 1144
✉ info@creativetalentlimited.com
🖥 www.creativetalentlimited.com

Jamie Stephen Represents 9 Upper Wimpole Street, London, W1G 6LJ, United Kingdom
✆ **(0845) 3733510/(07957) 784810** ☎ **(020) 7681 1027**
✉ **jamie@jamiestephen.com**
✉ **www.jamiestephen.com**
See ad in showcase

Jan Baldwin 11 Gibraltar Walk, London, E2 7LH, United Kingdom
✆ (020) 7729 2664/(07860) 352952 ☎ (020) 7729 3861
✉ studio@janbaldwin.co.uk
🖥 www.janbaldwin.co.uk

Jan Van Endert@Valeriehersleven Boundary House (3rd Floor), 91-93 Charterhouse Street, London, EC1M 6HR, United Kingdom
✆ (07775) 717474
✉ me@valeriehersleven.com
🖥 www.valeriehersleven.com

Jan Willem Scholten@David Edmunds Represents Unit 105, 54-58 Kingsland Road, London, E2 8DP, United Kingdom
✆ (020) 7739 1166/(07785) 580024
✉ info@davidedmundsrepresents.com
🖥 www.davidedmundsrepresents.com

Jane Bird 3 Mandela Street, Camden Town, London, NW1 0DU, United Kingdom
✆ /(07966) 510341
✉ emailme@janebird.co.uk

Jane Linders Alternative Photography 2419 Country Place, Maryland Heights, United States of America
✆ 314 576 7155
✉ janelinders@sbcglobal.net
🖥 www.jlinders2.photosite.com

Jane Maxwell-Hystop@Private View Artists Agency 17A Swan Hill, Shrewsbury, SY1 1NL, United Kingdom
✆ (01743) 350355/☎ (01743) 233923
✉ create@pvuk.com
🖥 www.pvuk.com

Jane Sumner Wantley Manor, Henfield, West Sussex, BN5 9JL, United Kingdom
✆ (01273) 491664/(07836) 735744 ☎ (01273) 491647
✉ janesumner@onetel.net.uk
🖥 www.janesumner.com

Janne Savon Photography 30 Wyatt Road, London, N5 2JU, United Kingdom
✆ (07932) 017367
✉ info@jannesavon.com
🖥 www.jannesavon.com/

Jason Andrews Photography 22 Station Road, London, N21 3RB, United Kingdom
✆ (07967) 581455
✉ jason_andrews@onetel.com
🖥 www.jasonandrews.co.uk

Jason Bye, Norwich, NR1 1NR, United Kingdom
✆ (07966) 173930
✉ mail@jasonbye.com
🖥 www.jasonbye.com

Jason Hawkes The Red House, Red House Drive, Sonning Common, Reading, RG4 9NL, United Kingdom
✆ 0118-924 2946/(07768) 525392
✉ library@jasonhawkes.com
🖥 www.jasonhawkes.com

Jason Hetherington@Pearce Stoner Associates 12B Links Yard, Spelman Street, London, E1 5LX, United Kingdom
✆ (020) 7247 7100/☎ (020) 7247 7144
✉ info@pearcestoner.com
🖥 www.pearcestoner.com

Jason Hindley@Agent Orange 10 Swan Yard, London, N1 1SD, United Kingdom
✆ (020) 7226 0440/☎ (020) 7226 1613
✉ annika@agentorange.co.uk
🖥 www.agentorange.co.uk

Jason Joyce@WildeHague Ltd Suite 4, The Swan centre, Fishers Lane, London, W4 1RX, United Kingdom
✆ (020) 8747 9988/☎ (020) 8747 8228
✉ info@wildehague.com
🖥 www.wildehague.com

Jason Knott@Horton-Stephens Photographers' Agent 14 Peacock Yard, Iliffe Street, London, SE17 3LH, United Kingdom
✆ (020) 7252 7979/☎ (020) 7252 6409
✉ us@horton-stephens.com
🖥 www.horton-stephens.com

Jason Shenai 48 Belsize Square, London, NW3 4HN, United Kingdom
✆ (020) 7794 9194/(07767) 756534 ☎ (020) 7435 0133
✉ jason@milim.com
🖥 www.milim.com

Jason Tozer 12 Mallow Street, London, EC1Y 8RQ, United Kingdom
(020) 7490 3360/ (020) 7490 3370
jt@jasontozer.com
www.jasontozer.com

JASPA Photography Holland Park Avenue, London, W11 3RA, United Kingdom
(07757) 324135
office@jaspaphoto.com
www.jaspaphoto.com

Jasper James@Alex Vaughan 59 Lambeth Walk, London, SE11 6DX, United Kingdom
(020) 7735 6623/(07775) 630137
me@alexvaughan.com
www.alexvaughan.com

Jasper White@Traffic Unit P102, 23 - 28 Penn Street, London, N1 7DL, United Kingdom
020 7739 6090
rebecca@rebeccavalentine.com
www.trafficphotographic.com

Jay Maidment@Blowup 146 Amyand Park Road, St. Margaret's, Twickenham, TW1 3HY, United Kingdom
(020) 8744 0210/ (020) 8892 2521
orders@blowup.net
www.blowup.net

Jay Myrdal Old School House, High Street, Stanford in the Vale, Faringdon, Oxfordshire, SN7 8LH, United Kingdom
(01367) 710168/(07768) 000013
jay@myrdal.com
www.myrdal.com

Jay Whitcombe Unit 3 Dickson House, 3 Grove Road, Richmond, Surrey, TW10 6SP, United Kingdom
(020) 8948 4151/ (020) 8948 4151

Jayawardene Travel Photo Library 7a Napier Road, Wembley, Middlesex, HA0 4UA, United Kingdom
(020) 8795 3581/ (020) 8795 4083

Jaypark Studios Brunel Park, Bumpers Farm Industrial Estate, Chippenham, Wiltshire, SN14 6NQ, United Kingdom
(01249) 655117/ (01249) 660740
jaypark@btconnect.com
www.jaypark.co.uk

Jean Cazals, London, W11 1SA, United Kingdom
(020) 7460 0683/(07860) 777143
info@jeancazals.com
www.jeancazals.net

Jean Gaumy@Magnum Photos 63 Gee Street, London, EC1V 3RS, United Kingdom
(020) 7490 1771/ (020) 7608 0020
magnum@magnumphotos.co.uk
www.magnumphotos.com

Jean-Claude Winkler Photography 13A Glenrosa Street, London, SW6 2QY, United Kingdom
(07765) 367 517
contact@jean-claudewinkler.com
www.jean-claudewinkler.com

Jean-Francois Carly@Webber Represents Ltd 25 Lexington Street, Soho, London, W1F 9AG, United Kingdom
(020) 7439 0678/ (020) 7439 0543
london@webberrepresents.com
www.webberrepresents.com

Jean-Luc Benard@Andrea Walji Agency 6 Brewer Street, London, W1F 0SB, United Kingdom
(020) 7439 4144/(07789) 871871 (020) 7439 4133
andrea@andreawalji.com
www.andreawalji.com

Jean-Luc BÈnard 44 Ennismore Avenue, London, W4 1SF, United Kingdom
(020) 8742 3142/(07836) 699128 (020) 8400 1786
jlb@jeanlucbenard.com
www.jeanlucbenard.com

Jean-Pierre Khazem@Bill Charles London Ltd. Unit 3E1, Zetland House, 5-25 Scrutton Street, London, EC2A 4HJ, United Kingdom
020 7033 9284/020 2033 9285
london@billcharles.com
www.billcharles.com

Jeff Mermelstein@Bill Charles London Ltd. Unit 3E1, Zetland House, 5-25 Scrutton Street, London, EC2A 4HJ, United Kingdom
020 7033 9284/020 2033 9285
london@billcharles.com
www.billcharles.com

Jemma Watts@Yara Gremoli Photographers Agent Studio 210, Canalot Studios, 222 Kensal Road, London, W10 5BN, United Kingdom
(0870) 8501209/(07880) 627413 (0870) 8501209
yara@sbmanagement.org
www.yaragremoli.com

Jenny Acheson@Axiom Photographic Agency The Pall Mall Deposit, 124-128 Barlby Road, London, W10 6BL, United Kingdom
(020) 8964 9970/ (020) 8964 8440
info@axiomphotographic.com
www.axiomphotographic.com

Jenny Hands@WildeHague Ltd Suite 4, The Swan centre, Fishers Lane, London, W4 1RX, United Kingdom
(020) 8747 9988/ (020) 8747 8228
info@wildehague.com
www.wildehague.com

Jenny van Sommers@C L M Top Floor, 19 All Saints Road, London, W11 1HE, United Kingdom
(020) 7750 2999/ (020) 7792 8507
clm@clmuk.com
www.clmuk.com

Jenny Zarins@A & R Photographic 16A Crane Grove, London, N7 8LE, United Kingdom
(020) 7607 3030/ (020) 7607 2190
info@aandrphotographic.co.uk
www.aandrphotographic.co.uk

Jens Lucking, SW11 4PF, United Kingdom
/07715 422444
www.jenslucking.co.uk

Jens Marott@Creative Talent (UK) Limited 78 York Street, London, W1H 1DP, United Kingdom
(020) 7439 1877/ (020) 7434 1144
info@creativetalentlimited.com
www.creativetalentlimited.com

Jeremy Browne 7 French Weir Avenue, Taunton, Somerset, TA1 1XH, United Kingdom
(01823) 331812/(07721) 464673 (020) 8341 1676
jeremy.browne@talk21.com
www.jeremybrowne.com

Jeremy Hilder 73 Erlanger Road, London, SE14 5TQ, United Kingdom
(020) 7639 8374/ (020) 7639 8374
mail@jeremyhilder.com
www.jeremyhilder.com

Jeremy Hirsch 41 The Avenue, London, NW6 7NR, United Kingdom
(07850) 253034
jeremyhirsch@hotmail.com

Jeremy Hopley Unit 13B, Rosemary Works, Branch Place, London, N1 5PH, United Kingdom
(020) 7613 5352/ (020) 7739 9617
jeremy@jeremyhopley.com
www.jeremyhopley.com

Jeremy Hudson @ Sharon Brandman Agency No 2 Elmhurst Close, Bushey, WD23 2QB
845 800 9003/ sharon@sharonbrandman.com
www.sharonbrandman.com
See ad in showcase

Jeremy Hudson Unit 14, Parsons Green Depot, Parsons Green, London, SW6 4HH, United Kingdom
(020) 7736 9933/ (020) 8736 7337
jeremy@hudsonphoto.co.uk
www.hudsonphoto.co.uk

Jeremy Matthews 215 Earlsfield Road, London, SW18 3DE, United Kingdom
(07831) 254320
info@jeremymatthews.co.uk
www.jeremymatthews.co.uk

Jeremy Murch@Webber Represents Ltd 25 Lexington Street, Soho, London, W1F 9AG, United Kingdom
(020) 7439 0678/ (020) 7439 0543
london@webberrepresents.com
www.webberrepresents.com

Jeremy Rendell 10 Florin Court, 8 Dock Street, London, E1 8JR, United Kingdom
(07860) 277411
jeremy.rendell@btconnect.com
www.jeremyrendell.com

Jerry Berndt@Akehurst Creative Management Ltd, London, United Kingdom
(020) 7624 2366
na@nickyakehurst.com
www.akehurstcreativemanagement.com

Jerry Oke@Mark George 5 St. George's Court, 131 Putney Bridge Road, Putney, London, SW15 2PA, United Kingdom
(020) 8877 9922/(07771) 595 999 (020) 8870 5533
mg@markgeorge.com
www.markgeorge.com

Jerry Young 60 Camberwell Grove, Camberwell, London, SE5 8RE, United Kingdom
(020) 7701 6224/(07973) 725189
jer@jerryyoung.co.uk
www.jerryyoung.co.uk

Jess Kappell 71 White Lion Street, London, N1 9PP, United Kingdom
(020) 7837 8374/ (020) 7837 7837

Jess Koppel@Noelle Pickford 27 Britton Street, London, EC1M 5UD, United Kingdom
(020) 7336 6773/ (020) 7336 7043
info@noellerepresents.com
www.noellerepresents.com

Jesse Seaward 16 ClayHall Court, St Stephens's Road, Bow, London, E3 5JE
07970 266 907/ info@jesseseaward.co.uk
www.jesseseaward.co.uk
See ad in showcase

Jessica Backhaus@S Management 15 Rocks Lane, London, SW13 0BD, United Kingdom
(020) 8487 9655/ (020) 8487 9541
fiona@smanagement.co.uk
www.smanagement.co.uk

Jessica Strang 504 Brody House, Strype Street, London, E1 7LQ, United Kingdom
(020) 7247 8982/ (020) 7247 8982
jessica@jessicastrang.plus.com

Jessops Ltd 20 Westborough, Scarborough, North Yorkshire, YO11 1UH, United Kingdom
(01723) 365024/ (01723) 363334
www.jessops.com

Jez Matthews@Jamie Stephen Represents 9 Upper Wimpole Street, London, W1G 6LJ, United Kingdom
(0845) 3733510/(07957) 784810 (020) 7681 1027
jamie@jamiestephen.com
www.jamiestephen.com

Jhon Kevern, United Kingdom
(07092) 200505
contact@jhonkevern.co.uk
www.kevern.co.uk

Jill Mead@Tattersall Love 40 Langham Street, W1W 7AS, United Kingdom
(020) 7637 5737/ (020) 7637 5747
mail@tattersall-love.com
www.tattersall-love.com

Jillian Lochner@Germaine Walker Photographers' Agent Crayford House, 49A Tabley Road, London, N7 0NA, United Kingdom
(020) 7697 8291/(07867) 780272 (020) 7619 9051
germaine@germaine.co.uk
www.germaine.co.uk

Jim Cooper@Re:fresh Suit 4, The Swans Centre, Fishers Lane, London, W4 1RX, United Kingdom
(020) 8747 8080/ (020) 8747 8228
info@refresh-agency.com
www.refresh-agency.com

Jim Fenwick, United Kingdom
(07976) 292436
jim@jimfenwick.com
www.jimfenwick.com

Jim Forrest 97 Streathbourne Road, London, SW17 8RA, United Kingdom
(020) 8767 4230/(07836) 738841
jim@jimforrest.net

Jim Friedman@Début Art & The Coningsby Gallery 30 Tottenham Street, London, W1T 4RJ, United Kingdom
(020) 7636 1064/ (020) 7580 7017
info@debutart.com
www.debutart.com

Jim Goldberg@Magnum Photos 63 Gee Street, London, EC1V 3RS, United Kingdom
(020) 7490 1771/ (020) 7608 0020
magnum@magnumphotos.co.uk
www.magnumphotos.com

Jim Henderson Photography Crooktree, Kincardine O'Neil, Aboyne, Aberdeenshire, AB34 4JD, United Kingdom
✆ (01339) 882149/☎ (01339) 882149
✉ JHende7868@aol.com
🖳 www.jimhendersonphotography.com

Jim Holmes@Axiom Photographic Agency The Pall Mall Deposit, 124-128 Barlby Road, London, W10 6BL, United Kingdom
✆ (020) 8964 9970/☎ (020) 8964 8440
✉ info@axiomphotographic.com
🖳 www.axiomphotographic.com

Jim Maskrey Photo Imaging Staleigh Manor, Whitmoor Lane, Guildford, Surrey, GU4 7QB, United Kingdom
✆ (01483) 236940/☎ (01483) 236190
✉ jim@maskrey.co.uk
🖳 www.jimmaskrey.co.uk

Jim Naughten@Axiom Photographic Agency The Pall Mall Deposit, 124-128 Barlby Road, London, W10 6BL, United Kingdom
✆ (020) 8964 9970/☎ (020) 8964 8440
✉ info@axiomphotographic.com
🖳 www.axiomphotographic.com

Jim Watters 4 Brook Street, Twyford, Reading, RG10 9NX, United Kingdom
✆ 0118-934 2797/07702) 433847 ☎ 0118-934 2797
✉ jimwatters@macunlimited.net
🖳 www.redstart.net/jameswatters/index.html

Jim Wheeler c/o Industrial Image, 168 Leahurst Road, London, SE13 5NL, United Kingdom
✆ (020) 8297 8080/(07860) 652735 ☎ (020) 8297 8181
✉ jimwheeler@industrialimage.co.uk
🖳 www.industrialimage.co.uk

Jo Bradbury 31 Brundretts Road, Chorlton, Manchester, M21 9DA, United Kingdom
✆ 0161-881 6925
✉ jo@jobradbury.co.uk
🖳 www.jobradbury.co.uk

Jo Broughton, London, United Kingdom
✆ (07801) 503953
✉ jobroughton@yahoo.com
🖳 www.myspace.com/jobroughton

Jo Clark 2nd Floor, 202B Camden Lock, London, NW1 8AF, United Kingdom
✆ (020) 7267 7267/☎ (020) 7267 7495
✉ jo@joclark.com
🖳 www.joclark.com

Jo Crowther, London, United Kingdom
✆ (07778) 358131/(07778) 358131

Jo Sax@Jo Clark 2nd Floor, 202B Camden Lock, London, NW1 8AF, United Kingdom
✆ (020) 7267 7267/☎ (020) 7267 7495
✉ jo@joclark.com
🖳 www.joclark.com

Jo Talbot & Sue Young 6M Hyde Park Mansions, Cabbell Street, London, NW1 5BJ, United Kingdom
✆ **(020) 7262 0189/(07850) 353468 ☎ (020) 7262 2160**
✉ **joandsue@btconnect.com**
🖳 **www.joandsue.com**
See ad in showcase

Jo Tyler@Sarah Kaye Representation Ltd 38 Queen's Gate, London, SW7 5HR, United Kingdom
✆ (020) 7225 5005/☎ (020) 7225 0109
✉ sarah@sarahkaye.com
🖳 www.sarahkaye.com

Joakim BorÈn Photography 14 Monroe House, New Orleans Walk, London, N19 3UG, United Kingdom
✆ (07917) 1591350
✉ contact@joakimboren.com
🖳 www.joakimboren.com

Joanna Agis@Début Art & The Coningsby Gallery 30 Tottenham Street, London, W1T 4RJ, United Kingdom
✆ (020) 7636 1064/☎ (020) 7580 7017
✉ info@debutart.com
🖳 www.debutart.com

Joanna Henderson@Sarah Kaye Representation Ltd 38 Queen's Gate, London, SW7 5HR, United Kingdom
✆ (020) 7225 5005/☎ (020) 7225 0109
✉ sarah@sarahkaye.com
🖳 www.sarahkaye.com

Joaquim Barreto 110 Blackheath Road, Greenwich, London, SE10 8DA, United Kingdom
✆ (020) 7760 6646/(07910) 539957
✉ joaquim@ocular-group.com
🖳 www.joaquimbarreto.com

Jocelyn Bain Hogg@Jo Talbot & Sue Young 6M Hyde Park Mansions, Cabbell Street, London, NW1 5BJ, United Kingdom
✆ (020) 7262 0189/(07850) 353468 ☎ (020) 7262 2160
✉ joandsue@btconnect.com
🖳 www.joandsue.com

Jochen Braun@Milc Studio 7, Zeus House, 16-30 Provost Street, London, N1 7NG, United Kingdom
✆ (020) 7278 8838/☎ (0870) 0941564
✉ gemma@milc.co.uk
🖳 www.milc.co.uk

Joe Beynon@Axiom Photographic Agency The Pall Mall Deposit, 124-128 Barlby Road, London, W10 6BL, United Kingdom
✆ (020) 8964 9970/☎ (020) 8964 8440
✉ info@axiomphotographic.com
🖳 www.axiomphotographic.com

Joe Cornish Topcliffe House, Low Green, Middlesbrough, Cleveland, TS9 6PT, United Kingdom
✆ (01642) 722487
✉ joecornish@phonecoop.coop
🖳 www.joecornish.com

Joe Fairs Photography, London, United Kingdom
✆ (07973) 193745
✉ joe@fairsphotography.co.uk
🖳 www.fairsphotography.co.uk

Joe McGorty@Stem Agency Top Floor, 23 Charlotte Road, London, EC2A 3PB, United Kingdom
✆ (07790) 026628
✉ will@stemagency.com
🖳 www.stemagency.com

Joe Pepler Photographer 2 Coombe Cottages, Bluebell Lane, Sharpthorne, East Grinstead, West Sussex, RH19 4PF, United Kingdom
✆ (07950) 403554
✉ info@peplerpictures.com
🖳 www.peplerpictures.com

Joe Windsor-Williams Ltd 2 The Old Works, Black Cut, St. Albans, Hertfordshire, AL1 1PT, United Kingdom
✆ (020) 7581 4400
✉ tracy@joeww.com
🖳 www.joeww.com

Joff Lee 30 Warner Street, Ground Floor, London, EC1R 5EX, United Kingdom
✆ (020) 7837 8218/☎ (020) 7278 0063
✉ joff@jofflee.co.uk
🖳 www.jofflee.co.uk

Johanna Parkin@A & R Photographic 16A Crane Grove, London, N7 8LE, United Kingdom
✆ (020) 7607 3030/☎ (020) 7607 2190
✉ info@aandrphotographic.co.uk
🖳 www.aandrphotographic.co.uk

John Akehurst@C L M Top Floor, 19 All Saints Road, London, W11 1HE, United Kingdom
✆ (020) 7750 2999/☎ (020) 7792 8507
✉ clm@clmuk.com
🖳 www.clmuk.com

John ALflatt@Alexandra Von Ziechmann Flat 1, 90 Sutherland Avenue, London, W9 2QR, United Kingdom
✆ (020) 7289 4248/(07962) 082691
🖳 www.alexandravz.com

John Aparicio 2nd Floor, Unit 12, 23-28 Penn Street, London, N1 5DL, United Kingdom
✆ (020) 7729 2166/(07710) 080140
✉ john@johnaparicio.co.uk
🖳 www.johnaparicio.co.uk

John Arnison White Ash, Barrowby Lane, Leeds, LS15 8PT, United Kingdom
✆ (01326) 41915
✉ johnarnison@whiteashhouse.freeserve.co.uk

John Balsom@The Katy Barker Agency Ltd 11 Mason's Arms Mews, Maddox Street, London, W1S 1NX, United Kingdom
✆ (020) 7493 3933/☎ (020) 7493 3311
✉ catherine@katybarker.com
🖳 www.katybarker.com

John Barlow Photography, United Kingdom
✆ (07831) 527662
✉ john@johnbarlow.com
🖳 www.johnbarlow.com

John Baxter Photographer 7 Bridge Street, Appleby-in-Westmorland, Cumbria, CA16 6QH, United Kingdom
✆ (01768) 353172/(07971) 253843 ☎ (01768) 352546
✉ john@johnbaxter.co.uk
🖳 www.johnbaxter.co.uk

John Bellars, Chiswick, London, W4, United Kingdom
✆ (07973) 733959
✉ john_bellars@yahoo.co.uk
🖳 www.johnbellars.com

John Bennett@Jamie Stephen Represents 9 Upper Wimpole Street, London, W1G 6LJ, United Kingdom
✆ (0845) 3733510/(07957) 784810 ☎ (020) 7681 1027
✉ jamie@jamiestephen.com
🖳 www.jamiestephen.com

John Bigglestone & Co. Wharf Studios, 13a The Wharf, Couch Lane, Devizes, Wiltshire, SN10 1EB, United Kingdom
✆ (01380) 720599
✉ upstarts@phototutor-online.com
🖳 www.thewharfstudio.com

John Blythe@Sharon Brandman Agency No 2 Milner Court, Bridgewater Way, Bushey, WD23 4UB, United Kingdom
✆ 020 8950 9213/07973 305575 ☎ 020 8950 7990
✉ sharon@sharonbrandman.com
🖳 www.sharonbrandman.com

John Brown Studio 3, 21 Wren Street, London, WC1X 0HS, United Kingdom
✆ (07836) 264866/☎ (07957) 205705
✉ johnbrownphoto@yahoo.co.uk

John Cleare Hill Cottage, Fonthill Gifford, Salisbury, SP3 6QW, United Kingdom
✆ (01747) 820320/☎ (01747) 820320
✉ cleare@btinternet.com
🖳 www.mountaincamera.com

John Cocking 49 Towles Pastures, Castle Donington, Derby, DE74 2RX, United Kingdom
✆ (01332) 814746/(07831) 200977 ☎ (01332) 855010
✉ mail@jcp.eclipse.co.uk
🖳 www.contactfashionphotographers.com

John Cole 29 Godwin Road, Hastings, East Sussex, TN35 5JR, United Kingdom
✆ (01424) 436644/(07958) 491179
✉ gully@johncole.co.uk
🖳 www.folio.johncole.co.uk

John Cooper 194 Mottram Road, Stalybridge, Cheshire, SK15 2RT, United Kingdom
✆ 0161-338 2201
✉ cooper.john0@btinternet.com

John Cooper Collection East Chase, Bowerchalke, Salisbury, SP5 5RB, United Kingdom
✆ (01722) 780076/☎ (01722) 780076
✉ info@johncoopercollection.co.uk
🖳 www.johncoopercollection.co.uk

John Crane Unit 2, Culford House, London, N1 5RA, United Kingdom
✆ (01803) 770543/(07970) 755589 ☎ (01803) 770543

John Cumming@Wendy Jackson Tag Creative, 29 Clerkenwell Road, London, EC1M 5TA, United Kingdom
✆ (020) 3217 2241/(07711) 084801 ☎ (020) 7439 1971
✉ wjackson@tagworldwide.com
🖳 www.wendyjackson.co.uk

John Daniels@Beth Coyne Agency, London, NW6 1GF, United Kingdom
✆ (020) 7431 8981/☎ (020) 7813 9750
✉ info@bethcoyne.com
🖳 www.bethcoyne.com

John Davis@Gina Phillips Represents Ltd 6 Leverton Place, London, NW5 2PL, United Kingdom
✆ (020) 7284 2022/☎ (020) 7424 0272
✉ info@ginaphillips.co.uk
🖳 www.ginaphillips.co.uk

John de Koning Kombuisweg 11, Amsterdam, 1041 AV, Netherlands
✆ 00 31 20 640 4782/00 31 65 391 8190 ☎ 00 31 20 640 6182
✉ studio@kingly.nl
🖳 www.kingly.nl

John Dickinson 5 Moat Road, East Grinstead, West Sussex, RH19 3JZ, United Kingdom
✆ (01342) 314377
✉ dickinbar@aol.com

John Eckart 232 Meanwood Road, The Old Chapel, Leeds, LS7 2AH, United Kingdom
℡ 0113-262 8811/✆ 0113-262 8822
✉ john@johneckart.co.uk
🖥 www.johneckart.co.uk

John Edward Linden@Arcaid Picture Library Parc House, 25-37 Cowleaze Road, Kingston upon Thames, Surrey, KT2 6DZ, United Kingdom
℡ (020) 8546 4352/✆ (020) 8541 5230
✉ arcaid@arcaid.co.uk
🖥 www.arcaid.co.uk

John Falzon 1 William Blake House, The Lanterns, Bridge Lane, London, SW11 3AD, United Kingdom
℡ (020) 7978 4175/✆ (020) 7978 4176
✉ info@lanternsstudios.com
🖥 www.lanternsstudios.com

John Ferro Sims 11 Parkhill Road, London, NW3 2YH, United Kingdom
℡ (020) 7586 0780/✆ (020) 7586 3790
✉ john@henrymoorestudio.co.uk
🖥 simspix.co.uk

John Flowerdew Gainsborough Cottage, Oxted Green, Godalming, Surrey, GU8 5DA, United Kingdom
℡ (01483) 813709/(07836) 702600 ✆ (01483) 424575
✉ sales@studioj.co.uk
🖥 www.studioj.co.uk

John Freebrey 37 Church Road, Hanwell, London, W7 3BD, United Kingdom
℡ (020) 8840 3176/✆ (020) 8840 3176
🖥 www.thedigitaldarkcloth.com

John Frye 4 Hounslow Avenue, Hounslow, TW3 2DX, United Kingdom
℡ (020) 8894 6573/(07766) 321789
✉ photographer@johnfrye.co.uk

John Garrett Flat C, 1 Amor Road, London, W6 0AN, United Kingdom
℡ (020) 8932 7719/✆ (020) 8932 7720

John Glover Photography The Oast Houses, Headley Lane, Liphook, Hampshire, GU30 7RN, United Kingdom
℡ (01428) 751925/(07973) 307078 ✆ (01428) 751191
✉ john@johnglover.co.uk
🖥 www.johnglover.co.uk

John Glynn 26 Station View, South Queensferry, Edinburgh, EH30 9DA, United Kingdom
℡ 0131-331 2093/(07770) 450217
✉ jgp@dalmeny.force9.co.uk
🖥 www.johnglynnphotography.com

John Greenwood 10 Gauden Road, London, SW4 6LT, United Kingdom
℡ (020) 7498 7100/(07973) 114428 ✆ (020) 7498 7300
✉ j_greenwood@btinternet.com

John Hudson@Sarah Kaye Representation Ltd 38 Queen's Gate, London, SW7 5HR, United Kingdom
℡ (020) 7225 5005/✆ (020) 7225 0109
✉ sarah@sarahkaye.com
🖥 www.sarahkaye.com

John Hulme Photography 17a Marine Square, Brighton, BN2 1DN, United Kingdom
℡ (01273) 601005/✆ (01273) 601005
✉ jphulme@yahoo.com
🖥 www.johnhulme.net

John J. Breen 61 High Street, Little Milton, Oxford, OX44 7PU, United Kingdom
℡ (01844) 278380/(07885) 655998 ✆ (01844) 278380
✉ johnjbreen@monochromeblue.com
🖥 www.monochromeblue.com

John Knill Amber House, Ovington, Alresford, Hampshire, SO24 0RE, United Kingdom
℡ (01962) 732151/(07976) 796758
✉ john@johnknill.com
🖥 www.johnknill.com

John Lawrence-Jones Studio D, 416 Fulham Road, London, SW6 1EB, United Kingdom
℡ (020) 7733 0055/(07778) 650937

John Londei Unit 5, 11 Wyfold Road, London, SW6 6SE, United Kingdom
℡ (020) 7381 8972/✆ (020) 7381 8971
✉ john@johnlondei.co.uk
🖥 www.johnlondei.co.uk

John Mac@Angela Woods 4 The Carlton Tavern, 73 Grafton Road, London, NW5 4BB, United Kingdom
℡ (020) 7284 3417/(07850) 263077 ✆ (020) 7482 2466
✉ angela@angelawoods.com
🖥 www.angelawoods.com

John Mason 14 Doughty Mews, London, WC1N 2PG, United Kingdom
℡ (020) 7251 4402/(07785) 280680
✉ masonfoto@btinternet.com
🖥 www.johmasonphoto.com

John Michael Wood April Cottage, 32 Oak Lane, Wilmslow, Cheshire, SK9 6AF, United Kingdom
℡ (0845) 6584314/(07957) 861632

John Midgley@Bill Charles London Ltd. Unit 3E1, Zetland House, 5-25 Scrutton Street, London, EC2A 4HJ, United Kingdom
℡ 020 7033 9284/020 2033 9285
✉ london@billcharles.com
🖥 www.billcharles.com

John Minoprio Parrys Lodge, Sarn Road, Threapwood, Malpas, Cheshire, SY14 7AW, United Kingdom
℡ (01948) 770309/✆ (01948) 770452
✉ john@minophoto.co.uk
🖥 www.minophoto.co.uk

John Mottershaw Photography 2 Commercial Road, Grindleford, Hope Valley, Derbyshire, S32 2HA, United Kingdom
℡ (01433) 631418
✉ john@johnmottershaw.com
🖥 www.johnmottershaw.com

John O'Grady 11 Wellesley Park, Wellington, Somerset, TA21 8PT, United Kingdom
℡ (01823) 662329/(07802) 613911
✉ john.ogrady@virgin.net
🖥 www.corbinogradystudio.co.uk

John Offenbach@Mark George 5 St. George's Court, 131 Putney Bridge Road, Putney, London, SW15 2PA, United Kingdom
℡ (020) 8877 9922/(07771) 595 999 ✆ (020) 8870 5533
✉ mg@markgeorge.com
🖥 www.markgeorge.com

John Parker@Mark George 5 St. George's Court, 131 Putney Bridge Road, Putney, London, SW15 2PA, United Kingdom
℡ (020) 8877 9922/(07771) 595 999 ✆ (020) 8870 5533
✉ mg@markgeorge.com
🖥 www.markgeorge.com

John Parkinson Photographic Agent Unit 17, 1-10 Summer's Street, London, EC1R 5BD, United Kingdom
℡ (020) 7278 6882/✆ (020) 7278 1251
✉ johnparkinsonagency@btinternet.com
🖥 www.johnparkinsonagency.co.uk

John Paul Gregory 34 Cheviot Gardens, London, NW2 1QE, United Kingdom
℡ (020) 8209 1357

John Paul Photography 12 Diriebught Road, Inverness, IV2 3QW, United Kingdom
℡ (01463) 221682/(07836) 310162
✉ john@jp-photo.demon.co.uk
🖥 www.photographerprofessional.com

John Quinn at Magenta The Mission Church, Hexham Road, Blucher Village, Newcastle upon Tyne, NE15 9SU, United Kingdom
℡ 0191-264 8888/(07732) 063530
✉ info@johnquinnat.co.uk
🖥 www.johnquinn.eu

John R. Ward 63 Shakespeare Road, London, W7 1LU, United Kingdom
℡ (020) 8579 1325/✆ (020) 8723 9984
🖥 www.johnrward.co.uk

John Rahim Photography 34b King Charles Road, Surbiton, Surrey, KT5 8PY, United Kingdom
℡ (020) 8339 9946
✉ john@rahim.co.uk
🖥 www.johnrahim.com

John Rensten@Traffic Unit P102, 23 - 28 Penn Street, London, N1 7DL, United Kingdom
℡ 020 7739 6090
✉ rebecca@rebeccavalentine.com
🖥 www.trafficphotographic.com

John Reynolds Photographer Studio 7, Chandlery House, 40 Gowers Walk, London, E1 8BH, United Kingdom
℡ (07973) 453363
✉ john@clickclickclick.net
🖥 www.clickclickclick.net

John Ross@L P A (Lisa Pritchard Agency) 3rd Floor, Block A, Morelands, 5-23 Old Street, London, EC1V 9HL, United Kingdom
℡ (020) 7250 1362/✆ (020) 7250 1357
✉ info@lisapritchard.com
🖥 www.lisapritchard.com

John Shelley @ JS Library International 101A Brondesbury Park, London, NW2 5JL, United Kingdom
℡ (020) 8451 2668/✆ (020) 8459 8517
✉ js@online24.co.uk
🖥 www.jslibrary.com www.jslibraryprints.com

John Slater 7 The Old Laundry, Alexander Studios, London, SW11 1YF, United Kingdom
℡ (020) 8874 2975/(07973) 380318
✉ john@compund-i.com
🖥 www.compund-i.com

John Spinks@East Photographic Ltd 8 Iron Bridge House, 3 Bridge Approach, London, NW1 8BD, United Kingdom
℡ (020) 7722 3444/✆ (020) 7722 3544
✉ roger@eastphotographic.com
🖥 www.eastphotographic.com

John Stone 14 Sandbourne Avenue, London, SW19 3EN, United Kingdom
℡ (020) 8540 0443/(07831) 251981
✉ john-stone@lineone.net

John Suett 85 Great Titchfield Street, London, W1W 6RJ, United Kingdom
℡ (020) 7580 1380/(07957) 353032
🖥 www.projectphotography.co.uk

John Swannell@Burnham Niker Unit 8, Canonbury Business Centre, 190A New North Road, London, N1 7BJ, United Kingdom
℡ (020) 7704 6565/✆ (020) 7704 8383
✉ enquiries@burnham-niker.com
🖥 www.burnham-niker.com

John T Brightmore The Lawns, Hinckley, Leicestershire, LE10 1DY, United Kingdom
℡ (01455) 440500/(07860) 227149 ✆ (01455) 440505
✉ johnbrightmore@btconnect.com

John Tickner 10 Damems Lane, Keighley, West Yorkshire, BD22 7AP, United Kingdom
℡ (01535) 601050/07967 604074
✉ john@johntickner.co.uk
🖥 www.johntickner.co.uk

John Turner Little Venhay, Meshaw, South Molton, Devon, EX36 4NQ, United Kingdom
℡ (01884) 860600/(07785) 232465 ✆ (0870) 7627531
✉ john@john-turner.co.uk
🖥 www.john-turner.co.uk

John Vink@Magnum Photos 63 Gee Street, London, EC1V 3RS, United Kingdom
℡ (020) 7490 1771/✆ (020) 7608 0020
✉ magnum@magnumphotos.co.uk
🖥 www.magnumphotos.com

John Walmsley Education Photos 8 Whitemore Road, Delmore, Guildford, Surrey, GU1 1QT, United Kingdom
℡ (01483) 511 666
✉ johnwalmsley@educationphotos.co.uk
🖥 www.educationphotos.co.uk

John Warburton-Lee Photography The Grange, Walcott, Sleaford, Lincolnshire, NG34 0ST, United Kingdom
℡ (01529) 497223/✆ (01529) 497223
✉ info@johnwarburtonlee.com
🖥 www.johnwarburtonlee.com

John Whitfield 2 Ilisse Yard, London, SE17 3QA, United Kingdom
℡ (020) 7703 5703/(07768) 525509
✉ johnwhitfield2@msn.com
🖥 www.johnwhitfield.com

John Wright Herald Way, Binley, Coventry, CV3 2NY, United Kingdom
℡ (024) 7665 3900/✆ (024) 7665 3902
✉ jwp@jwpschools.com
🖥 www.jwpschools.com

John-Paul Pietrus@A & R Photographic 16A Crane Grove, London, N7 8LE, United Kingdom
℡ (020) 7607 3030/✆ (020) 7607 2190
✉ info@aandrphotographic.co.uk
🖥 www.aandrphotographic.co.uk

Johnboyphoto Unit C, 1-19 Tewkesbury Road, Manor House, London, N15 6SE, United Kingdom
℡ (020) 8802 4653
✉ johnboyphoto@yahoo.co.uk
🖥 www.johnboyphoto.com

Johnny Boylan 21st Century, London, W1T 1NJ, United Kingdom
℡ (020) 7323 3822/(07831) 838829 ✆ (020) 7612 1010
✉ johnny@johnnyboylan.co.uk
🖥 www.johnnyboylan.co.uk

julian cotton
photographers agent

currently representing:

graeme ainscough   richard booth
steve cavalier   paul cordwell
laurence davis   paul fosbury
adam lawrence   leo mason
simon plant   graham precey

see pages in showcase for more details

e-mail: info@juliancotton.co.uk
web: www.juliancotton.co.uk

telephone: 020 7723 3100
mobile: 07932 151 999

Johnny Greig Photography 46 Ramsden Road, London,
SW12 8QY, United Kingdom
(020) 8772 1259/(07774) 134405
johnny@johnnygreig.com
www.johnnygreig.com

Johnny Haddock Flat 2, 81 Gloucester Street, London,
SW1V 4EB, United Kingdom
(020) 7834 5969/(07850) 121287 / (020) 7834 5969
johnnyhaddock@yahoo.co.uk
www.johnnyhaddock.co.uk

Jon Berkeley@Début Art & The Coningsby Gallery
30 Tottenham Street, London, W1T 4RJ, United Kingdom
(020) 7636 1064/ / 7580 7017
info@debutart.com
www.debutart.com

Jon Gray 110 Marylebone High Street, London, W1M
3DB, United Kingdom
(020) 7467 5681/(07778) 060073
jgray@aiulondon.com

Jon Hall 44 Leighton Road, London, NW5 2QE, United
Kingdom
(020) 7267 2988/ / (020) 7424 9252
jon@jonhallimages.com
www.jonhallimages.com

Jon Hempstead Retouching Top Floor 71, Sanshew
Street, London, N1 6LA, United Kingdom
(020) 7739 3844/(07960) 956182
jon@jonhempstead.co.uk

Jon Moss 5 Winwick Park Avenue, Winwick, Warrington,
WA2 8XB, United Kingdom
(01925) 242837/ / (01925) 242837
info@jonmoss.co.uk
www.jonmoss.co.uk

Jon Nash Photography 1 Walker Road, Maidenbower,
Crawley, West Sussex, RH10 7UA, United Kingdom
(01293) 887720/(07768) 860498 / (01293) 887720
jnash@easynet.co.uk

Jon Photography 65 High Street, Rode, Frome,
Somerset, BA11 6PB, United Kingdom
(07793) 962211
jonphotography@btinternet.com
www.jonphotography.com

Jon Prew The Church Hall, Camden Park Studios,
Camden Park Road, London, NW1 9AY, United Kingdom
(07771) 821525/ / (07771) 821525

Jon Spaull@Axiom Photographic Agency The Pall
Mall Deposit, 124-128 Barlby Road, London, W10 6BL,
United Kingdom
(020) 8964 9970/ / (020) 8964 8440
info@axiomphotographic.com
www.axiomphotographic.com

Jon Stewart 51 Calthorpe Street, London, WC1X 0HH,
United Kingdom
(020) 7278 5461/(07720) 046886
jon@jonstewartphotography.co.uk
www.jonstewartphotography.co.uk

Jon Welsh 33 Fairfield Road, Bournheath, Bromsgrove,
Worcestershire, B61 9JW, United Kingdom
(07814) 646077
jon@jonwelsh.com
www.jonwelsh.com

Jon Wyand 7 The Chase, Eastcote, Pinner, Middlesex,
HA5 1SJ, United Kingdom
(020) 8866 2652/(07802) 483903 / (020) 8866 2652
jon_wyand@blueyonder.co.uk

Jonas Bendiksen@Magnum Photos 63 Gee Street,
London, EC1V 3RS, United Kingdom
(020) 7490 1771/ / (020) 7608 0020
magnum@magnumphotos.co.uk
www.magnumphotos.com

Jonathan Broadbent 25 Delta Point, Delta Street,
London, E2 7BF, United Kingdom
(07952) 577780
jono.broadbent@orange.net
www.fletchersmanagement.com

Jonathan Butcher 336b Lewisham High Street, London,
SE13 6LE, United Kingdom
(07775) 565504
www.jonathanbutcher.com

Jonathan De Jongh The Half House, South Harting,
Petersfield, Hampshire, GU31 5QD, United Kingdom
(01730) 825889
jonthecamera@yahoo.com
www.jonathandejongh.co.uk

Jonathan De Villiers@The Katy Barker Agency Ltd
11 Mason's Arms Mews, Maddox Street, London, W1S
1NX, United Kingdom
(020) 7493 3933/ / (020) 7493 3311
catherine@katybarker.com
www.katybarker.com

Jonathan Faint Photography Twinkle Cottage, 22 North
Road, West Wickham, Kent, BR4 0JS, United Kingdom
(07782) 146008
jonnyfaint@yahoo.co.uk
www.jonathanfaint.co.uk

Jonathan Green Unit 12, Parsons Green Depot, 33-39
Parsons Green Lane, London, SW6 4HH, United Kingdom
/(07831) 220166
jon@jgreenphotography.co.uk
www.jgreenphotography.com

Jonathan Gregson@Pearson Lyle Management 3rd
Floor, 40 Bowling Green Lane, London, EC1R 0NE,
United Kingdom
(020) 7415 7061/ / (020) 7415 7059
contact@pearsonlyle.co.uk
www.pearsonlyle.com

Jonathan Hession@Blowup 146 Amyand Park Road,
St. Margaret's, Twickenham, TW1 3HY, United Kingdom
(020) 8744 0210/ / (020) 8892 2521
orders@blowup.net
www.blowup.net

Jonathan Keenan 5 Oak Street, Northern Quarter,
Manchester, M4 5JD, United Kingdom
0161-834 8585/(07968) 488551
studio@jkphotography.com
www.jkphotography.com

Jonathan Kitchen Flat 5, 220 Kingsland Road, London,
E2 8AX, United Kingdom
020 7033 1936/07789 992265
info@jonathankitchen.com
www.jonathankitchen.com

Jonathan Knowles 48A Chancellors Road, London, W6
9RS, United Kingdom
(020) 8741 7577/ / (020) 8748 9927
jk@jknowles.co.uk
www.jknowles.co.uk

Jonathan Lovekin@Paula Claridge Errochty House,
Calvine, Pitlochry, Perthshire, PH18 5UD, United Kingdom
(01796) 483308/(07850) 606303 / (01796) 483377

Jonathan Miller@C S B Management 40 Bowling
Green Lane, London, EC1R 0NE, United Kingdom
(020) 7415 7051/ / (020) 7415 7059
susie@csbmanagement.com
www.csbmanagement.com

Jonathan Minster@Vue Units 1 & 2 Elm Court, 1
Royal Oak Yard, London, SE1 3TP, United Kingdom
(020) 7403 5555/ / (020) 7403 2005
production@vue-us.com
www.vue-us.com

Jonathan Oakes 5 Hulme Street, Manchester, M1 5GL,
United Kingdom
0161-236 9045/(07831) 107405 / 0161-228 7502
jonathan@jonathanoakes.com
www.jonathanoakes.com

Jonathan Olley Photographer, United Kingdom
(020) 7812 9145/(07973) 893691
jonathan@jonathanolley.com
www.jonathanolley.com

Jonathan Pearson Photographer 119 Fortess Road,
London, NW5 2HR, United Kingdom
(07956) 402381
jonathan@silverface.fsnet.co.uk
www.davetyler.com

Jonathan Pollock Photographer Unit 216 The Business
Village, 3-9 Broomhill Road, London, SW18 4JQ, United
Kingdom
(020) 8877 9493/ / (020) 8877 9393
jonathan@jonathanpollock.com
www.jonathanpollock.com

Jonathan Root 21 Ferdinand Street, London, NW1 8EU,
United Kingdom
(020) 7485 5522/(07768) 292666
jonathan@jonathanroot.com
www.jonathanroot.com

Jonathan Syer Photographer Primrose Cottage,
Heaverham Road, Kemsing, Sevenoaks, Kent, TN15 6NF,
United Kingdom
(01732) 762168/ / (01732) 762168
info@jonathansyer.co.uk
www.jonathansyer.co.uk

Jonathan Tickner 56A Clerkenwell Road, London,
EC1M 5PX, United Kingdom
(020) 7251 6874/(07774) 422120 / (020) 7608 2138
jtickner@lineone.net

Jonathan Winstone Unit 8, Canes Lane, Weald Hall
Farm and Commercial Centre, Hastingwood, Harlow,
Essex, CM17 9LD, United Kingdom
(07958) 008187
contact@jonathanwinstone.co.uk
www.jonathanwinstone.co.uk

Jonathon Anderson & Edwin Low 18D Redcliffe
Gardens, London, SW10 9EX, United Kingdom
(020) 7351 2601/(07956) 247300 / (020) 7351 2601
andersonandlow1@yahoo.com
www.andersonandlow.com

Jonny Storey@Terri Manduca The Basement, 11 Elvaston Place, London, SW7 5QG, United Kingdom
✆ (020) 7581 5844/📠 (020) 7581 5822
✉ terri@terrimanduca.co.uk
🖥 www.terrimanduca.co.uk

Jose Lasheras@Sarah Kaye Representation Ltd 38 Queen's Gate, London, SW7 5HR, United Kingdom
✆ (020) 7225 5005/📠 (020) 7225 0109
✉ sarah@sarahkaye.com
🖥 www.sarahkaye.com

Jose Marti@Akehurst Creative Management Ltd, London, United Kingdom
✆ (020) 7624 2366
✉ na@nickyakehurst.com
🖥 www.akehurstcreativemanagement.com

Josef Koudelka@Magnum Photos 63 Gee Street, London, EC1V 3RS, United Kingdom
✆ (020) 7490 1771/📠 (020) 7608 0020
✉ magnum@magnumphotos.co.uk
🖥 www.magnumphotos.com

Joseph Ford@L P A (Lisa Pritchard Agency) 3rd Floor, Block A, Morelands, 5-23 Old Street, London, EC1V 9HL, United Kingdom
✆ (020) 7250 1362/📠 (020) 7250 1357
✉ info@lisapritchard.com
🖥 www.lisapritchard.com

Joseph Rodriguez@Bill Charles London Ltd. Unit 3E1, Zetland House, 5-25 Scrutton Street, London, EC2A 4HJ, United Kingdom
✆ 020 7033 9284/020 2033 9285
✉ london@billcharles.com
🖥 www.billcharles.com

Josh Cole@David Lambert 108 Oakley Street, London, SW3 5NR, United Kingdom
✆ (020) 7352 0033/(07747) 032 299 📠 (020) 7352 5553
✉ david@davidlambert.com
🖥 www.davidlambert.com

Josh Van Gelder@T Photographic 1 Heathgate Place, 75-83 Agincourt Road, London, London, NW3 2NU, United Kingdom
✆ (020) 7428 6070/📠 (020) 7428 6079
✉ peter@tphotographic.com
🖥 www.tphotographic.com

Joshua St. John.com 12 Springfield Grove, Sunbury-on-Thames, Middlesex, TW16 6NT, United Kingdom
✆ (07767) 684310
✉ josh1@netlineuk.net
🖥 www.stjohnphotography.com

Jouk Oosterhof@edsonwilliams photography consultancy 52 Brushfield Street, London, E1 6AJ, United Kingdom
✆ (020) 7375 2077/(07867) 517777 📠 (020) 7375 3077
✉ info@edsonwilliams.com
🖥 www.edsonwilliams.com

Joyce Morris, London, SW3 5TQ, United Kingdom
✆ (020) 7823 3238/(07850) 064222 📠 (020) 7376 7787
✉ joyce@joycemorris.co.uk
🖥 www.joycemorris.co.uk

Judith Katz 105 Philbeach Gardens, London, SW5 9ET, United Kingdom
✆ (020) 7385 4613/📠 (020) 7385 4613
✉ judith.katz@tiscali.co.uk

Julia Fullerton-Batten@Wendy Jackson Tag Creative, 29 Clerkenwell Road, London, EC1M 5TA, United Kingdom
✆ (020) 3217 2241/(07711) 084801 📠 (020) 7439 1971
✉ wjackson@tagworldwide.com
🖥 www.wendyjackson.co.uk

Julian Benjamin 7, Newman House, Garden Row, London, SE1 6HE, United Kingdom
✆ (07970) 285 899
✉ studio@julianbenjamin.co.uk
🖥 www.julianbenjamin.co.uk

Julian Calder 7 Nepean Street, London, SW15 5DW, United Kingdom
✆ (020) 8780 5352/📠 (020) 8780 2156
✉ juliancalder@btinternet.com
🖥 www.juliancalder.com

Julian Calverley Orchard House, 33 Oughtonhead Way, Hitchin, Hertfordshire, SG5 2LA
✆ 01462 441 251/07971 272815
✉ julian@juliancalverley.com
🖥 www.calverley.co.uk
See ad in showcase

Julian Cotton Photographers Agent 55 Upper Montague Street, London, W1H 1SF
✆ 020 7723 3100/020 7724 7555 ✉ info@juliancotton.co.uk
🖥 www.juliancotton.co.uk
See ad in showcase

Julian Dufort@Bill Charles London Ltd. Unit 3E1, Zetland House, 5-25 Scrutton Street, London, EC2A 4HJ, United Kingdom
✆ 020 7033 9284/020 2033 9285
✉ london@billcharles.com
🖥 www.billcharles.com

Julian Erwin Studio 9, 9-15 Elthorne Road, London, N19 4AJ, United Kingdom
✆ (07802) 266001/📠 (020) 7689 6662
✉ julian@photogra.demon.co.uk

Julian Hawkins 2 Patshull Road, London, NW5 2LB, United Kingdom
✆ (07973) 862006
✉ julianhawkins@enterprise.net
🖥 www.julian-hawkins.com

Julian Nieman 75 Dukes Avenue, London, N10 2PY, United Kingdom
✆ (020) 8883 1576
✉ j-nieman@dircon.co.uk
🖥 www.juliannieman-photographer.com

Julie Cook Photography Flat 21, Yates House, Roberta Street, London, E2 6NU, United Kingdom
✆ (07966) 284085
✉ julie.cook@virgin.net
🖥 www.juliecookphotography.com

Junction Eleven Ltd Unit 4 Jugglers Close, Off Wildmere Road, Banbury, Oxfordshire, OX16 3JU, United Kingdom
✆ 0121-627 5012/📠 0121-627 5038
✉ dan.burman@junctioneleven.com
🖥 www.junctioneleven.com

June Buck 54 Elthorne Park Road, London, W7 2JD, United Kingdom
✆ (020) 8579 6770/(07831) 377615
✉ junebuck@cutlerbuck.demon.co.uk

Jurgen Ziewe@Début Art & The Coningsby Gallery 30 Tottenham Street, London, W1T 4RJ, United Kingdom
✆ (020) 7636 1064/📠 (020) 7580 7017
✉ info@debutart.com
🖥 www.debutart.com

Justin de Deney 39 Loraine Mansions, Widdenham Road, London, N7 9SE, United Kingdom
✆ (07976) 432 645/📠 (020) 7607 6584
✉ justindedeney@blueyonder.co.uk
🖥 www.justindedeney.com

Justin Pumfrey Unit B, Riverside Business Centre, London, SW18 4LZ, United Kingdom
✆ (020) 8877 0202/(07850) 315427 📠 (020) 8877 0606
✉ justin@justinpumfrey.co.uk
🖥 www.justinpumfrey.co.uk

Justin Scobie Photography Tarradale Muir Croft, Muir of Tarradale, Muir of Ord, Ross-Shire, IV6 7QZ, United Kingdom
✆ (01463) 871790/📠 (01463) 871790
✉ mail@justinscobie.com
🖥 www.justinscobie.co.uk

Justin Windle Photography Unit 18, Wheelforge Way, Trafford Park, Manchester, M17 1EH, United Kingdom
✆ 0161-872 9222/(07831) 434068 📠 0161-872 9333
✉ justin@justinwindle.co.uk
🖥 www.justinwindle.co.uk

JWD Graphic 139 Winkworth Road, Banstead, Surrey, SM7 2JW, United Kingdom
✆ (01737) 353013/07973 520292
✉ jwmail@btinternet.com

JWPics Ltd 5 Treelands Walk, Salford, M5 3FU, United Kingdom
✆ (07810) 071924/📠 0161-872 4316
✉ jonwhitetd@blueyonder.co.uk
🖥 www.jwpics.co.uk

K L Photographers 128 Boroughbridge Road, York, Y026 6AL, United Kingdom
✆ (01904) 792338/📠 (01904) 781188
✉ info@klphoto.co.uk
🖥 www.klphoto.co.uk

Kaa Photographics 64 Ruskin Road, Carshalton, Surrey, SM5 3DH, United Kingdom
✆ (020) 8647 2007/(07889) 723878
✉ geoffrey@kaaphoto.demon.co.uk
🖥 www.kaaphotos.co.uk

Kai Feng@Milc Studio 7, Zeus House, 16-30 Provost Street, London, N1 7NG, United Kingdom
✆ (020) 7278 8838/ (0870) 0941564
✉ gemma@milc.co.uk
🖥 www.milc.co.uk

Kai Schwabe Fotografie Ander Weide 50, Bremen, D-28195, Germany
✆ 00 49 42 144 1520/📠 00 49 42 149 88359
✉ info@kaischwabe.de
🖥 www.kaischwabe.de

Kai Wiechmann@East Photographic Ltd 8 Iron Bridge House, 3 Bridge Approach, London, NW1 8BD, United Kingdom
✆ (020) 7722 3444/📠 (020) 7722 3544
✉ roger@eastphotographic.com
🖥 www.eastphotographic.com

Kai-Uwe Gundlach Arndtstrasse 24a, Hamburg, 22085, Germany
✆ 00 49 40 610 189/📠 00 49 40 610 213
✉ info@studiogundlach.de
🖥 www.studiogundlach.de

Karan Kapoor@Mutton Bones Ground Floor, 51 Balcombe Street, London, NW1 6HD, United Kingdom
✆ (020) 7723 8244/📠 (020) 7723 2770
✉ hello@muttonbones.co.uk
🖥 www.muttonbones.co.uk

Karen Collins@The Katy Barker Agency Ltd 11 Mason's Arms Mews, Maddox Street, London, W1S 1NX, United Kingdom
✆ (020) 7493 3933/📠 (020) 7493 3311
✉ catherine@katybarker.com
🖥 www.katybarker.com

Karen Howes 1 Ruston Mews, London, W11 1RB, United Kingdom
✆ (020) 7221 9922/📠 (020) 7221 9933
✉ karen@interior-archive.netkonect.co.uk
🖥 www.interiorarchive.com

Karin Berndl Unit 103, Phoenix Business Centre, London, E3 4AX, United Kingdom
✆ (07974) 070485
✉ karin@karinberndl.com
🖥 www.karinberndl.com

Karl Grant@Victoria Lees Management (VLM) 2 Fairview Gardens, Woodford Green, Essex, IG8 7DJ, United Kingdom
✆ (07710) 287220/📠 (020) 8504 8125
✉ victoria@victorialeesmanagement.co.uk
🖥 www.victorialeesmanagement.co.uk

Karoki Lewis@Axiom Photographic Agency The Pall Mall Deposit, 124-128 Barlby Road, London, W10 6BL, United Kingdom
✆ (020) 8964 9970/📠 (020) 8964 8440
✉ info@axiomphotographic.com
🖥 www.axiomphotographic.com

Kasal Make-Up & Hair 5d Third Avenue, Lancing, West Sussex, BN15 9PU, United Kingdom
✆ (07814) 687562
✉ lalaine@kasal.co.uk
🖥 www.kasal.co.uk

Kasal Make-Up & Hair Design & Photography Third Avenue, Lancing, West Sussex, BN15 9PU, United Kingdom
✆ (07973) 622629
✉ info@kasal.co.uk
🖥 www.kasal.co.uk

Kate Martin@WildeHague Ltd Suite 4, The Swan centre, Fishers Lane, London, W4 1RX, United Kingdom
✆ (020) 8747 9988/📠 (020) 8747 8228
✉ info@wildehague.com
🖥 www.wildehague.com

Kate Peters 34a Stavordale Road, London, N5 1NE, United Kingdom
✆ (020) 7226 9340/(07870) 738412
✉ post@katepeters.net
🖥 www.katepeters.net

Katherine Fawssett, London, United Kingdom
✆ (07956) 552363
✉ k@katherinefawssett.com
🖥 www.katherinefawssett.com

Kathy Morrison 7 Easton Terrace, Brighton, BN2 1DJ, United Kingdom
(07973) 443704/ (01273) 679218
kathy.morrison1@ntlworld.com

Katrien Franken Photography Kuipersstraat 105-3, Amsterdam, 1074, Netherlands
20 67 55 111
info@katrienfranken.com
www.katrienfranken.com

Kay Wahlig@Wood Associates 62 Bell Street, London, NW1 6SP, United Kingdom
(020) 7723 6600
info@wood-associates.co.uk
www.wood-associates.co.uk

Kayti Peschke@SK Creative Management 23 New Mount Street, Manchester, M4 4DE, United Kingdom
0161-953 4032/ (0870) 486 1940
info@skcreativemanagement.com
www.skcreativemanagement.com

Kaz Photographic Studio Rawreth Industrial Estate, Rayleigh, Essex, SS6 9RL, United Kingdom
(01268) 782582
clive@kaz-studio.co.uk
www.kaz-studio.co.uk

Keene Repro Ltd 33-41 Dallington Street, London, EC1V 0BB, United Kingdom
(020) 7251 2722/ (020) 7490 8736
contact@keenes.co.uk
www.keenes.co.uk

Keith Bernstein@Carolyn Trayler Photographers Agent Unit 566, 56 Gloucester Road, London, SW7 4UB, United Kingdom
(020) 7370 0712/ (020) 7370 0765
carolyn@trayler.co.uk
www.trayler.co.uk

Keith Gibson Digital Photography The Studio, Water Lane, Radcliffe on Trent, Nottingham, NG12 2DV, United Kingdom
0115-933 3085/(07850) 514825
keith-gibson@btconnect.com
www.keith-gibson.com

Keith Henderson@Ellison Lee 17 Quadrant Business Centre, 135 Salusbury Road, London, NW6 6RJ, United Kingdom
(020) 7624 2345/ (020) 7624 1100
info@ellisonlee.com
www.ellisonlee.com

Keith Hunter Photography 13 Oxford Road, Renfrew, PA4 0SJ, United Kingdom
0141-886 4503/(07831) 117980 0141-886 4509
keith@khp.demon.co.uk
www.arcblue.com/keith-hunter

Keith Meatheringham 20 Seafield Avenue, Osgodby, Scarborough, North Yorkshire, YO11 3QG, United Kingdom
(01723) 585141/(07802) 530583 (0871) 4338973
pix@dobsonagency.co.uk
www.dobsonagency.co.uk

Keith Miller Ltd 11 Towers Court, Duckworth Street, Blackburn, BB2 2JQ, United Kingdom
(01254) 696909/ (01254) 699813
info@millersphotography.co.uk
www.millersphotography.co.uk

Keith Ramsden 81 Tachbrook Street, London, SW1V 2QP, United Kingdom
(020) 7233 6339/(07976) 659351 (020) 7828 1952
krphotos@talktalk.net

Keith Shillitoe 6 Queens Keep, Park Road, Twickenham, TW1 2QA, United Kingdom
(07956) 334344/07956 334344
keithshillitoe@bolx.demon.co.uk
www.keithshillitoe.com

Keith Turnbull 21 Willow Road, Larkfield, Aylesford, Kent, ME20 6QZ, United Kingdom
(01732) 848187
kmturnbull@talk21.com
www.keithturnbull.co.uk

Keith Van Loen 35 Lordship Road, London, N16 0QH, United Kingdom
(07876) 203029
keith@keithvanloen.co.uk
www.keithvanloan.co.uk

Keith Yuill White Lodge, Maypole Road, Maldon, Essex, CM9 4SX, United Kingdom
(01621) 853143/(07802) 663549 (01621) 842221

Kelvin Murray Saint Lukes Hall, 120 Fortune Green Road, London, NW6 1DN, United Kingdom
(020) 7431 5414/ (020) 7435 5315
kelvin@kelvinmurray.com
www.kelvinmurray.com

Ken Champken 114 Pool Meadow, Hadley, Telford, Shropshire, TF1 5RP, United Kingdom
(07962) 041212
ken@champken.co.uk
www.champken.co.uk

Ken Christie 29 Southfields, East Molesey, Surrey, KT8 0BP, United Kingdom
(020) 8398 3997/(07831) 774232
kenchristie@ecosse.net
www.kenchristie.co.uk

Ken Griffiths@van Hauen Moore 14 Powis Mews, Notting Hill, London, W11 1JN, United Kingdom
(020) 7792 0022/ (020) 7792 8636
email@vanhauenmoore.com
www.vanhauenmoore.com

Ken Niven Photography 123 Ebury Street, London, SW1W 9QU, United Kingdom
(020) 7730 6458
ken@kennivenphotography.com
www.winkmanagement.co.uk

kennedypictures.com 29 Russell Road, London, W14 8HU, United Kingdom
(07810) 544719
dan@kennedypictures.com
www.kennedypictures.com

Kenneth Berry Studios Unit 7, Temple Street, Hull, HU5 1AD, United Kingdom
(01482) 470970/ (01482) 470970
kberrystudios@hotmail.com

Kent Larsson@Jamie Stephen Represents 9 Upper Wimpole Street, London, W1G 6LJ, United Kingdom
(0845) 3733510/(07957) 784810 (020) 7681 1027
jamie@jamiestephen.com
www.jamiestephen.com

Kerbe, 71 Denmark Villas, Hove, East Sussex, BN3 3TH, United Kingdom
(07775) 733588
info@kerbe.co.uk
www.kerbe.co.uk

Kerry Beckingsale The Olde Jell Cottage, 15 London Road, Bicester, Oxfordshire, OX26 6BU, United Kingdom
(01989) 220087
kerry.beckingsale@btinternet.com
www.savoirflare.co.uk

Keshco 28C Northiam Street, Hackney, London, E9 7HQ, United Kingdom
(020) 8986 7897
keshco@yahoo.co.uk
www.uk.geocities.com/keshco

Kevin Calvert Enterprise Way, Grovebury Road, Leighton Buzzard, Bedfordshire, LU7 4SZ, United Kingdom
(01525) 853700/(07831) 562152 (01525) 852111
kevin@calvertstudios.com
www.calvertstudios.com

Kevin Foord@T Photographic 1 Heathgate Place, 75-83 Agincourt Road, London, London, NW3 2NU, United Kingdom
(020) 7428 6070/ (020) 7428 6079
peter@tphotographic.com
www.tphotographic.com

Kevin Kingston@Renate Decker-Berry- Europe Unlimited 59 Lambeth Walk, London, SE11 6DX, United Kingdom
(020) 7735 6623/(07768) 251626 (0707) 5009648
renate@europeunlimited.com
www.europeunlimited.com

Kevin Leighton, United Kingdom
(07930) 559176
kevin@kevinleighton.com
www.kevinleighton.com

Kevin Mackintosh@Pearce Stoner Associates 12B Links Yard, Spelman Street, London, E1 5LX, United Kingdom
(020) 7247 7100/ (020) 7247 7144
info@pearcestoner.com
www.pearcestoner.com

Kevin Mallett@Jo Talbot & Sue Young 6M Hyde Park Mansions, Cabbell Street, London, NW1 5BJ, United Kingdom
(020) 7262 0189/(07850) 353468 (020) 7262 2160
joandsue@btconnect.com
www.joandsue.com

Kevin Martin@Axiom Photographic Agency The Pall Mall Deposit, 124-128 Barlby Road, London, W10 6BL, United Kingdom
(020) 8964 9970/ (020) 8964 8440
info@axiomphotographic.com
www.axiomphotographic.com

Kevin Nicholson Studio 13, 43 Carol Street, London, NW1 0HT, United Kingdom
(020) 7692 6606/ (020) 7485 6276
kev@kevinnicholson.com
www.kevinnicholson.com

Kevin Nixon Flat 2, Derwent Court, London, N8 9AT, United Kingdom
(020) 8340 4598/(07973) 760590
kevin.nixon1@virgin.net

Kevin Summers@Paula Claridge Errochty House, Calvine, Pitlochry, Perthshire, PH18 5UD, United Kingdom
(01796) 483308/(07850) 606303 (01796) 483377

Kim Knott@C S B Management 40 Bowling Green Lane, London, EC1R 0NE, United Kingdom
(020) 7415 7051/ (020) 7415 7059
susie@csbmanagement.com
www.csbmanagement.com

Kim McGillivray@Début Art & The Coningsby Gallery 30 Tottenham Street, London, W1T 4RJ, United Kingdom
(020) 7636 1064/ (020) 7580 7017
info@debutart.com
www.debutart.com

Kim Millar@Cormack Creative Management Ltd Suite 208, 95 Morrison Street, Glasgow, G5 8BE, United Kingdom
0141-429 6810/(07778) 323169 0141-429 2603
susie@cormackcreativemanagement.co.uk
www.cormackcreativemanagement.co.uk

Kingsley Barker@Inspired Reflection 28 Dayton Grove, Peckham, London, SE15 2NX, United Kingdom
(0870) 9193587/(07040) 402770 (0870) 9193588
deborah@inspiredreflection.com
www.inspiredreflection.com

Kip Meyer@Milc Studio 7, Zeus House, 16-30 Provost Street, London, N1 7NG, United Kingdom
(020) 7278 8838/ (0870) 0941564
gemma@milc.co.uk
www.milc.co.uk

Kiran Master 11 Blackbird Yard, Ravenscroft Street, London, E2 7RP, United Kingdom
(020) 7729 9236/ (020) 7613 3445

Kirk Verdi 225 Green Street, London, E7 8LL, United Kingdom
(020) 8472 8842/ (020) 8472 8882
kirkverdi@aol.com
www.verdistudios.com

Kit Houghton Houghton's Horses, Radlet Cottage, Spaxton, Bridgwater, Somerset, TA5 1DE, United Kingdom
(01278) 671362
kit@enterprise.net
www.houghtonshorses.com

Klaus Kalde Unit 1, 256 Hackney Road, London, E2 7SJ, United Kingdom
(020) 7729 5278/ (020) 7729 6802
k.kalde@btconnect.com
www.klauskalde.com

Knight & Hunt Photography The School House, Emery Street, Walsall, WS1 3AJ, United Kingdom
(01922) 635407/(07802) 607403 (01922) 622262

Knight + Daines Mill House Farm, Mill Street, Harlow, Essex, CM17 9JF, United Kingdom
(01279) 414744/ (01279) 635063
info@knight-daines.co.uk
www.knight-daines.co.uk

Kobi Israel Flat 27, Centre Point House, 15A St Giles High Street, London, WC2H 8LW, United Kingdom
(07815) 100598
kobi@kobiisrael.com
www.kobiisrael.com

Kos Photography 7 Spice Court, London, SW11 3UU, United Kingdom
(020) 7801 0066/ (020) 7801 0055
kos@kosphotos.com
www.kospictures.com

Kostas Grivas 39 Burntwood Lane, Wandsworth, London, SW17 0JY, United Kingdom
(020) 8947 4533/078 60 101027 (020) 8947 4533

Kristian Schuller@T Photographic 1 Heathgate Place, 75-83 Agincourt Road, London, London, NW3 2NU, United Kingdom
(020) 7428 6070/ (020) 7428 6079
peter@tphotographic.com
www.tphotographic.com

Kristin Peters@Tattersall Love 40 Langham Street, London, W1W 7AS, United Kingdom
(020) 7637 5737/ (020) 7637 5747
mail@tattersall-love.com
www.tattersall-love.com

Kristine Skovli Photography Flat A, 22 Morval Road, London, SW2 1DQ, United Kingdom
(07947) 332514
kristine@kskovli.com
www.kskovli.com

Kulbir Thandi@David Lambert 108 Oakley Street, London, SW3 5NR, United Kingdom
(020) 7352 0033/(07747) 032 299 / (020) 7352 5553
david@davidlambert.com
www.davidlambert.com
See ad in showcase

Kyoko Hamada@Bill Charles London Ltd. Unit 3E1, Zetland House, 5-25 Scrutton Street, London, EC2A 4HJ, United Kingdom
020 7033 9284/020 2033 9285
london@billcharles.com
www.billcharles.com

L P A (Lisa Pritchard Agency) 3rd Floor, Block A, Morelands, 5-23 Old Street, London, EC1V 9HL, United Kingdom
(020) 7250 1362/ (020) 7250 1357
info@lisapritchard.com
www.lisapritchard.com

Lacey@Pearce Stoner Associates 12B Links Yard, Spelman Street, London, E1 5LX, United Kingdom
(020) 7247 7100/ (020) 7247 7144
info@pearcestoner.com
www.pearcestoner.com

Laetitia Negre 134 Kingsland Road, London, E2 8DY, United Kingdom
(07960) 932317
info@laetitianegre.com
www.laetitianegre.com

Lane End Studios High Street, Lane End, High Wycombe, Buckinghamshire, HP14 3JG, United Kingdom
(01494) 882291/ (01494) 881826
reflectons@clara.net
www.reflectionsphoto-graphics.co.uk

Lansdowne Photography 4 Lansdowne Terrace, Gosforth, Newcastle upon Tyne, NE3 1HN, United Kingdom
0191-284 4096/(07778) 506565 / 0191-213 0858
info@lansdowne-photography.co.uk
www.lansdowne-photography.co.uk

Lapidge Photography 1 Richmond Close, Aylestone, Leicester, LE2 8AY, United Kingdom
(07949) 953915
enquiries@sl-photography.co.uk
www.sl-photography.co.uk

Larry Dunstan@Wyatt-Clarke & Jones 26 Mortimer Street, London, W1W 7RB, United Kingdom
(020) 7580 7570/(07958) 712658 / (020) 7903 5330
office@wyattclarkejones.com
www.wyattclarkejones.com

Larry Fink@Bill Charles London Ltd. Unit 3E1, Zetland House, 5-25 Scrutton Street, London, EC2A 4HJ, United Kingdom
020 7033 9284/020 2033 9285
london@billcharles.com
www.billcharles.com

Larry Sultan@Bill Charles London Ltd. Unit 3E1, Zetland House, 5-25 Scrutton Street, London, EC2A 4HJ, United Kingdom
020 7033 9284/020 2033 9285
london@billcharles.com
www.billcharles.com

Larry Towell@Magnum Photos 63 Gee Street, London, EC1V 3RS, United Kingdom
(020) 7490 1771/ (020) 7608 0020
magnum@magnumphotos.co.uk
www.magnumphotos.com

Larry Wooden 93 Lethe Grove, Colchester, CO2 8RH, United Kingdom
(01206) 572287
3dcreations@ukcompanies.org
www.3dcreations.ukcompanies.org

Lars H@Areia London Studio1, 42 Theobalds Road, London, WC1X 8NW, United Kingdom
(020) 7404 8600/ (020) 7404 8601
info@areia.com
www.areia.com

Lars Stenman@Freddie Brazil 211 Abercairn Road, London, SW16 5AJ, United Kingdom
(020) 8764 2801/(07711) 753072 / (020) 8764 2801
frederick.brazil@btconnect.com
www.freddiebrazil.com

Laughtons Photographic Supplies Ltd The Coach House, Mill Road, Wilmslow, Cheshire, SK9 1BW, United Kingdom
(01625) 537744/ (01625) 537782
laughtonsphoto@aol.com

Laura Ashman 48 Deanhill Court, Upper Richmond Road West, London, SW14 7DL, United Kingdom
(07932) 075605
mail@lauraashman.com
www.lauraashman.com

Laura Hart@ERA Management Ltd 120 The Beaux Arts Building, 10-18 Manor Gardens, London, N7 6JT, United Kingdom
(020) 7281 5996/ (020) 7281 6202
kate@eramanagement.com
www.eramanagement.com

Laura Knox Photography Unit 21 Jack's Place, 6 Corbet Place, London, E1 6NN,
020 7426 2111
laura@lauraknox.com
www.lauraknox.com

Laurel Studio 12 Aberdeen Terrace, Northampton, NN5 7AD, United Kingdom
(01604) 456197
info@laurelstudio.com
www.laurelstudio.com

Lauren Winsor 51 Hayes Lane, Kenley, Surrey, CR8 5LF, United Kingdom
(07743) 864765
lauren@proteinos.com

Laurence Cendrowicz 7 Bramshill Mansions, 85 Dartmouth Park Hill, London, NW5 1JG, United Kingdom
(020) 7281 1388/(07973) 729374 / (020) 7281 1388
l.cendrowicz@dial.pipex.com
www.laurencecendrowicz.com

Laurence Coates 9 Fruiterers Close, Sittingbourne, Kent, ME9 0PB, United Kingdom
01795 475353/079 76 252515

Laurence Davis@Julian Cotton Photographers Agent 55 Upper Montagu Street, London, W1H 1SF, United Kingdom
(020) 7723 3100/ (020) 7724 7555
info@juliancotton.co.uk
www.juliancotton.co.uk

Laurence Dutton Photography Ltd 57 Farringdon Road, London, EC1M 3JB, United Kingdom
(020) 7813 2099/ (020) 7242 6447
lol@laurence-dutton.co.uk
www.laurence-dutton.co.uk

Laurence Haskell 48 Lancaster Mews, London, W2 3QQ, United Kingdom
(020) 7723 3144/ (020) 7706 1844
laurence@laurencehaskell.com
www.laurencehaskell.com

Laurence Winram Unit 4, 130 Leith Walk, Edinburgh, EH6 5DT, United Kingdom
0131-555 1417/(07973) 205401
studio@lwinram.com
www.lwinram.com

Laurie Evans 11 James Cameron House, 12 Castlehaven Road, London, NW1 8QW, United Kingdom
(020) 7284 2140/(07713) 410922
laurieevans@btconnect.com
www.laurieevans.co.uk

Laurie Lewis 176 Camden Road, London, NW1 9HG, United Kingdom
(020) 7267 0315

Lawrence Jessop Photographer 40 West Street, Stratford-upon-Avon, Warwickshire, CV37 6DN, United Kingdom
(07767) 222204/ (01789) 415469
lj@ljessop.com
www.ljessop.com

Le Click Studio Ltd 14 North Star Drive, Leighton Buzzard, Bedfordshire, LU7 3DP, United Kingdom
(07866) 556044/ (01525) 850089
enquiry@leclickstudio.com
www.leclickstudio.com

Leah Gordon@Axiom Photographic Agency The Pall Mall Deposit, 124-128 Barlby Road, London, W10 6BL, United Kingdom
(020) 8964 9970/ (020) 8964 8440
info@axiomphotographic.com
www.axiomphotographic.com

Lee Atherton, Oxfordshire, United Kingdom
(07711) 823066
leeatherton@fsmail.net
www.contact-me.net/leeatherton

Lee Broomfield@MAP 72 Rochester Place, London, NW1 9JX, United Kingdom
(020) 7424 9144/ (020) 7284 3274
info@mapltd.com
www.mapltd.com

Lee Jenkins@C L M Top Floor, 19 All Saints Road, London, W11 1HE, United Kingdom
(020) 7750 2999/ (020) 7792 8507
clm@clmuk.com
www.clmuk.com

Lee McPherson Photography Flat 3, 126, Minnis Road, Birchington, Kent, CT7 9QB, United Kingdom
(01843) 845567
lee@leemcpherson.com

Lee Powers@Burnham Niker Unit 8, Canonbury Business Centre, 190A New North Road, London, N1 7BJ, United Kingdom
(020) 7704 6565/ (020) 7704 8383
enquiries@burnham-niker.com
www.burnham-niker.com

Lee Robinson Photography Studio Cottage, 1 Knatchbull Row, Plain Road, Smeeth, Ashford, Kent, TN25 6QX, United Kingdom
(01303) 813563/ (01303) 813563
studio@leejorobinson.com
www.leejorobinson.com

Lee Southgate 72 Rivington Street, London, EC2A 3AY, United Kingdom
(020) 7613 3203/(07973) 296237 / (020) 7684 0236
lee@leesouthgate.demon.co.uk

Lena Modigh, London, United Kingdom
(07779) 726622
post@lenamodigh.co.uk
www.lenamodigh.co.uk

Leo Mason@Julian Cotton Photographers Agent 55 Upper Montagu Street, London, W1H 1SF, United Kingdom
(020) 7723 3100/ (020) 7724 7555
info@juliancotton.co.uk
www.juliancotton.co.uk

Leon Chew@Bill Charles London Ltd. Unit 3E1, Zetland House, 5-25 Scrutton Street, London, EC2A 4HJ, United Kingdom
020 7033 9284/020 2033 9285
london@billcharles.com
www.billcharles.com

Leon Pearce Millyard Studios, Millyard, Guildford Street, Luton, LU1 2NR, United Kingdom
(01582) 404888/ (01582) 455089
leon@leonpearce.com
www.leonpearce.com

Leon Steele Top Floor, 71 Fanshawe Street, London, N1 6LA, United Kingdom
(020) 7739 3944
www.leonsteele.com

Leonard Freed@Magnum Photos 63 Gee Street, London, EC1V 3RS, United Kingdom
(020) 7490 1771/ (020) 7608 0020
magnum@magnumphotos.co.uk
www.magnumphotos.com

Leonardo Ferrante 254B Acton Lane, London, W4 5DJ, United Kingdom
(020) 8994 1203/(07885) 941741 / (020) 8994 1203
leonardo@photos44.freeserve.co.uk

Les Wies 75 Camden Mews, London, NW1 9BY, United Kingdom
(020) 7284 1187/ (020) 7284 1187

Lesley Dilcock@Pearson Lyle Management 3rd Floor, 40 Bowling Green Lane, London, EC1R 0NE, United Kingdom
(020) 7415 7061/ (020) 7415 7059
contact@pearsonlyle.co.uk
www.pearsonlyle.co.uk

Leslie Turtle PO Box 6275, Wareham, Dorset, BH20 9AG, United Kingdom
(020) 7731 6076/(07976) 855880
picturebusiness@easynet.co.uk
www.picturebusiness.co.uk

Lester Pugh Photography 3 Ashdown Close, Angmering, Littlehampton, West Sussex, BN16 4DZ, United Kingdom
(01903) 776283
info@lpphoto.co.uk
www.lpphoto.co.uk

Leticia Valverdes, London, United Kingdom
(07905) 469889
leticia@leticiavalverdes.com
www.leticiavalverdes.com

Lewis Mulatero@Alan Wickes 135 Downton Avenue, London, SW2 3TX, United Kingdom
(020) 8674 2242/(07774) 259352
a.wickes@btinternet.com
www.alanwickes.com

Liam Bailey Photography 3a Iliffe Yard, London, SE17 3QA, United Kingdom
(020) 7703 3535/(07973) 412477
mail@liambailey.com
www.liambailey.com

Liam Kennedy@Wyatt-Clarke & Jones 26 Mortimer Street, London, W1W 7RB, United Kingdom
(020) 7580 7570/(07958) 712658 / (020) 7903 5330
office@wyattclarkejones.com
www.wyattclarkejones.com

Lightwork Scenics School House, Winton, Kirkby Stephen, Cumbria, CA17 4HP, United Kingdom
(01768) 371829/ (01768) 372561
barry.stacey@lineone.net

Likwiduk Unit 54, Springfield Commercial Centre, Farsley, Leeds, LS28 5LY, United Kingdom
0113-256 8000
info@likwiduk.co.uk
www.likwid.co.uk

Lincolnshire Cam 1 Mill Cottages, Mill Lane, Heighington, Lincoln, LN4 1RQ, United Kingdom
(01522) 792629
rosey@lincolnshirecam.co.uk
www.lincolnshirecam.co.uk

Linda Burgess 46 Ursula Street, Battersea, London, SW11 3DW, United Kingdom
(020) 7585 1018/(07950) 915556 / (020) 7585 1018
www.lindaburgessphotography.com

Link Picture Library 41a The Downs, London, SW20 8HG, United Kingdom
(020) 8944 6933/(07947) 884517
library@linkpicturelibrary.com
www.linkpicturelibrary.com

Lionel Guyou@Terrie Tanaka Management 101 Talbot Road, London, W11 2AT, United Kingdom
(020) 7792 3500/ (020) 7792 2600
danni@terrietanaka.com
www.terrietanaka.com

Lisa Hooley@Jo Talbot & Sue Young 6M Hyde Park Mansions, Cabbell Street, London, NW1 5BJ, United Kingdom
(020) 7262 0189/(07850) 353468 / (020) 7262 2160
joandsue@btconnect.com
www.joandsue.com

Lise Sarfati@Magnum Photos 63 Gee Street, London, EC1V 3RS, United Kingdom
(020) 7490 1771/ (020) 7608 0020
magnum@magnumphotos.co.uk
www.magnumphotos.co.uk

Liz Artindale 3rd Floor, 71 Leonard Street, London, EC2A 4QU, United Kingdom
(020) 7739 8940/(07850) 566177 (020) 7739 4813
liz@lizartindale.co.uk
www.lizartindale.co.uk
See ad

Liz Collins 755 Washington Street, New York, 10014, United States of America
00 1 212 206 0737/ 00 1 212 463 7267
info@artandcommerce.com

Liz Garnett 6 Mountbatten Way, Brabourne Lees, Ashford, Kent, TN25 6PZ, United Kingdom
(01303) 812678/(07802) 365438
liz@lizgarnett.com
www.lizgarnett.com

Liz Greg@Creative Talent (UK) Limited 78 York Street, London, W1H 1DP, United Kingdom
(020) 7439 1877/ (020) 7434 1144
info@creativetalentlimited.com
www.creativetalentlimited.com

Lizzie Orme Unit 10 Waterside, 44-48 Wharf Road, London, N1 7UX, United Kingdom
(020) 7608 0018/(07831) 161665 / (020) 7608 0017
l.orme@btinternet.com
www.lizzieorme.co.uk

Lol Keegan@Wyatt-Clarke & Jones 26 Mortimer Street, London, W1W 7RB, United Kingdom
(020) 7580 7570/(07958) 712658 / (020) 7903 5330
office@wyattclarkejones.com
www.wyattclarkejones.com

Lonely Cloud 7c Hartington Gardens, Edinburgh, EH10 4LD, United Kingdom
(07730) 617055
d.m.fleetwood@gmail.com
www.lonely-cloud.co.uk

LOOK: Photographers & Production Room 8, 94 Oxford Street, Sydney, 2010, Australia
00 61 29 380 8822/ 00 61 29 380 8988
shoot@lookproduction.com
www.lookproduction.com

Lottie Davies 133 Petherton Road, London, N5 2RS, United Kingdom
(020) 7354 2713/(07976) 431345 / (020) 7354 2713
lottie@lottiedavies.com
www.lottiedavies.com

Louisa Parry@Process 5 Choumert Mews, Choumert Road, London, SE15 4BD, United Kingdom
(020) 7277 8400/(07950) 311425 / (020) 7277 7223
info@processphotography.com
www.processphotography.com

Louise Forrester 88 Hotham Road, Putney, London, SW15 1QP, United Kingdom
(07949) 764022
louforrester@hotmail.com
www.homepages.gold.ac.uk/louise/photos.htm

Louise Murray 32 Marsden Road, London, SE15 4EE, United Kingdom
(020) 3183 1036/(07808) 720016
louise@louisemurray.com
www.louisemurray.com

Louise Samuelsen, United Kingdom

Louise Samuelson Photography 49 Lynette Avenue, London, SW4 9HF, United Kingdom
(07981) 230365
louise@louisesamuelsen.com
www.louisesamuelsen.com

Lourdas Photography 12 Crossdeep Gardens, Twickenham, TW1 4QU, United Kingdom
(020) 8892 6864/(07703) 249548 / (020) 8892 6864
info@lourdas.co.uk
www.lourdas.co.uk

Lu Jeffery Photographer Providence Mill, Gorsey Bank, Wirksworth, Derbyshire, DE4 4AD, United Kingdom
(01629) 825222/(07976) 814417
lujeffery@w3z.co.uk
www.the-aop.org/LuJeffery

Luc Beziat@Jo Talbot & Sue Young 6M Hyde Park Mansions, Cabbell Street, London, NW1 5BJ, United Kingdom
(020) 7262 0189/(07850) 353468 / (020) 7262 2160
joandsue@btconnect.com
www.joandsue.com

Lucia Munoz Photographers 275 Avalon, Rosemere, J7A 3C7, Canada
00 1 514 892 5058/ 00 1 450 621 9744
info@luciamunoz.com
www.luciamunoz.com

Luciana Val & Franco Musso@The Katy Barker Agency Ltd 11 Mason's Arms Mews, Maddox Street, London, W1S 1NX, United Kingdom
(020) 7493 3933/ (020) 7493 3311
catherine@katybarker.com
www.katybarker.com

Lucinda Lambton@Arcaid Picture Library Parc House, 25-37 Cowleaze Road, Kingston upon Thames, Surrey, KT2 6DZ, United Kingdom
(020) 8546 4352/ (020) 8541 5230
arcaid@arcaid.co.uk
www.arcaid.co.uk

Lucinda Symons 17 Ursula Street, London, SW11 3DW, United Kingdom
(020) 7924 7509/(07831) 377960
mail@symonshatton.co.uk
www.lucindasymons.com

Lucy Barden Photography 2 High Moorgate, Kearstwick, Carnforth, Lancashire, LA6 2EG, United Kingdom
(01524) 273224/(07951) 180125
info@lucybarden.co.uk
www.lucybarden.co.uk

Lucy Davies@Axiom Photographic Agency The Pall Mall Deposit, 124-128 Barlby Road, London, W10 6BL, United Kingdom
(020) 8964 9970/ (020) 8964 8440
info@axiomphotographic.com
www.axiomphotographic.com

Lucy Weller@Début Art & The Coningsby Gallery 30 Tottenham Street, London, W1T 4RJ, United Kingdom
(020) 7636 1064/ (020) 7580 7017
info@debutart.com
www.debutart.com

Ludovic Roy Photographer 65 Rue De Javel, Paris, 75015, France
00 33 1 4575 5594/ 00 33 1 4575 5594
lrpp@noos.fr
www.ludovic-roy.com

Ludwig Haskins Flat 2, 52 St. James Road, Sutton, Surrey, SM1 2TS, United Kingdom
(020) 8404 2337/ (020) 8404 2338
ludwighaskins@yahoo.com
www.ludwig-haskins.com

Luis Monteiro Photography 88A Offord Road, London, N1 1PF, United Kingdom
(07859) 032033
info@luismonteirophoto.com
www.luismonteirophoto.com

Lukas David Flat 39, Cherwell House, Church Street Estate, London, NW8 8PT, United Kingdom
(07962) 547019
lukasdavid@lukasdavid.com
www.lukasdavid.com

Luke Hayes, London, United Kingdom
(07904) 106765
luke@lukehayes.com
www.lukehayes.com

Luke Kelly 18 St Leonards Court, St Leonards Road, London, SW14 7NG, United Kingdom
(020) 8878 2823
lukeookelly@tiscali.co.uk

Luke Kirwan@Blunt Management The Courtyard Studio 2, Old Grammarphone Works, London, W10 5BZ, United Kingdom
(020) 8960 2041/(07979) 900068 / (020) 8960 2039
info@bluntlondon.com
www.bluntlondon.com

Luke White@Axiom Photographic Agency The Pall Mall Deposit, 124-128 Barlby Road, London, W10 6BL, United Kingdom
(020) 8964 9970/ (020) 8964 8440
info@axiomphotographic.com
www.axiomphotographic.com

Lux Photo Digital 117 Chapman Street, London, E1 2PH, United Kingdom
(020) 7790 5533
info@luxphotodigital.co.uk
www.luxphotodigital.co.uk

Lynn Hilton Photography 11 Sylvan Hill, London, SE19 2QB, United Kingdom
(07831) 163844
lynn@lynnhilton.com
www.lynnhilton.com

Lynn Jackett@Victoria Lees Management (VLM) 2 Fairview Gardens, Woodford Green, Essex, IG8 7DJ, United Kingdom
(07710) 287220/ (020) 8504 8125
victoria@victorialeesmanagement.co.uk
www.victorialeesmanagement.co.uk

M & M Management Studio B, 11 Edith Grove, London, SW10 0JZ, United Kingdom
(020) 7823 3723/ (020) 7351 3714
admin@mmmanagement.com
www.mmmanagement.com

M & M Studios Ltd Millers Yard, Hayseech Road, Halesowen, West Midlands, B63 3PD, United Kingdom
✆ 0121-501 3868/✆ 0121-585 5377
✉ info@mandmstudios.co.uk
🖥 www.mandmstudios.co.uk

M Ashdown Photography Flat 3a, 45 Preston Park Avenue, Brighton, BN1 6HG, United Kingdom
✆ (07862) 213691
✉ info@mashdownphotography.com
🖥 www.mashdownphotography.com

M B P 14/18 New Hall Hey Business Park, Rossendale, Lancashire, BB4 6HR, United Kingdom
✆ (01706) 242900/✆ (01706) 242901
✉ info@mbp2.co.uk
🖥 www.mbp2.co.uk

M C P A 21 Kelful Close, Eastrea, Whittlesey, Peterborough, PE7 2EL, United Kingdom
✆ (07958) 643502
✉ mike@mc-pa.co.uk
🖥 www.mc-pa.co.uk

M D O Studio Hurstmere Close, Grayshott, Hindhead, Surrey, GU26 6TR, United Kingdom
✆ (07968) 245901
✉ hurstmerec@hotmail.com
🖥 www.modelling.org.uk

M L P 14 Victoria Road, London, N4 3SQ, United Kingdom
✆ (020) 8374 2167
✉ marcel@marcellam.com
🖥 www.marcellam.com

M R P 21 Orsman Road, London, N1 5RA, United Kingdom
✆ (020) 7613 1562
✉ mrp-london@ukonline.co.uk
🖥 www.mrp-images.com

M2 Visions 20 Wimploe Road, Uxbridge, Middlesex, UB7 7RJ, United Kingdom
✆ (01895) 465029
✉ info@m2visions.com
🖥 www.m2visions.com

Maak Roberts@Defrance 47 Rethelstrasse, Deusseldorf, 40237, Germany
✆ 00 49 211 87 67 89/✆ 00 49 211 87 67 89
✉ defrance@defrance.de
🖥 www.defrance.de

Maconochie Photography 4 Meard Street, Soho, London, W1F 0EF, United Kingdom
✆ (020) 7439 3159/✆ (020) 7439 2552
✉ info@macphoto.co.uk
🖥 www.macphoto.co.uk

Magali Deporte@Axiom Photographic Agency The Pall Mall Deposit, 124-128 Barlby Road, London, W10 6BL, United Kingdom
✆ (020) 8964 9970/✆ (020) 8964 8440
✉ info@axiomphotographic.com
🖥 www.axiomphotographic.com

Magic Marbles 155 Locket Road, Harrow, Middlesex, HA3 7NY, United Kingdom
✆ (020) 8427 6823
✉ isabelle@magicmarbles.co.uk
🖥 www.magicmarbles.co.uk

Magnum Photos 63 Gee Street, London, EC1V 3RS, United Kingdom
✆ (020) 7490 1771/✆ (020) 7608 0020
✉ magnum@magnumphotos.co.uk
🖥 www.magnumphotos.com

Magnus Hastings Photography 46 Cheshire Street, London, E2 6EH, United Kingdom
✆ (020) 7033 9757
✉ magnus@magnushastings.co.uk
🖥 www.magnushastings.co.uk

Magnus Marding@E S P Agency 1st Floor, 63 Charlotte Street, London, W1T 4PG, United Kingdom
✆ (020) 7209 1626/✆ (020) 7209 1627
✉ info@esp-agency.com
🖥 www.esp-agency.com

Malcolm Russell Duthy Hall, Great Guildford Street, London, SE1 0ES, United Kingdom
✆ (020) 7261 0360
🖥 www.duthyhall.com

Malcolm White Ltd Rowlands Cottage, Manor Lodge Road, Rowland's Castle, Hampshire, PO9 6BA, United Kingdom
✆ (023) 9241 0178/(07778) 160522
✉ malcolm@whitepix.co.uk
🖥 www.whitepix.co.uk

Malin Ngoie@Re:fresh Suit 4, The Swans Centre, Fishers Lane, London, W4 1RX, United Kingdom
✆ (020) 8747 8080/✆ (020) 8747 8228
✉ info@refresh-agency.com
🖥 www.refresh-agency.com

Mansfield Fyffe Photography 4 The Courtyard, Alexander Studios, Haydon Way, London, SW11 1YF, United Kingdom
✆ (020) 7207 8777/✆ (020) 7207 8787
✉ info@mansfieldfyffe.co.uk
🖥 www.mansfieldfyffe.co.uk

MAP 72 Rochester Place, London, NW1 9JX, United Kingdom
✆ (020) 7424 9144/✆ (020) 7284 3274
✉ info@mapltd.com
🖥 www.mapltd.com

Marc Beaussart@Areia London Studio1, 42 Theobalds Road, London, WC1X 8NW, United Kingdom
✆ (020) 7404 8600/✆ (020) 7404 8601
✉ info@areia.com
🖥 www.areia.com

Marc Burden 126 Morley Road, London, E10 6LL, United Kingdom
✆ (020) 8558 1112/(07850) 341330
🖥 www.marcburden.com

Marcel Malherbe@Arcaid Picture Library Parc House, 25-37 Cowleaze Road, Kingston upon Thames, Surrey, KT2 6DZ, United Kingdom
✆ (020) 8546 4352/✆ (020) 8541 5230
✉ arcaid@arcaid.co.uk
🖥 www.arcaid.co.uk

Marco Marezza@Victoria Lees Management (VLM) 2 Fairview Gardens, Woodford Green, Essex, IG8 7DJ, United Kingdom
✆ (07710) 287220/✆ (020) 8504 8125
✉ victoria@victorialeesmanagement.co.uk
🖥 www.victorialeesmanagement.co.uk

Marco Palumbo@Sarah Kaye Representation Ltd 38 Queen's Gate, London, SW7 5HR, United Kingdom
✆ (020) 7225 5005/✆ (020) 7225 0109
✉ sarah@sarahkaye.com
🖥 www.sarahkaye.com

One specialism - making things look beautiful.

See www.junctioneleven.com for the fuller picture.

junction eleven

Experienced team led by our Head of Photography

State-of-the-art digital equipment

Off J11 M40 Jugglers Close Banbury Oxfordshire OX16 3JU
Tel 01295 700122 email info@junctioneleven.com

Marco Santucci Photography 85 Essex Road, London, N1 2SF, United Kingdom
✆ (020) 7226 7705/✆ (020) 7226 9563
✉ email@marcosantucci.com
🖥 www.marcosantucci.com

Marcus Lyon The Glassworks, 1C Montford Place, London, SE11 5DE, United Kingdom
✆ (020) 7735 9933/(07831) 591959 ✆ (020) 7735 9273
✉ ml@theglassworks.co.uk
🖥 **www.marcuslyon.com**
See ad in showcase

Marcus Peel@Axiom Photographic Agency The Pall Mall Deposit, 124-128 Barlby Road, London, W10 6BL, United Kingdom
✆ (020) 8964 9970/✆ (020) 8964 8440
✉ info@axiomphotographic.com
🖥 www.axiomphotographic.com

Marcus Peel Photography 8 Medfield Street, Roehampton, London, SW15 4JZ, United Kingdom
✆ (020) 8788 3771/✆ (020) 8788 3771
✉ info@marcuspeelphotography.co.uk
🖥 www.marcuspeelphotography.co.uk

Marcus Philipp-Sauer@Mutton Bones Ground Floor, 51 Balcombe Street, London, NW1 6HD, United Kingdom
✆ (020) 7723 8244/✆ (020) 7723 2770
✉ hello@muttonbones.co.uk
🖥 www.muttonbones.co.uk

Marden Smith@Terri Manduca The Basement, 11 Elvaston Place, London, SW7 5QG, United Kingdom
✆ (020) 7581 5844/✆ (020) 7581 5822
✉ terri@terrimanduca.co.uk
🖥 www.terrimanduca.co.uk

Mareike Foecking@Defrance 47 Rethelstrasse, Deusseldorf, 40237, Germany
✆ 00 49 211 87 67 89/✆ 00 49 211 87 67 89
✉ defrance@defrance.de
🖥 www.defrance.de

Maria Moore@Sarah Lane Represents 56 Bidwell Gardens, London, N11 2AU, United Kingdom
✆ (07901) 552520/✆ (020) 8292 4001
✉ sarah@sarahlanerepresents.com
🖥 www.sarahlanerepresents.com

Marie O'Hara Photography Jasmine Cottage, Bushcombe Lane, Cheltenham, Gloucestershire, GL52 9QL, United Kingdom
✆ (01242) 674631/(07860) 287787
✉ marie@ohara.to
🖥 www.garden-collection.com

Marie-Louise Avery 1 Cahill Street, London, EC1Y 8PH, United Kingdom
✆ (020) 7251 2316/(07860) 436668 ✆ (020) 7251 3481
✉ creative@marielouiseavery.co.uk
🖥 www.marielouiseavery.co.uk

Marie-Louise Avery @Sharon Brandman Agency, No 2 Elmhurst Close, Bushey, WD23 2QB
✆ 847 800 9003/✉ sharon@sharonbrandman.com
🖥 **www.sharonbrandman.com**
See ad in showcase

Marijke De Gruyter@Defrance 47 Rethelstrasse, Deusseldorf, 40237, Germany
✆ 00 49 211 87 67 89/✆ 00 49 211 87 67 89
✉ defrance@defrance.de
🖥 www.defrance.de

Marilyn Silverstone@Magnum Photos 63 Gee Street, London, EC1V 3RS, United Kingdom
(020) 7490 1771/ (020) 7608 0020
magnum@magnumphotos.co.uk
www.magnumphotos.com

Marino Parisotto@Adrenalin Management Temple Works, Brett Passage, London, E8 1JR, United Kingdom
(020) 8986 3939/ (020) 8986 3665
info@adrenalinmanagement.com
www.adrenalinmanagement.com

Marius Alexander Wasps, 2 West Park Place, Edinburgh, EH11 2DP, United Kingdom
0131-539 9100/(07889) 913485
marius@mariusalexander.com
www.mariusalexander.com

Marius W. Hansen@Z Photographic The Mezzanine, 5 Dryden Street, Covent Garden, London, WC2E 9NW, United Kingdom
(020) 7829 8455/(07917) 302 491 (020) 7240 5600
zuk@zphotographic.com
www.zphotographic.com

Marius Wolfram@Defrance 47 Rethelstrasse, Deusseldorf, 40237, Germany
00 49 211 87 67 89/ 00 49 211 87 67 89
defrance@defrance.de
www.defrance.de

Mark Azavedo 1D Moulins Road, London, E9 7EL, United Kingdom
(020) 8985 2161/(07768) 585857 (020) 8985 2161
azavedo@btinternet.com
www.photosource.co.uk/azavedo.htm

Mark Bader The White Room, 45 Morrish Road, London, SW2 4EE, United Kingdom
(020) 8674 7517/(07979) 964994
mark@baderpics.co.uk

Mark Brome Photographer 6 Aston Works, Back Lane, Aston, Bampton, Oxfordshire, OX18 2DQ, United Kingdom
(07885) 950725
click@markbrome.com
www.markbrome.com

Mark Crick 1 Madeira Road, London, SW16 2DB, United Kingdom
(020) 8677 2760/079 73 843104
mcrick@globalnet.co.uk
www.markcrick.com

Mark Cummins 2 Windermere Avenue, Queen's Park, London, NW6 6LN, United Kingdom
(020) 8964 0423/(07976) 739058
typofoto@dircon.co.uk

Mark Davidson Unit 6, Kimberley Court, Kimberley Road, London, NW6 7SL, United Kingdom
(020) 7624 6664
www.markdavidson.com

Mark Dutton@SK Creative Management 23 New Mount Street, Manchester, M4 4DE, United Kingdom
0161-953 4032/ (0870) 486 1940
info@skcreativemanagement.com
www.skcreativemanagement.com

Mark Ellis Photography 3-4 Pond Close, Walkern Road, Stevenage, Hertfordshire, SG1 3QP, United Kingdom
(01438) 727792
info@mark-ellis.co.uk

Mark Fiennes@Arcaid Picture Library Parc House, 25-37 Cowleaze Road, Kingston upon Thames, Surrey, KT2 6DZ, United Kingdom
(020) 8546 4352/ (020) 8541 5230
arcaid@arcaid.co.uk
www.arcaid.co.uk

Mark Follon Digital & Film Unit 4, George Leigh Street, Manchester, M4 6BD, United Kingdom
0161-205 5409/ 0161-205 5409
mark@markfollon.com
www.markfollon.com

Mark George 5 St. George's Court, 131 Putney Bridge Road, Putney, London, SW15 2PA, United Kingdom
(020) 8877 9922/(07771) 595 999 (020) 8870 5533
mg@markgeorge.com
www.markgeorge.com

Mark Gibson 250 York Road, London, SW11 3SJ, United Kingdom
(020) 7228 9085/(07768) 696227
mark@markgibsonphotography.com
www.markgibsonphotography.com

Mark H Bennett Studio Pictures, Unit 3, Queensway Trading Estate, Birmingham, B5 5JU, United Kingdom
0121-666 6022/(07976) 960628 0121-233 2109

Mark Hamilton@Cormack Creative Management Ltd Suite 208, 95 Morrison Street, Glasgow, G5 8BE, United Kingdom
0141-429 6810/(07778) 323169 0141-429 2603
susie@cormackcreativemanagement.co.uk
www.cormackcreativemanagement.co.uk

Mark Harrison 54 Claremont Road, Tunbridge Wells, Kent, TN1 1TF, United Kingdom
(01892) 530977/(07860) 678314 (01892) 530977
markharrison@btinternet.com
www.markharrisonphotography.com

Mark Harwood Studio 12, The Waterside, London, N1 7SF, United Kingdom
(020) 7490 8787/(07702) 233721
mail@markharwood.plus.com
www.markharwoodstudio.co.uk

Mark Harwood Photography 12 The Waterside, 44-48 Wharf Road, London, N1 7SF, United Kingdom
(020) 7490 8787/(07702) 233721 (020) 7490 1009
info@markharwood.plus.com
www.markharwoodstudio.co.uk

Mark Henderson Photography 68 Cordwallis Road, Maidenhead, Berkshire, SL6 7BR, United Kingdom
(01628) 778247
mark@hendersonphoto.co.uk
www.hendersonphoto.co.uk

Mark Jordan Photography 31 Brander Road, Leeds, LS9 6PP, United Kingdom
0113-228 8333
info@markjordanphotography.co.uk
ww.markjordanphotography.co.uk

Mark King@Wendy Jackson Tag Creative, 29 Clerkenwell Road, London, EC1M 5TA, United Kingdom
(020) 3217 2241/(07711) 084801 (020) 7439 1971
wjackson@tagworldwide.com
www.wendyjackson.co.uk

Mark Lawrence Croft House, The Street, All Cannings, Devizes, Wiltshire, SN10 3PA, United Kingdom
(01380) 860 339
studio@aurastudios.co.uk
www.aurastudios.co.uk

Mark Leary@van Hauen Moore 14 Powis Mews, Notting Hill, London, W11 1JN, United Kingdom
(020) 7792 0022/ (020) 7792 8636
email@vanhauenmoore.com
www.vanhauenmoore.com

Mark Mason The Old Church Hall, Percy Street, Oxford, OX4 3AF, United Kingdom
(01865) 244600/ (01865) 794795
mail@mmstudios.co.uk
www.mmstudios.co.uk

Mark Plummer@S Management 15 Rocks Lane, London, SW13 0BD, United Kingdom
(020) 8487 9655/ (020) 8487 9541
fiona@smanagement.co.uk
www.smanagement.co.uk

Mark Polyblank@Annabelle Dalton 20 Glebe Street, London, W4 2BG, United Kingdom
(020) 8742 1883/(07973) 392625 (020) 8742 1856
daltphotog@aol.com
www.annabelledalton.com

Mark Power@Magnum Photos 63 Gee Street, London, EC1V 3RS, United Kingdom
(020) 7490 1771/ (020) 7608 0020
magnum@magnumphotos.co.uk
www.magnumphotos.com

Mark Richard Harrison Photographer 78 Clementina Road, London, E10 7LT, United Kingdom
(07901) 632500
mark@markrichardphotography.co.uk
www.markrichardphotography.com

Mark Stewardson Photography 76 Lower High Street, Cradley Heath, West Midlands, B64 5AJ, United Kingdom
(01384) 569291/ (01384) 567003
mark@shotbymark.co.uk
www.shotbymark.co.uk

Mark Taylor Photography 32 Charter Close, Boston, Lincolnshire, PE21 9PD, United Kingdom
(07976) 956657
info@alienzoo.co.uk
www.alienzoo.co.uk

Mark Thompson 19 Wray Crescent, London, N4 3LN, United Kingdom
(020) 7263 0503/(07956) 382530
mark@thompson-photography.com
www.thompson-photography.com

Mark Turnbull Photography Studio, The Old Trueman Brewery, 91 Brick Lane, London, E1 6QL, United Kingdom
(01892) 616154/(07973) 640835
photography@mark-turnbull.co.uk
www.mark-turnbull.co.uk

Mark Weeks Photography 4a Kettering Street, London, SW16 6QA, United Kingdom
(020) 8644 7488/(07890) 987860
mark@markweeksphotography.com
www.markweeksphotography.com

Mark Williams, Fun Valley, 7985, South Africa
0027 21 789 1409/(07831) 855797 0027 21 789 1409
mark@markwilliamsphoto.com
www.markwilliamsphoto.com

Mark Wragg Gate Studios, Walkers Place, Lacey Road, London, SW15 1PP, United Kingdom
(020) 8780 1186/(07836) 238225 (020) 8789 0140
mark@markwragg.com
www.markwragg.co.uk

Marmalade Photographics 104 Heathwood Gardens, London, SE7 8ER, United Kingdom
(020) 8854 1973
wendy@marmaladephotos.co.uk
www.marmaladephotos.co.uk

Martin Barraud Unit 26, 63 Clerkenwell Road, London, EC1M 5NP, United Kingdom
(020) 7336 6188/(07774) 264588 (020) 7336 0177
barraudm@aol.com
www.barraud.com

Martin Beckett@Alex Vaughan 59 Lambeth Walk, London, SE11 6DX, United Kingdom
(020) 7735 6623/(07775) 630137
me@alexvaughan.com
www.alexvaughan.com

Martin Beddall Chennells House, Rusper Road, Horsham, West Sussex, RH12 5QW, United Kingdom
(01403) 273908/(07973) 407330
info@martinbeddall.com
www.martinbeddall.com

Martin Bennett@Traffic Unit P102, 23 - 28 Penn Street, London, N1 7DL, United Kingdom
020 7739 6090
rebecca@rebeccavalentine.com
www.trafficphotographic.com

Martin Bennett - Photographer 77 Coppermill Lane, London, E17 7HA, United Kingdom
(07770) 886216
info@martinbennett.com
www.martinbennett.com

Martin Black 360 Alexandra Park Road, London, N22 7BD, United Kingdom
(020) 8365 7117/(07831) 300191 (020) 8374 0927
martinblack@mac.com
www.martinblackphoto.com

Martin Brent@Process 5 Choumert Mews, Choumert Road, London, SE15 4BD, United Kingdom
(020) 7277 8400/(07950) 311425 (020) 7277 7223
info@processphotography.com
www.processphotography.com

Martin Brent Photography The Coach House, Spirehouse Lane, Burcot, Bromsgrove, Worcestershire, B60 1PL, United Kingdom
(01527) 879567/(07770) 812668 (01527) 879567
mb@martinbrent.com
www.martinbrent.com

Martin Breschinski Unit B 29 Landor Road, London, SW9 9RT, United Kingdom
(020) 7627 0330/(07976) 425726 (0870) 7064693
martin@breschinski.com
www.breschinski.com

Martin Brigdale 42 Mornington Terrace, London, NW1 7RT, United Kingdom
(020) 7387 8806/ (020) 7388 2790
brigdale.trent@virgin.net

Martin Cameron Photographer 8 Sunningdale, Grantham, Lincolnshire, NG31 9PF, United Kingdom
(07973) 195918
martin@martincameron.co.uk
www.martincameron.co.uk

Martin Dawe Photography 347 Edinburgh Avenue, Slough, SL1 4TU, United Kingdom
(01753) 828828/ (01753) 828822
hello@martindawedesign.co.uk
www.martindawedesign.co.uk

Martin Ellis Photography 11 Wrights Close, London, SE13 5HP, United Kingdom
📞 (020) 8297 9288
✉ martinellis6@yahoo.com

Martin Evening Photography Ltd Unit 20, Red Square, London, N16 9AB, United Kingdom
📞 020 7249 1864/07979 811419 📠 020 7503 3445
✉ martin@martinevening.com
🖥 www.martinevening.com

Martin Haswell Clarson, Inner Down, Bristol, BS32 4PR, United Kingdom
📞 (01454) 417234
🖥 www.mhdi.co.uk

Martin Hill, London, United Kingdom
📞 (07802) 457977

Martin Hooper@Jamie Stephen Represents 9 Upper Wimpole Street, London, W1G 6LJ, United Kingdom
📞 (0845) 3733510/(07957) 784810 📠 (020) 7681 1027
✉ jamie@jamiestephen.com
🖥 www.jamiestephen.com

Martin Levenson 15 Waterside, 44/48 Wharf Road, London, N1 7UX, United Kingdom
📞 (020) 7253 2000/(07831) 389235
✉ martin@levenson.co.uk
🖥 www.levenson.co.uk

Martin O'Neill@Début Art & The Coningsby Gallery 30 Tottenham Street, London, W1T 4RJ, United Kingdom
📞 (020) 7636 1064/ 📠 (020) 7580 7017
✉ info@debutart.com
🖥 www.debutart.com

Martin Parr@Magnum Photos 63 Gee Street, London, EC1V 3RS, United Kingdom
📞 (020) 7490 1771/ 📠 (020) 7608 0020
✉ magnum@magnumphotos.co.uk
🖥 www.magnumphotos.com

Martin Peters 4 Bollans Court, Aldwark, York, YO1 7PQ, United Kingdom
📞 (01904) 629211/078 50 771779 📠 (01904) 629211
✉ martinpeters100@hotmail.com
🖥 www.martin-peters.com

Martin Philbert 2811 California Street, San Francisco, 94115, United States of America
📞 415 290 0404
✉ martin@martinphilbert.com
🖥 www.martinphilbert.com

Martin Riedl 3 Water Lane, London, NW1 8NZ, United Kingdom
📞 (020) 7428 9262/(07831) 879095 📠 (020) 7482 1822
✉ mriedl@easynet.co.uk
🖥 www.martinriedl.co.uk

Martin Roper Photographer's Agent 158a Chamberlayne Road, London, NW10 3JS, United Kingdom
📞 (020) 8964 4780/(0779) 9410942
✉ martin.roper@btinternet.com
🖥 www.martinroper.com

Martin Shallcross Photography 26 Gracedale Road, London, SW16 6SW, United Kingdom
📞 (07831) 374362/ 📠 (020) 8769 0860
✉ martfoto@mac.com
🖥 www.martfoto.net

Martin Thompson@Wendy Jackson Tag Creative, 29 Clerkenwell Road, London, EC1M 5TA, United Kingdom
📞 (020) 3217 2241/(07711) 084801 📠 (020) 7439 1971
✉ wjackson@tagworldwide.com
🖥 www.wendyjackson.co.uk

Martin Usborne Studio 4, 1 Hoxton Square, London, N1 6NU, United Kingdom
📞 (07747) 607930
✉ musborne@hotmail.com
🖥 www.martinusborne.com

Martin Wonnacott@edsonwilliams photography consultancy 52 Brushfield Street, London, E1 6AJ, United Kingdom
📞 (020) 7375 2077/(07867) 517777 📠 (020) 7375 3077
✉ info@edsonwilliams.com
🖥 www.edsonwilliams.com

Martine Franck@Magnum Photos 63 Gee Street, London, EC1V 3RS, United Kingdom
📞 (020) 7490 1771/ 📠 (020) 7608 0020
✉ magnum@magnumphotos.co.uk
🖥 www.magnumphotos.com

Martine Hamilton-Knight@Arcaid Picture Library Parc House, 25-37 Cowleaze Road, Kingston upon Thames, Surrey, KT2 6DZ, United Kingdom
📞 (020) 8546 4352/ 📠 (020) 8541 5230
✉ arcaid@arcaid.co.uk
🖥 www.arcaid.co.uk

Martyn James Brooks 27d Wood Vale, London, SE23 3DS,
📞 07976 280052
✉ martyn@martynjamesbrooks.com
🖥 www.martynjamesbrookes.com

Martyn Thompson@E S P Agency 1st Floor, 63 Charlotte Street, London, W1T 4PG, United Kingdom
📞 (020) 7209 1626/ 📠 (020) 7209 1627
✉ info@esp-agency.com
🖥 www.esp-agency.com

Mary Dunkin 6 Wrentham Avenue, London, NW10 3HA, United Kingdom
📞 (020) 8969 8043
✉ marydunkin@btopenworld.com
🖥 www.the-aop.org

Mary Robert Oculus Studios, 47 Creffield Road, London, W5 3RR, United Kingdom
📞 (020) 8993 4378/(07967) 644416
✉ mary@oculus-studios.demon.co.uk

Massimo Vitali @Bill Charles London Ltd. Unit 3E1, Zetland House, 5-25 Scrutton Street, London, EC2A 4HJ, United Kingdom
📞 020 7033 9284/020 2033 9285
✉ london@billcharles.com
🖥 www.billcharles.com

Mathias Baumann@Defrance 47 Rethelstrasse, Deusseldorf, 40237, Germany
📞 00 49 211 87 67 89/ 📠 00 49 211 87 67 89
✉ defrance@defrance.de
🖥 www.defrance.de

Matt Antrobus 1A Chance Street, London, E1 6JT, United Kingdom
📞 (020) 7729 1881/(07850) 664431
✉ matt@mattantrobus.com
🖥 www.mattantrobus.com

LISA PRITCHARD AGENCY/

TELEPHONE
+44 (0) 20 7250 1362
LISAPRITCHARD.COM

LPA/ FUTURES

Matt Cooke Photography 115 Tower Street, Brightling Sea, Essex, CO7 0AN, United Kingdom
℡ /(07831) 570289
✉ info@mattcooke.co.uk
🖥 www.mattcooke.co.uk

Matt Harris 10 Disraeli Road, London, W5 5HP, United Kingdom
℡ (07850) 955585
✉ mattharris@dial.pipex.com
🖥 www.mattharris.co.uk

Matt Prince 84 Hawkley Road, London, N16 0TJ, United Kingdom
℡ (07973) 382260
✉ matt@glossy.co.uk
🖥 www.glossy.co.uk

Matt Swift Photography Stone Cottage, Little Longstone, Bakewell, Derbyshire, DE45 1NN, United Kingdom
℡ (01629) 640469/(07905) 897862
✉ matt@mattswift.co.uk
🖥 www.mattswift.co.uk

Matt Wain Photography 19 Grahame Avenue, Pangbourne, Reading, RG8 7LF, United Kingdom
℡ (01189) 844 844
✉ polly@mattwain.com
🖥 www.mattwain.com

Matthais Neidhart@Upper Orange Nostitzstrasse 15, Berlin, 10961, Germany
℡ 49 178 6121661/ 49 30 6121661
✉ mail@upperorange.com
🖥 www.upperorange.de

Matthew Andrews Photographer 18 Montpelier Street, Brighton, BN1 3DJ, United Kingdom
℡ (01273) 747614/ (01273) 747614
✉ post@matthewandrews.co.uk
🖥 www.matthewandrews.co.uk

Matthew Barlow@Germaine Walker Photographers' Agent Crayford House, 49A Tabley Road, London, N7 0NA, United Kingdom
℡ (020) 7697 8291/(07867) 780272 ✆ (020) 7619 9051
✉ germaine@germaine.co.uk
🖥 www.germaine.co.uk

Matthew Cant Photography 34 Claygate Road, Ealing, London, W13 9XG, United Kingdom
℡ (020) 8579 1534/(07956) 525042
✉ mc@mattcant.com
🖥 www.mattcant.com

Matthew Cooper@Début Art & The Coningsby Gallery 30 Tottenham Street, London, W1T 4RJ, United Kingdom
℡ (020) 7636 1064/ (020) 7580 7017
✉ info@debutart.com
🖥 www.debutart.com

Matthew Donaldson 211B Kentish Town Road, London, NW5 2JU, United Kingdom
℡ (020) 7482 1278/(07973) 513960
✉ matthew@matthewdonaldson.com
🖥 www.matthewdonaldson.com

Matthew John Naylor 22B Pepys Road, London, SE14 5SB, United Kingdom
℡ (020) 7207 0776/(07799) 624161
✉ matthewjnaylor@ntlworld.com

Matthew Murray@Horton-Stephens Photographers' Agent 14 Peacock Yard, Iliffe Street, London, SE17 3LH, United Kingdom
℡ (020) 7252 7979/ (020) 7252 6409
✉ us@horton-stephens.com
🖥 www.horton-stephens.com

Matthew Murray (represented by) Horton Stevens 14 Peacock Yard, Llisse street, London, SE17 3LH, United Kingdom
℡ (020) 7252 7979/(07811) 168404
✉ matthew@matthew-murray.co.uk
🖥 www.matthew-murray.co.uk

Matthew Stylianou@The White Agency 60 Epirus Road, Fulham, London, SW6 7UH, United Kingdom
℡ (020) 7381 2004/(07970) 619277 ✆ (020) 7386 8479
✉ annabel@thewhiteagency.com
🖥 www.thewhiteagency.com

Matthew Ward Studio 6, 9 Park Hill, London, SW4 9NS, United Kingdom
℡ (020) 8772 1900/(07850) 611778
✉ matthew@matthewwardphotography.com
🖥 www.matthewwardphotography.com

Matthias Kerfante Photography Aimies Street, London, SW11, United Kingdom
℡ (07850) 167289
✉ mail@mattpictures.com
🖥 www.mattpictures.com

Matthu Placek@Bill Charles London Ltd. Unit 3E1, Zetland House, 5-25 Scrutton Street, London, EC2A 4HJ, United Kingdom
℡ 020 7033 9284/020 2033 9285
✉ london@billcharles.com
🖥 www.billcharles.com

Maureen Barrymore@Adrenalin Management Temple Works, Brett Passage, London, E8 1JR, United Kingdom
℡ (020) 8986 3939/ (020) 8986 3665
✉ info@adrenalinmanagement.com
🖥 www.adrenalinmanagement.com

Maurice Scheltens@The Katy Barker Agency Ltd 11 Mason's Arms Mews, Maddox Street, London, W1S 1NX, United Kingdom
℡ (020) 7493 3933/ (020) 7493 3311
✉ catherine@katybarker.com
🖥 www.katybarker.com

Maurizio Conte Via Tartini 11/a, Milano, 20158, Italy
℡ 00 39 02 4548 6183/00 39 33 3379 1252
✉ maurizio.conte@fastwebnet.it
🖥 www.maurizioconte.com

Max Baker 74 Lavenham Road, London, SW18 5HE, United Kingdom
℡ (020) 8874 3343/(07980) 893512
✉ max@magnimax.net
🖥 www.maxbaker.com

Max Ballatore Via Botteghelle 6, Naples, 80143, Italy
℡ 00 390 81 58 45 92 9/ 00 390 81 58 45 92 9
✉ info@maxballatore.com
🖥 www.maxballatore.com

Max Forsythe 1a The Terrace, Richmond Hill, Richmond, Surrey, TW10 6RN, United Kingdom
℡ (020) 8948 6888
✉ max@maxforsythe.com
🖥 www.maxforsythe.com

Max Oppenheim@Jo Talbot & Sue Young 6M Hyde Park Mansions, Cabbell Street, London, NW1 5BJ, United Kingdom
℡ (020) 7262 0189/(07850) 353468 ✆ (020) 7262 2160
✉ joandsue@btconnect.com
🖥 www.joandsue.com

Maya Goded@Magnum Photos 63 Gee Street, London, EC1V 3RS, United Kingdom
℡ (020) 7490 1771/ (020) 7608 0020
✉ magnum@magnumphotos.co.uk
🖥 www.magnumphotos.com

Maynard Firth 78 Bellenden Road, London, SE15 4RQ, United Kingdom
℡ (020) 7732 0527/(07973) 551387 ✆ (020) 7732 0527
🖥 www.maynardfirth.co.uk

Media Wisdom Photography Ltd 5 Lindsay Road, Hampton, Middlesex, TW12 1DR, United Kingdom
℡ (020) 8979 3328/(07971) 686151
✉ abi@mediawisdom.co.uk
🖥 www.mediawisdom.co.uk

Meena Julien Flat 4, Danes House, Sutton Way, London, W10 5HB, United Kingdom
℡ (07737) 120854
✉ meenakaren@hotmail.com
🖥 www.meenajulien.com

Mel Grundy Oakbase House, Trafford Street, Chester, CH1 3HP, United Kingdom
℡ (01244) 391391/ (01244) 370237
✉ mel@oakbase.co.uk
🖥 www.oakbase.co.uk

Mel Yates@Sarah Kaye Representation Ltd 38 Queen's Gate, London, SW7 5HR, United Kingdom
℡ (020) 7225 5005/ (020) 7225 0109
✉ sarah@sarahkaye.com
🖥 www.sarahkaye.com

Melvyn Vincent Spotlight Studios, Canonbury Yard, 202 New North Road, London, N1 7BJ, United Kingdom
℡ (020) 7354 8850/(07831) 287066
✉ mel@melvynvincent.com
🖥 www.melvynvincent.com

Mercer Design & Photography Chapel Studio, Downhead, Shepton Mallet, Somerset, BA4 4LQ, United Kingdom
℡ (01749) 880523/ (01749) 880690
✉ tim@mercerdesign.co.uk
🖥 www.mercerdesign.co.uk

Merle Moustafa 6 Tonstall Road, Epsom, Surrey, KT19 9DP, United Kingdom
℡ (07702) 194193
✉ info@merlemoustafa.com
🖥 www.merlemoustafa.com

Mervyn Franklyn@Horton-Stephens Photographers' Agent 14 Peacock Yard, Iliffe Street, London, SE17 3LH, United Kingdom
℡ (020) 7252 7979/ (020) 7252 6409
✉ us@horton-stephens.com
🖥 www.horton-stephens.com

Metcalfe Lancaster 20 Hanson Street, London, W1W 6UF, United Kingdom
℡ **(020) 7580 8875 (07778) 331771 (020) 7580 8689**
✉ **julie@metcalfelancaster.com**
🖥 **www.metcalfelancaster.com**
See ad in showcase

Metropolis St. Michael's Hall, Bennett Road, Leeds, LS6 3HN, United Kingdom
℡ 0113-274 9474/(07718) 782440
✉ andy@snakey.net
🖥 www.snakey.net

Metz & Racine@Siobhan Squire 111 Shoreditch High Street, London, E1 6JN, United Kingdom
℡ (020) 7739 8985/ (020) 7729 5125
✉ siobhan@siobhansquire.com
🖥 www.siobhansquire.com

Micha Bar-Am@Magnum Photos 63 Gee Street, London, EC1V 3RS, United Kingdom
℡ (020) 7490 1771/ (020) 7608 0020
✉ magnum@magnumphotos.co.uk
🖥 www.magnumphotos.com

Michael Birt 21 Parson's Green Lane, London, SW6 4HH, United Kingdom
℡ (020) 7371 5154/ (020) 7471 8977
✉ michael@michael-birt.com
🖥 www.michael-birt.com

Michael Black 1 Glebelands Road, Prestwich, Manchester, M25 1NE, United Kingdom
℡ 0161-798 8054/(07885) 629941
✉ mike@mikeblackphotographer.co.uk
🖥 www.mikeblackphotographer.co.uk

Michael Blissett 27-28 Roper Close, Canterbury, Kent, CT2 7EP, United Kingdom
℡ (01227) 768133/(07889) 299000
✉ michael.blissett@btinternet.com
🖥 www.blissett.co.uk

Michael Bright 49 Grove Park Terrace, Fishponds, Bristol, BS16 2BL, United Kingdom
℡ 0117-965 5345
✉ mkbright@cablenet.co.uk

Michael Brockway East View, Taylors Lane, Chichester, West Sussex, PO18 8QQ, United Kingdom
℡ (01243) 572600
✉ brockphoto@tiscali.co.uk
🖥 www.michaelbrockwayphotography.com

Michael Carsley The Basement, 35 Tottenham Street, London, W1P 9PE, United Kingdom
℡ (020) 7637 3937/ (020) 7323 2026
✉ carsley.photo@netmatters.co.uk
🖥 www.photographystore.com

Michael Chevis The Studio, West Street, Midhurst, West Sussex, GU29 9NF, United Kingdom
℡ (01730) 814864/(07734) 982525
✉ info@michaelchevis.com
🖥 www.michaelchevis.com

Michael Clement 136B Leathwaite Road, London, SW11 6RP, United Kingdom
℡ (020) 7228 9697/(07976) 216050 ✆ (020) 7228 9697
🖥 www.michaelclement.com

Michael Coyne@Axiom Photographic Agency The Pall Mall Deposit, 124-128 Barlby Road, London, W10 6BL, United Kingdom
℡ (020) 8964 9970/ (020) 8964 8440
✉ info@axiomphotographic.com
🖥 www.axiomphotographic.com

Michael Crockett, London, SW15 3ZB, United Kingdom
℡ (0845) 6039304/(07788) 817632 ✆ (0871) 4334723
✉ studio@michaelcrockett.com
🖥 www.michaelcrockett.com

Michael Danner Zelterstrasse 14, Berlin, 10439, Germany
📞 00 49 17 520 26704
✉ hello@michaeldanner.com
🖥 www.michaeldanner.com

Michael Davies 56A Clerkenwell Road, London, EC1M 5PX, United Kingdom
📞 (020) 7253 8101/(07831) 424739 📠 (020) 7608 2138
✉ mdphoto@lineone.net

Michael Dmochowski Phoenix, Flaunden Lane, Feldon, Bovingdon, Hemel Hempstead, Hertfordshire, HP3 0PA, United Kingdom
📞 (01442) 831702/(07831) 321202 📠 (01442) 834858
✉ miked@avnet.co.uk
🖥 www.thedemo.co.uk

Michael Duff Wynlic, Bull Lane, Lenham Heath, Maidstone, Kent, ME17 2JA, United Kingdom
📞 (01622) 858460/(07850) 835003
✉ michael.duff@btconnect.com

Michael Dunning The Clock House, Sheepstead, Marcham, Abingdon, Oxfordshire, OX13 6QG, United Kingdom
📞 (01865) 390108/(07941) 386021
✉ m@michaeldunning.com
🖥 www.michaeldunning.com

Michael Eastell 82 Clerkenwell Road, London, EC1M 5RJ, United Kingdom
📞 (020) 7608 2877/ 📠 (020) 7490 0642
✉ publiphoto@aol.com

Michael Harding Photography 85 Stanthorpe Road, London, SW16 2EA, United Kingdom
📞 (020) 8677 4412/(07860) 920769
✉ michael@mharding.com
🖥 www.mharding.com

Michael Harvey 215 217, Cold Harbour Lane, London, SW9 8RU, United Kingdom
📞 (020) 7274 9434
✉ info@michaelharveyphoto.com
🖥 www.michaelharveyphoto.com

Michael Heffernan@L P A (Lisa Pritchard Agency) 3rd Floor, Block A, Morelands, 5-23 Old Street, London, EC1V 9HL, United Kingdom
📞 (020) 7250 1362/ 📠 (020) 7250 1357
✉ info@lisapritchard.com
🖥 www.lisapritchard.com

Michael Johns (GBFE) 2 Grove Road, Amersham, Buckinghamshire, HP6 6ND, United Kingdom
📞 (01494) 728892/(07801) 657062 📠 (01494) 728892
✉ michaeleditor@btinternet.com

Michael Johnson Hunters Lodge, Beggar Hill, Chelmsford, CM4 0PE, United Kingdom
📞 (01277) 354271/ 📠 (01277) 356236
✉ mail@michaeljohnsonphotography.co.uk

Michael Kay Solar Studios, Unit H, Lombard Business Park, 20-26 Purley Way, Croydon, CR0 3JP, United Kingdom
📞 (020) 8664 8500/ 📠 (020) 8664 8570
✉ images@solar-studios.com
🖥 www.solar-studios.com

Michael Kenna@Maconochie Photography 4 Meard Street, Soho, London, W1F 0EF, United Kingdom
📞 (020) 7439 3159/ 📠 (020) 7439 2552
✉ info@macphoto.co.uk
🖥 www.macphoto.co.uk

Michael Lee 36 Monks Walk, Reigate, Surrey, RH2 0SS, United Kingdom
📞 (01737) 243185/(07860) 691143
✉ mike-lee1@ntlworld.com

Michael Lewis@David Edmunds Represents Unit 105, 54-58 Kingsland Road, London, E2 8DP, United Kingdom
📞 (020) 7739 1166/(07785) 580024
✉ info@davidedmundsrepresents.com
🖥 www.davidedmundsrepresents.com

Michael Michaels Unit 10, 69 St. Marks Road, London, W10 6JG, United Kingdom
📞 (020) 8964 5555
✉ mike@michaelmichaels.com
🖥 www.michaelmichaelsphotography.com

Michael Molloy 4 The Shrubbery, Grosvenor Road, London, E11 2EL, United Kingdom
📞 (020) 8530 2741
✉ info@michaelmolloy.co.uk
🖥 michaelmolloy.co.uk

Michael Prince@Mutton Bones Ground Floor, 51 Balcombe Street, London, NW1 6HD, United Kingdom
📞 (020) 7723 8244/ 📠 (020) 7723 2770
✉ hello@muttonbones.co.uk
🖥 www.muttonbones.co.uk

Michael Roberts@Maconochie Photography 4 Meard Street, Soho, London, W1F 0EF, United Kingdom
📞 (020) 7439 3159/ 📠 (020) 7439 2552
✉ info@macphoto.co.uk
🖥 www.macphoto.co.uk

Michael Schnabel@Valeriehersleven Boundary House (3rd Floor), 91-93 Charterhouse Street, London, EC1M 6HR, United Kingdom
📞 (07775) 717474
✉ me@valeriehersleven.com
🖥 www.valeriehersleven.com

Michael St. Maur Sheil Wyastone Cottage, Buckland, Faringdon, Oxfordshire, SN7 8QR, United Kingdom
📞 (01367) 870276/(07860) 508679 📠 (01367) 870641
✉ sheilphoto@compuserve.com
🖥 www.sheilphoto.co.uk

Michael Trevillion Trevillion Images, 75 Jeddo Road, London, W12 9ED, United Kingdom
📞 (020) 8740 9005/(07775) 686362
✉ info@trevillion.com
🖥 www.trevillion.com

Michael Tummings@Pearce Stoner Associates 12B Links Yard, Spelman Street, London, E1 5LX, United Kingdom
📞 (020) 7247 7100/ 📠 (020) 7247 7144
✉ info@pearcestoner.com
🖥 www.pearcestoner.com

Michael Westmoreland 358 Victoria Park Road, Leicester, LE2 1XF, United Kingdom
📞 0116-270 5828
✉ michael@westmoreland.demon.co.uk
🖥 www.invisiblephotography.com

Michael Whitestone Hill House, Far Wells Road, Bisley, Stroud, Gloucestershire, GL6 7AQ, United Kingdom
📞 (01452) 771066/(07970) 071566
✉ michael@michaelwhitestone.co.uk
🖥 www.michaelwhitestone.co.uk

Michael Wildsmith Photography 2nd Floor, 1-6 Falconberg Court, London, W1D 3AB, United Kingdom
📞 (07976) 839492
✉ michael@michaelwildsmith.com

Love Organic

Gill Orsman photographer
+44 (0) 1273 887627   info@gillorsman.com   www.gillorsman.com

Michael Woolley@Sarah Kaye Representation Ltd 38 Queen's Gate, London, SW7 5HR, United Kingdom
📞 (020) 7225 5005/ 📠 (020) 7225 0109
✉ sarah@sarahkaye.com
🖥 www.sarahkaye.com

Michel Haddi@Z Photographic The Mezzanine, 5 Dryden Street, Covent Garden, London, WC2E 9NW, United Kingdom
📞 (020) 7829 8455/(07917) 302 491 📠 (020) 7240 5600
✉ zuk@zphotographic.com
🖥 www.zphotographic.com

Michele Jorsling The Studio, 55 Leroy Street, London, SE1 4SN, United Kingdom
📞 (07973) 764393
✉ mjorsling@aol.com

Michelle Garrett, 28 Edith Road, London, W14 9BB, United Kingdom
📞 (020) 7603 8759/ 📠 (020) 7603 8510
✉ michelle.garrett@ukonline.co.uk
🖥 www.garden-photographers.com

Miguel Rio Branco@Magnum Photos 63 Gee Street, London, EC1V 3RS, United Kingdom
📞 (020) 7490 1771/ 📠 (020) 7608 0020
✉ magnum@magnumphotos.co.uk
🖥 www.magnumphotos.com

Miguel Rosales@Milc Studio 7, Zeus House, 16-30 Provost Street, London, N1 7NG, United Kingdom
📞 (020) 7278 8838/ (0870) 0941564
✉ gemma@milc.co.uk
🖥 www.milc.co.uk

Mikael Eliasson Photographer 18 Principal Square, Chelmer Road, London, E9 6AF, United Kingdom
📞 (07776) 220077
✉ mail@mikaeleliasson.com
🖥 www.mikaeleliasson.com

Mikael Gothage Photographs 258 Queensbridge Road, London, E8 3NB, United Kingdom
📞 (07880) 641 031
✉ info@gothage.com
🖥 www.gothage.com

Mikami Photography 25 Weybourne Street, London, SW18 4HG, United Kingdom
📞 (020) 8947 9941/(07860) 323185
✉ chris@mikami.co.uk
🖥 www.mikami.co.uk

Mike Bruce Gate Studios, Walkers Place, London, SW15 1PP, United Kingdom
📞 (020) 8788 7827/ 📠 (020) 8789 0140
✉ mike@gatestudios.com
🖥 www.gatestudios.com

Mike Caldwell St Anne's, Petersfield Road, Winchester, Hampshire, SO23 0JD, United Kingdom
📞 (01962) 863693/(07836) 708167 📠 (01962) 877617
✉ mike@mikecaldwell.co.uk
🖥 www.mikecaldwell.co.uk

Mike Cooper Photography Unit 19C, Barton Hill Trading Estate, Bristol, BS5 9BD, United Kingdom
📞 0117 955 1345/(07860) 439820 📠 0117 955 1456
✉ mike@mike-cooper.com
🖥 www.mike-cooper.com

Mike Diver@Yara Gremoli Photographers Agent
Studio 210, Canalot Studios, 222 Kensal Road, London,
W10 5BN, United Kingdom
(0870) 8501209/(07880) 627413 (0870) 8501209
yara@sbmanagement.org
www.yaragremoli.com

Mike Ellis Photography 65 Leonard Street, London,
EC2A 4QS, United Kingdom
(020) 7613 4313/(07860) 275287 (020) 7739 5512
mike@mikeellisphotography.com
www.mikeellisphotography.com

Mike Figgis@Maconochie Photography 4 Meard
Street, Soho, London, W1F 0EF, United Kingdom
(020) 7439 3159/ (020) 7439 2552
info@macphoto.co.uk
www.macphoto.co.uk

Mike Galletly Studio 3, The People's Hall, 2 Olaf Street,
London, W11 4BE, United Kingdom
(020) 7221 0925/ (020) 7229 1136
mikegalletly@talk21.com
www.living-landscape.com

Mike Hughes Photography 10 Bladen Drive, Rushmere
St. Andrew, Ipswich, IP4 5UG, United Kingdom
(01473) 716 838/(07836) 710226 (01473) 716 838
mike@airshots.co.uk
www.airshots.co.uk

Mike Marlowe No 23, 29 Eugene Way, Eastbourne, East
Sussex, BN23 5BH, United Kingdom
(07788) 122886
mm@mikemarlowe.co.uk
www.mikemarlowe.co.uk

Mike McGoran 6 Apollo Studios, Charlton Kings Road,
London, NW5 2SB, United Kingdom
(020) 7284 4875/ (020) 7284 4875
www.mikemcgoran.com

Mike Moran 33 Warner Road, Ware, Hertfordshire,
SG12 9JL, United Kingdom
(01920) 466003/(07801) 615952
mikemoran@moran19.fsnet.co.uk
www.photography-london.co.uk

Mike Owen, London, United Kingdom
(020) 7439 1877

Mike Parsons@Coochie Management 26 Harcourt
Street, Marylebone, London, W1H 4HW, United Kingdom
(020) 7724 9700/(07802) 795620 (020) 7724 2598
amanda@coochie-management.com
www.coochie-management.com

Mike Prior Photography 7 The Old Laundry, Hayden
Way, London, SW11 1YF, United Kingdom
(020) 7207 1964/(07721) 646464 (020) 7207 1965
info@mikeprior.com
www.mikeprior.com

Mike Roberts 27 Greenway Gardens, Greenford,
Middlesex, UB6 9TU, United Kingdom
(020) 8578 9047/ (020) 8575 7244
onlyhorsespics@aol.com
www.onlyhorsespictures.com

**Mike Shepherd@Début Art & The Coningsby
Gallery** 30 Tottenham Street, London, W1T 4RJ, United
Kingdom
(020) 7636 1064/ (020) 7580 7017
info@debutart.com
www.debutart.com

Mike Torrington 15 Shurland Avenue, East Barnet,
Hertfordshire, EN4 8DE, United Kingdom
(020) 8440 2304
info@miketorrington.com
www.miketorrington.com

Mike Venables@Photographic Techniques Ltd 1b
Montague Road, Wimbledon Broadway, London, SW19
1TB, United Kingdom
(020) 8542 2444/ (020) 8542 3444
images@phototech.co.uk
www.phototech.co.uk

Mike Woodward 15 Lynmouth Drive, Sully, Penarth,
South Glamorgan, CF64 5TP, United Kingdom
(029) 2053 0314/(07860) 536247

Miki Slingsby Fine Art Photography 306 The Glass
Building, 226 Arlington Road, London, NW1 7HY, United
Kingdom
(020) 7485 4367

Milc Studio 7, Zeus House, 16-30 Provost Street, London,
N1 7NG, United Kingdom
(020) 7278 8838/ (0870) 0941564
gemma@milc.co.uk
www.milc.co.uk

Mill Yard Studios Mill Yard, 24A Guildford Street,
Luton, LU1 2NR, United Kingdom
(01582) 483828/ (01582) 455089
info@millyard.co.uk
www.millyard.co.uk

Mills Media Ltd 2 Morpeth Wharf, 12 Quays, Wirral,
Merseyside, CH41 1LF, United Kingdom
0151-649 3600/ 0151-649 3700
sales@millsmediagroup.com
www.millsmediagroup.com

Minerva Aldrete Flat 13, Partridge House, Stafford
Road, London, E3 5EZ, United Kingdom
(07803) 162434
miny78mail@yahoo.com
www.minervaaldrete.com

Mischa Richter@E S P Agency 1st Floor, 63 Charlotte
Street, London, W1T 4PG, United Kingdom
(020) 7209 1626/ (020) 7209 1627
info@esp-agency.com
www.esp-agency.com

Mitch Epstein@Bill Charles London Ltd. Unit 3E1,
Zetland House, 5-25 Scrutton Street, London, EC2A 4HJ,
United Kingdom
020 7033 9284/020 2033 9285
london@billcharles.com
www.billcharles.com

Mitchell-McGree Garden Design 3 Poppyhills Road,
Camberley, Surrey, GU15 4ES, United Kingdom
(01276) 469141
mitchell@lifeworld.wanadoo.co.uk
www.mitchell-mcgree.com

Moe Kafer 20 Crowborough Road, London, SW17 9QQ,
United Kingdom
(07748) 902759
moekafer@f2s.com
www.moekafer.com

Moira O'Hara Photography Ground Floor, 1 Chalcot
Square, London, NW1 8YB, United Kingdom
(07802) 932584
moiraohara@mac.com
www.moiraohara.co.uk

Momin's Photography 112 Goodmayes Road,
Goodmayes, Ilford, Essex, IG3 9UZ, United Kingdom
(020) 8554 0355/(07949) 194101
momin@mominsphotography.co.uk
www.mominsphotography.co.uk

Monica Curtin Flat 8, 25 De Vere Gardens, London, W8
5AN, United Kingdom
(020) 7938 1474/(07779) 112374 (020) 7938 1474
monicacurtin@hotmail.com

Monokul Studio Hristo Vakarelski 11 bl 5 app 3, Sofia,
1700, Bulgaria
00 359 888 655 350
monokul@abv.bg
www.momchilristov.com

Montage Studio Gallery 12 Church Street, Castleton,
Whitby, North Yorkshire, YO21 2EQ, United Kingdom
(01287) 660159
glowpix@ntlworld.com
www.glow.co.uk

Monty Rakusen's Studio The Orchard, Toulston Cottage,
Leeds Road, Toulston, Tadcaster, North Yorkshire, LS24
9NA, United Kingdom
(01937) 830052/(07778) 411337 (01937) 830052
info@rakusen.co.uk
www.rakusen.co.uk

Mooney Photo Ltd 25 Armitage Bridge Mills, Armitage
Bridge, Huddersfield, HD4 7NR, United Kingdom
(020) 7193 6637/ (01484) 660575
admin@mooneyphoto.com
www.mooneyphoto.com

Morgan Lockyer 1 Albion Yard, Regent Quarter, Kings
Cross, London, N1 9ED, United Kingdom
(020) 7837 4600
charlotte@morganlockyer.com
www.morganlockyer.com

Morley von Sternberg@Arcaid Picture Library Parc
House, 25-37 Cowleaze Road, Kingston upon Thames,
Surrey, KT2 6DZ, United Kingdom
(020) 8546 4352/ (020) 8541 5230
arcaid@arcaid.co.uk
www.arcaid.co.uk

Morten Laursen@Webber Represents Ltd 25
Lexington Street, Soho, London, W1F 9AG, United
Kingdom
(020) 7439 0678/ (020) 7439 0543
london@webberrepresents.com
www.webberrepresents.com

Mouse In The House 7 Canham Mews, Canham Road,
London, W3 7SR, United Kingdom
(020) 8740 4634
mike@mouseinthehouse.co.uk
www.mouseinthehouse.co.uk

Moy Williams Photography 10 Booth Street, Salford,
Manchester, M3 5DG, United Kingdom
0161 839 6660/(07836) 770977 0161 839 8300
moy@moyphotography.com
www.moyphotography.com

Murray King Images Studio St. Ives, St. Ives, Cornwall,
TR26 2AF, United Kingdom
(01736) 796303/(07976) 055651 (01736) 796303
mk@imagesofcornwall.com
www.imagesofcornwall.com

Murray Lenton 5 Brief Street, London, SE5 9RD, United
Kingdom
(020) 7733 6769/(07941) 427458
murray.lenton@btinternet.com
www.theatrephotography.co.uk

**Mutton Bones Ground Floor, 51 Balcombe Street,
London, NW1 6HD, United Kingdom**
(020) 7723 8244/ (020) 7723 2770
hello@muttonbones.co.uk
www.muttonbones.co.uk
See ad in showcase

Mydas Photography 28 Montague Hall Place, Bushey,
WD23 1QG, United Kingdom
(020) 8950 0393/(07769) 700550
maurice@mydasphotography.com
www.mydasphotography.com

N M P Photo 211 Westbourne Park Road, W11
1EA, United Kingdom
(020) 7243 0074
info@nmpphoto.co.uk
www.nmpphoto.co.uk

Nadav Kander Unit D, Imperial Works, Perren Street,
London, NW5 3ED, United Kingdom
(020) 7485 6789/ (020) 7485 4321
mail@nadavkander.com
www.nadavkander.com

Nadav Kander @Bill Charles London Ltd. Unit 3E1,
Zetland House, 5-25 Scrutton Street, London, EC2A 4HJ,
United Kingdom
020 7033 9284/020 2033 9285
london@billcharles.com
www.billcharles.com

Nadege Meriau@Wyatt-Clarke & Jones 26 Mortimer
Street, London, W1W 7RB, United Kingdom
(020) 7580 7570/(07958) 712658 (020) 7903 5330
office@wyattclarkejones.com
www.wyattclarkejones.com

Nadia MacKenzie 43 Palmerston Road, London, SW14
7QA, United Kingdom
(020) 8876 2664/(07831) 284473
nadia@nadiamackenzie.com
www.nadiamackenzie.com

Naked Alphabet Studio 4 The Workshops, 43 Carol
Street, London, NW1 0HT, United Kingdom
info@makedalphabet.com
www.nakedalphabet.com

Naki Kouyioumtzis@Axiom Photographic Agency
The Pall Mall Deposit, 124-128 Barlby Road, London,
W10 6BL, United Kingdom
(020) 8964 9970/ (020) 8964 8440
info@axiomphotographic.com
www.axiomphotographic.com

Nancy Coste@Valerieherleven Boundary House (3rd
Floor), 91-93 Charterhouse Street, London, EC1M 6HR,
United Kingdom
(07775) 717474
me@valerieherleven.com
www.valerieherleven.com

Nancy Honey@L P A (Lisa Pritchard Agency) 3rd
Floor, Block A, Morelands, 5-23 Old Street, London, EC1V
9HL, United Kingdom
(020) 7250 1362/ (020) 7250 1357
info@lisapritchard.com
www.lisapritchard.com

Nanette Hoogslag@Début Art & The Coningsby Gallery 30 Tottenham Street, London, W1T 4RJ, United Kingdom
(020) 7636 1064/ (020) 7580 7017
info@debutart.com
www.debutart.com

Natasha Unit 4, Clapham North Art Centre, 26-32 Voltaire Road, London, SW4 6DH, United Kingdom
(07733) 113073
natasha@natashapiris.co.uk
www.natashapiris.co.uk

Nathan Willock Photographer 15 Levyne Court, Pine Street, London, EC1R 0JQ, United Kingdom
(020) 7837 5083/(07973) 393559 (020) 7837 5083
nathan@nw-photographer.co.uk
www.nathanwillock.com

National News Press Agency 4/5 Academy Buildings, Fanshaw Street, London, N1 6LQ, United Kingdom
(020) 7684 3000/ (020) 7684 3030
pix@nationalnews.co.uk
www.nationalpictures.co.uk

Neal Wilson Unit 1, The Studio, 23 Daleham Mews, London, NW3 5DB, United Kingdom
(07973) 437183
neal@nealwilson.com
www.nealwilson.com

Neil Barclay@Axiom Photographic Agency The Pall Mall Deposit, 124-128 Barlby Road, London, W10 6BL, United Kingdom
(020) 8964 9970/ (020) 8964 8440
info@axiomphotographic.com
www.axiomphotographic.com

Neil Barstow 93 Holland Road, Hove, East Sussex, BN3 1JP, United Kingdom
(01273) 774704/(07778) 160201
info@neilbarstow.co.uk
www.neilbarstow.co.uk

Neil Cooper Photography Grove Park, Modbury, Ivybridge, Devon, PL21 0SX, United Kingdom
(01548) 830011
neil@neilcooper.co.uk
www.neilcooper.co.uk

Neil Holden 4a Pasley Street, Plymouth, PL2 1DR, United Kingdom
(01752) 550357/(07799) 602206
neil@neilholden.net
www.neilholden.net

Neil Hudson Photography West Park Studios, Clayton Wood Road, Ring Road, Leeds, LS16 6RA, United Kingdom
0113-230 5222/(07836) 215715 0113-230 5222
neil@mosaicimaging.co.uk

Neil Leslie@Début Art & The Coningsby Gallery 30 Tottenham Street, London, W1T 4RJ, United Kingdom
(020) 7636 1064/ (020) 7580 7017
info@debutart.com
www.debutart.com

Neil Marriott, Mellis, United Kingdom
(07976) 735618
neil@neilmarriott.com
www.neilmarriott.com

Neil Mersh@Sarah Kaye Representation Ltd 38 Queen's Gate, London, SW7 5HR, United Kingdom
(020) 7225 5005/ (020) 7225 0109
sarah@sarahkaye.com
www.sarahkaye.com

Neill Menneer Belgrave Lodge, Upper Camden Place, Bath, Somerset, BA1 5JA, United Kingdom
(01225) 483151/(07970) 235052 (01225) 446394
ncm@ktwo.co.uk
www.neillmenneer.com

Neils Obee 6 Atlas Mews, Ramsgate Street, London, E8 2NE, United Kingdom
(020) 7923 0182

Neville Hornsey 128 Brick Lane, London, E1 6RU, United Kingdom
(07775) 912771
neville@applez.co.uk
www.applez.co.uk

New Dimension Photography 1 Pickering Street, Armley, Leeds, LS12 2QG, United Kingdom
0113-279 7175/(07932) 627669 0113-279 5228
info@ndp-leeds.co.uk
www.ndp-leeds.co.uk

NewsCast 4 Cannon Hill, London, London, N14 7HG, United Kingdom
(020) 8886 5895/ (020) 8882 8334
photo@newscast.co.uk
www.newscast.co.uk

NewsPics Ltd Hunter House, 150 Hutton Road, Shenfield, Brentwood, Essex, CM15 8NL, United Kingdom
(01277) 201215/ (01277) 226450
admin@newspics.co.uk
www.newspics.co.uk

Niall Clutton@Arcaid Picture Library Parc House, 25-37 Cowleaze Road, Kingston upon Thames, Surrey, KT2 6DZ, United Kingdom
(020) 8546 4352/ (020) 8541 5230
arcaid@arcaid.co.uk
www.arcaid.co.uk

Nic Kirley 1 Portsmouth Road, Thames Ditton, Surrey, KT7 0SY, United Kingdom
(020) 8398 0184/(07836) 670997 (020) 8398 0184

Nic Milner (GBCT) Birchenhall Farm, Old Storridge, Worcester, WR6 5HT, United Kingdom
(01866) 833306/(07973) 158627 (01866) 833306
nicmilner@btinternet.com

Nic Randall 61 Cranfield, Woodford, Plymouth, PL7 4PF, United Kingdom
(01752) 340847/(07831) 436645 (01752) 340847
nicam@btinternet.com
www.nicrandall.com

Nicholas Gentilli Associates Unit D4, Jaggard Way, London, SW12 8SG, United Kingdom
(020) 8772 1717/(07836) 262313 (020) 8772 1710
nicholas@nicholasgentilli.com
www.nicholasgentilli.com

Nicholas Gentilli Photography Unit d4, Jaggard Way, London, SW12 8SG, United Kingdom
(020) 8772 1717/ (020) 8772 1710
nicholas@nicholasgentilli.com
www.nicholasgentilli.com

Nicholas Kane@Arcaid Picture Library Parc House, 25-37 Cowleaze Road, Kingston upon Thames, Surrey, KT2 6DZ, United Kingdom
(020) 8546 4352/ (020) 8541 5230
arcaid@arcaid.co.uk
www.arcaid.co.uk

Nicholas Rigg 27 Gransden Avenue, London, E8 3QA, United Kingdom
(020) 8533 7457/ (020) 8533 6713
nickrigg@f2s.com
www.nicholasrigg.co.uk

Nichole Rees@A & R Photographic 16A Crane Grove, London, N7 8LE, United Kingdom
(020) 7607 3030/ (020) 7607 2190
info@aandrphotographic.com
www.aandrphotographic.co.uk

Nick Brown 2A Baguley Road, Sale Moor, Manchester, M33 2GB, United Kingdom
0161-962 8002/(07831) 831049
nick@nickbrownphoto.com
www.nickbrownphoto.com

Nick Carter 190 Dale Valley Road, Southampton, SO16 6QW, United Kingdom
(023) 8077 8400/(07976) 919021 (023) 8077 9211
nickcarterphoto@easynet.co.uk
www.photohall.com

Nick Carter Photo 190 Dale Valley Road, Southampton, SO16 6QW, United Kingdom
(023) 8077 8400/07976 919021 (023) 8077 9211
nickcarterphoto@easynet.co.uk
www.nickcarterphoto.com

Nick Clements@Terrie Tanaka Management 101 Talbot Road, London, W11 2AT, United Kingdom
(020) 7792 3500/ (020) 7792 2600
danni@terrietanaka.com
www.terrietanaka.com

Nick Cole@Sarah Kaye Representation Ltd 38 Queen's Gate, London, SW7 5HR, United Kingdom
(020) 7225 5005/ (020) 7225 0109
sarah@sarahkaye.com
www.sarahkaye.com

Nick Coughlin 16 Mannering Road, Aigburgh, Liverpool, L17 8TR, United Kingdom
0151-283 1029/(07976) 278210 0151-283 1029
coughlin.photo@virgin.net

Nick Cunard 21 Hobsons Place, London, E1 5HH, United Kingdom
(07721) 653062
nick@nickcunard.co.uk
www.nickcunard.co.uk

Nick Daly@L P A (Lisa Pritchard Agency) 3rd Floor, Block A, Morelands, 5-23 Old Street, London, EC1V 9HL, United Kingdom
(020) 7250 1362/ (020) 7250 1357
info@lisapritchard.com
www.lisapritchard.com

Nick David 3 Horton Road, London, E8 1DP, United Kingdom
(020) 7254 2737
nick@nickdavid.co.uk
www.nickdavid.co.uk

Nick Dawe@Arcaid Picture Library Parc House, 25-37 Cowleaze Road, Kingston upon Thames, Surrey, KT2 6DZ, United Kingdom
(020) 8546 4352/ (020) 8541 5230
arcaid@arcaid.co.uk
www.arcaid.co.uk

Nick Delaney 67 Hartopp Road, Leicester, LE2 1WG, United Kingdom
(07812) 049794
nick@nickdelaney.com
www.nickdelaney.com

Nick Dimbleby High Street, Syresham, Brackley, Northamptonshire, NN13 5HL, United Kingdom
(07710) 912522/ (01280) 851148
mail@nickdimbleby.com
www.nickdimbleby.com

Nick Dolding@Horton-Stephens Photographers' Agent 14 Peacock Yard, Iliffe Street, London, SE17 3LH, United Kingdom
(020) 7252 7979/ (020) 7252 6409
us@horton-stephens.com
www.horton-stephens.com

Nick Georghiou@Wyatt-Clarke & Jones 26 Mortimer Street, London, W1W 7RB, United Kingdom
(020) 7580 7570/(07958) 712658 (020) 7903 5330
office@wyattclarkejones.com
www.wyattclarkejones.com

Nick Guttridge 47 Cheadle Court, Henderson Drive, London, NW8 8UD, United Kingdom
(020) 7289 0602/ (020) 7289 0628
mail@nickguttridge.com
www.nickguttridge.com

Nick Ivins@Jo Talbot & Sue Young 6M Hyde Park Mansions, Cabbell Street, London, NW1 5BJ, United Kingdom
(020) 7262 0189/(07850) 353468 (020) 7262 2160
joandsue@btconnect.com
www.joandsue.com

Nick McGowan-Lowe Photography Unit 114, John Player Building, Stirling Enterprise Park, Stirling, FK7 7RP, United Kingdom
(01786) 474448/ (01786) 478443
nick@nml.uk.com
www.nml.uk.com

Nick Meek@Siobhan Squire 111 Shoreditch High Street, London, E1 6JN, United Kingdom
(020) 7739 8985/ (020) 7729 5125
siobhan@siobhansquire.com
www.siobhansquire.com

Nick Meers, Herefordshire, United Kingdom
(07961) 829829
nick@meersphoto.com
www.nickmeers.com

Nick Pope@Tattersall Love 40 Langham Street, London, W1W 7AS, United Kingdom
(020) 7637 5737/ (020) 7637 5747
mail@tattersall-love.com
www.tattersall-love.com

Nick Powell 115 Gloucester Avenue, London, NW1 8LB, United Kingdom
(020) 7586 3386/ (020) 7586 3386
nick@gloucesterave.demon.co.uk
www.nickpowellassociates.co.uk

Nick Robinson 101A Anderton Street, Chorley, Lancashire, PR7 2AY, United Kingdom
078 89 294102/078 89 294102 (01257) 265039
nick.robinson17@btinternet.com
www.nick-robinson-photography.co.uk

Nick Stylianou@Milc Studio 7, Zeus House, 16-30 Provost Street, London, N1 7NG, United Kingdom
(020) 7278 8838/ (0870) 0941564
gemma@milc.co.uk
www.milc.co.uk

Nick Townend Photographic Services 21 Holly Road, Hounslow, TW3 1UN, United Kingdom
(07739) 643568/ (01328) 830627
nick.townend@virgin.net
www.njtphoto.co.uk

Nick Treviss Photography Depot 14, Parsons Green Depot, Parsons Green, London, SW6 4HH, United Kingdom
(020) 7168 3868/(07712) 000583
info@nicktreviss.com
www.nicktreviss.com

Nick Veasey Radar Studios, Coldblow Lane, Thurnham, Maidstone, Kent, ME14 3LR, United Kingdom
(01622) 737722/ (01622) 738644
nick@nickveasey.com
www.nickveasey.com

Nick Wood Pavement Studios, 40-48 Bromells Road, London, SW4 0BG, United Kingdom
(020) 7720 2273/(07836) 500577
nick@nickwoodphoto.com
www.nickwoodphoto.com

Nick Wright, London, SW4 9NS, United Kingdom
(020) 7622 5223

Nicky Emmerson@T Photographic 1 Heathgate Place, 75-83 Agincourt Road, London, London, NW3 2NU, United Kingdom
(020) 7428 6070/ (020) 7428 6079
peter@tphotographic.com
www.tphotographic.com

Nicky Gissing@Début Art & The Coningsby Gallery 30 Tottenham Street, London, W1T 4RJ, United Kingdom
(020) 7636 1064/ (020) 7580 7017
info@debutart.com
www.debutart.com

Nicky Ryan Photography, London, United Kingdom
(07973) 620623
info@nickyryan.co.uk
www.nickyryan.co.uk

Nicola Gotts Photographer 124 Warwards Lane, Birmingham, B29 7RD, United Kingdom
0121-472 3355
www.nicolagotts.co.uk

Nicola Hippisley@Inspired Reflection 28 Dayton Grove, Peckham, London, SE15 2NX, United Kingdom
(0870) 9193587/(07040) 402770 (0870) 9193588
deborah@inspiredreflection.com
www.inspiredreflection.com

Nicola Jeffries 9 St. Lukes Close, Whitstable, Kent, CT5 4FB, United Kingdom
(07976) 160842
nj@nicolajeffries.co.uk
www.nicolajeffries.co.uk

Nicolas Clerc@The Katy Barker Agency Ltd 11 Mason's Arms Mews, Maddox Street, London, W1S 1NX, United Kingdom
(020) 7493 3933/ (020) 7493 3311
catherine@katybarker.com
www.katybarker.com

Nicolas Herbert 35 Abingdon Close, London, NW1 9UT, United Kingdom
(07791) 705390
nicolas.herbert@gmail.com

Nicolas Tikhomiroff@Magnum Photos 63 Gee Street, London, EC1V 3RS, United Kingdom
(020) 7490 1771/ (020) 7608 0020
magnum@magnumphotos.co.uk
www.magnumphotos.com

Nicolas Tucker 24 Hasker Street, London, SW3 2LG, United Kingdom
(020) 7589 4976/ (020) 7589 4976
nic@nictucker.com
www.nictucker.com

Nicole Nodland Flat 27, Advance House, 109 Ladbroke Grove, London, W11 1PG, United Kingdom
(07957) 161097/ (020) 7221 6044
nicnodland@aol.com
www.pearcestoner.com

Nigel Allsop 25 Glyn Mansions, Earsby Street, London, W14 8HX, United Kingdom
(020) 7603 0046/ (020) 7603 0046
cartierbresson@hotmail.com

Nigel Davies 86 Croxted Road, London, SE21 8NP, United Kingdom
(07850) 285355
nigel@nigeldavies.co.uk
www.nigeldavies.co.uk

Nigel Haynes Still Life Photography 60 Astbury Road, London, SE15 2NJ, United Kingdom
(020) 7652 4541

Nigel Hudson Thistle Cottage, Great Bedwyn, Marlborough, Wiltshire, SN8 3LH, United Kingdom
(01672) 870957/(07778) 806767 (01672) 870957
nigel@nigelhudson.co.uk
www.nigelhudson.co.uk

Nigel Limb Top Floor, 134-146 Curtain Road, London, London, EC2A 3AR, United Kingdom
(020) 7739 4199/ (0870) 0524 242
nigel@crs.demon.co.uk
www.curtainroadstudios.com

Nigel Millard Studio Dunstone Court, Widecombe-in-the-Moor, Newton Abbot, Devon, TQ13 7TH, United Kingdom
(01364) 621335/(0797) 0020003
info@nigelmillard.co.uk
www.nigelmillard.co.uk

Nigel Riches, London, United Kingdom
(01264) 860078/(07702) 124981
nigel.riches@virgin.net
(info@adrenalinmanagement.com)
www.nigelriches.co.uk

Nigel Riches Photography Ltd 7 Round Hill, London, SE26 4RF, United Kingdom
(020) 8742 1532/ (020) 8742 1532
nigel.riches@virgin.net

Nigel Taylor Photography Ltd Britannia Road, Sale, Cheshire, M33 2AA, United Kingdom
0161-969 5433/(07770) 275312 0161-962 8286
nigel@taylor.u-net.com
www.nigeltaylorphoto.co.uk

Nikos Economopoulos@Magnum Photos 63 Gee Street, London, EC1V 3RS, United Kingdom
(020) 7490 1771/ (020) 7608 0020
magnum@magnumphotos.co.uk
www.magnumphotos.com

Nils Jorgensen 18 Vine Hill, London, EC1R 5DZ, United Kingdom
(020) 7278 7294/ (020) 7837 4812
www.rexfeatures.com

No Fluffy Rugs & Cloudy Backgrounds The Photographers Studio, 16 Langston Priory Workshops, Kingham, Chipping Norton, Oxfordshire, OX7 6UP, United Kingdom
(01608) 683989
ella@cobert.fsnet.co.uk
www.nofluffyrugs-photography.co.uk

Nobby Clark, London, United Kingdom
(020) 7924 0302
nobby@nobbyclark.co.uk

Noelle Hoeppe@Mark George 5 St. George's Court, 131 Putney Bridge Road, Putney, London, SW15 2PA, United Kingdom
(020) 8877 9922/(07771) 595 999 (020) 8870 5533
mg@markgeorge.com
www.markgeorge.com

Noelle Pickford 27 Britton Street, EC1M 5UD, United Kingdom
(020) 7336 6773/ (020) 7336 7043
info@noellerepresents.com
www.noellerepresents.com

Noonwright Ltd 2 Seven Dials Court, 3 Shorts Garden, Covent Garden, London, WC2H 9AT, United Kingdom
(020) 7240 7277/ (020) 7240 7278
mail@noonwright.co.uk
www.noonwright.com

Noorie Parvez 114 St Ann's Hill, London, SW18 2RR, United Kingdom
(020) 8874 3960
www.noorie.co.uk

Norbert Galea 171 Acton Lane, Chiswick, London, W4 5HN, United Kingdom
(020) 8995 0585/(07944) 665405
norbert@ngstudio.freeserve.co.uk

Norbert Kniat@Andrea Walji Agency 6 Brewer Street, London, W1F 0SB, United Kingdom
(020) 7439 4144/(07789) 871871 (020) 7439 4133
andrea@andreawalji.com
www.andreawalji.com

Norbert Schoerner@C L M Top Floor, 19 All Saints Road, London, W11 1HE, United Kingdom
(020) 7750 2999/ (020) 7792 8507
clm@clmuk.com
www.clmuk.com

Norma Walton 23 Reed Close, Bridgwater, Somerset, TA6 6UX, United Kingdom
(07710) 298793
norma.walton@btinternet.com
www.normawalton.com

Norman Hollands 1k Woodstock Studios, 36 Woodstock Grove, London, W12 8LE, United Kingdom
(020) 8749 9990/(07970) 257778 (020) 8749 9777
normanhollands@mac.com

Norman McBeath 4 Learmonth Gardens Mews, Edinburgh, EH4 1EX, United Kingdom
0131-343 2375/(07796) 944719
nm@normanmcbeath.com
www.normanmcbeath.com

Northern Photography 30 Fitzroy Drive, Leeds, LS8 1RP, United Kingdom
0113-293 0339/ 0113-293 0339
john-north@ntlworld.com
www.northern-photography.co.uk

Norwyn Ltd 1 Hardy Close, Nelson Business Center, Preston, PR2 2XP, United Kingdom
(01772) 739985/ (01772) 739984
info@norwyn.co.uk
www.norwyn.co.uk

O'Reilly Studio 60 Belmont Park, London, SE13 5BM, United Kingdom
(020) 8297 8972/ (020) 8297 8972
info@oreillystudio.com

Oakes Studios Broadway House, 60 Calthorpe Road, Edgbaston, Birmingham, B15 1TN, United Kingdom
(07958) 712088
graham@oakesstudios.com
www.oakesstudios.com

Oli Tennent@Agent Pandora 12 Stonells Road, London, SW11 6HQ, United Kingdom
(07966) 181825
pandora@agentpandora.com
www.agentpandora.com

Oliver Beamish 49 Dorien Road, London, SW20 8EL, United Kingdom
(07973) 354259
oliver@beamishcreative.com
www.beamishcreative.com

Oliver Burston@Début Art & The Coningsby Gallery 30 Tottenham Street, London, W1T 4RJ, United Kingdom
(020) 7636 1064/ (020) 7580 7017
info@debutart.com
www.debutart.com

Oliver Gordon@Wilde Representation 314 Mare Street, London, E8 1HA, United Kingdom
(020) 8653 4466/(07810) 795036 (01424) 201070
sian@wilderepresentation.com
www.wilderepresentation.com

Oliver Hunter 73 Parkholme Road, London, E8 3AQ, United Kingdom
(020) 7241 1924/ (020) 7241 1924
olyhun@hotmail.com

Oliver Upton@Blowup 146 Amyand Park Road, St. Margaret's, Twickenham, TW1 3HY, United Kingdom
(020) 8744 0210/ (020) 8892 2521
orders@blowup.net
www.blowup.net

Olivia Beasley@Burnham Niker Unit 8, Canonbury Business Centre, 190A New North Road, London, N1 7BJ, United Kingdom
(020) 7704 6565/ (020) 7704 8383
enquiries@burnham-niker.com
www.burnham-niker.com

Olly Ball 55b Chapel Lane, Wilmslow, Cheshire, SK9 5JH, United Kingdom
(01625) 526813/ (01625) 526813
olly@ollyball.com
www.ollyball.co.uk

Oly Barnsley@T Photographic 1 Heathgate Place, 75-83 Agincourt Road, London, London, NW3 2NU, United Kingdom
(020) 7428 6070/ (020) 7428 6079
peter@tphotographic.com
www.tphotographic.com

Omer Knaz@Hungry Tiger Unit 16, The Piper Building, Peterborough Road, London, SW6 3EF, United Kingdom
- (020) 7751 8600/ (020) 7751 8618
- studio@hungrytiger.co.uk
- www.hungrytiger.co.uk

One Ninety Three 193 Moseley Street, Digbeth, Birmingham, B12 0RT, United Kingdom
- 0121-608 6666/ 0121-608 9666
- studio@oneninetythree.com
- www.oneninetythree.com

One Shot Photography 30 Hartland Road, London, NW1 8DD, United Kingdom
- (07961) 407158
- info@1shot.com
- www.1shot.uk.com

Ormathwaite 35 Earlsferry Way, Islington, London, N1 0DZ, United Kingdom
- 020 7609 5608/07957 450174/ 020 7609 5608
- ormathwaite.photos@virgin.net
- www.ormathwaite.co.uk

Otello Damonte@Martin Dawe Photography 347 Edinburgh Avenue, Slough, SL1 4TU, United Kingdom
- (01753) 828828/ (01753) 828822
- hello@martindawedesign.co.uk
- www.martindawedesign.co.uk

Othello De'Souza-Hartley 26 Banner House, Roscoe, London, EC1M 8SX, United Kingdom
- (020) 7193 2830/(07886) 510727
- othello@othellodesouzahartley.com
- www.othellodesouzahartley.com

P M Photography The Old Stables, High Street, Bryngwran, Holyhead, Gwynedd, LL65 3PP, United Kingdom
- (01407) 720407/(07774) 808613
- paul.mattock@virgin.net
- www.pmphotography.co.uk

P R T Photography Unit 1A, Darcy Business Centre, Darcy Business Park, Neath, SA10 6EJ, United Kingdom
- (01792) 815670/(07798) 877398
- info@paulthomasphotography.com
- www.paulthomasphotography.com

P W I 43-44 Hoxton Square, London, N1 6PB, United Kingdom
- (020) 7739 5577/(07704) 519564 / (020) 7729 0560
- susan@pwis.com
- www.pwis.com

P.J. Gates Photography Unit H, London Stone Business Estate, London, SW8 3QR, United Kingdom
- (020) 7498 8233/ (020) 7498 8649
- pjgates@wanadoo.co.uk

Packshot Company Ltd 43 Carol Street, Camden Town, London, NW1 0HT, United Kingdom
- **(020) 7267 0700/ (020) 7267 7721**
- **lee@packshot.com**
- **www.packshot.com**
- **See ad in showcase**

Packshot Factory 39-41 New Oxford Street, London, WC1A 1BN, United Kingdom
- **(020) 7379 3080/ (020) 7240 9568**
- **martin@packshotfactory.co.uk**
- **www.packshotfactory.co.uk**
- **See ad in showcase**

Paddy Cutts 25 Hollies Road, Ealing, London, W5 4UU, United Kingdom
- (020) 8568 4960/ (020) 8560 9965
- paddy@animalsunlimited.co.uk
- www.animalsunlimited.co.uk

Paddy Eckersley@David Edmunds Represents Unit 105, 54-58 Kingsland Road, London, E2 8DP, United Kingdom
- (020) 7739 1166/(07785) 580024
- info@davidedmundsrepresents.com
- www.davidedmundsrepresents.com

Page One 11 West Avenue, West Bridgford, Nottingham, NG2 7NL, United Kingdom
- 0115-981-8880/ 0115-981-4404
- abi@pageonephotographers.com
- www.pageonephotographers.com

Pan 3Sixty Ltd Biggin Hall Lane, Thurlaston, Rugby, Warwickshire, CV23 9LD, United Kingdom
- (0845) 6443605
- info@pan3sixty.com
- www.pan3sixty.com

Pank Sethi Photography & Digital Art 6 Lichfield Road, London, N9 9HD, United Kingdom
- (07919) 436 836
- pank@panksethi-photography.co.uk
- www.panksethi-photography.co.uk

Panoptika Bourgueralt, Chevannes, Billy Chevannes, 58270, France
- 00 33 3 86 60 20 53
- photo@panoptika.net
- www.panoptika.net

Panoscan 34 Rita Road, London, SW8 1JU, United Kingdom
- (020) 7582 8750/ (020) 7793 0467
- cinebuild@btclick.com
- www.cinebuild.com

Panteli Illustration, London, United Kingdom
- (020) 7272 9940/(07961) 878346 / (020) 7272 9940
- imaging@panteli.net
- www.panteli.net

Paolo Pellegrin@Magnum Photos 63 Gee Street, London, EC1V 3RS, United Kingdom
- (020) 7490 1771/ (020) 7608 0020
- magnum@magnumphotos.co.uk
- www.magnumphotos.com

Papilio Natural History & Travel Library 155 Station Road, Herne Bay, Kent, CT6 5QA, United Kingdom
- (01227) 360996
- library@papiliophotos.com
- www.papiliophotos.com

Parallax Models 63 Clerkenwell Road, London, EC1M 5NP, United Kingdom
- (020) 7253 6777/(07770) 328003
- steve@stevecolman.biz

Pat Doyle 17 Willow Street, London, EC2A 4BH, United Kingdom
- (020) 7729 0727

PAT Features 1610, Sector 18-D, Chandigarth, 10018, India
- 00 91 172 272 5641/00 91 941 721 0101
- thakurparamjit@yahoo.co.uk

Pat Shirreff-Thomas (IVCA) 5 Morris Street, Hook, Hampshire, RG27 9NT, United Kingdom
- (01256) 767090/(07831) 519217 / (01256) 767612
- www.greenshoots.co.uk

Patrice De Villiers@Carolyn Trayler Photographers Agent Unit 566, 56 Gloucester Road, London, SW7 4UB, United Kingdom
- (020) 7370 0712/ (020) 7370 0765
- carolyn@trayler.co.uk
- www.trayler.co.uk

Patricia Niven Photographer 115 Crescent House, Goswell Road, London, EC1Y 0SJ, United Kingdom
- (07958) 665629
- info@patricianiven.com
- www.patricianiven.com

Patrick Blake 8 Chippenham Mews, London, W9 2AW, United Kingdom
- (020) 7286 5148/(07947) 644545 / (020) 7266 2335
- info@patrickblake.com
- www.patrickblake.com

Patrick Coughlin 14A Hesper Mews, London, SW5 0HH, United Kingdom
- (020) 7373 7859
- patrickcoughlin@btconnect.com
- www.patrickcoughlin.co.uk

Patrick Eagar 1 Queensberry Place, Friars Lane, Richmond, Surrey, TW9 1NW, United Kingdom
- (020) 8940 9269/ (020) 8332 1229
- patrick@patrickeagar.com
- www.patrickeagar.com

Patrick Gosling 28 Jeraldine Road, London, SW18 2NT, United Kingdom
- /(07831) 587350
- patrick@patrickgosling.com
- www.patrickgosling.com

Patrick Llewelyn-Davies 1 Dallington Street, London, EC1V 0BH, United Kingdom
- (020) 7253 2838/(07866) 622478
- patrick@llewelyn-davies.com
- www.llewelyn-davies.com/indexchb.html

Patrick Morgan@Début Art & The Coningsby Gallery 30 Tottenham Street, London, W1T 4RJ, United Kingdom
- (020) 7636 1064/ (020) 7580 7017
- info@debutart.com
- www.debutart.com

Patrick Ryan@Victoria Lees Management (VLM) 2 Fairview Gardens, Woodford Green, Essex, IG8 7DJ, United Kingdom
- (07710) 287220/ (020) 8504 8125
- victoria@victorialeesmanagement.co.uk
- www.victorialeesmanagement.co.uk

Patrick Thimbleby Photography 47a Springfield Road, Harrow, Middlesex, HA1 1QF, United Kingdom
- (020) 8427 9747/ (020) 8427 9747
- pat@thimbleby.org
- www.patrickthimbleby.com

Patrick Zachmann@Magnum Photos 63 Gee Street, London, EC1V 3RS, United Kingdom
- (020) 7490 1771/ (020) 7608 0020
- magnum@magnumphotos.co.uk
- www.magnumphotos.com

Pau Ros, London, N16 6UN, United Kingdom
- (020) 8806 2090
- pau@blueyonder.co.uk
- www.pauros.com

Paul & Paul 88a Walcot Street, Bath, BA1 5BD, United Kingdom
- (020) 7209 1444/ (01225) 471847
- paulhames@thewalcotstudio.com
- www.paulandpaul.co.uk

Paul Andrews 14 Dixon Close, Aylesbury, Buckinghamshire, HP21 8FU, United Kingdom
- (07921) 801402
- pd_andrewss@yahoo.co.uk

Paul Anton 2C Macfarlane Road, London, W12 7JY, United Kingdom
- (020) 8749 0264/ (020) 8740 8873
- info@paulscape.com
- www.paulscape.com

Paul Barbera@edsonwilliams photography consultancy 52 Brushfield Street, London, E1 6AJ, United Kingdom
- (020) 7375 2077/(07867) 517777 / (020) 7375 3077
- info@edsonwilliams.com
- www.edsonwilliams.com

Paul Beard Photo Agency PBPA House, 33 Sanctuary Close, Worcester, WR2 5PY, United Kingdom
- (01905) 749959
- pbphotography@btconnect.com
- http://home.btconnect.com/pbphotography

Paul Bevitt 3A The Courtyard, 44 Gloucester Avenue, London, NW1 8JD, United Kingdom
- (020) 7586 8500/ (020) 7586 8868
- paul@paulbevitt.co.uk
- www.paulbevitt.com

Paul Biddle@Sharon Brandman Agency No 2 Milner Court, Bridgewater Way, Bushey, WD23 4UB, United Kingdom
- 020 8950 9213/07973 305575 / 020 8950 7990
- sharon@sharonbrandman.com
- www.sharonbrandman.com

Paul Bock Photography 128 Pitt Street, Edinburgh, EH6 4DD, United Kingdom
- 0131-553 6333/(07860) 539130
- paul@paulbock.com
- www.paulbock.com

Paul Bricknell 2 Bleeding Heart Yard, London, EC1N 8SJ, United Kingdom
- (020) 7404 6044/(07836) 687415
- info@paulbricknell.com
- www.paulbricknell.com

Paul Brooking The Old Wall, 6 The Upper Butts, Brentford, Middlesex, TW8 8DA, United Kingdom
- (020) 8560 4900
- info@paulbrooking.com
- www.paulbrooking.com

Paul Bussell Photography 19 Shaftesbury Way, Strawberry Hill, Twickenham, TW2 5RN, United Kingdom
- **(020) 8898 6006/(07836) 263388 / (020) 8995 1199**
- **paul@paulbussell.com**
- **www.paulbussell.com**
- **See ad in showcase**

Paul Campbell 14 Oldfield Road, Hampton, Middlesex, TW12 2AB, United Kingdom
- (020) 8941 1725
- paul@paulcampbellsnaps.com
- www.paulcampbellphotographer.com

Paul Carter 7 College Road, Woolston, Southampton, SO19 9GD, United Kingdom
(023) 8043 6191/ (023) 8043 1070
paul@paulcarter-photographer.co.uk
www.paulcarter-photographer.co.uk

Paul Cooper 73 High Street, Hampton Hill, Middlesex, TW12 1NH, United Kingdom
(020) 8979 4942/(07966) 518310 (020) 8979 4942
paul@hamptonhillstudios.co.uk
www.hamptonhillstudios.co.uk

Paul Cordwell@Julian Cotton Photographers Agent 55 Upper Montagu Street, London, W1H 1SF, United Kingdom
(020) 7723 3100/ (020) 7724 7555
info@juliancotton.co.uk
www.juliancotton.co.uk

Paul Cordwell Photographer 3 Century Park, Garrison Lane, Birmingham, B9 4NZ, United Kingdom
(07831) 416477/0121-766 8444
paul@paulcordwell.com
www.paulcordwell.co.uk

Paul Corey Photography, Ennis, Co. Clare, Ireland, Republic of
00 353 897 671 716
paul@paulcorey.ie
www.paulcorey.ie

Paul Dance 115 Epping Way, Witham, Essex, CM8 1ND, United Kingdom
(07860) 376464
pauldancephoto@yahoo.co.uk

Paul Dawson 1 Gloucester Road, Harrow, Middlesex, HA1 4PP, United Kingdom
(07976) 977195
pauldawson@pdphoto.com
www.pdphoto.com

Paul Farnham Flat C, The Vicarage, 152 Commercial Street, London, E1 6NU, United Kingdom
(07881) 554601
info@paulfarnham.com
www.paulfarnham.com

Paul Felix Hornbeam House, Robinson Lane, Cirencester, Gloucestershire, GL7 7EN, United Kingdom
(01285) 831703/ (01285) 831045
photos@paulfelix.co.uk
www.paulfelix.co.uk

Paul Fisher 53 Laitwood Road, Balham, London, SW12 9QH, United Kingdom
(020) 8675 2463/(07710) 198315
paul@paulfisherphotos.com
www.paulfisherphotos.com

Paul Fosbury@Julian Cotton Photographers Agent 55 Upper Montagu Street, London, W1H 1SF, United Kingdom
(020) 7723 3100/ (020) 7724 7555
info@juliancotton.co.uk
www.juliancotton.co.uk

Paul Fusco@Magnum Photos 63 Gee Street, London, EC1V 3RS, United Kingdom
(020) 7490 1771/ (020) 7608 0020
magnum@magnumphotos.co.uk
www.magnumphotos.com

Paul Graham Photography 41 Fourth Avenue, Millerston, Glasgow, G33 6JZ, United Kingdom
(0141) 7794985
paul@paulgraham.org
www.paulgraham.org

Paul Graves@Upper Orange Nostitzstrasse 15, Berlin, 10961, Germany
49 178 6121661/ 49 30 6121661
mail@upperorange.com
www.upperorange.de

Paul Greenwood@Hungry Tiger Unit 16, The Piper Building, Peterborough Road, London, SW6 3EF, United Kingdom
(020) 7751 8600/ (020) 7751 8618
studio@hungrytiger.co.uk
www.hungrytiger.co.uk

Paul Groom Photography 16 Cherry Orchard, Wotton-under-Edge, Gloucestershire, GL12 7HT, United Kingdom
(07917) 224480
paul@paulgroomphotography.com
www.paulgroomphotography.com

Paul Hackett@Axiom Photographic Agency The Pall Mall Deposit, 124-128 Barlby Road, London, W10 6BL, United Kingdom
(020) 8964 9970/ (020) 8964 8440
info@axiomphotographic.com
www.axiomphotographic.com

Paul Harness BSc (Hons) LBIPP DipM 41 Pondfields Drive, Kippax, Leeds, LS25 7HJ, United Kingdom
0113-286 0909
info@paulharness.co.uk
www.paulharness.co.uk

Paul Hartley 23 Hurlingham Studios, Ranelagh Gardens, London, SW6 3PA, United Kingdom
(020) 7731 0244/ (020) 7384 2567
info@hartleystudios.com
www.hartleystudios.com
See ad in showcase

Paul Johnson 25 Dorset Avenue, East Grinstead, West Sussex, RH19 2AB, United Kingdom
(01342) 317000
www.pjphoto.co.uk

Paul Jones 15 Rudyard Road, Salford, M6 7QN, United Kingdom
0161-279 1856/(07802) 167972 0161-279 1856
info@pauljones-photographer.com
www.pauljones-photographer.com

Paul Keep Studio 4, 65 Leonard Street, London, EC2A 4QS, United Kingdom
(020) 7739 2413/(07850) 065914 (020) 7739 2413
www.contact-me.net/paulkeep

Paul King Unit 21, Perseverance Works, London, E2 8DD, United Kingdom
(020) 7739 9679/(07860) 538888 (020) 7613 2417
pk@paul-king.com
www.paul-king.com

Paul Lund 20 Elm Road, Ewell Village, Epsom, Surrey, KT17 2EU, United Kingdom
(020) 8394 2390/(07831) 559 880 (020) 8394 2390
mail@paullund.com
www.paullund.com

Paul Medley Photography & Design 28 Fairacres Road, Oxford, OX4 1TF, United Kingdom
(01865) 723316
info@paulmedley.co.uk
www.paulmedley.co.uk

Paul Mellor 87 Clerkenwell Road, London, EC1R 5BX, United Kingdom
(020) 7405 0013/ (020) 7405 8877
paul@paulmellorphotography.co.uk
www.paulmellorphotography.co.uk

Paul Miles@Axiom Photographic Agency The Pall Mall Deposit, 124-128 Barlby Road, London, W10 6BL, United Kingdom
(020) 8964 9970/ (020) 8964 8440
info@axiomphotographic.com
www.axiomphotographic.com

Paul Murphy@van Hauen Moore 14 Powis Mews, Notting Hill, London, W11 1JN, United Kingdom
(020) 7792 0022/ (020) 7792 8636
email@vanhauenmoore.com
www.vanhauenmoore.com

Paul Noble Photographic Unit 4, Teknol House, Burgess Hill, West Sussex, RH15 9LH, United Kingdom
(01444) 232367/(07860) 654724
paul@pnoblephoto.com
www.pnoblephoto.net

Paul Pickard Photography The Studio, Ranton, Stafford, ST18 9JX, United Kingdom
(07720) 238997
paulpickardfolio@yahoo.com
www.paulpickard.com

Paul Quayle@Axiom Photographic Agency The Pall Mall Deposit, 124-128 Barlby Road, London, W10 6BL, United Kingdom
(020) 8964 9970/ (020) 8964 8440
info@axiomphotographic.com
www.axiomphotographic.com

Paul Quinn@Tattersall Love 40 Langham Street, London, W1W 7AS, United Kingdom
(020) 7637 5737/ (020) 7637 5747
mail@tattersall-love.com
www.tattersall-love.com

Paul Raeside 36 St. Johns Square, Clerkenwell, London, EC1V 4JJ, United Kingdom
(07836) 554266
mail@paulraeside.com
www.paulraeside.com

Paul Reas@Marco Santucci Photography 85 Essex Road, London, N1 2SF, United Kingdom
(020) 7226 7705/ (020) 7226 9563
email@marcosantucci.com
www.marcosantucci.com

Paul Rider@Shoot Production Ltd 23 Glebe Road, London, N8 7DA, United Kingdom
(020) 8442 9171/ (020) 8348 7404
adele@shootgroup.com
www.shootgroup.com

Paul Smith@Mark George 5 St. George's Court, 131 Putney Bridge Road, Putney, London, SW15 2PA, United Kingdom
(020) 8877 9922/(07771) 595 999 (020) 8870 5533
mg@markgeorge.com
www.markgeorge.com

Paul Spencer 22 Denmark Terrace, Brighton, BN1 3AN, United Kingdom
(07880) 742711
paolospencer@mac.com
www.paulaspencer.eu

Paul Thompson@Noelle Pickford 27 Britton Street, London, EC1M 5UD, United Kingdom
(020) 7336 6773/ (020) 7336 7043
info@noellerepresents.com
www.noellerepresents.com

Paul Tozer 103 Packington Square, London, N1 7UA, United Kingdom
(020) 7359 9231/(07831) 805787
paul@paulttozer.com
www.paultozer.com

Paul Venning 1 Stable Yard, Danemere Street, London, SW15 1LT, United Kingdom
(07836) 738842
paul@paulvenning.co.uk
www.paulvenning.co.uk

Paul Wakefield@Wendy Jackson Tag Creative, 29 Clerkenwell Road, London, EC1M 5TA, United Kingdom
(020) 3217 2241/(07711) 084801 (020) 7439 1971
wjackson@tagworldwide.com
www.wendyjackson.co.uk

Paul Watt Photography The Studio, 630 Lanark Road, Edinburgh, EH14 5EW, United Kingdom
0131-453 4088/(07831) 709058 0131-453 4088
admin@paulwatt.co.uk
www.paulwatt.co.uk

Paul Watts Photography Trelawney Lodge, Keveral Lane, Seaton, Torpoint, Cornwall, PL11 3JJ, United Kingdom
(01503) 250673/ (01503) 250383
paul@imageclick.co.uk
www.imageclick.co.uk

Paul Webster 11 Parke Road, London, SW13 9NF, United Kingdom
(020) 8748 5786/(07860) 247562 (020) 8748 5786
info@paulsnap.com
www.paulsnap.com
See ad in showcase

Paul Westlake@A & R Photographic 16A Crane Grove, London, N7 8LE, United Kingdom
(020) 7607 3030/ (020) 7607 2190
info@aandrphotographic.com
www.aandrphotographic.co.uk

Paul Wetherell@MAP 72 Rochester Place, London, NW1 9JX, United Kingdom
(020) 7424 9144/ (020) 7284 3274
info@mapltd.com
www.mapltd.com

Paul Williams 6 Cedar Way, London, NW1 0PD, United Kingdom
(020) 7387 2637
www.big30films.com

Paul Winch-Furness 11 Hawthorn Hill, Letchworth Garden City, Hertfordshire, SG6 4HE, United Kingdom
(01462) 442282/(07836) 311359
mail@paulwf.co.uk
www.paulwf.co.uk

Paul Zak@Burnham Niker Unit 8, Canonbury Business Centre, 190A New North Road, London, N1 7BJ, United Kingdom
(020) 7704 6565/ (020) 7704 8383
enquiries@burnham-niker.com
www.burnham-niker.com

Paul@Paul@Swerve Photography 29-31 Saffron Hill, London, EC1N 8SW, United Kingdom
/(07967) 628769
info@swervephotography.com
www.swervephotography.com

Paula Claridge Errochty House, Calvine, Pitlochry, Perthshire, PH18 5UD, United Kingdom
(01796) 483308/(07850) 606303 (01796) 483377

Paula Glassman 37 Stapleton Hall Road, London, N4 3QE, United Kingdom
✆ (07973) 360150
✎ paula@paulaglassman.com
🖥 www.paulaglassman.com

Pauline Lord 4 Thornhill Road, Islington, London, N1 1HW, United Kingdom
✆ (020) 7609 4439/✆ (020) 7609 4439
✎ paulinaphotos@beeb.net

Peak Photographer Sunny Hill, Milford, Belper, Derbyshire, DE56 0QR, United Kingdom
✆ (07976) 969096
✎ mail@peakphotographer.co.uk
🖥 www.peakphotographer.co.uk

Pearce Stoner Associates 12B Links Yard, Spelman St, London, E1 5LX, United Kingdom
✆ (020) 7247 7100/✆ (020) 7247 7144
✎ info@pearcestoner.com
🖥 www.pearcestoner.com

Pearson Lyle Management 3rd Fl, 40 Bowling Green Ln, London, EC1R 0NE, United Kingdom
✆ (020) 7415 7061/✆ (020) 7415 7059
✎ contact@pearsonlyle.co.uk
🖥 www.pearsonlyle.co.uk

Peartree Rental Ltd Lower Ground Floor, 53 Central St, London, EC1V 8AD, United Kingdom
✆ (020) 7251 2044/078 41260777 ✆ (020) 7251 2455
✎ info@peartreerental.com
🖥 www.peartreerental.com

Pedro Alvarez@van Hauen Moore 14 Powis Mews, Notting Hill, London, W11 1JN, United Kingdom
✆ (020) 7792 0022/✆ (020) 7792 8636
✎ email@vanhauenmoore.com
🖥 www.vanhauenmoore.com

Peer Lindgreen@Wyatt-Clarke & Jones 26 Mortimer St, London, W1W 7RB, United Kingdom
✆ (020) 7580 7570/07958) 712658 ✆ (020) 7903 5330
✎ office@wyattclarkejones.com
🖥 www.wyattclarkejones.com

Penny Cottee@Vue Units 1 & 2 Elm Ct, 1 Royal Oak Yd, London, SE1 3TP, United Kingdom
✆ (020) 7403 5555/✆ (020) 7403 2005
✎ production@vue-us.com
🖥 www.vue-us.com

Penrose Photographer The Studio, Wroxham Road, Poole, Dorset, BH12 1HB, United Kingdom
✆ (01202) 762310
✎ mail@penrosephotographer.co.uk
🖥 www.penrosephotographer.co.uk

Perfect Pictures 49 Alexandra Road, Denton, Gravesend, Kent, DA12 2QG, United Kingdom
✆ (01474) 327742
✎ sales@perfect-pictures.net
🖥 www.perfect-pictures.net

Personal Paparazzi 3 Elm Grove, Prestwich, Manchester, M25 3DN, United Kingdom
✆ (07725) 029978

Pete Chinn Unit 4A, The Old Malt House, Little Anne Street, Bristol, BS2 9EB, United Kingdom
✆ 0117-955 5449/(07831) 700834 ✆ 0117-954 1158
✎ mail@petechinn.com
🖥 www.petechinn.com

Pete Cronin Photography 14 Lakes Road, Keston, Kent, BR2 6BN, United Kingdom
✆ (01689) 858719
✎ pete@petecronin.com
🖥 www.petecronin.com

Pete Gardner Unit 27, Chelsea Warf, 15 Lots Road, London, SW10 0QJ, United Kingdom
✆ (020) 7351 1932/07860 787860
✎ mail@petegardner.co.uk
🖥 www.petegardner.co.uk

Pete Rushton 79 Warwick Street, Birmingham, B12 0NH, United Kingdom
✆ 01332 863 110/✆ 0121-766 5149
✎ info@peterushton.com

Pete Seaward 6 Church End, Bletchingdon, Kidlington, Oxfordshire, OX5 3DL, UK
✆ (01869) 351393
✎ pete@peteseaward.com
🖥 www.peteseaward.com

Peter A. Defty The Spire, Leeds Road, Halifax, West Yorkshire, HX3 8NU, United Kingdom
✆ (01422) 200788/(07973) 460729 ✆ (01422) 200788
✎ peter@drifty.demon.co.uk
🖥 www.the-aop.org

Peter Arnold Flat A, 36 Eaton Square, London, SW1W 9DH, United Kingdom
✆ (020) 7235 6663/(07971) 560410 ✆ (020) 7235 6663
✎ peter@menexposed.co.uk
🖥 www.menexposed.co.uk

Peter Beavis 54 Fairlawn Grove, London, W4 5EH, United Kingdom
✆ (07860) 758861
✎ peter@peterbeavis.com
🖥 www.peterbeavis.com

Peter Birch 23 Gibb Street, Birmingham, B9 4AA, United Kingdom
✆ 0121-773 2116/(07860) 452988 ✆ 0121-773 5939
✎ mail@peterbirch.co.uk
🖥 www.peterbirch.co.uk

Peter Chatterton 83 Lilliput Road, Poole, Dorset, BH14 8JX, United Kingdom
✆ (01202) 706565/(07973) 229283 ✆ (01202) 706565
✎ pete@photo4.net
🖥 www.photo4.net

Peter Christian@John Parkinson Photographic Agent Unit 17, 1-10 Summer's Street, London, EC1R 5BD, United Kingdom
✆ (020) 7278 6882/✆ (020) 7278 1251
✎ johnparkinsonagency@btinternet.com
🖥 www.johnparkinsonagency.co.uk

Peter Davis 21 Bleachfield Street, Alcester, Warwickshire, B49 5BB, United Kingdom
✆ (07720) 722971

Peter Day Photographer Unit 7, Riverside Workshops, 28 Park Street, London, SE1 9EQ, United Kingdom
✆ (020) 7378 7780
✎ peter@peterdayphoto.com
🖥 www.peterdayphoto.com

Peter Dench@Jo Talbot & Sue Young 6M Hyde Park Mansions, Cabbell Street, London, NW1 5BJ, United Kingdom
✆ (020) 7262 0189/(07850) 353468 ✆ (020) 7262 2160
✎ joandsue@btconnect.com
🖥 www.joandsue.com

studio fulham

ORLEBAR BROWN
BEACH + SWIM SHORTS

Fashion - Accessories - Products - Packshots
London studio & on location in the UK & Europe

t: +44 207 7751 3030

w: www.StudioFulham.com   e: info@StudioFulham.com

Peter Dixon 11 Gibralter Walk, London, E2 7LH, United Kingdom
✆ (020) 7729 2664/(07770) 303229 ✆ (020) 7729 3861
✎ peterdixon99@hotmail.com

Peter Durkes Unit 27, Dehavalland Studios, 20 Theydon Road, London, E5 9NY, United Kingdom
✆ (020) 8806 9900/✆ (020) 8806 0200
✎ peter.durkes@btinternet.com

Peter Funch@Bonakdar Cleary 35 Charles Square, London, N1 6HT, United Kingdom
✆ (020) 7490 1155
✎ bc@bonakdarcleary.com
🖥 www.bonakdarcleary.com

Peter Giles Suite 4, 34700 Skylark Drive, Union City, 94587, United States of America
✆ 00 1 510 477 8841
✎ info@petergilesphoto.com
🖥 www.petergilesphoto.com

Peter Granser@Valeriehersleven Boundary House (3rd Floor), 91-93 Charterhouse Street, London, EC1M 6HR, United Kingdom
✆ (07775) 717474
✎ me@valeriehersleven.com
🖥 www.valeriehersleven.com

Peter Hannert 250 Mercer Street D404, New York, 10012, United States of America
✆ 212 375 8589
✎ info@hannert.com
🖥 www.hannert.com

Peter Higgins 40 Armadale Court, Westcote Road, Reading, RG30 2DF, United Kingdom
✆ 0118-950 0943/(07702) 074927

Peter Howard Smith 4 Claremont Road, Marlow, Buckinghamshire, SL7 1BW, United Kingdom
✆ (01628) 481200
✎ phsphoto@btinternet .com
🖥 www.peterhowardsmith.com

Peter Humfreys Photography Ltd Unit 60 Wycombe Air Park, Clay Lane, Booker, Marlow, Buckinghamshire, SL7 3DJ, United Kingdom
✆ (01494) 510980
✎ pete@petespix..com
🖥 www.petespix.com

Peter J Carey 157 Junction Road, Islington, London, N19 5PZ, United Kingdom
✆ (020) 7272 6516

Peter J. Millard 94 Jeddo Road, London, W12 9EG, United Kingdom
✆ (020) 8749 6752
🖥 www.petermillard.com

Peter Kidd 22 Vanbrugh Hill, London, SE3 7UF, **United Kingdom**
✆ **(07973) 315122**
✎ **p.kidd7@ntlworld.com**
See ad

Peter Knab 37 Wycombe Square, London, W8 7JD, United Kingdom
✆ (020) 7727 0997
✎ peter.knab@btinternet.com
🖥 www.lebaou.com

Peter Lake 14 WILLIOW ROAD, GREAT DUNMOW, ESSEX, CM61ZG, United Kingdom
✆ 01371 859 581/(07958) 715730
✎ peterlakephoto@yahoo.com

Peter Lavery@Swerve Photography 29-31 Saffron Hill, London, EC1N 8SW, United Kingdom
📞 (07967) 628769
✍ info@swervephotography.com
🖥 www.swervephotography.com

Peter Lavery Photography Brandiers Farm, Minety, Malmesbury, Wiltshire, SN16 9PZ, United Kingdom
📞 (01666) 860960/(07887) 711163 /📠 (01666) 860742
✍ peter@peterlavery.com
🖥 www.peterlavery.com

Peter MacKertich Invicta Works, 8 Graces Mews, London, SE5 8JF, United Kingdom
📞 (020) 7701 4989/(07973) 952071 /📠 (020) 7701 4989
✍ peter@petermackertich.com
🖥 www.petermackertich.com

Peter Marlow@Magnum Photos 63 Gee Street, London, EC1V 3RS, United Kingdom
📞 (020) 7490 1771/📠 (020) 7608 0020
✍ magnum@magnumphotos.co.uk
🖥 www.magnumphotos.com

Peter Marshall 22 Hearne Road, Strand on the Green, Chiswick, London, W4 3NJ, United Kingdom
📞 (07976) 275071
✍ ps.marshall@virgin.net

Peter Mason 10 Cranleigh Mews, London, SW11 2QL, United Kingdom
📞 **(07774) 496414**
✍ **peter@petermason.biz**
🖥 **www.petermason.biz**
See ad in showcase

Peter Meech 9 Beech Avenue, High Wycombe, Buckinghamshire, HP14 3EQ, United Kingdom
📞 (01494) 883334/(07721) 444497
✍ peter@petermeech.co.uk
🖥 www.petermeech.co.uk

Peter Meer Photography Spot Studios, Canonbury Road, 202 New North Road, London, N1 7BJ, United Kingdom
📞 (07802) 726662
✍ peter@petermeer.co.uk
🖥 www.petermeer.co.uk

Peter Messett 38b The Grove, Biggin Hill, Westerham, Kent, TN16 3TB, United Kingdom
📞 (01959) 574302/(07050) 134363 /📠 (01959) 574302
✍ pmphotography@btinternet.com
🖥 www.pm-photgrahy.co.uk

Peter Mountain@Blowup 146 Amyand Park Road, St. Margaret's, Twickenham, TW1 3HY, United Kingdom
📞 (020) 8744 0210/📠 (020) 8892 2521
✍ orders@blowup.net
🖥 www.blowup.net

Peter Packer Landscape Photographer Hillside House, Cottesmore Road, Ashwell, Oakham, Leicestershire, LE15 7LJ, United Kingdom
📞 (01572) 757702
✍ peter@peterpacker.com
🖥 www.peterpacker.com

Peter Phipp Longfield Cottage, 3B Uplands Close, London, SW14 7AS, United Kingdom
📞 (020) 8878 2226/📠 (020) 8392 2920
✍ photography@peterphipp.co.uk
🖥 www.peterphipp.co.uk

Peter Pugh-Cook 52 Borstal Street, Rochester, Kent, ME1 3HL, United Kingdom
📞 (07711) 895785

Peter Quinnell@Début Art & The Coningsby Gallery 30 Tottenham Street, London, W1T 4RJ, United Kingdom
📞 (020) 7636 1064/📠 (020) 7580 7017
✍ info@debutart.com
🖥 www.debutart.com

Peter Rayner, London, United Kingdom
📞 (020) 8964 9970

Peter Sanders Photography 24 Meades Lane, Chesham, Buckinghamshire, HP5 1ND, United Kingdom
📞 (01494) 773674/📠 (01494) 773674
✍ photos@petersanders.com
🖥 www.petersanders.com

Peter Scholey Partnership 73 Old Park Avenue, Sheffield, S8 7DQ, United Kingdom
📞 0114-274 7662
🖥 www.peterscholey.co.uk

Peter Smith Shimpling Place, Diss, Norfolk, IP21 4UB, United Kingdom
📞 (01379) 740404/(07778) 281228
✍ info@photosmithuk.com
🖥 www.photosmithuk.com

Peter Smith Studio No 4 Millers Cottage, Belvedere Creek, Faversham, Kent, ME14 7LN, United Kingdom
📞 (01795) 538000/(07850) 769503
✍ photos@petersmith.co.uk
🖥 www.petersmith.co.uk

Peter Thompson Photography, 11 Ashling Court, Nottingham, NG2 3JA, United Kingdom
📞 0115-986 5888/(07711) 556634 /📠 (07092) 316410
✍ itsfab@petethompsons.co.uk
🖥 www.petethompsons.co.uk

Peter Waldman The Studio, 1 Langtry Road, London, NW8 0AJ, United Kingdom
📞 (020) 7328 7221

Peter Williams 68 Bolingbroke Grove, London, SW11 6HD, United Kingdom
📞 (020) 7228 2298/(07958) 325022 /📠 (020) 7801 0965
✍ peter@peashooter.org
🖥 www.peashooter.org

Peter Wilson@Axiom Photographic Agency The Pall Mall Deposit, 124-128 Barlby Road, London, W10 6BL, United Kingdom
📞 (020) 8964 9970/📠 (020) 8964 8440
✍ info@axiomphotographic.com
🖥 www.axiomphotographic.com

Peter Wood Studio 3, 20 Albert Street, London, NW1 7NU, United Kingdom
📞 (020) 7388 9089/📠 (020) 7387 0627

Phil Ashley 3 Dee Road, Richmond, Surrey, TW9 2JN, United Kingdom
📞 (020) 8332 7707/(07976) 887879 /📠 (020) 8332 1932
✍ phil@philashley.com
🖥 www.philashley.com

Phil Babb@Anthea Bowen Willow Tree Cottage, Cloghams Green, Leaden Roding, Dunmow, Essex, CM6 1WG, United Kingdom
📞 (01279) 876640/(07860) 389352
✍ anthea@antheabowen.com
🖥 www.antheabowen.com

Phil Boorman Photography 12 Willowbrook Laboratory Units, Crickhowell Road, St. Mellons, Cardiff, CF3 0EF, United Kingdom
📞 (029) 2079 8132/7973141902
✍ studio@philboorman.co.uk
🖥 www.philboorman.co.uk

Phil Bradshaw 19 Bransby Rise, Old Hall Green, Leeds, LS28 5UR, United Kingdom
📞 0113-255 8349/📠 0113-255 8349

Phil Cawley The Mews, Charlton Place, Ardwick, Manchester, M12 6HS, United Kingdom
📞 0161-273 7050/(07973) 186623
✍ mail@philcawley.com
🖥 www.philcawley.com

Phil Jason Graphic Eye Ltd, Shire House, Monk Sherborne Road, Ramsdell, Basingstoke, Hampshire, RG26 5PR, United Kingdom
📞 (01256) 851210/📠 (01256) 850484
✍ graphiceye@compuserve.com
🖥 www.graphiceyeltd.co.uk

Phil Sills@Mutton Bones Ground Floor, 51 Balcombe Street, London, NW1 6HD, United Kingdom
📞 (020) 7723 8244/📠 (020) 7723 2770
✍ hello@muttonbones.co.uk
🖥 www.muttonbones.co.uk

Phil Starling 17 Monnery Road, Tufnell Park, London, N19 5SA, United Kingdom
📞 (020) 7272 6470/(07850) 660544 /📠 (020) 7272 0855
✍ pstarling@gn.apc.org
🖥 www.philstarling.co.uk

Phil Surbey Photographers 3-4 Pond Close, Walkern Road, Stevenage, Hertfordshire, SG1 3QP, United Kingdom
📞 (01438) 353500/(07860) 241155 /📠 (01438) 353520
✍ phil@surbey.net
🖥 www.surbey.net

Philip Ashwin Oakbank, 19 Simister Lane, Manchester, M25 2RS, United Kingdom
📞 0161-773 5624/(07860) 237116
✍ philip@philipashwin.co.uk
🖥 www.philipashwin.co.uk

Philip Berryman Upper Ground Flat, 58 Holland Road, London, London, W14 8BB, United Kingdom
📞 (020) 7610 4848/(07850) 002311 /📠 (020) 7610 4848
✍ philip_berryman@hotmail.com
🖥 www.philipberryman.com

Philip Bier 55 North View Road, London, N8 7LN, United Kingdom
📞 (020) 8348 3050/📠 (020) 8348 5850
✍ philip@bierphotography.co.uk
🖥 www.bierphotography.co.uk

Philip Dowell 7 Kingsley Close, London, N2 0ES, United Kingdom
📞 (020) 8455 6657

Philip Gatward 9 The Old School House, 2 Lansdowne Drive, London, E8 3EZ, United Kingdom
📞 (020) 7683 0284/(07802) 654785
✍ philip@philipgatward.com
🖥 www.philipgatward.com

Philip Holden Bali Hai, Michaels Field, Mumbles, Swansea, SA3 4JB, United Kingdom
📞 (01792) 367571/(07949) 532323
✍ phil@philholdenphotography.com
🖥 www.philholdenphotography.com

Philip Jones Griffiths@Magnum Photos 63 Gee Street, London, EC1V 3RS, United Kingdom
📞 (020) 7490 1771/📠 (020) 7608 0020
✍ magnum@magnumphotos.co.uk
🖥 www.magnumphotos.com

Philip Lee Harvey@van Hauen Moore 14 Powis Mews, Notting Hill, London, W11 1JN, United Kingdom
📞 (020) 7792 0022/📠 (020) 7792 8636
✍ email@vanhauenmoore.com
🖥 www.vanhauenmoore.com

Philip Newton@Philip North-Coombes 8 Dashwood Court, Ashton, Rowant, Watlington, Oxfordshire OX49 52A, United Kingdom
📞 (07785) 381697/📠 (01865) 882742
✍ pepnorthcoombes@btinternet.com
🖥 www.philipnorthcoombes.com

Philip Sharrock 25 Thomas Avenue, Radcliffe-on-Trent, Nottingham, NG12 2HT, United Kingdom
📞 (07703) 985977
✍ philip.sharrock@ntlworld.com
🖥 www.philipsharrock-photography.co.uk

Philip Sharrock Creative Ltd 25 Thomas Avenue, Radcliffe-on-Trent, Nottingham, NG12 2HT, United Kingdom
📞 (07703) 985977
✍ philip.sharrock@ntlworld.com
🖥 www.t3-studios.co.uk

Philip Webb 27 Warple Way, London, W3 0RX, United Kingdom
📞 (020) 8749 7808/📠 (020) 8749 7808
✍ focuson2@aol.com

Philip Wight Motor Co 36a Queen Marys Avenue, Watford, WD18 7JP, United Kingdom
📞 (01923) 220000/📠 (01923) 235938
✍ phil@click4cars.co.uk
🖥 www.click4cars.co.uk

Philip Wilkins 3 New North House, 190A New North Road, London, N1 7BJ, United Kingdom
📞 /(07956) 524411 /📠 (020) 7704 8863
✍ p.wilkins@btinternet.com
🖥 www.philipwilkinsphotography.com

Philip-Lorca Di Corcia@MAP 72 Rochester Place, London, NW1 9JX, United Kingdom
📞 (020) 7424 9144/📠 (020) 7284 3274
✍ info@mapltd.com
🖥 www.mapltd.com

Philippa Bogle Photography, United Kingdom
📞 (07866) 070272
🖥 www.cga.org.uk/philippabogle

Philippe Halsmann@Magnum Photos 63 Gee Street, London, EC1V 3RS, United Kingdom
📞 (020) 7490 1771/📠 (020) 7608 0020
✍ magnum@magnumphotos.co.uk
🖥 www.magnumphotos.com

Phillimore Photography Apartment 10, 42 Speires Whaf, Glasgow, G4 9TH, United Kingdom
📞 0141-332 0666/📠 0141-332 0777
✍ martin@phillimore-photography.com
🖥 www.phillimore-photography.com

Phillip North Coombes@M & M Management Studio B, 11 Edith Grove, London, SW10 0JZ, United Kingdom
📞 (020) 7823 3723/📠 (020) 7351 3714
✍ admin@mmmanagement.com
🖥 www.mmmanagement.com

Photo 64 15 Cressdale Drive, Glasgow, G45 9PN, United Kingdom
✆ (07971) 697236
✉ mail@photo64.com
🖥 www.photo64.com

Photo Dreams 101 Burford, Brookside, Telford, Shropshire, TF3 1LJ, United Kingdom
✆ (01952) 279110
✉ ian@photodreams.co.uk
🖥 www.photodreams.co.uk

Photo Fiction 14 Tremes Close, Marshfield, Chippenham, Wiltshire, SN14 8TB, United Kingdom
✆ (07973) 631185
✉ mail@photofiction.co.uk
🖥 www.photofiction.co.uk

Photo Visual 315 London Road, Westcliff-on-Sea, Essex, SS0 7BX, United Kingdom
✆ (01702) 348296
✉ info@photo-visual.com
🖥 www.photo-visual.com

Photo William King Studio 2, The Old Malthouse, 2-4 Pennywell Road, Bristol, BS5 0TJ, United Kingdom
✆ (0117) 941 1600/ (0117) 941 1700
✉ will@photo.uk.com
🖥 www.photo.uk.com

Photographer J. Thue 55 Reynolds House, London, E2 9JR, United Kingdom
✆ (07910) 418383
✉ jacob@iabook.co.uk
🖥 www.jthue.iabook.co.uk

Photographic Techniques Ltd 1b Montague Road, Wimbledon Broadway, London, SW19 1TB, United Kingdom
✆ (020) 8542 2444/ (020) 8542 3444
✉ images@phototech.co.uk
🖥 www.phototech.co.uk

Photographics Bowling Green, East Chiltington, Lewes, East Sussex, BN7 3QU, United Kingdom
✆ (01273) 890621

Photography 199 Camberwell Grove, London, SE5 8JU, United Kingdom
✆ (07768) 862620
✉ enquiry@charlessturge.com
🖥 www.charlessturge.com

Photolink Creative Group, The Old School House, Thirsk Street, Ardwick Green, Manchester, M12 6PN, United Kingdom
✆ 0161-273 7551/ 0161-274 3326
✉ contact@photolink.co.uk
🖥 www.photolink.co.uk

Photoworx 5 Griggs Place, London, SE1 3AB, United Kingdom
✆ (020) 7394 8615
✉ contact@webphotoworx.com
🖥 www.webphotoworx.com

Pia Tryde@Creative Talent (UK) Limited 78 York Street, London, W1H 1DP, United Kingdom
✆ (020) 7439 1877/ (020) 7434 1144
✉ info@creativetalentlimited.com
🖥 www.creativetalentlimited.com

Pic-Biz Ltd Hawber House, Hawber Lane, Silsden, Keighley, West Yorkshire, BD20 0LP, United Kingdom
✆ (08709) 905266/ (08709) 905267
✉ jeoff@pic-biz.co.uk
🖥 www.pic-biz.co.uk

Pictii Photography & Design Ltd Old School, Victoria Road, Brora, Sutherland, KW9 6LN, United Kingdom
✆ (01408) 622600
✉ info@pictii.com
🖥 www.pictii.com

Picture Business PO Box 6275, Wareham, Dorset, BH20 9AG, United Kingdom
✆ (020) 7731 6076/(07976) 855880
✉ picturebusiness@easynet.co.uk
🖥 www.picturebusiness.co.uk

Picture It Foxhill, 36 Ruskin Road, Eastleigh, Hampshire, SO50 4JS, United Kingdom
✆ (023) 8064 1237/(07802) 605250 (023) 861 1731
✉ info@pictureit-uk.com
🖥 www.pictureit-uk.com

Picture Workshop 45 Highgate Place, Highgate, Birmingham, B12 0DD, United Kingdom
✆ 0121-440 2342/(07768) 937739 0121-440 2844
✉ chris@pictureworkshop.co.uk
🖥 www.pictureworkshop.co.uk

Picturebyte Ltd The Coppice, 384 Wilbraham Road, Chorlton-Cum-Hardy, Manchester, M21 0UW, United Kingdom
✆ (07007) 788346/07836 508884
✉ studio@picturebyte.co.uk
🖥 www.picturebyte.co.uk

Pierre d'Alancaisez Photography 16 Lake Street, Oxford, OX1 4RN, United Kingdom
✆ (07813) 183482/ (0870) 1694700
✉ pierre@petitpoi.net
🖥 www.petitpoi.net

Piers Golden Whitehouse, 4 Haybridge House, London, E5 9NB, United Kingdom
✆ **(020) 8442 4240/(07958) 533510 (020) 8442 4240**
✉ **piers@goldenphoto.com**
🖥 **www.goldenphoto.com**
See ad in showcase

Piet Johnson@Sarah Lane Represents 56 Bidwell Gardens, London, N11 2AU, United Kingdom
✆ (07901) 552520/ (020) 8292 4001
✉ sarah@sarahlanerepresents.com
🖥 www.sarahlanerepresents.com

Pieter Boer Fotografie Grevelingenstraat 22-2, Amsterdam, 1078 KP, Netherlands
✆ 00 31 20 675 4129/00 31 65 422 7758 00 31 20 675 4129
✉ fotoboer@x54all.nl

Pinpoint Photography Unit 30, Park Farm Estate, 100 Acre Lane, Wivelsfield Green, Haywards Heath, West Sussex, RH17 7RU, United Kingdom
✆ (01273) 890600
✉ info@pinpointphotography.co.uk
🖥 www.pinpointphotography.co.uk

Pip Calvert, London, United Kingdom
✆ (020) 7439 1877

Pixel Canvas 8 Cyrus Court, Emersons Green, Bristol, BS16 7AX, United Kingdom
✆ 0117-909 0076/(07950) 094529 0117-909 0076
✉ tom@pixelcanvas.co.uk
🖥 www.pixelcanvas.co.uk

Pixel Studios 6 Anne Hathaway Drive, Church Down, Gloucester, GL3 2PX, United Kingdom
✆ (01452) 545540/(07860) 391058
✉ pixelstudios@blueyonder.co.uk

Pixel Visual Communications Ltd Shieling House, Invincible Road, Farnborough, Hampshire, GU14 7QU, United Kingdom
✆ (01252) 375750/ (01252) 521155
✉ mail@pixelvisual.com
🖥 www.pixelvisual.com

Pixelate Imaging 8 Flitcroft Street, London, WC2H 8DL, United Kingdom
✆ **(020) 7240 9808/ (020) 7240 9188**
✉ **studio@pixelate.biz**
🖥 **www.pixelate.biz**
See ad in showcase

Plastic Sandwich White Lodge, 252 Finchley Road, London, NW3 7AA, United Kingdom
✆ (020) 7431 3211/ (020) 7435 5799
✉ info@plasticsandwich.com
🖥 www.plasticsandwich.com

Platman Photography 10 Daubeney Road, London, E50 ES, United Kingdom
✆ (020) 8986 7348/(07973) 747248
✉ lara@platmanphotography.com
🖥 www.platmanphotography.com

Playground Photographic 109a Omnibus House, 39-41 North Road, London, N7 9DP, United Kingdom
✆ (020) 7697 4433
✉ info@playgroundphotographic.com
🖥 www.playgroundphotographic.com

PLC 7 Edith Grove, London, SW10 0JZ, United Kingdom
✆ (020) 7352 4008/(07774) 694140 (020) 7351 9969
✉ julia@plcinternational.com
🖥 www.plcinternational.com

PLN Management Second Floor, 79 Barlby Road, London, W10 6AZ,
✆ +44 (0) 203 181 0003
✉ info@plnmanagement.com
🖥 www.planmanagement.com

Polly Wreford@Sarah Kaye Representation Ltd 38 Queen's Gate, London, SW7 5HR, United Kingdom
✆ (020) 7225 5005/ (020) 7225 0109
✉ sarah@sarahkaye.com
🖥 www.sarahkaye.com

Positive Image The Laurels, 29 Moss Lane, Hyde, Cheshire, SK14 6BD, United Kingdom
✆ (01457) 763129/(07770) 692510 (01457) 763129
✉ posimage@btopenworld.com
🖥 www.posimage.mcmail.com

Powerhouse Digital Photography Ltd Rodley House Studio, Coal Hill Lane, Rodley, Leeds, LS13 1DJ, United Kingdom
✆ 0113-204 7000/ 0113-229 4200
✉ neil@powerhousephoto.co.uk
🖥 www.powerhousephoto.co.uk

Precision Unit 18, Green Lane 3 Industrial Estate, Letchworth Garden City, Hertfordshire, SG6 1HP, United Kingdom
✆ (01462) 670270/ (01462) 670370
✉ anne@precision-uk.com
🖥 www.precision-uk.com

Private View Artists Agency 17A Swan Hill, Shrewsbury, SY1 1NL, United Kingdom
✆ (01743) 350355/ (01743) 233923
✉ create@pvuk.com
🖥 www.pvuk.com

Process 5 Choumert Mews, Choumert Road, London, SE15 4BD, United Kingdom
✆ **(020) 7277 8400/(07950) 311425 (020) 7277 7223**
✉ **info@processphotography.com**
🖥 **www.processphotography.com**
See ad in showcase

Professional Sport UK Ltd 18-19 Shaftesbury Quay, Hertford, SG14 1SF, United Kingdom
✆ (01992) 505000/ (01992) 505020
✉ pictures@prosport.co.uk
🖥 www.professionalsport.com

Projekt Photography Ltd 85 Great Titchfield Street, London, W1W 6RJ, United Kingdom
✆ (020) 7580 1380/(07957) 353032

Pronin Photography 286 Barrow Street, Jersey City, 7302, United States of America
✆ 00 1 201 332 3289
✉ apronin@apronin.com
🖥 www.apronin.com

Prudence Cumming Associates Ltd 28 Dover Street, London, W1F 4NA, United Kingdom
✆ (020) 7629 6430/ (020) 7495 2458
✉ info@prudencecumming.co.uk
🖥 www.prudencecumming.co.uk

Publifoto 82-84 Clerkenwell Road, London, EC1M 5RJ, United Kingdom
✆ (020) 7608 2877/ (020) 7490 0642
✉ publifoto@aol.com

Purkiss Images 5 Thamesgate Close, Richmond, Surrey, TW10 7YS, United Kingdom
✆ (07831) 817585/ (020) 8948 6635
✉ akp@photshot.com
🖥 purkiss-images.net

Push Button Studios 2 Windermere Avenue, Queen's Park, London, NW6 6LN, United Kingdom
✆ (020) 8964 0423
✉ typofoto@dircon.co.uk

Pyramid Photographics 21 Beverley Drive, Berry Hill, Mansfield, Nottinghamshire, NG18 4QL, United Kingdom
✆ (01623) 620670/(07976) 851857
✉ pyramid@ntlworld.com

Q A Photos Ltd La Rosiere, 24620 Les Eyzies, Les Eyzies, 24620, France
✆ (01303) 894141 (diverted from UK)
✉ pix@qaphotos.com
🖥 www.qaphotos.com

Quantum Photography Abbey Mills Studio, Abbey Road, Leeds, LS5 3HP, United Kingdom
✆ 0113-274 0077/ 0113-278 4883
✉ info@quantumstudios.co.uk
🖥 www.quantumstudios.co.uk

Quentin Photography 9A-1403 Jindian Garden, 9 Wenhuiyan Beilu, Haidian, Beijing, 100088, China, People's Republic of
✆ 10 622 68947/ 10 622 68914
✉ info@quentinphotography.com
🖥 www.quentinphotography.com

R P M Ltd New Court, 82 Station Road, Hampton, Middlesex, TW12 2AX, United Kingdom
✆ (020) 8939 3700/ (020) 8941 5556
✉ enquiries@rpmltd..com
🖥 www.rpmltd.com

R.T. Quayle 3 Roman Road, Meols, Wirral, Merseyside, CH47 6AG, United Kingdom
0151-632 1402/(07889) 524125 0151-632 1802
info@rogerquayle.com
www.rogerquayle.com

Rab Letham Photography 160 Havelock Road, London, SW19 8HB, United Kingdom
(020) 8542 9897/(07968) 783972
rab@rab-photo.com
www.rab-photo.com

Rachel Annie Bridgen@Germaine Walker Photographers' Agent Crayford House, 49A Tabley Road, London, N7 0NA, United Kingdom
(020) 7697 8291/(07867) 780272 (020) 7619 9051
germaine@germaine.co.uk
www.germaine.co.uk

Radka & RenÈ@David Edmunds Represents Unit 105, 54-58 Kingsland Road, London, E2 8DP, United Kingdom
(020) 7739 1166/(07785) 580024
info@davidedmundsrepresents.com
www.davidedmundsrepresents.com

Raf Makda 165 Sanerstead Road, Croydon, CR2 0PH, United Kingdom
(020) 8240 1340/(07973) 634202
mail@rafmakda.com
www.rafmakda.com

Raghu Rai@Magnum Photos 63 Gee Street, London, EC1V 3RS, United Kingdom
(020) 7490 1771/ (020) 7608 0020
magnum@magnumphotos.co.uk
www.magnumphotos.com

Rago & Waring The Chapel, Chapel Lane, Normanby-by-Spital, Market Rasen, Lincolnshire, LN8 2HG, United Kingdom
(01673) 878615/ (01673) 878615
protoangel@btinternet.com
www.protoangelwebdesign.co.uk

Rainer Elstermann@Process 5 Choumert Mews, Choumert Road, London, SE15 4BD, United Kingdom
(020) 7277 8400/(07950) 311425 (020) 7277 7223
info@processphotography.com
www.processphotography.com

Ralf Pulmanns@ERA Management Ltd 120 The Beaux Arts Building, 10-18 Manor Gardens, London, N7 6JT, United Kingdom
(020) 7281 5996/ (020) 7281 6202
kate@eramanagement.com
www.eramanagement.com

Ranald Mackechnie 215-217 Cold Harbour Lane, London, SW9 8RU, United Kingdom
(07973) 219652
ranald@ranaldmac.com
www.ranaldmac.com

Ray Barret@Jo Talbot & Sue Young 6M Hyde Park Mansions, Cabbell Street, London, NW1 5BJ, United Kingdom
(020) 7262 0189/(07850) 353468 (020) 7262 2160
joandsue@btconnect.com
www.joandsue.com

Ray Burmlston@Shoot Production Ltd 23 Glebe Road, London, N8 7DA, United Kingdom
(020) 8442 9171/ (020) 8348 7404
adele@shootgroup.com
www.shootgroup.com

Ray Cockle 48 Avondale Avenue, Esher, Surrey, KT10 0DA, United Kingdom
(020) 8224 5080/07831 311680
raycockle@ntlworld.com
www.raycockle.com

Ray Harwood 47 Worton Gardens, Isleworth, Middlesex, TW7 4BD, United Kingdom
(020) 8560 7106
rayharwood1@talktalk.net

Ray Lowe Photography 121-123 Crossbrook Street, Cheshunt, Hertfordshire, EN8 8LY, United Kingdom
(01992) 636152
info@raylowestudios.co.uk
www.raylowestudios.co.uk

Ray Massey Camden Park Studios, The Church Hall, Camden Park Road, London, NW1 9AY, United Kingdom
(020) 7267 9550/(07831) 606342 (020) 7267 5612
ray@raymassey.com
www.raymassey.com
See ad in showcase

Ray Watkins@SK Creative Management 23 New Mount Street, Manchester, M4 4DE, United Kingdom
0161-953 4032/ (0870) 486 1940
info@skcreativemanagement.com
www.skcreativemanagement.com

Ray Watkins Photography Studio 1 Meadow Oak Drive, Oakfield Grange, Liverpool, L25 3SZ, United Kingdom
(07860) 364225/ 0151-428 8593
info@raywatkins.com
www.raywatkins.com

Raymond Depardon@Magnum Photos 63 Gee Street, London, EC1V 3RS, United Kingdom
(020) 7490 1771/ (020) 7608 0020
magnum@magnumphotos.co.uk
www.magnumphotos.com

Raymond Thatcher Photography 18 Queen Street, Maidenhead, Berkshire, SL6 1HZ, United Kingdom
(01628) 625381/ (01628) 778921
raymondthatcher1@talktalk.net
www.raymondthatcherphotography.co.uk

Raymondo Marcus 7 Chiswick High Road, London, W4 2ND, United Kingdom
(01628) 485692/(07831) 649000
r.marcus@raymondomarcus.com
www.raymondomarcus.com

Re:fresh Suit 4, The Swans Centre, Fishers Lane, London, W4 1RX, United Kingdom
(020) 8747 8080/ (020) 8747 8228
info@refresh-agency.com
www.refresh-agency.com

Rebecca Bernstein c/o Digital Peninsula Network, 1-2 Old Brewery Yard, Penzance, Cornwall, TR18 2SL, United Kingdom
(07931) 561911
info@rebeccabernstein.co.uk
www.rebeccabernstein.co.uk

REDEYE Media Ltd York, YO1 6WX, United Kingdom
(01904) 337419/(07811) 325932 (01904) 339811
mail@redeye.uk.com
www.redeye.uk.com

Redseal@Début Art & The Coningsby Gallery 30 Tottenham Street, London, W1T 4RJ, United Kingdom
(020) 7636 1064/ (020) 7580 7017
info@debutart.com
www.debutart.com

Refinery Photographers 10 Pittbrook House, Ardwick, Manchester, M12 6JX, United Kingdom
0161-273 5511
ianclegg@refinerygroup.co.uk
www.refinerygroup.co.uk

Refinery Photographic 10 Pittbrook Street, Manchester, M12 6JX, United Kingdom
0161-273 5511
laffan@refinerygroup.co.uk
www.refineryphotographic.co.uk

Reg Wilkins, London, United Kingdom
(020) 7684 1019
reg@regwilkins.com
www.regwilkins.com

Renate Decker-Berry- Europe Unlimited 59 Lambeth Walk, London, SE11 6DX, United Kingdom
(020) 7735 6623/(07768) 251626 (0707) 5009648
renate@europeunlimited.com
www.europeunlimited.com

Rene Burri@Magnum Photos 63 Gee Street, London, EC1V 3RS, United Kingdom
(020) 7490 1771/ (020) 7608 0020
magnum@magnumphotos.co.uk
www.magnumphotos.com

Revolver Photography 83 Fitzwilliam Street, Huddersfield, HD1 5LG, United Kingdom
(01484) 453400/(07770) 528374
paul@revolverphoto.com
www.revolverphoto.com

Rhys Jones Images 100 Eaton Crescent, Swansea, SA1 4QR, United Kingdom
(07790) 490368/(01792) 470429
info@rhysjonesimages.com
www.rhysjonesimages.com

Ric Frazier Productions 3790 Dunn Drive cl, Los Angeles, 90094, United States of America
00 1 310 559 1441
ric@frazierproductions.com
www.frazierproductions.com

Ric Gemmell Calderwood House, 15 Stanbrook Close, Southend, Reading, RG7 6EW, United Kingdom
0118-974 5077/(07860) 338956 0118-974 5077
ric@ricgemmell.com
www.ricgemmell.com

Richard Ansett@Horton-Stephens Photographers' Agent 14 Peacock Yard, Iliffe Street, London, SE17 3LH, United Kingdom
(020) 7252 7979/ (020) 7252 6409
us@horton-stephens.com
www.horton-stephens.com

Richard Bailey Photography 8 Oman Avenue, Cricklewood, London, NW2 6BG, United Kingdom
(020) 8450 4148/(07956) 971520 (020) 8450 4686
richard@richardbaileyphotography.co.uk
www.richardbaileyphotography.co.uk

Richard Bayburtt 101 Davenport Road, London, SE6 2AU, United Kingdom
(07745) 904601
richardbaybutt@hotmail.com
www.richardbaybutt.com

Richard Booth@Julian Cotton Photographers Agent 55 Upper Montagu Street, London, W1H 1SF, United Kingdom
(020) 7723 3100/ (020) 7724 7555
info@juliancotton.co.uk
www.juliancotton.co.uk

Richard Bradbury 72 Thornton Avenue, London, W4 1QQ, United Kingdom
(07768) 352100
info@rbradbury.com
www.rbradbury.com
See ad in showcase

Richard Bryant@Arcaid Picture Library Parc House, 25-37 Cowleaze Road, Kingston upon Thames, Surrey, KT2 6DZ, United Kingdom
(020) 8546 4352/ (020) 8541 5230
arcaid@arcaid.co.uk
www.arcaid.co.uk

Richard Seymour @ Sharon Brandman Agency No 2 Elmhurst Close, Bushey, WD23 2QB
848 800 9003/ sharon@sharonbrandman.com
www.sharonbrandman.com
See ad in showcase

Richard Clark, London, United Kingdom
(020) 8679 9118/(07973) 326092
richardclark@richardclark.com
www.richardclark.com

Richard Clive Photography Bedford House Studios, Nunnington, York, YO62 5UX, United Kingdom
(01439) 748237/(07778) 636954
richard@clivephotography.co.uk
www.clivephotography.co.uk

Richard Cooke Manor House, Church Street, Cogenhoe, Northampton, NN7 1LS, United Kingdom
(01604) 890556/(07712) 653595 (01604) 890556
richard@richard-cooke.com
www.richard-cooke.com

Richard Foster Melmoth Hall, 27 Eustace Road, London, SW6 1JB, United Kingdom
(020) 7381 2727/ (020) 7381 0027
richard@richardfoster.com
www.richardfoster.com

Richard Goulding@SK Creative Management 23 New Mount Street, Manchester, M4 4DE, United Kingdom
0161-953 4032/ (0870) 486 1940
info@skcreativemanagement.com
www.skcreativemanagement.com

Richard Jackson Photography Countryside Studios, Forest Hall, Bishop's Stortford, Hertfordshire, CM22 7BT, United Kingdom
0137-1859 658/(07831) 469635 (01279) 718937
richard@rjpstudios.co.uk
www.rjpstudios.co.uk

Richard Jenkins 5a Rucklidge Avenue, London, NW10 4QA, United Kingdom
(07957) 651478
info@rjenkins.co.uk
www.rjenkins.co.uk

Richard Jung Photography 13 Comeragh Road, 1st Floor, London, W14 9HP, United Kingdom
(020) 7381 3693/(07921) 626675
richard@richardjungphotography.com
www.richardjungphotography.com

Richard Kalvar@Magnum Photos 63 Gee Street, London, EC1V 3RS, United Kingdom
(020) 7490 1771/ (020) 7608 0020
magnum@magnumphotos.co.uk
www.magnumphotos.com

Richard Kelly 8 Heron Close, Ascot, Berkshire, SL5 8NG, United Kingdom
☎ (07909) 994414
✉ info@richardkkelly.com
🖥 www.richardkkelly.com

Richard Kluczynski Photography 16 Kent Road, East Molesey, Surrey, KT8 9JZ, United Kingdom
☎ (020) 8941 0047
✉ info@rkphoto.co.uk
🖥 www.rkphoto.co.uk

Richard Lewisohn Photography 15 Moorhouse Road, London, W2 5DH, United Kingdom
☎ (07956) 395901/ (020) 7243 4689
✉ richard@lewisohn.co.uk
🖥 www.lewisohn.co.uk

Richard Maxted@Jo Clark 2nd Floor, 202B Camden Lock, London, NW1 8AF, United Kingdom
☎ (020) 7267 7267/ (020) 7267 7495
✉ jo@joclark.com
🖥 www.joclark.com

Richard Meats Burtons Hollow, Burtons Lane, Chalfont St. Giles, Buckinghamshire, HP8 4BA, United Kingdom
☎ (01494) 762634/(07774) 478706
✉ mcarbon2@aol.com
🖥 www.richardmeats.com

Richard Mountney 19A Broad Wynd, Leith, Edinburgh, EH6 6QZ, United Kingdom
☎ 0131-555 0630/(07747) 606680
✉ email@richardmountney.com
🖥 www.richardmountney.com

Richard Mummery 74 Riversdale Road, London, N5 2JZ, United Kingdom
☎ (07785) 243568
✉ richard@richardmummery.com
🖥 www.richardmummery.com

Richard Newton 25 Green End, Granborough, Buckingham, MK18 3NT, United Kingdom
☎ (01296) 670465/(07785) 364132 (01296) 670030
✉ rich.newton@btinternet.com

Richard Nolan-Neylan, United Kingdom
☎ (020) 7502 0839/(07778) 999835
✉ richard.nolanneylan@blueyonder.co.uk
🖥 www.richardnolan-neylan.co.uk

Richard Pentin Photography 170 Trinity Road, London, SW17 7HT, United Kingdom
☎ (07796) 265210
✉ richardpentin@yahoo.co.uk
🖥 www.richardpentinphotography.com

Richard Pinches@Victoria Lees Management (VLM) 2 Fairview Gardens, Woodford Green, Essex, IG8 7DJ, United Kingdom
☎ (07710) 287220/ (020) 8504 8125
✉ victoria@victorialeesmanagement.co.uk
🖥 www.victorialeesmanagement.co.uk

Richard Pinches Photography Marlow Road, Henley-on-Thames, Oxfordshire, RG9 3AA, United Kingdom
☎ (01491) 577789
✉ rich@pinchesphoto.co.uk
🖥 www.richardpinches.co.uk

Richard Porter Photography 9 Baytree Road, Brixton, London, SW2 5RR, United Kingdom
☎ (020) 7274 7811/(07736) 458311
✉ porterrichard@btinternet.com
🖥 www.richardporterphotography.co.uk

Richard Powers@Arcaid Picture Library Parc House, 25-37 Cowleaze Road, Kingston upon Thames, Surrey, KT2 6DZ, United Kingdom
☎ (020) 8546 4352/ (020) 8541 5230
✉ arcaid@arcaid.co.uk
🖥 www.arcaid.co.uk

Richard Prescott Unicorn Lodge, Bottom House Farm, Cropswell Road, Nottingham, NG13 9HD, United Kingdom
☎ (01949) 869409/(07831) 368073 (01949) 869409
✉ info@richardprescott.com
🖥 www.richardprescott.com

Richard Pullar Unit 44, Kingsway Place, Sans Walk, London, EC1R 0LU, United Kingdom
☎ **(020) 7490 2188/ (020) 7251 6255**
✉ **richard@richardpullar.com**
🖥 **www.richardpullar.com**
See ad in showcase

Richard Seymour@Sharon Brandman Agency, No 2 Milner Court, Bridgewater Way, Bushey, WD23 4UB, United Kingdom
☎ **020 8950 9213/07973 305575 020 8950 7990**
✉ **sharon@sharonbrandman.com**
🖥 **www.sharonbrandman.com**
See ad in showcase

Richard Sibley 53 St. Michaels Close, Lambourn, Hungerford, Berkshire, RG17 8FA, United Kingdom
☎ (07785) 725486
✉ mail@richardsibley.co.uk
🖥 www.richardsibley.co.uk

Richard Smith, Richmond, Surrey, United Kingdom
☎ (07831) 206461
✉ richsmith.pics@virgin.net
🖥 www.richardsmithphoto.com

Richard Waite 14 Analby Road, Teddington, TW11 0PU, United Kingdom
☎ (020) 8288 0362/(07973) 664862
✉ mail@richardwaite.com
🖥 www.richardwaite.com

Richard Young Rex Features, 18 Vine Hill, London, EC1R 5DZ, United Kingdom
☎ (020) 7278 7294/ (020) 7696 0974
✉ interstock@rexfeatures.com
🖥 www.rexfeatures.com

Richie Hopson@Stem Agency Top Floor, 23 Charlotte Road, London, EC2A 3PB, United Kingdom
☎ (07790) 026628
✉ will@stemagency.com
🖥 www.stemagency.com

Rick Chapman 70-71 Wells Street, London, W1P 3QD, United Kingdom
☎ (020) 7636 9119/078 01 800969 (020) 7636 9120
✉ rickchapman@genie.co.uk
🖥 www.rickchapman.co.uk

Rick Cordell 91 The De Beauvoir Road, London, N1 4EL, United Kingdom
☎ (020) 7249 4243/ (020) 7275 0215
✉ rickcordell@blueyonder.co.uk

Rick Fawcett 33 Moreton Terrace, Pimlico, London, SW1V 2NS, United Kingdom
☎ (020) 7828 3302/(07956) 261526
✉ rick@rickfawcett.com

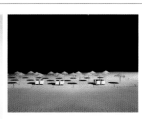

Paul O'Connor · People, Lifestyle & Portraiture
Dan Jones · Food
David Oxberry · Exteriors, Interiors, People & Still life
Rooney · Reportage Still life & Locations
David Sykes · Still life
Edgar Martins · Contemporary landscape

swerve
photography

www.swervephotography.com +44 (0) 7967 628 769 lucy@swervephotography.com

Rick Guest@East Photographic Ltd 8 Iron Bridge House, 3 Bridge Approach, London, NW1 8BD, United Kingdom
✆ (020) 7722 3444/✆ (020) 7722 3544
✉ roger@eastphotographic.com
⌨ www.eastphotographic.com

Rick Tomlinson Photography 10 Birmingham Road, Cowes, Cowes, Isle of Wight, PO31 7BH, United Kingdom
✆ (01983) 248512
✉ photos@rick-tomlinson.com
⌨ www.rick-tomlinson.com

Ripley & Ripley The Granary, Donyatt, Ilminster, Somerset, TA19 0RN, United Kingdom
✆ (07739) 745495/✆ (01460) 57330
✉ studio@ripleyandripley.com
⌨ www.ripleyandripley.com

River Studio 305 The Custard Factory, Gibb Street, Birmingham, B9 4AA, United Kingdom
✆ 0121-624 4777/(07860) 824101 ✆ 0121-693 3993
✉ info@riverstudio.co.uk
⌨ www.riverstudio.co.uk

Rob Brimson 101 Hadley Road, Barnet, Hertfordshire, EN5 5QR, United Kingdom
✆ (020) 8449 2680

Rob Decelis Unit 26, 63 Clerkenwell Road, London, EC1N 5NP, United Kingdom
✆ (020) 7253 6611/079 73 153395 ✆ (020) 7253 6611
✉ radecelis@ukonline.co.uk
⌨ www.decelis.com

Rob Lawson@Wilde Representation 314 Mare Street, London, E8 1HA, United Kingdom
✆ (020) 8653 4466/(07810) 795036 ✆ (01424) 201070
✉ sian@wilderepresentation.com
⌨ www.wilderepresentation.com

Rob Mitchell Units 12 & 13, Enterprise Estate, Guildford, Surrey, GU1 1RB, United Kingdom
✆ (020) 7823 9410/✆ (01483) 450773
✉ rob@rob-mitchell.co.uk
⌨ www.rob-mitchell.co.uk

Rob Payne@Agent Orange 10 Swan Yard, London, N1 1SD, United Kingdom
✆ (020) 7226 0440/✆ (020) 7226 1613
✉ annika@agentorange.co.uk
⌨ www.agentorange.co.uk

Rob Penn@Axiom Photographic Agency The Pall Mall Deposit, 124-128 Barlby Road, London, W10 6BL, United Kingdom
✆ (020) 8964 9970/✆ (020) 8964 8440
✉ info@axiomphotographic.com
⌨ www.axiomphotographic.com

Rob Steel@Metcalfe Lancaster 20 Hanson Street, London, W1W 6UF, United Kingdom
✆ (020) 7580 8875/(07778) 331771 ✆ (020) 7580 8689
✉ julie@metcalfelancaster.com
⌨ www.metcalfelancaster.com

Rob Turner 13 Doughty Mews, London, WC1N 2PG, United Kingdom
✆ (020) 7405 6465/(07767) 660286 ✆ (020) 7404 6855
⌨ www.robturnerphoto.com

Rob White 57 Farringdon Road, London, EC1M 3JB, United Kingdom
✆ (020) 7831 0012/✆ (020) 7831 0012
✉ rob@robwhite-photo.co.uk
⌨ www.robwhite-photo.co.uk

Rob Wyatt Photography Unit 55, Alston Drive, Bradwell Abbey, Milton Keynes, MK13 9HB, United Kingdom
✆ (01908) 220902/✆ (01908) 314860
✉ info@robwyattphotography.com
⌨ www.robwyattphotography.com

Robert Alens 21 Lanercost Road, Brixton, London, SW2 3DP, United Kingdom
✆ (020) 8674 2211
✉ robert@robertalensphotographer.com
⌨ www.robertalensphotographer.com

Robert Barber Setterfields, Christmas Common, Watlington, Oxfordshire, OX49 5HL, United Kingdom
✆ (01491) 614431

Robert Bluffield Photography 37 Station Road, Woburn Sands, Milton Keynes, MK17 8RX, United Kingdom
✆ (01908) 582645/✆ (01908) 584800
✉ robert@bluffield.fsnet.co.uk
⌨ www.robertbluffield.co.uk

Robert Brady Photography 83/4 St. Stephen Street, Edinburgh, EH3 5AG, United Kingdom
✆ 0131-2205223/✆ (07713) 399578
✉ rob@robertbradyphotography.com
⌨ www.robertbradyphotography.com

Robert Burton 64 Stevenage Road, Hitchin, Herts, SG4 9DR,
✆ 07834 606576
✉ bert@robertburton.co.uk
⌨ www.robertburton.co.uk

Robert Daly Unit A223 - 226, Riverside business Centre, Haldane Place, London, SW18 4UQ, United Kingdom
✆ (020) 8874 4171

Robert Estall Photo Agency 12-14 Swan Street, Boxford, Sudbury, Suffolk, CO10 5NZ, United Kingdom
✆ (01787) 210111/✆ (01787) 211440
✉ robertestall@mac.com
⌨ www.africanceremonies.com

Robert Fairer 3 The School, 38 Burns Road, London, SW11 5GY, United Kingdom
✆ (020) 7207 9000/✆ (020) 7652 8090
✉ robertfairer@hotmail.com
⌨ www.robertfairer.com

Robert Greshoff Hiltons Wharf, 30 Lorman Road, London, SE10 9QX, United Kingdom
✆ (020) 8858 4343/(07778) 839978
⌨ www.greshoff.co.uk

Robert H. Judges 42 Church Road, Horspath, OX33 1RU, United Kingdom
✆ (01865) 874418/(07860) 920519
✉ rob@rjudges.demon.co.uk
⌨ www.robjudges.com

Robert Hall Gate Studios, Walkers Place, London, SW15 1PP, United Kingdom
✆ (020) 8789 6928/(07956) 943794 ✆ (020) 8789 0140
✉ robert@roberthallphoto.co.uk
⌨ www.roberthallphoto.co.uk

Robert Holmes 10A Printing House Yard, 15 Hackney Road, London, E2 7PR, United Kingdom
✆ (020) 7739 7418/(07710) 779426
⌨ www.robertholmesimages.com

Robert Jobling 55 Montrouge Crescent, Epsom, Surrey, KT17 3PB, United Kingdom
✆ (01737) 350557/(07968) 832098
✉ robertjobling@aol.com

Robert Morris Images Attleboro House, Temple Walk, Matlock Bath, Matlock, Derbyshire, DE4 3PG, United Kingdom
✆ 1629 582035
✉ robertmorrisimages.co.uk
⌨ www.robertmorrisimageds.co.uk

Robert R. Capa@Magnum Photos 63 Gee Street, London, EC1V 3RS, United Kingdom
✆ (020) 7490 1771/✆ (020) 7608 0020
✉ magnum@magnumphotos.co.uk
⌨ www.magnumphotos.com

Robert Rebec Photography 26 Crowndale Road, London, NW1 1TT, United Kingdom
✆ (07788) 598791
✉ robert@robertrebec.com
⌨ www.robertrebec.com

Robert Simpson Photography Annesley Coach House, Bank, Lyndhurst, Hampshire, SO43 7FD, United Kingdom
✆ (023) 8028 4970/(07836) 535025
✉ robert@robertsimopson.biz
⌨ www.robertsimpson.net

Robert Unsworth Flat 13, 59 Standen Road, London, SW18 5TF, United Kingdom
✆ (020) 8870 3248/(07879) 826210

Robert Wilkinson The Whitehouse, West Grove, Walton-on-Thames, Surrey, KT12 5PE, United Kingdom
✆ (01932) 880022/(07836) 546556 ✆ (01932) 880018
✉ rob.wilkinson@photoshot.com
⌨ www.robertwilkinson.co.uk

Robert Wilson@Catherine Collins The Power Station, Coronet Street, London, N1 6HD, United Kingdom
✆ (020) 7739 8678/(07785) 571187 ✆ (020) 7739 8489
✉ catherine@catherinecollins.co.uk
⌨ www.catherinecollins.co.uk

Robert Workman Studio 103B, The Business Village, Broomhill Road, Wandsworth, London, SW18 4JQ, United Kingdom
✆ (020) 7385 5442
✉ bob@robertworkman.demon.co.uk
⌨ www.robertworkman.demon.co.uk

Robin Broadbent@The Katy Barker Agency Ltd 11 Mason's Arms Mews, Maddox Street, London, W1S 1NX, United Kingdom
✆ (020) 7493 3933/✆ (020) 7493 3311
✉ catherine@katybarker.com
⌨ www.katybarker.com

Robin Derrick@C L M Top Floor, 19 All Saints Road, London, W11 1HE, United Kingdom
✆ (020) 7750 2999/✆ (020) 7792 8507
✉ clm@clmuk.com
⌨ www.clmuk.com

Robin Laurance 44 Stratfield Road, Oxford, OX2 7BQ, United Kingdom
✆ (01865) 557517/(07831) 101021
✉ robinlaurance@compuserve.com

Robin MacDougall Hilltop, Church Road, Rotherfield, East Sussex, TN6 3LG, United Kingdom
✆ (07880) 707238
✉ robin@robinmacdougall.com
⌨ www.robinmacdougall.com

Robin Manford 34 Powderham Road, Hartley Vale, Plymouth, PL3 5SG, United Kingdom
✆ (07980) 377243
✉ info@robinmanford.co.uk
⌨ www.robinmanford.co.uk

Robin Matthews Beechwood Studio, Priorsfield Road, Godalming, Surrey, GU7 2RG, United Kingdom
✆ (020) 7924 1919/(07860) 551435
✉ robin@rmphotos.com
⌨ www.rmphotos.co.uk

Robin Preston@Esser Assocs 2nd Floor North, 6 Buckingham Street, London, WC2N 6BU, United Kingdom
✆ (020) 7976 2915/(07778) 149149 ✆ (01372) 464326
✉ rob.esser@virgin.net
⌨ www.davidesser.com

Robin Skjoldborg@Gina Phillips Represents Ltd 6 Leverton Place, London, NW5 2PL, United Kingdom
✆ (020) 7284 2022/✆ (020) 7424 0272
✉ info@ginaphillips.co.uk
⌨ www.ginaphillips.co.uk

Robin Weaver Photographer 77 Livingstone Road, Derby, DE23 6PS, United Kingdom
✆ (01332) 770241/(07903) 057682 ✆ (01332) 770241
✉ info@robinweaver.co.uk
⌨ www.robinweaver.co.uk

Rod Howe Unit 102, 134-146 Curtain Road, London, EC2A 3AR, United Kingdom
✆ (020) 7729 3880/(07941) 164985 ✆ (020) 7729 3880
✉ rod@rodhowe.com
⌨ www.rodhowe.com

Roddy Paine Unit 22, Colebrook Industrial Estate, Tunbridge Wells, Kent, TN2 3DG, United Kingdom
✆ (01892) 522523
✉ roddy.paine@virgin.net
⌨ www.roddypaine.co.uk

Roderick Field 111 Rainville Court, Rainville Road, London, W6 9HJ, United Kingdom
✆ (07961) 152740
✉ roderickfield@btinternet.com
⌨ www.roderickfield.com

Rodolphe Foucher Photography 630 East 14 Street #10, Stockholm, 15594, Sweden
✆ 00 46 8 553 430 44
✉ info@rodolphefoucher.com
⌨ www.rodolpherfoucher.com

Rodolphe Oditch@Gina Phillips Represents 6 Leverton Place, London, NW5 2PL, United Kingdom
✆ (020) 7284 2022/✆ (020) 7424 0272
✉ info@ginaphillips.co.uk
⌨ www.ginaphillips.co.uk

Roger Askew Photography 4 Temple Cloisters, Junction Road, Oxford, OX4 2YG, United Kingdom
✆ (01865) 402848/(07971) 404571
✉ roger@rogeraskewphotography.co.uk
⌨ www.rogeraskewphotography.co.uk

Roger Di Vito, United Kingdom
✆ (020) 8568 5674/(07711) 947084 ✆ (020) 8569 7650
✉ roger.divito@clara.co.uk

Roger Eaton 33 Lime Grove, London, W12 8EE, United Kingdom
✆ (07831) 606310/✆ (0870) 1272165
✉ roger@rogereaton.com
⌨ www.rogereaton.com

Roger Payling@Jamie Stephen Represents 9 Upper Wimpole Street, London, W1G 6LJ, United Kingdom
✆ (0845) 3733510/(07957) 784810 ✆ (020) 7681 1027
✉ jamie@jamiestephen.com
⌨ www.jamiestephen.com

Rohan Van Twest 134 Robertson Street, London, SW8 3TZ, United Kingdom
(020) 7627 2868/(07836) 204239
rohan@rohanvantwest.com
www.rohanvantwest.com

Rolph Gobits@Jo Talbot & Sue Young 6M Hyde Park Mansions, Cabbell Street, London, NW1 5BJ, United Kingdom
(020) 7262 0189/(07850) 353468 (020) 7262 2160
joandsue@btconnect.com
www.joandsue.com

Rolph Gobits Studio Ltd The Coach House, 1 Winfrith Road, London, SW18 3BE, United Kingdom
(020) 8877 9181/(07785) 292599
rolph.gobits@btinternet.com
www.lensmodern.com

Romilly Lockyer 55 Effingham Road, Long Ditton, Surbiton, Surrey, KT6 5LA, United Kingdom
(020) 8339 0896/(07770) 275524 (020) 8339 0896
romilly@lineone.net
www.Romilly.com

Ron Bambridge Photographer 1-5 Poland Street, London, W1F 8NA, United Kingdom
(020) 7486 7588/ (020) 7486 7588
ron.bambridge@btinternet.com
www.ronbambridge.com

Ron Davies Photography 1 Coronation Road, Crosby, Liverpool, L23 5RD, United Kingdom
0151-931 2301/(07860) 434144 0151-931 2301
ron@rdphoto.demon.co.uk
www.rondaviesphoto.co.uk

Ron Evans Garden Images 31 High Meadow, Cannock Wood, Rugeley, Staffordshire, WS15 4RJ, United Kingdom
(01543) 676343/(07941) 822361
ron@evans01543.freeserve.co.uk
www.ronevans.co.uk

Ron Sutherland 16 Park Steps, St Georges Fields, London, W2 2YQ, United Kingdom
(020) 7402 7363/(01736) 798060
ron@surfbeach.co.uk

Ron Taylor Studio 152 North High Street, Musselburgh, Midlothian, EH21 6AR, United Kingdom
0131-653 2700/ 0131-653 2700
rontaylor@easynet.co.uk

Rooney@Swerve Photography 29-31 Saffron Hill, London, EC1N 8SW, United Kingdom
/(07967) 628769
info@swervephotography.com
www.swervephotography.com

Rory Carnegie@Siobhan Squire 111 Shoreditch High Street, London, E1 6JN, United Kingdom
(020) 7739 8985/ (020) 7729 5125
siobhan@siobhansquire.com
www.siobhansquire.com

Rosendorf 117 Northen Avenue, No 4, Decatur, 30030, United States of America
00 1 404 229 7445
studio@rosendorf.us
rosendorf.us

Rosie Beckett 102 Cole Park Road, Twickenham, TW1 1JA, United Kingdom
(020) 8255 1574/(07973) 193071
rosiebeckett@mac.com

Ross Vincent Pictures Studio 202, Barford Street, Digbeth, Birmingham, B5 7EP, United Kingdom
0121-666 6022
pictures@rossvincent.co.uk
www.rossvincent.co.uk

Rowena Dugdale@Début Art & The Coningsby Gallery 30 Tottenham Street, London, W1T 4RJ, United Kingdom
(020) 7636 1064/ (020) 7580 7017
info@debutart.com
www.debutart.com

Roy A. Giles 7 Scarsdale Studio, 21A Stratford Road, London, W8 6RE, United Kingdom
(020) 7937 2940/(07785) 233981 (020) 7937 9907
gileswartz@aol.com

Roy Mehta 31 Harrow View, Harrow, Middlesex, HA1 1RE, United Kingdom
(07785) 583528
roy@roymehta.com
www.roymehta.com

Roy Pagett Photography 19 Pheasant Walk, Littlemore, Oxford, OX4 4XX, United Kingdom
(01865) 747239
roypagett@hotmail.com
www.roy-pagett-photography.co.uk

Roy Powell Photography 71 Cuckfield Crescent, Worthing, West Sussex, BN13 2EB, United Kingdom
(01903) 266606
roy@p2roy.co.uk
www.roypowellphotography.co.uk

Roy Victor 2A Park Walk, Chelsea, London, SW10 0AD, United Kingdom
(020) 7351 7269

Rui Faria@Areia London Studio1, 42 Theobalds Road, London, WC1X 8NW, United Kingdom
(020) 7404 8600/ (020) 7404 8601
info@areia.com
www.areia.com

Rupert Marlow Photography Littleworth Corner, Lower Littleworth, Amberley, Stroud, Gloucestershire, GL5 5AW, United Kingdom
(07887) 943590
rupert@rupertmarlow.com
www.rupertmarlow.com

Rupert Truman 15A Luttrell Avenue, London, SW15 6PD, United Kingdom
(020) 8789 7768/(07774) 494994
r@rupert-truman.com
www.rupert-truman.com

Russell Falkingham 12 Astwood Mews, London, SW7 4DE, United Kingdom
(020) 7373 4928/(07941) 121443
russ.falkingham@btconnect.com
www.russellfalkingham.co.uk

Russell Sadur, London, United Kingdom
(07970) 693044
russ@sadur.com
www.sadur.com

Russells Commercial Photography 17 Elm Grove, London, SW19 4HE, United Kingdom
(020) 8947 6177/ (020) 8944 2064
dave@russellsphoto.co.uk
www.russellsphoto.co.uk

Ruth Garner 15 York Road, North Weald, Epping, Essex, CM16 6HT, United Kingdom
(01992) 523244
poot1907@yahoo.co.uk

Ruth Jenkinson Chelmsford Road, Felstead, Essex, United Kingdom
(020) 7608 2429/(07850) 625199
photography@ruthjenkinson.co.uk

Ruud Baan@edsonwilliams photography consultancy 52 Brushfield Street, London, E1 6AJ, United Kingdom
(020) 7375 2077/(07867) 517777 (020) 7375 3077
info@edsonwilliams.com
www.edsonwilliams.com

Ruy Teixeira@Tattersall Love 40 Langham Street, London, W1W 7AS, United Kingdom
(020) 7637 5737/ (020) 7637 5747
mail@tattersall-love.com
www.tattersall-love.com

S B Photography 63 Brunswick Road, Edinburgh, EH7 5PD, United Kingdom
0131-659 6262/(07850) 030187 0131-659 6262
ronnie@sbphotography.co.uk
www.sbphotography.co.uk

S C L Photographic Services 16 Bull Lane, Edmonton, London, N18 1SX, United Kingdom
(020) 8807 0725/ (020) 8807 2539
steven@sclimage.net
www.sclimage.net

S Management 15 Rocks Lane, London, SW13 0BD, United Kingdom
(020) 8487 9655/ (020) 8487 9541
fiona@smanagement.co.uk
www.smanagement.co.uk

Sage Sohier@Bill Charles London Ltd. Unit 3E1, Zetland House, 5-25 Scrutton Street, London, EC2A 4HJ, United Kingdom
020 7033 9284/020 2033 9285
london@billcharles.com
www.billcharles.com

Sally Fear 2 Rosedale Terrace, Dalling Road, London, W6 0HF, United Kingdom
(020) 8748 6436
sally@sallyfear.com

Sally Griffyn 164 Nelson Road, London, N8 9RN, United Kingdom
(020) 8341 9724/(07866) 385366
sally@sacredjourneys.co.uk
www.sacredjourneys.co.uk

Sam Ashley, London, N16, United Kingdom
(07941) 330538
photosam@hotmail.com
www.samashley.com

Sam Burnett Photography 6a Waldram Crescent, London, SE23 3LW, United Kingdom
(07985) 606055
sam@sb-photography.net
www.sb-photography.net

Sam Haskins@The Katy Barker Agency Ltd 11 Mason's Arms Mews, Maddox Street, London, W1S 1NX, United Kingdom
(020) 7493 3933/ (020) 7493 3311
catherine@katybarker.com
www.katybarker.com

Sam Logan@Blunt Management The Courtyard Studio 2, Old Grammarphone Works, London, W10 5BZ, United Kingdom
(020) 8960 2041/(07979) 900068 (020) 8960 2039
info@bluntlondon.com
www.bluntlondon.com

Sam Robinson Photography The Shop, 64 Halliford Street, London, N1 3HF, United Kingdom
(020) 7704 8887/07976 287848
info@sam-robinson.com
www.sam-robinson.com

Sam Stowell Studio 1, 28-30 Churchfield Road, W3 6EB, United Kingdom
(07956) 448527
samstowell_29@msn.com
www.samstowell.com

Samuel Ashfield Photography, Bristol, United Kingdom
(01454) 326250/(07974) 878099 (01454) 326976
sam@samuelashfield.com
www.samuelashfield.com

Samuel Hicks@van Hauen Moore 14 Powis Mews, Notting Hill, London, W11 1JN, United Kingdom
(020) 7792 0022/ (020) 7792 8636
email@vanhauenmoore.com
www.vanhauenmoore.com

Sanders Nicolson Charity House, 14-15 Perseverance Works, London, E2 8DD, United Kingdom
(020) 7739 6987/ (020) 7729 4056
mail@sandersnicolson.com
www.sandersnicolson.com

Sandra Lane@Sarah Kaye Representation Ltd 38 Queen's Gate, London, SW7 5HR, United Kingdom
(020) 7225 5005/ (020) 7225 0109
sarah@sarahkaye.com
www.sarahkaye.com

Sandra Lousada@Creative Talent (UK) Limited 78 York Street, London, W1H 1DP, United Kingdom
(020) 7439 1877/ (020) 7434 1144
info@creativetalentlimited.com
www.creativetalentlimited.com

Sandro Hyams 37 Lyndhurst Avenue, London, London, N12 0LX, United Kingdom
(020) 8362 0966/(07941) 918819
sh@sandrohyams.com
www.sandrohyams.com

Sandy Porter Kamarsan, Valley Road, Swanage, Dorset, BH19 3DX, United Kingdom
(01929) 480806/ (01929) 480806
sandy@gnss.com

Sara Morris 23-28 Penn Street, London, N1 5DL, United Kingdom
(020) 7729 3740/ (020) 7729 9410
sara.studio@virgin.net
www.saramorris.co.uk

Sara Wilson@Gina Phillips Represents Ltd 6 Leverton Place, London, NW5 2PL, United Kingdom
(020) 7284 2022/ (020) 7424 0272
info@ginaphillips.co.uk
www.ginaphillips.co.uk

Sarah Daw Cameo House, 11 Bear Street, London, WC2H 7AS, United Kingdom
(020) 7930 6996/ (020) 7930 5002
hello@sarahdaw.com
www.sarahdawproduction.com

Sarah Jones@Début Art & The Coningsby Gallery 30 Tottenham Street, London, W1T 4RJ, United Kingdom
(020) 7636 1064/ (020) 7580 7017
info@debutart.com
www.debutart.com

Sarah Kaye Representation Ltd 38 Queen's Gate, London, SW7 5HR, United Kingdom
(020) 7225 5005/ (020) 7225 0109
sarah@sarahkaye.com
www.sarahkaye.com

Sarah King Studio 66, Cheylesmore House, Ebury Bridge Road, London, SW1W 8QZ, United Kingdom
(020) 7730 5589/(07774) 480626
sarahking.photographer@btinternet.com
www.sarah-king.com

Sarah Lane Represents 56 Bidwell Gardens, London, N11 2AU, United Kingdom
(07901) 552520/ (020) 8292 4001
sarah@sarahlanerepresents.com
www.sarahlanerepresents.com

Sarah Louise Photography 175 Derby Road, Chellaston, Derby, DE73 5SB, United Kingdom
(07791) 531887/ (01332) 727752
dancingperfect@hotmail.com
www.sarahlouisephotography.com

Sarah Ramsay 9 Edis Street, London, NW1 8LG, United Kingdom
(020) 7586 1975/(07770) 430678
slrphotography@blueyonder.co.uk
www.slrphotography.co.uk

Sarkis Boyadjian 55 Coram Street, London, WC1N 1HB, United Kingdom
(07788) 444705
sarkfoto@lineone.net

Sasha Bezzubov@Bill Charles London Ltd. Unit 3E1, Zetland House, 5-25 Scrutton Street, London, EC2A 4HJ, United Kingdom
020 7033 9284/020 2033 9285
london@billcharles.com
www.billcharles.com

Sasha Gusov@Axiom Photographic Agency The Pall Mall Deposit, 124-128 Barlby Road, London, W10 6BL, United Kingdom
(020) 8964 9970/ (020) 8964 8440
info@axiomphotographic.com
www.axiomphotographic.com

Schnaps Photography Condover Mews, Condover, Shrewsbury, SY5 7BG, United Kingdom
(01743) 875007/ (01743) 875005
info@schnaps.co.uk
www.schnaps.co.uk

Scott Johnston 2 Dale Hill, Blackwell, Bromsgrove, Worcestershire, B60 1QJ, United Kingdom
0121-445 2384/(07775) 998090 / 0121-445 2649
scott@scottjphoto.co.uk

Scott Morrison Photography 9 Brassmill Enterprise Centre, Brassmill Lane, Bath, BA1 3JN, United Kingdom
(01225) 463555/ (01225) 463222
info@scottstudio.co.uk
www.scottstudio.co.uk

sdimaging 53 Sandgate High Street, Sandgate, Folkestone, Kent, CT20 3AH, United Kingdom
(01303) 256666/(07930) 316601
info@sdimaging.co.uk
www.sdimaging.co.uk

Seal Studio 26 Pulteney Road, Bath, BA2 4EZ, United Kingdom
(01225) 445 734/ (01225) 445734
post@sealstudio.com
www.sealstudio.com

Sealand Aerial Photography Ltd Pitlands Farm, Up Marden, Chichester, West Sussex, PO18 9JP, United Kingdom
(023) 9263 1468/ (023) 9263 1890
sales@sealandap.co.uk
www.sealandap.co.uk

Seamus Ryan@Vue Units 1 & 2 Elm Court, 1 Royal Oak Yard, London, SE1 3TP, United Kingdom
(020) 7403 5555/ (020) 7403 2005
production@vue-us.com
www.vue-us.com

Sean Myers@Tattersall Love 40 Langham Street, London, W1W 7AS, United Kingdom
(020) 7637 5737/ (020) 7637 5747
mail@tattersall-love.com
www.tattersall-love.com

Sebetenzo@Sergio Larrain@Magnum Photos 63 Gee Street, London, EC1V 3RS, United Kingdom
(020) 7490 1771/ (020) 7608 0020
magnum@magnumphotos.co.uk
www.magnumphotos.com

Sergio Veranes@Adrenalin Management Temple Works, Brett Passage, London, E8 1JR, United Kingdom
(020) 8986 3939/ (020) 8986 3665
info@adrenalinmanagement.com
www.adrenalinmanagement.com

Shahny Raitz Von Frentz 38 Chiswick Lane, London, W4 2JQ, United Kingdom
(020) 8994 4797/(07903) 921525
shahnyrvf@btinternet.com
www.shahnyraitzvonfrentz.com www.srvfinteriors.com

Sharon Brandman Agency No 2 Elmhurst Close, Bushey, WD23 2QB
845 800 9003/ sharon@sharonbrandman.com
www.sharonbrandman.com
See ad in showcase

harp Photography 14 Devonshire Place, Brighton, BN2 1QA, United Kingdom
(07775) 895477
info@janesharp.com
www.JaneSharp.com

Shaun Higson Flat 4, 165-169 Lewisham Way, London, SE14 6QP, United Kingdom
(020) 8694 8961/(07836) 672690
higson@pics.freeserve.co.uk

Shaw & Shaw 40 Cheltenham Road, Manchester, M21 9QN, United Kingdom
(07989) 409826
j.shaw@shawandshaw.co.uk
www.shawandshaw.co.uk

Shed 16 Studios 16 Olga Road, Nottingham, NG3 2NW, United Kingdom
0115-941 9416
robin.culley.co.uk
www.robinculley.co.uk

Sheila Rock@Terri Manduca The Basement, 11 Elvaston Place, London, SW7 5QG, United Kingdom
(020) 7581 5844/ (020) 7581 5822
terri@terrimanduca.co.uk
www.terrimanduca.co.uk

Shirley Beljon 5 John Islip Street, London, SW1P 4PU, United Kingdom
(020) 7630 1145

Shirley Hart Creative Consultants 19 Ulundi Road, London, SE3 7UQ, United Kingdom
(020) 8853 2987/(07867) 806250
shirleyhart@btinternet.com
www.shirleyhart.com

Shoot Me Senseless Photography Osler Road, Old Headington, Oxford, OX3 9BH, United Kingdom
(07876) 021870
david@shootmesenseless.com
www.shootmesenseless.com

Shoot Production Ltd 23 Glebe Road, London, N8 7DA, United Kingdom
(020) 8442 9171/ (020) 8348 7404
adele@shootgroup.com
www.shootgroup.com

Shoot The Moon Photography Concept House, Naval Street, Manchester, M4 6AX, United Kingdom
0161-205 7417/ 0161-205 8623
elaine@shoot-the-moon.co.uk
www.stmphotography.co.uk

ShootingHip.com 62 Patrick's Cops Road, Liss, Hampshire, GU33 7DW, United Kingdom
(07730) 876651
rob@shootinghip.com
www.shootinghip.com

ShowBizLondon Ltd, London, NW1 0XQ, United Kingdom
(0870) 3212019/ (0870) 4324310
chb@showbizlondon.com
www.showbizlondon.com

Sian Irvine@Beth Coyne Agency, London, NW6 1GF, United Kingdom
(020) 7431 8981/ (020) 7813 9750
info@bethcoyne.com
www.bethcoyne.com

Sien Web 74a St. Marys Road, London, NW10 4AX, United Kingdom
(020) 8965 6138
contact@sienweb.com
www.sienweb.com

Silverscene Photography Office 3, 142 Union Street, Plymouth, PL1 3HL, United Kingdom
(01752) 604266/(07944) 145992
leepengelly@aol.com
www.silverscenephoto.co.uk

Simen Johan@Bill Charles London Ltd. Unit 3E1, Zetland House, 5-25 Scrutton Street, London, EC2A 4HJ, United Kingdom
020 7033 9284/020 2033 9285
london@billcharles.com
www.billcharles.com

Simmons Aerofilms Ltd 32-34 Station Close, Potters Bar, Hertfordshire, EN6 1TL, United Kingdom
(01707) 648390/ (01707) 648399
library@aerofilms.com
www.simmonsaerofilms.com

Simon Annand@Akehurst Creative Management Ltd, London, United Kingdom
(020) 7624 2366
na@nickyakehurst.com
www.akehurstcreativemanagement.com

Simon Bevan@Tattersall Love 40 Langham Street, London, W1W 7AS, United Kingdom
(020) 7637 5737/ (020) 7637 5747
mail@tattersall-love.com
www.tattersall-love.com

Simon Bremner@Victoria Lees Management (VLM) 2 Fairview Gardens, Woodford Green, Essex, IG8 7DJ, United Kingdom
(07710) 287220/ (020) 8504 8125
victoria@victorialeesmanagement.co.uk
www.victorialeesmanagement.co.uk

Simon Brown@Jo Clark 2nd Floor, 202B Camden Lock, London, NW1 8AF, United Kingdom
(020) 7267 7267/ (020) 7267 7495
jo@joclark.com
www.joclark.com

Simon Buckley 3 Lions Fold, Sale, Cheshire, M33 6JF, United Kingdom
/(07770) 426888
mail@simonbuckleyphoto.co.uk

Simon Butcher 28 Liddell Gardens, London, NW10 3QD, United Kingdom
(020) 8960 9456/(07850) 555826
simon@zebu.co.uk
www.simon-butcher.co.uk

Simon Clark Photography 17 Helsby Court, Pollitt Drive, St John's Wood, London, NW8 8JQ, United Kingdom
(07779) 100009
siclarkphoto@yahoo.co.uk
www.siclark.com

Simon Emery Associates 48 Blenheim Crescent, South Croydon, Surrey, CR2 6BP, United Kingdom
(020) 8239 7200
charlotte@seaphotography.com
www.seaphotography.com

Simon Fowler@Shoot Production Ltd 23 Glebe Road, London, N8 7DA, United Kingdom
(020) 8442 9171/ (020) 8348 7404
adele@shootgroup.com
www.shootgroup.com

Simon Frederick Fotography 26-28 Hammersmith Grove, London, W6 7BA, United Kingdom
(07789) 201072
simon@simonfrederick.com
www.simonfrederick.com

Simon Harding, Forty Six, 3 Oaks Road, Wythall, Birmingham, B47 6HQ, United Kingdom
(01564) 200 199/(07836) 211278
simonharding@tiscali.co.uk
www.simonhardingphotography.com

Simon Harris@Milc Studio 7, Zeus House, 16-30 Provost Street, London, N1 7NG, United Kingdom
(020) 7278 8838/ (0870) 0941564
gemma@milc.co.uk
www.milc.co.uk

Simon Holben@David Lambert 108 Oakley Street, London, SW3 5NR, United Kingdom
(020) 7352 0033/(07747) 032 299 / (020) 7352 5553
david@davidlambert.com
www.davidlambert.com

Simon King Photography 13A Heaten Road, Willington, Manchester, M20 4PX, United Kingdom
✆ (07885) 201404
✉ simon@skingphoto.com
🖥 www.skingphoto.com

Simon Le-Fevre 118 Churchfield Road, London, W3 6BY, United Kingdom
✆ (020) 8993 2236/(07770) 755307 ✍ (020) 8993 2236

Simon Leibowitz Photography 119 Ashurst Road, London, N12 9AA, United Kingdom
✆ (020) 8492 0693/ ✍ (020) 8343 7255
✉ simon@slphotography.co.uk
🖥 www.slphotography.co.uk

Simon Lewis Photographer 35 Swan Island, Strawberry Vale, Twickenham, TW1 4RP, United Kingdom
✆ (07860) 235544
✉ mail@simonlewisphotography.com
🖥 www.simonlewisphotography.com

Simon Livingstone 41-43 Commercial Street, Birmingham, B1 1RS, United Kingdom
✆ 0121-643 2123/ ✍ 0121-246 5101
✉ simon.livingstone@newsteam.co.uk
🖥 www.newsteam.co.uk

Simon Mackney Photography Top Floor, 348 Caledonian Road, Islington, London, N1 1DU, United Kingdom
✆ (07830) 131817
✉ simon@simonmackney.co.uk
🖥 www.simonmackney.co.uk

Simon Marsden The Presbytery, Hainton, Market Rasen, Lincolnshire, LN8 6LR, United Kingdom
✆ (01507) 313646/ ✍ (01507) 313646
✉ info@marsdenarchive.com
🖥 www.marsdenarchive.com

Simon McComb 18 Townshend Terrace, Richmond, Surrey, TW9 1XL, United Kingdom
✆ (020) 8408 0495/(07802) 585028
🖥 www.simonmccomb.co.uk

Simon Mills (PMA)@Carolyn Trayler Photographers Agent Unit 566, 56 Gloucester Road, London, SW7 4UB, United Kingdom
✆ (020) 7370 0712/ ✍ (020) 7370 0765
✉ carolyn@trayler.co.uk
🖥 www.trayler.co.uk

Simon Page-Ritchie@Catherine Collins The Power Station, Coronet Street, London, N1 6HD, United Kingdom
✆ (020) 7739 8678/(07785) 571187 ✍ (020) 7739 8489
✉ catherine@catherinecollins.co.uk
🖥 www.catherinecollins.co.uk

Simon Pask N1 Studios, 1st Floor, 6-8 Vestry Street, London, N1 7RE, United Kingdom
✆ (020) 7251 2414/(07768) 735637 ✍ (020) 7490 2392
✉ simon@simonpask.com
🖥 www.simonpask.com

Simon Pugh 7 Ezra Street, London, E2 7RH, United Kingdom
✆ (020) 7729 4812/(07770) 428172 ✍ (020) 7256 0367
✉ simon.pugh@virgin.net

Simon Punter 103 Elm Drive, Hove, East Sussex, BN3 7JA, United Kingdom
✆ (01273) 770730/(07074) 770730 ✍ (01273) 773999
✉ photo@simonpunter.com

Simon Saffery Unit 3, Abbeymount Techbase, 2 Easter Road, Edinburgh, EH7 5AN, United Kingdom
✆ 0131-659 6575/(07710) 739471 ✍ 0131-659 6575
✉ s.safferyphoto@virgin.net
🖥 www.sports-portraits.co.uk

Simon Scarboro@Re:fresh Suit 4, The Swans Centre, Fishers Lane, London, W4 1RX, United Kingdom
✆ (020) 8747 8080/ ✍ (020) 8747 8228
✉ info@refresh-agency.com
🖥 www.refresh-agency.com

Simon Songhurst Photography 2 Mapesbury Road, London, NW2 4HX, United Kingdom
✆ (07961) 107777/7894711144
✉ info@simonsonghurst.com
🖥 www.simonsonghurst.com

Simon Statpoole 130 Britannia Drive, Ashton-on-Ribble, Preston, PR2 2YD, United Kingdom
✆ (07989) 567194

Simon Stock@Burnham Niker Unit 8, Canonbury Business Centre, 190A New North Road, London, N1 7BJ, United Kingdom
✆ (020) 7704 6565/ ✍ (020) 7704 8383
✉ enquiries@burnham-niker.com
🖥 www.burnham-niker.com

Simon Stuart-Miller Oak Lodge, Nanstallon, Bodmin, Cornwall, PL30 5LQ, United Kingdom
✆ (020) 8540 7198/(07979) 914492 ✍ (020) 8540 7198
✉ simon@simonstuartmiller.com
🖥 www.simonstuart-miller.com

Simon Thorpe, London, United Kingdom
✆ /(07966) 261 532
✉ simon@simonthorpeimages.com
🖥 www.simonthorpeimages.com
www.simonthorpeimages.com simonthorpeimages.com

Simon Towsley@Agent Pandora 12 Stonells Road, London, SW11 6HQ, United Kingdom
✆ (07966) 181825
✉ pandora@agentpandora.com
🖥 www.agentpandora.com

Simon Turtle 42 Probert Road, London, SW2 1BW, United Kingdom
✆ (020) 7737 7521/07973 229743
✉ mail@simonturtle.com
🖥 www.simonturtle.com

Simon Walton@Creative Talent (UK) Limited 78 York Street, London, W1H 1DP, United Kingdom
✆ (020) 7439 1877/ ✍ (020) 7434 1144
✉ info@creativetalentlimited.com
🖥 www.creativetalentlimited.com

Simon Warmer Fotografie BV Dukdalfweg 38, Amsterdam, 1041-BE, Netherlands
✆ 00 31 20 692 3955/ ✍ 00 31 20 693 1511
✉ simon@simonwarmer.nl
🖥 http |/www.simonwarmer.nl

Simon Warner Whitestone Farm, Stanbury, Keighley, West Yorkshire, BD22 0JW, United Kingdom
✆ (01535) 644644/(07932) 106056 ✍ (01535) 644644
✉ photos@simonwarner.co.uk
🖥 www.simonwarner.co.uk

Simon Warren Studio 12, Waterside, London, N1 7SH, United Kingdom
✆ (020) 7253 1711/(07836) 322711 ✍ (020) 7490 1009
🖥 www.simonwarren.com

Siobhan Squire 111 Shoreditch High Street, London, E1 6JN, United Kingdom
✆ (020) 7739 8985/ ✍ (020) 7729 5125
✉ siobhan@siobhansquire.com
🖥 www.siobhansquire.com

SK Creative Management 23 New Mount Street, Manchester, M4 4DE, United Kingdom
✆ 0161-953 4032/ ✍ (0870) 486 1940
✉ info@skcreativemanagement.com
🖥 www.skcreativemanagement.com

Skinny Dip 1st Floor, 45-46 Poland Street, London, W1F 7NA, United Kingdom
✆ (020) 7292 0901/ ✍ (020) 7734 0758
✉ info@skinnydip.co.uk
🖥 www.skinnydip.co.uk

Skye Parrot@Blunt Management The Courtyard Studio 2, Old Grammarphone Works, London, W10 5BZ, United Kingdom
✆ (020) 8960 2041/(07979) 900068 ✍ (020) 8960 2039
✉ info@bluntlondon.com
🖥 www.bluntlondon.com

Slomon & Pettitt Photography 96 Clandon Road, Chatham, Kent, ME5 8UT, United Kingdom
✆ (0845) 2260 939
✉ tony@salomonpettitt.co.uk
🖥 www.slomanpettit.co.uk

Slyde Media 134 Windy House Lane, Sheffield, S2 1BY, United Kingdom
✆ (07719) 280804
✉ slydeproductions@hotmail.com
🖥 www.slydemedia.plus.uk

Smith n Smith 6 Creekside, London, SE8 4SA, United Kingdom
✆ (07738) 942194
✉ info@smithnsmith.com
🖥 www.smithnsmith.com

Smudgesphotos Miltonmuir House, Arbuthnott, Laurencekirk, Kincardineshire, AB30 1PB, United Kingdom
✆ (01561) 361900
✉ hasmudge1@tiscali.co.uk
🖥 myweb.tiscali.co.uk/smudgephotos

Sniffy Dog@Coochie Management 26 Harcourt Street, Marylebone, London, W1H 4HW, United Kingdom
✆ (020) 7724 9700/(07802) 795620 ✍ (020) 7724 2598
✉ amanda@coochie-management.com
🖥 www.coochie-management.com

Sofia Sanchez & Mauro Mongiello@The Katy Barker Agency Ltd 11 Mason's Arms Mews, Maddox Street, London, W1S 1NX, United Kingdom
✆ (020) 7493 3933/ ✍ (020) 7493 3311
✉ catherine@katybarker.com
🖥 www.katybarker.com

Solid 111 Shoreditch High Street, London, E1 6JN, United Kingdom
✆ (020) 7729 1991/ ✍ (020) 7729 5125
✉ info@solid.co.uk
🖥 www.solid.co.uk

Soma Design 21 Westfield Avenue, Woking, Surrey, GU22 9PH, United Kingdom
✆ (01483) 764491/ ✍ (01483) 764491
✉ calvers@soma-design.co.uk
🖥 www.soma-design.co.uk

SomaPhotos 1 Sly Street, London, E1 2LE, United Kingdom
✆ (07766) 753300
✉ hugh@somaphotos.com
🖥 www.somaphotos.com

Sonia Halliday Photographs 22 Bates Lane, Aylesbury, Buckinghamshire, HP22 5SL, United Kingdom
✆ (01296) 612266/ ✍ (01296) 612266
✉ info@soniahalliday.com
🖥 www.soniahalliday.com

Sonja Fowler Photography Flat 2, Gye House, Solon New Road Estate, London, SW4 7LU, United Kingdom
✆ (07951) 431122
✉ sonjafowler@hotmail.com
🖥 www.sonjafowlerphotography.com

Sophie Broadbridge@Coochie Management 26 Harcourt Street, Marylebone, London, W1H 4HW, United Kingdom
✆ (020) 7724 9700/(07802) 795620 ✍ (020) 7724 2598
✉ amanda@coochie-management.com
🖥 www.coochie-management.com

Sophie Klerk@Début Art & The Coningsby Gallery 30 Tottenham Street, London, W1T 4RJ, United Kingdom
✆ (020) 7636 1064/ ✍ (020) 7580 7017
✉ info@debutart.com
🖥 www.debutart.com

Sophie Marsham@Début Art & The Coningsby Gallery 30 Tottenham Street, London, W1T 4RJ, United Kingdom
✆ (020) 7636 1064/ ✍ (020) 7580 7017
✉ info@debutart.com
🖥 www.debutart.com

Soulscapes Design and Photography Saint Osmunds Road, Lower Parkstone, Poole, Dorset, BH14 9JN, United Kingdom
✆ (01202) 723696
✉ enquiries@soulscapes.co.uk
🖥 www.soulscapes.co.uk

Spencer Cartwright Photography 207 Layton Road, Blackpool, FY3 8ES, United Kingdom
✆ (01253) 399492
✉ spencer@spencercartwright.co.uk
🖥 www.spencercartwright.co.uk

Spike Powell 7 The Thoroughfare, Woodbridge, Suffolk, IP12 1AA, United Kingdom
✆ (01394) 384666/(07860) 379870 ✍ (01394) 382091
✉ spikepowell@btconnect.com

Spiros Politis@Agent Orange 10 Swan Yard, London, N1 1SD, United Kingdom
✆ (020) 7226 0440/ ✍ (020) 7226 1613
✉ annika@agentorange.co.uk
🖥 www.agentorange.co.uk

Square Moon Photography Springfield Coachhouse, Park Road, Bingley, West Yorkshire, BD16 4LR, United Kingdom
✆ (07831) 208113

Stantham Studios 4 Northcote Place, Newcastle, Staffordshire, ST5 1HU, United Kingdom
✆ (07831) 354302
✉ info@statham.net
🖥 www.statham.net

Stefan May Archive Oettingenstrae 36, Munich, 80538, Germany
✆ 00 49 89 21 66 55 55/ ✍ 00 49 89 21 66 55 56
✉ archive@stefanmay.com

Stefan Ruiz@The Katy Barker Agency Ltd 11 Mason's Arms Mews, Maddox Street, London, W1S 1NX, United Kingdom
(020) 7493 3933/ (020) 7493 3311
catherine@katybarker.com
www.katybarker.com

Stefano Massimo@Stella Pye The Basement, 22 Castellain Road, London, W9 1EZ, United Kingdom
(020) 7286 8200/(07956) 501977 (020) 7286 8400
stella@stellapye.com
www.stellapye.com

Stem Agency Top Floor, 23 Charlotte Road, London, EC2A 3PB, United Kingdom
(07790) 026628
will@stemagency.com
www.stemagency.com

Stephan Minder@Defrance 47 Rethelstrasse, Deusseldorf, 40237, Germany
00 49 211 87 67 89/ 00 49 211 87 67 89
defrance@defrance.de
www.defrance.de

Stephan Schacher@Bill Charles London Ltd. Unit 3E1, Zetland House, 5-25 Scrutton Street, London, EC2A 4HJ, United Kingdom
020 7033 9284/020 2033 9285
london@billcharles.com
www.billcharles.com

Stephane Bourson 41b rue de chaillot, Paris, 75116, France
00 33 6 13 58 77 39
steph@sbourson.com
www.sbourson.com

Stephanie Hafner@Jo Clark 2nd Floor, 202B Camden Lock, London, NW1 8AF, United Kingdom
(020) 7267 7267/ (020) 7267 7495
jo@joclark.com
www.joclark.com

Stephanie Rushton 16 Reservoir Studios, 547 Cable Street, London, E1W 3EW, United Kingdom
(020) 7780 9838/(07798) 862243 (020) 7780 9838
info@stephanierushton.com
www.stephanierushton.com

Stephen Barnett 29 Culverden Park Road, Tunbridge Wells, Kent, TN4 9RB, United Kingdom
(01892) 546307/(07831) 244920
www.stephenbarnett.com

Stephen Bond Blackditch Barns, Bartlow, Cambridge, CB1 6PW, United Kingdom
(01223) 890980/(07703) 332890
stephen@stephenbond.com
www.stephenbond.com

Stephen Coe 16 Railey Mews, London, NW5 2PA, United Kingdom
(020) 7267 3377

Stephen Dodd Bigcheese, 10 Windle Court, Clayhill, Neston, CH64 3UH, United Kingdom
0151-336 8882/(07774) 944943 0151-336 8371
photography@bigcheese.co.uk
www.bigcheese.co.uk

Stephen Hayward 45 Broom House Lane, London, SW6 3DP, United Kingdom
(020) 7736 8307/(07973) 122791 (020) 7384 1545
stephenjhayward@compuserve.com
www.contact-uk.com/stephenhayward

Stephen Hepworth Photographer Overdale, The Hills, Bradwell, Hope Valley, Derbyshire, S33 9GZ, United Kingdom
(01433) 623586
stephen@stephenhepworth.com
www.stephenhepworth.com

Stephen Hopkinson Photography Ltd 12 Billsmore Green, Solihull, West Midlands, B92 9LN, United Kingdom
0121-680 2716/ 0121-248 8153
stephenphoto3@aol.com
www.stephenhopkinsonphoto.co.uk

Stephen Hyde 57 Maldon Road, London, W3 6SZ, United Kingdom
(020) 8993 4599/(07831) 345856 (020) 8248 2584
steve@londonphotography.co.uk
www.londonphotography.co.uk

Stephen Mallaby The Studio, 14 Railway Approach, East Grinstead, West Sussex, RH19 1BP, United Kingdom
(01342) 321493/ (01342) 323300
steve@mallaby.co.uk
www.mallaby.co.uk

Stephen Markeson Chearsley Hill Cottage, Chilton Road, Chearsley, Aylesbury, Buckinghamshire, HP18 0DN, United Kingdom
(01844) 208791/(07836) 623372 (01844) 201838
stephen@stephenmarkeson.com
www.stephenmarkeson.com

Stephen Marshall Johnston 75 Haverhill Road, London, SW12 0HE, United Kingdom
(07775) 991834
steve@stevejohnstonphoto.com
www.stevejohnstonphoto.com

Stephen Marwood 20 Bowling Green Lane, London, EC1R 0BD, United Kingdom
(020) 7490 7706/(07759) 463181 (020) 7336 8280
mail@stephenmarwood.com
www.stephenmarwood.com

Stephen Oliver Unit 12B, Rosemary Works, London, N1 5PH, United Kingdom
(020) 7613 0366/(07973) 324839
oliver@photow.com
www.photow.com

Stephen Robson 18 Caterham Road, London, SE13 5AR, United Kingdom
(020) 8852 3556
stephenje.robson@virgin.net

Stephen Shepherd 11 Barn Way, Cirencester, Gloucestershire, GL7 2LY, United Kingdom
(07798) 836 147
steve@shepherdphoto.co.uk
www.shepherdphoto.co.uk

Stephen Shore@Bill Charles London Ltd. Unit 3E1, Zetland House, 5-25 Scrutton Street, London, EC2A 4HJ, United Kingdom
020 7033 9284/020 2033 9285
london@billcharles.com
www.billcharles.com

Stephen Vaughan, Tunbridge Wells, Kent, TN2 5YW, United Kingdom
(01892) 519316/07748 962376
info@stephenvaughan.co.uk
www.stephenvaughan.co.uk

Stephen Ward Photography Ltd The Red House, Water Lane, Hollingworth, Hyde, Cheshire, SK14 8HT, United Kingdom
(01457) 764220/ (08700) 528 375
stephen@swp.uk.com
www.swp.uk.com

SternREP 1801 Lincoln Blvd #148, Venice, 90291, United States of America
00 1 310 574 0076/ 00 1 310 496 2626
andrea:sternrep.com
www.sternrep.com

Steve Aland Photography Hoylake Business Centre, 42 Birkenhead Road, Hoylake, Wirral, Merseyside, CH47 3BW, United Kingdom
0151-630 1600/(07760) 112211
info@stevealand.co.uk
www.stevealand.co.uk

Steve Atkins Photography, Sherborne, Dorset, DT9, United Kingdom
(07743) 958353
steve@steveatkinsphotography.com
www.steveatkinsphotography.com

Steve Bardens Photography 5 Little Western Street, Brighton, BN1 2PU, United Kingdom
(01273) 770798
steve@stevebardens.com
www.stevebardens.com

Steve Baxter 4 Poplar Mews, Uxbridge Road, London, W12 7JS, United Kingdom
(020) 8749 4588/(07712) 623500 (020) 8749 4299
baxter.photography@btconnect.com
www.stevebaxter.com

Steve Benbow@Axiom Photographic Agency The Pall Mall Deposit, 124-128 Barlby Road, London, W10 6BL, United Kingdom
(020) 8964 9970/ (020) 8964 8440
info@axiomphotographic.com
www.axiomphotographic.com

Steve Bielschowsky Unit 10, 21 Wren Street, London, WC1X 0HF, United Kingdom
(020) 7278 2228/(07831) 674677 (020) 7833 4691
www.bielschowsky.com

Steve Bisgrove Via F.Siacci 13, Rome, 197, Italy
00 39 6 807 7521/00 39 33 9119 0970
steve.bisgrove@infinito.it
www.contact-me.net/SteveBisgrove

Steve Bond Photography 3 Stone Cottages, Furnace Lane, Lamberhurst, Tunbridge Wells, Kent, TN3 8LF, United Kingdom
(01892) 891690/(07778) 177 690
steve@stevebond.co.uk
www.stevebond.co.uk

Steve Cavalier@Julian Cotton Photographers Agent 55 Upper Montagu Street, London, W1H 1SF, United Kingdom
(020) 7723 3100/ (020) 7724 7555
info@juliancotton.co.uk
www.juliancotton.co.uk

Steve Davey 15 Ballater Road, London, SW2 5QS, United Kingdom
(020) 7924 0856/(07710) 757433
steve@stevedavey.com
www.stevedavey.com

Steve Emby@Yara Gremoli Photographers Agent Studio 210, Canalot Studios, 222 Kensal Road, London, W10 5BN, United Kingdom
(0870) 8501209/(07880) 627413 (0870) 8501209
yara@sbmanagement.org
www.yaragremoli.com

Steve Gale 4 Ribblesdale Road, London, N8 7EP, United Kingdom
(020) 8348 7724/(07831) 372198
sgale@dircon.co.uk
www.celticlandscapes.com

Steve Hall Photography 27 Cambridge Close, Harlington, Doncaster, South Yorkshire, DN5 7JX, United Kingdom
(01709) 888512/(07957) 870693
info@photographyyorkshire.com
www.photographyyorkshire.com

Steve Harries@East Photographic Ltd 8 Iron Bridge House, 3 Bridge Approach, London, NW1 8BD, United Kingdom
(020) 7722 3444/ (020) 7722 3544
roger@eastphotographic.com
www.eastphotographic.com

Steve Hoskins@Angela Woods 4 The Carlton Tavern, 73 Grafton Road, London, NW5 4BB, United Kingdom
(020) 7284 3417/(07850) 263077 (020) 7482 2466
angela@angelawoods.com
www.angelawoods.com

Steve MacarÈ Photography 59 Dragon Avenue, Harrogate, North Yorkshire, HG1 5DS, United Kingdom
(01423) 561809/(07711) 937562 (01423) 548843
stevemacare@ntlworld.com

Steve McCurry@Magnum Photos 63 Gee Street, London, EC1V 3RS, United Kingdom
(020) 7490 1771/ (020) 7608 0020
magnum@magnumphotos.co.uk
www.magnumphotos.com

Steve McDonough, 9 Victoria Mews, London, E8 1GP, United Kingdom
(020) 7249 7274/(07885) 890336 (020) 7249 7274
smcfoto@btinternet.com
www.smcfolio.co.uk

Steve Moore M & M Studios, Millers Yard, Hayseech Road, Halesowen, West Midlands, B63 3PD, United Kingdom
0121-501 3868/ 0121-585 5377
info@mandmstudios.co.uk
www.mandmstudios.co.uk

Steve Orino Photography 128 De Beauvoir Road, London, N1 4DJ, United Kingdom
(07774) 117284
steve@orino-photo.co.uk
www.orino-photo.co.uk

Steve Painter Photography 6 Bates Close, Larkfield, Aylesford, Kent, ME20 6TG, United Kingdom
(01732) 849259
steve@stevepainterphotography.co.uk
www.stevepainterphotography.co.uk

Steve Payne 1st Floor Building D, The Chocolate Factory, Clarendon Road, London, N22 6XJ, United Kingdom
(020) 8889 6609
stevepaynephotog@btconnect.com
www.stevepaynephotography.co.uk

Steve Rawlings@Début Art & The Coningsby Gallery 30 Tottenham Street, London, W1T 4RJ, United Kingdom
📞 (020) 7636 1064/📠 (020) 7580 7017
✉ info@debutart.com
🖥 www.debutart.com

Steve Shipman@Beth Coyne Agency, London, NW6 1GF, United Kingdom
📞 (020) 7431 8981/📠 (020) 7813 9750
✉ info@bethcoyne.com
🖥 www.bethcoyne.com

Steve Smith 6 Westville Road, London, W12 9BD, United Kingdom
📞 (020) 8749 7578/(07798) 523986 📠 (020) 8723 4734

Steve Smith Photography Flat 1, Locksmith Court, 151 Albion Road, London, N16 9JU, United Kingdom
📞 (07747) 622338/📠 (020) 7613 1198
✉ steve@stevesmithphoto.com
🖥 www.stevesmithphoto.com

Steve Tanner 2 Bleeding Heart Yard, Off Greville Street, London, EC1N 8SJ, United Kingdom
📞 (020) 7430 0074/(07956) 270210
✉ steve@stevetanner.eu
🖥 www.stevetanner.eu

Steve Teague Photo Fourways, Mill End, Standon, Ware, Hertfordshire, SG11 1LP, United Kingdom
📞 (01920) 823947/(07774) 735860
✉ teague@btconnect.com
🖥 www.steveteague.co.uk

Steve Theodorou Studio 21, 21 Liddell Road, London, NW6 2EW, United Kingdom
📞 (020) 7328 5582/📠 (020) 7624 9334
✉ info@studio21photo.com
🖥 www.studio21photo.com

Steve Thompson 21 Arnot Way, Higher Bebington, Wirral, Merseyside, CH63 8LP, United Kingdom
📞 0151-650 2221/(07850) 098799
✉ steve@stevethomsonphoto.com
🖥 www.stevethomsonphoto.com

Steve Thornton 18b Abbey Road, Grimsby, North East Lincolnshire, DN32 0HW, United Kingdom
📞 (0845) 1662103/(07970) 220892
✉ stevethornton@ntlworld.com
🖥 www.stevethornton.co.uk

Steve Wakeham Ground Floor Studio, 10-11 Bishops Terrace, London, SE11 4UE, United Kingdom
📞 (020) 7735 7788/(07831) 885244 📠 (020) 7735 9944
✉ steve@stevewakeham.com
🖥 www.stevewakeham.com

Steve Williams 25c Somerfield Road, London, N4 2JN, United Kingdom
📞 (07932) 683736
✉ swilliams@systechgroup.net

Steven Allen Lindon House, The Green, York, YO62 4AA, United Kingdom
📞 (01653) 628687/(07775) 607585 📠 (01653) 628687
✉ mail@steveallenphotography.com
🖥 www.steveallenphotography.com

Steven Behr Bearsden, Bourneside, Virginia Water, Surrey, GU25 4LZ, United Kingdom
📞 (01344) 844428/(07973) 719060
✉ info@stockfile.co.uk
🖥 www.stockfile.co.uk

Steven Morris Photography, London, United Kingdom
📞 (07973) 523160
✉ steven@stevenmorris.com
🖥 www.stevenmorris.com

Stewart Grant 66 Vassall Road, London, SW9 6HY, United Kingdom
📞 (020) 7735 8111/(07973) 327991
✉ info@stewartgrant.co.uk
🖥 www.stewartgrant.co.uk

Stewart Jackson Photography 47 Low Moor Lane, Woolley, Wakefield, West Yorkshire, WF4 2LJ, United Kingdom
📞 (01924) 257967
✉ stoot1@mac.com
🖥 www.stewartjacksonphotography.co.uk

Stoneman & Metcalf Photographers Ltd Unit 1, Highbury Villas, Kingsdown, Bristol, BS2 8BX, United Kingdom
📞 0117-929 1813/(07714) 518142 📠 0117-925 0528
✉ mail@stonemanandmetcalf.com
🖥 www.stonemanandmetcalf.com

Stones Imaging The Hayloft Studio, Home Farm, Wakefield Road, Swillington, Leeds, LS26 8UA, United Kingdom
📞 0113-287 6700/(07913) 160852
✉ stonesimaging@btconnect.com
🖥 www.commercialfoto.com

Storm Studios Unit 7, Orchard Business Centre, Tonbridge, Kent, TN9 1QG, United Kingdom
📞 (01732) 770158/📠 (01732) 770160
✉ studio@stormukcom.demon.co.uk
🖥 www.storm.uk.com

Struan Wallace The Studio, 16 Gibraltar Walk, London, E2 7LH, United Kingdom
📞 (020) 7739 4406/📠 (020) 7739 8784
✉ struan@struan-wallace.co.uk
🖥 www.struan-wallace.co.uk

Structuraleye 9 Mount Pleasant, Hitchin, Hertfordshire, SG5 2BG, United Kingdom
📞 (01462) 436973/(07773) 192423
✉ jo@structuraleye.co.uk
🖥 www.structuraleye.co.uk

Stu Booth Digital Photography Unit 43, Wassage Way, Droitwich, Worcestershire, WR9 0NX, United Kingdom
📞 (01905) 796411/📠 (01905) 796411
✉ stu@boothphotography.co.uk
🖥 www.stubooth.co.uk

Stuart Boreham Eastworth Road, Chertsey, Surrey, KT16 8DW, United Kingdom
📞 01932 563318/(07976) 445772 📠 0193-270-6175
✉ stuart@boreham.co.uk
🖥 www.boreham.co.uk

Stuart Brown 19 Smeaton Road, London, SW18 5JJ, United Kingdom
📞 (020) 8874 8154/(07831) 443038
✉ stuart@stuartbrown99.wanadoo.co.uk

Peter Kidd

www.peterkidd.net

Stuart Chorley@Sharon Brandman Agency No 2 Milner Court, Bridgewater Way, Bushey, WD23 4UB, United Kingdom
℡ 020 8950 9213/07973 305575 ℡ 020 8950 7990
✉ sharon@sharonbrandman.com
🖥 www.sharonbrandman.com

Stuart Clark Salisbury House, 15 Aberford Road, Leeds, LS25 1PZ, United Kingdom
℡ 0113-286 2547

Stuart F Hall@Carolyn Trayler Photographers Agent Unit 566, 56 Gloucester Road, London, SW7 4UB, United Kingdom
℡ (020) 7370 0712/ (020) 7370 0765
✉ carolyn@trayler.co.uk
🖥 www.trayler.co.uk

Stuart Franklin@Magnum Photos 63 Gee Street, London, EC1V 3RS, United Kingdom
℡ (020) 7490 1771/ (020) 7608 0020
✉ magnum@magnumphotos.co.uk
🖥 www.magnumphotos.com

Stuart Frawley Eclipse Studios, Oldtye Place, 3 London Road South, Redhill, RH1 3AZ, United Kingdom
℡ (01737) 642020/(07973) 354576
✉ eclipsestudios@btinternet.com
🖥 www.eclipsephotostudio.co.uk

Stuart Hamilton@Alan Wickes 135 Downton Avenue, London, SW2 3TX, United Kingdom
℡ (020) 8674 2242/(07774) 259352
✉ a.wickes@btinternet.com
🖥 www.alanwickes.com

Stuart Haygarth@Début Art & The Coningsby Gallery 30 Tottenham Street, London, W1T 4RJ, United Kingdom
℡ (020) 7636 1064/ (020) 7580 7017
✉ info@debutart.com
🖥 www.debutart.com

Stuart MacGregor 7 Cedar Way, Camley Street, London, NW1 0PD, United Kingdom
℡ (020) 7388 9652
✉ stuartmacgregor@btclick.com

Stuart Roy Three Gables, Wood Farm, Earlswood, Solihull, West Midlands, B94 5SQ, United Kingdom
℡ (01564) 702947/(07836) 777213 ℡ (01564) 702947
✉ stuart@julieroy.freeserve.co.uk

Stuart West 30 Stone Street, Boxford, Sudbury, Suffolk, CO10 5NR, United Kingdom
℡ (01787) 211525/(07711) 356633
✉ stuartwest@btinternet.com
🖥 www.foodPhotographers.com/stuartwest

Studio 11 Unit 11 Benson Road, Nuffield Industrial Estate, Poole, Dorset, BH17 0GB, United Kingdom
℡ (01202) 330505
✉ info@studio-11.co.uk
🖥 www.studio-11.co.uk

Studio 2 Gill Farm, Gill Lane, Ashford, Kent, TN25 7HZ, United Kingdom
℡ (01233) 721511
✉ trevor@studio2uk.com
🖥 www.studio2uk.com

Studio 2 Photography Studio House, Invar Business Park, Invar Road, Swinton, Manchester, M27 9HF, United Kingdom
℡ 0161-728 8959
✉ paulb@thestudio.co.uk
🖥 www.studio-2.co.uk

Studio 202 Barford Street, Birmingham, B5 7EP, United Kingdom
℡ 0121-622 2221/(07976) 853336 ℡ 0121-622 2124
✉ studio202@btopenworld.com

Studio 21 Ltd 21 Liddell Road, West Hampstead, London, NW6 2EW, United Kingdom
℡ (020) 7328 5582/ (020) 7624 9334
✉ info@studio21photo.com
🖥 www.studio21photo.com

Studio 8 Photography 7 Northdown Road, Belmont, Surrey, SM2 6DY, United Kingdom
℡ (020) 8770 2108
✉ colin@studio8.co.uk
🖥 www.studio8.co.uk

Studio Argent Ltd School Lane, Knowsley Business Park, Prescot, Merseyside, L34 9EN, United Kingdom
℡ 0151-548 7722/ 0151-549 1713
✉ images@studioargent.co.uk
🖥 www.studioargent.co.uk

Studio D Photography 234 Church Street, Blackpool, FY1 3PX, United Kingdom
℡ (01253) 290191/ (01253) 290182
✉ paul@studiodphotography.co.uk
🖥 www.studiodphotography.co.uk

Studio Fulham Unit 22, Sulivan Enterprise Centre, Sulivan Road, London, SW6 3DJ, United Kingdom
℡ **(020) 7751 3030**
✉ **info@studiofulham.com**
🖥 **www.studiofulham.com**
See ad in showcase

Studio Lianski 3 Tiverton Dr, Wilmslow, Cheshire, SK9 2TJ, United Kingdom
℡ (01625) 549622
✉ studio_ilianski@yahoo.co.uk
🖥 www.ilianski.com

Studio M K 96 Puxley Road, Deanshanger, Milton Keynes, MK19 6LP, United Kingdom
℡ (01908) 260440/078 08 272423
✉ johnc@studiomk.co.uk
🖥 www.studiomk.co.uk

Studio P W D Ltd 48 Beaconsfield Road, Christchurch, Dorset, BH23 1QT, United Kingdom
℡ (01202) 382731
✉ mail@studiopwd.co.uk
🖥 www.studiopwd.co.uk

Studio Vivid Unit 14, Albion Park, Leeds, LS12 2EJ, United Kingdom
℡ 0113-245 9201/(07710) 090423 ℡ 0113-245 9202
✉ info@studiovivid.com
🖥 www.studiovivid.com

Stunning Corporate Photography 20 Elizebeth Road, Henley-on-Thames, Oxfordshire, RG9 1RG, United Kingdom
℡ (07884) 471232
✉ chb@stunningphoto.com
🖥 www.stunningphoto.com

Sue Allatt 10 Hatton Place, London, EC1N 8RU, United Kingdom
℡ (020) 7242 0024/(07860) 224735 ℡ (020) 7242 6200
✉ info@sueallatt.com
🖥 www.sueallatt.com

Sue Anderson 15 Riverview Park, Newcastleton, Roxburghshire, TD9 0TF, United Kingdom
℡ (01387) 375065/(07799) 693619 ℡ (01387) 375065
✉ info@islandfocus.co.uk
🖥 www.islandfocus.co.uk

Sue Atkinson 18 Grafton Mews, London, W1T 5JG, United Kingdom
℡ (020) 7387 5577
✉ sue@atkinsonroles.co.uk
🖥 www.sueatkinson.co.uk

Sue Baker, Rickmansworth, Hertfordshire, WD3 5YT, United Kingdom
℡ (01923) 282549/07850 667877
✉ suebaker05@yahoo.co.uk
🖥 www.suebaker05.com

Sue Cunningham 56 Chatham Road, Kingston upon Thames, Surrey, KT1 3AA, United Kingdom
℡ (020) 8541 3024/ (020) 8541 5388
✉ pictures@scphotographic.com
🖥 www.scphotographic.com

Sue Evans 8 Wells Street, Cardiff, CF11 6DW, United Kingdom
℡ (029) 2022 8367
✉ sue.evans7@virgin.net
🖥 www.ffotofictions.com

Sue Hiscoe Photography Upper Woodhead, Krumlin, Halifax, West Yorkshire, HX4 0EQ, United Kingdom
℡ (01422) 824422/ (01422) 824433
✉ sue@suehiscoe.com
🖥 www.suehiscoe.com

Sue Packer@Creative Talent (UK) Limited 78 York Street, London, W1H 1DP, United Kingdom
℡ (020) 7439 1877/ (020) 7434 1144
✉ info@creativetalentlimited.com
🖥 www.creativetalentlimited.com

Sue Parkhill@Coochie Management 26 Harcourt Street, Marylebone, London, W1H 4HW, United Kingdom
℡ (020) 7724 9700/(07802) 795620 ℡ (020) 7724 2598
✉ amanda@coochie-management.com
🖥 www.coochie-management.com

Sumner Partnership Ltd 29 Grove Hill Road, London, SE5 8DF, United Kingdom
℡ (020) 7501 6477
✉ edmund@edmundsumner.co.uk
🖥 www.edmundsumner.co.uk

Sunlight Studios Bulevardi 19 D31, Helsinki, 120, Finland
℡ 00 358 500 500 087
✉ peikko@anttiviitala.com
🖥 www.anttiviitala.com

Susan Meiselas@Magnum Photos 63 Gee Street, London, EC1V 3RS, United Kingdom
℡ (020) 7490 1771/ (020) 7608 0020
✉ magnum@magnumphotos.co.uk
🖥 www.magnumphotos.com

Sutton Motor Sport Images The Chapel, 61 Watling Street, Towcester, Northamptonshire, NN12 6AG, United Kingdom
℡ (01327) 352188/ (01327) 359355
✉ customerservices@sutton-images.com
🖥 www.sutton-images.com

Suzanne Grala Photography, Epsom, Surrey, KT17 4WY, United Kingdom
℡ /07976) 428966
✉ suzi@suzanne.grala.co.uk
🖥 www.suzanne.grala.co.uk

Sven Arnstein 29-31 Saffron Hill, London, EC1N 8SW, United Kingdom
℡ (07860) 288822
✉ svenire@aol.com
🖥 www.staystill.com

Swerve Photography 29-31 Saffron Hill, London, EC1N 8SW, United Kingdom
℡ **(07967) 628769**
✉ **info@swervephotography.com**
🖥 **www.swervephotography.com**
See ad in showcase

Sydney Harris 4 Brookland Close, London, NW11 6DJ, United Kingdom
℡ (020) 8458 0137
✉ photoharris@aol.com

Sylvain Deleu Photography 71 Southey Road, Harringhey, London, N15 5LJ, United Kingdom
℡ (07870) 649 206
✉ sylvaindeleu@mac.com
🖥 www.sylvaindeleu.com

Sylvia Bernat Photography 15 Sussex Square, Brighton, BN2 5AA, United Kingdom
℡ (07810) 228730
✉ sylviabernat@hotmail.com
🖥 www.sylviabernatphotography.com

Synergy Communications Ltd 250-252 Goswell Road, London, EC1V 7EB, United Kingdom
℡ (020) 7251 0303/ (020) 7251 0323
✉ info@synergy-communications.co.uk
🖥 www.synergy-communications.co.uk

T & N Enterprises Unit 5, 54 Cavell Street, London, E1 2HP, United Kingdom
℡ (020) 7423 9150/077 10 298793
✉ info@tnenterprises.co.uk
🖥 www.tnenterprises.co.uk

T M 2 Photography Unit C4, Wyther Lane Industrial Estate, Wyther Drive, Leeds, LS5 3AP, United Kingdom
℡ 0113-278 9585/ 0113-274 1163
✉ team@tm2photography.co.uk
🖥 www.tm2photography.co.uk

T Photographic 1 Heathgate Place, 75-83 Agincourt Road, London, London, NW3 2NU, United Kingdom
℡ (020) 7428 6070/ (020) 7428 6079
✉ peter@tphotographic.com
🖥 www.tphotographic.com

Tara Darby@East Photographic Ltd 8 Iron Bridge House, 3 Bridge Approach, London, NW1 8BD, United Kingdom
℡ (020) 7722 3444/ (020) 7722 3544
✉ roger@eastphotographic.com
🖥 www.eastphotographic.com

Tara Fisher@Tara Moore@Angela Woods 4 The Carlton Tavern, 73 Grafton Road, London, NW5 4BB, United Kingdom
℡ (020) 7284 3417/(07850) 263077 ℡ (020) 7482 2466
✉ angela@angelawoods.com
🖥 www.angelawoods.com

Tattersall Love 40 Langham Street, London, W1W 7AS, United Kingdom
℡ (020) 7637 5737/ (020) 7637 5747
✉ mail@tattersall-love.com
🖥 www.tattersall-love.com

Ted Humble-Smith@The White Agency 60 Epirus Road, Fulham, London, SW6 7UH, United Kingdom
℡ (020) 7381 2004/(07970) 619277 ℡ (020) 7386 8479
✉ annabel@thewhiteagency.com
🖥 www.thewhiteagency.com

Terence Broady 127 Highlands Heath, Putney, London, SW15 3TZ, United Kingdom
℡ (020) 8788 5325

Teresa Cottrell@Creative Talent (UK) Limited 78 York Street, London, W1H 1DP, United Kingdom
- (020) 7439 1877/ (020) 7434 1144
- info@creativetalentlimited.com
- www.creativetalentlimited.com

Terri Manduca The Basement, 11 Elvaston Place, London, SW7 5QG, United Kingdom
- (020) 7581 5844/ (020) 7581 5822
- terri@terrimanduca.co.uk
- www.terrimanduca.co.uk

Terrie Tanaka Management 101 Talbot Road, London, W11 2AT, United Kingdom
- (020) 7792 3500/ (020) 7792 2600
- danni@terrietanaka.com
- www.terrietanaka.com

Terry Hudson@Dave Tyler Associates 8 Portland Mews, London, W1V 3FJ, United Kingdom
- (07071) 202470/(07860) 364225 / (01438) 871680
- dave@davetyler.com
- www.davetyler.com

Terry McCormick Basement Studio 2, Panther House, London, WC1X 0AP, United Kingdom
- (020) 7837 5115/(07860) 555868 / (020) 7278 9074

Terry O'Neill@M & M Management Studio B, 11 Edith Grove, London, SW10 0JZ, United Kingdom
- (020) 7823 3723/ (020) 7351 3714
- admin@mmmanagement.com
- www.mmmanagement.com

Terry Payne Packshot & Food Photographer First Floor, Building D, The Chocolate Factory, Clarendon Road, London, N22 6XJ,
- 020 8889 6609
- terry.payne1@ntlworld.com
- www.terrypaynephotog.co.uk

Terry Richardson@The Katy Barker Agency Ltd 11 Mason's Arms Mews, Maddox Street, London, W1S 1NX, United Kingdom
- (020) 7493 3933/ (020) 7493 3311
- catherine@katybarker.com
- www.katybarker.com

Terry Ryan Photography 193 Charles Street, Leicester, LE1 1LA, United Kingdom
- 0116-254 4661/078 36 509584 / 0116-247 0933
- tryan@terryryan.co.uk
- www.terryryan.co.uk

Terry Trott Photography The Studio, 24 School Lane, Sittingbourne, Kent, ME9 9NL, United Kingdom
- (01795) 472833/(07831) 465253
- terry@terrytrottphotography.co.uk
- www.terrytrottphotography.co.uk

Tessa Musgrave The Old Water Tower, Herne Common, Herne Bay, Kent, CT6 7JZ, United Kingdom
- (01227) 361303/(07710) 035999
- contact@theoldwatertower.co.uk
- www.tessamusgrave.co.uk

Tessa Newmark 23 Streatham Common South, London, SW16 3BX, United Kingdom
- (07973) 241227
- tessa@tessanewmark.co.uk
- www.tessanewmark.co.uk

Tessa Traeger 7 Rossetti Studios, 72 Flood Street, London, SW3 5TF, United Kingdom
- (020) 7352 3641/ (020) 7352 4846
- info@tessatraeger.com
- www.tessatraeger.com

Tessa Verder@Freddie Brazil 211 Abercairn Road, London, SW16 5AJ, United Kingdom
- (020) 8764 2801/(07711) 753072 / (020) 8764 2801
- frederick.brazil@btconnect.com
- www.freddiebrazil.com

The Constructive 141a Constantine Road, London, NW3 2LR, United Kingdom
- (020) 7871 7618
- info@theconstructive.co.uk
- www.theconstructive.co.uk

The Creative Store Ltd Studio House, 142 Merton Hall Road, London, SW19 3PZ, United Kingdom
- (020) 8543 3855
- sales@thecreativestore.co.uk
- www.thecreativestore.co.uk

The Estate of Jeanloup Sieff@Maconochie Photography 4 Meard Street, Soho, London, W1F 0EF, United Kingdom
- (020) 7439 3159/ (020) 7439 2552
- info@macphoto.co.uk
- www.macphoto.co.uk

The Exotic Garden Company 6 Cotman Road, Thorpe, Norwich, NR1 4AF, United Kingdom
- (01603) 623167
- info@exoticgarden.com
- www.exoticgarden.com

The Helmut Newton Estate@Maconochie Photography 4 Meard Street, Soho, London, W1F 0EF, United Kingdom
- (020) 7439 3159/ (020) 7439 2552
- info@macphoto.co.uk
- www.macphoto.co.uk

The Image Store The Studio, West Hill, St. Helier, Jersey, JE2 3HB, United Kingdom
- (01534) 769933/(07797) 715489 / (01534) 789191
- peter-trenchard@jerseymail.co.uk
- www.peter-trenchard.com

The Internet Design Co. Studio 212, The Wasp Factory, Glasgow, G31 2HF, United Kingdom
- (0800) 0527463/(07774) 251384
- chb@theinternetdesignco.com
- www.theinternetdesignco.com

The John Hytch Photography Partnership Chapel House, 256 Gloucester Road, Cheltenham, Gloucestershire, GL51 8NR, United Kingdom
- (01242) 576727/(07702) 280433 / (01242) 227622
- john.hp@virgin.net
- www.hytchphotography.com

The Katy Barker Agency Ltd 11 Mason's Arms Mews, Maddox Street, London, W1S 1NX, United Kingdom
- (020) 7493 3933/ (020) 7493 3311
- catherine@katybarker.com
- www.katybarker.com

The Marsden Archive The Presbytery, Hainton, Market Rasen, Lincolnshire, LN8 6LR, United Kingdom
- (01507) 313646/ (01507) 313646
- info@marsdenarchive.com
- www.marsdenarchive.com

The Office London Unit 18, Chocolate Studios, 7 Shepherdess Place, London, N1 7LJ, United Kingdom
- (020) 7336 6006/ (020) 7336 6060
- kayte@theofficelondon.com
- www.theofficelondon.com

The Photographers' Gallery 5 & 8 Great Newport Street, London, WC2H 7HY, United Kingdom
- (020) 7831 1772/ (020) 7836 9704
- info@photonet.org.uk
- www.photonet.org.uk

The Rational Gallery, London, United Kingdom
- (020) 8881 0633
- info@therationalgallery.co.uk
- www.therationalgallery.co.uk

The Stone Studio of Petersfield 45 High Street, Petersfield, Hants, GU32 3JR,
- 01730 269966
- mail@thestonestudio.co.uk
- www.thestonestudio.co.uk

The Street Studios 2 Dunston Street, London, E8 4EB, United Kingdom
- (020) 7923 9430/ (020) 7923 9429
- mail@streetstudios.co.uk
- www.streetstudios.co.uk

The White Agency 60 Epirus Road, Fulham, London, SW6 7UH, United Kingdom
- (020) 7381 2004/(07970) 619277 / (020) 7386 8479
- annabel@thewhiteagency.com
- www.thewhiteagency.com

Thearle Photography 24 York Street, Cowes, Isle of Wight, PO31 7BS, United Kingdom
- (01983) 281727/(07711) 795689
- thearle@btinternet.com
- www.thearlephotography.com

Theo Cohen Unit 23, Quadrant Business Centre, 135 Salusbury Road, London, NW6 6RJ, United Kingdom
- (020) 7644 6160/(07976) 414709 / (020) 7624 7111
- www.theo-photography.co.uk

Thierry Van Biesen@Terri Manduca The Basement, 11 Elvaston Place, London, SW7 5QG, United Kingdom
- (020) 7581 5844/ (020) 7581 5822
- terri@terrimanduca.co.uk
- www.terrimanduca.co.uk

Thomas Dworzak@Magnum Photos 63 Gee Street, London, EC1V 3RS, United Kingdom
- (020) 7490 1771/ (020) 7608 0020
- magnum@magnumphotos.co.uk
- www.magnumphotos.com

Thomas Hoeffgen@Milc Studio 7, Zeus House, 16-30 Provost Street, London, N1 7NG, United Kingdom
- (020) 7278 8838/ (0870) 0941564
- gemma@milc.co.uk
- www.milc.co.uk

Thomas Hoepker@Magnum Photos 63 Gee Street, London, EC1V 3RS, United Kingdom
- (020) 7490 1771/ (020) 7608 0020
- magnum@magnumphotos.co.uk
- www.magnumphotos.com

Thomas Martin 8 Cyrus Court, Emersons Green, Bristol, BS16 7AX, United Kingdom
- 0117-909 0076/ 0117-909 0076
- tom@pixelcanvas.co.uk
- www.pixelcanvas.co.uk

Thomas Skiffington@S Management 15 Rocks Lane, London, SW13 0BD, United Kingdom
- (020) 8487 9655/ (020) 8487 9541
- fiona@smanagement.co.uk
- www.smanagement.co.uk

Thornton Howdle Photographic 4 Carter Terrace, Whitkirk, Leeds, LS15 7AH, United Kingdom
- 0113-257 9041/(07932) 372216
- thorntonhowdle@mac.com
- www.thorntonhowdle.com

Thymann@Wyatt-Clarke & Jones 26 Mortimer Street, London, W1W 7RB, United Kingdom
- (020) 7580 7570/(07958) 712658 / (020) 7903 5330
- office@wyattclarkejones.com
- www.wyattclarkejones.com

Tif Hunter 18A Wilds Rents, London, SE1 4QG, United Kingdom
- (020) 7403 8879
- tif.hunter@virgin.net
- www.tifhunter.com

Tim Ainsworth 24 Midlands Street, Ardwick, Manchester, M12 6LB, United Kingdom
- 0161-272 8885/ 0161-272 8884
- www.timainsworth.com

Tim Ashton@Début Art & The Coningsby Gallery 30 Tottenham Street, London, W1T 4RJ, United Kingdom
- (020) 7636 1064/ (020) 7580 7017
- info@debutart.com
- www.debutart.com

Tim Booth The Penthouse Flat, 283 Longsdale Road, London, SW13 9QB, United Kingdom
- (020) 8487 8524
- timbooth@timbooth.com
- www.timbooth.com

Tim Bowden Lower Ground Floor, 7 Mallow Street, London, EC1Y 8RQ, United Kingdom
- (020) 7490 3500/(07831) 397096 / (020) 7253 6676
- t.bowden@netcomuk.co.uk
- www.timbowdenfood.com

Tim Bret-Day 33 Riding House Street, London, W1W 7DZ, United Kingdom
- (020) 7580 4243/ (020) 7580 4266
- tim@timbretday.com
- www.timbretday.com

Tim Brightmore 16 York Central, 70 York Way, London, N1 9AG, United Kingdom
- **(020) 7278 4747/(07850) 914707** / **(020) 7278 4775**
- **mail@timbrightmore.co.uk**
- **www.timbrightmore.co.uk**
- See ad in showcase

Tim Brown 32B Queens Grove, London, NW8 6HJ, United Kingdom
- (020) 7586 2295/(07879) 640804 / (020) 7586 2142
- tim@timbrownphotography.co.uk
- www.timbrownphotography.co.uk

Tim Dry Basement Flat, 66 Princes Square, London, W2 4NY, United Kingdom
- (020) 7727 6185/(07932) 403381
- tim@timdry.co.uk
- www.timdry.co.uk

Tim Flach@ Tim Goffe, London, United Kingdom
- (020) 8673 9574/(07976) 356608
- tim@timgoffe.com
- www.timgoffe.com

Tim Green 13 Harris Street, Bradford, West Yorkshire, BD1 5HU, United Kingdom
- (01274) 732656/(07768) 305059
- tim.studio@virgin.net
- www.timgreenphotography.com

Tim Grevatt Hill House, 4 Staple Orchard, Totnes, Devon, TQ9 6FJ, United Kingdom
✆ (01803) 867722/✆ (01803) 867722
✉ info@grevatt.co.uk
🖳 www.grevatt.co.uk

Tim Gutt@Webber Represents Ltd 25 Lexington Street, Soho, London, W1F 9AG, United Kingdom
✆ (020) 7439 0678/✆ (020) 7439 0543
✉ london@webberrepresents.com
🖳 www.webberrepresents.com

Tim Hall@Axiom Photographic Agency The Pall Mall Deposit, 124-128 Barlby Road, London, W10 6BL, United Kingdom
✆ (020) 8964 9970/✆ (020) 8964 8440
✉ info@axiomphotographic.com
🖳 www.axiomphotographic.com

Tim Hawkins 35 Nansen Road, London, SW11 5NS, United Kingdom
✆ /(07836) 586999 /✆ (020) 7924 2972
✉ timspix@dial.pipex.com

Tim Hetherington Thornhill Wharf, Islington, London, N1 0IU, United Kingdom
✆ (020) 7833 4704/(07831) 228219
✉ tim-h@btconnect.com
🖳 www.tim-h.com

Tim Hill Unit C2 Lower, Bounds Green Industrial Estate, North Way, London, N11 2UD, United Kingdom
✆ (020) 8368 1222
✉ tim@timhill.co.uk
🖳 www.timhill.co.uk

Tim Kent@Vue Units 1 & 2 Elm Court, 1 Royal Oak Yard, London, SE1 3TP, United Kingdom
✆ (020) 7403 5555/✆ (020) 7403 2005
✉ production@vue-us.com
🖳 www.vue-us.com

Tim Kent Photographer Unit 13, 33 Rushworth Street, London, SE1 0RB, United Kingdom
✆ (020) 7633 0868/✆ (020) 7633 9239

Tim Lomas Photography 22 Nuns Lane, St Albans, Hertfordshire, AL1 2HR,
✆ 7968066191
✉ tim@timlomas.com
🖳 www.timlomas.com

Tim MacPherson@Carolyn Trayler Photographers Agent Unit 566, 56 Gloucester Road, London, SW7 4UB, United Kingdom
✆ (020) 7370 0712/✆ (020) 7370 0765
✉ carolyn@trayler.co.uk
🖳 www.trayler.co.uk

Tim Malyon Middle Coombe Farm, Huntsham, Tiverton, Devon, EX16 7QQ, United Kingdom
✆ (01884) 821176/✆ (01884) 821350
✉ timal@gn.apc.org

Tim Mercer Chapel Studio, Downhead, Shepton Mallet, Somerset, BA4 4LQ, United Kingdom
✆ **(01749) 880523/** ✆ **(01749) 880690**
✉ **tim@mercerdesign.co.uk**
🖳 **www.mercerdesign.co.uk**
See ad in showcase

Tim Morris Photographer Unit 3, Innovation Studios, 4 Long Street, London, E2 8HS, United Kingdom
✆ (020) 7729 2690
✉ tim@timmorrisphotographer.com
🖳 www.timmorrisphotographer.com

Tim Motion 91 St. Marks Road, London, W10 6JS, United Kingdom
✆ (020) 8960 6102/(07785) 772110 ✆ (020) 8960 6102
✉ tim@timmotion.com
🖳 www.timmotion.com

Tim O'Leary 63a Montagu Square, London, W1H 2LU, United Kingdom
✆ (020) 7402 2924/(07968) 529205
✉ tim@timoleary.co.uk
🖳 www.timoleary.co.uk

Tim O'Sullivan Productions Ltd 6 Crescent Road, Brighton, BN2 3RP, United Kingdom
✆ (01273) 708640/(07836) 343628
✉ info@timosullivan.co.uk
🖳 www.timosullivan.co.uk

Tim Pestridge Photography@Design 11 Walnut Close, Exminster, Exeter, EX6 8SZ, United Kingdom
✆ (01392) 825718
✉ studio@timpestridge.co.uk
🖳 www.timpestridge.co.uk

Tim Platt Photographer 97 Alberta Street, Kennington, London, SE17 3RU, United Kingdom
✆ (020) 7793 8500/(07774) 444776 ✆ (020) 7793 9500
✉ tim@timplatt.co.uk
🖳 www.timplatt.co.uk

Tim Richmond@Ellison Lee 17 Quadrant Business Centre, 135 Salusbury Road, London, NW6 6RJ, United Kingdom
✆ (020) 7624 2345/✆ (020) 7624 1100
✉ info@ellisonlee.com
🖳 www.ellisonlee.com

Tim Robberts Photography, Stratford-upon-Avon, Warwickshire, CV37 9SJ, United Kingdom
✆ (07913) 440001
✉ tim@timrobberts.com
🖳 www.timrobberts.com

Tim Robinson 8 Wells Street, Cardiff, CF1 8DW, United Kingdom
✆ (029) 2022 8367
✉ tim.robinson7@virgin.net

Tim Rose@Martin Dawe Photography 347 Edinburgh Avenue, Slough, SL1 4TU, United Kingdom
✆ (01753) 828828/✆ (01753) 828822
✉ hello@martindawedesign.co.uk
🖳 www.martindawedesign.co.uk

Tim Simmons, London, United Kingdom
✆ (020) 7729 0234
✉ tim@timsimmons.co.uk

Tim White 74 Burnfoot Avenue, London, SW6 5EA, United Kingdom
✆ (020) 7736 8845
✉ timwhitefoto@clara.co.uk

Tim Wren@Metcalfe Lancaster 20 Hanson Street, London, W1W 6UF, United Kingdom
✆ (020) 7580 8875/(07778) 331771 ✆ (020) 7580 8689
✉ julie@metcalfelancaster.com
🖳 www.metcalfelancaster.com

Timothy Allen@Axiom Photographic Agency The Pall Mall Deposit, 124-128 Barlby Road, London, W10 6BL, United Kingdom
✆ (020) 8964 9970/✆ (020) 8964 8440
✉ info@axiomphotographic.com
🖳 www.axiomphotographic.com

Timothy Foster 137 Stoke Newington Church Street, London, N16 0UH, United Kingdom
✆ (07970) 837788
✉ mail@timothyfoster.co.uk
🖳 www.timothyfoster.co.uk

Titchfield Studios Titchfield Studios, 4 Ryecroft, Fareham, Hampshire, PO14 4PZ, United Kingdom
✆ (01489) 582925/✆ (01489) 885107
✉ info@tichfieldstudios.co.uk
🖳 www.tichfieldstudios.co.uk

Toby Adamson@Axiom Photographic Agency The Pall Mall Deposit, 124-128 Barlby Road, London, W10 6BL, United Kingdom
✆ (020) 8964 9970/✆ (020) 8964 8440
✉ info@axiomphotographic.com
🖳 www.axiomphotographic.com

Toby Maudsley@Mark Gibson 250 York Road, London, SW11 3SJ, United Kingdom
✆ (020) 7228 9085/(07768) 696227
✉ mark@markgibsonphotography.com
🖳 www.markgibsonphotography.com

Toby McFarlan Pond@MAP 72 Rochester Place, London, NW1 9JX, United Kingdom
✆ (020) 7424 9144/✆ (020) 7284 3274
✉ info@mapltd.com
🖳 www.mapltd.com

Toby Savage 42 Cradock Road, Clarendon Park, Leicester, LE2 1TD, United Kingdom
✆ 0116-270 6506/(07785) 902530 ✆ 0116-270 6506
✉ toby@tobysavage.co.uk
🖳 www.tobysavage.co.uk

Tom Ang 59 Grantham Road, London, SW9 9ED, United Kingdom
✆ (07958) 701393
✉ tomang@cap.ndirect.co.uk

Tom Baker 8 Culburnie, Kiltarlity, Beauly, Inverness-Shire, IV4 7JJ, United Kingdom
✆ (01463) 741301/(07970) 491755 ✆ (01463) 741301
✉ info@scotphot.com
🖳 www.scotphot.com

Tom Collins@Blowup 146 Amyand Park Road, St. Margaret's, Twickenham, TW1 3HY, United Kingdom
✆ (020) 8744 0210/✆ (020) 8892 2521
✉ orders@blowup.net
🖳 www.blowup.net

Tom Corbett@T Photographic 1 Heathgate Place, 75-83 Agincourt Road, London, NW3 2NU, United Kingdom
✆ (020) 7428 6070/✆ (020) 7428 6079
✉ peter@tphotographic.com
🖳 www.tphotographic.com

Tom Craig@Bill Charles London Ltd. Unit 3E1, Zetland House, 5-25 Scrutton Street, London, EC2A 4HJ, United Kingdom
✆ 020 7033 9284/020 2033 9285
✉ london@billcharles.com
🖳 www.billcharles.com

Tom Graty St Vincent's School House, Greenside Street, Openshaw, Manchester, M11 2EX, United Kingdom
✆ 0161-231 6099/(07710) 373739
✉ tom@graty.com
🖳 www.ukcommercialphotographer.com

Tom Hanley 41 Harefield, Esher, Surrey, KT10 9TG, United Kingdom
✆ (020) 8972 9165
✉ tomhanley31@hotmail.com
🖳 www.tomhanleyphotography.com

Tom Hunter@MAP 72 Rochester Place, London, NW1 9JX, United Kingdom
✆ (020) 7424 9144/✆ (020) 7284 3274
✉ info@mapltd.com
🖳 www.mapltd.com

Tom Leighton 17 Cedar Court, Sheen Lane, London, SW14 8LY, United Kingdom
✆ (020) 8876 8497/(07831) 591969 ✆ (020) 8876 9755
✉ tomleighton@blueyonder.co.uk

Tom Main Burndale, Glen Road, Lumphanan, Banchory, Kincardineshire, AB31 4SL, United Kingdom
✆ (01339) 883508/(07767) 894770
✉ tom@tommainphotography.com
🖳 www.tommainphotography.com

Tom Parker 1 Mansion House, Main Street, Carnforth, Lancashire, LA6 1LQ, United Kingdom
✆ (01524) 781995

Tom Pollock Photography Tanzaro House, Ardwick Green North, Manchester, M12 6FZ, United Kingdom
✆ (0161) 2744436/✆ (0161) 3742225
✉ tom@tompollock.co.uk
🖳 www.tompollock.co.uk

Tom Watson@edsonwilliams photography consultancy 52 Brushfield Street, London, E1 6AJ, United Kingdom
✆ (020) 7375 2077/(07867) 517777 ✆ (020) 7375 3077
✉ info@edsonwilliams.com
🖳 www.edsonwilliams.com

Tom Willcocks@Victoria Lees Management (VLM) 2 Fairview Gardens, Woodford Green, Essex, IG8 7DJ, United Kingdom
✆ (07710) 287220/✆ (020) 8504 8125
✉ victoria@victorialeesmanagement.co.uk
🖳 www.victorialeesmanagement.co.uk

Tony Bowran@Dave Tyler Associates 8 Portland Mews, London, W1V 3FJ, United Kingdom
✆ (07071) 202470/(07860) 364225 ✆ (01438) 871680
✉ dave@davetyler.com
🖳 www.davetyler.com

Tony Briggs@Mutton Bones Ground Floor, 51 Balcombe Street, London, NW1 6HD, United Kingdom
✆ (020) 7723 8244/✆ (020) 7723 2770
✉ hello@muttonbones.co.uk
🖳 www.muttonbones.co.uk

Tony Burrett 3-4 The Mews, Beckenham, Kent, BR3 1BQ, United Kingdom
✆ (020) 8658 8918/✆ (020) 8650 7393
✉ anthonygburrett@aol.com
🖳 www.anthonyburrett.co.uk

Tony Cambio Imaging The Green, Little Addington, Kettering, Northamptonshire, NN14 4BB, United Kingdom
✆ (01933) 651340
✉ info@cambio.uk.com
🖳 www.cambio.uk.com

Tony Chau@Germaine Walker Photographers' Agent Crayford House, 49A Tabley Road, London, N7 0NA, United Kingdom
✆ (020) 7697 8291/(07867) 780272 ✆ (020) 7619 9051
✉ germaine@germaine.co.uk
🖳 www.germaine.co.uk

Tony Cousins Photography T B C Studios, The Old Cider Mill, Purton, Berkeley, Gloucestershire, GL13 9HP, United Kingdom
✆ (01453) 511408/(07973) 800707
✎ tony@tbcstudios.co.uk
▭ www.tbcstudios.co.uk

Tony Gibson 180 Hoppers Road, Winchmore Hill, London, N21 3JY, United Kingdom
✆ (020) 8886 3995/(07973) 867226 ✆ (020) 8245 9802
✎ tony@tonygibson.net
▭ www.tonygibson.net

Tony Harris 183 Dawes Road, London, SW6 7QP, United Kingdom
✆ (020) 7385 8158/(07836) 201229 ✆ (020) 7385 8159
✎ tony@tonyhphoto.com
▭ www.tonyhphoto.com

Tony Hopewell@Traffic Unit P102, 23 - 28 Penn Street, London, N1 7DL, United Kingdom
✆ 020 7739 6090
✎ rebecca@rebeccavalentine.com
▭ www.trafficphotographic.com

Tony Hutchings 7 Luke Street, London, EC2A 4PX, United Kingdom
✆ (020) 7729 8181/✆ (020) 7729 9322
▭ www.tonyhutchings.co.uk

Tony Latham Studio Five. The Hanger, Perseverance Works, 38 Kingsland Road, London, E2 8DA, United Kingdom
✆ (020) 7739 6253/(07831) 473954 ✆ (020) 7739 0443
✎ tony.latham@btconnect.com
▭ www.tonylatham.com

Tony Lord c/o Ceta, 1-5 Poland Street, London, W1F 8NA, United Kingdom
✆ (020) 7289 5156/078 50 738286
✎ tony@tonylordy.com
▭ www.tonylordy.com

Tony McConnell 99 Faringdon Road, London, EC1R 3BN, United Kingdom
✆ (020) 7278 0560/(07836) 509275 ✆ (020) 7278 0460
✎ tony@tonymcconnell.com
▭ www.tonymcconnell.com

Tony Nathan The Little Cottage, 31 High Street, Cranley, Guildford, Surrey, GU6 8AS, United Kingdom
✆ (01483) 275149
✎ nathanstudio@hotmail.com
▭ www.nathan-weddings-photographers.com

Tony Robins 56 Sherard Road, Eltham, London, SE9 6EP, United Kingdom
✆ (020) 8488 7815/(07976) 281779 ✆ (020) 8488 7849
✎ trassocs@hotmail.com
▭ www.tonyrobins.co.uk

Tony Rusecki Photography 43 Delamere Road, London, W5 3JL, United Kingdom
✆ (020) 8566 0919
✎ photography@tonyrusecki.co.uk
▭ www.tonyrusecki.co.uk

Tony Russell Photogrphy 30 Spratt Hall Road, London, E11 2RQ, United Kingdom
✆ (020) 8530 4030/(07831) 103843
✎ tonyrussellphoto@hotmail.com

Tony Slade Photography 51 Turnfurlong, Aylesbury, Buckinghamshire, HP21 7PS, United Kingdom
✆ (07890) 990246/✆ (01296) 415488
✎ tony@tonyslade.com
▭ www.tonyslade.com

Topsy Korean 176 Camden Road, London, NW1 9HG, United Kingdom
✆ (020) 7267 0315/(07789) 286974

Town & Country Productions Ltd Parry's Lodge, Threapwood, Malpas, Cheshire, SY14 7AW, United Kingdom
✆ (01948) 770 309/✆ (01948) 770452
✎ john@minophoto.co.uk
▭ www.minophoto.co.uk

Tracey Gibbs Photography Ltd 54 Oldfield Road, Salford, M5 4LZ, United Kingdom
✆ 0161-743 0008/(07801) 413161 ✆ 0161-736 3935
✎ info@traceygibbs.co.uk
▭ www.traceygibbs.co.uk

Tracy Morgan Animal Photography Lace Cottage, Harbury Close, Lane End, High Wycombe, Buckinghamshire, HP14 3HB, United Kingdom
✆ (01494) 883176/(07802) 483993
✎ tracymorgan@animalphotographer.co.uk
▭ www.animalphotographer.co.uk

Trafalgar Photographic Studios Ltd Robin Business Centre, Leeds Road, Bradford, West Yorkshire, BD10 9TE, United Kingdom
✆ (01274) 610600/✆ (01274) 610500
✎ info@trafalgarstudios.co.uk
▭ www.trafalgarstudios.co.uk

Traffic Unit P102, 23 - 28 Penn Street, London, N1 7DL, United Kingdom
✆ 020 7739 6090
✎ rebecca@rebeccavalentine.com
▭ www.trafficphotographic.com

Tramp 2 Kendrey Gardens, Twickenham, TW2 7PA, United Kingdom
✆ (07968) 958825
✎ sophie_blackman@hotmail.com
▭ www.tramped.co.uk

Transworld Eye 64 Gloucester Road, Kingston upon Thames, Surrey, KT1 3RB, United Kingdom
✆ (020) 8546 4066

Traveller 45-49 Brompton Road, Knightsbridge, London, SW3 1DE, United Kingdom
✆ (020) 7589 0500/✆ (020) 7581 1357
✎ duncan.mills@wexas.com
▭ www.traveller.org.uk

Trent Parke@Magnum Photos 63 Gee Street, London, EC1V 3RS, United Kingdom
✆ (020) 7490 1771/✆ (020) 7608 0020
✎ magnum@magnumphotos.co.uk
▭ www.magnumphotos.co.uk

Trevor Beynon 7 Jardine House, The Harrovian Business Village, Bessborough Road, Harrow, Middlesex, HA1 3EX, United Kingdom
✆ (020) 8422 7099/✆ (020) 8422 4411
✎ trevorbeynon@btconnect.com
▭ www.trevorbeynon.co.uk

Trevor Burrows Photography Studio 8/23, Mary Feacole Road, Plymouth, PL1 3JY, United Kingdom
✆ (01752) 666633/✆ (01752) 666633
✎ trevor@trevorburrowsphoto.com
▭ www.trevorburrowsphoto.com

Trevor Richards 40 Kings Hall Road, Beckenham, Kent, BR3 1LS, United Kingdom
✆ (020) 8249 3862/✆ (020) 8249 0583
✎ trphoto@dircon.co.uk
▭ www.trphoto.dircon.co.uk

Trevor Sutton Studio 2, Gill Farm, Gill Lane, Ashford, Kent, TN25 7HZ, United Kingdom
✆ (01233) 721511
✎ info@studio2uk.com
▭ www.studio2uk.com

Trizeps Photography & Mediadesign Langoth & Fallnhauser GnbR, Zollergasse 13, Wien, 1070, Austria
✆ 00 33 1 526 3393/✆ 00 33 1 526 6020
✎ studio@trizeps.com

Turpin & Kloss Ltd 306a St. Pauls Road, London, N1 2LH, United Kingdom
✆ (020) 7354 8568
✎ samk@turpinandkloss.com
▭ www.turpinandkloss.com

Twobobrocket 9-11 Harvie Street, Glasgow, G51 1BW, United Kingdom
✆ 0141-427 9111/✆ 0141-427 5888
✎ paul@twobobrocket.co.uk
▭ www.twobobrocket.co.uk

Uli Mattes Photography Neumann Reichardtstr 33, Hamburg, 22041, Germany
✆ 40 65 64 90 4/✆ 40 65 67 36 4
✎ mail@uli-mattes.de
▭ www.uli-mattes.de

Uli Weber@Terri Manduca The Basement, 11 Elvaston Pl, London, SW7 5QG, United Kingdom
✆ (020) 7581 5844/✆ (020) 7581 5822
✎ terri@terrimanduca.co.uk
▭ www.terrimanduca.co.uk

Ulla Nyeman@Ellison Lee 17 Quadrant Business Centre, 135 Salusbury Road, London, NW6 6RJ, United Kingdom
✆ (020) 7624 2345/✆ (020) 7624 1100
✎ info@ellisonlee.com
▭ www.ellisonlee.com

Ulrike Leyens 2 Independent Place, London, E8 2HE, United Kingdom
✆ (020) 7249 8384/✆ (020) 7249 8384
✎ ulrike@leyens.com
▭ www.leyens.com

Ultimate Images 9 Blenheim Close, Upminster, Essex, RM14 1SH, United Kingdom
✆ (07854) 170711
✎ paul@ultimateimage.co.uk
▭ www.ultimate-images.co.uk

Unichrome Creative 23-25 Great Sutton Street, London, EC1V 0DN, United Kingdom
✆ (020) 7251 8811/✆ (020) 7251 8812
✎ info@unichrome-creative.com
▭ www.unichrome-creative.com

Upper Orange Nostitzstrasse 15, Berlin, 10961, Germany
✆ 49 178 6121661/✆ 49 30 6121661
✎ mail@upperorange.com
▭ www.upperorange.de

V.K. Guy Ltd Browhead Cottage, Troutbeck, Windermere, Cumbria, LA23 1PJ, United Kingdom
✆ (01539) 433519/✆ (01539) 413971
✎ vic@vkguy.co.uk
▭ www.vkguy.co.uk

Valerie Bennett 34-36 Bedford Square, London, WC1B 3ES, United Kingdom
✆ (020) 7636 0974/✆ (020) 7414 0782
✎ arch-assoc@aaschool.ac.uk

Valerie Phillips@Webber Represents Ltd 25 Lexington Street, Soho, London, W1F 9AG, United Kingdom
✆ (020) 7439 0678/✆ (020) 7439 0543
✎ london@webberrepresents.com
▭ www.webberrepresents.com

Valeriehersleven Boundary House (3rd Floor), 91-93 Charterhouse Street, London, EC1M 6HR, United Kingdom
✆ (07775) 717474
✎ me@valeriehersleven.com
▭ www.valeriehersleven.com

van Hauen Moore 14 Powis Mews, Notting Hill, London, W11 1JN, United Kingdom
✆ (020) 7792 0022/✆ (020) 7792 8636
✎ email@vanhauenmoore.com
▭ www.vanhauenmoore.com

Vanessa Berberian Photography 142a Regents Park Road, London, NW1 8XL, United Kingdom
✆ (07984) 026 633
✎ vlb@alum.dartmouth.org
▭ wwwvanessaberberian.com

Vanessa Davies@T Photographic 1 Heathgate Place, 75-83 Agincourt Road, London, London, NW3 2NU, United Kingdom
✆ (020) 7428 6070/✆ (020) 7428 6079
✎ peter@tphotographic.com
▭ www.tphotographic.com

Vanessa Ellis Photography 20 Linden Road, Hampton, Middlesex, TW12 2JB, United Kingdom
✆ (07752) 943575
✎ vanessa@vanessaellis.co.uk
▭ www.vanessaellis.co.uk

Vava Ribeiro@Big Active Ltd Unit 6.01, The Tea Building, 56 Shoreditch High Street, London, E16 JJ, United Kingdom
✆ (020) 7739 5601/✆ (020) 7739 7479
✎ contact@bigactive.com
▭ www.bigactive.com

Velvet Park 90 Lots Road, Unit 41, London, SW10 0QD, United Kingdom
✆ (020) 7352 5578/(07789) 248021
✎ info@velvetpark.com
▭ www.velvetpark.com

Vera Kodajova@van Hauen Moore 14 Powis Mews, Notting Hill, London, W11 1JN, United Kingdom
✆ (020) 7792 0022/✆ (020) 7792 8636
✎ email@vanhauenmoore.com
▭ www.vanhauenmoore.com

Verena 461 Forest Road, Walthamstow, London, E17 5LD, United Kingdom
✆ (020) 8257 7233
✎ verena@verena-online.com
▭ www.verena-online.com

Verity Welstead@Creative Talent (UK) Limited 78 York Street, London, W1H 1DP, United Kingdom
✆ (020) 7439 1877/✆ (020) 7434 1144
✎ info@creativetalentlimited.com
▭ www.creativetalentlimited.com

Veronica Walford Photography 27 Moreton Place, London, SW1V 2NL, United Kingdom
✆ (07779) 241635
✎ veronica@veronicawalford.co.uk
▭ www.veronicawalford.co.uk

Veronique Leplat, London, United Kingdom
📞 (07973) 964 758
✉ veroniqueleplat@hotmail.com
🖥 www.infinityfolio.co.uk

Veronique Vial@Mutton Bones Ground Floor, 51 Balcombe Street, London, NW1 6HD, United Kingdom
📞 (020) 7723 8244/📠 (020) 7723 2770
✉ hello@muttonbones.com
🖥 www.muttonbones.co.uk

Vic Huber Photography 1731 Reynolds Avenue, Irvine, 92614-5711, United States of America
📞 00 1 949 261 5844/00 1 949 632 3949 📠 00 1 949 261 5973
✉ steve_bishop@vichuber.com
🖥 www.vichuber.com

Vicki Couchman@Axiom Photographic Agency The Pall Mall Deposit, 124-128 Barlby Road, London, W10 6BL, United Kingdom
📞 (020) 8964 9970/📠 (020) 8964 8440
✉ info@axiomphotographic.com
🖥 www.axiomphotographic.com

Vicky Fleming-Brown@Cormack Creative Management Ltd Suite 208, 95 Morrison Street, Glasgow, G5 8BE, United Kingdom
📞 0141-429 6810/(07778) 323169 📠 0141-429 2603
✉ susie@cormackcreativemanagement.co.uk
🖥 www.cormackcreativemanagement.co.uk

Victor Albrow 7 Links Gardens Lane, Edinburgh, EH6 7JQ, United Kingdom
📞 0131-554 8644/(07860) 958690 📠 0131-555 1609
✉ victor@albrow.com
🖥 www.albrow.com

Victor Yuan@Pearce Stoner Associates 12B Links Yard, Spelman Street, London, E1 5LX, United Kingdom
📞 (020) 7247 7100/📠 (020) 7247 7144
✉ info@pearcestoner.com
🖥 www.pearcestoner.com

Victoria Blackie Ltd 1b Nightingale Road, Wendover, Aylesbury, Buckinghamshire, HP22 6JX, United Kingdom
📞 **(07831) 423177**
✉ **vicblack@tinyworld.co.uk**
🖥 **www.victoriablackie.co.uk**
See ad in showcase

Victoria Carew-Hunt 6 Woodhayes Road, Wimbledon, London, SW19 4RJ, United Kingdom
📞 (020) 8946 6038/📠 (020) 8944 8171
✉ vch@carew-hunt.com
🖥 www.carew-hunt.com

Victoria Lees Management (VLM) 2 Fairview Gardens, Woodford Green, Essex, IG8 7DJ, United Kingdom
📞 (07710) 287220/📠 (020) 8504 8125
✉ victoria@victorialeesmanagement.co.uk
🖥 www.victorialeesmanagement.co.uk

Victoria Upton, London, United Kingdom
📞 (020) 7992 0226/(07976) 358919
🖥 www.victoriaupton.com

Vietnam Travel, Hanoi HN, 10000, Vietnam, Socialist Republic of
📞 00 84 4945479/📠 00 84 4945482
✉ links@landingvietnam.com
🖥 www.landingvietnam.com/exchange-list.aspx

Vincent Dixon@Izzy King 22 Alder Lodge, 73 Stevenage Road, London, SW6 6NP, United Kingdom
📞 (07961) 168086/📠 (020) 7381 9726
✉ izzy@izzyking.co.uk
🖥 www.izzyking.co.uk

Vincent Oliver 20 Green Lane, Chislehurst, Kent, BR7 6AG, United Kingdom
📞 (020) 8467 2465/(07768) 004518
✉ vsoliver@aol.com
🖥 www.photo-i.co.uk

Vincent Paul Bennett 196 Guildford Park Avenue, Guildford, Surrey, GU2 7NH, United Kingdom
📞 (01483) 579042
✉ enquiry@vincentpaul.co.uk
🖥 www.vincentpaul.co.uk

Vinh Van Phan 87 The Alders, Aldrington Road, London, SW16 1TW, United Kingdom
📞 (07798) 861 291
✉ vinh@vinhvanphan.com
🖥 www.vinhvanphan.com

Visage Unit 54, Springfield Commercial Centre, Farsley, Leeds, LS28 5LY, United Kingdom
📞 0113-256 5433/(07860) 735421
✉ dave@visage-photography.com

Vision Photography 159 Brooke Street, Chorley, Lancashire, PR6 0NG, United Kingdom
📞 (01257) 410941
✉ frankz10@hotmail.com
🖥 www.visionphotos.com

Vollans Photography 26-28 Cheapside, Knaresborough, North Yorkshire, HG5 8AX, United Kingdom
📞 (01423) 862626/📠 (01423) 869697
✉ vollansphotography@supanet.com
🖥 www.vollansphotography.co.uk

Voveris Photography Flat 1, 14 Park Road, Westcliff-on-Sea, Essex, SS0 7PE, United Kingdom
📞 (07999) 245888
✉ arun@voverisphotography.com
🖥 www.voverisphotography.com

Vue Units 1 & 2 Elm Court, 1 Royal Oak Yard, London, SE1 3TP, United Kingdom
📞 (020) 7403 5555/📠 (020) 7403 2005
✉ production@vue-us.com
🖥 www.vue-us.com

Vyner Street Studios 23 Vyner Street, London, E2 9DG, United Kingdom
📞 (020) 9983 3744
✉ ha@howardallman.com
🖥 www.howardallman.com

W.G. Photo Southdownview Road, Worthing, West Sussex, BN14 8NJ, United Kingdom
📞 (01903) 200528/📠 (01903) 200528
✉ mike@wgphoto.co.uk
🖥 www.wgphoto.co.uk

Ward Philipson Group Ltd Halifax Road, Dunston Industrial Estate, Gateshead, Tyne & Wear, NE11 9HW, United Kingdom
📞 0191-460 5915/(07768) 061347 📠 0191-460 8540
✉ hitcham@wardphilipson.co.uk
🖥 www.wardphilipson.co.uk

Warren Smith Photography The Lost Space, 33 Livingston Road, Hove, East Sussex, BN3 3WP, United Kingdom
📞 (07919) 346521
✉ info@warrensmithphotography.com
🖥 www.warrensmithphotography.com

Wayne Miller@Magnum Photos 63 Gee Street, London, EC1V 3RS, United Kingdom
📞 (020) 7490 1771/📠 (020) 7608 0020
✉ magnum@magnumphotos.co.uk
🖥 www.magnumphotos.com

Wayne Parker@Sarah Lane Represents 56 Bidwell Gardens, London, N11 2AU, United Kingdom
📞 (07901) 552520/📠 (020) 8292 4001
✉ sarah@sarahlanerepresents.com
🖥 www.sarahlanerepresents.com

Webber Represents Ltd 25 Lexington Street, Soho, London, W1F 9AG, United Kingdom
📞 (020) 7439 0678/📠 (020) 7439 0543
✉ london@webberrepresents.com
🖥 www.webberrepresents.com

Wellfield Studios Ltd 12-14 Wellfield Road, London, SW16 2BT, United Kingdom
📞 (020) 8696 7011
✉ alisonmetcalfe@homechoice.co.uk

Wendy Carrig@A & R Photographic 16A Crane Grove, London, N7 8LE, United Kingdom
📞 (020) 7607 3030/📠 (020) 7607 2190
✉ info@aandrphotographic.com
🖥 www.aandrphotographic.co.uk

Wendy Jackson Tag Creative, 29 Clerkenwell Road, London, EC1M 5TA, United Kingdom
📞 **(020) 3217 2241/(07711) 084801** 📠 **(020) 7439 1971**
✉ **wjackson@tagworldwide.com**
🖥 **www.wendyjackson.co.uk**
See ad in showcase

Werner Bischof@Magnum Photos 63 Gee Street, London, EC1V 3RS, United Kingdom
📞 (020) 7490 1771/📠 (020) 7608 0020
✉ magnum@magnumphotos.co.uk
🖥 www.magnumphotos.com

WG Photo Southdownview Road, Worthing, West Sussex, BN14 8NJ, United Kingdom
📞 (01903) 200 528/(07801) 699288 📠 (01903) 200 528
✉ mike@wgphoto.co.uk
🖥 www.wgphoto.co.uk

Whiskey UK Ltd 7 Walburt Road, Hyburry, London, N5 1QS, United Kingdom
📞 (0700) 0740240/(07885) 338071
✉ andy@photofolio.net
🖥 www.photofolio.net

Whitepix Rowlands Cottage, Mannor Lodge Road, Rowlands Castle, Rowland's Castle, Hampshire, PO9 6BA, United Kingdom
📞 (023) 9241 0178
✉ malcom@whitepix.co.uk
🖥 www.whitepix.co.uk

Wilde Representation 314 Mare Street, London, E8 1HA, United Kingdom
📞 (020) 8653 4466/(07810) 795036 📠 (01424) 201070
✉ sian@wilderepresentation.com
🖥 www.wilderepresentation.com

WildeHague Ltd Suite 4, The Swan centre, Fishers Lane, London, W4 1RX, United Kingdom
📞 (020) 8747 9988/📠 (020) 8747 8228
✉ info@wildehague.com
🖥 www.wildehague.com

Wildpear Studio 70 Hill Street, Richmond, Surrey, TW9 1TW, United Kingdom
📞 (020) 8948 2300
✉ studio@wildpear.com
🖥 www.wildpear.com

Will Sanders@Agent Orange 10 Swan Yard, London, N1 1SD, United Kingdom
📞 (020) 7226 0440/📠 (020) 7226 1613
✉ annika@agentorange.co.uk
🖥 www.agentorange.co.uk

Will Thom@Tattersall Love 40 Langham Street, London, W1W 7AS, United Kingdom
📞 (020) 7637 5737/📠 (020) 7637 5747
✉ mail@tattersall-love.com
🖥 www.tattersall-love.com

Will Whipple@Milc Studio 7, Zeus House, 16-30 Provost Street, London, N1 7NG, United Kingdom
📞 (020) 7278 8838/📠 (0870) 0941564
✉ gemma@milc.co.uk
🖥 www.milc.co.uk

Will White 39a South Park Road, London, SW19 8RS, United Kingdom
📞 (020) 854 26100/(07973) 396256
✉ will@willwhitephotographer.com
🖥 www.willwhitephotographer.com

William Davies@Gina Phillips Represents Ltd 6 Leverton Place, London, NW5 2PL, United Kingdom
📞 (020) 7284 2022/📠 (020) 7424 0272
✉ info@ginaphillips.co.uk
🖥 www.ginaphillips.co.uk

William De La Hey Mertoun Glebe, St. Boswells, Melrose, Roxburghshire, TD6 0DY, United Kingdom
📞 (01835) 824650/(07831) 551030
✉ bill@delahey.com
🖥 www.delahey.com

William King Studio 2, The Old Malt House, Pennywell Road, Bristol, BS5 0TJ, United Kingdom
📞 0117-941 1600/07973 317 438
✉ will@photo.uk.com
🖥 www.photo.uk.com

William Shaw@Axiom Photographic Agency The Pall Mall Deposit, 124-128 Barlby Road, London, W10 6BL, United Kingdom
📞 (020) 8964 9970/📠 (020) 8964 8440
✉ info@axiomphotographic.com
🖥 www.axiomphotographic.com

Wimbledon Photographic Ventures 324 Cannon Hill Lane, London, SW20 9HL, United Kingdom
📞 (020) 8417 0016/(07900) 977613
✉ mboardman2000@hotmail.com
🖥 www.boardmanphotography.co.uk

Windmill Photographic Advertising Studios 128 Burntwood Lane, Caterham, Surrey, CR3 6TB, United Kingdom
📞 (01883) 334778/(07836) 369266
✉ roger@windmillphotographic.com
🖥 www.windmillphotgraphic.com

Winfried Heinze 63b West Hill, London, SW15 2UL, United Kingdom
📞 (020) 8874 0335/📠 (020) 8875 0995
✉ winfried@heinze.plus.com
🖥 www.winfriedheinze.co.uk

With Associates 2 Glebe Road, London, E2 0RE, United Kingdom
📞 (020) 7923 4757
✉ hello@withassociates.com
🖥 www.withassociates.com

Wonderfuel 118 Hatherley Gardens, London, E6 3HQ, United Kingdom
☎ 020 8548 1358
✎ info@wonderfuel.co.uk
💻 www.wonderfuel.co.uk

Wood Associates 62 Bell Street, London, NW1 6SP, United Kingdom
☎ (020) 7723 6600
✎ info@wood-associates.co.uk
💻 www.wood-associates.co.uk

Woollams & Woollams 21 Birchvale Drive, Romiley, Stockport, Cheshire, SK6 4LD, United Kingdom
☎ 0161-494 9400/(07710) 443318 📠 0161-494 9400
✎ ian@woollams.co.uk
💻 www.woollams.co.uk

www.photolinaker.com 294 Windsor Road, Maidenhead, Berkshire, SL6 2DT, United Kingdom
☎ (01628) 784550
✎ paula@photolinaker.com
💻 www.photolinaker.com

www.robertkacala.com 25, Hythe House, Swan Road, London, SE16 4LG, United Kingdom
☎ (07939) 863363
✎ photo@robertkacala.com
💻 www.robertkacala.com

www.womenphotographers.com Morgan House, Walton Grove, Aylesbury, Buckinghamshire, HP21 7U, United Kingdom
☎ (01494) 880882/ 📠 (01494) 880892
✎ info@womenphotographers.com
💻 www.womenphotographers.com

Wyatt-Clarke & Jones 26 Mortimer Street, London, W1W 7RB, United Kingdom
☎ (020) 7580 7570/(07958) 712658 📠 (020) 7903 5330
✎ office@wyattclarkejones.com
💻 www.wyattclarkejones.com
See ad

Xavier Harcq 131 Avenue Demey, Brussels, B-1160, Belgium
☎ 2 672 68 80/4 75 65 76 42 📠 2 672 70 20
✎ xavier.harcq@skynet.be
💻 www.harcq.com
See ad in showcase

Yann Coatsaliou 15 Av Julien, Nice, 6100, France
☎ 4 93 98 75 27/6 03 00 01 43
✎ coatsaliou@wanadoo.fr

Yann Robert@Andrea Walji Agency 6 Brewer Street, London, W1F 0SB, United Kingdom
☎ (020) 7439 4144/(07789) 871871 📠 (020) 7439 4133
✎ andrea@andreawalji.com
💻 www.andreawalji.com

Yara Gremoli Photographers Agent Studio 210, Canalot Studios, 222 Kensal Road, London, W10 5BN, United Kingdom
☎ (0870) 8501209/(07880) 627413 📠 (0870) 8501209
✎ yara@sbmanagement.org
💻 www.yaragremoli.com

Yellow Munky The Crescent, Caerphilly, Mid Glamorgan, CF83 2SW, United Kingdom
☎ (07900) 288363
✎ info@yellowmunky.co.uk
💻 www.yellowmunky.co.uk

Yuo 5 Ryal Mile Mansions, Edinburgh, EH1 1QN, United Kingdom
☎ (07903) 939779
✎ info@yuoyuo.co.uk
💻 www.yuoyuo.co.uk

Z Photographic The Mezzanine, 5 Dryden Street, Covent Garden, London, WC2E 9NW, United Kingdom
☎ (020) 7829 8455/(07917) 302 491 📠 (020) 7240 5600
✎ zuk@zphotographic.com
💻 www.zphotographic.com

Zabriskie Studios 95 Downfield Drive, Sedgley, Dudley, West Midlands, DY3 1RY, United Kingdom
☎ (07951) 918377
✎ hedyneash@yahoo.co.uk

Zap Art Studio 4, 59 Neville Road, London, N16 8SW, United Kingdom
☎ (020) 7923 3618/ 📠 (020) 7923 3618
✎ bernard@zap-art.com
💻 www.zap-art.com

ADVERTISING

Adam Dawe Hangar 9, Perserverance Works, 38 Kingsland Road, London, E2 8DD, United Kingdom
☎ (020) 7613 3262/ 📠 (020) 7613 2152
✎ mail@adamdawe.com
💻 www.adamdawe.com

Adam Tolner 10A Printing House Yard, Hackney Road, London, E2 7PR, United Kingdom
☎ (020) 7739 6329/ 📠 (020) 7739 6213
✎ at@adamtolner.com
💻 www.adamtolner.com

Artseens Images The Hub, 123 Star Lane, London, E16 4PZ, United Kingdom
☎ (020) 7055 0005/ 📠 (020) 7055 0005
✎ info@artseens.com
💻 www.artseens.com

Basement Photographic Unit 22, Soho Mills, Wooburn Green, High Wycombe, Buckinghamshire, HP10 0PF, United Kingdom
☎ (01628) 529900/ 📠 (01628) 851039
✎ studio@basementphoto.com
💻 www.basementphoto.com
See ad in showcase

Ben Fisher Photography 45-46 Charlotte Road, London, EC2A 3PD, United Kingdom
☎ (020) 7613 1623/(07976) 659605 📠 (020) 7613 1623
✎ contact@benfisherphotography.com
💻 www.benfisherphotography.com
See ad in showcase

Ben Fitchett B/21 Phipp Street, London, EC2A 4NP, United Kingdom
☎ (07977) 490106/ 📠 (020) 7033 9446
✎ ben@parallax.fsnet.co.uk
💻 www.benfitchett.com

Brainstorm Interactive, London, NW5, United Kingdom
☎ (020) 7485 9585
✎ carl@newmedia.demon.co.uk
💻 www.newmedia.demon.co.uk

Brian Galloway 77 Peterborough Road, London, SW6 3BT, United Kingdom
☎ (07973) 386904
✎ brian@gallowayphoto.co.uk
💻 www.gallowayphoto.co.uk

Bruce Anderson Photography 126 Shoreditch High Street, London, E1 6JE, United Kingdom
☎ (020) 7729 2299/(07930) 406668
✎ bruce@bruceanderson.co.uk
💻 www.bruceanderson.co.uk

Bullock Partners Photography Poplars Farm, Knightcote, Southam, Warwickshire, CV47 2SF, United Kingdom
☎ (07710) 295956
✎ jax@bullockpartners.co.uk
💻 www.bullockpartners.com

Carol kwok 41b Fairholme Road, London, W14 9JZ, United Kingdom
☎ (020) 7385 9222
✎ carol@carolkwok.com
💻 www.carolkwok.com

Colin Bell Photography Unit E, Purdon Street, Glasgow, G11 6AF, United Kingdom
☎ 0141-334 8008/(07787) 573155 📠 0141-334 8008
✎ colin@colinbellphotography.com
💻 www.colinbellphotography.com

Colin Campbell 23-28 Penn Street, London, N1 5DL, United Kingdom
☎ (020) 7729 3740/ 📠 (020) 7729 9410
✎ colin.studio@virgin.net
💻 www.colincampbell-photo.com

Colin Peacock Photographic The Rectory, Berwick Lane, Compton Greenfield, Bristol, BS35 5RU, United Kingdom
☎ (01454) 633545/ 📠 (01454) 633575
✎ cpeacock@dircon.co.uk
💻 www.colinpeacockphotographer.com

CRE8 Photography Ltd 2nd Floor, 145-157 St. John Street, London, EC1V 4PY, United Kingdom
☎ (07909) 975144
✎ info@cre8photo.com
💻 www.cre8photo.com

Creative Edge Design & Advertising 1st Floor Donald Hendry Building, Auchincruive, Ayr, KA6 5HW, United Kingdom
☎ (01292) 521404/ 📠 (01292) 521693
✎ paul@cedge.co.uk
💻 www.cedge.co.uk

Dave Brown 55 Farringdon Road, London, EC1M 3JB, United Kingdom
☎ (020) 7404 9888/ 📠 (020) 7404 9800
✎ dave@davebrownstudio.co.uk
💻 www.davebrownstudio.co.uk
See ad in showcase

Esser Assocs 2nd Floor North, 6 Buckingham Street, London, WC2N 6BU, United Kingdom
☎ (020) 7976 2915/(07778) 149149 📠 (01372) 464326
✎ rob.esser@virgin.net
💻 www.davidesser.com
See ad in showcase

David George 55 Lansdowne Drive, London, E8 3EP, United Kingdom
☎ (07973) 410031
✎ david@david-george.co.uk
💻 www.david-george.co.uk

David Parfitt Photography 3 Lever Street, London, EC1V 3QU, United Kingdom
☎ (020) 7251 1427/ 📠 (020) 7608 0628
✎ david@davidparfitt.com
💻 www.davidparfitt.com
See ad in showcase

wyatt Clarke & Jones

Leon Steele
Peer Lindgreen
Nick Georghiou
Andy Glass
Lol Keegan
Chris Frazer Smith
Adam Hinton
Liam Kennedy
Nadège Mériau
Larry Dunstan

The White House
26 Mortimer Street
London W1W 7RB
+44 20 7580 7570
www.wyattclarkejones.com

ADVERTISING

David Rees Photography 33 Kirkwood Road, London, SE15 3XT, United Kingdom
(020) 7639 3896/(07889) 379946 / (020) 7639 3896
mail@davidreesphotography.com
www.davidreesphotography.com

Dominic Harris@Martin Roper Photographer's Agent 158a Chamberlayne Road, London, NW10 3JS, United Kingdom
(020) 8964 4780/(0779) 9410942
martin.roper@btinternet.com
www.martinroper.com

Edward Edwards Jewellery Photographer 16 The Vale, London, W3 7SB, United Kingdom
(020) 8749 8887/ (020) 8749 8884
studio@edwardsphotography.co.uk
www.edwardsphotography.co.uk

Erwin Olaf Ijselstraat 26-28, Amsterdam, 1078 CJ, Netherlands
20 692 3438/ 20 694 1291
info@erwinolaf.com
www.erwinolaf.com

Gary Bryan Photography Limited Holborn Studios, 49-50 Eagle Wharf Road, London, N1 7ED,
7973825574
gary@garybryanphotography.com
www.garybryanphotography.com

Gary Ombler 10 Swan Court, Oxfordshire, OX28 6EA,
1993771468
gary@garyombler.com
www.garyombler.com

Gill Orsman 1 The Old Church Hall, 15 Ditchling Rise, Brighton, BN1 4QL, United Kingdom
(01273) 887627/(07831) 855324 / (0870) 3502761
info@gillorsman.com
www.gillorsman.com
See ad in showcase

Iain McKell, London, United Kingdom
(020) 8968 8668/(07802) 756800 / (020) 8968 8668
iain@iainmckell.com
www.iainmckell.com

Inspired Reflection 28 Dayton Grove, Peckham, London, SE15 2NX, United Kingdom
(0870) 9193587/(07040) 402770 / (0870) 9193588
deborah@inspiredreflection.com
www.inspiredreflection.com

Jo Talbot & Sue Young 6M Hyde Park Mansions, Cabbell Street, London, NW1 5BJ, United Kingdom
(020) 7262 0189/(07850) 353468 / (020) 7262 2160
joandsue@btconnect.com
www.joandsue.com
See ad in showcase

Joaquim Barreto 110 Blackheath Road, Greenwich, London, SE10 8DA, United Kingdom
(020) 7760 6646/(07910) 539957
joaquim@ocular-group.com
www.joaquimbarreto.com

John Quinn at Magenta The Mission Church, Hexham Road, Blucher Village, Newcastle upon Tyne, NE15 9SU, United Kingdom
0191-264 8888/(07732) 063530
info@johnquinnat.co.uk
www.johnquinn.eu

Jonathan Green Unit 12, Parsons Green Depot, 33-39 Parsons Green Lane, London, SW6 4HH, United Kingdom
/(07831) 220166
jon@jgreenphotography.co.uk
www.jgreenphotography.co.uk

Jonathan Pollock Photographer Unit 216 The Business Village, 3-9 Broomhill Road, London, SW18 4JQ, United Kingdom
(020) 8877 9493/ (020) 8877 9393
jonathan@jonathanpollock.com
www.jonathanpollock.com

Jonathan Winstone Unit 8, Canes Lane, Weald Hall Farm and Commercial Centre, Hastingwood, Harlow, Essex, CM17 9LD, United Kingdom
(07958) 008187
contact@jonathanwinstone.co.uk
www.jonathanwinstone.co.uk

JWD Graphic 139 Winkworth Road, Banstead, Surrey, SM7 2JW, United Kingdom
(01737) 353013/07973 520292
jwmail@btinternet.com

Laurence Dutton Photography Ltd 57 Farringdon Road, London, EC1M 3JB, United Kingdom
(020) 7813 2099/ (020) 7242 6447
lol@laurence-dutton.co.uk
www.laurence-dutton.com

Leon Pearce Millyard Studios, Millyard, Guildford Street, Luton, LU1 2NR, United Kingdom
(01582) 404888/ (01582) 455089
leon@leonpearce.com
www.leonpearce.com

M C P A 21 Kelful Close, Eastrea, Whittlesey, Peterborough, PE7 2EL, United Kingdom
(07958) 643502
mike@mc-pa.co.uk
www.mc-pa.co.uk

Mark Brome Photographer 6 Aston Works, Back Lane, Aston, Bampton, Oxfordshire, OX18 2DQ, United Kingdom
(07885) 950725
click@markbrome.com
www.markbrome.com

Mark Turnbull Photography Studio, The Old Trueman Brewery, 91 Brick Lane, London, E1 6QL, United Kingdom
(01892) 616154/(07973) 640835
photography@mark-turnbull.co.uk
www.mark-turnbull.co.uk

Martin Roper Photographer's Agent 158a Chamberlayne Road, London, NW10 3JS, United Kingdom
(020) 8964 4780/(0779) 9410942
martin.roper@btinternet.com
www.martinroper.com

Matthias Kerfante Photography Aimies Street, London, SW11, United Kingdom
(07850) 167289
mail@mattpictures.com
www.mattpictures.com

Mike Ellis Photography 65 Leonard Street, London, EC2A 4QS, United Kingdom
(020) 7613 4313/(07860) 275287 / (020) 7739 5512
mike@mikeellisphotography.com
www.mikeellisphotography.com

Milc Studio 7, Zeus House, 16-30 Provost Street, London, N1 7NG, United Kingdom
(020) 7278 8838/ (0870) 0941564
gemma@milc.co.uk
www.milc.co.uk

Mutton Bones Ground Floor, 51 Balcombe Street, London, NW1 6HD, United Kingdom
(020) 7723 8244/ (020) 7723 2770
hello@muttonbones.co.uk
www.muttonbones.co.uk
See ad in showcase

Olly Ball 55b Chapel Lane, Wilmslow, Cheshire, SK9 5JH, United Kingdom
(01625) 526813/ (01625) 526813
olly@ollyball.co.uk
www.ollyball.co.uk

Packshot Company Ltd 43 Carol Street, Camden Town, London, NW1 0HT, United Kingdom
(020) 7267 0700/ (020) 7267 7721
lee@packshot.com
www.packshot.com

Patrick Llewelyn-Davies 1 Dallington Street, London, EC1V 0BH, United Kingdom
(020) 7253 2838/(07866) 622478
patrick@llewelyn-davies.com
www.llewelyn-davies.com/indexchb.html

Paul Hartley 23 Hurlingham Studios, Ranelagh Gardens, London, SW6 3PA, United Kingdom
(020) 7731 0244/ (020) 7384 2567
info@hartleystudios.com
www.hartleystudios.com
See ad in showcase

Paul Webster 11 Parke Road, London, SW13 9NF, United Kingdom
(020) 8748 5786/(07860) 247562 / (020) 8748 5786
info@paulsnap.com
www.paulsnap.com
See ad in showcase

Pearson Lyle Management 3rd Floor, 40 Bowling Green Lane, London, EC1R 0NE, United Kingdom
(020) 7415 7061/ (020) 7415 7059
contact@pearsonlyle.co.uk
www.pearsonlyle.co.uk
See ad in showcase

Peter Beavis 54 Fairlawn Grove, London, W4 5EH, United Kingdom
(07860) 758861
peter@peterbeavis.com
www.peterbeavis.com

Philip North-Coombes Barnard Gate Farm, Barnard Gate, Witney, Oxfordshire, OX29 6XE, United Kingdom
(07785) 381697/ (01865) 882742
pepnorthcoombes@btinternet.com
www.philipnorthcoombes.com

Photo Elevate 1 Rosemary Crescent, Tiptree, Colchester, Essex, CO5 0XA,
07757 417066
photo-elevate@hotmail.co.uk
www.photo-elevate.com

Piers Golden Whitehouse, 4 Haybridge House, London, E5 9NB, United Kingdom
(020) 8442 4240/(07958) 533510 / (020) 8442 4240
piers@goldenphoto.com
www.goldenphoto.com
See ad in showcase

Ray Massey Camden Park Studios, The Church Hall, Camden Park Road, London, NW1 9AY, UK
(020) 7267 9550/(07831) 606342 / (020) 7267 5612
ray@raymassey.com
www.raymassey.com
See ad in showcase

Raymondo Marcus 7 Chiswick High Road, London, W4 2ND, United Kingdom
(01628) 485692/(07831) 649000
r.marcus@raymondomarcus.com
www.raymondomarcus.com

Richard Lewisohn Photography 15 Moorhouse Road, London, W2 5DH, United Kingdom
(07956) 395901/ (020) 7243 4689
richard@lewisohn.co.uk
www.lewisohn.co.uk

Richard Pullar Unit 44, Kingsway Place, Sans Walk, London, EC1R 0LU, United Kingdom
(020) 7490 2188/ (020) 7251 6255
richard@richardpullar.com
www.richardpullar.com
See ad in showcase

Robert Burton 64 Stevenage Road, Hitchin, Herts, SG4 9DR,
07834 606576
bert@robertburton.co.uk
www.robertburton.com

Romilly Lockyer 55 Effingham Road, Long Ditton, Surbiton, Surrey, KT6 5LA, United Kingdom
(020) 8339 0896/(07770) 275524 / (020) 8339 0896
romilly@lineone.net
www.Romilly.com

Sara Morris 23-28 Penn Street, London, N1 5DL, United Kingdom
(020) 7729 3740/ (020) 7729 9410
sara.studio@virgin.net
www.saramorris.co.uk

Shoot The Moon Photography Concept House, Naval Street, Manchester, M4 6AX, United Kingdom
0161-205 7417/ 0161-205 8623
elaine@shoot-the-moon.co.uk
www.stmphotography.co.uk

Stephanie Rushton 16 Reservoir Studios, 547 Cable Street, London, E1W 3EW, United Kingdom
(020) 7780 9838/(07798) 862243 / (020) 7780 9838
info@stephanierushton.com
www.stephanierushton.com

Stephen Marshall Johnston 75 Haverhill Road, London, SW12 0HE, United Kingdom
(07775) 991834
steve@stevejohnstonphoto.com
www.stevejohnstonphoto.com

Studio Fulham Unit 22, Sulivan Enterprise Centre, Sulivan Road, London, SW6 3DJ, United Kingdom
(020) 7751 3030
info@studiofulham.com
www.studiofulham.com

StudioTime Photography Studio 25, 10 Martello St, London Fields, London, E8 3PE,
020 7241 2816
info@studiotime.org
www.studiotimeadvertising.com

Sue Baker, Rickmansworth, Hertfordshire, WD3 5YT, United Kingdom
☎ (01923) 282549/07850 667877
✉ suebaker05@yahoo.co.uk
🖥 www.suebaker05.com

Terry Payne Packshot & Food Photographer First Floor, Building D, The Chocolate Factory, Clarendon Road, London, N22 6XJ,
☎ 020 8889 6609
✉ terry.payne1@ntlworld.com
🖥 www.terrypaynephotog.co.uk

The Street Studios 2 Dunston Street, London, E8 4EB, United Kingdom
☎ (020) 7923 9430/ (020) 7923 9429
✉ mail@streetstudios.co.uk
🖥 www.streetstudios.co.uk

Tim Brightmore 16 York Central, 70 York Way, London, N1 9AG, United Kingdom
☎ **(020) 7278 4747/(07850) 914707** **(020) 7278 4775**
✉ **mail@timbrightmore.co.uk**
🖥 **www.timbrightmore.co.uk**
See ad in showcase

Tim O'Leary 63a Montagu Square, London, W1H 2LU, United Kingdom
☎ (020) 7402 2924/(07968) 529205
✉ tim@timoleary.co.uk
🖥 www.timoleary.co.uk

Tony Latham Studio Five. The Hanger, Perseverance Works, 38 Kingsland Road, London, E2 8DA, UK
☎ (020) 7739 6253/(07831) 473954 (020) 7739 0443
✉ tony.latham@btconnect.com
🖥 www.tonylatham.com

Town & Country Productions Ltd Parry's Lodge, Threapwood, Malpas, Cheshire, SY14 7AW, United Kingdom
☎ (01948) 770 309/ (01948) 770452
✉ john@minophoto.co.uk
🖥 www.minophoto.co.uk

Trevor Richards 40 Kings Hall Road, Beckenham, Kent, BR3 1LS, United Kingdom
☎ (020) 8249 3862/ (020) 8249 0583
✉ trphoto@dircon.co.uk
🖥 www.trphoto.dircon.co.uk

Vincent Paul Bennett 196 Guildford Park Avenue, Guildford, Surrey, GU2 7NH, United Kingdom
☎ (01483) 579042
✉ enquiry@vincentpaul.co.uk
🖥 www.vincentpaul.co.uk

AERIAL

Countrywide Photographic 116 Ellingham Industrial Centre, Ellingham Way, Ashford, Kent, TN23 6LZ, United Kingdom
☎ (01233) 666868
✉ info@countrywidephotographic.co.uk
🖥 www.countrywidephotographic.co.uk

Infoterra Ltd Atlas House, 41 Wembley Road, Leicester, LE3 1UT, United Kingdom
☎ 0116-273 2391/(07901) 655438 0116-273 2400
✉ info@infoterra-global.com
🖥 www.infoterra.co.uk

James King Photographer Unit 19c Barton Hill trad est, Maze Street, Bristol, BS5 9BD,
☎ 1179350839
✉ james@jameskingphotographer.co.uk
🖥 www.jameskingphotographer.co.uk

Photo Elevate 1 Rosemary Crescent, Tiptree, Colchester, Essex, CO5 0XA,
☎ 07757 417066
✉ photo-elevate@hotmail.co.uk
🖥 www.photo-elevate.com

Rupert Marlow Photography Littleworth Corner, Lower Littleworth, Amberley, Stroud, Gloucestershire, GL5 5AW, United Kingdom
☎ (07887) 943590
✉ rupert@rupertmarlow.com
🖥 www.rupertmarlow.com

Sealand Aerial Photography Ltd Pitlands Farm, Up Marden, Chichester, West Sussex, PO18 9JP, United Kingdom
☎ (023) 9263 1468/ (023) 9263 1890
✉ sales@sealandap.co.uk
🖥 www.sealandap.co.uk

ANIMALS

Angela Woods 4 The Carlton Tavern, 73 Grafton Road, London, NW5 4BB, United Kingdom
☎ (020) 7284 3417/(07850) 263077 (020) 7482 2466
✉ angela@angelawoods.com
🖥 www.angelawoods.com

Dave Brown 55 Farringdon Road, London, EC1M 3JB, United Kingdom
☎ **(020) 7404 9888/ (020) 7404 9800**
✉ **dave@davebrownstudio.co.uk**
🖥 **www.davebrownstudio.co.uk**
See ad in showcase

James King Photographer Unit 19c Barton Hill trad est, Maze Street, Bristol, BS5 9BD,
☎ 1179350839
✉ james@jameskingphotographer.co.uk
🖥 www.jameskingphotographer.co.uk

Tessa Newmark 23 Streatham Common South, London, SW16 3BX, United Kingdom
☎ (07973) 241227
✉ tessa@tessanewmark.co.uk
🖥 www.tessanewmark.co.uk

Yara Gremoli Photographers Agent Studio 210, Canalot Studios, 222 Kensal Road, London, W10 5BN, United Kingdom
☎ (0870) 8501209/(07880) 627413 (0870) 8501209
✉ yara@sbmanagement.org
🖥 www.yaragremoli.com

ARCHITECTURE

Alex Orrow Photographer 38 Bavent Road, London, SE5 9RY, United Kingdom
☎ (07768) 152 787
✉ alex@alexorrow.co.uk
🖥 www.alexorrow.co.uk

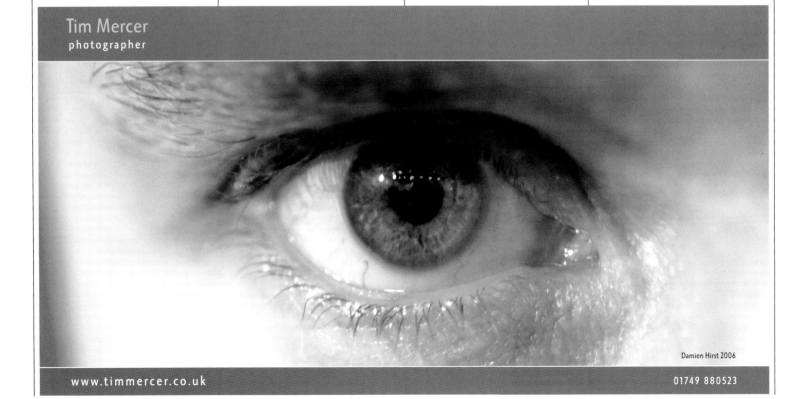

Tim Mercer
photographer

Damien Hirst 2006

www.timmercer.co.uk   01749 880523

Andrew Holt 67Connaught Gardens, London, N10 3LG, United Kingdom
(020) 8444 1888/070 50 264264
contact@andrew-holt.com
www.andrew-holt.com

CLB Photo 8 Highbury Hill, Lower Ground, London, N5 1AL,
7733206857
www.lopzphoto.co.uk

Clive Sawyer 6 Linnet Lane, Camber Sands, East Sussex, TN31 7SL, United Kingdom
(01797) 222213/(07738) 715354
clive@clivephotographer.com
www.clivephotographer.com

Colin Bell Photography Unit E, Purdon Street, Glasgow, G11 6AF, United Kingdom
0141-334 8008/(07787) 573155 0141-334 8008
colin@colinbellphotography.com
www.colinbellphotography.com

Construction Photography 2 Whitacre Mews, 26-34 Stannary Street, London, SE11 4AB, United Kingdom
(020) 7820 6200/(07946) 705650
lucy@constructionphotography.com
www.constructionphotography.com

David Parmiter 27 Lottage Road, Aldbourne, Marlborough, Wiltshire, SN8 2EB, United Kingdom
(01672) 540949/(07973) 205275 (01672) 540949
david@davidparmiter.co.uk
www.davidparmiter.co.uk

Daydream Linton House, 164-180 Union Street, London, SE1 0LH,
+44 (0) 20 7096 1471/+44 (0) 20 7117 1636
ralph@daydream.co.uk
www.daydream.co.uk

James Brittain Photography Studio 22, 33-35 St John Square, London, Greater London, EC1M 4DS,
020 7490 5203
mail@jamesbrittain.co.uk
www.jamesbrittain.co.uk

James King Photographer Unit 19c Barton Hill trad est, Maze Street, Bristol, BS5 9BD,
1179350839
james@jameskingphotographer.co.uk
www.jameskingphotographer.co.uk

James Willis 83 Longlands Court, Denbigh Terrace, London, London, W11 2QG, United Kingdom
(020) 7792 1150/(07836) 226597
info@jwillisphoto.com
www.jwillisphoto.com

Liz Artindale 3rd Floor, 71 Leonard Street, London, EC2A 4QU, United Kingdom
(020) 7739 8940/(07850) 566177 (020) 7739 4813
liz@lizartindale.co.uk
www.lizartindale.co.uk

Lonely Cloud 7c Hartington Gardens, Edinburgh, EH10 4LD, United Kingdom
(07730) 617055
d.m.fleetwood@gmail.com
www.lonely-cloud.co.uk

Ludwig Haskins Flat 2, 52 St. James Road, Sutton, Surrey, SM1 2TS, United Kingdom
(020) 8404 2337/ (020) 8404 2338
ludwighaskins@yahoo.com
www.ludwig-haskins.com

Mark Bury Photography 158 Sheen Road, Richmond, Surrey, TW9 1UU,
0776 9705656
info@markbury.co.uk
www.markbury.co.uk

Media Wisdom Photography Ltd 5 Lindsay Road, Hampton, Middlesex, TW12 1DR, United Kingdom
(020) 8979 3328/(07971) 686151
abi@mediawisdom.co.uk
www.mediawisdom.co.uk

Neill Menneer Belgrave Lodge, Upper Camden Place, Bath, Somerset, BA1 5JA, United Kingdom
(01225) 483151/(07970) 235052 (01225) 446394
ncm@ktwo.co.uk
www.neillmenneer.com

Photo Elevate 1 Rosemary Crescent, Tiptree, Colchester, Essex, CO5 0XA,
07757 417066
photo-elevate@hotmail.co.uk
www.photo-elevate.com

Rowland Roques-O'Neil Studio 15, The Tay Building, 2a Wrentham Avenue, London, NW10 3HA,
020 8969 4482
rowland@rolypics.com
www.rolypics.com

Tessa Newmark 23 Streatham Common South, London, SW16 3BX, United Kingdom
(07973) 241227
tessa@tessanewmark.co.uk
www.tessanewmark.co.uk

ART

Adrian Houston Amberley Studio, 32A Goldney Road, London, W9 2AX, United Kingdom
(020) 7289 1419/(07850) 475105 (020) 7289 1419
adrian@adrianhouston.co.uk
www.adrianhouston.co.uk

Chaos 94 Bradshaw Close, Winbledon, London, SW19 8NL,
020 8944 1692/ 020 8944 1692
to-chaos@hotmail.co.uk
www.chaos-gallery.co.uk

James King Photographer Unit 19c Barton Hill trad est, Maze Street, Bristol, BS5 9BD,
1179350839
james@jameskingphotographer.co.uk
www.jameskingphotographer.co.uk

Razzdesign.com 108 / 3F2, Edinburgh, EH3 9HX, United Kingdom
(07792) 161591
steve@razzdesign.com
www.stephenrasmussen.com

Voveris Photography Flat 1, 14 Park Road, Westcliff-on-Sea, Essex, SS0 7PE, United Kingdom
(07999) 245888
arun@voverisphotography.com
www.voverisphotography.com

BEAUTY

Augustbound Unit 4, 2 Millers Terrace, London, E8 2DP,
7944488761
augustbound@yahoo.co.uk
www.reneaugust.com

Henry Arden Photography 7 The Old Laundry, Haydon Way, London, SW11 1YF, United Kingdom
(020) 8871 1274/07860 384633 020 7207 1965
henry@henryarden.com
www.henryarden.com
See ad in showcase

James King Photographer Unit 19c Barton Hill trad est, Maze Street, Bristol, BS5 9BD,
1179350839
james@jameskingphotographer.co.uk
www.jameskingphotographer.co.uk

Matthias Kerfante Photography Aimies Street, London, SW11, United Kingdom
(07850) 167289
mail@mattpictures.com
www.mattpictures.com

Milc Studio 7, Zeus House, 16-30 Provost Street, London, N1 7NG, United Kingdom
(020) 7278 8838/ (0870) 0941564
gemma@milc.co.uk
www.milc.co.uk

Piers Golden Whitehouse, 4 Haybridge House, London, E5 9NB, United Kingdom
(020) 8442 4240/(07958) 533510 (020) 8442 4240
piers@goldenphoto.com
www.goldenphoto.com
See ad in showcase

Raymondo Marcus 7 Chiswick High Road, London, W4 2ND, United Kingdom
(01628) 485692/(07831) 649000
r.marcus@raymondomarcus.com
www.raymondomarcus.com

Richard Booth The Old Kiln, Watts Gallery, Guildford, Surrey, GU3 1DQ, United Kingdom
(01483) 812007/(07866) 767067 (01483) 810093
richard@rbphusion.co.uk
www.richardbooth.co.uk

Voveris Photography Flat 1, 14 Park Road, Westcliff-on-Sea, Essex, SS0 7PE, United Kingdom
(07999) 245888
arun@voverisphotography.com
www.voverisphotography.com

BOATS

Bruce Head Photographer The Studio, 1 Avenue Approach, Bury St. Edmunds, Suffolk, IP32 6BA, United Kingdom
(01284) 760159/(07885) 370980
bruce@brucehead.com
www.fabfoodphotography.com

The Mad Agency Mad House, Horton, Wimborne, Dorset, BH21 7JH,
01258 840841/ 01258 840849
lisa@themadagency.com
www.themadagency.com

BUSINESS/CORPORATE

Agent Pandora 12 Stonells Road, London, SW11 6HQ, United Kingdom
(07966) 181825
pandora@agentpandora.com
www.agentpandora.com

Albada Studios Unit 83, Portmanmoor Road Industrial Estate, Ocean Way, Cardiff, CF24 5HB,
02920 495123
adrian@albada.co.uk
www.albada.co.uk

Amos Schliack Unit 8, 220 Kingsland Road, London, E2 8DF, United Kingdom
(020) 7033 9972/(07906) 449 776
amos@london.com
www.amosschliack.com

Andrew Holt 67Connaught Gardens, London, N10 3LG, United Kingdom
(020) 8444 1888/070 50 264264
contact@andrew-holt.com
www.andrew-holt.com

Asvisual - Architectural Photography 2 Eddy Street, Berkhamsted, Hertfordshire, HP4 1DQ, United Kingdom
(07747) 103334
andy@asvisual.co.uk
www.asvisual.co.uk

CLB Photo 8 Highbury Hill, Lower Ground, London, N5 1AL,
7733206857
www.lopzphoto.co.uk

Colin Bell Photography Unit E, Purdon Street, Glasgow, G11 6AF, United Kingdom
0141-334 8008/(07787) 573155 0141-334 8008
colin@colinbellphotography.com
www.colinbellphotography.com

Construction Photography 2 Whitacre Mews, 26-34 Stannary Street, London, SE11 4AB, United Kingdom
(020) 7820 6200/(07946) 705650
lucy@constructionphotography.com
www.constructionphotography.com

CRE8 Photography Ltd 2nd Floor, 145-157 St. John Street, London, EC1V 4PY, United Kingdom
(07909) 975144
info@cre8photo.com
www.cre8photo.com

Daydream Linton House, 164-180 Union Street, London, SE1 0LH,
+44 (0) 20 7096 1471/+44 (0) 20 7117 1636
ralph@daydream.co.uk
www.daydream.co.uk

Gill Orsman 1 The Old Church Hall, 15 Ditchling Rise, Brighton, BN1 4QL, United Kingdom
(01273) 887627/(07831) 855324 (0870) 3502761
info@gillorsman.com
www.gillorsman.com

Inspired Reflection 28 Dayton Grove, Peckham, London, SE15 2NX, United Kingdom
(0870) 9193587/(07040) 402770 (0870) 9193588
deborah@inspiredreflection.com
www.inspiredreflection.com

James King Photographer Unit 19c Barton Hill trad est, Maze Street, Bristol, BS5 9BD,
1179350839
james@jameskingphotographer.co.uk
www.jameskingphotographer.co.uk

James Willis 83 Longlands Court, Denbigh Terrace, London, London, W11 2QG, United Kingdom
(020) 7792 1150/(07836) 226597
info@jwillisphoto.com
www.jwillisphoto.com

John Quinn at Magenta The Mission Church, Hexham Road, Blucher Village, Newcastle upon Tyne, NE15 9SU, United Kingdom
0191-264 8888/(07732) 063530
info@johnquinnat.co.uk
www.johnquinn.eu

Julian Calder 7 Nepean Street, London, SW15 5DW, United Kingdom
(020) 8780 5352/ (020) 8780 2156
juliancalder@btinternet.com
www.juliancalder.com

Laura Ashman 48 Deanhill Court, Upper Richmond Road West, London, SW14 7DL, United Kingdom
(07932) 075605
mail@lauraashman.com
www.lauraashman.com

Liz Artindale 3rd Floor, 71 Leonard Street, London, EC2A 4QU, United Kingdom
(020) 7739 8940/(07850) 566177 (020) 7739 4813
liz@lizartindale.co.uk
www.lizartindale.co.uk

Mark Turnbull Photography Studio, The Old Trueman Brewery, 91 Brick Lane, London, E1 6QL, United Kingdom
(01892) 616154/(07973) 640835
photography@mark-turnbull.co.uk
www.mark-turnbull.co.uk

Mike Cooper Photography Unit 19C, Barton Hill Trading Estate, Bristol, BS5 9BD, United Kingdom
0117 955 1345/(07860) 439820 0117 955 1456
mike@mike-cooper.com
www.mike-cooper.com

Mike Ellis Photography 65 Leonard Street, London, EC2A 4QS, United Kingdom
(020) 7613 4313/(07860) 275287 (020) 7739 5512
mike@mikeellisphotography.com
www.mikeellisphotography.com

Phil Ashley 3 Dee Road, Richmond, Surrey, TW9 2JN, United Kingdom
(020) 8332 7707/(07976) 887879 (020) 8332 1932
phil@philashley.com
www.philashley.com

Photo Elevate 1 Rosemary Crescent, Tiptree, Colchester, Essex, CO5 0XA,
07757 417066
photo-elevate@hotmail.co.uk
www.photo-elevate.com

Richard Booth The Old Kiln, Watts Gallery, Guildford, Surrey, GU3 1DQ, United Kingdom
(01483) 812007/(07866) 767067 (01483) 810093
richard@rbphusion.co.uk
www.richardbooth.co.uk

Richard Lewisohn Photography 15 Moorhouse Road, London, W2 5DH, United Kingdom
(07956) 395901/ (020) 7243 4689
richard@lewisohn.co.uk
www.lewisohn.co.uk

Rupert Marlow Photography Littleworth Corner, Lower Littleworth, Amberley, Stroud, Gloucestershire, GL5 5AW, United Kingdom
(07887) 943590
rupert@rupertmarlow.com
www.rupertmarlow.com

Sealand Aerial Photography Ltd Pitlands Farm, Up Marden, Chichester, West Sussex, PO18 9JP, United Kingdom
(023) 9263 1468/ (023) 9263 1890
sales@sealandap.co.uk
www.sealandap.co.uk

StudioTime Photography Studio 25, 10 Martello St, London Fields, London, E8 3PE,
020 7241 2816
info@studiotime.org
www.studiotimeadvertising.com

Terry Payne Packshot & Food Photographer First Floor, Building D, The Chocolate Factory, Clarendon Road, London, N22 6XJ,
020 8889 6609
terry.payne1@ntlworld.com
www.terrypaynephotog.co.uk

Tim O'Leary 63a Montagu Square, London, W1H 2LU, United Kingdom
(020) 7402 2924/(07968) 529205
tim@timoleary.co.uk
www.timoleary.co.uk

Wildpear Studio 70 Hill Street, Richmond, Surrey, TW9 1TW, United Kingdom
(020) 8948 2300
studio@wildpear.com
www.wildpear.com

CARS

Agent Pandora 12 Stonells Road, London, SW11 6HQ, United Kingdom
(07966) 181825
pandora@agentpandora.com
www.agentpandora.com

The Angela Woods Agency 4 The Carlton Tavern, 73 Grafton Road, London, NW5 4BB, United Kingdom
(020) 7284 3417/(07850) 263077 (020) 7482 2466
angela@angelawoods.com
www.angelawoods.com
See ad in showcase

Car Photo Library 28 Fernside Road, Talbot Park, Bournemouth, BH9 2LB, United Kingdom
(01202) 528849/(07785) 537928
davidkimber@carphoto.co.uk
www.carphoto.co.uk

Colin Campbell 23-28 Penn Street, London, N1 5DL, United Kingdom
(020) 7729 3740/ (020) 7729 9410
colin.studio@virgin.net
www.colincampbell-photo.com

Esser Assocs 2nd Floor North, 6 Buckingham Street, London, WC2N 6BU, United Kingdom
(020) 7976 2915/(07778) 149149 (01372) 464326
rob.esser@virgin.net
www.davidesser.com
See ad in showcase

James King Photographer Unit 19c Barton Hill trad est, Maze Street, Bristol, BS5 9BD,
1179350839
james@jameskingphotographer.co.uk
www.jameskingphotographer.co.uk

Leon Pearce Millyard Studios, Millyard, Guildford Street, Luton, LU1 2NR, United Kingdom
(01582) 404888/ (01582) 455089
leon@leonpearce.com
www.leonpearce.com

Michael Harding Photography 85 Stanthorpe Road, London, SW16 2EA, United Kingdom
(020) 8677 4412/(07860) 920769
michael@mharding.com
www.mharding.com

Packshot Company Ltd 43 Carol Street, Camden Town, London, NW1 0HT, United Kingdom
(020) 7267 0700/ (020) 7267 7721
lee@packshot.com
www.packshot.com

Patrick Llewelyn-Davies 1 Dallington Street, London, EC1V 0BH, United Kingdom
(020) 7253 2838/(07866) 622478
patrick@llewelyn-davies.com
www.llewelyn-davies.com/indexchb.html

Richard Booth The Old Kiln, Watts Gallery, Guildford, Surrey, GU3 1DQ, United Kingdom
(01483) 812007/(07866) 767067 (01483) 810093
richard@rbphusion.co.uk
www.richardbooth.co.uk

Unichrome Creative 23-25 Great Sutton Street, London, EC1V 0DN, United Kingdom
(020) 7251 8811/ (020) 7251 8812
info@unichrome-creative.com
www.unichrome-creative.com

Yara Gremoli Photographers Agent Studio 210, Canalot Studios, 222 Kensal Road, London, W10 5BN, United Kingdom
(0870) 8501209/(07880) 627413 (0870) 8501209
yara@sbmanagement.org
www.yaragremoli.com

CELEBRITIES

Dani Brubaker Photography 2805 Tennyson Place, Hermosa Beach, Los Angeles, 90254,
310-463-4157
studio@danibrubaker.com
www.danibrubaker.com

Henry Arden Photography 7 The Old Laundry, Haydon Way, London, SW11 1YF, United Kingdom
(020) 8871 1274/07860 384633 020 7207 1965
henry@henryarden.com
www.henryarden.com
See ad in showcase

James King Photographer Unit 19c Barton Hill trad est, Maze Street, Bristol, BS5 9BD,
1179350839
james@jameskingphotographer.co.uk
www.jameskingphotographer.co.uk

Mike Prior Photography 7 The Old Laundry, Hayden Way, London, SW11 1YF, United Kingdom
(020) 7207 1964/(07721) 646464 (020) 7207 1965
info@mikeprior.com
www.mikeprior.com

Milc Studio 7, Zeus House, 16-30 Provost Street, London, N1 7NG, United Kingdom
(020) 7278 8838/ (0870) 0941564
gemma@milc.co.uk
www.milc.co.uk

Raymondo Marcus 7 Chiswick High Road, London, W4 2ND, United Kingdom
(01628) 485692/(07831) 649000
r.marcus@raymondomarcus.com
www.raymondomarcus.com

Stephanie Rushton 16 Reservoir Studios, 547 Cable Street, London, E1W 3EW, United Kingdom
(020) 7780 9838/(07798) 862243 (020) 7780 9838
info@stephanierushton.com
www.stephanierushton.com

CHILDREN

Agent Pandora 12 Stonells Road, London, SW11 6HQ, United Kingdom
(07966) 181825
pandora@agentpandora.com
www.agentpandora.com

The Angela Woods Agency 4 The Carlton Tavern, 73 Grafton Road, London, NW5 4BB, United Kingdom
(020) 7284 3417/(07850) 263077 (020) 7482 2466
angela@angelawoods.com
www.angelawoods.com
See ad in showcase

Basement Photographic Unit 22, Soho Mills, Wooburn Green, High Wycombe, Buckinghamshire, HP10 0PF, United Kingdom
(01628) 529900/ (01628) 851039
studio@basementphoto.com
www.basementphoto.com
See ad in showcase

Bay Hippisley@Martin Roper Photographer's Agent 158a Chamberlayne Road, London, NW10 3JS, United Kingdom
(020) 8964 4780/(0779) 9410942
martin.roper@btinternet.com
www.martinroper.com

Dani Brubaker Photography 2805 Tennyson Place, Hermosa Beach, Los Angeles, 90254,
310-463-4157
studio@danibrubaker.com
www.danibrubaker.com

David Rees Photography 33 Kirkwood Road, London, SE15 3XT, United Kingdom
(020) 7639 3896/(07889) 379946 (020) 7639 3896
mail@davidreesphotography.com
www.davidreesphotography.com

Inspired Reflection 28 Dayton Grove, Peckham, London, SE15 2NX, United Kingdom
(0870) 9193587/(07040) 402770 (0870) 9193588
deborah@inspiredreflection.com
www.inspiredreflection.com

James King Photographer Unit 19c Barton Hill trad est, Maze Street, Bristol, BS5 9BD,
1179350839
james@jameskingphotographer.co.uk
www.jameskingphotographer.co.uk

Laura Ashman 48 Deanhill Court, Upper Richmond Road West, London, SW14 7DL, United Kingdom
(07932) 075605
mail@lauraashman.com
www.lauraashman.com

Marcus Lyon The Glassworks, 1C Montford Place, London, SE11 5DE, United Kingdom
☎ **(020) 7735 9933/(07831) 591959** 📠 **(020) 7735 9273**
✉ ml@theglassworks.co.uk
🖥 www.marcuslyon.com
See ad in showcase

Martin Roper Photographer's Agent
158a Chamberlayne Road, London, NW10 3JS, United Kingdom
☎ (020) 8964 4780/(0779) 9410942
✉ martin.roper@btinternet.com
🖥 www.martinroper.com

Mike Prior Photography 7 The Old Laundry, Hayden Way, London, SW11 1YF, United Kingdom
☎ (020) 7207 1964/(07721) 646464 📠 (020) 7207 1965
✉ info@mikeprior.com
🖥 www.mikeprior.com

Peter Mason 10 Cranleigh Mews, London, SW11 2QL, United Kingdom
☎ **(07774) 496414**
✉ peter@petermason.biz
🖥 www.petermason.biz
See ad in showcase

Richard Pentin Photography 170 Trinity Road, London, SW17 7HT, United Kingdom
☎ (07796) 265210
✉ richardpentin@yahoo.co.uk
🖥 www.richardpentinphotography.com

Sue Baker, Rickmansworth, Hertfordshire, WD3 5YT, United Kingdom
☎ (01923) 282549/07850 667877
✉ suebaker05@yahoo.co.uk
🖥 www.suebaker05.com

Tessa Newmark 23 Streatham Common South, London, SW16 3BX, United Kingdom
☎ (07973) 241227
✉ tessa@tessanewmark.co.uk
🖥 www.tessanewmark.co.uk

Victoria Blackie Ltd 1b Nightingale Road, Wendover, Aylesbury, Buckinghamshire, HP22 6JX, United Kingdom
☎ (07831) 423177
✉ vicblack@tinyworld.co.uk
🖥 www.victoriablackie.co.uk

Wildpear Studio 70 Hill Street, Richmond, Surrey, TW9 1TW, United Kingdom
☎ (020) 8948 2300
✉ studio@wildpear.com
🖥 www.wildpear.com

CLOTHES/COSMETICS

David Parfitt Photography 3 Lever Street, London, EC1V 3QU, United Kingdom
☎ **(020) 7251 1427**/📠 **(020) 7608 0628**
✉ david@davidparfitt.com
🖥 www.davidparfitt.com
See ad in showcase

James King Photographer Unit 19c Barton Hill trad est, Maze Street, Bristol, BS5 9BD,
☎ 1179350839
✉ james@jameskingphotographer.co.uk
🖥 www.jameskingphotographer.co.uk

Joaquim Barreto 110 Blackheath Road, Greenwich, London, SE10 8DA, United Kingdom
☎ (020) 7760 6646/(07910) 539957
✉ joaquim@ocular-group.com
🖥 www.joaquimbarreto.com

Matthias Kerfante Photography Aimies Street, London, SW11, United Kingdom
☎ (07850) 167289
✉ mail@mattpictures.com
🖥 www.mattpictures.com

Packshot Company Ltd 43 Carol Street, Camden Town, London, NW1 0HT, United Kingdom
☎ (020) 7267 0700/📠 (020) 7267 7721
✉ lee@packshot.com
🖥 www.packshot.com

Packshot Factory 39-41 New Oxford Street, London, WC1A 1BN, United Kingdom
☎ **(020) 7379 3080**/📠 **(020) 7240 9568**
✉ martin@packshotfactory.co.uk
🖥 www.packshotfactory.co.uk
See ad in showcase

Paul Hartley 23 Hurlingham Studios, Ranelagh Gardens, London, SW6 3PA, United Kingdom
☎ **(020) 7731 0244**/📠 **(020) 7384 2567**
✉ info@hartleystudios.com
🖥 www.hartleystudios.com
See ad in showcase

Richard Booth The Old Kiln, Watts Gallery, Guildford, Surrey, GU3 1DQ, United Kingdom
☎ (01483) 812007/(07866) 767067 📠 (01483) 810093
✉ richard@rbphusion.co.uk
🖥 www.richardbooth.co.uk

Studio Fulham Unit 22, Sulivan Enterprise Centre, Sulivan Road, London, SW6 3DJ, United Kingdom
☎ (020) 7751 3030
✉ info@studiofulham.com
🖥 www.studiofulham.com

DRINK

Agent Pandora 12 Stonells Road, London, SW11 6HQ, United Kingdom
☎ (07966) 181825
✉ pandora@agentpandora.com
🖥 www.agentpandora.com

Bruce Head Photographer The Studio, 1 Avenue Approach, Bury St. Edmunds, Suffolk, IP32 6BA, United Kingdom
☎ (01284) 760159/(07885) 370980
✉ bruce@brucehead.com
🖥 www.fabfoodphotography.com

James King Photographer Unit 19c Barton Hill trad est, Maze Street, Bristol, BS5 9BD,
☎ 1179350839
✉ james@jameskingphotographer.co.uk
🖥 www.jameskingphotographer.co.uk

Jonathan Pollock Photographer Unit 216 The Business Village, 3-9 Broomhill Road, London, SW18 4JQ, United Kingdom
☎ (020) 8877 9493/📠 (020) 8877 9393
✉ jonathan@jonathanpollock.com
🖥 www.jonathanpollock.com

Kai Schwabe Fotografie Ander Weide 50, Bremen, D-28195, Germany
☎ 00 49 42 144 1520/📠 00 49 42 149 88359
✉ info@kaischwabe.de
🖥 www.kaischwabe.de

Oliver Beamish 49 Dorien Road, London, SW20 8EL, United Kingdom
☎ (07973) 354259
✉ oliver@beamishcreative.com
🖥 www.beamishcreative.com

Packshot Company Ltd 43 Carol Street, Camden Town, London, NW1 0HT, United Kingdom
☎ (020) 7267 0700/📠 (020) 7267 7721
✉ lee@packshot.com
🖥 www.packshot.com

Packshot Factory 39-41 New Oxford Street, London, WC1A 1BN, United Kingdom
☎ **(020) 7379 3080**/📠 **(020) 7240 9568**
✉ martin@packshotfactory.co.uk
🖥 www.packshotfactory.co.uk
See ad in showcase

Paul Webster 11 Parke Road, London, SW13 9NF, United Kingdom
☎ **(020) 8748 5786/(07860) 247562** 📠 **(020) 8748 5786**
✉ info@paulsnap.com
🖥 www.paulsnap.com
See ad in showcase

Peter Kidd 22 Vanbrugh Hill, London, SE3 7UF, United Kingdom
☎ **(07973) 315122**
✉ p.kidd7@ntlworld.com
See ad in showcase

Ray Massey Camden Park Studios, The Church Hall, Camden Park Road, London, NW1 9AY, United Kingdom
☎ **(020) 7267 9550/(07831) 606342** 📠 **(020) 7267 5612**
✉ ray@raymassey.com
🖥 www.raymassey.com
See ad in showcase

Shoot The Moon Photography Concept House, Naval Street, Manchester, M4 6AX, United Kingdom
☎ 0161-205 7417/📠 0161-205 8623
✉ elaine@shoot-the-moon.co.uk
🖥 www.stmphotography.co.uk

Terry Payne Packshot & Food Photographer First Floor, Building D, The Chocolate Factory, Clarendon Road, London, N22 6XJ,
☎ 020 8889 6609
✉ terry.payne1@ntlworld.com
🖥 www.terrypaynephotog.co.uk

Tim Brightmore 16 York Central, 70 York Way, London, N1 9AG, United Kingdom
☎ **(020) 7278 4747/(07850) 914707** 📠 **(020) 7278 4775**
✉ mail@timbrightmore.co.uk
🖥 www.timbrightmore.co.uk

EDITORIAL

Adam Dawe Hangar 9, Perserverance Works, 38 Kingsland Road, London, E2 8DD, United Kingdom
☎ (020) 7613 3262/📠 (020) 7613 2152
✉ mail@adamdawe.com
🖥 www.adamdawe.com

Albada Studios Unit 83, Portmanmoor Road Industrial Estate, Ocean Way, Cardiff, CF24 5HB,
☎ 02920 495123
✉ adrian@albada.co.uk
🖥 www.albada.co.uk

Andrew Wiard 15 Pembroke Road, London, N10 2HR, United Kingdom
☎ (07973) 219201
✉ andrew@reportphotos.com
🖥 www.wiard.co.uk

Augustbound Unit 4, 2 Millers Terrace, London, E8 2DP,
☎ 7944488761
✉ augustbound@yahoo.co.uk
🖥 www.reneaugust.com

Ben Fisher Photography 45-46 Charlotte Road, London, EC2A 3PD, United Kingdom
☎ **(020) 7613 1623/(07976) 659605** 📠 **(020) 7613 1623**
✉ contact@benfisherphotography.com
🖥 www.benfisherphotography.com
See ad in showcase

Ben Mostyn Photography Farleigh, Orchard Lane, Old Boars Hill, Oxford, Oxfordshire, OX1 5JH,
☎ 01865 730138
✉ info@benmostyn.com
🖥 www.benmostyn.com

Blerim Racaj 9 George Mews, London, NW1 2EU, United Kingdom
☎ (07792) 959732
✉ info@blerimracaj.com
🖥 www.blerimracaj.com

CLB Photo 8 Highbury Hill, Lower Ground, London, N5 1AL,
☎ 7733206857
🖥 www.lopzphoto.co.uk

CRE8 Photography Ltd 2nd Floor, 145-157 St. John Street, London, EC1V 4PY, United Kingdom
☎ (07909) 975144
✉ info@cre8photo.com
🖥 www.cre8photo.com

Dani Brubaker Photography 2805 Tennyson Place, Hermosa Beach, Los Angeles, 90254,
☎ 310-463-4157
✉ studio@danibrubaker.com
🖥 www.danibrubaker.com

David Parmiter 27 Lottage Road, Aldbourne, Marlborough, Wiltshire, SN8 2EB, United Kingdom
☎ (01672) 540949/(07973) 205275 📠 (01672) 540949
✉ david@davidparmiter.co.uk
🖥 www.davidparmiter.co.uk

Erwin Olaf Ijselstraat 26-28, Amsterdam, 1078 CJ, Netherlands
☎ 20 692 3438/📠 20 694 1291
✉ info@erwinolaf.com
🖥 www.erwinolaf.com

Gary Ombler 10 Swan Court, Oxfordshire, OX28 6EA,
☎ 1993771468
✉ gary@garyombler.com
🖥 www.garyombler.com

Inspired Reflection 28 Dayton Grove, Peckham, London, SE15 2NX, United Kingdom
☎ (0870) 9193587/(07040) 402770 📠 (0870) 9193588
✉ deborah@inspiredreflection.com
🖥 www.inspiredreflection.com

Joaquim Barreto 110 Blackheath Road, Greenwich, London, SE10 8DA, United Kingdom
✆ (020) 7760 6646/(07910) 539957
✉ joaquim@ocular-group.com
🖳 www.joaquimbarreto.com

Jonathan Winstone Unit 8, Canes Lane, Weald Hall Farm and Commercial Centre, Hastingwood, Harlow, Essex, CM17 9LD, United Kingdom
✆ (07958) 008187
✉ contact@jonathanwinstone.co.uk
🖳 www.jonathanwinstone.co.uk

Julian Calder 7 Nepean Street, London, SW15 5DW, United Kingdom
✆ (020) 8780 5352/✎ (020) 8780 2156
✉ juliancalder@btinternet.com
🖳 www.juliancalder.com

M C P A 21 Kelful Close, Eastrea, Whittlesey, Peterborough, PE7 2EL, United Kingdom
✆ (07958) 643502
✉ mike@mc-pa.co.uk
🖳 www.mc-pa.co.uk

Mark Turnbull Photography Studio, The Old Trueman Brewery, 91 Brick Lane, London, E1 6QL, United Kingdom
✆ (01892) 616154/(07973) 640835
✉ photography@mark-turnbull.co.uk
🖳 www.mark-turnbull.co.uk

Richard Pentin Photography 170 Trinity Road, London, SW17 7HT, United Kingdom
✆ (07796) 265210
✉ richardpentin@yahoo.co.uk
🖳 www.richardpentinphotography.com

Robert Burton 64 Stevenage Road, Hitchin, Herts, SG4 9DR,
✆ 07834 606576
✉ bert@robertburton.co.uk
🖳 www.robertburton.co.uk

Sara Morris 23-28 Penn Street, London, N1 5DL, United Kingdom
✆ (020) 7729 3740/✎ (020) 7729 9410
✉ sara.studio@virgin.net
🖳 www.saramorris.co.uk

Terry Payne Packshot & Food Photographer First Floor, Building D, The Chocolate Factory, Clarendon Road, London, N22 6XJ,
✆ 020 8889 6609
✉ terry.payne1@ntlworld.com
🖳 www.terrypaynephotog.co.uk

Tim O'Leary 63a Montagu Square, London, W1H 2LU, United Kingdom
✆ (020) 7402 2924/(07968) 529205
✉ tim@timoleary.co.uk
🖳 www.timoleary.co.uk

Town & Country Productions Ltd Parry's Lodge, Threapwood, Malpas, Cheshire, SY14 7AW, United Kingdom
✆ (01948) 770 309/✎ (01948) 770452
✉ john@minophoto.co.uk
🖳 www.minophoto.co.uk

Trevor Richards 40 Kings Hall Road, Beckenham, Kent, BR3 1LS, United Kingdom
✆ (020) 8249 3862/✎ (020) 8249 0583
✉ trphoto@dircon.co.uk
🖳 www.trphoto.dircon.co.uk

Wildpear Studio 70 Hill Street, Richmond, Surrey, TW9 1TW, United Kingdom
✆ (020) 8948 2300
✉ studio@wildpear.com
🖳 www.wildpear.com

EQUESTRIAN

James King Photographer Unit 19c Barton Hill trad est, Maze Street, Bristol, BS5 9BD,
✆ 1179350839
✉ james@jameskingphotographer.co.uk
🖳 www.jameskingphotographer.co.uk

Town & Country Productions Ltd Parry's Lodge, Threapwood, Malpas, Cheshire, SY14 7AW, United Kingdom
✆ (01948) 770 309/✎ (01948) 770452
✉ john@minophoto.co.uk
🖳 www.minophoto.co.uk

EVENTS

Ivor Tetteh-Lartey 25 Corbie Wynd, Duddingston, Edinburgh, EH15 3RP, United Kingdom
✆ 0131-657 2427/(07770) 732137 ✎ 0131-657 2427
✉ ivor@tetteh-lartey.co.uk
🖳 www.tetteh-lartey.co.uk

Neill Menneer Belgrave Lodge, Upper Camden Place, Bath, Somerset, BA1 5JA, United Kingdom
✆ (01225) 483151/(07970) 235052 ✎ (01225) 446394
✉ ncm@ktwo.co.uk
🖳 www.neillmenneer.com

EXHIBITIONS

Erwin Olaf Ijselstraat 26-28, Amsterdam, 1078 CJ, Netherlands
✆ 20 692 3438/✎ 20 694 1291
✉ info@erwinolaf.com
🖳 www.erwinolaf.com

James King Photographer Unit 19c Barton Hill trad est, Maze Street, Bristol, BS5 9BD,
✆ 1179350839
✉ james@jameskingphotographer.co.uk
🖳 www.jameskingphotographer.co.uk

Photo Elevate 1 Rosemary Crescent, Tiptree, Colchester, Essex, CO5 0XA,
✆ 07757 417066
✉ photo-elevate@hotmail.co.uk
🖳 www.photo-elevate.com

FASHION

Andrea Klarin@edsonwilliams photography consultancy 52 Brushfield Street, London, E1 6AJ, United Kingdom
✆ (020) 7375 2077/(07867) 517777 ✎ (020) 7375 3077
✉ info@edsonwilliams.com
🖳 www.edsonwilliams.com

Anne Dokter Photography Amstelkade 171-1, Amsterdam, The Netherlands, 1078 az,
✆ +31 20 6721244
✉ info@annedokter.com
🖳 www.annedokter.com

Augustbound Unit 4, 2 Millers Terrace, London, E8 2DP,
✆ 7944488761
✉ augustbound@yahoo.co.uk
🖳 www.reneaugust.com

Ben Fisher Photography 45-46 Charlotte Road, London, EC2A 3PD, United Kingdom
✆ (020) 7613 1623/(07976) 659605 ✎ (020) 7613 1623
✉ contact@benfisherphotography.com
🖳 www.benfisherphotography.com

Bruce Anderson Photography 126 Shoreditch High Street, London, E1 6JE, United Kingdom
✆ (020) 7729 2299/(07930) 406668
✉ bruce@bruceanderson.co.uk
🖳 www.bruceanderson.co.uk

Cereinyn 4 Church Studios, Camden Park Road, London, NW1 9AY,
✆ 7809777957
✉ info@cereinyn.com
🖳 www.cereinyn.com

CLB Photo 8 Highbury Hill, Lower Ground, London, N5 1AL,
✆ 7733206857
🖳 www.lopzphoto.co.uk

Dani Brubaker Photography 2805 Tennyson Place, Hermosa Beach, Los Angeles, 90254,
✆ 310-463-4157
✉ studio@danibrubaker.com
🖳 www.danibrubaker.com

Henry Arden Photography 7 The Old Laundry, Haydon Way, London, SW11 1YF, United Kingdom
✆ (020) 8871 1274/07860 384633 ✎ 020 7207 1965
✉ henry@henryarden.com
🖳 www.henryarden.com
See ad in showcase

Iain McKell London, United Kingdom
✆ (020) 8968 8668/(07802) 756800 ✎ (020) 8968 8668
✉ iain@iainmckell.com
🖳 www.iainmckell.com

James King Photographer Unit 19c Barton Hill trad est, Maze Street, Bristol, BS5 9BD,
✆ 1179350839
✉ james@jameskingphotographer.co.uk
🖳 www.jameskingphotographer.co.uk

Joaquim Barreto 110 Blackheath Road, Greenwich, London, SE10 8DA, United Kingdom
✆ (020) 7760 6646/(07910) 539957
✉ joaquim@ocular-group.com
🖳 www.joaquimbarreto.com

Ludwig Haskins Flat 2, 52 St. James Road, Sutton, Surrey, SM1 2TS, United Kingdom
✆ (020) 8404 2337/✎ (020) 8404 2338
✉ ludwighaskins@yahoo.com
🖳 www.ludwig-haskins.com

Matthias Kerfante Photography Aimies Street, London, SW11, United Kingdom
✆ (07850) 167289
✉ mail@mattpictures.com
🖳 www.mattpictures.com

Milc Studio 7, Zeus House, 16-30 Provost Street, London, N1 7NG, United Kingdom
✆ (020) 7278 8838/✎ (0870) 0941564
✉ gemma@milc.co.uk
🖳 www.milc.co.uk

Philip North-Coombes Barnard Gate Farm, Barnard Gate, Witney, Oxfordshire, OX29 6XE, United Kingdom
✆ (07785) 381697/✎ (01865) 882742
✉ pepnorthcoombes@btinternet.com
🖳 www.philipnorthcoombes.com

Raymondo Marcus 7 Chiswick High Road, London, W4 2ND, United Kingdom
✆ (01628) 485692/(07831) 649000
✉ r.marcus@raymondomarcus.com
🖳 www.raymondomarcus.com

Stephanie Rushton 16 Reservoir Studios, 547 Cable Street, London, E1W 3EW, United Kingdom
✆ (020) 7780 9838/(07798) 862243 ✎ (020) 7780 9838
✉ info@stephanierushton.com
🖳 www.stephanierushton.com

Studio Fulham Unit 22, Sulivan Enterprise Centre, Sulivan Road, London, SW6 3DJ, United Kingdom
✆ (020) 7751 3030
✉ info@studiofulham.com
🖳 www.studiofulham.com

Sue Baker, Rickmansworth, Hertfordshire, WD3 5YT, United Kingdom
✆ (01923) 282549/07850 667877
✉ suebaker05@yahoo.co.uk
🖳 www.suebaker05.com

Tom Watson@edsonwilliams photography consultancy 52 Brushfield Street, London, E1 6AJ, United Kingdom
✆ (020) 7375 2077/(07867) 517777 ✎ (020) 7375 3077
✉ info@edsonwilliams.com
🖳 www.edsonwilliams.com

Victoria Blackie Ltd 1b Nightingale Road, Wendover, Aylesbury, Buckinghamshire, HP22 6JX, United Kingdom
✆ (07831) 423177
✉ vicblack@tinyworld.co.uk
🖳 www.victoriablackie.co.uk

Voveris Photography Flat 1, 14 Park Road, Westcliff-on-Sea, Essex, SS0 7PE, United Kingdom
✆ (07999) 245888
✉ arun@voverisphotography.com
🖳 www.voverisphotography.com

Wildpear Studio 70 Hill Street, Richmond, Surrey, TW9 1TW, United Kingdom
✆ (020) 8948 2300
✉ studio@wildpear.com
🖳 www.wildpear.com

Yara Gremoli Photographers Agent Studio 210, Canalot Studios, 222 Kensal Road, London, W10 5BN, United Kingdom
✆ (0870) 8501209/(07880) 627413 ✎ (0870) 8501209
✉ yara@sbmanagement.org
🖳 www.yaragremoli.com

FLOWERS

Carol Sharp 71 Leonard Street, London, EC2A 4QU, United Kingdom
✆ (020) 7729 8040/✎ (020) 7729 7909
✉ carol@carolsharp.co.uk
🖳 www.carolsharp.co.uk

Gill Orsman 1 The Old Church Hall, 15 Ditchling Rise, Brighton, BN1 4QL, United Kingdom
✆ (01273) 887627/(07831) 855324 ✎ (0870) 3502761
✉ info@gillorsman.com
🖳 www.gillorsman.com

James King Photographer Unit 19c Barton Hill trad est, Maze Street, Bristol, BS5 9BD,
☎ 1179350839
✉ james@jameskingphotographer.co.uk
🖥 www.jameskingphotographer.co.uk

Terry Payne Packshot & Food Photographer First Floor, Building D, The Chocolate Factory, Clarendon Road, London, N22 6XJ,
☎ 020 8889 6609
✉ terry.payne1@ntlworld.com
🖥 www.terrypaynephotog.co.uk

FOOD

Agent Pandora 12 Stonells Road, London, SW11 6HQ, United Kingdom
☎ (07966) 181825
✉ pandora@agentpandora.com
🖥 www.agentpandora.com

Albada Studios Unit 83, Portmanmoor Road Industrial Estate, Ocean Way, Cardiff, CF24 5HB,
☎ 02920 495123
✉ adrian@albada.co.uk
🖥 www.albada.co.uk

Amos Schliack Unit 8, 220 Kingsland Road, London, E2 8DF, United Kingdom
☎ (020) 7033 9972/(07906) 449 776
✉ amos@london.com
🖥 www.amosschliack.com

Andy Seymour 82 Princedale Road, Holland Park, London, W11 4NL, United Kingdom
☎ **(020) 7221 2021/ (020) 7792 0702**
✉ **andy@andyseymour.co.uk**
🖥 **www.andyseymour.co.uk**
See ad in showcase

Bay Hippisley@Martin Roper Photographer's Agent 158a Chamberlayne Road, London, NW10 3JS, United Kingdom
☎ (020) 8964 4780/(0779) 9410942
✉ martin.roper@btinternet.com
🖥 www.martinroper.com

Carol Sharp 71 Leonard Street, London, EC2A 4QU, United Kingdom
☎ (020) 7729 8040/ (020) 7729 7909
✉ carol@carolsharp.co.uk
🖥 www.carolsharp.co.uk

CLB Photo 8 Highbury Hill, Lower Ground, London, N5 1AL,
☎ 7733206857
🖥 www.lopzphoto.co.uk

Jonathan Pollock Photographer Unit 216 The Business Village, 3-9 Broomhill Road, London, SW18 4JQ, United Kingdom
☎ (020) 8877 9493/ (020) 8877 9393
✉ jonathan@jonathanpollock.com
🖥 www.jonathanpollock.com

Kai Schwabe Fotografie Ander Weide 50, Bremen, D-28195, Germany
☎ 00 49 42 144 1520/ 00 49 42 149 88359
✉ info@kaischwabe.de
🖥 www.kaischwabe.de

Martin Roper Photographer's Agent 158a Chamberlayne Road, London, NW10 3JS, United Kingdom
☎ (020) 8964 4780/(0779) 9410942
✉ martin.roper@btinternet.com
🖥 www.martinroper.com

Mike Cooper Photography Unit 19C, Barton Hill Trading Estate, Bristol, BS5 9BD, United Kingdom
☎ 0117 955 1345/(07860) 439820 0117 955 1456
✉ mike@mike-cooper.com
🖥 www.mike-cooper.com

Oliver Beamish 49 Dorien Road, London, SW20 8EL, United Kingdom
☎ (07973) 354259
✉ oliver@beamishcreative.com
🖥 www.beamishcreative.com

Packshot Company Ltd 43 Carol Street, Camden Town, London, NW1 0HT, United Kingdom
☎ (020) 7267 0700/ (020) 7267 7721
✉ lee@packshot.com
🖥 www.packshot.com

Paul Webster 11 Parke Road, London, SW13 9NF, United Kingdom
☎ **(020) 8748 5786/(07860) 247562 (020) 8748 5786**
✉ **info@paulsnap.com**
🖥 **www.paulsnap.com**
See ad in showcase

Pearson Lyle Management 3rd Floor, 40 Bowling Green Lane, London, EC1R 0NE, United Kingdom
☎ (020) 7415 7061/ (020) 7415 7059
✉ contact@pearsonlyle.co.uk
🖥 www.pearsonlyle.co.uk

Peter Kidd 22 Vanbrugh Hill, London, SE3 7UF, United Kingdom
☎ (07973) 315122
✉ p.kidd7@ntlworld.com

Shoot The Moon Photography Concept House, Naval Street, Manchester, M4 6AX, United Kingdom
☎ 0161-205 7417/ 0161-205 8623
✉ elaine@shoot-the-moon.co.uk
🖥 www.stmphotography.co.uk

Terry Payne Packshot & Food Photographer First Floor, Building D, The Chocolate Factory, Clarendon Road, London, N22 6XJ,
☎ 020 8889 6609
✉ terry.payne1@ntlworld.com
🖥 www.terrypaynephotog.co.uk

TNG Food Photography 54 Byron Gardens, Tilbury, Essex, RM18 8BD,
☎ 07870 641109
✉ info@tngfoodphotography.com
🖥 www.tngfoodphotography.com

Tony Harris 183 Dawes Road, London, SW6 7QP, United Kingdom
☎ (020) 7385 8158/(07836) 201229 (020) 7385 8159
✉ tony@tonyhphoto.com
🖥 www.tonyhphoto.com

FURNITURE

David Parmiter 27 Lottage Road, Aldbourne, Marlborough, Wiltshire, SN8 2EB, United Kingdom
☎ (01672) 540949/(07973) 205275 (01672) 540949
✉ david@davidparmiter.co.uk
🖥 www.davidparmiter.co.uk

Daydream Linton House, 164-180 Union Street, London, SE1 0LH,
☎ +44 (0) 20 7096 1471/+44 (0) 20 7117 1636
✉ ralph@daydream.co.uk
🖥 www.daydream.co.uk

James King Photographer Unit 19c Barton Hill trad est, Maze Street, Bristol, BS5 9BD,
☎ 1179350839
✉ james@jameskingphotographer.co.uk
🖥 www.jameskingphotographer.co.uk

Packshot Company Ltd 43 Carol Street, Camden Town, London, NW1 0HT, United Kingdom
☎ (020) 7267 0700/ (020) 7267 7721
✉ lee@packshot.com
🖥 www.packshot.com

HEALTH & FITNESS

Romilly Lockyer 55 Effingham Road, Long Ditton, Surbiton, Surrey, KT6 5LA, United Kingdom
☎ (020) 8339 0896/(07770) 275524 (020) 8339 0896
✉ romilly@lineone.net
🖥 www.Romilly.com

INTERIORS

Adrian Houston Amberley Studio, 32A Goldney Road, London, W9 2AX, United Kingdom
☎ (020) 7289 1419/(07850) 475105 (020) 7289 1419
✉ adrian@adrianhouston.co.uk
🖥 www.adrianhouston.co.uk

Charlotte Murphy 56 Romola Road, London, SE24 9AZ, United Kingdom
☎ (020) 8516 9048/(07774) 487 874

CLB Photo 8 Highbury Hill, Lower Ground, London, N5 1AL,
☎ 7733206857
🖥 www.lopzphoto.co.uk

David Parmiter 27 Lottage Road, Aldbourne, Marlborough, Wiltshire, SN8 2EB, United Kingdom
☎ (01672) 540949/(07973) 205275 (01672) 540949
✉ david@davidparmiter.co.uk
🖥 www.davidparmiter.co.uk

Focusing Ltd Unit 6, New Milton Bus. Center, Wick Drive, New Milton, Hampshire, BH25 6RQ,
☎ 01425 617800
✉ info@focusingltd.com
🖥 www.focusingltd.com

Inspired Reflection 28 Dayton Grove, Peckham, London, SE15 2NX, United Kingdom
☎ (0870) 9193587/(07040) 402770 (0870) 9193588
✉ deborah@inspiredreflection.com
🖥 www.inspiredreflection.com

James King Photographer Unit 19c Barton Hill trad est, Maze Street, Bristol, BS5 9BD,
☎ 1179350839
✉ james@jameskingphotographer.co.uk
🖥 www.jameskingphotographer.co.uk

Jonathan Green Unit 12, Parsons Green Depot, 33-39 Parsons Green Lane, London, SW6 4HH, United Kingdom
☎ /(07831) 220166
✉ jon@jgreenphotography.co.uk
🖥 www.jgreenphotography.co.uk

Liz Artindale 3rd Floor, 71 Leonard Street, London, EC2A 4QU, United Kingdom
☎ (020) 7739 8940/(07850) 566177 (020) 7739 4813
✉ liz@lizartindale.co.uk
🖥 www.lizartindale.co.uk

Oliver Beamish 49 Dorien Road, London, SW20 8EL, United Kingdom
☎ (07973) 354259
✉ oliver@beamishcreative.com
🖥 www.beamishcreative.com

Paul Barbera@edsonwilliams photography consultancy 52 Brushfield Street, London, E1 6AJ, United Kingdom
☎ (020) 7375 2077/(07867) 517777 (020) 7375 3077
✉ info@edsonwilliams.com
🖥 www.edsonwilliams.com

Pearson Lyle Management 3rd Floor, 40 Bowling Green Lane, London, EC1R 0NE, United Kingdom
☎ (020) 7415 7061/ (020) 7415 7059
✉ contact@pearsonlyle.co.uk
🖥 www.pearsonlyle.co.uk

Tessa Newmark 23 Streatham Common South, London, SW16 3BX, United Kingdom
☎ (07973) 241227
✉ tessa@tessanewmark.co.uk
🖥 www.tessanewmark.co.uk

Tony Harris 183 Dawes Road, London, SW6 7QP, United Kingdom
☎ (020) 7385 8158/(07836) 201229 (020) 7385 8159
✉ tony@tonyhphoto.com
🖥 www.tonyhphoto.com

JEWELLERY

Bruce Anderson Photography 126 Shoreditch High Street, London, E1 6JE, United Kingdom
☎ (020) 7729 2299/(07930) 406668
✉ bruce@bruceanderson.co.uk
🖥 www.bruceanderson.co.uk

Edward Edwards Jewellery Photographer 16 The Vale, London, W3 7SB, United Kingdom
☎ (020) 8749 8887/ (020) 8749 8884
✉ studio@edwardsphotography.co.uk
🖥 www.edwardsphotography.co.uk

James King Photographer Unit 19c Barton Hill trad est, Maze Street, Bristol, BS5 9BD,
☎ 1179350839
✉ james@jameskingphotographer.co.uk
🖥 www.jameskingphotographer.co.uk

Patrick Llewelyn-Davies 1 Dallington Street, London, EC1V 0BH, United Kingdom
☎ (020) 7253 2838/(07866) 622478
✉ patrick@llewelyn-davies.com
🖥 www.llewelyn-davies.com/indexchb.html

Paul Hartley 23 Hurlingham Studios, Ranelagh Gardens, London, SW6 3PA, United Kingdom
☎ **(020) 7731 0244/ (020) 7384 2567**
✉ **info@hartleystudios.com**
🖥 **www.hartleystudios.com**
See ad in showcase

Terry Payne Packshot & Food Photographer First Floor, Building D, The Chocolate Factory, Clarendon Road, London, N22 6XJ,
☎ 020 8889 6609
✉ terry.payne1@ntlworld.com
🖥 www.terrypaynephotog.co.uk

Tim Brightmore 16 York Central, 70 York Way, London, N1 9AG, United Kingdom
☎ **(020) 7278 4747/(07850) 914707 (020) 7278 4775**
✉ **mail@timbrightmore.co.uk**
🖥 **www.timbrightmore.co.uk**
See ad in showcase

LANDSCAPES

Adrian Houston Amberley Studio, 32A Goldney Road, London, W9 2AX, United Kingdom
☎ (020) 7289 1419/(07850) 475105 / (020) 7289 1419
✉ adrian@adrianhouston.co.uk
🖥 www.adrianhouston.co.uk

Agent Pandora 12 Stonells Road, London, SW11 6HQ, United Kingdom
☎ (07966) 181825
✉ pandora@agentpandora.com
🖥 www.agentpandora.com

Albada Studios Unit 83, Portmanmoor Road Industrial Estate, Ocean Way, Cardiff, CF24 5HB,
☎ 02920 495123
✉ adrian@albada.co.uk
🖥 www.albada.co.uk

Armitage Online Solutions 1 Tall Trees, Lancaster, Lancashire, LA1 2LD,
☎ 0845 094 3795/ 0845 094 3795
✉ andrew@armitage-online.co.uk
🖥 www.armitage-online.co.uk

Clive Sawyer 6 Linnet Lane, Camber Sands, East Sussex, TN31 7SL, United Kingdom
☎ (01797) 222213/(07738) 715354
✉ clive@clivephotographer.com
🖥 www.clivephotographer.com

Esser Assocs 2nd Floor North, 6 Buckingham Street, London, WC2N 6BU, United Kingdom
☎ (020) 7976 2915/(07778) 149149 / (01372) 464326
✉ rob.esser@virgin.net
🖥 www.davidesser.com
See ad in showcase

James Bareham@edsonwilliams photography consultancy 52 Brushfield Street, London, E1 6AJ, United Kingdom
☎ (020) 7375 2077/(07867) 517777 / (020) 7375 3077
✉ info@edsonwilliams.com
🖥 www.edsonwilliams.com

James King Photographer Unit 19c Barton Hill trad est, Maze Street, Bristol, BS5 9BD,
☎ 1179350839
✉ james@jameskingphotographer.co.uk
🖥 www.jameskingphotographer.co.uk

Liz Artindale 3rd Floor, 71 Leonard Street, London, EC2A 4QU, United Kingdom
☎ (020) 7739 8940/(07850) 566177 / (020) 7739 4813
✉ liz@lizartindale.co.uk
🖥 www.lizartindale.co.uk

Michael Harding Photography 85 Stanthorpe Road, London, SW16 2EA, United Kingdom
☎ (020) 8677 4412/(07860) 920769
✉ michael@mharding.com
🖥 www.mharding.com

Paul Webster 11 Parke Road, London, SW13 9NF, United Kingdom
☎ (020) 8748 5786/(07860) 247562 / (020) 8748 5786
✉ info@paulsnap.com
🖥 www.paulsnap.com
See ad in showcase

Photo Elevate 1 Rosemary Crescent, Tiptree, Colchester, Essex, CO5 0XA,
☎ 07757 417066
✉ photo-elevate@hotmail.com
🖥 www.photo-elevate.com

Rupert Marlow Photography Littleworth Corner, Lower Littleworth, Amberley, Stroud, Gloucestershire, GL5 5AW, United Kingdom
☎ (07887) 943590
✉ rupert@rupertmarlow.com
🖥 www.rupertmarlow.com

Tim O'Leary 63a Montagu Square, London, W1H 2LU, United Kingdom
☎ (020) 7402 2924/(07968) 529205
✉ tim@timoleary.co.uk
🖥 www.timoleary.co.uk

LIFESTYLE

Adrian Houston Amberley Studio, 32A Goldney Road, London, W9 2AX, United Kingdom
☎ (020) 7289 1419/(07850) 475105 / (020) 7289 1419
✉ adrian@adrianhouston.co.uk
🖥 www.adrianhouston.co.uk

Basement Photographic Unit 22, Soho Mills, Wooburn Green, High Wycombe, Buckinghamshire, HP10 0PF, United Kingdom
☎ (01628) 529900/ (01628) 851039
✉ studio@basementphoto.com
🖥 www.basementphoto.com
See ad in showcase

Henry Arden Photography 7 The Old Laundry, Haydon Way, London, SW11 1YF, United Kingdom
☎ (020) 8871 1274/07860 384633 / 020 7207 1965
✉ henry@henryarden.com
🖥 www.henryarden.com
See ad in showcase

Inspired Reflection 28 Dayton Grove, Peckham, London, SE15 2NX, United Kingdom
☎ (0870) 9193587/(07040) 402770 / (0870) 9193588
✉ deborah@inspiredreflection.com
🖥 www.inspiredreflection.com

James King Photographer Unit 19c Barton Hill trad est, Maze Street, Bristol, BS5 9BD,
☎ 1179350839
✉ james@jameskingphotographer.co.uk
🖥 www.jameskingphotographer.co.uk

John Quinn at Magenta The Mission Church, Hexham Road, Blucher Village, Newcastle upon Tyne, NE15 9SU, United Kingdom
☎ 0191-264 8888/(07732) 063530
✉ info@johnquinnat.co.uk
🖥 www.johnquinn.eu

Jonathan Green Unit 12, Parsons Green Depot, 33-39 Parsons Green Lane, London, SW6 4HH, United Kingdom
☎ /(07831) 220166
✉ jon@jgreenphotography.co.uk
🖥 www.jgreenphotography.co.uk

Marcus Lyon The Glassworks, 1C Montford Place, London, SE11 5DE, United Kingdom
☎ (020) 7735 9933/(07831) 591959 / (020) 7735 9273
✉ ml@theglassworks.co.uk
🖥 www.marcuslyon.com
See ad in showcase

Mark Turnbull Photography Studio, The Old Trueman Brewery, 91 Brick Lane, London, E1 6QL, United Kingdom
☎ (01892) 616154/(07973) 640835
✉ photography@mark-turnbull.co.uk
🖥 www.mark-turnbull.co.uk

Mike Cooper Photography Unit 19C, Barton Hill Trading Estate, Bristol, BS5 9BD, United Kingdom
☎ 0117 955 1345/(07860) 439820 / 0117 955 1456
✉ mike@mike-cooper.com
🖥 www.mike-cooper.com

Mike Ellis Photography 65 Leonard Street, London, EC2A 4QS, United Kingdom
☎ (020) 7613 4313/(07860) 275287 / (020) 7739 5512
✉ mike@mikeellisphotography.com
🖥 www.mikeellisphotography.com

Milc Studio 7, Zeus House, 16-30 Provost Street, London, N1 7NG, United Kingdom
☎ (020) 7278 8838/ (0870) 0941564
✉ gemma@milc.co.uk
🖥 www.milc.co.uk

Packshot Company Ltd 43 Carol Street, Camden Town, London, NW1 0HT, United Kingdom
☎ (020) 7267 0700/ (020) 7267 7721
✉ lee@packshot.com
🖥 www.packshot.com

Packshot Factory 39-41 New Oxford Street, London, WC1A 1BN, United Kingdom
☎ (020) 7379 3080/ (020) 7240 9568
✉ martin@packshotfactory.co.uk
🖥 www.packshotfactory.co.uk
See ad in showcase

Peter Beavis 54 Fairlawn Grove, London, W4 5EH, United Kingdom
☎ (07860) 758861
✉ peter@peterbeavis.com
🖥 www.peterbeavis.com

Peter Mason 10 Cranleigh Mews, London, SW11 2QL, United Kingdom
☎ (07774) 496414
✉ peter@petermason.biz
🖥 www.petermason.biz
See ad in showcase

Philip North-Coombes Barnard Gate Farm, Barnard Gate, Witney, Oxfordshire, OX29 6XE, United Kingdom
☎ (07785) 381697/ (01865) 882742
✉ pepnorthcoombes@btinternet.com
🖥 www.philipnorthcoombes.com

Piers Golden Whitehouse, 4 Haybridge House, London, E5 9NB, United Kingdom
☎ (020) 8442 4240/(07958) 533510 / (020) 8442 4240
✉ piers@goldenphoto.com
🖥 www.goldenphoto.com
See ad in showcase

Romilly Lockyer 55 Effingham Road, Long Ditton, Surbiton, Surrey, KT6 5LA, United Kingdom
☎ (020) 8339 0896/(07770) 275524 / (020) 8339 0896
✉ romilly@lineone.net
🖥 www.Romilly.com

Sue Baker, Rickmansworth, Hertfordshire, WD3 5YT, United Kingdom
☎ (01923) 282549/07850 667877
✉ suebaker05@yahoo.co.uk
🖥 www.suebaker05.com

Tony Latham Studio Five. The Hanger, Perseverance Works, 38 Kingsland Road, London, E2 8DA, United Kingdom
☎ (020) 7739 6253/(07831) 473954 / (020) 7739 0443
✉ tony.latham@btconnect.com
🖥 www.tonylatham.com

Trevor Richards 40 Kings Hall Road, Beckenham, Kent, BR3 1LS, United Kingdom
☎ (020) 8249 3862/ (020) 8249 0583
✉ trphoto@dircon.co.uk
🖥 www.trphoto.dircon.co.uk

Victoria Blackie Ltd 1b Nightingale Road, Wendover, Aylesbury, Buckinghamshire, HP22 6JX, United Kingdom
☎ (07831) 423177
✉ vicblack@tinyworld.co.uk
🖥 www.victoriablackie.co.uk

Wonderfuel 118 Hatherley Gardens, London, E6 3HQ, United Kingdom
☎ 020 8548 1358
✉ info@wonderfuel.co.uk
🖥 www.wonderfuel.co.uk

Zac Macaulay Photography 20 Leigh Road, Cobham, Surrey, KT11 2LD, United Kingdom
☎ (020) 8941 1238/(07990) 592000
✉ zac@zacmacaulay.com
🖥 www.zacmacaulay.com

LIQUID

David Parfitt Photography 3 Lever Street, London, EC1V 3QU, United Kingdom
☎ (020) 7251 1427/ (020) 7608 0628
✉ david@davidparfitt.com
🖥 www.davidparfitt.com
See ad in showcase

Jonathan Pollock Photographer Unit 216 The Business Village, 3-9 Broomhill Road, London, SW18 4JQ, United Kingdom
☎ (020) 8877 9493/ (020) 8877 9393
✉ jonathan@jonathanpollock.com
🖥 www.jonathanpollock.com

Peter Kidd 22 Vanbrugh Hill, London, SE3 7UF, United Kingdom
☎ (07973) 315122
✉ p.kidd7@ntlworld.com

Ray Massey Camden Park Studios, The Church Hall, Camden Park Road, London, NW1 9AY, United Kingdom
☎ (020) 7267 9550/(07831) 606342 / (020) 7267 5612
✉ ray@raymassey.com
🖥 www.raymassey.com
See ad in showcase

LOCATIONS

Bruce Head Photographer The Studio, 1 Avenue Approach, Bury St. Edmunds, Suffolk, IP32 6BA, United Kingdom
☎ (01284) 760159/(07885) 370980
✉ bruce@brucehead.com
🖥 www.fabfoodphotography.com

Clive Sawyer 6 Linnet Lane, Camber Sands, East Sussex, TN31 7SL, United Kingdom
☎ (01797) 222213/(07738) 715354
✉ clive@clivephotographer.com
🖥 www.clivephotographer.com

David Parmiter 27 Lottage Road, Aldbourne, Marlborough, Wiltshire, SN8 2EB, United Kingdom
☎ (01672) 540949/(07973) 205275 / (01672) 540949
✉ david@davidparmiter.co.uk
🖥 www.davidparmiter.co.uk

David Roy Imaginaire, 79 Broomhill Road, Witton Village, Birmingham, B23 5AF, United Kingdom
✆ (07973) 305938/📱 0121-386 2640
✉ david@imaginaire-photo.co.uk
🖥 www.imaginaire-photo.co.uk

Focusing Ltd Unit 6, New Milton Bus. Center, Wick Drive, New Milton, Hampshire, BH25 6RQ,
✆ 01425 617800
✉ info@focusingltd.com
🖥 www.focusingltd.com

Gary Ombler 10 Swan Court, Oxfordshire, OX28 6EA,
✆ 1993771468
✉ gary@garyombler.com
🖥 www.garyombler.com

James King Photographer Unit 19c Barton Hill trad est, Maze Street, Bristol, BS5 9BD,
✆ 1179350839
✉ james@jameskingphotographer.co.uk
🖥 www.jameskingphotographer.co.uk

Michael Harding Photography 85 Stanthorpe Road, London, SW16 2EA, United Kingdom
✆ (020) 8677 4412/(07860) 920769
✉ michael@mharding.com
🖥 www.mharding.com

Neill Menneer Belgrave Lodge, Upper Camden Place, Bath, Somerset, BA1 5JA, United Kingdom
✆ (01225) 483151/(07970) 235052 📠 (01225) 446394
✉ ncm@ktwo.co.uk
🖥 www.neillmenneer.com

Oliver Beamish 49 Dorien Road, London, SW20 8EL, United Kingdom
✆ (07973) 354259
✉ oliver@beamishcreative.com
🖥 www.beamishcreative.com

Peter Beavis 54 Fairlawn Grove, London, W4 5EH, United Kingdom
✆ (07860) 758861
✉ peter@peterbeavis.com
🖥 www.peterbeavis.com

Photo Elevate 1 Rosemary Crescent, Tiptree, Colchester, Essex, CO5 0XA,
✆ 07757 417066
✉ photo-elevate@hotmail.co.uk
🖥 www.photo-elevate.com

Ray Massey Camden Park Studios, The Church Hall, Camden Park Road, London, NW1 9AY, United Kingdom
✆ **(020) 7267 9550/(07831) 606342 📠 (020) 7267 5612**
✉ **ray@raymassey.com**
🖥 **www.raymassey.com**
See ad in showcase

Richard Bradbury 72 Thornton Avenue, London, W4 1QQ, United Kingdom
✆ **(07768) 352100**
✉ **info@rbradbury.com**
🖥 **www.rbradbury.com**
See ad in showcase

Robert Burton 64 Stevenage Road, Hitchin, Herts, SG4 9DR,
✆ 07834 606576
✉ bert@robertburton.co.uk
🖥 www.robertburton.co.uk

Sealand Aerial Photography Ltd Pitlands Farm, Up Marden, Chichester, West Sussex, PO18 9JP, United Kingdom
✆ (023) 9263 1468/📠 (023) 9263 1890
✉ sales@sealandap.co.uk
🖥 www.sealandap.co.uk

Shoot The Moon Photography Concept House, Naval Street, Manchester, M4 6AX, United Kingdom
✆ 0161-205 7417/📠 0161-205 8623
✉ elaine@shoot-the-moon.co.uk
🖥 www.stmphotography.co.uk

PACKAGING

Albada Studios Unit 83, Portmanmoor Road Industrial Estate, Ocean Way, Cardiff, CF24 5HB,
✆ 02920 495123
✉ adrian@albada.co.uk
🖥 www.albada.co.uk

Focusing Ltd Unit 6, New Milton Bus. Center, Wick Drive, New Milton, Hampshire, BH25 6RQ,
✆ 01425 617800
✉ info@focusingltd.com
🖥 www.focusingltd.com

Gary Ombler 10 Swan Court, Oxfordshire, OX28 6EA,
✆ 1993771468
✉ gary@garyombler.com
🖥 www.garyombler.com

James King Photographer Unit 19c Barton Hill trad est, Maze Street, Bristol, BS5 9BD,
✆ 1179350839
✉ james@jameskingphotographer.co.uk
🖥 www.jameskingphotographer.co.uk

Kai Schwabe Fotografie Ander Weide 50, Bremen, D-28195, Germany
✆ 00 49 42 144 1520/📠 00 49 42 149 88359
✉ info@kaischwabe.de
🖥 www.kaischwabe.de

LSD | Brand Designer L Martinez 983, (Martinez), Buenos Aires, 1460,
✆ 54 11 4798 1760/📠 54 11 4798 1760
✉ luzsoldano@sion.com
🖥 www.luzsoldano.com

Terry Payne Packshot & Food Photographer First Floor, Building D, The Chocolate Factory, Clarendon Road, London, N22 6XJ,
✆ 020 8889 6609
✉ terry.payne1@ntlworld.com
🖥 www.terrypaynephotog.co.uk

PEOPLE

Angela Woods 4 The Carlton Tavern, 73 Grafton Road, London, NW5 4BB, United Kingdom
✆ **(020) 7284 3417/(07850) 263077 📠 (020) 7482 2466**
✉ **angela@angelawoods.com**
🖥 **www.angelawoods.com**
See ad in showcase

Bay Hippisley@Martin Roper Photographer's Agent 158a Chamberlayne Road, London, NW10 3JS, United Kingdom
✆ (020) 8964 4780/(0779) 9410942
✉ martin.roper@btinternet.com
🖥 www.martinroper.com

Brian Galloway 77 Peterborough Road, London, SW6 3BT, United Kingdom
✆ (07973) 386904
✉ brian@gallowayphoto.co.uk
🖥 www.gallowayphoto.co.uk

Bruce Head Photographer The Studio, 1 Avenue Approach, Bury St. Edmunds, Suffolk, IP32 6BA, United Kingdom
✆ (01284) 760159/(07885) 370980
✉ bruce@brucehead.com
🖥 www.fabfoodphotography.com

Colin Bell Photography Unit E, Purdon Street, Glasgow, G11 6AF, United Kingdom
✆ 0141-334 8008/(07787) 573155 📠 0141-334 8008
✉ colin@colinbellphotography.com
🖥 www.colinbellphotography.com

Dave Brown 55 Farringdon Road, London, EC1M 3JB, United Kingdom
✆ **(020) 7404 9888/📠 (020) 7404 9800**
✉ **dave@davebrownstudio.co.uk**
🖥 **www.davebrownstudio.co.uk**
See ad in showcase

Esser Assocs 2nd Floor North, 6 Buckingham Street, London, WC2N 6BU, United Kingdom
✆ **(020) 7976 2915/(07778) 149149 📠 (01372) 464326**
✉ **rob.esser@virgin.net**
🖥 **www.davidesser.com**
See ad in showcase

David Rees Photography 33 Kirkwood Road, London, SE15 3XT, United Kingdom
✆ (020) 7639 3896/(07889) 379946 📠 (020) 7639 3896
✉ mail@davidreesphotography.com
🖥 www.davidreesphotography.com

David Roy Imaginaire, 79 Broomhill Road, Witton Village, Birmingham, B23 5AF, United Kingdom
✆ (07973) 305938/📱 0121-386 2640
✉ david@imaginaire-photo.co.uk
🖥 www.imaginaire-photo.co.uk

Erwin Olaf Ijselstraat 26-28, Amsterdam, 1078 CJ, Netherlands
✆ 20 692 3438/📠 20 694 1291
✉ info@erwinolaf.com
🖥 www.erwinolaf.com

Henry Arden Photography 7 The Old Laundry, Haydon Way, London, SW11 1YF, United Kingdom
✆ **(020) 8871 1274/(07860 384633 📠 020 7207 1965**
✉ **henry@henryarden.com**
🖥 **www.henryarden.com**
See ad in showcase

Ivor Tetteh-Lartey 25 Corbie Wynd, Duddingston, Edinburgh, EH15 3RP, United Kingdom
✆ 0131-657 2427/(07770) 732137 📠 0131-657 2427
✉ ivor@tetteh-lartey.co.uk
🖥 www.tetteh-lartey.co.uk

John Quinn at Magenta The Mission Church, Hexham Road, Blucher Village, Newcastle upon Tyne, NE15 9SU, United Kingdom
✆ 0191-264 8888/(07732) 063530
✉ info@johnquinn.co.uk
🖥 www.johnquinn.eu

Julian Calder 7 Nepean Street, London, SW15 5DW, United Kingdom
✆ (020) 8780 5352/📠 (020) 8780 2156
✉ juliancalder@btinternet.com
🖥 www.juliancalder.com

Laura Ashman 48 Deanhill Court, Upper Richmond Road West, London, SW14 7DL, United Kingdom
✆ (07932) 075605
✉ mail@lauraashman.com
🖥 www.lauraashman.com

Liz Artindale 3rd Floor, 71 Leonard Street, London, EC2A 4QU, United Kingdom
✆ (020) 7739 8940/(07850) 566177 📠 (020) 7739 4813
✉ liz@lizartindale.co.uk
🖥 www.lizartindale.co.uk

Ludwig Haskins Flat 2, 52 St. James Road, Sutton, Surrey, SM1 2TS, United Kingdom
✆ (020) 8404 2337/📠 (020) 8404 2338
✉ ludwighaskins@yahoo.com
🖥 www.ludwig-haskins.com

Marcus Lyon The Glassworks, 1C Montford Place, London, SE11 5DE, United Kingdom
✆ **(020) 7735 9933/(07831) 591959 📠 (020) 7735 9273**
✉ **ml@theglassworks.co.uk**
🖥 **www.marcuslyon.com**
See ad in showcase

Mark Turnbull Photography Studio, The Old Trueman Brewery, 91 Brick Lane, London, E1 6QL, United Kingdom
✆ (01892) 616154/(07973) 640835
✉ photography@mark-turnbull.co.uk
🖥 www.mark-turnbull.co.uk

Michael Harding Photography 85 Stanthorpe Road, London, SW16 2EA, United Kingdom
✆ (020) 8677 4412/(07860) 920769
✉ michael@mharding.com
🖥 www.mharding.com

Mike Cooper Photography Unit 19C, Barton Hill Trading Estate, Bristol, BS5 9BD, United Kingdom
✆ 0117 955 1345/(07860) 439820 📠 0117 955 1456
✉ mike@mike-cooper.com
🖥 www.mike-cooper.com

Mike Ellis Photography 65 Leonard Street, London, EC2A 4QS, United Kingdom
✆ (020) 7613 4313/(07860) 275287 📠 (020) 7739 5512
✉ mike@mikeellisphotography.com
🖥 www.mikeellisphotography.com

Mike Prior Photography 7 The Old Laundry, Hayden Way, London, SW11 1YF, United Kingdom
✆ (020) 7207 1964/(07721) 646464 📠 (020) 7207 1965
✉ info@mikeprior.com
🖥 www.mikeprior.com

Neill Menneer Belgrave Lodge, Upper Camden Place, Bath, Somerset, BA1 5JA, United Kingdom
✆ (01225) 483151/(07970) 235052 📠 (01225) 446394
✉ ncm@ktwo.co.uk
🖥 www.neillmenneer.com

Peter Beavis 54 Fairlawn Grove, London, W4 5EH, United Kingdom
✆ (07860) 758861
✉ peter@peterbeavis.com
🖥 www.peterbeavis.com

Peter Mason 10 Cranleigh Mews, London, SW11 2QL, United Kingdom
✆ **(07774) 496414**
✉ **peter@petermason.biz**
🖥 **www.petermason.biz**
See ad in showcase

Phil Ashley 3 Dee Road, Richmond, Surrey, TW9 2JN, United Kingdom
✆ (020) 8332 7707/(07976) 887879 ✆ (020) 8332 1932
✉ phil@philashley.com
🖥 www.philashley.com

Piers Golden Whitehouse, 4 Haybridge House, London, E5 9NB, United Kingdom
✆ **(020) 8442 4240/(07958) 533510** ✆ **(020) 8442 4240**
✉ piers@goldenphoto.com
🖥 **www.goldenphoto.com**
See ad in showcase

Richard Booth The Old Kiln, Watts Gallery, Guildford, Surrey, GU3 1DQ, United Kingdom
✆ (01483) 812007/(07866) 767067 ✆ (01483) 810093
✉ richard@rbphusion.com
🖥 www.richardbooth.co.uk

Richard Bradbury 72 Thornton Avenue, London, W4 1QQ, United Kingdom
✆ **(07768) 352100**
✉ **info@rbradbury.com**
🖥 **www.rbradbury.com**
See ad in showcase

Richard Lewisohn Photography 15 Moorhouse Road, London, W2 5DH, United Kingdom
✆ (07956) 395901/ ✆ (020) 7243 4689
✉ richard@lewisohn.co.uk
🖥 www.lewisohn.co.uk

Richard Pentin Photography 170 Trinity Road, London, SW17 7HT, United Kingdom
✆ (07796) 265210
✉ richardpentin@yahoo.co.uk
🖥 www.richardpentinphotography.com

Robert Burton 64 Stevenage Road, Hitchin, Herts, SG4 9DR,
✆ 07834 606576
✉ bert@robertburton.co.uk
🖥 www.robertburton.co.uk

Romilly Lockyer 55 Effingham Road, Long Ditton, Surbiton, Surrey, KT6 5LA, United Kingdom
✆ (020) 8339 0896/(07770) 275524 ✆ (020) 8339 0896
✉ romilly@lineone.net
🖥 www.Romilly.com

Stephanie Rushton 16 Reservoir Studios, 547 Cable Street, London, E1W 3EW, United Kingdom
✆ (020) 7780 9838/(07798) 862243 ✆ (020) 7780 9838
✉ info@stephanierushton.com
🖥 www.stephanierushton.com

Stephen Marshall Johnston 75 Haverhill Road, London, SW12 0HE, United Kingdom
✆ (07775) 991834
✉ steve@stevejohnstonphoto.com
🖥 www.stevejohnstonphoto.com

Sue Baker, Rickmansworth, Hertfordshire, WD3 5YT, United Kingdom
✆ (01923) 282549/07850 667877
✉ suebaker05@yahoo.co.uk
🖥 www.suebaker05.com

Tim O'Leary 63a Montagu Square, London, W1H 2LU, United Kingdom
✆ (020) 7402 2924/(07968) 529205
✉ tim@timoleary.co.uk
🖥 www.timoleary.co.uk

Tony Harris 183 Dawes Road, London, SW6 7QP, United Kingdom
✆ (020) 7385 8158/(07836) 201229 ✆ (020) 7385 8159
✉ tony@tonyhphoto.com
🖥 www.tonyhphoto.com

Tony Latham Studio Five. The Hanger, Perseverance Works, 38 Kingsland Road, London, E2 8DA, United Kingdom
✆ (020) 7739 6253/(07831) 473954 ✆ (020) 7739 0443
✉ tony.latham@btconnect.com
🖥 www.tonylatham.com

Victoria Blackie Ltd 1b Nightingale Road, Wendover, Aylesbury, Buckinghamshire, HP22 6JX, United Kingdom
✆ (07831) 423177
✉ vicblack@tinyworld.co.uk
🖥 www.victoriablackie.co.uk

Wonderfuel 118 Hatherley Gardens, London, E6 3HQ, United Kingdom
✆ 020 8548 1358
✉ info@wonderfuel.co.uk
🖥 www.wonderfuel.co.uk

PORTRAIT

Albada Studios Unit 83, Portmanmoor Road Industrial Estate, Ocean Way, Cardiff, CF24 5HB,
✆ 02920 495123
✉ adrian@albada.co.uk
🖥 www.albada.co.uk

Amos Schliack Unit 8, 220 Kingsland Road, London, E2 8DF, United Kingdom
✆ (020) 7033 9972/(07906) 449 776
✉ amos@london.com
🖥 www.amosschliack.com

Ben Fisher Photography 45-46 Charlotte Road, London, EC2A 3PD, United Kingdom
✆ (020) 7613 1623/(07976) 659605 ✆ (020) 7613 1623
✉ contact@benfisherphotography.com
🖥 www.benfisherphotography.com

Ben Fitchett B/21 Phipp Street, London, EC2A 4NP, United Kingdom
✆ (07977) 490106/ ✆ (020) 7033 9446
✉ ben@parallax.fsnet.co.uk
🖥 www.benfitchett.com

Ben Mostyn Photography Farleigh, Orchard Lane, Old Boars Hill, Oxford, Oxfordshire, OX1 5JH,
✆ 01865 730138
✉ info@benmostyn.com
🖥 www.benmostyn.com

Charlotte Murphy 56 Romola Road, London, SE24 9AZ, United Kingdom
✆ (020) 8516 9048/(07774) 487 874

CRE8 Photography Ltd 2nd Floor, 145-157 St. John Street, London, EC1V 4PY, United Kingdom
✆ (07909) 975144
✉ info@cre8photo.com
🖥 www.cre8photo.com

David Rees Photography 33 Kirkwood Road, London, SE15 3XT, United Kingdom
✆ (020) 7639 3896/(07889) 379946 ✆ (020) 7639 3896
✉ mail@davidreesphotography.com
🖥 www.davidreesphotography.com

Dominic Harris@Martin Roper Photographer's Agent 158a Chamberlayne Road, London, NW10 3JS, United Kingdom
✆ (020) 8964 4780/(0779) 9410942
✉ martin.roper@btinternet.com
🖥 www.martinroper.com

Focusing Ltd Unit 6, New Milton Bus. Center, Wick Drive, New Milton, Hampshire, BH25 6RQ,
✆ 01425 617800
✉ info@focusingltd.com
🖥 www.focusingltd.com

James King Photographer Unit 19c Barton Hill trad est, Maze Street, Bristol, BS5 9BD,
✆ 1179350839
✉ james@jameskingphotographer.co.uk
🖥 www.jameskingphotographer.co.uk

Joaquim Barreto 110 Blackheath Road, Greenwich, London, SE10 8DA, United Kingdom
✆ (020) 7760 6646/(07910) 539957
✉ joaquim@ocular-group.com
🖥 www.joaquimbarreto.com

Joe Doyle Photography 4 Victoria Drive, Eastbourne, East Sussex, BN20 8JS, United Kingdom
✆ (01323) 737735

Jouk Oosterhof@edsonwilliams photography consultancy 52 Brushfield Street, London, E1 6AJ, United Kingdom
✆ (020) 7375 2077/(07867) 517777 ✆ (020) 7375 3077
✉ info@edsonwilliams.com
🖥 www.edsonwilliams.com

Julian Calder 7 Nepean Street, London, SW15 5DW, United Kingdom
✆ (020) 8780 5352/ ✆ (020) 8780 2156
✉ juliancalder@btinternet.com
🖥 www.juliancalder.com

Mark Turnbull Photography Studio, The Old Trueman Brewery, 91 Brick Lane, London, E1 6QL, United Kingdom
✆ (01892) 616154/(07973) 640835
✉ photography@mark-turnbull.co.uk
🖥 www.mark-turnbull.co.uk

Martin Roper Photographer's Agent 158a Chamberlayne Road, London, NW10 3JS, United Kingdom
✆ (020) 8964 4780/(0779) 9410942
✉ martin.roper@btinternet.com
🖥 www.martinroper.com

Michael Harding Photography 85 Stanthorpe Road, London, SW16 2EA, United Kingdom
✆ (020) 8677 4412/(07860) 920769
✉ michael@mharding.com
🖥 www.mharding.com

Mike Ellis Photography 65 Leonard Street, London, EC2A 4QS, United Kingdom
✆ (020) 7613 4313/(07860) 275287 ✆ (020) 7739 5512
✉ mike@mikeellisphotography.com
🖥 www.mikeellisphotography.com

Peter Kidd 22 Vanbrugh Hill, London, SE3 7UF, United Kingdom
✆ (07973) 315122
✉ p.kidd7@ntlworld.com

Ray Massey Camden Park Studios, The Church Hall, Camden Park Road, London, NW1 9AY, United Kingdom
✆ (020) 7267 9550/(07831) 606342 ✆ (020) 7267 5612
✉ ray@raymassey.com
🖥 www.raymassey.com

Richard Bradbury 72 Thornton Avenue, London, W4 1QQ, United Kingdom
✆ (07768) 352100
✉ info@rbradbury.com
🖥 www.rbradbury.com

Richard Lewisohn Photography 15 Moorhouse Road, London, W2 5DH, United Kingdom
✆ (07956) 395901/ ✆ (020) 7243 4689
✉ richard@lewisohn.co.uk
🖥 www.lewisohn.co.uk

Richard Pullar Unit 44, Kingsway Place, Sans Walk, London, EC1R 0LU, United Kingdom
✆ (020) 7490 2188/ ✆ (020) 7251 6255
✉ richard@richardpullar.com
🖥 www.richardpullar.com

Robert Burton 64 Stevenage Road, Hitchin, Herts, SG4 9DR,
✆ 07834 606576
✉ bert@robertburton.co.uk
🖥 www.robertburton.co.uk

Rupert Marlow Photography Littleworth Corner, Lower Littleworth, Amberley, Stroud, Gloucestershire, GL5 5AW, United Kingdom
✆ (07887) 943590
✉ rupert@rupertmarlow.com
🖥 www.rupertmarlow.com

Stephanie Rushton 16 Reservoir Studios, 547 Cable Street, London, E1W 3EW, United Kingdom
✆ (020) 7780 9838/(07798) 862243 ✆ (020) 7780 9838
✉ info@stephanierushton.com
🖥 www.stephanierushton.com

Stephen Marshall Johnston 75 Haverhill Road, London, SW12 0HE, United Kingdom
✆ (07775) 991834
✉ steve@stevejohnstonphoto.com
🖥 www.stevejohnstonphoto.com

StudioTime Photography Studio 25, 10 Martello St, London Fields, London, E8 3PE,
✆ 020 7241 2816
✉ info@studiotime.org
🖥 www.studiotimeadvertising.com

Tessa Newmark 23 Streatham Common South, London, SW16 3BX, United Kingdom
✆ (07973) 241227
✉ tessa@tessanewmark.co.uk
🖥 www.tessanewmark.co.uk

Tony Latham Studio Five. The Hanger, Perseverance Works, 38 Kingsland Road, London, E2 8DA, United Kingdom
✆ (020) 7739 6253/(07831) 473954 ✆ (020) 7739 0443
✉ tony.latham@btconnect.com
🖥 www.tonylatham.com

Victoria Blackie Ltd 1b Nightingale Road, Wendover, Aylesbury, Buckinghamshire, HP22 6JX, United Kingdom
✆ (07831) 423177
✉ vicblack@tinyworld.co.uk
🖥 www.victoriablackie.co.uk

Wildpear Studio 70 Hill Street, Richmond, Surrey, TW9 1TW, United Kingdom
✆ (020) 8948 2300
✉ studio@wildpear.com
🖥 www.wildpear.com

Wonderfuel 118 Hatherley Gardens, London, E6 3HQ, United Kingdom
- 020 8548 1358
- info@wonderfuel.co.uk
- www.wonderfuel.co.uk

REPORTAGE

Adrian Houston Amberley Studio, 32A Goldney Road, London, W9 2AX, United Kingdom
- (020) 7289 1419/(07850) 475105 / (020) 7289 1419
- adrian@adrianhouston.co.uk
- www.adrianhouston.co.uk

Amos Schliack Unit 8, 220 Kingsland Road, London, E2 8DF, United Kingdom
- (020) 7033 9972/(07906) 449 776
- amos@london.com
- www.amosschliack.com

Andrew Wiard 15 Pembroke Road, London, N10 2HR, United Kingdom
- (07973) 219201
- andrew@reportphotos.com
- www.wiard.co.uk

CRE8 Photography Ltd 2nd Floor, 145-157 St. John Street, London, EC1V 4PY, United Kingdom
- (07909) 975144
- info@cre8photo.com
- www.cre8photo.com

David Rees Photography 33 Kirkwood Road, London, SE15 3XT, United Kingdom
- (020) 7639 3896/(07889) 379946 / (020) 7639 3896
- mail@davidreesphotography.com
- www.davidreesphotography.com

James King Photographer Unit 19c Barton Hill trad est, Maze Street, Bristol, BS5 9BD,
- 1179350839
- james@jameskingphotographer.co.uk
- www.jameskingphotographer.co.uk

Julian Calder 7 Nepean Street, London, SW15 5DW, United Kingdom
- (020) 8780 5352/ (020) 8780 2156
- juliancalder@btinternet.com
- www.juliancalder.com

Marcus Lyon The Glassworks, 1C Montford Place, London, SE11 5DE, United Kingdom
- (020) 7735 9933/(07831) 591959 / (020) 7735 9273
- ml@theglassworks.co.uk
- www.marcuslyon.com

Mike Ellis Photography 65 Leonard Street, London, EC2A 4QS, United Kingdom
- (020) 7613 4313/(07860) 275287 / (020) 7739 5512
- mike@mikeellisphotography.com
- www.mikeellisphotography.com

Ray Massey Camden Park Studios, The Church Hall, Camden Park Road, London, NW1 9AY, United Kingdom
- (020) 7267 9550/(07831) 606342 / (020) 7267 5612
- ray@raymassey.com
- www.raymassey.com

Richard Lewisohn Photography 15 Moorhouse Road, London, W2 5DH, United Kingdom
- (07956) 395901/ (020) 7243 4689
- richard@lewisohn.co.uk
- www.lewisohn.co.uk

Richard Pentin Photography 170 Trinity Road, London, SW17 7HT, United Kingdom
- (07796) 265210
- richardpentin@yahoo.co.uk
- www.richardpentinphotography.com

Wonderfuel 118 Hatherley Gardens, London, E6 3HQ, United Kingdom
- 020 8548 1358
- info@wonderfuel.co.uk
- www.wonderfuel.co.uk

ROOM SETS

Basement Photographic Unit 22, Soho Mills, Wooburn Green, High Wycombe, Buckinghamshire, HP10 0PF, United Kingdom
- (01628) 529900/ (01628) 851039
- studio@basementphoto.com
- www.basementphoto.com

Erwin Olaf Ijselstraat 26-28, Amsterdam, 1078 CJ, Netherlands
- 20 692 3438/ 20 694 1291
- info@erwinolaf.com
- www.erwinolaf.com

Gary Ombler 10 Swan Court, Oxfordshire, OX28 6EA,
- 1993771468
- gary@garyombler.com
- www.garyombler.com

Oliver Beamish 49 Dorien Road, London, SW20 8EL, United Kingdom
- (07973) 354259
- oliver@beamishcreative.com
- www.beamishcreative.com

Packshot Company Ltd 43 Carol Street, Camden Town, London, NW1 0HT, United Kingdom
- (020) 7267 0700/ (020) 7267 7721
- lee@packshot.com
- www.packshot.com

Richard Bradbury 72 Thornton Avenue, London, W4 1QQ, United Kingdom
- (07768) 352100
- info@rbradbury.com
- www.rbradbury.com

Trevor Richards 40 Kings Hall Road, Beckenham, Kent, BR3 1LS, United Kingdom
- (020) 8249 3862/ (020) 8249 0583
- trphoto@dircon.co.uk
- www.trphoto.dircon.co.uk

STILL LIFE

Adam Dawe Hangar 9, Perserverance Works, 38 Kingsland Road, London, E2 8DD, United Kingdom
- (020) 7613 3262/ (020) 7613 2152
- mail@adamdawe.com
- www.adamdawe.com

Adam Tolner 10A Printing House Yard, Hackney Road, London, E2 7PR, United Kingdom
- (020) 7739 6329/ (020) 7739 6213
- at@adamtolner.com
- www.adamtolner.com

Agent Pandora 12 Stonells Road, London, SW11 6HQ, United Kingdom
- (07966) 181825
- pandora@agentpandora.com
- www.agentpandora.com

Angela Woods 4 The Carlton Tavern, 73 Grafton Road, London, NW5 4BB, United Kingdom
- (020) 7284 3417/(07850) 263077 / (020) 7482 2466
- angela@angelawoods.com
- www.angelawoods.com

Anthony Lanneretonne Photographer 34, bd de l'hopital, Nice, Paris, France, 75005,
- +33 (0) 6 60 26 82 79
- contact@anthonylanneretonne.com
- www.anthonylanneretonne.com

Axel Michel 44 Oakington Road, London, W9 2DH, United Kingdom
- (020) 7286 4681/ (020) 7286 4681
- axelm@btinternet.com
- www.axelmichel.com

Basement Photographic Unit 22, Soho Mills, Wooburn Green, High Wycombe, Buckinghamshire, HP10 0PF, United Kingdom
- (01628) 529900/ (01628) 851039
- studio@basementphoto.com
- www.basementphoto.com

Bay Hippisley@Martin Roper Photographer's Agent 158a Chamberlayne Road, London, NW10 3JS, United Kingdom
- (020) 8964 4780/(0779) 9410942
- martin.roper@btinternet.com
- www.martinroper.com

Ben Fitchett B/21 Phipp Street, London, EC2A 4NP, United Kingdom
- (07977) 490106/ (020) 7033 9446
- ben@parallax.fsnet.co.uk
- www.benfitchett.com

Bruce Anderson Photography 126 Shoreditch High Street, London, E1 6JE, United Kingdom
- (020) 7729 2299/(07930) 406668
- bruce@bruceanderson.co.uk
- www.bruceanderson.co.uk

Carol Sharp 71 Leonard Street, London, EC2A 4QU, United Kingdom
- (020) 7729 8040/ (020) 7729 7909
- carol@carolsharp.co.uk
- www.carolsharp.co.uk

Colin Bell Photography Unit E, Purdon Street, Glasgow, G11 6AF, United Kingdom
- 0141-334 8008/(07787) 573155 / 0141-334 8008
- colin@colinbellphotography.com
- www.colinbellphotography.com

Colin Campbell 23-28 Penn Street, London, N1 5DL, United Kingdom
- (020) 7729 3740/ (020) 7729 9410
- colin.studio@virgin.net
- www.colincampbell-photo.com

Dave Brown 55 Farringdon Road, London, EC1M 3JB, United Kingdom
- (020) 7404 9888/ (020) 7404 9800
- dave@davebrownstudio.co.uk
- www.davebrownstudio.co.uk

Esser Assocs 2nd Floor North, 6 Buckingham Street, London, WC2N 6BU, United Kingdom
- (020) 7976 2915/(07778) 149149 / (01372) 464326
- rob.esser@virgin.net
- www.davidesser.com

David Parfitt Photography 3 Lever Street, London, EC1V 3QU, United Kingdom
- (020) 7251 1427/ (020) 7608 0628
- david@davidparfitt.com
- www.davidparfitt.com

Edward Edwards Jewellery Photographer 16 The Vale, London, W3 7SB, United Kingdom
- (020) 8749 8887/ (020) 8749 8884
- studio@edwardsphotography.co.uk
- www.edwardsphotography.co.uk

Inspired Reflection 28 Dayton Grove, Peckham, London, SE15 2NX, United Kingdom
- (0870) 9193587/(07040) 402770 / (0870) 9193588
- deborah@inspiredreflection.com
- www.inspiredreflection.com

James King Photographer Unit 19c Barton Hill trad est, Maze Street, Bristol, BS5 9BD,
- 1179350839
- james@jameskingphotographer.co.uk
- www.jameskingphotographer.co.uk

Jonathan Green Unit 12, Parsons Green Depot, 33-39 Parsons Green Lane, London, SW6 4HH, United Kingdom
- /(07831) 220166
- jon@jgreenphotography.co.uk
- www.jgreenphotography.co.uk

Jonathan Pollock Photographer Unit 216 The Business Village, 3-9 Broomhill Road, London, SW18 4JQ, United Kingdom
- (020) 8877 9493/ (020) 8877 9393
- jonathan@jonathanpollock.com
- www.jonathanpollock.com

Kai Schwabe Fotografie Ander Weide 50, Bremen, D-28195, Germany
- 00 49 42 144 1520/ 00 49 42 149 88359
- info@kaischwabe.de
- www.kaischwabe.de

Laurence Dutton Photography Ltd 57 Farringdon Road, London, EC1M 3JB, United Kingdom
- (020) 7813 2099/ (020) 7242 6447
- lol@laurence-dutton.co.uk
- www.laurence-dutton.com

Ludwig Haskins Flat 2, 52 St. James Road, Sutton, Surrey, SM1 2TS, United Kingdom
- (020) 8404 2337/ (020) 8404 2338
- ludwighaskins@yahoo.com
- www.ludwig-haskins.com

Martin Wonnacott@edsonwilliams photography consultancy 52 Brushfield Street, London, E1 6AJ, United Kingdom
- (020) 7375 2077/(07867) 517777 / (020) 7375 3077
- info@edsonwilliams.com
- www.edsonwilliams.com

Oliver Beamish 49 Dorien Road, London, SW20 8EL, United Kingdom
- (07973) 354259
- oliver@beamishcreative.com
- www.beamishcreative.com

Packshot Company Ltd 43 Carol Street, Camden Town, London, NW1 0HT, United Kingdom
✆ (020) 7267 0700/✆ (020) 7267 7721
✉ lee@packshot.com
🖥 www.packshot.com

Packshot Factory 39-41 New Oxford Street, London, WC1A 1BN, United Kingdom
✆ (020) 7379 3080/✆ (020) 7240 9568
✉ martin@packshotfactory.co.uk
🖥 www.packshotfactory.co.uk

Patrick Llewelyn-Davies 1 Dallington Street, London, EC1V 0BH, United Kingdom
✆ (020) 7253 2838/(07866) 622478
✉ patrick@llewelyn-davies.com
🖥 www.llewelyn-davies.com/indexchb.html

Paul Hartley 23 Hurlingham Studios, Ranelagh Gardens, London, SW6 3PA, United Kingdom
✆ (020) 7731 0244/✆ (020) 7384 2567
✉ info@hartleystudios.com
🖥 www.hartleystudios.com

Paul Webster 11 Parke Road, London, SW13 9NF, United Kingdom
✆ (020) 8748 5786/(07860) 247562/✆ (020) 8748 5786
✉ info@paulsnap.com
🖥 www.paulsnap.com

Pearson Lyle Management 3rd Floor, 40 Bowling Green Lane, London, EC1R 0NE, United Kingdom
✆ (020) 7415 7061/✆ (020) 7415 7059
✉ contact@pearsonlyle.co.uk
🖥 www.pearsonlyle.co.uk

Peter Kidd 22 Vanbrugh Hill, London, SE3 7UF, United Kingdom
✆ (07973) 315122
✉ p.kidd7@ntlworld.com

Phil Ashley 3 Dee Road, Richmond, Surrey, TW9 2JN, United Kingdom
✆ (020) 8332 7707/(07976) 887879/✆ (020) 8332 1932
✉ phil@philashley.com
🖥 www.philashley.com

Ray Massey Camden Park Studios, The Church Hall, Camden Park Road, London, NW1 9AY, United Kingdom
✆ (020) 7267 9550/(07831) 606342/✆ (020) 7267 5612
✉ ray@raymassey.com
🖥 www.raymassey.com

Richard Pullar Unit 44, Kingsway Place, Sans Walk, London, EC1R 0LU, United Kingdom
✆ (020) 7490 2188/✆ (020) 7251 6255
✉ richard@richardpullar.com
🖥 www.richardpullar.com

Sara Morris 23-28 Penn Street, London, N1 5DL, United Kingdom
✆ (020) 7729 3740/✆ (020) 7729 9410
✉ sara.studio@virgin.net
🖥 www.saramorris.co.uk

Shoot The Moon Photography Concept House, Naval Street, Manchester, M4 6AX, United Kingdom
✆ 0161-205 7417/✆ 0161-205 8623
✉ elaine@shoot-the-moon.co.uk
🖥 www.stmphotography.co.uk

Stephen Marshall Johnston 75 Haverhill Road, London, SW12 0HE, United Kingdom
✆ (07775) 991834
✉ steve@stevejohnstonphoto.com
🖥 www.stevejohnstonphoto.com

Terry Payne Packshot & Food Photographer First Floor, Building D, The Chocolate Factory, Clarendon Road, London, N22 6XJ,
✆ 020 8889 6609
✉ terry.payne1@ntlworld.com
🖥 www.terrypaynephotog.co.uk

Tim Brightmore 16 York Central, 70 York Way, London, N1 9AG, United Kingdom
✆ (020) 7278 4747/(07850) 914707/✆ (020) 7278 4775
✉ mail@timbrightmore.co.uk
🖥 www.timbrightmore.co.uk

Wonderfuel 118 Hatherley Gardens, London, E6 3HQ, United Kingdom
✆ 020 8548 1358
✉ info@wonderfuel.co.uk
🖥 www.wonderfuel.co.uk

Yara Gremoli Photographers Agent Studio 210, Canalot Studios, 222 Kensal Road, London, W10 5BN, United Kingdom
✆ (0870) 8501209/(07880) 627413/✆ (0870) 8501209
✉ yara@sbmanagement.org
🖥 www.yaragremoli.com

TRANSPORT

Car Photo Library 28 Fernside Road, Talbot Park, Bournemouth, BH9 2LB, United Kingdom
✆ (01202) 528849/(07785) 537928
✉ davidkimber@carphoto.co.uk
🖥 www.carphoto.co.uk

James King Photographer Unit 19c Barton Hill trad est, Maze Street, Bristol, BS5 9BD,
✆ 1179350839
✉ james@jameskingphotographer.co.uk
🖥 www.jameskingphotographer.co.uk

Leon Pearce Millyard Studios, Millyard, Guildford Street, Luton, LU1 2NR, United Kingdom
✆ (01582) 404888/✆ (01582) 455089
✉ leon@leonpearce.com
🖥 www.leonpearce.com

Wonderfuel 118 Hatherley Gardens, London, E6 3HQ, United Kingdom
✆ 020 8548 1358
✉ info@wonderfuel.co.uk
🖥 www.wonderfuel.co.uk

TRAVEL

Ben Fisher Photography 45-46 Charlotte Road, London, EC2A 3PD, United Kingdom
✆ (020) 7613 1623/(07976) 659605/✆ (020) 7613 1623
✉ contact@benfisherphotography.com
🖥 www.benfisherphotography.com

Clive Sawyer 6 Linnet Lane, Camber Sands, East Sussex, TN31 7SL, United Kingdom
✆ (01797) 222213/(07738) 715354
✉ clive@clivephotographer.com
🖥 www.clivephotographer.com

Dominic Harris@Martin Roper Photographer's Agent 158a Chamberlayne Road, London, NW10 3JS, United Kingdom
✆ (020) 8964 4780/(0779) 9410942
✉ martin.roper@btinternet.com
🖥 www.martinroper.com

James King Photographer Unit 19c Barton Hill trad est, Maze Street, Bristol, BS5 9BD,
✆ 1179350839
✉ james@jameskingphotographer.co.uk
🖥 www.jameskingphotographer.co.uk

Martin Roper Photographer's Agent 158a Chamberlayne Road, London, NW10 3JS, United Kingdom
✆ (020) 8964 4780/(0779) 9410942
✉ martin.roper@btinternet.com
🖥 www.martinroper.com

Piers Golden Whitehouse, 4 Haybridge House, London, E5 9NB, United Kingdom
✆ (020) 8442 4240/(07958) 533510/✆ (020) 8442 4240
✉ piers@goldenphoto.com
🖥 www.goldenphoto.com

Richard Pentin Photography 170 Trinity Road, London, SW17 7HT, United Kingdom
✆ (07796) 265210
✉ richardpentin@yahoo.co.uk
🖥 www.richardpentinphotography.com

Tony Harris 183 Dawes Road, London, SW6 7QP, United Kingdom
✆ (020) 7385 8158/(07836) 201229/✆ (020) 7385 8159
✉ tony@tonyhphoto.com
🖥 www.tonyhphoto.com

Wonderfuel 118 Hatherley Gardens, London, E6 3HQ, United Kingdom
✆ 020 8548 1358
✉ info@wonderfuel.co.uk
🖥 www.wonderfuel.co.uk

UNDERWATER

James King Photographer Unit 19c Barton Hill trad est, Maze Street, Bristol, BS5 9BD,
✆ 1179350839
✉ james@jameskingphotographer.co.uk
🖥 www.jameskingphotographer.co.uk

Ray Massey Camden Park Studios, The Church Hall, Camden Park Road, London, NW1 9AY, United Kingdom
✆ (020) 7267 9550/(07831) 606342/✆ (020) 7267 5612
✉ ray@raymassey.com
🖥 www.raymassey.com

Romilly Lockyer 55 Effingham Road, Long Ditton, Surbiton, Surrey, KT6 5LA, United Kingdom
✆ (020) 8339 0896/(07770) 275524/✆ (020) 8339 0896
✉ romilly@lineone.net
🖥 www.Romilly.com

Zac Macaulay Photography 20 Leigh Road, Cobham, Surrey, KT11 2LD, United Kingdom
✆ (020) 8941 1238/(07990) 592000
✉ zac@zacmacaulay.com
🖥 www.zacmacaulay.com

VEHICLES

James King Photographer Unit 19c Barton Hill trad est, Maze Street, Bristol, BS5 9BD,
✆ 1179350839
✉ james@jameskingphotographer.co.uk
🖥 www.jameskingphotographer.co.uk

James King Photographer Unit 19c Barton Hill trad est, Maze Street, Bristol, BS5 9BD,
✆ 1179350839
✉ james@jameskingphotographer.co.uk
🖥 www.jameskingphotographer.co.uk

Leon Pearce Millyard Studios, Millyard, Guildford Street, Luton, LU1 2NR, United Kingdom
✆ (01582) 404888/✆ (01582) 455089
✉ leon@leonpearce.com
🖥 www.leonpearce.com

Yara Gremoli Photographers Agent Studio 210, Canalot Studios, 222 Kensal Road, London, W10 5BN, United Kingdom
✆ (0870) 8501209/(07880) 627413/✆ (0870) 8501209
✉ yara@sbmanagement.org
🖥 www.yaragremoli.com

SUBSCRIBE TO CREATIVE REVIEW TODAY FOR JUST £64

BY PHONE
0207 292 3703
ONLINE
CREATIVEREVIEW.CO.UK/SUBSCRIBE.PHP

PEEPSHOW.ORG.UK

Photographic Services

mono: (gr) *the only one*

Oops! - here's our real logo

see it again on our DPS

HOLBORN
STUDIOS LTD

**HOLBORN
STUDIOS LTD**

polis: (gr) *in town*

Turn 5 pages for more details

Advertising showcase:
Photographic services
02.

Four large daylight hire studios, digital capture
packages, lighting hire, set building, parking
and catering in London's hippest quarter.
2 Dunston Street, London E8 4EB
+44 (0)20 7923 9430

www.streetstudios.co.uk

street studios

HOLBORN
STUDIOS LTD

49-50 Eagle Wharf Road
London N1 7ED
+44 (0) 20 7490 4099
www.holbornstudios.com

Discover London's Largest Studios

15 stages | 20 acres

SUPPORTED BY

LONDON DEVELOPMENT AGENCY

WORKING FOR THE MAYOR OF LONDON

020 7363 3336 | info@3mills.com | www.3mills.com

Photography courtesy of Steve Harries. www.eastphotographic.com

SNAP

STUDIO HIRE__FULL PRODUCTION__LIGHTING/DIGITAL RENTAL__LOCATION LIBRARY

Wimbourne House
151-155 New North Road
London N1 6TA

t +44.207.684.7555
f +44.207.684.7556
e richard@snap-pro.com
www.snap-pro.com

drive-in coved studios | **imaging services** | **catering** | **large car park** | **equipment hire**

park
royal
studios

studio **3**	80' x 47' x 20'
studio **4**	80' x 47' x 20'
studio **5**	110' x 65' x 20'
studio **6**	73' x 41' x 23'
studio **A**	30' x 18' x 13'
studio **B**	54' x 23' x 10'

Park Royal Studios, 1 Barretts Green Road, London, NW10 7AE
e **info@parkroyalstudios.com**   w **www.parkroyalstudios.com**

DON'T SHOOT!
UNTIL YOU'VE SEEN OUR LOCATIONS

We are the photographers' first choice, so if you're looking for somewhere to shoot, **visit the ultimate location library**

www.amazingspace.co.uk

or **call 020 7251 6661**

We've been doing this for 15 years so we must be doing something right!

the ultimate location library
amazing
space

thislittlefish
creating a big splash

TECHNICAL DEPT
HDR PHOTOGRAPHY
BACKPLATE CAPTURE
TECHNICAL SUPERVISION

We can help you get a
360° understanding of
the potential for including
CG in your workflow. Our
skilled technicians can take
to the road with your own
photographers, providing
matched and accurate
High Dynamic Range
Images (HDRI) to light
up your projects.

soho : london

t : +44 (0)20 7534 0810

e : info@thislittlefish.com

www.thislittlefish.com

CGI DEPT
3D MODELLING
RENDERING
3D LIGHTING

We're not all about cars
and packshots — from
basic scanning to creating
CAD data, modelling and
real-time rendering we
make projects that break
barriers. Our skills in
combining CG, HDRI and
stunning backplates open
up the creative possibilities
for your ideas to flourish.

Picture Perfection

SADDINGTONBAYNES.COM
RETOUCHING | CGI

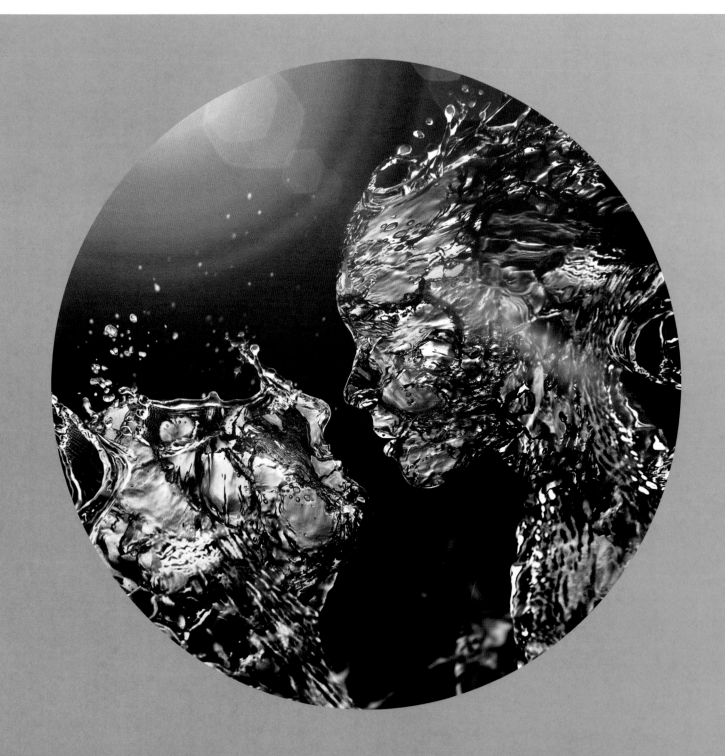

ActTwo.biz

london 020 7863 9570
new york 212 226 8753

Um-cgi.com

london 020 7863 9570
new york 212 226 8753

thislittlefish
creating a big splash

REPROGRAPHICS DEPT
COLOUR MANAGMENT
CERTIFIED PROOFS
QUALITY ASSURED

We make sure that all the
hard work and effort you
put in on the creative isn't
wasted on a bad print job,
with a fully managed ICC
workflow and certified
contract proofs.

RETOUCHING DEPT
HDRI/BACKPLATE PREP
COMPOSITING
CREATIVE RETOUCHING

With a vast amount of
experience working on
automotive and high-end
advertising projects, we
integrate with CG and
rendering processes to
achieve photoreal results.

soho : london

t : +44 (0)20 7534 0810

e : info@thislittlefish.com

www.thislittlefish.com

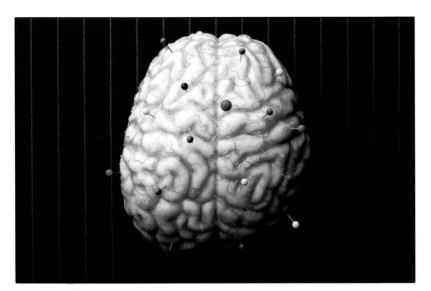

The whole Nation's gone Crunchy Nuts.

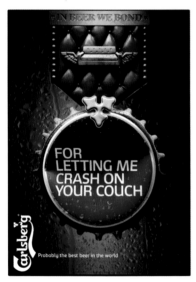

IN BEER WE BOND

FOR LETTING ME CRASH ON YOUR COUCH

Carlsberg

Probably the best beer in the world

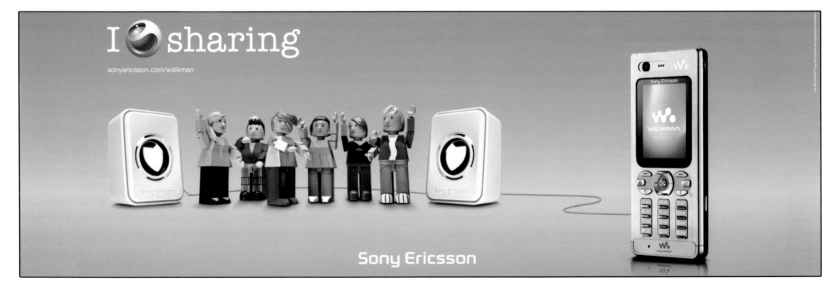

I ♥ sharing

sonyericsson.com/walkman

Sony Ericsson

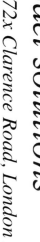

m del solutions

72x Clarence Road, London N22 8PW

info@modelsolutions.co.uk
www.modelsolutions.co.uk

020 8881 2333

tim weare & partners
creative modelmakers

t • 01580 860808

w • wearemodels.co.uk   e • tim@wearemodels.co.uk

ASSET MANAGEMENT SERVICES

Bold Endeavours Ltd 7 Manor Park, Staines, Middlesex, TW18 4XE,
☎ 01784 460 064
✉ derek@boldendeavours.com
🖥 www.big-easy-footage-library-software.co.uk

Daydream Linton House, 164-180 Union Street, London, SE1 0LH,
☎ +44 (0) 20 7096 1471/+44 (0) 20 7117 1636
✉ ralph@daydream.co.uk
🖥 www.daydream.co.uk

Junction Eleven Ltd Unit 4 Jugglers Close, Off Wildmere Road, Banbury, Oxfordshire, OX16 3JU, United Kingdom
☎ 0121-627 5012/ 0121-627 5038
✉ dan.burman@junctioneleven.com
🖥 www.junctioneleven.com

BUREAU SERVICES

Arhiann Direct 22 Saville Road Industrial Estate, Peterborough, PE3 7PR, United Kingdom
☎ (01733) 346739
✉ rob@arhiann.com
🖥 www.arhiann.com

Automatic Television Ltd 35 Bedfordbury, Covent Garden, London, WC2N 4DU, United Kingdom
☎ (020) 7240 2073/ (020) 7379 5210
✉ info@autotv.co.uk
🖥 www.autotv.co.uk

BlueChip Admin Services 30, Pennyacre Road, Teignmouth, Devon, TQ14 8LB, United Kingdom
☎ 01626 774143/ 01626 779059
✉ bluechipcasework@yahoo.co.uk
🖥 www.bluechipadmin.co.uk

Colourtech Unit 2 Stafford Close, Fairwood Industrial Estate, Ashford, Kent, TN23 4TT, United Kingdom
☎ 01233 642020/ 01233 632040
✉ Sarah@colourtechgroup.com
🖥 www.colourtechgroup.com

Creative Sponge 1 Netherconesford, King Street, Norwich, NR1 1PH, United Kingdom
☎ (01603) 622766/ (01603) 622347
✉ info@creativesponge.co.uk
🖥 www.creativesponge.co.uk

Dunns Professional Imaging Ltd Chester Road, Cradley Heath, West Midlands, B64 6AA, United Kingdom
☎ (01384) 564770/ (01384) 637165
✉ enquiries@dunns.co.uk
🖥 www.dunns.co.uk

Face Creative Services Ltd 2-10 Baron Street, London, N1 9LL, United Kingdom
☎ (020) 7713 9777/ (020) 7713 9788
✉ colin.harding@facecreative.co.uk

Immediate Image The Church, 145F Crouch Hill, London, N8 9QH, United Kingdom
☎ (020) 8442 7007/(07986) 532225 (0871) 5617761
✉ info@immediateimage.co.uk
🖥 www.immediateimage.co.uk

Jupiter Associates Ltd 21 The Waldrons, Croydon, CR0 4HB, United Kingdom
☎ (020) 8688 6133/ (020) 8688 0316
✉ studio@jupiterassociates.co.uk
🖥 www.jupiterassociates.co.uk

Mass Technology (UK) Ltd 36b Evington Road, Leicester, Leicestershire, LE2 1HG,
☎ 0116 25 44 171
✉ masstechnology@hotmail.com
🖥 www.masstechnologyonline.com

Newport/South East Wales Meeting & Conference Bureau Civic Centre, Godfrey Road, Newport, Gwent, NP20 4UR, United Kingdom
☎ (01633) 233327/ (01633) 232334
✉ lynne.richards@newport.gov.uk
🖥 www.newport.gov.uk

Phil Kashdan Design, Print & Display Ltd The Studio, 47 Povey Cross Road, Horley, Surrey, RH6 0AG,
☎ 01293 773129/ 01293 773129
✉ phil@pk-design.com

R I 3S 87A Upper Brockley Road, London, SE4 1TF, United Kingdom
☎ (07764) 794095
✉ rossiignatova@ri3s.co.uk
🖥 www.ri3s.co.uk

Rocket Group 3-5 Alexandra Terrace, Alexandra Road, Aldershot, Hampshire, GU11 3HU, United Kingdom
☎ (01252) 670600/ (01292) 670810
✉ sales@rocketuk.com
🖥 www.rocketuk.com

CREATIVE SERVICES

1minus1 93-94 West Street, Farnham, Surrey, GU9 7EB, United Kingdom
☎ (0870) 0501280
✉ signup@1minus1.com
🖥 www.1minus1.com

2wisted Ltd 117 Queens Court, Queens Way, London, W2 4QS, United Kingdom
☎ (07836) 315031
✉ info@2wisted.co.uk
🖥 www.2wisted.co.uk

4D Modelshop Ltd The Railway Arches, 120 Leman Street, London, E1 8EU, United Kingdom
☎ (020) 7264 1288/ (020) 7264 1299
✉ info@modelshop.co.uk
🖥 www.modelshop.co.uk

6th Degree Ltd Suite 6, Bank Chambers, 29 High Street, Ewell, Epsom, Surrey, KT17 1SB, United Kingdom
☎ 020 8786 3664/ 020 8786 3665
✉ idegree@6thdegreeltd.com
🖥 www.6thdegreeltd.com

72 Point PR Media Centre, Abbey Wood Business Park, Emma Chris Way, Filton, Bristol, BS34 7JU, United Kingdom
☎ 0117-906 6524/ 0117-906 6501
✉ jay@72point.com
🖥 www.72point.com

A Fish in Sea The Royal Victoria, Patriotic Building, Fitzhugh Grove, London, SW18 3SX, United Kingdom
☎ (0800) 0582450/(07789) 727325
✉ info@afishinsea.co.uk
🖥 www.afishinsea.co.uk

A Plus 2 Foresters Cottages, Barnet Wood Road, Bromley, BR2 8HJ, United Kingdom
☎ (020) 8462 4666/ (020) 8462 4666
✉ office@kidsplus.wanadoo.co.uk
🖥 www.kidsplusagency.co.uk

AFA Creations Ltd 4 Glastonbury Road, Sully, Penarth, South Glamorgan, CF64 5PZ, United Kingdom
☎ (029) 2053 0438
✉ john@afa-creations.com
🖥 www.afa-creations.com

Aid Visual 3 Goodrich Road, London, SE22 9EH, United Kingdom
☎ (020) 8693 9334
✉ laurence@visualaid.co.uk
🖥 www.visualaid.co.uk

Alandra Rosh Ltd 343a Green Lanes, London, N4 1DZ, United Kingdom
☎ (020) 8809 5598/ (020) 8809 5598
✉ info@alandrarosh.com
🖥 www.alandrarosh.com

Alice Palace 35 Briar Close, Evesham, Worcestershire, WR11 4JJ, United Kingdom
☎ (01386) 48363/(07990) 687670
✉ alice@alicepalace.co.uk
🖥 www.alicepalace.co.uk

Art Factory 6 Barns Street, Ayr, KA7 1XA, United Kingdom
☎ (01292) 886677/ (01292) 263127
✉ ask@art-factory.co.uk
🖥 www.art-factory.co.uk

ArtActive 3 Queens Road, Twickenham, Middlesex, TW1 4EZ,
☎ 7900242997
✉ info@leecampbell.co.uk
🖥 www.artactive.org.uk

Ascanio Creative PO Box 103, Briarcliff Manor, 10510, United States of America
☎ 00 1 914 806 0476
✉ info@ascaniocreative.com

ascent London Limited 49 Queen Victoria Street, London, EC4N 4SA, United Kingdom
☎ 020 76531913/ 020 76531914
✉ info@ascentlondon.co.uk
🖥 www.ascentlondon.co.uk

Assembly 3rd Floor, 38 Turner Street, London, E1 2AS, United Kingdom
☎ (020) 7265 8856
🖥 www.assemblylondon.com

B K E Business Services Ltd 77 Oxford Street, Pontycymmer, Bridgend, Bridgend, Mid Glamorgan, CF32 8DD, United Kingdom
☎ 01656 871605
✉ louise@bkebusiness.co.uk
🖥 www.bkebusinessservices.co.uk

B M N Ltd Unit 6 Windmill Business Village, Brooklands Close, Sunbury-on-Thames, Middlesex, TW11 8EB, United Kingdom
☎ (01932) 733100/ (01932) 733133
🖥 www.bmn-systems.com

B S I Group Ltd BSI House, 1 Blackbrook Park Avenue, Taunton, Somerset, TA1 2PF, United Kingdom
☎ (0870) 8304244/ (0870) 1278070
✉ reades@bsi.co.uk
🖥 www.bsi.co.uk

B2 1 The Mistal, Farnley, Otley, West Yorkshire, LS21 2QG, United Kingdom
☎ (01943) 468890/ (01943) 463526

Bell Pottinger North Fernbank House, Springwood Way, Tytherington Business Park, Macclesfield, Cheshire, SK10 2XA, United Kingdom
☎ (01625) 506444
✉ cwarham@bellpottingernorth.co.uk
🖥 www.bellpottingernorth.co.uk

Benson Cairns Communications 30B/9 Chambers St, Edinburgh, EH1 1HR, United Kingdom
☎ 0131 220 3785/ 0131 220 3786
✉ rachelle@bensoncairns.co.uk
🖥 www.bensoncairns.com

Better Start Here Ashford Road, Faversham, Kent, ME13 8XL, United Kingdom
☎ 0789 0617 747
✉ info@betterstarthere.co.uk
🖥 www.betterstarthere.co.uk

Bionicmedia Old Steyne House, 21-22 Old Steine, Brighton, BN1 1EL, United Kingdom
☎ (01273) 648384
✉ dhuff@bionicmedia.co.uk
🖥 www.bionicmedia.co.uk

Birbeck University of London Malet Street, Bloomsbury, London, WC1E 7HX, United Kingdom
☎ (020) 7079 0736
✉ m.hoek@bbk.ac.uk
🖥 www.bbk.ac.uk

Black & Ginger 14 Colquitt Street, Liverpool, L1 4DE, United Kingdom
☎ (07782) 201620
✉ alex@blackandginger.com
🖥 www.blackandginger.com

BlackOrange Ltd 5 Victoria Court, Bank Square, Morley, Leeds, LS27 9SE, United Kingdom
☎ (0845) 1307308
✉ info@blackorange.co.uk
🖥 www.blackorange.co.uk

Blitz the Net 10 Argyle Street, Bath, BA2 4BQ, United Kingdom
☎ (01225) 422333
✉ garry@blitzthenet.com
🖥 www.blitzthenet.com

Blood Group Illustrations 45 Queens Park Rise, Brighton, BN2 9ZF, United Kingdom
☎ (01273) 700540
✉ jackjackpatrick@gmail.com

Blue Gorilla Studios 353 Vosseller Avenue, Bound Brook, 8805, United States of America
☎ 00 1 732 302 9122
✉ bobtobey@bluegorilla.com
🖥 www.bluegorilla.com

Blue Skies Graphic Design Ltd 37 Oldfield Road, London Colney, St. Albans, Hertfordshire, AL2 1HZ, United Kingdom
☎ (01727) 822633
✉ peterch@blueskiesdes.plus.com

Blueberry Recruitment Ealing Studios, Ealing Green, London, W5 5EP, United Kingdom
☎ (0871) 8550086/(07961) 148767 (07092) 119411
✉ info@blueberryrecruitment.co.uk
🖥 www.blueberryrecruitment.co.uk

Blueskystudio Bluebell Cottage, Steeple Lane, St. Ives, Cornwall, TR26 2GY, United Kingdom
☎ (01736) 793740
✉ kerry@blueskystudio.co.uk
🖥 www.blueskystudio.co.uk

Bold Endeavours Ltd 7 Manor Park, Staines, Middlesex, TW18 4XE,
01784 460 064
derek@boldendeavours.com
www.big-easy-footage-library-software.co.uk

Border Line Arts Ltd 5 Dryden Street, London, WC2E 9NB, United Kingdom
(020) 7829 8413/ (020) 7836 1904
info@borderlinearts.co.uk
www.borderlinearts.co.uk

Brand Central 14 Seacourt Road, Oxford, OX2 9LD, United Kingdom
(01865) 422201/ (01865) 422382
info@brandcentralstation.co.uk
www.brandcentralstation.co.uk

Brand Puppy Union Chapel, Common Street, Ravenstone, Olney, Buckinghamshire, MK46 5AF, United Kingdom
(01908) 551692
rob.phillips@brandpuppy.co.uk
www.brandpuppy.co.uk

Breeze Communications 40 Whiteladies Road, Bristol, BS8 2LG, United Kingdom
(0117)-923 7822
info@breezecommunications.co.uk
www.breezecommunications.co.uk

Brenda May Ramsey 43 Beacontree Road, London, E11 3AX, United Kingdom
(020) 8530 7577
brenda@brendamayramsey.co.uk
www.brendamayramsey.co.uk

Brett Mead Flat 51, 41 Provost Street, London, N1 7NB, United Kingdom
(07784) 983782

Brever Web Design Edinburgh 60a Craigour Drive, Edinburgh, EH17 7NT, United Kingdom
(0845) 129 8534
info@breverwebdesign.com
www.breverwebdesign.com

Built from scratch design New Plot, 1-2 Ivy cottages, Chapmans Lane, St Pauls Cray, Orpington, Kent, BR5 3JA, United Kingdom
01689 897740/ 01689 897740
Info@builtfromscratch-design.co.uk
www.builtfromscratch-design.co.uk

C J H Productions 18 All Saints Road, Studio 14, London, W11 1HH, United Kingdom
(020) 7229 2488/ (020) 7229 2481
camilla@cjhproductions.com
www.cjhproductions.com

Calligraphy and Heraldic Art Studio 6C, Clapham North Art Centre, 26-32 Voltaire Road, London, SW4 6DH, United Kingdom
(020) 7720 8883
paulantonioscribe@yahoo.co.uk
www.paulantonioscribe.com

Camilla Johnson-Hill Studio 14, 18 All Saints Road, London, W11 1HH, United Kingdom
(020) 7229 2488/ (020) 7229 2481
camilla@cjhproductions.com
www.cjhproductions.com

Capital Calligraphy 65 Elmbridge Avenue, Surbiton, Surrey, KT5 9EZ, United Kingdom
(07961) 105151
brett@capitalcalligraphy.co.uk
capitalcalligraphy.co.uk

Carl Middleton 1 Chapel Close, Chapel Street, Braunton, Devon, EX33 1EA, United Kingdom
(07867) 768971
middleton@mail.com

Catwalk Creations 63, March Court, Warwick Drive, London, SW15 6LE, United Kingdom
(07834) 470117
nicola@catwalkcreations.com
www.catwalkcreations.com

Charles Ward Photography Farm Studios, London End, Earls Barton, Northampton, NN6 0EZ, United Kingdom
(01604) 812465/ (01604) 812778
craig@charlesward.com
www.charlesward.com

Charlyvia Cantave Corp 1067 New York Avenue, Brooklyn, United States of America
00 1 347 678 6543/ 00 1 718 940 0108
charlyviacantave@aol.com

Chris Colville-Walker 3 Hacon Square, Richmond Road, London, E8 3QR, United Kingdom
(07940) 725499
christopher@colville-walker.co.uk
www.colville-walker.co.uk

Christopher Radley 433 Liverpool Road, Islington, London, N7 8PR, United Kingdom
(020) 7609 2993
radders@radders.fsnet.co.uk

Cite - The Internet Agency 42 Duke Street, Leicester, LE1 6WA, United Kingdom
0116-254 9888
daf@cite.co.uk
www.cite.co.uk

Clever Ltd. Milldown, Kingston Road, Lewes, East Sussex, BN7 3NB, United Kingdom
(01273) 487744
mikeb@cleverworks.co.uk
www.cleverworks.co.uk

Conrad Davies Design The Mistal, 3 Farnley Park, Otley, West Yorkshire, LS21 2QF, United Kingdom
(01943) 850088
conrad@conraddavies.com
www.conraddavies.com

Consider Hyde Park House, 5 Manfred Road, Putney, London, SW15 2RS, United Kingdom
(0870) 4296209/ (0870) 4296208
info@considercreative.co.uk
www.considercreative.co.uk

Copywrite Corporation 12 The Inner Silk Mill, Malmesbury, Wiltshire, SN16 9LP, United Kingdom
(01666) 824130/ (01666) 825397
lee@faberfaber.com
www.faberfaber.com

Creative Artworker & Packaging Designer Flat 3, Europa House, 11 Marsham Way, Gerrards Cross, Buckinghamshire, SL9 8BQ, United Kingdom
(01753) 899352
pm.day@vigin.net
www.foliofinder.com

Creative Design in Marketing India Mill Business Centre, Darwen, Lancashire, BB3 1AE, United Kingdom
(01254) 777752/ (01254) 777759
claire@cd-marketing.co.uk
www.cd-marketing.co.uk

Creative Edge Design & Advertising 1st Floor Donald Hendry Building, Auchincruive, Ayr, KA6 5HW, United Kingdom
(01292) 521404/ (01292) 521693
paul@cedge.co.uk
www.cedge.co.uk

Creative Graphics 22 Ansari Road, 1st Floor, Daryaganj, New Delhi, 110002, India
0091 11 2324 6574/ 00 91 11 2956 5598
info@creativegraphicsindia.com
www.creativegraphicsindia.com

Creative Management P.O.Box 72280, Office 61, Building 8, Dubai Media City, Dubai, United Arab Emirates
00 97 14 391 4318
emma@cm-ww.com
www.cm-ww.com

Creative Soup 6 Inverleith Avenue, Edinburgh, EH3 5PT, United Kingdom
0131-551 5202
creativesoupuk@aol.com

Creative Sponge 1 Netherconesford, King Street, Norwich, NR1 1PH, United Kingdom
(01603) 622766/ (01603) 622347
info@creativesponge.co.uk
www.creativesponge.co.uk

creativepool 42 Oakworth Road, London, W10 6DQ, United Kingdom
0208 9692483
listings@creativepool.co.uk
www.creativepool.co.uk

CyDmp.co.uk Flat 120, 1d Belvedere Road, London, SE1 7GH, United Kingdom
(020) 8123 6823/ (0871) 714 2823
info@cydmp.co.uk
www.cydmp.co.uk

D D B Mexico Leibinitz 11 - 3∞ Floor, Mexico DF, 11590, Mexico
00 52 63 36 00
mcampo@ddmexico.com

D N A Creative 52 New Street, Pudsey, West Yorkshire, LS28 8PE, United Kingdom
(07760) 252890
noonan.hq@ntlworld.com
www.dnacreative.co.uk

D W P Imaging Ltd Windsor House, 9-15 Adelaide Street, Luton, LU1 5BJ, United Kingdom
(01582) 400123/(07976) 220017 / (01582) 483362
info@dwpimaging.com
www.dwpimaging.com

Dance Theatre Projects 48 St. Peter's Street, London, N1 8JT, United Kingdom
(020) 7354 9586
v.bridson@dancetheatreprojects.org
www.dancetheatreprojects.org

David and Associates 67-69 Whitfield Street, London, W1T 4HF,
david@davidandassociates.co.uk
www.davidandassociates.co.uk

David Bevan Creative Artist 87 Lime Grove Close, Beaumont Leys, Leicester, LE4 0UG,
0116 2259463/ 0116 2259463
david.bevan55@ntlworld.com

David Hardy 66B Haydn Park Road, London, W12, United Kingdom
/07887 572 580
contactme@davidhardy.co.uk
www.davidhardy.co.uk

Daydream Linton House, 164-180 Union Street, London, SE1 0LH,
+44 (0) 20 7096 1471/+44 (0) 20 7117 1636
ralph@daydream.co.uk
www.daydream.co.uk

design@djhunter 133 Ravensbourne Avenue, Bromley, BR2 0AZ, United Kingdom
(020) 8466 7196/ (020) 8466 7196
design@djhunter.co.uk

Design73 26 Kingswear Road, Ruislip, Middlesex, HA4 6AY, United Kingdom
(01895) 460942/ (01895) 460942
martin@design73.co.uk
www.design73.co.uk

Designbern 31 Yorkland Avenue, Welling, Kent, DA16 2LE, United Kingdom
(07855) 856529
bern@designbern.com
www.designbern.com

Designcrew Creative Media Centre, 45 Robertson Street, Hastings, East Sussex, TN34 1HL,
01424 205 499/01424 205 499
danny@designcrew.co.uk
www.designcrew.co.uk

Digital One Marynarska 11, Warsaw, 2674, Poland
00 48 22 444 0 819/ 00 48 22 444 0 887
z.nowicki@digitalone.pl
www.digitalone.pl

Digitronix Ltd 22a&b Lightcliffe Road, Brighouse, West Yorkshire, HD6 2DJ, United Kingdom
(01484) 380100/ (01484) 380101
ask@digitronix.co.uk
www.digitronix.co.uk

Dirty Ego Creative 93 Southwell Road East, Rainworth, Mansfield, Nottinghamshire, NG21 0DE, United Kingdom
(07981) 056208
info@dirtyegocreative.co.uk
www.dirtyegocreative.co.uk

Discodog Ltd 23 Spittal Street, Edinburgh, EH3 9DZ, United Kingdom
(0870) 7775885
mail@discodog.co.uk
www.discodog.co.uk

Dizine Studioz 34 Chiddlingford Court, Somerset Avenue, Blackpool, FY1 5RE, United Kingdom
(07709) 129586
craig@dizinestudioz.co.uk
www.dizinestudioz.co.uk

DL Design Associates Limited 38a Duke Street, Chelmsford, CM1 1HY,
01245 299047/ 01245 299047
darren@dl-design.co.uk
www.dl-design.co.uk

Dolby Gallery The Design Factory, The Old Surgery, 30 West Street, Oundle, Peterborough, PE8 4EF, United Kingdom
(01832) 273801
dolbygallery@design-factory.co.uk
www.dolbygallery.com

DOT 16 High Street, Lewes, East Sussex, BN7 2LN, United Kingdom
✆ (01273) 477700
✉ tellmemore@dotco.co.uk
🖥 www.dotco.co.uk

Dragonfly Media 3 Berkeley Crescent, Clifton, Bristol, Avon, BS8 1HA,
✆ 0845 6520 888/✆ 0845 6520 808
✉ jon@dragonfly-media.co.uk
🖥 www.dragonfly-media.co.uk

Drawn Design Flat 34, Belgrave Court, Wellesley Road, London, W4 1LG, United Kingdom
✆ (020) 8994 4373/✆ (020) 8994 4373
✉ david@drawndesign.com
🖥 www.drawndesign.com

Elfin Presentations 191-205 Cambridge Heath Road, London, E2 0EL, United Kingdom
✆ (020) 7729 6744/✆ (020) 7729 9318
✉ info@elfinpresentations.co.uk
🖥 www.elfinpresentations.co.uk

Elliott Young Ltd Millennium House, 7 High Street, Hampton, Middlesex, TW12 2SA, United Kingdom
✆ (0845) 0540070/✆ (0870) 7627106
✉ daniel@elliottyoung.co.uk
🖥 www.elliottyoung.co.uk

Ephemera Design 65 South Drive, Bolton, BL2 3NL, United Kingdom
✆ (01204) 459922
✉ mark@fmra.co.uk
🖥 www.fmra.co.uk

Event Communications Ltd India House, 45 Curlew St, London, SE1 2ND, United Kingdom
✆ (020) 7378 9900/✆ (020) 7378 9911
✉ info@eventcomm.com
🖥 www.eventcomm.com

Exploding Monkey Ltd 50 Buttesland Street, Hoffman Square, Hoxton, London, N1 6BY, United Kingdom
✆ (020) 7253 9123/✆ (07092) 808516
✉ stephen@explodingmonkey.com
🖥 www.explodingmonkey.com

FaberFaber Partnership 12 The Inner Silk Mill, Malmesbury, Wiltshire, SN16 9LP, United Kingdom
✆ (01666) 824130/✆ (01666) 825397
✉ lee@faberfaber.com
🖥 www.faberfaber.com

Faces 349 Yorktown Road, College Town, Sandhurst, Berkshire, GU47 0PX, United Kingdom
✆ (01276) 38888/✆ (01276) 38111
✉ info@faces.co.uk
🖥 www.faces.co.uk

Five Eight 13-19 Vine Hill, London, EC1R 5DX, United Kingdom
✆ (020) 7837 1347
✉ subs@fiveeight.net
🖥 www.fiveeight.net

Fluid Business Communications Unit 1, Europa Park, Croft Way, Witham, Essex, CM8 2FN, United Kingdom
✆ (01376) 515573
✉ john@fluid-communications.com
🖥 www.fluid-communications.com

Fly on the Wire Ltd 4th Floor Argyle House, Marketgait, Dundee, DD1 1QP, United Kingdom
✆ (01382) 228947/✆ (0870) 1366817
✉ anique@flyonthewire.com
🖥 www.flyonthewire.com

Flying Mouse 68 Rennets, Wood Road, London, SE9 2NH, United Kingdom
✆ (07780) 707092/✆ (020) 8850 1294
✉ digital@rtwork.co.uk

Forth Generation Richmond Bridge House, 421 Richmond Road, Richmond, Surrey, TW1 2EX, United Kingdom
✆ (020) 8744 2811/(07789) 987531 /✆ (020) 8744 2669
✉ steve@forthgeneration.co.uk
🖥 www.forthgeneration.co.uk

Four Graphics Unit 4, 80 Willow Walk, London, SE1 5SY, United Kingdom
✆ (020) 7231 7070/✆ (020) 7231 0072
✉ info@fourgraphics.co.uk
🖥 www.fourgraphics.co.uk

Frukt Music 54 - 56 Compton Street, London, EC1V 0ET, United Kingdom
✆ (020) 7837 1347
✉ jack@fruktmusic.com
🖥 www.fruktmusic.com

Funky Concepts 5 Lansdowne Close, Coseley, Bilston, West Midlands, WV14 9TR, United Kingdom
✆ (01902) 651239/✆ (01902) 651239
✉ info@funkyconecpts.co.uk
🖥 www.funkyconcepts.co.uk

FuseBoxDesign Ltd St. Nicholas Chare, Newcastle upon Tyne, NE1 1RJ, United Kingdom
✆ 0191-245 7101/✆ 0191-245 7111
✉ louise@fuseboxdesign.co.uk
🖥 www.fuseboxdesign.co.uk

Fusioncom Via della Magliana, 63, Rome, 146, Italy
✆ 00 39 06 553 4061/✆ 00 39 06 5538 1440
✉ frankstahlberg@fusioncom.it
🖥 www.fusioncom.it

Genius Loci 15 Primrose Close, Goldsithney, Penzance, Cornwall, TR20 9JL, United Kingdom
✆ (01736) 719342
✉ sue.aston@geniusloci.co.uk
🖥 www.geniusloci.co.uk

Georgiou Digital Imaging & Design 71 Grosvenor Road, London, N9 8RG, United Kingdom
✆ (07762) 707370
✉ mario@georgiou.com
🖥 www.georgiou.com

Gibson & Holt The Hive, Burton Street, Nottingham, NG1 4BU, United Kingdom
✆ 0115-848 4733/✆ 0115-848 4612
✉ susieholt@hotmail.com

Glidden Design Ltd 2 Braidburn Terrace, Edinburgh, EH10 6ES, United Kingdom
✆ 0131-447 3399/(07973) 432572 /✆ 0131-447 3399
✉ andy@gliddendesign.com
🖥 www.gliddendesign.com

Glo London 32 Stratford Road, London, W8 6QF, United Kingdom
✆ (020) 7938 1330/✆ (020) 7938 3120
✉ kate@glolondon.com
🖥 www.glolondon.com

GMID Design for Business Prospect House, 3 Prospect Place, Swansea, SA1 1QP, United Kingdom
✆ (01792) 641350/✆ (01792) 301548
✉ studio@gmid.net
🖥 www.gmid.net

Go Vicinity Graphic Design Canterbury, Kent, CT1 9DY, United Kingdom
✆ (01227) 477061
✉ info@govicinity.com
🖥 www.govicinity.com

Hardings Design to Print Aintree Avenue, White Horse Business Park, Trowbridge, Wiltshire, BA14 0XB, United Kingdom
✆ (01225) 752888/✆ (01225) 752666
✉ alan@hardingsprinters.co.uk
🖥 www.hardingsprinters.co.uk

Harvestcrafts 86 Julians Road, Newport, Gwent, NP19 7RX, United Kingdom
✆ (01633) 215161
✉ craftyron@aol.com

Hawkins Design 9b Burwood Road, Walton-on-Thames, Surrey, KT12 4AB, United Kingdom
✆ (01932) 234847
✉ info@hawkinsdesign.co.uk
🖥 www.hawkinsdesign.co.uk

Heyward Rigby Communications Beckwell House, Woodford Halse, Daventry, Northamptonshire, NN11 3QS, United Kingdom
✆ (01327) 262497/✆ (01327) 262785
✉ tom@heywardrigby.co.uk
🖥 www.heywardrigby.co.uk

Hookson Ltd 30 Annandale Street Lane, Edinburgh, EH7 4LS, United Kingdom
✆ 0131-524 7940/✆ 0131-524 7941
✉ creative@hookson.co
🖥 www.hookson.com

Hypermania Design Forum House, Stirling Road, Chichester, West Sussex, PO19 7DN, United Kingdom
✆ (01243) 785678/✆ (01243) 785678
✉ sean@hypermania.co.uk
🖥 www.hypermania.com

iceni Productions Ltd The Studio, Long Lane, Fradley, Lichfield, Staffordshire, WS13 8NX, United Kingdom
✆ (01283) 792990/✆ (01283) 792993
✉ studio@iceni-tv.co.uk
🖥 www.iceni-tv.co.uk

ICG - Intereurope Communications Group Windy Harbour Barn, Harbour Lane, Warton, Preston, PR4 1YB, United Kingdom
✆ (01772) 679383/✆ (01772) 631440
✉ peter@icgonline.co.uk
🖥 www.icgonline.co.uk

Ignite 34 Grange Court, North Grange Mount, Leeds, LS6 2BZ, United Kingdom
✆ 0113-230 2795
✉ studio@ignitedesign.co.uk
🖥 www.ignitedesign.co.uk

Image and Music Little Orchard, Trenewan, Looe, Cornwall, PL13 2QD, United Kingdom
✆ (01503) 272633/(07779) 703281
✉ admin@imageandmusic.com
🖥 www.imageandmusic.com

Infidels Suite 131 Victoria Junction, Gate 4 Prestwich Street, Green Point, Cape Town, 8005, South Africa
✆ 00 27 21 425 78 78/✆ 00 27 21 425 69 15
✉ info@infidels.co.za
🖥 www.infidels.co.za

Ink & Colors Ltd 27 Old Gloucester Street, London, WC1N 3XX, United Kingdom
✆ (020) 7558 8374
✉ info@inkandcolors.com
🖥 www.inkandcolors.com

Inspire Carlton Mills, Pickering Street, Leeds, LS12 2QG, United Kingdom
✆ 0113-224 4800/✆ 0113-224 4801
✉ lindsay.kemp@logistik.co.uk
🖥 www.logistik-inspire.co.uk

Interactive Pages Ltd Eastern Court, 182-190 Newmarket Road, Cambridge, CB5 8HE, United Kingdom
✆ (01223) 502080
✉ dr.cb@interactivepages.co.uk
🖥 www.interactive-pages.co.uk

Interior Motives 163 High Street, Musselburgh, Midlothian, EH21 7DE, United Kingdom
✆ 0131-665 7172/✆ 0131-665 8217
✉ enquiries@interiormotivesltd.com
🖥 www.interiormotivesltd.com

Irrational Design 122 Hollydale Road, London, SE15 2TQ, United Kingdom
✆ (07956) 512509
✉ andy.knowles@irrational.info
🖥 www.irrational.info

James Cartledge Graphic Design 16 Fairfax Road, Teddington, Middlesex, TW11 9DH, United Kingdom
✆ (07971) 544712/✆ (020) 8977 7828
✉ james@jamescartledge.co.uk
🖥 www.jamescartledge.co.uk

Jebens Design Ltd 32 Dale Street, London, W4 2BL, United Kingdom
✆ (020) 8995 2929/✆ (020) 8995 2949
✉ info@jebensdesign.co.uk
🖥 www.jebensdesign.co.uk

Jo Groeneveld 2 Studd Street, London, N1 0QJ, United Kingdom
✆ (020) 7354 1290
✉ jo@passionateaboutdesign.co.uk
🖥 www.passionateaboutdesign.co.uk

John Brown Design 1 Arundel Gardens, Rayleigh, Essex, SS6 9GS, United Kingdom
✆ (01268) 786442/✆ (0870) 1166144
✉ studio@johnbrowndesign.co.uk
🖥 www.johnbrowndesign.co.uk

John Vernon Design The Studio, 24 Alric Avenue, New Malden, Surrey, KT3 4JN, United Kingdom
✆ (020) 8942 8273
✉ mail@johnvernon-design.co.uk
🖥 www.johnvernon-design.co.uk

Johnny Grey Ltd Fyning Copse, Rogate, Petersfield, Hampshire, GU31 5DH, United Kingdom
✆ (01730) 821424
✉ miles@johnnygrey.co.uk
🖥 www.johnnygrey.co.uk

Jump Marketing Gladstone Court, 179 Canongate, Edinburgh, EH8 8BN, United Kingdom
✆ 0131-523 1560/✆ 0131-558 1229
✉ moyra@jumpmarketing.co.uk
🖥 www.jumpmarketing.co.uk

JWD Graphic 139 Winkworth Road, Banstead, Surrey, SM7 2JW, United Kingdom
✆ (01737) 353013/07973 520292
✉ jwmail@btinternet.com

CREATIVE SERVICES

Karen Bergen Web Design Wood Green, London, N22, United Kingdom
(07799) 252942
offers@karenbergen.co.uk
www.karenbergen.co.uk

Karen Spinks 63 Alberta Road, Enfield, Middlesex, EN1 1JA, United Kingdom
(07881) 884740
karencrowley@blueyonder.co.uk
www.advertisingontap.co.uk

Karl Smith Lighting Design 28 Elm Row, Edinburgh, EH7 4RR, United Kingdom
(0871) 5200261/(0871) 5200261
office@karl-smith.com
www.karl-smith.com

Keshco 28C Northiam Street, Hackney, London, E9 7HQ, United Kingdom
(020) 8986 7897
keshco@yahoo.co.uk
www.uk.geocities.com/keshco

Knob Snobs Flat 39, Cadogan House, Beaufort Street, London, SW3 5BL, United Kingdom
(020) 8767 7443
sales@knob-snobs.co.uk
www.knob-snobs.co.uk

Kopanska 13 Grosvenor Crescent, Glasgow, G12 9AF, United Kingdom
0141-342 4539
info@kopanska.com
www.kopanska.com

Kr8iv Universal Square, Devonshire, Manchester, M12 6JH, United Kingdom
0161-276 3141
thepeople@kr8iv.co.uk
www.kr8iv.co.uk

LaGrafica 3 Ivor Park, Brynsadler, Pontyclun, Mid Glamorgan, CF72 9BF, United Kingdom
(07782) 660 855/(01443) 222 860
dan@lagrafica.co.uk
www.lagrafica.co.uk

Lake Associates Pax House, Headington Hill, Headington, Oxford, OX3 0BT, United Kingdom
(01865) 744798/(01865) 744954
q@lakeassociates.biz
www.lakeassociates.biz

Lee Grainge
London, United Kingdom
(07791) 043526
info@leegrainge.com
www.leegrainge.com

Leming Design Studio
Kharkiv, 61000, Ukraine
00 380 50 2240450
admin@lemingdesign.com
lemingdesign.com

LIMA Graphics Ltd 12 Yew Tree Walk, Frimley, Camberley, Surrey, GU16 8LG, United Kingdom
(01276) 507570/(07979) 502991/(0870) 1992932
lisa@limagraphics.co.uk
www.limagraphics.co.uk

Lokinlado Design 117 Eton Rise, Eton College Road, London, NW3 2DD, United Kingdom
(020) 7483 2425
lokinlado@gmail.com
www.lokinlado.com

London Creative 4th Floor, Gt. Titchfield House, 14-18 Gt. Titchfield Street, London, W1W 8BD, United Kingdom
(020) 7255 1616/(020) 7255 1617
office@londoncreative.com
www.londoncreative.com

Lonedog Multimedia 5 Cove Hollow, Groomsport, Bangor, County Down, BT19 6HT, United Kingdom
(028) 9146 8224
aoife@lonedog.co.uk
www.lonedog.co.uk

Longneck Afgan Road 27, Battersea, London, SW11 2QD,
7506018062
vlad@longneck.ro
www.longneck.ro

LSD | Brand Designer L Martinez 983, (Martinez), Buenos Aires, 1460,
54 11 4798 1760/54 11 4798 1760
luzsoldano@sion.com
www.luzsoldano.com

Luke Moloney, Architect 24 Queen Street, Dumfries, Dumfriesshire, DG1 2JF,
01387 259338/01387 259338
info@lukemoloneyarchitect.co.uk
www.lukemoloneyarchitect.co.uk

M O D Films 9 Wyndham Street, London, W1H 1DB, United Kingdom
(020) 7723 4674/(020) 7723 4764
reception@modfilms.com
www.modfilms.com

M&M Creative High Trees, Bishops Down Park Road, Tunbridge Wells, Kent, TN4 8XU,
01892 533103
mike@mandmcreative.co.uk
www.mandmcreative.co.uk

mabox 120-122 Bermondsey Street, London, SE1 3TX, United Kingdom
(08709) 908677/(08708) 406871
tim@mabox.co.uk
www.mabox.co.uk

Mandarin 55-63 Goswell Road, London, EC1V 7EN, United Kingdom
(020) 7837 2222/(020) 7490 5882
nick@mandarin.org.uk
www.mandarin.org.uk

Maria Chryssikos
London, United Kingdom
(020) 8579 5121/07817 739614/(08700) 517452
maria@productiondesign.demon.co.uk

Mark Russell 16 Porpen Road, London, SW2 5RT, United Kingdom
07881 904476
open@resaturate.com
www.resaturate.com

Marsh & Malone Bower Cottage, High Street, Limpsfield, Oxted, Surrey, RH8 0DY, United Kingdom
(01883) 730610/(01883) 370600
tony@marshandmalone.co.uk
www.marshandmalone.co.uk

MCC Creative 4, Park Farm, Chichester Road, Arundel, West Sussex, BN18 0AG,
01903 885 235
dan@m-c-c.biz
www.mcccreative.co.uk

Melissa Allen Design 48 Llyswen Road, Cardiff, CF23 6PP, United Kingdom
(029) 2075 6239
mel@melissaallendesign.com
www.melissaallendesign.com

Mercy Design 59 Seel Street, The Basement, Liverpool, L1 4AZ, United Kingdom
(07931) 221494
joe@mercydesign.co.uk
www.mercydesign.co.uk

Meta One Ltd Creative Media Centre, Robertson Street, Hastings, East Sussex, TN34 1HL, United Kingdom
(01424) 205420
info@metaone.co.uk
www.metaone.co.uk

Metro Imaging 76 Clerkenwell Road, London, EC1M 5TN, United Kingdom
(020) 7865 0000/(020) 7865 0001
info@metroimaging.co.uk
www.metroimaging.co.uk

Modus Media Ltd 18 Iliffe Yard, London, SE17 3QA, United Kingdom
0207 77406045
info@modus-media.com
www.modus-media.com

Monastery Design 2 Roseneath, Bramhall, Stockport, Cheshire, SK7 3LP, United Kingdom
0161-485 4777/0161-485 6444
mail@monasterydesign.co.uk
www.monasterydesign.co.uk

Motion Blur Ltd Bryn Hyfryd, Bryncroes, Pwllheli, Gwynedd, LL53 8ET, United Kingdom
(01758) 730777
pix@motionblur.tv
www.motionblur.tv

My Mate Dave Designs 5 Buchanan Ct, Buchanan Dr, Luton, Beds, LU2 0SA,
7736939770
d.sweeney@ntlworld.com
www.mymatedaves.com

N K D Unit 10a, Acton Business Centre, School Road, London, NW10 6TD, United Kingdom
(020) 8961 3300/(020) 8961 3300
nkd@theirstudio.freeserve.co.uk
www.nk-d.co.uk

Nena Carney Design The Coach House, 2a Blakeney Road, Beckenham, Kent, BR3 1HA, United Kingdom
(020) 8658 9838/7802769400
n@nenacarneydesign.com
www.nenacarneydesign.com

New Crane Ltd 20 Upper Ground, London, SE1 9PD, United Kingdom
(020) 7633 0266/(020) 7775 7705
info@7publishing.co.uk
www.newcrane.com

Nicola L Robinson Mynachdy, Cardiff, Glamorgan, CF14 3AG,

nlrobinson@thesurrealdemon.co.uk
www.thesurrealdemon.co.uk

Nomas Creative Ltd Widbury Farmhouse, Widbury Hill, Ware, Hertfordshire, SG12 7QE, United Kingdom
(01920) 462302
studio@nomascreative.com
www.nomascreative.com

Noonwright Ltd 2 Seven Dials Court, 3 Shorts Garden, Covent Garden, London, WC2H 9AT, United Kingdom
(020) 7240 7277/(020) 7240 7278
mail@noonwright.co.uk
www.noonwright.com

Northstar Marketing & Design Northstar House, 5 Ferns Mead, Farnham, Surrey, GU9 7XP, United Kingdom
(01252) 734070/(01252) 734071
info@northstarmarketng.co.uk
www.northstarmarketing.co.uk

NotOnlyButAlso Ltd 44-46 Old Steine, Brighton, BN1 1NH, United Kingdom
(01273) 229909/(01273) 229895
nick@notonlybutalso.net
www.notonlybutalso.net

Object Marketing Object House, 7 Poplar Mews, Uxbridge Road, London, W12 7JS, United Kingdom
(020) 8762 9292/(020) 8762 9299
contact@objectmarketing.com
www.objectmarketing.com

Oceanic Design Highview, Little Staughton, Bedford, MK44 2BH, United Kingdom
(01234) 378171/(07092) 023480
phil@oceanicdesign.com
www.oceanicdesign.com

ODS Business Services Ltd ODS Building, (Specrum) meadway, Westlea, Swindon, SN5 7UT, United Kingdom
01793 421 300/01793 425 155
sales@ods-businessservices.com
www.ods-businessservices.com

one-or-more.com 1 Longley Road, London, SW17 9LA, United Kingdom
(020) 8767 3376/(020) 8767 3424
info@one-or-more.com
www.one-or-more.com

Onnpoint Design 1-5 Jeffries Passage, Guildford, Surrey, GU1 4AP, United Kingdom
(01483) 510515/(01483) 510519
info@onnpoint.co.uk
www.onnpoint.co.uk

Onscreen Graphics, Leagrave, Luton, LU3 4WD, United Kingdom
01582 584134
info@osgx.co.uk
www.osgx.co.uk

Open Creative Ltd Unit 10, Catapult Too Centre, Parade Street, St. Helens, Merseyside, WA10 1LX, United Kingdom
(01744) 732077/(01744) 732078
studio@opencreative.co.uk
www.opencreative.co.uk

Orgill Advertising Ltd Unit 19/20, Scott Business Park, Beacon Park Road, Plymouth, PL2 2PB, United Kingdom
(01752) 201601/(01752) 201611
sarah@orgilladvertising.co.uk
www.orgilladvertising.co.uk

Osei-Tutu 68 Hackney Close, Borehamwood, Hertfordshire, WD6 2SL, United Kingdom
(020) 8386 1032
info@osei-tutu.co.uk
www.osei-tutu.co.uk

Ouside The Lines 4 Trerice Fields, Praze, Camborne, Cornwall, TR14 0JS, United Kingdom
(07886) 864130
sarah@outsidethelines.co.uk
www.outsidethelines.co.uk

Own It University of The Arts London (LCC), Elephant & Castle, London, SE1 6SB, United Kingdom
(020) 7514 7985/ (020) 7514 7313
info@own-it.org
www.own-it.org

P T E 123 Regents Park Road, London, NW1 8BE, United Kingdom
(020) 7722 5566/ (020) 7586 4133
info@ptemedia.com
www.ptemedia.com

Palmer Hamilton Partnership 87 Comber Grove, Camberwell, London, SE5 0LD, United Kingdom
(020) 7708 2134
info@palmerhamilton.co.uk
www.palmerhamilton.co.uk

Pantechnicon The Glass Mill, 1 Battersea Bridge Road, London, SW11 3BZ, United Kingdom
(020) 7228 1133/ (020) 7326 8398
info@pantechnicon.co.uk
www.pantechnicon.co.uk

Panthers Purrfections 1 Thorne Street, London, SW13 0PT, United Kingdom
(020) 8876 0468
jasonapanther@yahoo.co.uk
www.pantherspurrfections.co.uk

Paul Crampton Hay Wood House, 40 New Road, Darbridge, West Midlands, DY8 1PA, United Kingdom
(07855) 361640/ (01384) 372928
paul@paulcrampton.com
www.paulcrampton.com

Peter Jaques 4 Stourvale Gardens, Chandler's Ford, Eastleigh, Hampshire, SO53 3NE, United Kingdom
(023) 8027 0513
peter@peterjaques.co.uk
www.peterjaques.co.uk

Peter Layton and Associates Ltd Unit 7, The Leather Market, Weston Street, London, SE1 3ER, United Kingdom
(020) 7403 2800/ (020) 7403 7778
info@peterlaytonglass.co.uk
www.peterlaytonglass.co.uk

Phew Design The Courtyard, Crowhill Farm, Ravensden Road, Wilden, Bedford, MK44 2QS, United Kingdom
(0845) 1259070/ (0845) 1259070
matthew.burgess@phewdesign.com
www.phewdesign.com

Phil Bicker/MAP 72 Rochester Place, London, NW1 9JX, United Kingdom
(020) 7424 9144/ (020) 7284 3274
info@mapltd.com
www.mapltd.com

Pipeline Design 43 Maiden Lane, London, WC2E 7LL, United Kingdom
(020) 7836 5070/ (020) 7240 4123
dawn@pipelinedesign.com
www.pipelinedesign.it

Pixel DNA Ltd Hydra Clarkson House, PO Box 37, Sheffield, S6 3AH, United Kingdom
0114-224 6145
marc@pixel-dna.com
www.pixel-dna.com

Platform3 Web Ltd 3 Wilkes Street, London, E1 6QF, United Kingdom
(020) 7375 2973
info@platform-3.co.uk
www.platform-3.co.uk

Platform44 Sparkhouse Studios, Rope Walk, Lincoln, LN6 7DQ, United Kingdom
(01522) 837241/ (01522) 837201
projects@platform44.com
www.platform44.com

Polepeople Ltd The bonmarshy Centre, 241-251 Ferndale Road, London, SW9 8BJ, United Kingdom
(020) 7737 0831/ (0870) 1353335
info@polepeople.co.uk
www.polepeople.co.uk

Prism Visual Analysis Unit 521, The Greenhouse, Gibb Street, Birmingham, B9 4AA, United Kingdom
0121-224 8270
ben@prismvisualanalysis.com
www.prismvisualanalysis.com

PropertyMall Covent Garden, London, WC2B 5AA, United Kingdom
(020) 7611 5040/ 2076115041
manager@propertymall.com
www.propertymall.com

Proudspark 1 Palace Place, Brighton, BN1 1EF, United Kingdom
(01273) 223637/ (01273) 323219
sam@prooudspark.co.uk
www.proudspark.co.uk

Psolutions Unlimited 44 Chapmans Road, Sundridge, Sevenoaks, Kent, TN14 6DR, United Kingdom
(01959) 562192/(07799) 534191
helen@psolutions-unlimited.co.uk
www.psolutions-unlimited.co.uk

Punch NMC Fern House, 53 Padbrook, Limpsfield, Surrey, RH8 0DZ,
01883 730073
andrew.richardson@thinkpunch.co.uk
www.thinkpunch.co.uk

Radium Audio Ltd 7 Leicester Road, Sale, Manchester, M33 7DU,
0161 282 0768
andrew@radium-audio.com
www.radium-audio.com

Radley Yeldar 24 Charlotte Road, London, EC2A 3PB, United Kingdom
(020) 7033 0700
j.ellis@ry.com
www.ry.com

Raucous Creative Services 5 Oak Lane, Wilmslow, Cheshire, SK9 6AA, United Kingdom
(01625) 530697
paul@raucous.co.uk

Reality 3D 17 St Clements Road, Parkstone, Poole, Dorset, BH15 3PB, United Kingdom
(07973) 534171
Steve@reality3d.co.uk
www.reality3d.co.uk

RedLime 18 Friary Road, Newark, Nottinghamshire, NG24 1LE, United Kingdom
(01636) 677229/ (01636) 677339
sally@redlime.co.uk
www.redlime.co.uk

Resolution Creative 204 Latimer Road, London, W10 6QY, United Kingdom
(020) 8969 7333/ (020) 8969 7444
info@resolveandcreate.co.uk
www.resolveandcreate.co.uk

Richard Evans Design & Art Direction Unit 24, Ransomes Dock Business Centre, 35-37 Parkgate Road, London, SW11 4NP, United Kingdom
(020) 7223 7135/ (020) 7223 7140
rich@rdevans.com
www.rdevans.com

Run2 Design 13 Norton Road, Loddon, Norwich, NR14 6JN, United Kingdom
(01508) 522002/ (01508) 522002
studio@run2design.co.uk
www.run2design.co.uk

Safety First Design 3 Gibson Green, Witham St Hughs, Lincoln, LN6 9GA, United Kingdom
(07753) 740589
enquiries@safetyfirstdesign.co.uk
www.safetyfirstdesign.co.uk

Sally Bargman 2 Washington Road, London, SW13 9BE, United Kingdom
(07875) 416807/(07976) 271312
sallybargman@hotmail.com
www.sallyandjohncreative.co.uk

Sasha Studios 370a Camden Road, London, N7 0LG, United Kingdom
(07913) 201667
sashastudios@yahoo.com
www.sashastudios.com

Scene The Granary, Sandpit Lane, Bledlow, Princes Risborough, Buckinghamshire, HP27 9QQ, United Kingdom
(01844) 275863
info@sceneoutside.com
www.sceneoutside.com

Scootman Music & Sound Design 2021 21st Avenue South, Suite C-100, Nashville, 37212, United States of America
615 319 9556/615 319 9556 615 777 2122
scott@scootmanmusic.com
www.scootmanmusic.com

Sennep 6 Disney Street, Borough, London, SE1 1JF, United Kingdom
(020) 7357 9200
info@sennep.com
www.sennep.com

Sensedance 1425 Third Avenue, #3c, New York, 10028, United States of America
212 717 6869/ 212 717 6869
sensedance@sensedance.org
www.sensedance.org

Shape Construction & Design Totom House, 70 Stanley Gardens, London, W3 7SZ, United Kingdom
(07958) 526148
james@shapeconstruction.co.uk
www.shapeconstruction.co.uk

Shop Film Production Co. Mallard Cottage, Newtown Road, Ramsbury, Wiltshire, SN8 2PP, United Kingdom
(01672) 521272/(07836) 576093
cof@appleinter.net

Signs of all Kinds 797 Lea Bridge Road, London, E17 9DS, United Kingdom
(020) 8521 7900/ (020) 8521 1150

Skim New Media Ltd Studio one, Canalot Studios, 222 Kensal Road, London, W10 5BN, United Kingdom
(020) 8960 7989/ (020) 8960 8609
info@skim.co.uk
www.skim.co.uk

Sleepymonkey Creative Media Ltd 33 Siddeley Avenue, Coventry, CV3 1FZ, United Kingdom
(07723) 314436
info@sleepymonkey.co.uk
www.sleepymonkey.co.uk

Smoothe Ground Floor, Block A, 6 Corbett Place, London, E1 6NH, United Kingdom
(020) 7490 4300/ (020) 7490 9480
info@smoothe.com
www.smoothe.com

Smoothe Ltd Ist Floor, E Office, 1 portland Street, Manchester, M13 be, United Kingdom
08708 - 909 836
samcrothers@smoothe.com
www.smoothe.com

Social Fabric UK Ltd William Blake House, 8 Marshall Street, London, W1F 7EJ, United Kingdom
(020) 7788 7876
us@thesocialfabric.com
www.thesocialfabric.com

SomaPhotos 1 Sly Street, London, E1 2LE, United Kingdom
(07766) 753300
hugh@somaphotos.com
www.somaphotos.com

SONAA Unit 204 @ Tea Building, 56 Shoreditch High Street, London, E1 6JJ, United Kingdom
(020) 7729 0387/ (020) 7012 1104
pat.fahy@sonaa.co.uk
www.sonaa.co.uk

Spiral Communications Pte Ltd 28 Maxwell Road, 02-15A, Red Dot Traffic Building, Singapore,
+65 65347184/ +65 63278902
enquiry@spiralcomms.com
www.spiralcomms.com

Spotless Design 39 Atalanta Street, Fulham, London, SW6 6TU, United Kingdom
(020) 7168 7526/(07971) 002292 (020) 7681 4375
info@spotlessdesign.com
www.spotlessdesign.com

Spur Creative Workshop 169b Davidson Road, Croydon, CR0 6DP, United Kingdom
(020) 8405 3436/07940 790580
phil@spurcreative.com
www.spurcreative.co.uk

Stream UK Media Services Ltd Studio 522, 53-79 Highgate Road, London, NW5 1TL, United Kingdom
(020) 7387 6090/ (020) 7419 1819
jessica@streamuk.com
www.streamuk.com

Stretchmark 22 Laburnum Lane, Newhey, Rochdale, Lancashire, OL16 4LP, United Kingdom
(07980) 224261
mark_hoolaham_554@hotmail.com

Studio North 51 Bengal, Manchester, M4 6LN, United Kingdom
0161-237 5151/ 0161-237 5131
nick@studionorth.co.uk
www.studionorth.co.uk

Stylo Design Bedford Chambers, The Piazza, Covent Garden, London, WC2E 8HA, United Kingdom
(020) 7836 9474
ben@stylodesign.co.uk
www.stylodesign.co.uk

Subcircle Creative 5 Luther Mews, Brighton, BN2 9YR, United Kingdom
✆ (01273) 675428
✉ studio@subcircle.co.uk
🖥 www.subcircle.co.uk

Sure Creation 76 Palmerston Crescent, Plumstead, London, SE18 2TS, United Kingdom
✆ (020) 8317 4977
✉ ziv@surecreation.com
🖥 www.surecreation.com

T & N Enterprises Unit 5, 54 Cavell Street, London, E1 2HP, United Kingdom
✆ (020) 7423 9150/077 10 298793
✉ info@tnenterprises.co.uk
🖥 www.tnenterprises.co.uk

T D A Marketing Communications Apex House, Bank Street, Lutterworth, Leicestershire, LE17 4AG, United Kingdom
✆ (01455) 558377/📠 (01455) 559845
✉ tda@tda-marketing.com
🖥 www.tda-marketing.com

Tabbhousepublishers 8 Church Streed, Padstow, Cornwall, PL28 8BG, United Kingdom
✆ (01841) 532316/📠 (01841) 532316
✉ Books@tabb-house.fsnet.co.uk

Tank 49-50 Great Marlborough Street, London, W1F 7JR, United Kingdom
✆ (020) 7434 0110/📠 (020) 7434 9232
✉ mail@tankmagazine.com
🖥 www.tankmagazine.com

Taylor Creative Services Unit 3, 21 Wren Street, London, WC1X 0HF, United Kingdom
✆ (020) 7278 4009/📠 (020) 7837 1942
✉ scott.freeman@taylorcreative.co.uk
🖥 www.taylorcreative.co.uk

Techdesign.co.uk 2 Pellor Cottages, Pellor Road, Breage, Helston, Cornwall, TR13 9QL, United Kingdom
✆ (01326) 574289
✉ info@techdesigns.co.uk
🖥 www.techdesigns.co.uk

The Artistry Ltd 28 Vansittart Street, New Cross, London, SE14 6JQ, United Kingdom
✆ (020) 3132 4826
✉ info@theartistry.co.uk
🖥 www.theartistry.co.uk

The Design Inn 28 Upper Hamilton Road, Brighton, BN1 5DF, United Kingdom
✆ (07903) 389990
✉ liavittone@yahoo.co.uk

The Gate Marketing & Design Ltd Murlain Business Centre, Union Street, Chester, CH1 1QP, United Kingdom
✆ (01244) 357242/📠 (01244) 357215
✉ info@thegatemarketing.com
🖥 www.thegatemarketing.com

The Invisible Picture Company 56 Falconer Road, Bushey, WD23 3AW, United Kingdom
✆ (020) 8950 2901
✉ terry@invisiblepicture.com
🖥 www.invisiblepicturecompany.com

The One Off 55 Derby Road, Melbourne, Derby, DE73 8SE, United Kingdom
✆ (01332) 694555/(07967) 505335 📠 (01332) 694556
✉ adam@theoneoff.com
🖥 www.theoneoff.com

The Tinsley Lockhart Group 44 West Preston Street, Edinburgh, EH8 9PY, United Kingdom
✆ 0131-466 7767
✉ creative@tinsleylockhart.com
🖥 www.tinsleylockhart.com

The Wax Mill Partenrship The Raylor Centre, James Street, York, YO24 4BP, United Kingdom
✆ (01904) 422114

Think Smart Marketing Unit B2, Arc Progress, Beckerings Park, Lidlington, Bedford, MK43 0RD, United Kingdom
✆ (01525) 288828/📠 (01525) 288904
✉ marka@thinksmartmarketing.co.uk
🖥 www.thinksmartmarketing.co.uk

Thought by Design 47 Greys Road, Henley-on-Thames, Oxfordshire, RG9 1SB, United Kingdom
✆ (01491) 411439/(07967) 729085 📠 (01491) 411439
✉ info@thoughtbydesign.co.uk
🖥 www.thoughtbydesign.co.uk

Threerooms Ltd 13 Mayfield Drive, Stapleford, Nottingham, NG9 8JF, United Kingdom
✆ 0115-877 9429
✉ info@threerooms.com
🖥 www.threerooms.com

Tortoy 43c Quaker Street, London, E1 6SN, United Kingdom
✆ (020) 7426 0866/077867 20020
✉ hector@tortoy.com
🖥 www.tortoy.com

Triptych Events UK 24 Lansdowne Street, Hove, East Sussex, BN3 1FQ, United Kingdom
✆ (07917) 10248
✉ joe@triptychevents.co.uk
🖥 www.triptychevents.co.uk

Visual Source The Barn, Bottom Road, West Wycombe, High Wycombe, Buckinghamshire, HP14 4BS, United Kingdom
✆ (01494) 481482
✉ info@visualsource.co.uk
🖥 www.visualsource.co.uk

Vocal Coach Studio Berry Hill, Mansfield, Nottinghamshire, NG18 4HZ, United Kingdom
✆ 01623 474464
✉ business@vocalcoachstudio.co.uk
🖥 www.vocalcoachstudio.co.uk

Vpress Ltd Church Mews, Church Street, Cheltenham, Gloucestershire, GL50 3HA, United Kingdom
✆ (0870) 2005858
✉ info@vpress.co.uk
🖥 www.vpress.co.uk

Walls Have Ears Leeds, LS25 7RW, United Kingdom
✆ (07977) 733862
✉ stewart@wallshaveears.co.uk
🖥 www.wallshaveears.co.uk

Willis Reddick Partnership 10 Ivanhoe Avenue, Carryduff, Belfast, BT8 8BN, United Kingdom
✆ (028) 9081 5996/📠 (028) 9081 5996
✉ info@willisreddick.com
🖥 www.willisreddick.com

Wonderfuel 118 Hatherley Gardens, London, E6 3HQ, United Kingdom
✆ 020 8548 1358
✉ info@wonderfuel.co.uk
🖥 www.wonderfuel.co.uk

Worldspan Marketing Commodore House, Cae Eithin, Abergele, Clwyd, LL22 8LJ, United Kingdom
✆ (01492) 531070/📠 (01492) 536053
✉ nina.sardar@worldspan.co.uk
🖥 www.worldspanmarketing.com

@www Digital 3 Printing House Yard, Hackney Road, London, E2 7PR, United Kingdom
✆ (020) 7749 8660/📠 (020) 7749 8677
✉ barnaby.hobbs@atwww.com
🖥 www.atwww.com

Yolk Design Flat 3, 66 Hamilton Terrace, London, NW8 9UJ, United Kingdom
✆ (07771) 994497
✉ scsosnov@yahoo.com

Yovina.co.uk 55 Whippendell Road, Watford, Hertfordshire, WD18 7LY,
✆ 077 37 45 7663
✉ jess@yovina.co.uk 🖥 www.yovina.co.uk

Zacella Since 1982 87 Roberts Road, High Wycombe, Buckinghamshire, HP13 6XD, United Kingdom
✆ (07763) 842297
✉ zacella@hotmail.com

DIGITAL IMAGING AND RETOUCHING

46gradinord s.a.s. Via Esterle 11, Trento, 38100,
✆ 3.93384E+11/📠 3.90461E+12
✉ stefano@46gradinord.com
🖥 www.46gradinord.com

8ball Multimedia Unit L, The Eurocentre, North River Road, Great Yarmouth, Norfolk, NR30 1TE, United Kingdom
✆ (01493) 857473
✉ joseph@8ballmultimedia.com
🖥 www.8ballmedia.com

A D S Visual Group 246-250 Seaward Street, Kinning Park, Glasgow, G41 1NG, United Kingdom
✆ 0141-420 1266/📠 0141-420 1345
✉ info@ads-visual.com
🖥 www.ads-visual.com

Acrom Photographic Lab Ltd 19 Heathmans Road, London, SW6 4TJ, United Kingdom
✆ (020) 7751 9922/📠 (020) 7751 9955
✉ mail@acrom.co.uk
🖥 www.acrom.co.uk

Act Two 3rd Floor, 16 Bishops Bridge Road, London, W2 6AA
✆ 0207 863 9570/0207 863 9571 ✉ info@acttwo.biz
✉ www.acttwo.biz
See ad in showcase

Admagic Ltd The Green Building, 50-54 Beak Street, London, W1F 9RN, United Kingdom
✆ (020) 7388 4114/(07802) 753 643 📠 (020) 7439 1971
✉ supplies@admagic.com
🖥 www.fusionpremedia.co.uk

Advance Digital Print 91 Great Titchfield Street, London, W1W 6RW, United Kingdom
✆ (020) 7580 8763/📠 (020) 7637 4149
✉ gavin.last@advancerepro.net
🖥 www.advancerepro.co.uk

Alternity 26 St. Michaels Court, St. Leonards Road, London, E14 6PS, United Kingdom
✆ (020) 7515 7995
✉ stevecook@alternity.co.uk
🖥 www.alternity.co.uk

Andrew Weir Retouching 25 Alderney Road, London, E1 4EG, United Kingdom
✆ (07817) 215065
✉ andrewrussellweir@hotmail.com

Andy Graham Flat 14, Abney Park Court, 230 Stoke Newington High Street, London, N16 7HF, United Kingdom
✆ (020) 7254 0494
✉ andy.graham@mac.com
🖥 www.andygraham.biz

Ann Mulqueeney Retouching 49 Park Road North, Newton-le-Willows, Merseyside, WA12 9TA, United Kingdom
✆ (07779) 117986
✉ annmulqueeney@freeuk.com

Artext 28 Sedley Rise, Loughton, Essex, IG10 1LT, United Kingdom
✆ (020) 8508 1328
✉ simon@artext.co.uk

Arthur Phillips 38 Aragon Avenue, Thames Ditton, Surrey, KT7 0PX, United Kingdom
✆ (020) 8398 0077/📠 (020) 8398 0077
✉ arthur@computerillustration.co.uk
🖥 www.computerillustration.co.uk

Bare Essence Photography 14 Jalan Anggerik Liparis 31/153, Kota Kemuning, Shah Alam, Selangor, 40460, Malaysia
✆ 00 60 35 121 6387
✉ debbieyw@streamyx.com
🖥 debbieyip.fotopages.com

Bayeux Ltd 78 Newman Street, London, W1T 3BT, United Kingdom
✆ (020) 7436 1066/📠 (020) 7436 8005
✉ info@bayeux.co.uk
🖥 www.bayeux.co.uk

Blaze Creative Ltd 77 East Road, London, N1 6AH, United Kingdom
✆ (020) 7253 0099/📠 (020) 7253 4358
✉ mail@blaze-creative.co.uk
🖥 www.blaze-creative.co.uk

Blaze Image 111 Talbot Road, London, W11 2AT, United Kingdom
✆ (020) 7229 4334/📠 (020) 7229 4334

Blueskystudio Bluebell Cottage, Steeple Lane, St. Ives, Cornwall, TR26 2GY, United Kingdom
✆ (01736) 793740
✉ kerry@blueskystudio.co.uk
🖥 www.blueskystudio.co.uk

Bold Endeavours Ltd 7 Manor Park, Staines, Middlesex, TW18 4XE,
✆ 01784 460 064
✉ derek@boldendeavours.com
🖥 www.big-easy-footage-library-software.co.uk

Bolton Colour Lab 362 Shorley Old Road, Bolton, BL1 6AG, United Kingdom
✆ (01204) 847592
✉ boltoncolourlabs@btconnect.com
🖥 www.boltoncolourlabs.co.uk

Brever Web Design Edinburgh 60a Craigour Drive, Edinburgh, EH17 7NT, United Kingdom
✆ (0845) 129 8534
✉ info@breverwebdesign.com
🖥 www.breverwebdesign.com

C C Imaging Ltd 7 Scala Court, Leatheley Road, Leeds, LS10 1JD, United Kingdom
☎ 0113-244 8329/🖷 0113-244 0115
✉ ccimaging@btconnect.com
🖥 www.ccimaging.co.uk

C W A Studios Ltd 10 Treadaway Technical Centre, Treadaway Hill, Loudwater, High Wycombe, Buckinghamshire, HP10 9RS, United Kingdom
☎ (01628) 530676/🖷 (01628) 810085
✉ info@cwa-studios.com
🖥 www.cwa-studios.com

Catwalk Creations 63, March Court, Warwick Drive, London, SW15 6LE, United Kingdom
☎ (07834) 470117
✉ nicola@catwalkcreations.com
🖥 www.catwalkcreations.com

Ceta Imaging 1/5 Poland Street, London, W1F 8NA, United Kingdom
☎ (020) 7434 1235/🖷 (020) 7434 9283
✉ info@cetaimaging.com
🖥 www.cetaimaging.com

Chau Digital 19 Rosebery Avenue, London, EC1R 4SP, United Kingdom
☎ (020) 7833 3938/🖷 (020) 7837 9130
✉ sales@chaudigital.com
🖥 www.chaudigital.com

Christopher Liddington Photography 14 Lewes Road, London, N12 9NL, United Kingdom
☎ (07740) 336676
✉ info@christopherliddington.com
🖥 www.christopherliddington.com

Christopher McMurray Photography The Design Foundry, Smith Way, Ossett, West Yorkshire, WF5 9JZ, United Kingdom
☎ (01924) 884400/(07774) 182078 /🖷 (01924) 884420
✉ cmcmurray@thedesignfoundry.co.uk
🖥 www.mcphoto.co.uk

Cinebuild Ltd Studio House, 34 Rita Road, London, SW8 1JU, United Kingdom
☎ (020) 7582 8750/(07836) 220441 /🖷 (020) 7793 0467
✉ cinebuild@btclick.com
🖥 www.cinebuild.com

Colour Management.net 93 Holland Road, Hove, East Sussex, BN3 1JP, United Kingdom
☎ (01273) 774704/(07778) 160201
✉ info@neilbarstow.co.uk
🖥 www.colourmanagement.net

Colour Network Studio B9, 3A Queensly Court, Glasgow, G33 4DB, United Kingdom
☎ 0141-774 8388/🖷 0141-774 9797
✉ rgray@colour-network.co.uk
🖥 www.colour-network.co.uk

Colourworks 70-71 Well Street, London, W1T 3QE, United Kingdom
☎ (020) 7636 0820/🖷 (020) 7636 0820
✉ colourworks@ukonline.co.uk

Cosmetic Ink 204 Latimer Road, London, W10 6QY,
☎ 2089694411/2089606286
✉ joe@cosmeticink.tv
🖥 www.cosmeticink.tv

Creative Edge Design & Advertising 1st Floor Donald Hendry Building, Auchincruive, Ayr, KA6 5HW, United Kingdom
☎ (01292) 521404/🖷 (01292) 521693
✉ paul@cedge.co.uk
🖥 www.cedge.co.uk

Creative Image Unit 3, 231 Stoke Newington Church Street, London, N16 9HP, United Kingdom
☎ (020) 7254 4141/(07887) 568007
✉ laurence@laurence-davis.co.uk
🖥 www.laurence-davis.co.uk

D W P Imaging Ltd Windsor House, 9-15 Adelaide Street, Luton, LU1 5BJ, United Kingdom
☎ (01582) 400123/(07976) 220017 /🖷 (01582) 483362
✉ info@dwpimaging.com
🖥 www.dwpimaging.com

D Z Studios Studio I, Trinity Buoy Wharf, Docklands, London, E14 0JY, United Kingdom
☎ (0844) 8404 130/🖷 (0871) 242 1685
✉ mardi@d-z.co.uk
🖥 www.d-z.co.uk

David Calvert Photography 1 Hillhead, Perry Green, Much Hadham, Hertfordshire, SG10 6DU, United Kingdom
☎ (01279) 843050
✉ enquiries@calvert.biz
🖥 www.calvert.biz

David Peters Studios Unit 14, Fordhouse Road Industrial Estate, Wolverhampton, WV10 9XB, United Kingdom
☎ (01902) 397739/🖷 (01902) 397001
✉ dp@davidpeters.co.uk
🖥 www.davidpeters.co.uk

Digital Photo Services Top Floor, Export House, 25-31 Ironmonger Row, London, EC1V 3QN, United Kingdom
☎ (020) 7033 4421/(07830) 146285 /🖷 (020) 7490 3384
✉ info@digitalphotoservices.co.uk
🖥 www.digitalphotoservices.co.uk

Digitronix Ltd 22a&b Lightcliffe Road, Brighouse, West Yorkshire, HD6 2DJ, United Kingdom
☎ (01484) 380100/🖷 (01484) 380101
✉ ask@digitronix.co.uk
🖥 www.digitronix.co.uk

Display Graphics Ltd Unit J 112, Tower Bridge Business Complex, 100 Clements Road, London, SE16 4DG, United Kingdom
☎ (020) 7231 8881/🖷 (020) 7231 0025
✉ sales@display-graphics.co.uk
🖥 www.display-graphics.co.uk

Dragonfly Media 3 Berkeley Crescent, Clifton, Bristol, Avon, BS8 1HA,
☎ 0845 6520 888/🖷 0845 6520 808
✉ jon@dragonfly-media.co.uk
🖥 www.dragonfly-media.co.uk

Ed Ironside Galleon House, 3 Fore Street, Calstock, Cornwall, PL18 9RN, United Kingdom
☎ (01822) 832574/(07973) 335509
✉ ed@bremweb.co.uk
🖥 www.bremweb.co.uk

eme Digital 3 Millharbour, London, E14 9XP, United Kingdom
☎ (020) 7538 8105/🖷 (020) 7538 3130
✉ enquiries@emedigital.co.uk
🖥 www.emedigital.co.uk

Emma Hughes 120 Latchmere Road, Kingston upon Thames, Surrey, KT2 5TT, United Kingdom
☎ (020) 8546 7199/(07971) 957596
✉ emma@lesandemma.co.uk

Enhanced Images Ltd The Stables, 21A St. James Road, East Grinstead, West Sussex, RH19 1DL, United Kingdom
☎ (01342) 327574/🖷 (01342) 326540
✉ info@enhancedimages.co.uk
🖥 www.enhancedimages.co.uk

Exe Valley Dataset Ltd 43 Marsh Green Road West, Marsh Barton Trading Estate, Exeter, EX2 8PN, United Kingdom
☎ (01392) 426464/🖷 (01392) 491066
✉ sales@evdataset.co.uk
🖥 www.evdataset.co.uk

Fiction Imaging 1 Lynton Road, London, N8 8SR, United Kingdom
☎ (020) 8374 8044
✉ info@fictionimaging.co.uk
🖥 www.fictionimaging.co.uk

FixerLabs Unit 62, Wenta Business Centre, Watford, WD24 7ND, United Kingdom
☎ (01923) 226655
✉ info@fixerlabs.com
🖥 www.fixerlabs.com

Flying Colours 45-47 Broadwick Street, London, W1F 9QP, United Kingdom
☎ (020) 7734 3577/🖷 (020) 7494 1559
✉ david@negs.co.uk
🖥 www.negs.co.uk

FreelanceImages The Core Business Centre, Milton Hill, Steventon, Abingdon, Oxfordshire, OX13 6AB, United Kingdom
☎ (01235) 828 286/(07919) 181830
✉ garethlewis@freelanceimages.co.uk
🖥 www.freelanceimages.co.uk

Gask & Hawley Ltd 3 Commerce Way, Avocado Court, Trafford Park, Manchester, M17 1HW, United Kingdom
☎ 0161-869 5880/🖷 0161-873 7501
✉ dave.hatton@gaskandhawley.com
🖥 www.gaskandhawley.com

Genesis Imaging (Chelsea) Unit D2, The Depot, 2 Michael Road, London, SW6 2AD, United Kingdom
☎ (020) 7731 2227/🖷 (020) 7731 8778
✉ chelsea@genesisimaging.co.uk
🖥 www.genesisimaging.co.uk

Genesis Imaging (City) The Depo, 2 Michael Road, Fulham, London, SW6 2AD, United Kingdom
☎ (020) 7731 2227/🖷 (020) 7731 8778
✉ city@genesisimaging.co.uk
🖥 www.genesisimaging.co.uk

Genie Imaging Unit D4, Jaggard Way, London, SW12 8SG, United Kingdom
☎ (020) 8772 1700/🖷 (020) 8772 1710
✉ orders@genieimaging.co.uk
🖥 www.genieimaging.co.uk

Georgiou Digital Imaging & Design 71 Grosvenor Road, London, N9 8RG, United Kingdom
☎ (07762) 707370
✉ mario@georgiou.com
🖥 www.georgiou.com

Glorious Productions 6 Hoxton Square, Top Floor, London, N1 6NU, United Kingdom
☎ (020) 7729 9510/(07718) 878454
✉ keith@gloriousproductions.co.uk
🖥 www.gloriousproductions.co.uk

GMID Design for Business Prospect House, 3 Prospect Place, Swansea, SA1 1QP, United Kingdom
☎ (01792) 641350/🖷 (01792) 301548
✉ studio@gmid.net
🖥 www.gmid.net

Graham Naylor Flat 7, Albany, 20 St. John's Avenue, London, SW15 2AA, United Kingdom
☎ (07789) 488956
✉ info@grahamnaylor.co.uk
🖥 www.grahamnaylor.co.uk

GreatPortraits.co.uk Arle Court, Hatherley Lane, Cheltenham, Gloucestershire, GL51 6PN, United Kingdom
☎ (01242) 255000
✉ sqw@c2000.com
🖥 www.greatportraits.co.uk

Hand Colouring Helena Zakrzewska-Rucinska Invicta Works, 8 Graces Mews, London, SE5 8JF, United Kingdom
☎ (020) 7701 4865/7920042865
✉ helena@helenazr.com
🖥 www.helenazr.com

Happy Finish Unit 36, Cremer Business Centre, 37 Cremer Street, London, E2 8HD, United Kingdom
☎ 07830 136796/🖷 (020) 7739 6164
✉ kate@happyfinish.net
🖥 www.happyfinish.net

Harrogate Photographic Labs Bower House, Station Parade, Harrogate, North Yorkshire, HG1 1UF, United Kingdom
☎ (01423) 501066/🖷 (01423) 501066
✉ tony@photo-labs.com
🖥 www.photo-labs.com

Holborn Studios 49-50 Eagle Wharf Road, London, N1 7ED, United Kingdom
☎ **(020) 7490 4099**/🖷 **(020) 7253 8120**
✉ **reception@holborn-studios.co.uk**
🖥 **www.holbornstudios.com**
See ad in showcase

Horst Kolo 60 Hamilton Road, London, NW11 9EJ, United Kingdom
☎ (020) 8458 6364/🖷 (020) 7435 3873
✉ horst@horstkolo.co.uk
🖥 www.horstkolo.co.uk

Ian Headland
London, United Kingdom
☎ (020) 7253 3007
✉ ian.headland@btconnect.com
🖥 www.ianheadland.com

Image 1 Ltd The Old Forge, 38a North Road, Preston, Brighton, BN1 6SP, United Kingdom
☎ (01273) 543888/🖷 (01273) 236365
✉ info@image1.co.uk
🖥 www.image1.co.uk

Images of Empire British Empire & Commonwealth Museum, Clock Tower Yard, Temple Meads, Bristol, BS1 6QH, United Kingdom
☎ 0117-929 3851/🖷 0117-929 3852
✉ info@imagesofempire.com
🖥 www.imagesofempire.com

Imaginart Ltd 8 Shambles, York, YO1 7LZ, United Kingdom
☎ (01904) 623895
✉ grahame@imaginart.co.uk
🖥 www.imaginart.co.uk

DIGITAL IMAGING AND RETOUCHING

Immediate Image The Church, 145F Crouch Hill, London, N8 9QH, United Kingdom
(020) 8442 7007/(07986) 532225 (0871) 5617761
info@immediateimage.co.uk
www.immediateimage.co.uk

Inatif 14 Durnsford Road, Wimbledon, London, SW19 8HQ, United Kingdom
(020) 8605 2526/(020) 8605 2526
sales@inatif.co.uk
www.inatif.co.uk

Isis London 14a Rosebery Ave, London, EC1R 4TD, UK
(020) 7833 8335/(07748) 124327 (020) 7833 0510
isis@isislondon.co.uk
www.isislondon.co.uk

Jessop Group Ltd Jessop House, 98 Scudamore Road, Leicester, LE3 1TZ, United Kingdom
0116-232 0033/0116-232 0060
www.jessops.com

Joan Blencowe Imaging The Lodge, 155 Lascelles Hall Road, Huddersfield, HD5 0BE, United Kingdom
(01484) 513363
imaging@frogs-eye.com
www.frogs-eye.com

John Prior MCSD Braemoor, Heath End Road, High Wycombe, Buckinghamshire, HP15 6HL, United Kingdom
(01494) 711664
john@johnprior.co.uk
www.johnprior.co.uk

Johnboyphoto Unit C, 1-19 Tewkesbury Road, Manor House, London, N15 6SE, United Kingdom
(020) 8802 4653
johnboyphoto@yahoo.co.uk
www.johnboyphoto.com

Jon Hempstead Retouching Top Floor 71, Sanshew Street, London, N1 6LA, United Kingdom
(020 7739 3844/(07960) 956182
jon@jonhempstead.co.uk

Julian Tewkesbury 1 Britten Drive, Barnstaple, Devon, EX32 8AQ, United Kingdom
(01271) 343507
julian@juliantewkesbury.com
www.juliantewkesbury.com

Junction Eleven Ltd Unit 4 Jugglers Close, Off Wildmere Road, Banbury, Oxfordshire, OX16 3JU, UK
0121-627 5012/0121-627 5038
dan.burman@junctioneleven.com
www.junctioneleven.com

K L Imaging 128 Boroughbridge Road, York, YO26 6AL, United Kingdom
(01904) 792338/(01904) 781188
info@klphoto.co.uk
www.klphoto.co.uk

Kostas Grivas 39 Burntwood Lane, Wandsworth, London, SW17 0JY, United Kingdom
(020) 8947 4533/078 60 101027 (020) 8947 4533

Kr8iv Universal Square, Devonshire, Manchester, M12 6JH, United Kingdom
0161-276 3141
thepeople@kr8iv.co.uk
www.kr8iv.co.uk

Lee John Rouse 404 St. Albans Road, Watford, WD24 6PJ, United Kingdom
(01923) 247538/(07968) 196914
studio@leejohnrouse.co.uk
www.leejohnrouse.co.uk

Lightbox Creative Services Ltd 65 Clerkenwell Road, London, EC1R 5BL, United Kingdom
(020) 7421 1122/ (020) 7421 1144
sales@lightboxes.co.uk
www.lightboxes.co.uk

LM Retouch 10 Gwindra Road, St. Stephen, St. Austell, Cornwall, PL26 7NG, United Kingdom
(07725) 534305
lucy@lmretouch.co.uk
www.lmretouch.co.uk

London Digital Printing Group Ltd Kirkman House, 12-14 Whitfield Street, London, W1T 2RF, United Kingdom
(020) 7637 4440/ (020) 7637 4441
lesbexfield@ldpg.com
www.ldpg.com

Longneck Afgan Road 27, Battersea, London, SW11 2QD,
7506018062
vlad@longneck.ro
www.longneck.ro

Major Retouch 59b Barrington Road, London, SW9 7JH, United Kingdom
(07981) 349321
robmajor@majorretouch.com
www.majorretouch.com

Mark Mason The Old Church Hall, Percy Street, Oxford, OX4 3AF, United Kingdom
(01865) 244600/ (01865) 794795
mail@mmstudios.co.uk
www.mmstudios.co.uk

Martin Bradbery 12 Crescent Road, London, N15 3LL, United Kingdom
(07971) 783384
mbradbery2002@yahoo.co.uk

Matrix Graphics Ltd 31 Lee Bank Business Centre, 55 Holloway Head, Birmingham, B1 1HP, United Kingdom
0121-643 2227/ 0121-643 1345
carl.prosser@matrixgraphics.co.uk
www.matrixgraphics.co.uk

Matt Crowther 16 Hillside, 74 Crouch End Hill, London, N8 8DN, United Kingdom
(07779) 250977/ (07779) 250977
matt@mattcrowther.com
www.mattcrowther.com

Matt Leech Flat 14, 53 Langton Road, London, SW9 6UG, United Kingdom
(07711) 686180

Matthew Burlem Retouching London, United Kingdom
(020) 7635 7516/(07778) 355652
matt@burlem.com
www.burlem.com

Matthew Lane 12 Verney Close, Tring, Hertfordshire, HP23 5LB, United Kingdom
(01442) 383699
matt@mattlane.info
www.mattlane.info

Moorefield Photographic 2 Old Hall Street, Liverpool, L3 9RQ, United Kingdom
0151-236 1611/ 0151-236 1677
info@moorefieldsphoto.com
www.moorefieldsphoto.com

Moorland Photographic & Digital Imaging Ltd 123 Moorland Road, Burslem, Stoke-on-Trent, ST6 1JD, United Kingdom
(01782) 814861/ (01782) 835907
enquiries@moorlandphoto.co.uk
www.moorlandphoto.co.uk

Neville Hornsey 128 Brick Lane, London, E1 6RU, United Kingdom
(07775) 912771
neville@applez.co.uk
www.applez.co.uk

NXMD 38 Heathdene Road, London, SW16 3PD, United Kingdom
(07986) 623628
jd@nxmd.co.uk
www.nxmd.co.uk

One Shot Photography 30 Hartland Road, London, NW1 8DD, United Kingdom
(07961) 407158
info@1shot.uk.com
www.1shot.uk.com

Pank Sethi Photography & Digital Art 6 Lichfield Rd, London, N9 9HD, United Kingdom
(07919) 436 836
pank@panksethi-photography.co.uk
www.panksethi-photography.co.uk

Paper Alligator Ltd 67 Wood End Lane, Northolt, Middlesex, UB5 4JW, United Kingdom
(07751) 310303
louisecunningham133@hotmail.com
www.louisecunningham.com

Parallax Models 63 Clerkenwell Road, London, EC1M 5NP, United Kingdom
(020) 7253 6777/(07770) 328003
steve@stevecolman.biz

Paul Carter 7 College Road, Woolston, Southampton, SO19 9GD, United Kingdom
(023) 8043 6191/ (023) 8043 1070
paul@paulcarter-photographer.co.uk
www.paulcarter-photographer.co.uk

Paul Noble Photographic Unit 4, Teknol House, Burgess Hill, West Sussex, RH15 9LH, United Kingdom
(01444) 232367/(07860) 654724
paul@pnoblephoto.net
www.pnoblephoto.net

Perceptive Photography Deacons Cottage, Cross in Hand Road, Heathfield, East Sussex, TN21 0UR, United Kingdom
(01435) 865214
info@perceptivephotography.com
www.perceptivephotography.com

Photo Digital Enhance Ltd 24 Langroyd Road, London, SW17 7PL, United Kingdom
(020) 8879 6222
admin@photodigitalenhance.co.uk
www.photodigitalenhance.co.uk

Photo-Stock Library 14 Neville Avenue, Anchorsholme, Blackpool, FY5 3BG, United Kingdom
(01253) 864598
enquiries@photo-stock.co.uk
www.photo-stock.co.uk

Photofusion Photography Centre 17a Electric Lane, London, SW9 8LA, United Kingdom
(020) 7733 3500/ (020) 7738 5509
library@photofusion.org
www.photofusionpictures.org

PictureSelect Staines, Middlesex, TW18 1XX, United Kingdom
(08701) 995070
info@pictureselect.com
www.pictureselect.com

Pinpoint Photography Unit 30, Park Farm Estate, 100 Acre Lane, Wivelsfield Green, Haywards Heath, West Sussex, RH17 7RU, United Kingdom
(01273) 890600
info@pinpointphotography.co.uk
www.pinpointphotography.co.uk

Pixel Canvas 8 Cyrus Court, Emersons Green, Bristol, BS16 7AX, United Kingdom
0117-909 0076/(07950) 094529 0117- 909 0076
tom@pixelcanvas.co.uk
www.pixelcanvas.co.uk

Poliprints 57 Lancaster Road, Barnet, Hertfordshire, EN4 8AS, United Kingdom
(020) 8441 4364/(07976) 900695 (020) 8449 0317
steve@leopold.co.uk
www.poliprints.com

Profolab Imaging Ltd Unit 4 Surrey Close, Granby Industrial Estate, Weymouth, Dorset, DT4 9TY, United Kingdom
(01305) 774098/ (01305) 778746
info@profolab.co.uk
www.profolab.co.uk

Qualitech Group Bramhall Technology Park, Pepper Road, Stockport, Cheshire, SK7 5BW, United Kingdom
0161-456 6866/ 0161-487 1588
sales@qualitech.co.uk
www.qualitech.co.uk

Quality Exposed Kiosk Two, The Martlets, Burgess Hill, West Sussex, RH15 9NN, United Kingdom
(01444) 257535
qualityexposed@btinternet.com
www.qualityexposed.co.uk

Red Roofrack 5 Calvert Avenue, London, E2 7JP, United Kingdom
(020) 7739 2461
tim@redroofrack.com
www.redroofrack.com

Robert Holder Twin Oaks, 14 Darren View, Bridgend, Mid Glamorgan, CF34 9SG, United Kingdom
(01656) 732944/(07796) 172129 (01656) 733895
rholder@freeuk.com

Robert McAulay 9A Oxford Gardens, London, W10 5UE, United Kingdom
(020) 8969 3070/ (020) 8969 3070
mcaulayrobert@hotmail.com

Saddington Baynes Studio 3 , 21 Wren Street, London, WC1X 0HF
020 7833 3032/020 7837 1942
info@saddingtonbaynes.com
www.saddingtonbaynes.com
The pioneers of digital retouching are once again leading the way, introducing the world's finest Agencies and Photographers to the exciting creative possibilities of CGI for Print, taking their concepts to new levels of creativity. **See ad in showcase**

Scarlet Creative Solutions Ltd 3 Yew Walk, Hoddesdon, Hertfordshire, EN11 8BB, United Kingdom
(0845) 4085402
solutions@scarletcreative.co.uk
www.scarletcreative.co.uk

Schafline 29 Darby Road, Liverpool, L19 9BP, United Kingdom
✆ 0151-494 2928/✆ 0151-494 3829
✉ jbs@pinsharp3d.co.uk
🖥 www.pinsharp3d.co.uk

sdimaging 53 Sandgate High Street, Sandgate, Folkestone, Kent, CT20 3AH, United Kingdom
✆ (01303) 256666/(07930) 316601
✉ info@sdimaging.co.uk
🖥 www.sdimaging.co.uk

Service Point 27 Prince of Wales Road, Norwich, NR1 1BG, United Kingdom
✆ (01603) 660061/✆ (01603) 630838
✉ norwich@servicepoint.com
🖥 www.servicepointuk.com

Smudgesphotos Miltonmuir House, Arbuthnott, Laurencekirk, Kincardineshire, AB30 1PB, United Kingdom
✆ (01561) 361900
✉ hasmudge1@tiscali.co.uk
🖥 myweb.tiscali.co.uk/smudgephotos

SOLUTIONS Photographic Manor Road, Luton, LU1 4ED, United Kingdom
✆ (01582) 725065/(07836) 248126
✉ rod@solphoto.co.uk
🖥 www.solphoto.co.uk

Sonoco Trident Unit 4, Connaught Road, Kingswood Business Park, Hull, HU7 3AP, United Kingdom
✆ (01482) 828 100/✆ (01482) 710 600
✉ david.keel@sonoco-trident.com
🖥 www.sonoco-trident.com

Spring Studios Ltd 10 Spring Place, Kentish Town, London, NW5 3BH, United Kingdom
✆ (020) 7267 8383/(07764) 331234/✆ (020) 7267 8481
✉ info@springstudios.com
🖥 www.springstudios.com

St James Retouching Unit 21, Jacks Place, 6 Corbet Place, London, E1 6NN, United Kingdom
✆ (020) 7426 2111/✆ (020) 7426 2111
✉ knoxy@st-james.uk.com
🖥 www.st-james.uk.com

Stan McGee Creative Imaging 7 Poplar Row, Theydon Bois, Essex, CM16 7HX, United Kingdom
✆ (01992) 814342/(07710) 037767
✉ stanmcgee@beeb.net

Stantham Studios 4 Northcote Place, Newcastle, Staffordshire, ST5 1HU, United Kingdom
✆ (07831) 354302
✉ info@statham.net
🖥 www.statham.net

Steve Gale 4 Ribblesdale Road, London, N8 7EP, United Kingdom
✆ (020) 8348 7724/(07831) 372198
✉ sgale@dircon.co.uk
🖥 www.celticlandscapes.com

Studio Studio House, Invar Business Park, Invar Road, Manchester, M27 9HF, United Kingdom
✆ 0161-793 7377/✆ 0161-793 7376
✉ info@thestudio.co.uk
🖥 www.thestudio.co.uk

T A G Creative, Adplates Group 29 Clerkenwell Road, London, EC1M 5TA, United Kingdom
✆ (020) 7251 4571/✆ (020) 7253 5355
✉ info@tagmedia.co.uk
🖥 www.tagmedia.co.uk

Tag Print 3-4 Bakers Yard, Bakers Row, London, EC1R 3DD, United Kingdom
✆ (020) 7837 0123/✆ (020) 7278 3364
🖥 www.tagworldwide.com

Tapestry Tapestry, 51-52 Frith Street, London, W1D 4SH, United Kingdom
✆ (020) 7896 3100/✆ (020) 7896 3009
✉ info@tapestry.co.uk
🖥 www.tapestry.co.uk

Taylor James 123-125 Curtain Road, Shorditch, London, EC2A 3BX, United Kingdom
✆ (020) 7739 4488/✆ (020) 7739 5958
✉ info@taylorjames.com
🖥 www.taylorjames.com

Technik Unit 4, River Park Industrial Estate, Billet Lane, Berkhamsted, Hertfordshire, HP4 1HL, United Kingdom
✆ (01442) 871117/✆ (01442) 869619
✉ sales@technik.com
🖥 www.technik.com

Terry Obiora 56 Falconer Road, Bushey, WD23 3AW, United Kingdom
✆ (07830) 071504
✉ info@terryobiora.com
🖥 www.terryobiora.com

Terry Payne Packshot & Food Photographer First Floor, Building D, The Chocolate Factory, Clarendon Road, London, N22 6XJ,
✆ 020 8889 6609
✉ terry.payne1@ntlworld.com
🖥 www.terrypaynephotog.co.uk

The Colour Company 1-5 Clerkenwell Road, London, EC1M 5PA, United Kingdom
✆ (020) 7251 1285/✆ (020) 7490 3818
✉ john@colourcompany.com
🖥 www.colourcompany.com

The D P C Ltd Linear House, Peyton Place, London, SE10 8RS, United Kingdom
✆ (020) 8858 8351/✆ (020) 8305 0268
✉ richard@thedpc.com
🖥 www.thedpc.com

The Dairy Studio 43 Bellenden Road, London, SE15 5BB, United Kingdom
✆ (020) 7639 2712/✆ 020 7732 8235
✉ info@thedairystudio.com
🖥 www.thedairystudio.com

The Invisible Picture Company 56 Falconer Road, Bushey, WD23 3AW, United Kingdom
✆ (020) 8950 2901
✉ terry@invisiblepicture.com
🖥 www.invisiblepicturecompany.com

This Little Fish 14a Dufours Place, London, W1F 7SN
✆ **020 7534 0810/✉ info@thislittlefish.com**
✉ **www.thislittlefish.com**
See ad in showcase

Tim Gravestock 197 Hempstead Road, Watford, WD17 3HG, United Kingdom
✆ (01923) 252460/07752 043046
✉ timgravestock@btconnect.com
🖥 www.takumigroup.net

Tom Ang 59 Grantham Road, London, SW9 9ED, United Kingdom
✆ (07958) 701393
✉ tomang@cap.ndirect.co.uk

Tom Langford Retoucher 44 Hermiston Avenue, London, N8 8NP, United Kingdom
✆ (07973) 923 210
✉ mail@tomlangford.net
🖥 www.tomlangford.net

Tony Slade Photography 51 Turnfurlong, Aylesbury, Buckinghamshire, HP21 7PS, United Kingdom
✆ (07890) 990246/✆ (01296) 415488
✉ tony@tonyslade.com 🖥 www.tonyslade.com

Tony Swinney 44 Hogshill Lane, Cobham, Surrey, KT11 2AQ, United Kingdom
✆ (07768) 993022
✉ tony@mustardpost.co.uk
🖥 www.mustardpost.co.uk

Touch Creative Ltd 8 Gatehill Road, Northwood, Middlesex, HA6 3QD, United Kingdom
✆ (01923) 825387/7773481607
✉ georgekepinski@onetel.com

Touch Digital 3 Ardleigh Road, London, N1 4HS, United Kingdom
✆ (020) 7684 7500/✆ (020) 7684 7499
✉ graeme@touchdigital.co.uk
🖥 www.touchdigital.co.uk

Transcolour Ltd Unit 1, 7 Tyers Gate, London, SE1 3HX, United Kingdom
✆ (020) 7403 0048
✉ juno.field@btinternet.co.uk

Unichrome Creative 23-25 Great Sutton Street, London, EC1V 0DN, United Kingdom
✆ (020) 7251 8811/✆ (020) 7251 8812
✉ info@unichrome-creative.com
🖥 www.unichrome-creative.com

Vincent Oliver 20 Green Lane, Chislehurst, Kent, BR7 6AG, United Kingdom
✆ (020) 8467 2465/(07768) 004518
✉ vsoliver@aol.com
🖥 www.photo-i.co.uk

Visual Aspects Ltd 18 Leather Lane, London, EC1N 7SU, United Kingdom
✆ (020) 7404 1290/✆ (020) 7404 1291
✉ info@visualaspects.co.uk
🖥 www.visualaspects.co.uk

Visual Communications 8 Manor Road, Chigwell, Essex, IG7 5PD, United Kingdom
✆ (020) 8504 9009/✆ (020) 8504 9030
✉ viscom2@aol.com
🖥 www.viscom-design.co.uk

Visualeyes Imaging Services 11 West Street, Covent Garden, London, WC2H 9NE, United Kingdom
✆ (020) 7836 3004/✆ (020) 7240 0079
✉ imaging@visphoto.co.uk
🖥 www.visphoto.co.uk

Voila Image Unit 5, 139A Stroud Green Road, London, N4 3PX, United Kingdom
✆ (020) 7263 4445/✆ (020) 7281 2681
✉ info@voilaimage.com
🖥 www.voilaimage.com

Wallcandy 295 View 146 Conway Street, Liverpool, L5 3BB, United Kingdom
✆ 0151-207 4531
✉ sales@wallcandyuk.com
🖥 www.wallcandyuk.com

HOME ECONOMISTS

Ailsa Cruickshank/HERS Agency Ltd Cleaveside, Bickleigh, Tiverton, Devon, EX16 8RB, United Kingdom
✆ (0870) 429 6499/✆ (01884) 855855
✉ hers@hersagency.co.uk
🖥 www.hersagency.co.uk

B C Connections Ltd 27a Erewash Square, Ilkeston, Derbyshire, DE7 5SP, United Kingdom
✆ 0115-977 0586/✆ (0870) 1319548
✉ bcconnection@emailaccount.com
🖥 www.bc-connections.com

Bethany Heald/HERS Agency Ltd Cleaveside, Bickleigh, Tiverton, Devon, EX16 8RB, United Kingdom
✆ (0870) 429 6499/✆ (01884) 855855
✉ hers@hersagency.co.uk
🖥 www.hersagency.co.uk

Brian Brooke Walker Brow Farm, Macclesfield Road, Whaley Bridge, High Peak, Derbyshire, SK23 7DR, United Kingdom
✆ (01663) 735212/(07798) 521269 ✆ (01663) 733616
✉ brianbrooke@btinternet.com
🖥 www.contact-me.net/brianbrooke

Carole Handslip/HERS Agency Ltd Cleaveside, Bickleigh, Tiverton, Devon, EX16 8RB, United Kingdom
✆ (0870) 429 6499/✆ (01884) 855855
✉ hers@hersagency.co.uk
🖥 www.hersagency.co.uk

Caroline Marson/HERS Agency Ltd Cleaveside, Bickleigh, Tiverton, Devon, EX16 8RB, United Kingdom
✆ (0870) 429 6499/✆ (01884) 855855
✉ hers@hersagency.co.uk
🖥 www.hersagency.co.uk

Christine Greaves/HERS Agency Ltd Cleaveside, Bickleigh, Tiverton, Devon, EX16 8RB, United Kingdom
✆ (0870) 429 6499/✆ (01884) 855855
✉ hers@hersagency.co.uk
🖥 www.hersagency.co.uk

Christine McFadden Oriel House, 71 Prior Park Road, Bath, BA2 4NF, United Kingdom
✆ (01225) 310593/(07980) 623164 ✆ (01225) 481558
✉ christine@mcfadden1.demon.co.uk

Clare Ferguson/HERS Agency Ltd Cleaveside, Bickleigh, Tiverton, Devon, EX16 8RB, United Kingdom
✆ (0870) 429 6499/✆ (01884) 855855
✉ hers@hersagency.co.uk
🖥 www.hersagency.co.uk

Clare Gordon-Smith 30 kersley Street, London, SW11 4PT, United Kingdom
✆ (020) 7924 6002
✉ clare.gordonsmith@btinternet.com

Creative Talent (UK) Limited 78 York Street, London, W1H 1DP, United Kingdom
✆ (020) 7439 1877/✆ (020) 7434 1144
✉ info@creativetalentlimited.com
🖥 www.creativetalentlimited.com

Dagmar Vesely/HERS Agency Ltd Cleaveside, Bickleigh, Tiverton, Devon, EX16 8RB, United Kingdom
✆ (0870) 429 6499/✆ (01884) 855855
✉ hers@hersagency.co.uk
🖥 www.hersagency.co.uk

Dawn Stock 15 Woodland Drive, Thorpe End, Norwich, NR13 5BH, United Kingdom
✆ (01603) 433174
✉ dawn_doc@hotmail.com

HOME ECONOMISTS

Denise Smart 70 Stokenchurch Place, Bradwell Common, Milton Keynes, MK13 8BY, United Kingdom
☎ (01908) 695379/(07759) 798281 📠 (01908) 695379
✉ denise.smart@virgin.net
🖥 www.denisesmart.com

Elaine Ngan 2A Clifton Road, London, SW19 4QT, United Kingdom
☎ (020) 8947 2899/(07831) 888654 📠 2089463245
✉ elainengan13@hotmail.com

Eliza Baird/HERS Agency Ltd Cleaveside, Bickleigh, Tiverton, Devon, EX16 8RB, United Kingdom
☎ (0870) 429 6499/ 📠 (01884) 855855
✉ hers@hersagency.co.uk
🖥 www.hersagency.co.uk

Entrust Food Safety 593 Clarkston Road, Glasgow, G44 3QD, United Kingdom
☎ 0141-577 7576
✉ Peter.davidson@entrustfoodsafety.co.uk
🖥 www.entrustfoodsafety.com

Gill McCormick Forest Dene, 26 Little Forest Road, Bournemouth, BH4 9NW, United Kingdom
☎ (01202) 759311/(07956) 258309 📠 (01202) 759311

Gizzi Erskine/HERS Agency Ltd Cleaveside, Bickleigh, Tiverton, Devon, EX16 8RB, United Kingdom
☎ (0870) 429 6499/ 📠 (01884) 855855
✉ hers@hersagency.co.uk
🖥 www.hersagency.co.uk

HERS Agency Ltd Cleaveside, Bickleigh, Tiverton, Devon, EX16 8RB, United Kingdom
☎ (0870) 429 6499/ 📠 (01884) 855855
✉ Hers@hersagency.co.uk
🖥 www.hersagency.co.uk
See ad in showcase

J C S 24 Windsor Avenue, Margate, Kent, CT9 2NQ, United Kingdom
☎ (01843) 571823
✉ jul_es10@hotmail.com

Jacqueline Bellefontaine 224 Long Lane, London, SE1 4QB, United Kingdom
☎ (020) 7407 5552/(07973) 333885
✉ info@jacquelinebellefontaine.co.uk
🖥 www.jacquelinebellefontaine.co.uk

Jan Zacharias Jan Zacharias Catering, Storeton Hall Farm, Storeton, Lever Causeway, Wirral, Merseyside, CH63 6HT, United Kingdom
☎ 0151-608 2352/(07885) 787752 📠 0151-608 2352
✉ janzachariascatering@hotmail.com
🖥 www.janzachariascatering.org.uk

Jennie Berresford/HERS Agency Ltd Cleaveside, Bickleigh, Tiverton, Devon, EX16 8RB, United Kingdom
☎ (0870) 429 6499/ 📠 (01884) 855855
✉ hers@hersagency.co.uk
🖥 www.hersagency.co.uk

Juicy Fruits 28 Mill Hill, Weston Colville, Cambridge, CB21 5NY, United Kingdom
☎ (01223) 290396/ 📠 (01223) 290212
✉ steven@juicyfruitsuk.com
🖥 www.juicyfruitsuk.com
See ad in showcase

Kathy Roche The Garden Flat, 282 Elgin Avenue, Maida Vale, London, W9 1JR, United Kingdom
☎ (020) 7286 5383/(07836) 288222 📠 (020) 7286 6947
✉ k.t.roche@dsl.pipex.com

Kit Chan/HERS Agency Ltd Cleaveside, Bickleigh, Tiverton, Devon, EX16 8RB, United Kingdom
☎ (0870) 429 6499/ 📠 (01884) 855855
✉ hers@hersagency.co.uk
🖥 www.hersagency.co.uk

Lesley Sendall 100A Bethune Road, London, N16 5BA, United Kingdom
☎ (020) 8800 2034/079 73 333823 📠 (020) 8800 2034
✉ lesley@lsendall.fsnet.co.uk

Linda Tubby
United Kingdom
☎ (07770) 945330

Lorna Rhodes 12 Highwoods Drive, Marlow Bottom, Marlow, Buckinghamshire, SL7 3PY, United Kingdom
☎ (01628) 483420/(07710) 488109 📠 (01628) 482111
✉ lornarhodes@aol.com
🖥 www.lornarhodes.co.uk

Lyn Rutherford
London, SE23 1EW, United Kingdom
☎ (020) 8699 3817/(07774) 816080

Lynne Clayton Abbey Oaks Farm House, Burstall Lane, Ipswich, IP8 3DH, United Kingdom
☎ (01473) 747388/(07774) 113989 📠 (01473) 744775
✉ lynneclayton@lineone.net

Mandy Phipps 2 Falconwood Road, Croydon, CR0 9BB, United Kingdom
☎ (01689) 843888
✉ amanda@foodstylingplus.co.uk

Marie-Ange Lapierre/HERS Agency Ltd Cleaveside, Bickleigh, Tiverton, Devon, EX16 8RB, United Kingdom
☎ (0870) 429 6499/ 📠 (01884) 855855
✉ hers@hersagency.co.uk
🖥 www.hersagency.co.uk

Martha Dunkerley/HERS Agency Ltd Cleaveside, Bickleigh, Tiverton, Devon, EX16 8RB, United Kingdom
☎ (0870) 429 6499/ 📠 (01884) 855855
✉ hers@hersagency.co.uk
🖥 www.hersagency.co.uk

Mary Luther/HERS Agency Ltd Cleaveside, Bickleigh, Tiverton, Devon, EX16 8RB, United Kingdom
☎ (0870) 429 6499/ 📠 (01884) 855855
✉ hers@hersagency.co.uk
🖥 www.hersagency.co.uk

Meg Jansz 8 Lessar Avenue, London, SW4 9HJ, United Kingdom
☎ (020) 8772 0542/(07932) 022881

HOME ECONOMISTS
STYLISTS
HAIR & MAKE-UP

Nicola Fowler/HERS Agency Ltd Cleaveside, Bickleigh, Tiverton, Devon, EX16 8RB, United Kingdom
✆ (0870) 429 6499/ ✆ (01884) 855855
✉ hers@hersagency.co.uk
🖥 www.hersagency.co.uk

Nicole Szabason/HERS Agency Ltd Cleaveside, Bickleigh, Tiverton, Devon, EX16 8RB, United Kingdom
✆ (0870) 429 6499/ ✆ (01884) 855855
✉ hers@hersagency.co.uk
🖥 www.hersagency.co.uk

Peta O'Brien 36 Clarence Mews, London, E5 8HL, United Kingdom
✆ (020) 8986 0087/(07768) 825255
✉ petaob@yahoo.co.uk

Pippa Cuthbert/HERS Agency Ltd Cleaveside, Bickleigh, Tiverton, Devon, EX16 8RB, United Kingdom
✆ (0870) 429 6499/ ✆ (01884) 855855
✉ hers@hersagency.co.uk
🖥 www.hersagency.co.uk

Sheila Bretherton 69 Stourbridge Road, Fairfield, Bromsgrove, Worcestershire, B61 9LY, United Kingdom
✆ (01527) 831820/(07717) 762633 ✆ (01527) 831820

Shoot People 3rd Floor, 202 City Road, London, EC1V 2PH, United Kingdom
✆ (020) 7253 0009/(07767) 313007 ✆ (020) 7253 0009
✉ victoria@shootpeople.com
🖥 www.shootpeople.com

Smutt Magazine 41 Kensington Road, Chichester, West Sussex, PO19 7XS,
✆ 70926368776
✉ lou.marshall@hotmail.com
🖥 www.smuttmagazine.com

Stephen Parkins-Knight/HERS Agency Ltd Cleaveside, Bickleigh, Tiverton, Devon, EX16 8RB, United Kingdom
✆ (0870) 429 6499/ ✆ (01884) 855855
✉ hers@hersagency.co.uk
🖥 www.hersagency.co.uk

The Food Business Ground Floor, St Georges House, 50 Adelaide Street, St. Albans, Hertfordshire, AL3 5BG, United Kingdom
✆ (01727) 832834/(07989) 304850 ✆ (01727) 832836
✉ sally@thefoodbusiness.co.uk

The Original Hat Box Cake Company Foxgloves, Dragon Lane, Manningford Bruce, Pewsey, Wiltshire, SN9 6JE, United Kingdom
✆ (01672) 564063
✉ suepalms@tiscali.co.uk

LIGHTING

Black Light 18 West Harbour Road, Granton, Edinburgh, EH5 1PN, United Kingdom
✆ 0131-551 2337/ ✆ 0131-551 6827
✉ enquiries@black-light.com
🖥 www.black-light.com

Blacklight Ltd 18 West Harbour Road, Granton, Edinburgh, EH5 1PN, United Kingdom
✆ 0131-551 2337/ ✆ 0131-551 6827
✉ edinburgh@black-light.com
🖥 www.black-light.com

Cinebuild Ltd Studio House, 34 Rita Road, London, SW8 1JU, United Kingdom
✆ (020) 7582 8750/(07836) 220441 ✆ (020) 7793 0467
✉ cinebuild@btclick.com
🖥 www.cinebuild.com

Daylight Co. Ltd 89-91 Scrubs Lane, London, NW10 6QU, United Kingdom
✆ (020) 8964 1200/ ✆ (020) 8964 1300
✉ info.uk@daylightcompany.com
🖥 www.daylightcompany.com

Kinetic Units 3 & 4, Cremer Business Centre, 37 Cremer Street, London, E2 8HD, United Kingdom
✆ (020) 7729 7442/ ✆ (020) 7749 4299
✉ info@go-kinetic.com
🖥 www.go-kinetic.com

LCA - Lights, Camera, Action Unit 30, The Metropolitan Centre, Taunton Road, Greenford, Middlesex, UB6 8UQ, United Kingdom
✆ (020) 8833 7600/ ✆ (020) 8575 8219
✉ sales@lcauk.com
🖥 www.lcauk.com

Paul Robinson (GBCT) 31 Stapleton Road, London, SW17 8BA, United Kingdom
✆ (020) 8682 4416/(07973) 255815
✉ paulrobinson@mail.com
🖥 www.paulrobinson-cameraman.com

Photon Beard Ltd Unit K3, Cherry Court Way, Leighton Buzzard, Bedfordshire, LU7 4UH, United Kingdom
✆ (01525) 850911/ ✆ (01525) 850922
✉ info@photonbeard.com
🖥 www.photonbeard.com

Pro Centre 5/6 Mallow Street, London, EC1Y 8RS, United Kingdom
✆ (020) 7490 3122/ ✆ (020) 7490 1292
✉ procentre@hasselblad.co.uk
🖥 www.procentre.co.uk

Roscolab Ltd Blanchard Works, Kangley Bridge Road, Sydenham, London, SE26 5AQ, United Kingdom
✆ (020) 8659 2300/ ✆ (020) 8659 3153
✉ marketing@rosco-europe.com
🖥 www.rosco.com

Sanctuary Photographic 32-36 Telford Way, London, W3 7XS, United Kingdom
✆ (020) 8743 1563/ ✆ (020) 8743 8075
✉ photographic@sanctuarystudios.co.uk
🖥 www.sanctuaryphotographic.co.uk

Snap Productions 151-155 New North Road, London, N1 6TA, United Kingdom
✆ (020) 7684 7555/ ✆ (020) 7684 7556
✉ rich@snap-pro.com
🖥 www.snap-pro.com
See ad in showcase

Contact Julia or Alice

Tel: +44 (0)870 429 6499
Fax: +44 (0)1884 855 855
hers@hersagency.co.uk
www.hersagency.co.uk

Digital asset management made easy.

See www.junctioneleven.com for the fuller picture.

junction eleven

State-of-the-art system | Simple to use

Secure & reliable | Access any time, anywhere

Off J11 M40 Jugglers Close Banbury Oxfordshire OX16 3JU
Tel 01295 700122 email info@junctioneleven.com

Sola (Solalights) Limited Unit 18, The Grand Union Center, West Row, Ladbroke Grove, London, W10 5AS, United Kingdom
- (020) 8960 1121/(07966) 430985 (020) 7117 1930
- solalights@mac.com
- www.solalights.com

Spot Professional Lightservice S.L. Calle Ramon Turrü 23, s.at, Barcelona, 8005, Spain
- 69 038 0205/ 93 221 6083
- barcelona@spot-lightservice.com
- www.spot-lightservice.com

Technical Lamps Milton Hall, Milton Road, Hampton, Middlesex, TW12 2LL, United Kingdom
- (020) 8979 6652/ (020) 8979 9007
- sales@techlamps.co.uk
- www.techlamps.co.uk

LOCATIONS

2Can Productions PO Box 668, Cardiff, CF11 1EZ,
- 0845 0545096/ 0845 0545097
- info@2canproductions.com
- www.2canproductions.com

365 Productions Ibiza 7830, Sant Josep de sa talai, San Jose, Spain
- 00 34 69 745 6967
- info@365-productions.com
- www.365-productions.com

A OK Locations Urb. Isla de Guadalimina Adosada 62, San Pedro de Alcantara, Malaga, 29670, Spain
- 00 34 952 88 0501/ 00 34 952 880 156
- yianniel@terra.es
- www.eventspain.es

Action Locations 5 Peterborough Villas, London, SW6 2AT, United Kingdom
- (020) 7871 0638/(07958) 204916
- renuka008@gmail.com

Airlie Gardens 9 Airlie Gardens, Flat 4 & 5, London, W8 7AJ, United Kingdom
- (020) 7792 8156
- naomi.sorkin@btopenworld.com

Alan Goodyear Classic Cars Engine Farm, 80 Cock Bank, Whittlesey, PE7 2HN, United Kingdom
- (01733) 840553/(07779) 387673 (01733) 840553
- alan@hotchkiss.to

Amazing Space Location Library 74 Clerkenwell Road, London, EC1M 5QA, United Kingdom
- **(020) 7251 6661/ (020) 7251 6808**
- **info@amazingspace.co.uk**
- **www.amazingspace.co.uk**
- See ad in showcase

Anglian Events - First For Film Food Unit 3, Lodge Farm, Park Lane, Kirton, Ipswich, Suffolk, IP10 0EA,
- 0845 4349535
- henry@anglianevents.co.uk
- www.firstforfilmfood.com

Anthea Bowen Willow Tree Cottage, Cloghams Green, Leaden Roding, Dunmow, Essex, CM6 1WG, United Kingdom
- (01279) 876640/(07860) 389352
- anthea@antheabowen.com
- www.antheabowen.com

Arti Printing Solutions 142 Axminster Crescent, Welling, Kent, DA16 1ET, United Kingdom
- (020) 8306 5992/ (020) 8306 5530
- shamjirabadia@hotmail.com

B P H P 50b Regina Road, London, N4 3PP, United Kingdom
- (07855) 520707
- ben@bphp.co.uk
- www.bphp.co.uk

BAC Venues Lavender Hill, Battersea, London, SW11 5TN, United Kingdom
- (020) 7326 8211/ (020) 7585 0704
- venues@bac.org.uk
- www.bacvenues.org.uk

Big Fish Film Productions Ltd 177 West Heath Road, London, NW3 7TT, United Kingdom
- (020) 8201 8555/ (020) 8201 8322
- info@big-fish-productions.co.uk
- www.big-fish-productions.co.uk

Blackbushe Airport Ltd Terminal Building, Blackbushe Airport, Blackwater, Camberley, Surrey, GU17 9LQ, United Kingdom
- (01252) 879449/ (01252) 874444
- blackbusheairport@bca-group.com
- www.blackbusheairport.co.uk

Bluebell Railway Sheffield Park Station, Uckfield, East Sussex, TN22 3QL, United Kingdom
- (01825) 720800/ (01825) 720804
- info@bluebell-railway.co.uk
- www.bluebell-railway.co.uk

Boardroom Productions 22b Iliffe Yard, London, SE17 3QA, United Kingdom
- (020) 7228 0225/ (020) 7223 9740
- jon.self@virgin.net
- www.sunnyhill1.co.uk

Bocek Production Cubuklu cad.agaclik mesire yeri, d+e burunbahce, beykoz, Istanbul, 34805,
- 00 9 02166801058
- selma@bocekyapim.com.tr
- www.bocekyapim.com.tr

Bristol Television Film Services Ltd Unit 12, Londonderry Farm, Keynsham Road, Willsbridge, Bristol, BS30 6EL, United Kingdom
- 0117-932 2046/ 0117-932 3335
- lara@btf-services.co.uk
- www.btf-services.co.uk

British Waterways London 1 Sheldon Square, Paddington Central, London, W2 6TT, United Kingdom
- (020) 7985 7200/ (020) 7985 7201
- enquiries.london@britishwaterways.co.uk
- www.britishwaterwayslondon.co.uk/press

Brocket Hall International Ltd Brocket Hall, Welwyn Garden City, Hertfordshire, AL8 7XG, United Kingdom
- (01707) 335241/(07831) 374757 (01707) 375166
- mail@brocket-hall.co.uk
- www.brocket-hall.co.uk

Brooklands Museum The Clubhouse, Brooklands Road, Weybridge, Surrey, KT13 0QN, United Kingdom
- (01932) 857381/ (01932) 855465
- info@brooklandsmuseum.com
- www.brooklandsmuseum.com

C B A V World Locations 3 rue de Turbigo, Paris, 75001, France
- 00 33 1 42 33 89 23/ 00 33 1 42 33 89 23
- paris@worldlocations.com
- www.worldlocations.com

C R Security (UK) Ltd 19 Reynolds Close, London, SW19 8Gj, United Kingdom
- (020) 8394 1772/ (020) 8224 7688
- crsecurit@aol.com
- www.crsecurity.tv

Cargo Overseas Limited Building 308, World Freight Terminal, Manchester International Airport, Manchester, M90 5PZ, United Kingdom
- 0161 498 6111/ 0161 498 6222
- groche@cargo-overseas.co.uk
- www.cargo-overseas.co.uk

Cars In Camera Unit 6-7 Cardiff Road Ind Estate, Cardiff Road, Watford, WD18 0DG, United Kingdom
- (01727) 836773/(07768) 932646 (01923) 238494
- info@carsincamera.com
- www.carsincamera.com

Caspar & Co. 24 Wisley Road, London, SW11 6NF, United Kingdom
- **(020) 7978 6622/(07768) 610177**
- **info@casparco.com**
- **www.casparco.com**
- See ad in showcase

Celebrity Catering Co. 11933 Ayres Avenue, Suite Three, Los Angeles, 90064, United States of America
- 00 1 310 454 9700
- celebritycatering@myway.com
- neonlightsentertainment.com/celebritycatering.html

Charisma Cabins Ltd Ash House, 8 Second Cross Road, Twickenham, TW2 5RF, United Kingdom
- (07860) 572299/ (020) 8755 4843
- enquiries@charismacabins.co.uk

Charlie Varley North Cottage, Upper Sheriff Farmhouse, Hammingden Lane, Ardingly, Haywards Heath, West Sussex, RH17 6SR, United Kingdom
- (01444) 891340/(07836) 322227
- charlie.varley@tiscali.co.uk

Chateau Impney Hotel & Impney Regent Centre Chateau Hotel, Droitwich Spar, Droitwich, Worcestershire, WR9 0BN, United Kingdom
- (01905) 774411/ (01905) 772371
- enquiries@chateau-impney.com
- www.chateau-impney.com

Check The Gate Rua Rodrigo Albuquerque e Melo 4, 4D, L.A. Velha, Lisboa, Portugal
- 00 351 91 819 6577
- jose@checkthegate.com
- www.checkthegate.com

Chicheley Hall Chicheley Hall, Chicheley, Newport Pagnell, Buckinghamshire, MK16 9JJ, United Kingdom
- (01234) 391 252/ (01234) 391 388
- katiephillips@chicheleyhall.co.uk
- www.chicheleyhall.co.uk

Cinebuild Ltd Studio House, 34 Rita Road, London, SW8 1JU, United Kingdom
- (020) 7582 8750/(07836) 220441 / (020) 7793 0467
- cinebuild@btclick.com
- www.cinebuild.com

Cole Hire Ltd Westar House, 690 Great West Road, Osterley, Isleworth, Middlesex, TW7 4PU, United Kingdom
- (020) 8568 0733
- colehire@demon.co.uk
- www.colehire.co.uk

Compass Locations Ltd 19 All Saints Road, London, W11 1HE, United Kingdom
- (020) 7750 6912/(07770) 274866 / (020) 7792 8507
- charles@compasslocations.com
- www.compasslocations.com

Deerhurst Road Shooting Location 28 Deerhurst Road, Streatham, London, SW16 2AN
- 020 8664 7129/07788 741908/
- gillian.milner@btinternet.com
- www.deerhurstroad.co.uk
- See ad in showcase

Diane Edwards 12 Burlington Lodge Studios, Rigault Road, London, SW6 4JJ, United Kingdom
- (020) 7736 7966/ (020) 7736 7966
- styling@dianedwards.com

Discover The World Arctic House, 8 Bolters Lane, Banstead, Surrey, SM7 2AR, United Kingdom
- (01737) 214214/ (01737) 362341
- enquiries@discover-the-world.co.uk
- www.discover-the-world.co.uk

Dixcot Locations Ltd Dixcot, 8 North Drive, London, SW16 1RL, United Kingdom
- (020) 8769 7144/(07775) 688590 / (020) 8769 4229
- juliet@dixcotlocations.com
- www.dixcotlocations.com

E T H O S Represents 23 Albert Square, London, SW8 1BS, United Kingdom
- (020) 7735 7006/ (020) 7735 7009
- ethosrepresents@btconect.com

Edwardian House Shoot Location 52 Westover Road, Wandsworth, London, SW18 2RH,
- 020 8870 6730
- mina@em-ltd.com
- www.edwardian-house.com

Edwin Shirley Trucking Ltd Marshgate Sidings, Marshgate Lane, London, E15 2PB, United Kingdom
- (020) 8522 1000/ (020) 8522 1002
- info@est-uk.com
- www.yourock-weroll.com

Epping Ongar Railway Ltd Station House, High Street, Ongar, Essex, CM5 9BN, United Kingdom
- (01277) 366616
- www.eorailway.co.uk

Eshott Hall Estate Eshott, Morpeth, Northumberland, NE65 9EP, United Kingdom
- (01670) 787000/ (01670) 786000
- enquiries@eshotthall.co.uk
- www.eshotthall.co.uk

Exel Chauffuer Services Ltd Warrington Business Park, Long Lane, Warrington, WA2 8TX, United Kingdom
- (01925) 245050/ (01925) 245050
- keith@xl-cars.co.uk
- www.xl-cars.co.uk

Fashion Executives Via Monte, Di Pieta, Milan, Italy, 20121,
- 7717366567/ 8700625674
- riz@fashionexecutives.com
- www.fashionexecutives.com

Film Concierge Services 4 Regis Place, London, SW2 5RE, United Kingdom
- (020) 7274 9011
- fcslondon@hotmail.com
- www.european-encounters.com

Firework Events 5 Hanover Road, Scarborough, North Yorkshire, YO11 1LS, United Kingdom
- (01723) 507357/(07990) 611953
- jmevents4@aol.com
- www.fireworkevents.co.uk

Florence House Hotel 2 Malvern Road, Southsea, Hampshire, PO5 2NA, United Kingdom
- (023) 9275 1666/ (023) 9273 4369
- info@florencehousehotel.co.uk
- www.florencehousehotel.co.uk

Footprint Locations Flat 2, 81 Endell Street, London, WC2H 9AJ,
- 07854 506947
- pjlobban@gmail.com

Exel Chauffuer Services Ltd Warrington Business

Geoff Morton (MBE) Hasholme Carr Farm, Skiff Lane, Holme-on-Spalding-Moor, York, YO43 4BD, United Kingdom
- (01430) 860393/(07768) 346905 / (01430) 860057
- m.morton306@btinternet.com

Great Western Society Ltd Didcot Railway Centre, Didcot, Oxfordshire, OX11 7NJ, United Kingdom
- (01235) 817200/ (01235) 510621
- didrlyc@globalnet.co.uk
- www.didcotrailwaycentre.org.uk

Greater London Conveniencies / John Anderson Hire Unit 5, Smallford Works, Smallford Lane, St. Albans, Hertfordshire, AL4 0SA, United Kingdom
- (01727) 822120/ (01727) 822886
- sales@superloo.co.uk
- www.superloo.co.uk

Harleyford Estate Ltd Henley Road, Marlow, Buckinghamshire, SL7 2DX, United Kingdom
- (01628) 471361/ (01628) 476647
- info@harleyford.co.uk
- www.harleyford.co.uk

Heathrow Airport Ltd Heathrow Point West 234, Bath Road, Harlington, Hayes, Middlesex, UB3 5AP, United Kingdom
- (020) 8745 7224/ (020) 8745 6061
- heathrowmediacentre@baa.com
- www.baa.com

Heritage Railway Association 10 Hurdeswell, Long Hanborough, Witney, Oxfordshire, OX29 8DH, United Kingdom
- (01993) 883384/ (01993) 883384
- www.ukhrail.uel.ac.uk

locationpartnership.com

The Location Partnership

- Location library
- Creative location finding
- Location management
- UK & International
- Stills production

www.locationpartnership.com

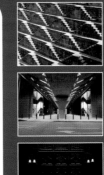

THE LOCATION PARTNERSHIP 82 BERWICK STREET SOHO LONDON W1F 8TP TEL: +44 (0)20 7734 0456 INFO@LOCATIONPARTNERSHIP.COM

Location Scouting, Management & Production

Location X is a collective of highly experienced location managers with combined decades of experience and specialist knowledge.

We can produce your entire shoot, or simply organise the locations. We have the most extensive network of location contacts in the UK and Europe, but our experience is truly global.

Advice is free: contact Roland to pick our brains, without the meter running.

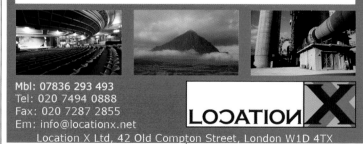

Mbl: 07836 293 493
Tel: 020 7494 0888
Fax: 020 7287 2855
Em: info@locationx.net
Location X Ltd, 42 Old Compton Street, London W1D 4TX

Hever Castle & Gardens & Tudor Village Hever, Edenbridge, Kent, TN8 7NG, United Kingdom
(01732) 865224/ (01732) 866796
mail@hevercastle.co.uk
www.hevercastle.co.uk

Historic Scotland Longmore House, Salisbury Place, Edinburgh, EH9 1SH, United Kingdom
0131-668 8926/ 0131-668 8888
hs.events@scotland.gsi.gov.uk
www.historic-scotland.gov.uk/filming/

Holborn Studios 49-50 Eagle Wharf Road, London, N1 7ED, United Kingdom
(020) 7490 4099/ (020) 7253 8120
reception@holborn-studios.co.uk
www.holbornstudios.com

House 62 Fortis Green, East Finchley, London, N2 9EN, United Kingdom
(020) 8883 2091/ (020) 8883 8713
sh@housestudio.co.uk
www.housestudio.co.uk

Inspace 37 Croxley Road, London, W9 3HH, United Kingdom
(020) 8968 4154/(07050) 189375 (0870) 0529927
info@inspacelocations.com
www.inspacelocations.com

Ironbridge Gorge Museum Trust Ltd Coach Road, Coalbrookdale, Telford, Shropshire, TF8 7DQ, United Kingdom
(01952) 435900/ (01952) 435999
marketing@ironbridge.org.uk
www.ironbridge.org.uk

J J Locations 10 Harris Lane, Shenley, Radlett, Hertfordshire, WD7 9EB, United Kingdom
(01923) 853932
info@jjlocations.co.uk
www.jjlocations.co.uk

Jennifer Beech Rose Cottage, High Street, Cavendish, Sudbury, Suffolk, CO10 8AW, United Kingdom
(01787) 280973
jenniferbeech@mac.com

John Anderson Hire Unit 5, Smallford Works, Smallford Lane, St. Albans, Hertfordshire, AL4 0SA, United Kingdom
(01727) 822485/ (01727) 822886
sales@superloo.co.uk
www.superloo.co.uk

John Leask & Son Esplanade, Lerwick, Shetland, ZE1 0LL, United Kingdom
(01595) 693162/ (01595) 693171
leasks@zetnet.co.uk
www.leaskstravel.co.uk

Jorvik 15-17 Coppergate Walk, York, YO1 9WT, United Kingdom
(01904) 543400/ (01904) 627097
enquiries@vikingjorvik.com
www.vikingjorvik.com

Karma Studio 1 Park Hill, Clapham, London, SW4 9NS, United Kingdom
(020) 7498 6888/ (020) 7498 7555
studio@karma-productions.com
www.karma-productions.com

Kent & East Sussex Railway Tenterden Town Station, Tenterden, Kent, TN30 6HE, United Kingdom
(0870) 6006074/ (01580) 765654
enquiries@kesr.org.uk
www.kesr.org.uk

Knebworth House Knebworth Park, Knebworth, Hertfordshire, SG3 6PY, United Kingdom
(01438) 812661/ (01438) 811908
info@knebworthhouse.com
www.knebworthhouse.com

Lake District Locations Gable Cottage, Eaglesfield, Cockermouth, Cumbria, CA13 0SD, United Kingdom
(01900) 823927/(07779) 956777 (01900) 823927
wiseelaine@hotmail.com

Lavish Locations Chiswick Town Hall, Heathfield Terrace, London, W4 4JN, United Kingdom
(020) 8742 2992/ (020) 8742 2836
info@lavishlocations.com
www.lavishlocations.com

Lays International Ltd Delta Way, Thorpe Industrial Est, Egham, Surrey, TW20 8RX, United Kingdom
(01784) 432100/(07720) 427750 (01784) 433200
sales@laysint.com
www.laysint.com

Lee Valley Regional Park Authority Myddelton House, Bulls Cross, Enfield, Middlesex, EN2 9HG, United Kingdom
(01992) 709831/ (01992) 709922
events@leevalleypark.org.uk
www.leevalleypark.org.uk

Leonora Sheppard Locations & Production 32A Brewster Gardens, London, W10 6AJ, United Kingdom
(020) 8969 7302/ (020) 8964 2668
mail@leonora.uk.com
www.leonora.uk.com

Location Manager Ltd 423 Fishguard Way, London, E16 2RU, United Kingdom
(07973) 934 542/ (0870) 130 4456
tom@thelocationmanager.co.uk
www.thelocationmanager.co.uk

Location Works UK Ltd 42 Old Compton Street, London, W1D 4TX, United Kingdom
(020) 7494 0888/ (020) 7287 2855
info@locationworks.com
www.locationworks.com
See ad in showcase

Location X 74 Swaby Road, London, SW18 3QZ, United Kingdom
(020) 8947 7597/(07836) 293493 (020) 8946 2987
roland@locationx.co.uk
www.locationx.net
See ad in showcase

Location25 25 Clapham Common South Side, London, SW4 7AB, United Kingdom
(020) 7720 6514/ (020) 7498 0040
info@location25.com
www.location25.com

Locations UK Location Library 16 Timbercroft, Epsom, Surrey, KT19 0DT, United Kingdom
(020) 8393 2423/ (020) 8393 2423
info@locations-uk.com
www.locations-uk.com

London Stansted Airport Enterprise House, Stansted, Essex, CM24 1QW, United Kingdom
(0870) 000 0303/ (01279) 662066
www.baa.com

London Underground Ltd 55 Broadway, London, SW1H 0BD, United Kingdom
(020) 7918 3610/ (020) 7918 4644
filmoffice@tube.tfl.gov.uk
www.tube.tfl.gov.uk/filming

Longleat Estate Office, Longleat, Warminster, Wiltshire, BA12 7NW, United Kingdom
(01985) 844400/ (01985) 844885
enquiries@longleat.co.uk
www.longleat.co.uk

Lord Flight R K Film & Location 63 Studio Villa Apartment, Charles Colley House, Whitehall Road, Uxbridge, Middlesex, UB8 2NZ, United Kingdom
(01895) 254285/ (01895) 850803

Luc Beziat France
contact@lucbeziat.com
www.lucbeziat.com

Martin Mere Wildfowl & Wetlands Trust Burscough, Ormskirk, Lancashire, L40 0TA, United Kingdom
(01704) 895181/ (01704) 892343
info@martinmere.co.uk
www.wwt.org.uk

Max Locations 94 Poverest Road, Orpington, Kent, BR5 2DQ, United Kingdom
(01689) 872836/ (01689) 872836
info@maxlocations.com
www.maxlocations.com

Michael Harvey 27 Selwyn Road, Edgbaston, Birmingham, B16 0SJ, United Kingdom
0121-455 8667/(07721) 500443 0121-455 8667
michael.harvey1@btinternet.com

Mid-Hants Railway (Watercress Line) P.L.C. The Railway Station, Alresford, Hampshire, SO24 9JG, United Kingdom
(01962) 733810/(07785) 752640 (01962) 735448
chriscornell@watercressline.co.uk
www.watercressline.co.uk

Midland International (Hire) Services Ltd Hollyfast House, Wall Hill Road, Coventry, CV5 9EL, United Kingdom
(024) 7633 6411/ (024) 7633 8007
fern@midland-international.co.uk
www.toilet-hire.com

Mike Liddall West London Film Office, 5th Floor Percival House, 14-16 Uxbridge Road, London, W5 2HL, United Kingdom
(020) 8825 7575/ (020) 8825 7667
liddallm@ealing.gov.uk
www.westlondonfilmoffice.co.uk

Military Advisory Services The Old Rectory, Alton Barnes, Marlborough, Wiltshire, SN8 4LB, United Kingdom
(01672) 851826/(07721) 422720 (01672) 851150
david.carson@abingdon.org.uk

Mills & MacCarthy Exhibitions Windsor Court, East Grinstead House, East Grinstead, West Sussex, RH19 1XA, United Kingdom
/ (01342) 336113
phewson@reedinfo.co.uk

Mission Control Locations Broomden Barn, Vineyard Lane, Ticehurst, Wadhurst, East Sussex, TN5 7LP, United Kingdom
(01580) 200346/(07860) 887652 (01580) 200438
chris@missioncontrollers.com

Motordrive Location Co 10 Harris Lane, Shenley, Hertfordshire, WD7 9EB, United Kingdom
✆ (01923) 853932/✆ (0871) 4335801
✎ info@motordrive.tv
▢ www.motordrive.tv

National Motor Museum Trading Ltd John Montague Building, Beaulieu, Brockenhurst, Hampshire, SO42 7ZN, United Kingdom
✆ (01590) 614664/(07818) 454522 ✆ (01590) 612655
✎ stephen.vokins@beaulieu.co.uk
▢ www.beaulieu.co.uk

National Trust 32 Queens Annes Gate, London, SW1H 9AB, United Kingdom
✆ (01793) 817571/✆ (01793) 817401
✎ enquiries@nationaltrust.org.uk
▢ www.nationaltrust.org.uk

Neovision Film Production & Services 7 rue Gardiol, Grande Saconnex, Genéva, CH-1218, Switzerland
✆ 22 741 12 09/79 357 54 17 ✆ 22 741 12 08
✎ info@neovisionprod.com
▢ www.neovisionprod.com

Nick Veasey Radar Studios, Coldblow Lane, Thurnham, Maidstone, Kent, ME14 3LR, United Kingdom
✆ (01622) 737722/✆ (01622) 738644
✎ nick@nickveasey.com
▢ www.nickveasey.com

Northern Film & Media Ltd Central Square, Forth Street, Newcastle upon Tyne, NE1 3PJ, United Kingdom
✆ 0191-269 9212/✆ 0191-269 9213
✎ locations@northernmedia.org
▢ www.northernmedia.org

O I C Locations 66 Charlotte Street, London, W1T 4QE, United Kingdom
✆ (020) 7419 1949/(07973) 172579 ✆ (020) 7419 1950
✎ info@oic.co.uk
▢ www.oic.co.uk

Oak Management Ltd 25 Clifton Road, Wallington, Surrey, SM6 8AL, United Kingdom
✆ (020) 8647 7800/✆ (020) 8254 9220
✎ info@oakmanagement.co.uk
▢ www.oakmanagement.co.uk

Online Film & TV Location Library Great Northern Warehouse, 275 Deansgate, Manchester, M3 4EL, United Kingdom
✆ (0845) 0450608/✆ (0845) 0450609
✎ info@northwestlocations.co.uk
▢ www.northwestlocations.co.uk

Page International Services 35 Cadogan Gardens, London, SW3 2TB, United Kingdom
✆ (020) 7730 1663/✆ (020) 7730 1663
✎ info@pagelocation.com
▢ www.pagelocation.com

Patrick Stuart Locations 104 Heathwood Gardens, London, SE7 8ER, United Kingdom
✆ (07970) 614063
✎ patrick@lemonia.org

Pennine Helicopters Ltd Oakdene Farm, Saddleworth, Greater Manchester, Lancashire, OL3 5LU, United Kingdom
✆ (01457) 820152/✆ (01457) 820153
✎ enquiries@penninehelis.co.uk
▢ www.penninehelis.co.uk

Peter Ker Associates International Ltd London, W1T 3PH, United Kingdom
✆ (0208) 964 4448/(07836) 210427 ✆ (020) 7580 8933
✎ pka@pka-ministry.com
▢ www.pka-ministry.com

Photo-Locations 29 Finlay Street, London, SW6 6HE, United Kingdom
✆ (07770) 928349/✆ (020) 7736 2929
✎ info@photo-locations.com
▢ www.photo-locations.com

Place Invaders 16 Farm Avenue, Swanley, Kent, BR8 7JA, United Kingdom
✆ (01322) 615030/(07831) 187888 ✆ (01322) 665714
✎ placeinvaders@aol.com

Plan It Locations 15500 Erwin Street, Suite 4009, Van Nuys, 91411, United States of America
✆ 818 376 6506/✆ 818 376 7606
✎ info@planitlocations.com
▢ www.planitlocations.com

PLC 7 Edith Grove, London, SW10 0JZ, United Kingdom
✆ (020) 7352 4008/(07774) 694140 ✆ (020) 7351 9969
✎ julia@plcinternational.com
▢ www.plcinternational.com

Pooch Palace The Lee, Great Missenden, Buckinghamshire, HP16 9NQ, United Kingdom
✆ (01494) 837420

Port of London Authority London River House, Royal Pier Road, 7 Harp Lane, Gravesend, Kent, DA12 2BG, United Kingdom
✆ (01474) 562200/✆ (01474) 562281
✎ pressoffice@pola.co.uk
▢ www.portoflondon.co.uk

Portsmouth Film Office Portsmouth City Council Civic Offices, Guildhall Square, Portsmouth, PO1 2AD, United Kingdom
✆ (023) 9283 4116/✆ (023) 9283 4159
✎ tourism@portsmouthcc.gov.uk
▢ www.visitportsmouth.co.uk

Powderham Castle Kenton, Exeter, EX6 8JQ, United Kingdom
✆ (01626) 890243/✆ (01626) 890729
✎ castle@powderham.co.uk
▢ www.powderham.co.uk

Property Repair 52 Montrose Terrace, Edinburgh, EH7 5DL, United Kingdom
✆ 0131-478 3391/✆ 1314777553
✎ info@propertyrepair.net
▢ www.propertyrepair.net

Pure Productions Unit 105, Canalot Studios, 222 Kensal Road, London, W10 5BN, United Kingdom
✆ (020) 8964 4664/✆ (020) 8694 4774
✎ info@pureproduction.net
▢ www.pureproduction.net

Remstor Services Ltd Unit 8, Cranford Way Industrial Estate, London, N8 9DG, United Kingdom
✆ (020) 8347 8855/✆ (020) 8340 7757
✎ mail@remstor.co.uk
▢ www.remstor.co.uk

Richard Godfrey 34 Avondale Road, Palmers Green, London, N13 4DU, United Kingdom
✆ (020) 8886 7342/(07973) 549137 ✆ (07970) 099048
✎ technical.office@virgin.net

Rural Location Finders Weir Farm, Oakridge Lynch, Stroud, Gloucestershire, GL6 7NR, United Kingdom
✆ (01285) 760781/✆ (01285) 760781

SHOOTFACTORY

locations | www.shootfactory.co.uk | +44 (0) 207 252 3900

Rural Locations & Location Services Benefold Farm, Petworth, West Sussex, GU28 9NX, United Kingdom
✆ (01798) 344066/(07836) 250882 ✆ (01798) 344077
✎ heritage_oak@btconnect.com

Saint Georges Hall William Brown Street, Liverpool, L1 1JJ, United Kingdom
✆ 0151-225 4457/✆ 0151-709 2252
✎ steve.neill@liverpool.gov.uk
▢ www.stgeorgeshall.com

Sally Mackie Locations Cownham Farm, Broadwell, Moreton-in-Marsh, Gloucestershire, GL56 0TT, United Kingdom
✆ (01451) 830294/(07860) 533355
✎ sally@mackie.biz
▢ www.sallymackie-locations.com

Sarah Eastel Locations 18 Box Road, Bathford, Bath, BA1 7QD, United Kingdom
✆ (01225) 858100/✆ (01225) 852860
✎ info@film-locations.co.uk
▢ www.film-locations.co.uk

Scottish Screen 2nd Floor, 249 West George Street, Glasgow, G2 4QE, United Kingdom
✆ 0141-302 1700/✆ 0141-302 1711
✎ info@scottishscreen.com
▢ www.scottishscreen.com

Screen & Music Travel Limited Colne House, High Street, Colnbrook, Slough, SL3 0LX, United Kingdom
✆ (01753) 764050/✆ (01753) 464051
✎ groups@screenandmusictravel.co.uk
▢ www.screenandmusictravel.co.uk

Screen West Midlands 9 Regent Place, Birmingham, B1 3NJ, United Kingdom
✆ 0121-265 7120/✆ 0121-265 7180
✎ info@screenwm.co.uk
▢ www.screenwm.co.uk

Severn Valley Railway (Holding) Plc The Railway Station, Bewdley, Worcestershire, DY12 1BG, United Kingdom
✆ (01299) 403816/✆ (01299) 400839
✎ grouptravel@svr.co.uk
▢ www.svr.co.uk

Shepperton Marina Ltd Shepperton Marina, Felix Lane, Shepperton, Middlesex, TW17 8NS, United Kingdom
✆ (01932) 243722/✆ (01932) 243152
✎ marina@boatshowrooms.com
▢ www.sheppertonmarina.com

Shoot People 3rd Floor, 202 City Road, London, EC1V 2PH, United Kingdom
✆ (020) 7253 0009/(07767) 313007 ✆ (020) 7253 0009
✎ victoria@shootpeople.com
▢ www.shootpeople.com

Shootfactory Ltd Studio 7.25 Alaska Buildings, London, SE1 3BD, United Kingdom
✆ **(020) 7252 3900**
✎ jk@shootfactory.co.uk
▢ www.shootfactory.co.uk
See ad in showcase

Shootspaces Ltd 92 Brondesbury Road, London, NW6 6RX, United Kingdom
✆ (020) 7912 9989/(07880) 636473 ✆ (020) 8723 0402
✎ helene@shootspaces.com
▢ www.shootspaces.com

Wheal's Far-Go Location Vehicles

We have been established since 1973 and in that time have covered shoots all over Europe and the UK. This wealth of unequalled experience is reflected in each of our individually designed fashion location vehicles, which are custom built and comprehensively equipped to the highest quality, to meet your every need. Our vehicles are modern, with plenty of working space. They can comfortably get to country locations and navigate the narrow streets of London. We enjoy the reputation of having the best location vehicles in Europe.

The vehicle in the photograph is our Mega Truck, so called as it is the ultimate location vehicle, built to the highest possible standard, regardless of cost.

T + 44 (0)20 8965 4600/+ 44 (0)20 8965 8200 • F + 44 (0)20 8965 0699
wfg@whealsfargo.com • www.whealsfargo.com

Silverstone Circuits Ltd
Silverstone, Towcester, Northamptonshire, NN12 8TN, United Kingdom
(0870) 4588200/ (0870) 4588250
www.silverstone-circuit.com

Site Unit Rentals Ltd Watlington Road, Cowley, Oxford, OX4 6SR, United Kingdom
(01865) 747025/ (01865) 774562
events@surhire.com
www.surhire.com

Snap Productions 151-155 New North Road, London, N1 6TA, United Kingdom
(020) 7684 7555/ (020) 7684 7556
rich@snap-pro.com
www.snap-pro.com
See ad in showcase

South West Scotland Screen Commission Gracefield Arts Centre, 28 Edinburgh Road, Dumfries, DG1 1JQ, United Kingdom
(01387) 263666/(07725) 065463 / (01387) 263666
screencom@dumgal.gov.uk
www.sw-scotland-screen.com

Space Photographic Film Location Loft 20, Haybridge House, 15 Mount Pleasant Hill, London, E5 9NB, United Kingdom
(07956) 326864/ (020) 8806 1273
www.spacelocationS.net

Space-2 Battersea Studios, 80 Silverthorne Road, London, SW8 3HE, United Kingdom
(07922) 224216
mark@space2online.com
www.space2online.com

Sports Workshop Promotions Ltd Jubilee Stand, Crystal Palace Sports Centre, London, SE19 2BH, United Kingdom
(020) 8659 4561/(07770) 994043 / (020) 8776 7772
info@sportspromotions.co.uk
www.sportspromotions.co.uk

Square Sail Shipyard Ltd Charlestown Harbour, St. Austell, Cornwall, PL25 3NJ, United Kingdom
(01726) 67526/(07782) 136914 / (01726) 61839
sextent@btconnect.com
www.square-sail.com

Steam Traction Ltd 1-23 Hertford Road, Enfield Highway, Enfield, Middlesex, EN3 5JD, United Kingdom
(020) 8804 1928/ (020) 8804 9512

Steve Mortimore The Garden Flat, 40 Elsworthy Road, London, NW3 3DL, United Kingdom
(07990) 542766
mortimores@aol.com

Sudeley Castle Gardens & Exhibitions Winchcombe, Cheltenham, Gloucestershire, GL54 5JD, United Kingdom
(01242) 602308/ (01242) 602959
enquiries@sudeley.org.uk
www.sudeleycastle.co.uk

Sue Quimby 1 Holyoake Cottage, Castle Road, Studley, Warwickshire, B80 7AD, United Kingdom
(01527) 857495/ (01527) 857465

Thai Model Sutton Farm House, Sutton, Witney, Oxfordshire, OX29 5RD, United Kingdom
(01865) 731309/ (01865) 883789
thaimodel@btconnect.com
www.thaimodel.co.uk

The Beach Studios
London and Kent, United Kingdom
(01797) 344 077
office@beachstudios.co.uk
www.beachstudios.co.uk

The Location Bank Postbus 16445, Amsterdam, 1001 RM, Netherlands
653 647 184
info@locationbank.nl
www.locationbank.nl

The Location Partnership 82 Berwick Street, London, W1F 8TP, United Kingdom
(020) 7734 0456/(07976) 249699 **(020) 7734 5411**
info@locationpartnership.com
www.locationpartnership.com
See ad in showcase

The Location Source 74 Sweaby Road, London, SW18 3QZ, United Kingdom
(020) 8947 7597/(07836) 593493 / (020) 8946 2987
info@locsource.com
www.locationx.net

The Production Team Unit 93, Cholmley Gardens, London, NW6 1UN, United Kingdom
(07836) 539671 / (020) 8693 5551
productionteam@hotmail.com

The Space Men 8-10 Lower James Street, London, W1F 9EL,
020 7534 5780/ 020 7534 5799
david@thespacemen.com
www.thespacemen.com

Thistle Film Facilities Silver Birches, Nairnside, Inverness, IV2 5BT, United Kingdom
(01463) 790 011/(07836) 217550 / (01463) 790 011
msharpthistle@compuserve.com

Tomo London Production Ltd Unit 305, Kingswharf, London, E8 4DS, United Kingdom
(020) 7249 5707/(07958) 954901 **(020) 7249 6557**
info@tomolondon.com
www.tomolondon.com
See ad in showcase

Traction Equipment Ltd Glover Street, Stafford, ST16 2NY, United Kingdom
(01785) 223355/ (01785) 211074
call@tractionequipment.co.uk
www.tractionequipment.co.uk

Troppo Property The Old Place, Lock Path, Dorney, Windsor, Berkshire, SL4 6QQ, United Kingdom
(01753) 827037/ (01753) 855022
sarah@pjsmith.co.uk
www.troppo.uk.com

Turk Film Services Ltd Turks Boat Yard, The Historic Dockyard, Chatham, Kent, ME4 2TZ, United Kingdom
(01634) 400110/ (01634) 400237
operations@turks.co.uk
www.turks.co.uk

Urban Circus The Arts Exchange, Millgreen, Congleton, Cheshire, CW12 1JG, United Kingdom
(01260) 276627/ (01260) 270777
info@arts-exchange.com
www.arts-exchange.com

Veronica Lowes 4 The Embankment, London, SW15 1LB, United Kingdom
(020) 8788 7028/(07860) 286144 / (020) 8789 2097
vlowes@hotmail.com

Vikki McCraw 5 Wheatfield Road, Edinburgh, EH11 2PT, United Kingdom
0131-337 9893
film@locations365.co.uk
www.locations365.co.uk

Warners Film & Location Transport 1216 Brunel Road, London, W3 7XR, United Kingdom
(020) 7586 6060/ (020) 7483 1755

Watermouth Castle Berrynarbor, Ilfracombe, Devon, EX34 9SL, United Kingdom
(01271) 863879/ (01271) 865864
www.watermouthcastle.com

West Country Locations Crosslands House, Ash Thomas, Tiverton, Devon, EX16 4NU, United Kingdom
(01884) 820888/(07774) 428309 / (01884) 821328
roger@westcountrylocations.co.uk
www.westcountrylocations.co.uk

West London Film Office 5th Floor, Percival House, 14-16 Uxbridge Road, London, London, W5 2HL, United Kingdom
(020) 8825 7575/ (020) 8825 7667
liddallm@ealing.gov.uk
www.westlondonfilmoffice.co.uk

Wheal's Far-Go Unit 5, 13-15 Sunbeam Road, London, NW10 6JP, United Kingdom
(020) 8965 4600/ (020) 8965 0699
wfg@whealsfargo.com
www.whealsfargo.com

Windermere Steamboat Museum Rayrigg Road, Windermere, Cumbria, LA23 1BN, United Kingdom
(01539) 445565/ (01539) 448769
post@steamboat.co.uk
www.steamboat.co.uk

World Locations 8533 Sunset Boulevard, Suite 106, West Hollywood, 90069, United States of America
00 1 310 659 0599/ 00 1 310 659 3292
info@worldlocations.com
www.worldlocations.com

Yorkshire Locations: Online Film & TV Locations Library Commercial House, 57 Great George Street, Leeds, LS1 3AJ, United Kingdom
(0845) 0450608/(07811) 180200 / (0845) 0450609
info@yorkshirelocations.co.uk
www.yorkshirelocations.co.uk

Zownir Locations Ltd Studio 9, The Village, 101 Amies Street, London, SW11 2JW, United Kingdom
(020) 7738 2002/ (020) 7652 1946
hq@zownirlocations.com
www.zownirlocations.com

MAKE-UP AND HAIR

Fashion Executives Via Monte, Di Pieta, Milan, Italy, 20121,
7717366567/ 8700625674
riz@fashionexecutives.com
www.fashionexecutives.com

Freelance Make-Up Artist Flat 1, 44 Anselm Road, Fulham, London, SW6 1LJ,
7929574010
charlotte_cowen@hotmail.com

Mel Lee Flat 10 Cedar House, 35 Melliss Avenue, Kew, Surrey, TW9 4BG,
7775557250
mel.lee1@hotmail.co.uk

MODELMAKERS

1:1 Modelmaking Ltd 101 Villiers Road, London, NW2 5QB, United Kingdom
📞 (020) 8459 4333/(07850) 808979
✉ andy@1-1modelmaking.co.uk
🖥 www.1-1modelmaking.co.uk

2D:3D 263 Abbeydale Road, Wembley, Wembley, Middlesex, HA0 1TW, United Kingdom
📞 (020) 8998 3199/📠 (020) 8998 7767
✉ rob@2d3d.co.uk
🖥 www.2d3d.co.uk

360 Models 7 Ty-Gwyn Road, Rhiwbina, Cardiff, CF14 6NF, United Kingdom
📞 (029) 2056 8837
✉ sales@360models.co.uk
🖥 www.360models.co.uk

3D Studios 2 Bedlam Mews, off Walnut Tree Walk, London, SE11 6DF, United Kingdom
📞 (020) 7735 7932/(07710) 809692 📠 (020) 7587 5105
✉ paul@3d-studios.co.uk
🖥 www.3d-studios.co.uk

3DD 3 Marlow Workshops, Arnold Circus, London, E2 7JN, United Kingdom
📞 (020) 7739 7933/📠 (020) 7739 7195
✉ sales@3dd.co.uk
🖥 www.3ddmodels.co.uk

4D Modelshop Ltd The Railway Arches, 120 Leman Street, London, E1 8EU, United Kingdom
📞 (020) 7264 1288/📠 (020) 7264 1299
✉ info@modelshop.co.uk
🖥 www.modelshop.co.uk

A D Modelmaking The Studio, 28 The Retreat, Frome, Somerset, BA11 5JU, United Kingdom
📞 (01373) 455455/📠 (01373) 455455
🖥 www.admodelmaking.com

Adam Howarth Models & Effects Unit 21, Wembley Commercial Centre, East Lane, Wembley, Middlesex, HA9 7UR, United Kingdom
📞 (07968) 073418
✉ adam@model-fx.net
🖥 www.model-fx.net

Adel Roostein Display Mannequins Ltd 9 Beaumont Avenue, London, W14 9LP, United Kingdom
📞 (020) 7381 1447/📠 (020) 7386 9594
✉ sales@adelrootstein.co.uk
🖥 www.rootstein.com

Alan Martin 71 Edwin Road, Twickenham, TW2 6SP, United Kingdom
📞 (020) 8287 2784/(07752) 431316

Albatross The Coach House, St. Pauls Waudenbury, Hitchin, Hertfordshire, SG4 8BP, United Kingdom
📞 (01438) 871688/(07971) 849893 📠 (01438) 871874
✉ enquiries@albatrossmodels.co.uk
🖥 www.albatrossmodels.co.uk

All Handmade Unit 6-8, Stapley Manor Farm, Long Lane, Odiham, Hook, Hampshire, RG29 1JE, United Kingdom
📞 (01256) 862111

Alpha 4 Ltd 24 Brunel Road, St. Leonards-on-Sea, East Sussex, TN38 9RT, United Kingdom
📞 (01424) 854485/📠 (01424) 854402
✉ info@alpha-4.co.uk
🖥 www.alpha-4.co.uk

Amorichi Design Ltd 2 Peel Street, Glasgow, G11 5LL, United Kingdom
📞 0141-581 6556
✉ shelley_001@hotmail.com

Andrew Hart Design Hamilton Close, South Mimms, Potters Bar, Hertfordshire, EN6 3PJ, United Kingdom
📞 (01707) 663300/📠 (01707) 663300
✉ ahdesign@clara.net
🖥 www.andrewhartdesign.co.uk

Andy Knight Ltd 2-6 Occupation Road, London, SE17 3BE, United Kingdom
📞 (020) 7252 5252/📠 (020) 7252 5111
✉ info@andyknight.co.uk
🖥 www.andyknight.co.uk

Angela Christie 14 West End Avenue, Pinner, Middlesex, HA5 1BJ, United Kingdom
📞 (020) 8868 5469/(07962) 027 921 📠 (020) 8868 5469
✉ angela@maet1.plus.com

Anorak 3 Bedlam Mews, Walnut Tree Walk, London, SE11 6DF, United Kingdom
📞 (020) 7582 5802/📠 (020) 7582 5802
✉ annabel@anorakmodels.fsnet.co.uk
🖥 www.anorakmodels.com

Applied Arts 22-27 The Oval, London, E2 9DT, United Kingdom
📞 (020) 7739 3155/(07841) 562256
✉ appliedarts@btconnect.com
🖥 www.appliedarts.co.uk

Arteffects 32 Bermondsey Wall West, London, SE16 4UB, United Kingdom
📞 (020) 7237 7453/📠 (020) 7237 7450
✉ steve@arteffects.co.uk
🖥 www.arteffects.co.uk

Artem Ltd Perivale Park, Horsenden Lane South, Perivale, Greenford, Middlesex, UB6 7RH, United Kingdom
📞 (020) 8997 7771/📠 (020) 8997 1503
✉ info@artem.com
🖥 www.artem.com

Arterial Artwork Ltd 11 Petten Close, Orpington, Kent, BR5 4QD, United Kingdom
📞 (01689) 834003/📠 (01689) 834003

Asylum Models & Effects 20 Thornsett Road, Earlsfield, London, SW18 4EF, United Kingdom
📞 (020) 8871 2988/📠 (020) 8874 8186
✉ enquiries@asylumsfx.com
🖥 www.asylumsfx.com

ATOM Ltd High Street, Sunningdale Village, Ascot, Berkshire, SL5 0NG, United Kingdom
📞 (01344) 620001/📠 (01344) 628028
✉ peterd@atomltd.com
🖥 www.atomltd.com

Avanti Model Makers 420 Manchester Road, London, E14 9ST, United Kingdom
📞 (020) 7536 3390/(07764) 603650

Aztec Model Makers 129-135 Fulwell Road, Teddington, Middlesex, TW11 0RJ, United Kingdom
📞 (020) 8977 2010
✉ info@aztec-modelmakers.co.uk
🖥 www.aztecmodelmakers.co.uk

Berry Place Modelmakers 1 Berry Place, Sebastian Street, London, EC1V 0HE, United Kingdom
📞 (020) 7490 8222/📠 (020) 7336 8482
✉ enquiries@berryplace.co.uk
🖥 www.berryplace.co.uk

deerhurst road shoot location

For bookings telephone Gillian on **07788 741908**
For more photographs and information visit
www.deerhurstroad.co.uk

Buyers & Sellers Ltd 120-122 Ladbroke Grove, London, W10 5NE, United Kingdom
📞 (020) 7243 5424/📠 (020) 7243 5201
✉ lowestprices@buyers-sellers.co.uk
🖥 www.buyersandsellersonline.co.uk

Capital Models Perseverance Works, Kingsland Road, London, E2 8DD, United Kingdom
📞 (020) 7729 8660/📠 (020) 7729 8670
✉ info@capitalmodels.co.uk
🖥 www.capitalmodels.co.uk

Carmel Said Unit 45, Stadium Business Centre, North End Road, Wembley, Middlesex, HA9 0AT, United Kingdom
📞 (020) 8795 3820/(07785) 770434 📠 (020) 8795 3830
✉ carmellouissaid@aol.com

Cars In Camera Unit 6-7 Cardiff Road Ind Estate, Cardiff Road, Watford, WD18 0DG, United Kingdom
📞 (01727) 836773/(07768) 932646 📠 (01923) 238494
✉ info@carsincamera.com
🖥 www.carsincamera.com

Chris Lovell Studio 2 Garden Cottages, Monkshatch, Guildford, Surrey, GU3 1DL, United Kingdom
📞 (01483) 810633/(07714) 096529 📠 (01483) 810633
✉ chrislovell.studio@virgin.net
🖥 www.chrislovellstudio.com

Clive Armitage 45 Gould Road, Twickenham, TW2 6RN, United Kingdom
📞 (020) 8894 4794/(07808) 346616 📠 (020) 8894 4794
✉ cliveart2003@yahoo.co.uk
🖥 www.clivearmitage.com

Cod Steaks Ltd 2 Cole Road, St. Philips, Bristol, BS2 0UG, United Kingdom
📞 0117-980 3910/📠 0117-972 8999
✉ mail@codsteaks.com
🖥 www.codsteaks.com

Cole Models 13 Hague Street, London, E2 6HN, United Kingdom
📞 (020) 7729 6686
✉ peter@colemodels.co.uk 🖥 www.colemodels.co.uk

Complete Fabrication Ltd Unit B110, Faircharm Studios, 8-12 Creekside, London, SE8 3DX, United Kingdom
📞 (020) 8694 9666/📠 (020) 8694 9669
✉ mail@completefabrication.com
🖥 www.completefabrication.com

Complete Fabrication Model Makers Ltd Unit 4b Lion Works, Station Road, Whittlesford, Cambridge, CB22 4WL, United Kingdom
📞 (01223) 836837/(07810) 648717 📠 (01223) 837437
✉ sebastian@compfab.co.uk
🖥 www.compfab.co.uk

Concept Creative Services Ltd Unit 1, Baird House, Dudley Innovations Centre, Pensnett Estate, Kingswinford, West Midlands, DY6 7YA, United Kingdom
📞 (01384) 400161/📠 (01384) 400190
✉ sales@concept-models.com
🖥 www.concept-models.com

Creative Glassfibre Models 266 Ralph Road, Shirley, Solihull, West Midlands, B90 3LF, United Kingdom
📞 0121-744 9226/(07778) 285997 📠 0121-744 9226
✉ s.kcreative@fsbdial.co.uk
🖥 www.creativemodelmaking.co.uk

Custom Creations Unit 39, 26-28 Queensway, Enfield, Middlesex, EN3 4SA, United Kingdom
(020) 8443 4444/(07715) 109208 (020) 8443 4444
info@themodelmaker.co.uk
www.customcreations.cc

Darius Wilson Associates Unit H2, Upper Brents Industrial Estate, Faversham, Kent, ME13 7DZ, United Kingdom
(01795) 591194/ (01795) 535982
dariuswils@aol.com
www.dariuswilson.com

DataCAM Models 18 Hewett Street, London, EC2A 3NN, United Kingdom
(020) 7655 4822
ashley@datacam.co.uk
www.datacam.co.uk

David Donkin Jarvis House, Jarvis Lane, Goudhurst, Kent, TN17 2NP, United Kingdom
(01580) 211474/ (01580) 211474
3d@daviddonkin.com
www.daviddonkin.com

Derek Allwood Units 6 & 7, Highgate Square Craft Centre, Birmingham, B12 0DU, United Kingdom
0121-440 4004/ 0121-440 4004

Direct Pocket Bikes 5 Cliffside, Wellingore, Lincoln, LN5 0DR, United Kingdom
(01522) 813680
sales@directpocketbikes.co.uk
www.directpocketbikes.co.uk

Donald Owen Wren House, 33 Hurst Green, Brightlingsea, Colchester, CO7 0HA, United Kingdom
01206 304154/(07977) 201175 01206 305760
owendonald@hotmail.com
www.donowen.co.uk

Elements Special Effects Ltd Unit P04, Acton Business Centre, London, NW10 6TD, United Kingdom
(020) 8961 4244/(07968) 613030 (020) 8961 4255
info@elementsfx.co.uk
www.elementsfx.co.uk

Elfin Presentations 191-205 Cambridge Heath Road, London, E2 0EL, United Kingdom
(020) 7729 6744/ (020) 7729 9318
info@elfinpresentations.co.uk
www.elfinpresentations.co.uk

Embtech Embroidery Rispain House, Whithorn, Newton Stewart, Wigtownshire, DG8 8NA, United Kingdom
(01988) 500223
alan@embtech.co.uk
www.embtech.co.uk

fatbelly.com St James House, 150 London Road, East Grinstead, West Sussex, RH19 1HB, United Kingdom
/ (01342) 336113
phewson@reedinfo.co.uk

Flic Models 18 Hewett Street, London, EC2A 3NN, United Kingdom
(020) 7377 6127/ (020) 7377 6129
workshop@flicmodels.com
www.flicmodels.com

Fulcrum Modelmakers Ltd 15-20 The Oval, Hoxton, London, E2 9DX, United Kingdom
(020) 7729 8920/ (020) 7739 7005
mail@fulcrummodelmakers.co.uk
www.fulcrummodelmakers.co.uk

G & E Unit 3, Newmans Estate, Ford Road, Clacton-on-Sea, Essex, CO15 3DS, United Kingdom
(01255) 221132
www.gande4u.com

Gail Armstrong/Illustration Ltd 2 Brooks Court, Cringle Street, London, SW8 5BX, United Kingdom
(020) 7720 5202/ (020) 7720 5920
team@illustrationweb.com
www.illustrationweb.com

Games Workshop Ltd Willow Road, Lenton, Nottingham, NG7 2WS, United Kingdom
0115-916 8000/ 0115-916 8008
www.games-workshop.com

Gems Studio 9 Dallington Street, London, EC1V 0LN, United Kingdom
(01923) 855858/ (01923) 855185
info@gems-studio.com
www.gems-studio.com

Godfrey Design Ltd Sandy Hill, Coggeshall Road, Bradwell, Braintree, Essex, CM77 8EU, United Kingdom
(01376) 552777/ (01376) 552776
sales@godfreydesigngroup.co.uk
www.godfreydesigngroup.co.uk

Hadlee Design Peyton Hall, Stone Street, Boxford, Sudbury, Suffolk, CO10 5NS, United Kingdom
(01787) 211649
c.hadlee@eggconnect.net

Harry Metcalfe 129 Chapman Street, London, E1 2PH, United Kingdom
(020) 7739 2530/ (020) 7702 7334
harry@harrymetcalfe.demon.co.uk

Helen Jones Studio 310, 3rd Floor, 5 Torrens Street, London, EC1V 1NQ, United Kingdom
(020) 7837 0509/ (020) 7837 0509
helenjonesstudio@hotmail.com
www.helenjonesonline.com

Hidden Modelshop 269 Wandsworth Bridge Road, London, SW6 2TX, United Kingdom
(020) 7751 8395
models@hiddenmodelshop.co.uk
www.hiddenmodelshop.co.uk

Hothouse IWG 10 St Leonards Road, Park Royal, London, NW10 6SY, United Kingdom
(020) 8961 3666/(07801) 612061 (020) 8961 3777
info@hothousefx.co.uk
www.hothousefx.co.uk

Houghton Wyatt 30 Woolpack Lane, Nottingham, NG1 1GA, United Kingdom
0115-958 2171/(07702) 104536 0115-958 2171
pete@houghtonwyatt.co.uk
www.houghtonwyatt.co.uk

John Ashton 29 Stalybridge Road, Mottram, Hyde, Cheshire, SK14 6NF, United Kingdom
/(07747) 088018
john@piersharayashton.freeserve.co.uk

John Dines The Mill House, Bodiam, Robertsbridge, East Sussex, TN32 5UN, United Kingdom
(01580) 850629
john@bodiam-mill.net
www.bodiam-mill.net

John Ryan 88 Whitton Road, Hounslow, TW3 2DF, United Kingdom
(020) 8570 1513/(07836) 244321 (020) 8570 1513

John Wright Studio 1, Centre Space, 6 Leonard Lane, Bristol, BS1 1EA, United Kingdom
0117-927 2854/ 0117-927 2606
www.jwmm.co.uk

Jon Steed Model Making 14 Windsor Street, London, N1 8QG, United Kingdom
(020) 7354 3344/ (020) 7288 1763
jonsteed@btconnect.com
www.jonsteed.com

Juicy Fruits 28 Mill Hill, Weston Colville, Cambridge, CB21 5NY, United Kingdom
(01223) 290396/ (01223) 290212
steven@juicyfruitsuk.com
www.juicyfruitsuk.com

K D Models 5 Host Street, Bristol, BS1 5BU, United Kingdom
0117-901 4040/ 0117-901 4001
ian.hollister@kinneirdufort.com
www.kinneirdufort.com

Kandor Modelmakers Ltd 1 Berry Place, Sebastian Street, London, EC1V 0HE, United Kingdom
(020) 7251 6366/ (020) 7608 3356
kandor@kandormodels.com
www.kandormodels.com

Kathy Wyatt 52 Egerton Road, Bishopston, Bristol, BS7 8HL, United Kingdom
0117-924 3929/ 0117-924 3929
kathy@kathywyatt.com
www.kathywyatt.com

Legs Productions Throstle Farm, Glossop Road, Little Hayfield, High Peak, Derbyshire, SK22 2NG, United Kingdom
(01663) 742255/ (01663) 742255
lyndone@onetel.com

London Associates 105 High Street, Berkhamsted, Hertfordshire, HP4 2DG, United Kingdom
(01442) 862631/ (01442) 874354
info@la-design.co.uk
www.la-design.co.uk

Mark Boyes Models & Props 14 Potter Street, Melbourne, Derby, DE73 1DW, United Kingdom
(01332) 864208/ (01332) 864208
mark1boyes@aol.com
www.mbmodelmaking.co.uk

Mark Russell Model Studio High Gardens, Garway Hill, Hereford, HR2 8RT, United Kingdom
(01981) 240730/(07836) 375248
themodelworkshop@highgardens.co.uk

Matthew Wurr Downswood Studios, Matching Road, Hatfield Heath, Bishop's Stortford, Hertfordshire, CM22 7AS, United Kingdom
(01279) 731734/(07836) 656060 (01279) 731735
matthew@wurr.co.uk
www.wurr.co.uk

Metro Models 2-6 Occupation Road, London, SE17 3BE, United Kingdom
(020) 7252 4545/ (020) 7252 5111
info@metromodels.co.uk
www.metromodels.co.uk

Mexicolore 28 Warriner Gardens, London, SW11 4EB, United Kingdom
(020) 7622 9577/ (020) 7498 3643
ian.mursell@btinternet.com
www.mexicolore.co.uk

Michael Sinclair Modelmakers 29 Blenheim Gardens, 6 Blenheim Studios, London, SW2 5EU, United Kingdom
(020) 8671 5051/(07780) 737719 (020) 8671 5051
msinc7@yahoo.com

Mike & Rosi Compton 11 Woodstock Road, Croydon, CR0 1JS, United Kingdom
(020) 8680 4364/(07900) 258646 (020) 8681 3126
mikeandrosicompton@btopenworld.com

Mimesis 1 Bedlam Mews, London, SE11 6DF, United Kingdom
(020) 7582 4303/(07973) 615948 (020) 7820 1562
martin@mimesis-models.com
www.mimesis-models.com

Minima Design Ltd The Technology Centre, Framlingham, Woodbridge, Suffolk, IP13 9EZ, United Kingdom
(01728) 727000/ (01728) 726546
design.pays@minima.co.uk
www.minima.co.uk

Model Solutions 72 X Clarence Road, London, N22 8PW, United Kingdom
(020) 8881 2333/(07973) 743554 (020) 8881 2233
info@modelsolutions.co.uk
www.modelsolutions.co.uk
See ad in showcase

Modelmaking & Graphic Services Ltd 9 Bath Buildings, Montpelier, Bristol, BS6 5PT, United Kingdom
0117-944 6050/ 0117-944 5973

Modelscape Adams House, Dickerage Lane, New Malden, Surrey, KT3 3SF, United Kingdom
(020) 8949 9286/ (020) 8949 7418
modelscape@btconnect.com
www.modelscape.co.uk

Mount Design Ltd Postley Road, Woburn Road Industrial Estate, Kempston, MK42 7BU, United Kingdom
(01234) 841148/ (01234) 840014
keith@mount-design.co.uk
www.mountdesign.com

Nancy Fouts The Old Vicarage, 52 Oakley Square, London, NW1 1NJ, United Kingdom
(020) 7388 6491/ (020) 7388 6491

Neal Scanlan Studio Ltd, The Chocolate Factory, 5 Clarendon Road, London, N22 6XJ, United Kingdom
(020) 8889 3800/(07710) 099217 2088890794
info@nsstudio.co.uk
www.nsstudio.co.uk

Ogle Models Ltd Birds Hill, Letchworth Garden City, Hertfordshire, SG6 1JA, United Kingdom
(01462) 682661/ (01462) 680131
sales@oglemodels.com
www.oglemodels.com

Ozturk & Robotica 17-23 Park Terrace Lane, Glasgow, G3 6BQ, United Kingdom
0141-353 2261/ 0141-353 2614
models@ozturk.co.uk
www.ozturk.co.uk

P D D Ltd 85-87 Richford Street, London, W6 7HJ, United Kingdom
(020) 8735 1111/ (020) 8735 1122
studio@pdd.co.uk
www.pdd.co.uk

Pams of Gainsborough Ltd Unit 30, Corringham Road Industrial Estate, Gainsborough, Lincolnshire, DN21 1QB, United Kingdom
📞 (01427) 610011/ 📠 (01427) 810174
✉ sales@pams.co.uk
🖥 www.pams.co.uk

Paul Cutler 54 Elthorne Park Road, London, W7 2JD, United Kingdom
📞 (020) 8579 6770/(07973) 601436
✉ cutler@cutlerbuck.demon.co.uk

Paul Keep Studio 4, 65 Leonard Street, London, EC2A 4QS, United Kingdom
📞 (020) 7739 2413/(07850) 065914 📠 (020) 7739 2413
🖥 www.contact-me.net/paulkeep

Pearson Matthews Ltd 9 Princess Mews, Horace Road, Kingston upon Thames, Surrey, KT1 2SZ, United Kingdom
📞 (020) 8547 0470/ 📠 (020) 8547 0123
✉ design@pearsonmatthews.com
🖥 www.pearsonmatthews.com

Pennicott Payne Ltd 10-16 Gwynne Road, Battersea, London, SW11 3UW, United Kingdom
📞 (020) 7228 6127/ 📠 (020) 7223 3332
✉ info@pplsfx.com
🖥 www.pplsfx.com

Peter Evans Studios Ltd 12-14 Tavistock Street, Dunstable, Bedfordshire, LU6 1NE, United Kingdom
📞 (01582) 725730/ 📠 (01582) 481329
✉ sales@peterevansstudios.co.uk

Peter Hutchinson Special Effects Copse Farm, South Litchfield, Overton, Basingstoke, Hampshire, RG25 3BP, United Kingdom
📞 (01256) 771000/(07836) 641313 📠 (01256) 773344
✉ hutchinsonb7@aol.com

Pilot Models Borders Lane, Etchingham, East Sussex, TN19 7AF, United Kingdom
📞 (01580) 819461/ 📠 (01580) 819461
✉ pilot3d@btconnect.com
🖥 pilot-models.demon.co.uk

Pipers 27-35 Bevenden Street, London, N1 6BH, United Kingdom
📞 (020) 7250 0530/ 📠 (020) 7251 0134
✉ info@pipers.co.uk
🖥 www.pipers.co.uk

Pollexprops/Firebrand Leac na Ban, Lochgilphead, Argyll, PA31 8PF, United Kingdom
📞 (01546) 870310/ 📠 (01546) 870678
✉ alex@firebrand.fsnet.co.uk
🖥 www.pollex-props.co.uk

Presentation Studios International 1st Floor, Block C, 38-40 Glasshill Street, London, SE1 0QR, United Kingdom
📞 (020) 7261 9271/ 📠 (020) 7928 6416
✉ psilondon@btclick.com
🖥 www.psiglobal.biz

Professor Patten's Punch & Judy 14 The Crest, Goffs Oak, Waltham Cross, Hertfordshire, EN7 5NP, United Kingdom
📞 (01707) 873262
🖥 www.dennispatten.co.uk

Progressive Modelmakers Ltd The Croft, Montague Road, Berkhamsted, Hertfordshire, HP4 3DZ, United Kingdom
📞 (01442) 866866/ 📠 (01442) 865655

Prototype Projects Ltd 1 Greenfield, Royston, Hertfordshire, SG8 5HN, United Kingdom
📞 (01763) 249760/ 📠 (01763) 249382
✉ info@prototypeprojects.com
🖥 www.prototypeprojects.com

Racecraft Ltd 125 Harris Way, Sunbury-on-Thames, Middlesex, TW16 7EL, United Kingdom
📞 (01932) 780580/ 📠 (01932) 780580
✉ info@racecraftonline.co.uk
🖥 www.racecraftonline.co.uk

Replica Food Ltd 11A Uplands Business Park, Blackhorse Lane, Walthamstow, London, E17 5QJ, United Kingdom
📞 (020) 8523 3523/ 📠 (020) 8523 3524
✉ sales@replica.co.uk
🖥 www.replica.co.uk

Rocky Road Productions Ltd 9 Wellington Road, Wimbledon Park, London, SW19 8EQ, United Kingdom
📞 (020) 8947 2404/ 📠 (020) 8947 2404
✉ john@rockyroad.fsnet.co.uk

Roger Singer 23 Colville Terrace, London, W11 2BU, United Kingdom
📞 (020) 7229 1078

Roger Southall 29 Chawn Park Drive, Stourbridge, West Midlands, DY9 0YF, United Kingdom
📞 (01384) 373945/ 📠 (01384) 373945
✉ rsouthall@btconnect.com

Russell Beck Studios Ltd Ground Floor, Richmond House, 1a Westgate Street, London, E8 3RL, United Kingdom
📞 (020) 8985 1813/ 📠 (020) 8525 1927
✉ office@russellbeckstudio.co.uk
🖥 www.russellbeckstudio.co.uk

S B Modelmakers.com The Warehouse, 7A Wilford Crescent West, Nottingham, NG2 2EZ, United Kingdom
📞 0115-986 2323/ 📠 0115-986 2323
✉ info@sbmodelmakers.com
🖥 www.sbmodelmakers.com

Sculpture Studios 3 Hornsby Square, Southfields Industrial Park, Laindon, Basildon, Essex, SS15 6SD, United Kingdom
📞 (01268) 418837/ 📠 (01268) 414118
✉ aden.hynes@virgin.net
🖥 www.sculpturestudios.co.uk

Side Effects Unit 13, Mulberry Business Centre, Quebec Way, London, SE16 7LB, United Kingdom
📞 (020) 7237 0007/ 📠 (020) 7207 0062
✉ sfx@lineone.net

Simon Millington & Associates Unit 2, 12 Verney Road, London, SE16 3DH, United Kingdom
📞 (020) 7231 5770/(07973) 600851 📠 (020) 7231 5591
✉ info@simonmillington.com
🖥 www.simonmillington.com

Simon Wilson Taxidermy Hire 14 Canterbury Way, Croxley Green, Rickmansworth, Hertfordshire, WD3 3SS, United Kingdom
📞 (01923) 212498/ 📠 (01923) 212498
✉ animatronic@btconnect.com
🖥 www.animatronicanimals.com

Juicy Fruits

Cambridge / London

model maker
food stylist

Steven Wheeler

01223 290 396
07860 792 082

www.juicyfruitsuk.com

MODELMAKERS

Snowdonia Taxidermy Studios School Bank Road, Llanrwst, Gwynedd, LL26 0HU, United Kingdom
(01492) 640664/ (01492) 641643
sales@taxidermy-uk.com
www.taxidermy-uk.com

Soft Sculptures by PAB Soft Options, 10 Woodhead Road, Glossop, Derbyshire, SK13 7RH, United Kingdom
(01457) 855067
pennywillow@freenet.co.uk

Solid Models 55 Field View, Bar Hill, Cambridge, CB3 8SY, United Kingdom
(01954) 206165/ (01223) 517732
prm@solidmodels.demon.co.uk

Stephen Greenfield Modelmakers Downs Farm, Reigate Road, Ewell, Epsom, Surrey, KT17 3BY, United Kingdom
(020) 8393 8770/(07831) 758953 (020) 8394 2803
stephen@sgmm.co.uk
www.sgmm.co.uk
See ad

Steve Wilsher Creative Effects Ltd 30 Church Road, Teddington, Middlesex, TW11 8PB, United Kingdom
(020) 8943 1066/(07768) 887716 (020) 8943 1065
swcfx@btinternet.com
www.swcfx.com

Stuart Roy Three Gables, Wood Farm, Earlswood, Solihull, West Midlands, B94 5SQ, United Kingdom
(01564) 702947/(07836) 777213 (01564) 702947
stuart@julieroy.freeserve.co.uk

Synapse Creative Ltd 18 Paramount Industrial Estate, Sandown Road, Watford, WD24 7XG, United Kingdom
(01923) 239444/ (01923) 237003
info@synapse-point7.com
www.synapse-point7.com

T P A Modelmakers Old Hay Oast, Brenchley, Tonbridge, Kent, TN12 7DG, United Kingdom
(01892) 835051/ (01892) 832176
tpamodelmakers@btconnect.com
www.tpamodelmakers.com

Tee Pee Stage Lighting 31 Chesterfield Avenue, Benfleet, Essex, SS7 4AJ, United Kingdom
(01268) 566844/ (01268) 566844

The Model Works Shepperton Studios, Studios Road, Shepperton, Middlesex, TW17 0QD, United Kingdom
(01932) 565433/ (01932) 568830
tiernan@jrebbeck.freeserve.co.uk

The Modelroom Kew Bridge Steam Museum, Green Dragon Lane, Brentford, Middlesex, TW8 0EN, United Kingdom
(020) 8758 9515/078121 64395 (020) 8878 6934
robert@themodelroom.com
www.themodelroom.com

Thorp Modelmakers Ltd Whitmore Lane, Sunningdale Village, Ascot, Berkshire, SL5 0NS, United Kingdom
(01344) 876776/ (01344) 876583
thorp@atomltd.com
www.atomltd.com

Tim Weare & Partners The Old Court House, 46-48 London Road, Hurst Green, Etchingham, East Sussex, TN19 7QP, United Kingdom
(01580) 860808/(07798) 518790 (01580) 860068
tim@wearemodels.co.uk
www.wearemodels.co.uk
See ad in showcase

Tripleostudio 58 Filsham Road, St. Leonards-on-Sea, East Sussex, TN38 0PA, United Kingdom
(01424) 200007/079 77 552258 (01424) 425583
tostudio@tesco.net

Van Der Graaf Perspex Productions 178A Glyn Road, London, E5 0JE, United Kingdom
(020) 8510 9977/ (020) 8510 9977
studio@van-der-graaf.co.uk
www.van-der-graaf.co.uk

Ventriloquist's Dummy Hire 14 The Crest, Goffs Oak, Waltham Cross, Hertfordshire, EN7 5NP, United Kingdom
(01707) 873262
dennis.patten@btinternet.com
www.dennispatten.co.uk

Windsor Workshop 68 Venn Street, London, SW4 8AX, United Kingdom
(020) 7627 1641/ (020) 7652 2712
www.windsorworkshopltd.co.uk

Wyebridge Interiors Hartleton, Bromsash, Ross-on-Wye, Herefordshire, HR9 7SB, United Kingdom
(01989) 780536/ (01989) 780536
info@wyebridge.com
www.wyebridge.com

MOUNTING AND LAMINATION

Acrom Photographic Lab Ltd 19 Heathmans Road, London, SW6 4TJ, United Kingdom
(020) 7751 9922/ (020) 7751 9955
mail@acrom.co.uk
www.acrom.co.uk

Andrews Professional Colour Laboratory Ltd Unit 2, Norfolk Drive, Ashford, Kent, TN23 4FB, United Kingdom
(01233) 620764
info@andrewsimaging.co.uk
www.andrewsimaging.co.uk

C 3 Imaging London City Ltd Lector Court, 153 Farringdon Road, London, EC1 3AF, United Kingdom
(020) 7833 9100/ (020) 7833 9119
work@c3londoncity.com
www.c3imaging.com

Chromagene Unit 3 Navigation Park, Lockside Road, Leeds, LS10 1EP, United Kingdom
0113-272 8500/ 0113-272 8501
sales@chromagene.co.uk
www.chromagene.co.uk

Clicks Group Ltd 10 Baker's Yard, Baker's Row, London, EC1R 3DD, United Kingdom
(020) 7278 2300/ (020) 7278 1550
info@clicks.co.uk
www.clicks-ds.co.uk

STEP HEN GREEN FIELD
MODELMAKERS
The Downs Farm, Reigate Road, Ewell, Surrey KT17 3BY
t: 020 8393 8770 e: stephen@sgmm.co.uk
www.sgmm.co.uk

Colab Digital Imaging Ltd Herald Way, Binley, Coventry, CV3 2NY, United Kingdom
(024) 7644 0404/ (024) 7644 4219
info@colab.com
www.colab.com

Colourcraft Ltd Snape Road, Hurdsfield Industrial Estate, Macclesfield, Cheshire, SK10 2NZ, United Kingdom
(01625) 427791/ (01625) 511110
enquiries@colourcraft.org.uk
www.colourcraft.org.uk

Covent Garden Laminates Ltd 13 Macklin Street, Covent Garden, London, WC2B 5NH, United Kingdom
(020) 7242 1960/ (020) 7242 1001
info@cgluk.net
www.cgluk.net
See ad

D A R Colourskill Ltd Unit 1, Cornwall Road, Hatch End, Middlesex, HA5 4JR, United Kingdom
(020) 8428 1055/ (020) 8428 3268
info@darimages.co.uk
www.darimages.co.uk

Display Graphics Ltd Unit J 112, Tower Bridge Business Complex, 100 Clements Road, London, SE16 4DG, United Kingdom
(020) 7231 8881/ (020) 7231 0025
sales@display-graphics.co.uk
www.display-graphics.co.uk

Eaveswood Colour 1 Keyfield, St. Albans, Hertfordshire, AL1 1QL, United Kingdom
(01727) 893770/(07880) 748778 (01727) 893391
sales@eaveswoodcolour.co.uk
www.eaveswoodcolour.co.uk

Genesis Imaging (Chelsea) Unit D2, The Depot, 2 Michael Road, London, SW6 2AD, United Kingdom
(020) 7731 2227/ (020) 7731 8778
chelsea@genesisimaging.co.uk
www.genesisimaging.co.uk

Genesis Imaging (City) The Depo, 2 Michael Road, Fulham, London, SW6 2AD, United Kingdom
(020) 7731 2227/ (020) 7731 8778
city@genesisimaging.co.uk
www.genesisimaging.co.uk

Home Counties Colour Services Ltd Suite 1, Ground Floor, Chaucer House, Biscot Road, Luton, LU3 1AX, United Kingdom
(01582) 816001/ (01582) 402410
sales@hccs.co.uk
www.hccs.co.uk

John E. Wright & Co. Ltd Blue Print House, 115 Huntingdon Street, Nottingham, NG1 3NF, United Kingdom
0115-950 6633/ 0115-958 5067
nottingham@johnewright.com
www.johnewright.com

Laminart Unit 21, Tower Workshops, London, SE1 3DG, United Kingdom
(020) 7232 0317/ (020) 7394 2847
info@laminart.co.uk
www.laminart.co.uk

Libran Laminations Unit 4, The Finishing Factory, 156 Coles Green Road, London, NW2 7HW, United Kingdom
(020) 8452 2006/ (020) 8452 4456
info@libranlaminations.co.uk
www.libranlaminatíons.co.uk

Mass Technology (UK) Ltd 36b Evington Road, Leicester, Leicestershire, LE2 1HG,
0116 25 44 171
masstechnology@hotmail.com
www.masstechnologyonline.com

Moorland Photographic & Digital Imaging Ltd 123 Moorland Road, Burslem, Stoke-on-Trent, ST6 1JD, United Kingdom
(01782) 814861/ (01782) 835907
enquiries@moorlandphoto.co.uk
www.moorlandphoto.co.uk

Phil Kashdan Design, Print & Display Ltd The Studio, 47 Povey Cross Road, Horley, Surrey, RH6 0AG,
01293 773129/ 01293 773129
phil@pk-design.com

Polyboard UK 25 Robinson Road, Bangor, County Down, BT19 6NJ, United Kingdom
(02891) 450780/ (02891) 450420
polyboard@btconnect.com
www.polyboard-uk.com

Service Point 49 Charles Street, Cardiff, CF10 2GD, United Kingdom
(029) 20 224316/ (029) 20 342712
cardiff@servicepointuk.com
www.servicepointuk.com

Shoot Photographic 123 Pancras Road, London, NW1 1UN, United Kingdom
(020) 7388 3132/ (020) 7387 3844
shootphoto@ukonline.co.uk

Studio Mounts 7 Dainford Close, Bromley, BR1 5QS, United Kingdom
(020) 8695 9515/ (020) 8695 0978
juliius@studiomounts.co.uk
www.studiomounts.co.uk

X Card Technology Unit 8, Cowley Mill Trading Estate, Longbridge Way, Uxbridge, Middlesex, UB8 2YG, United Kingdom
(01895) 256332/ (01895) 230902
info@xcardtechnology.com
www.xcardtechnology.com

PHOTOLABS

1st Option Representation 64 West Yard, Camden Lock Place, London, NW1 8AF, United Kingdom
(020) 7284 2345/ (020) 7284 2456
mail@1st-option.com
www.1st-option.com

A. Foster & Son Ltd 8 High Street, Horncastle, Lincolnshire, LN9 5BL, United Kingdom
(01507) 526861/ (01507) 526053
postbox@afosterandson.co.uk
www.afosterandson.co.uk

A.C. Cooper (Colour) Ltd 2nd Floor, 104 New Bond Street, London, W1S 1SU, United Kingdom
(020) 7629 7585/ (020) 7409 3449
info@accooper.com
www.accooper.com

Academy Photos 410 Coldharbour Lane, London, SW9 8LF, United Kingdom
(020) 7274 2602/ (020) 7733 8924
academyphotos@yahoo.co.uk
www.academyimaging.com

CGL
Covent Garden Laminates
13 Macklin Street
London WC2B 5NH
Tel: 020 7242 1940
Fax: 020 7242 1001
email: info@cgluk.net
http://www.cgluk.net

LARGE FORMAT PRINTS
EXHIBITION GRAPHICS
VINYL LETTERING
LAMINATING/ENCAPSULATION
COLOUR SCANNING
INCLUDING BOARDS

'Takes the effort out of finishing'

Acrom Photographic Lab Ltd 19 Heathmans Road, London, SW6 4TJ, United Kingdom
(020) 7751 9922/ (020) 7751 9955
mail@acrom.co.uk
www.acrom.co.uk

Adrian Ensor 69 Grafton Way, London, W1t 6JD, United Kingdom
(020) 7636 1739/ (020) 7580 7772

Allied Photolabs Ltd Allied House, Bay Tree Avenue, Leatherhead, Surrey, KT22 7UE, United Kingdom
(01372) 379933/ (01372) 372867
sales@alliedphotolabs.com
www.alliedphotolabs.com

Andrews Professional Colour Laboratory Ltd Unit 2, Norfolk Drive, Ashford, Kent, TN23 4FB, United Kingdom
(01233) 620764
info@andrewsimaging.co.uk
www.andrewsimaging.co.uk

Anglia Photoworks Ltd 66 Devonshire Road, Cambridge, CB1 2BL, United Kingdom
(01223) 357056
angliaphotoworks@gmail.com

Ashley Colour Laboratories 50 Ashley Road, Parkstone, Poole, Dorset, BH14 9BN, United Kingdom
(01202) 742508/ (01202) 715540
photoprint@ashleycolour.co.uk
www.ashleycolour.co.uk

Avoncolour Ltd 131 Duckmoor Road, Ashton Gate, Bristol, BS3 2BJ, United Kingdom
0117-963 3456/ 0117-966 3456
info@avoncolour.co.uk
www.avoncolour.co.uk

Axiom Photographic Agency The Pall Mall Deposit, 124-128 Barlby Road, London, W10 6BL, United Kingdom
(020) 8964 9970/ (020) 8964 8440
info@axiomphotographic.com
www.axiomphotographic.com

Black & White Revival Magpie Cottage, Moor End Road, Radwell, Bedford, MK43 7HX, United Kingdom
(01234) 782265/ (01234) 217263
helen.dawkins@tiscali.net

Black Sheep Display 141/149 Upper Newtownards Road, Belfast, BT4 3HX, United Kingdom
(028) 9065 7404/ (028) 9065 7919
info@blacksheepni.com
www.blacksheepdisplay.com

Blaze Image 111 Talbot Road, London, W11 2AT, United Kingdom
(020) 7229 4334/ (020) 7229 4334

Blowup 146 Amyand Park Road, St. Margaret's, Twickenham, TW1 3HY, United Kingdom
(020) 8744 0210/ (020) 8892 2521
orders@blowup.net
www.blowup.net

Bolton Colour Lab 362 Shorley Old Road, Bolton, BL1 6AG, United Kingdom
(01204) 847592
boltoncolourlabs@btconnect.com
www.boltoncolourlabs.co.uk

BT Photographic Express 74 Wood Lane, Timperley, Altrincham, Cheshire, WA15 7PL, United Kingdom
☎ 0161-980 5918/ 0161-903 9869
✉ neil@btphotographic.co.uk
🖳 www.btphotographic.co.uk

Bucks Laboratories 714-715 Banbury Avenue, Slough, SL1 4LR, United Kingdom
☎ (01753) 501501/ (01753) 691762
✉ mail@bucks.co.uk
🖳 www.bucks.co.uk

C C Imaging Ltd 7 Scala Court, Leatheley Road, Leeds, LS10 1JD, United Kingdom
☎ 0113-244 8329/ 0113-244 0115
✉ ccimaging@btconnect.com
🖳 www.ccimaging.co.uk

Ceta Imaging 1/5 Poland Street, London, W1F 8NA, United Kingdom
☎ (020) 7434 1235/ (020) 7434 9283
✉ info@cetaimaging.com
🖳 www.cetaimaging.com

Chromagene Unit 3 Navigation Park, Lockside Road, Leeds, LS10 1EP, United Kingdom
☎ 0113-272 8500/ 0113-272 8501
✉ sales@chromagene.co.uk
🖳 www.chromagene.co.uk

Click 2 Print 30A High Street, Hampton Hill, Middlesex, TW12 1PD, United Kingdom
☎ (020) 8943 4576/(07976) 404277
✉ click2print@orange.net
🖳 www.click-2-print.co.uk

Colab Digital Imaging Ltd Herald Way, Binley, Coventry, CV3 2NY, United Kingdom
☎ (024) 7644 0404/ (024) 7644 4219
✉ info@colab.com
🖳 www.colab.com

Colab Ltd 18 Cheltenham Trade Park, Arle Road, Cheltenham, Gloucestershire, GL51 8JU, United Kingdom
☎ (01242) 224219/ (01242) 254330
✉ cheltenham@colab.com
🖳 www.colab.co.uk

Colorama Digital Pro Lab & Studio 178 Wardour Street, London, W1F 8ZZ, United Kingdom
☎ (020) 7434 0649
✉ prolab1@colorama.co.uk
🖳 www.coloramaprolab.co.uk

Colorama Processing Laboratories Ltd 61 Webber Street, London, SE1 0RF, United Kingdom
☎ (020) 7261 1082/ (020) 7620 1208
✉ colorama@easynet.co.uk
🖳 www.colorama.co.uk

Colorworld Ltd, Norham Road, North Shields, Tyne & Wear, NE29 0YQ, United Kingdom
☎ 0191-259 6926/ 0191-257 6948
✉ lad@colorworldimaging.co.uk
🖳 www.colorworldimaging.co.uk

Colourcraft Ltd Snape Road, Hurdsfield Ind Est, Macclesfield, Cheshire, SK10 2NZ, United Kingdom
☎ (01625) 427791/ (01625) 511110
✉ enquiries@colourcraft.org.uk
🖳 www.colourcraft.org.uk

Colourshack High Street, Lane End, High Wycombe, Buckinghamshire, HP14 3JG, United Kingdom
☎ (01494) 882823/ (01494) 881826
✉ colourshack@supanet.com

D S Colour Labs Ltd 720 Wilmslow Road, Didsbury, Manchester, M20 2DW, United Kingdom
☎ 0161-445 3481/ 0161-445 2044
✉ jonathan.porter@btclick.com
🖳 www.dscolourlabs.co.uk

Dark Side Photographic 4 Helmet Row, London, EC1V 3QJ, United Kingdom
☎ (020) 7250 1200/ (020) 7250 1771
✉ info@darksidephoto.co.uk
🖳 www.darksidephoto.co.uk

Downtown Darkroom Ltd Little Britain House, 12 Valentine Place, London, SE1 8QH, United Kingdom
☎ (020) 7620 0911
✉ darkroom@silverprint.co.uk

Eastern 108 Market Street, Musselburgh, Midlothian, EH21 6QA, United Kingdom
☎ 0131-653 5700/ 0131-665 5335
✉ sales@eastern-info.co.uk
🖳 www.eastern-info.co.uk

Edinburgh Cameras 219 Bruntsfield Place, (Holy Corner), Edinburgh, EH10 4DH, United Kingdom
☎ 0131-447 9977/ 0131-447 7997
✉ sales@edinburghcameras.co.uk
🖳 www.edinburghcameras.co.uk

Express Imaging 544 Sauchiehall Street, Glasgow, G2 3LX, United Kingdom
☎ 0141-332 3381/ 0141-332 0722
✉ expressim@btclick.com
🖳 www.express-imaging.co.uk

F.E. Burman Ltd 20 Crimscott Street, London, SE1 5TF, United Kingdom
☎ (020) 7206 1000/ (020) 7206 1040
✉ info@feburman.co.uk
🖳 www.feburman.co.uk

F.E. Wrightson & Associates 47 West End, Kirkbymoorside, York, YO62 6AD, United Kingdom
☎ (01751) 431417/ (01751) 433331
✉ info@fewrightson.co.uk
🖳 www.fewrightson.co.uk

Fastline Photographic Station Rise, York, YO1 6HT, United Kingdom
☎ (01904) 522 575/ (01904) 522 575
✉ seamus@fastlinephotographic.com
🖳 www.fastlinephotographic.com

Flying Colours 45-47 Broadwick Street, London, W1F 9QP, United Kingdom
☎ (020) 7734 3577/ (020) 7494 1559
✉ david@negs.co.uk
🖳 www.negs.co.uk

Foto First Ltd 21 Cornwall Street, Plymouth, PL1 1NW, United Kingdom
☎ (01752) 663666
🖳 www.fotofirstdirect.com

Genesis Imaging (Chelsea) Unit D2, The Depot, 2 Michael Road, London, SW6 2AD, United Kingdom
☎ (020) 7731 2227/ (020) 7731 8778
✉ chelsea@genesisimaging.co.uk
🖳 www.genesisimaging.co.uk

Genesis Imaging (City) The Depo, 2 Michael Road, Fulham, London, SW6 2AD, United Kingdom
☎ (020) 7731 2227/ (020) 7731 8778
✉ city@genesisimaging.co.uk
🖳 www.genesisimaging.co.uk

Genie Imaging Unit D4, Jaggard Way, London, SW12 8SG, United Kingdom
☎ (020) 8772 1700/ (020) 8772 1710
✉ orders@genieimaging.co.uk
🖳 www.genieimaging.co.uk

Genix Imaging Ltd 32 Broadwick Street, London, W1F 8JB, United Kingdom
☎ (020) 7734 0742/ (020) 7434 1528
✉ sales@genix.co.uk
🖳 www.genix.co.uk

Gillman & Soame Trajan House, Mill Street, Oxford, OX2 0DJ, United Kingdom
☎ (01865) 263600/(07966) 258103 / (01865) 263636
✉ commercial@gillmanandsoame.co.uk
🖳 www.gillmanandsoame.co.uk

Gordon Bishop Associates 23A Paddington Street, London, W1U 5QT, United Kingdom
☎ (020) 7486 1464/ (020) 7487 2984
✉ g@blackandwhiteprocessing.com
🖳 www.blackandwhiteprocessing.com

Green Room Turnham Green, Terrace Mews, London, W4 1QU, United Kingdom
☎ (020) 8994 6551
✉ dantsantilis@aol.com

Hammer Lab Ltd Unit 2, Building 5, Long Street Workshops, Long Street, London, E2 8HJ, United Kingdom
☎ (020) 7033 2702
✉ hammerlabs@mac.com
🖳 www.hammerlab.co.uk

Harrogate Photographic Labs Bower House, Station Parade, Harrogate, North Yorkshire, HG1 1UF, United Kingdom
☎ (01423) 501066/ (01423) 501066
✉ tony@photo-labs.com
🖳 www.photo-labs.com

Hemingway Photographic Services 84 Barnsley Road, South Kirkby, Pontefract, West Yorkshire, WF9 3QE, United Kingdom
☎ (01977) 642986/ (01977) 642986

Hi-Speed Photos 60 Broadway, West Ealing, London, W13 0SU, United Kingdom
☎ (020) 8840 4850/ (020) 8840 1800
✉ sales@hi-speed.co.uk
🖳 www.hi-speed.co.uk

Home Counties Colour Services 79A Thorpe Road, Knights, Norwich, NR1 1UA, United Kingdom
☎ (01603) 630539/ (01603) 630539

Inatif 14 Durnsford Road, Wimbledon, London, SW19 8HQ, United Kingdom
☎ (020) 8605 2526/ (020) 8605 2526
✉ sales@inatif.co.uk
🖳 www.inatif.co.uk

Infoterra Ltd Atlas House, 41 Wembley Road, Leicester, LE3 1UT, United Kingdom
☎ 0116-273 2391/(07901) 655438 / 0116-273 2400
✉ info@infoterra-global.com
🖳 www.infoterra.co.uk

Isis London 14a Rosebery Avenue, London, EC1R 4TD, United Kingdom
☎ (020) 7833 8335/(07748) 124327 / (020) 7833 0510
✉ isis@isislondon.co.uk
🖳 www.isislondon.co.uk

Jessop Group Ltd Jessop House, 98 Scudamore Road, Leicester, LE3 1TZ, United Kingdom
☎ 0116-232 0033/ 0116-232 0060
🖳 www.jessops.com

Jessops 24 County Square, Ashford, Kent, TN23 1YB, United Kingdom
☎ (01233) 624835/ (01233) 613444
🖳 www.jessops.com

Just Photos 83b High Street, Banstead, Surrey, SM7 2NL, United Kingdom
☎ (01737) 371003
✉ lab@mhpstudios.co.uk
🖳 www.lab.mhpstudios.co.uk

K L Imaging 128 Boroughbridge Road, York, YO26 6AL, United Kingdom
☎ (01904) 792338/ (01904) 781188
✉ info@klphoto.co.uk
🖳 www.klphoto.co.uk

Keith Miller Ltd 11 Towers Court, Duckworth Street, Blackburn, BB2 2JQ, United Kingdom
☎ (01254) 696909/ (01254) 699813
✉ info@millersphotography.co.uk
🖳 www.millersphotography.co.uk

Klaus Kalde Unit 1, 256 Hackney Road, London, E2 7SJ, United Kingdom
☎ (020) 7729 5278/ (020) 7729 6802
✉ k.kalde@btconnect.com
🖳 www.klauskalde.com

L A T Photographic Somerset House, Somerset Road, Teddington, Middlesex, TW11 8RU, United Kingdom
☎ (020) 8251 3000/ (020) 8251 3001
✉ digital@latphoto.co.uk
🖳 www.latphoto.co.uk

Lancashire Colour Laboratories 11 Towers Court, Duckworth Street, Blackburn, BB2 2JQ, United Kingdom
☎ (01254) 263500/ (01254) 699813
✉ sales@millersphotography.co.uk
🖳 www.millersphotography.co.uk

Leach Colour Ltd Bradley Business Park, Dyson Wood Way, Bradley, Huddersfield, HD2 1GN, United Kingdom
☎ (01484) 551200/ (01484) 551211
✉ info@leachcolour.com
🖳 www.leachcolour.com

M P C Professional Digital & Photographic Imaging Ltd MPC House, Francis Road, Manchester, M20 4XP, United Kingdom
☎ 0161-445 3145/ 0161-445 5563
✉ info@mpclabs.co.uk
🖳 www.mpclabs.co.uk

M P S Photographic Image House, 17 Carlol Square, Newcastle upon Tyne, NE1 6UQ, United Kingdom
☎ 0191-232 3558/ 0191-261 0990
✉ mps@mps-photographic.co.uk
🖳 www.mps-photographic.co.uk

Manchester Colour Lab Ltd Archer Street, Great Moor, Stockport, Cheshire, SK2 7PN, United Kingdom
☎ 0161-456 4957/ 0161-419 9463
✉ info@mcl-ltd.com
🖳 www.mcl-ltd.com

Matchless Prints Ltd 36 Lambs Conduit Street, London, WC1N 3LJ, United Kingdom
☎ (020) 7405 8899
🖳 www.dannypope.com

Metro Imaging 76 Clerkenwell Road, London, EC1M 5TN, United Kingdom
☎ (020) 7865 0000/🖷 (020) 7865 0001
✎ info@metroimaging.co.uk
🖳 www.metroimaging.co.uk

Michael Chevis The Studio, West Street, Midhurst, West Sussex, GU29 9NF, United Kingdom
☎ (01730) 814864/(07734) 982525
✎ info@michaelchevis.com
🖳 www.michaelchevis.com

Moorefield Photographic 2 Old Hall Street, Liverpool, L3 9RQ, United Kingdom
☎ 0151-236 1611/🖷 0151-236 1677
✎ info@moorefieldsphoto.com
🖳 www.moorefieldsphoto.com

Othens on line in Greenwich Ltd Linear House, Peyton Place, London, SE10 8RS, United Kingdom
☎ (020) 8858 8351/🖷 (020) 8305 0268
✎ tony@othens.co.uk
🖳 www.othens.co.uk

Panther Professionals 87 Clerkenwell Road, London, EC1R 5BX, United Kingdom
☎ (020) 7405 0055/🖷 (020) 7405 8877
✎ panther@globalnet.co.uk
🖳 www.panther-imaging.com

Photo Finish Ltd 2-4 Market Hill, Douglas, Isle of Man, IM1 2BG, United Kingdom
☎ (01624) 628022/🖷 (01624) 616074
✎ photofinish@manx.net
🖳 www.photofinish.co.im

Photogenix 9 Commercial Road, Hereford, HR1 2BB, United Kingdom
☎ (01432) 274374
✎ tel23@tiscali.co.uk

Photographic Techniques Ltd 1b Montague Road, Wimbledon Broadway, London, SW19 1TB, United Kingdom
☎ (020) 8542 2444/🖷 (020) 8542 3444
✎ images@phototech.co.uk
🖳 www.phototech.co.uk

PIC Photos Ltd 9 Park Lane, Harefield, Middlesex, UB9 6BJ, United Kingdom
☎ (01895) 822100/🖷 (01895) 822500
✎ scott_picphotos@yahoo.com

Pro2col Imaging Ltd Unit 4, Great Jackson Street, Manchester, M15 4NP, United Kingdom
☎ 0161-228 0303/🖷 0161-236 9149
✎ sales@pro2col-imaging.co.uk
🖳 www.pro2col-imaging.co.uk

Promises Specialist Colour Processing Ltd Unit 9, Goldhawk Industrial Estate, 2A Brackenberry Road, London, W6 0BA, United Kingdom
☎ (020) 8749 2136/🖷 (020) 8740 9469
✎ kdg55@dial.pipex.com
🖳 www.promises.co.uk

Quality Exposed Kiosk Two, The Martlets, Burgess Hill, West Sussex, RH15 9NN, United Kingdom
☎ (01444) 257535
✎ qualityexposed@btinternet.com
🖳 www.qualityexposed.co.uk

R P Photographic Unit 1 Sleaford Industrial Estate, Sleaford Street, London, SW8 5AB, United Kingdom
☎ (020) 7720 3840/🖷 (020) 7498 9553
✎ rpphotographic@aol.com
🖳 www.rpphotographic.com

Redwood Photographic Laboratories Ltd 7 Brunel Court, Brunel Way, Colchester, CO4 9XW, United Kingdom
☎ (01206) 751241/(07887) 796635/🖷 (01206) 855134
✎ info@redwoodphoto.com
🖳 www.redwoodphoto.com

Reflections
Norwich, United Kingdom
☎ (01603) 630081/🖷 (01603) 765154
✎ reflections@btconnect.com
🖳 www.reflectionsnorwich.co.uk

Roy Snell (Silver Gelatine / Giclee) 54 Summerly Street, London, SW18 4EX, United Kingdom
☎ (020) 8946 7536/(07764) 354700
✎ print@roysnell.demon.co.uk

S C L Photographic Services 16 Bull Lane, Edmonton, London, N18 1SX, United Kingdom
☎ (020) 8807 0725/🖷 (020) 8807 2539
✎ steven@sclimage.net
🖳 www.sclimage.net

School Pictures International Burns Street, Mansfield, Nottinghamshire, NG18 5PT, United Kingdom
☎ (01623) 657777/🖷 (01623) 660957
✎ general@schoolpictures.net
🖳 www.schoolpictures.net

Shades Photographic Ltd Unit 2, Butt Road, Woking, Surrey, GU21 6JU, United Kingdom
☎ (01483) 740362
✎ shadesphoto@btinternet.com
🖳 www.shadesphoto.co.uk

Sherwood Laboratories Ltd Brunel Drive, Newark, Nottinghamshire, NG24 2EG, United Kingdom
☎ (01636) 700321/🖷 (01636) 640653
🖳 www.sherwood-labs.co.uk

South West Colour Labs 1 Aspen Way, Yalberton Industrial Estate, Paignton, Devon, TQ4 7QR, United Kingdom
☎ (01803) 666640/🖷 (01803) 409797
✎ sales@swcl.co.uk
🖳 www.swcl.co.uk

Steve MacarÈ Photography 59 Dragon Avenue, Harrogate, North Yorkshire, HG1 5DS, United Kingdom
☎ (01423) 561809/(07711) 937562/🖷 (01423) 548843
✎ stevemacare@ntlworld.com

Tapestry Tapestry, 51-52 Frith Street, London, W1D 4SH, United Kingdom
☎ (020) 7896 3100/🖷 (020) 7896 3009
✎ info@tapestry.co.uk
🖳 www.tapestry.co.uk

Taurus Colour Labs Unit 6, Kelvin Business Centre, Kelvin Way, Crawley, West Sussex, RH10 9SF, United Kingdom
☎ (01293) 553427
🖳 www.tauruscolourlabs.co.uk

Team Photographic 37 Endell Street, Covent Garden, London, WC2H 9BA, United Kingdom
☎ (020) 7240 2902/🖷 (020) 7240 4590
✎ hugh@teamphotographic.com
🖳 www.teamphotographic.com

Techniques Group Ltd 29-31 Greville Street, London, EC1N 8SU, United Kingdom
☎ (020) 7404 3175/🖷 (020) 7831 8173
✎ techniques@btconnect.com
🖳 www.techniquesgroup.co.uk

The Dark Room UK Ltd 15 Berkeley Mews, Upper High Street, Cheltenham, Gloucestershire, GL50 1DY, United Kingdom
☎ (01242) 239031/🖷 (01242) 239032
✎ process@the-darkroom.co.uk
🖳 www.the-darkroom.co.uk

The Lab (Soho) Ltd 51 Cleveland Street, London, W1T 4JH, United Kingdom
☎ (020) 7631 1111/🖷 (020) 7631 0011
✎ sales@thelab.co.uk
🖳 www.thelab.co.uk

The Photographers Workshop St Mary's Nursery, 103 Birchwood Road, Dartford, DA2 7HQ, United Kingdom
☎ (01322) 665264
✎ info@thephotographersworkshop.co.uk
🖳 www.thephotographersworkshop.co.uk

The Vault 1 Dorset Place, Brighton, BN2 1ST, United Kingdom
☎ (01273) 670 667
✎ info@thevaultimaging.co.uk
🖳 www.thevaultimaging.co.uk

Transcolour Ltd Unit 1, 7 Tyers Gate, London, SE1 3HX, United Kingdom
☎ (020) 7403 0048
✎ juno.field@btinternet.co.uk

Verdi Studios 225 Green Street, London, E7 8LL, United Kingdom
☎ (020) 8472 8842/🖷 (020) 8472 8882
✎ kirkverdi@aol.com
🖳 www.verdistudios.com

Visions 271-273 King Street, London, W6 9LZ, United Kingdom
☎ (020) 8748 0871/🖷 (020) 8563 0223
✎ visions@which.net
🖳 www.visionsphoto.co.uk

Visualeyes Imaging Services 11 West Street, Covent Garden, London, WC2H 9NE, United Kingdom
☎ (020) 7836 3004/🖷 (020) 7240 0079
✎ imaging@visphoto.co.uk
🖳 www.visphoto.co.uk

W.W. Winter Ltd 45 Midland Road, Derby, DE1 2SP, United Kingdom
☎ (01332) 345224/🖷 (01332) 345224
✎ office@wwwinter.co.uk
🖳 www.wwwinter.com

PHOTO EQUIPMENT AND RENTAL

A F M Lighting Ltd Waxlow Road, London, NW10 7NU, United Kingdom
☎ (020) 8233 7000/🖷 (020) 8233 7001
✎ info@afmlighting.com
🖳 www.afmlighting.com

Calumet Bradbourne Drive, Tilbrook, Milton Keynes, MK7 8AJ, United Kingdom
☎ (01908) 366344/🖷 (01908) 366857
🖳 www.calumetphoto.co.uk

Calumet - Belfast 3 Loughside Industrial Park, Dargan Crescent, Belfast, BT3 9JP, United Kingdom
☎ (028) 9077 7770/🖷 (028) 9077 4230
✎ belfast@calumetphoto.co.uk
🖳 www.calumetphoto.co.uk

Calumet - Birmingham 23 Aston Cross Business Centre, Wainwright Street, Aston, Birmingham, B6 5TH, United Kingdom
☎ 0121-326 7636/🖷 0121-328 1713
✎ tom.gately@calumetphoto.co.uk
🖳 www.calumetphoto.com

Calumet - Bristol 7 Montpelier Central Trading Estate, Station Road, Montpelier, Bristol, BS6 5EE, United Kingdom
☎ 0117-942 2000/🖷 0117-942 7722
✎ andy.adams@calumetphoto.co.uk
🖳 www.calumetphoto.com

Calumet - Edinburgh 3 Bonnington Business Centre, Tennant Street, Edinburgh, EH6 5HG, United Kingdom
☎ 0131-554 7648/🖷 0131-554 6105
✎ vanessa.cox@calumetphoto.co.uk
🖳 www.calumetphoto.com

Calumet - Glasgow Block 4, Unit 1, Oakbank Industrial Estate, off Garscube Road, Glasgow, G20 7LU, United Kingdom
☎ 0141-353 0875/🖷 0141-332 1275
✎ tommy.rodgers@calumetphoto.co.uk
🖳 www.calumetphoto.com

Calumet - Liverpool 7 Century Building, Summers Road, Brunswick Business Park, Liverpool, L3 4BL, United Kingdom
☎ 0151-709 1665/🖷 0151-709 6516
✎ liverpool@calumetphoto.co.uk
🖳 www.calumetphoto.com

Calumet - London 93-103 Drummond Street, London, NW1 2HJ, United Kingdom
☎ (020) 7380 1144/🖷 (020) 7387 3354
✎ film@calumetphoto.com
🖳 www.calumetphoto.com

Calumet - Manchester Unit 4, Downing Street Industrial Estate, Charlton Place, Manchester, M12 6HH, United Kingdom
☎ 0161-274 4455/🖷 0161-274 3406
✎ michael.collins@calumetphoto.co.uk
🖳 www.calumetphoto.com

Calumet - Nottingham 2 Nelson Street, Nottingham, NG1 1DR, United Kingdom
☎ 0115-958 6888/🖷 0115-959 9061
✎ nottingham@calumetphoto.co.uk
🖳 www.calumetphoto.com

Calumet Direct
Milton Keynes, United Kingdom
☎ (0800) 0964396/🖷 (0870) 6060061
🖳 www.calumetphoto.com

Calumet Photographic Ltd Unit 4, Charlton Place, Downing Street Industrial Estate, Manchester, M12 6HH, United Kingdom
☎ 0161-274 4455/🖷 0161-274 3406
✎ michael.collins@calumetphoto.co.uk
🖳 www.calumetphoto.com

Chau Digital 19 Rosebery Avenue, London, EC1R 4SP, United Kingdom
☎ (020) 7833 3938/🖷 (020) 7837 9130
✎ sales@chaudigital.com
🖳 www.chaudigital.com

Cinebuild Ltd Studio House, 34 Rita Road, London, SW8 1JU, United Kingdom
☎ (020) 7582 8750/(07836) 220441/🖷 (020) 7793 0467
✎ cinebuild@btclick.com
🖳 www.cinebuild.com

plastic sandwich

leather print books • slip cases • bike bags
mini books • custom presentation projects

www.plasticsandwich.com

t 020 7431 3211 • info@plasticsandwich.com

Digital Photo Services Top Floor, Export House, 25-31 Ironmonger Row, London, EC1V 3QN, United Kingdom
(020) 7033 4421/(07830) 146285 (020) 7490 3384
info@digitalphotoservices.co.uk
www.digitalphotoservices.co.uk

Edinburgh Cameras 219 Bruntsfield Place, (Holy Corner), Edinburgh, EH10 4DH, United Kingdom
0131-447 9977/ 0131-447 7997
sales@edinburghcameras.co.uk
www.edinburghcameras.co.uk

eme Digital 3 Millharbour, London, E14 9XP, United Kingdom
(020) 7538 8105/ (020) 7538 3130
enquiries@emedigital.co.uk
www.emedigital.co.uk

Equip 11 Balmoral Road, Romford, RM2 5XD, United Kingdom
(01708) 479898
sales@equip-u.com
www.equip-u.com

Express Imaging 544 Sauchiehall Street, Glasgow, G2 3LX, United Kingdom
0141-332 3381/ 0141-332 0722
expressim@btclick.com
www.express-imaging.co.uk

Fuji Photo Film (U.K.) Ltd 125 Finchley Road, London, NW3 6HY, United Kingdom
(020) 7586 5900/ (020) 7722 4259
www.fujifilm.co.uk

G W Digital & Photo Ltd Unit 7G, North Estate, Old Oxford Road, Piddington, High Wycombe, Buckinghamshire, HP14 3BE, United Kingdom
(01494) 880882/(07774) 637406 (01494) 880892
info@gwdigitalandphoto.com
www.gwdigitalandphoto.com

Kinetic Units 3 & 4, Cremer Business Centre, 37 Cremer Street, London, E2 8HD, United Kingdom
(020) 7729 7442/ (020) 7749 4299
info@go-kinetic.com
www.go-kinetic.com

Leeds PhotoVisual Ltd 20-22 Brunswick Centre, Bernard Street, London, WC1N 1AE, United Kingdom
(020) 7833 1661/ (020) 7833 1570
www.leedsphoto.co.uk

Morco Ltd 20 Oak Tree Business Park, Oak Tree Lane, Mansfield, Nottinghamshire, NG18 3HQ, United Kingdom
(01623) 422828/ (01623) 422818
sales@morco.uk.com
www.morco.uk.com

Peartree Rental Ltd Lower Ground Floor, 53 Central Street, London, EC1V 8AD, United Kingdom
(020) 7251 2044/078 41260777 (020) 7251 2455
info@peartreerental.com
www.peartreerental.com

Photo-Me International Church Road, Bookham, Surrey, KT23 3EU, United Kingdom
(01372) 453399/ (01372) 459064
info@photo-me.co.uk
www.photo-me.co.uk

Shooting Digital.co.uk 42B Medina Road, London, N7 7LA, United Kingdom
(020) 7502 5118/07856 687933 (020) 7686 2324
info@shootingdigital.co.uk
www.shootingdigital.co.uk

Snap Productions 151-155 New North Road, London, N1 6TA, United Kingdom
(020) 7684 7555/ (020) 7684 7556
rich@snap-pro.com
www.snap-pro.com
See ad in showcase

Switch Digital 21 Lanercost Road, Brixton, London, SW2 3DP, United Kingdom
(020) 8674 2255/ (020) 8674 1973
bookings@switch-digital.co.uk
www.switch-digital.co.uk

Technical Lamps Milton Hall, Milton Road, Hampton, Middlesex, TW12 2LL, United Kingdom
(020) 8979 6652/ (020) 8979 9007
sales@techlamps.co.uk
www.techlamps.co.uk

PORTFOLIOS

Delta Design Studio/Cathy Robert Studio 2, 14-16 Meredith Street, London, EC1R 0AE, United Kingdom
(020) 7837 7557/ (020) 7837 9878
info@cathyrobert.com
www.cathyrobert.com

Lucian Marin
Bucharest, 61079, Romania
721 230 631
lucian.marin@gmail.com
www.lucianmarin.ro

Paggraphicsandmedia 73C Ballards Lane, London, N3 1XT, United Kingdom
(020) 8371 9969
info@paggraphicsandmedia.com
www.paggraphicsandmedia.com

Plastic Sandwich White Lodge, 252 Finchley Road, London, NW3 7AA, United Kingdom
(020) 7431 3211/ (020) 7435 5799
info@plasticsandwich.com
www.plasticsandwich.com
See ad in showcase

Studio Mounts 7 Dainford Close, Bromley, BR1 5QS, United Kingdom
(020) 8695 9515/ (020) 8695 0978
juliius@studiomounts.co.uk
www.studiomounts.co.uk

STILLS

A Construction Production 9 Alpha Street, London, SE15 4NX, United Kingdom
(07971) 009015
ac.e@aconstructionproduction.com
www.aconstructionproduction.com

Arthur Productions Ltd 20 Benson Road, Croydon, CR0 4LQ, United Kingdom
(07973) 151406
sam.arthur@arthurproductions.com
www.arthurproductions.com

B P H P 50b Regina Road, London, N4 3PP, United Kingdom
(07855) 520707
ben@bphp.co.uk
www.bphp.co.uk

Bespoke Production 72 Belleville Road, London, SW11 6PP, United Kingdom
(020) 7585 2536/ (020) 7585 2536
info@bespokeproduction.com
www.bespokeproduction.com

C B A V World Locations 3 rue de Turbigo, Paris, 75001, France
00 33 1 42 33 89 23/ 00 33 1 42 33 89 23
paris@worldlocations.com
www.worldlocations.com

C J H Productions 18 All Saints Road, Studio 14, London, W11 1HH, United Kingdom
(020) 7229 2488/ (020) 7229 2481
camilla@cjhproductions.com
www.cjhproductions.com

Cameron Eccles 9 Alpha Street, London, SE15 4NX, United Kingdom
(07971) 009015
ac.e@aconstructionproduction.com
www.aconstructionproduction.com

Caspar & Co. 24 Wisley Road, London, SW11 6NF, United Kingdom
(020) 7978 6622/(07768) 610177
info@casparco.com
www.casparco.com

Charles Pearce Ltd 26 Devonshire Road, London, W4 2HD, United Kingdom
(020) 8995 3333
ava@charlespearce.co.uk
www.charlespearce.co.uk

Check The Gate Rua Rodrigo Albuquerque e Melo 4, 4D, L.A. Velha, Lisboa, Portugal
00 351 91 819 6577
jose@checkthegate.com
www.checkthegate.com

Creative Management P.O.Box 72280, Office 61, Building 8, Dubai Media City, Dubai, United Arab Emirates
00 97 14 391 4318
emma@cm-ww.com
www.cm-ww.com

Digital Photo Services Top Floor, Export House, 25-31 Ironmonger Row, London, EC1V 3QN, United Kingdom
(020) 7033 4421/(07830) 146285 (020) 7490 3384
info@digitalphotoservices.co.uk
www.digitalphotoservices.co.uk

Emma Wood 24 St. Lawrence Terrace, London, W10 5SX, United Kingdom
(020) 8960 1977/(07918) 112048

Fiona Watson Production 139 Capel Road, London, E7 0JT, United Kingdom
(020) 8478 3731
fiona@fionawatson.com
www.fionawatson.com

Flight Logistics The Cabair Building, Elstree Aerodrome, Borehamwood, Hertfordshire, WD6 3AW, United Kingdom
(0870) 620 8046/ (0870) 620 8047
operations@flight-logistics.co.uk
www.flightlogistics.tv

Freelink Unit 3 Jackson Terrace, 79-81 Buitenkant Street, Gardens, Cape Town, 8001, South Africa
☎ 21 461 7288/82 880 2230 📠 00 27 21 461 7299
✉ info@freelink.co.za
🖥 www.freelink.co.za

Gavin Schneider Productions Studio G6. Gate 1, Victoria Junction, Prestwich Street, Cape Town, 8005, South Africa
☎ 21 421 2200/ 📠 21 421 2202
✉ gavin@gsproductions.co.za
🖥 www.gsproductions.co.za

Infidels Suite 131 Victoria Junction, Gate 4 Prestwich Street, Green Point, Cape Town, 8005, South Africa
☎ 00 27 21 425 78 78/ 📠 00 27 21 425 69 15
✉ info@infidels.co.za
🖥 www.infidels.co.za

Jaine Bevan 1 Riverside, The Media Centre, St. Annes Road, St. Annes Park, Bristol, BS4 4ED, United Kingdom
☎ (07967) 362613
✉ bevan.jaine@virgin.net
🖥 www.jainebevan.com

James King Photographer Unit 19c Barton Hill trad est, Maze Street, Bristol, BS5 9BD,
☎ 1179350839
✉ james@jameskingphotographer.co.uk
🖥 www.jameskingphotographer.co.uk

Kathy Howes Freelance Art Buyer 3 Hawkfield Court, Woodlands Grove, Isleworth, Middlesex, TW7 6NU, United Kingdom
☎ (07958) 575848
✉ kathyhowes16@hotmail.com

Keith Meatheringham 20 Seafield Avenue, Osgodby, Scarborough, North Yorkshire, YO11 3QG, United Kingdom
☎ (01723) 585141/(07802) 530583 📠 (0871) 4338973
✉ pix@dobsonagency.co.uk
🖥 www.dobsonagency.co.uk

Leonora Sheppard Locations & Production 32A Brewster Gardens, London, W10 6AJ, United Kingdom
☎ (020) 8969 7302/ 📠 (020) 8964 2668
✉ mail@leonora.uk.com
🖥 www.leonora.uk.com

Louise De Ville Morel 3 Heber Road, Cricklewood, London, NW2 6AB, United Kingdom
☎ (020) 8450 6148/(07966) 173913 📠 (020) 8450 1574
✉ lou@unconventionalproductions.com
🖥 www.unconventionalproductions.com

Marissa Coram 164 Woodseer Street, London, E1 5HQ, United Kingdom
☎ (020) 7247 0242/(07879) 695234
✉ marissa@marisacoram.com
🖥 www.marisacoram.com

Neovision Film Production & Services 7 rue Gardiol, Grande Saconnex, Genéva, CH-1218, Switzerland
☎ 22 741 12 09/79 357 54 17 📠 22 741 12 08
✉ info@neovisionprod.com
🖥 www.neovisionprod.com

One Production 48 Poland Street, London, W1F 7ND, United Kingdom
☎ (020) 7734 9766/ 📠 (020) 7287 2313
✉ info@oneproduction.com
🖥 www.oneproduction.com

Picnic Productions Black Door, 34 Clifton Road, London, NW10 4RB,
☎ 020 8961 6100
✉ nicole@picnicproductions.com
🖥 www.picnicproductions.com

PLC 7 Edith Grove, London, SW10 0JZ, United Kingdom
☎ (020) 7352 4008/(07774) 694140 📠 (020) 7351 9969
✉ julia@plcinternational.com
🖥 www.plcinternational.com

Rachael Phillips Associates
United Kingdom
☎ (0845) 058 0642/(07793) 276500 📠 (0871) 661 2184
✉ rp@rachaelphillips.co.uk
🖥 www.rachaelphillips.co.uk

Santa Monica Productions Spain Carril De La Granadilla, Guadalcina Alta, San Pedro Alcantara, Spain
☎ 95 288 0501/ 📠 95 288 0156
✉ info@santa-monica-productions.com
🖥 www.santa-monica-productions.com

Shoot People 3rd Floor, 202 City Road, London, EC1V 2PH, United Kingdom
☎ (020) 7253 0009/(07767) 313007 📠 (020) 7253 0009
✉ victoria@shootpeople.com
🖥 www.shootpeople.com

Site4View Productions 799 Broadway ~608, New York, 10003, United States of America
☎ 00 1 212 614 8500/ 📠 00 1 212 614 8586
✉ ik@site4view.com
🖥 www.site4view.com

Steve Mortimore The Garden Flat, 40 Elsworthy Road, London, NW3 3DL, United Kingdom
☎ (07990) 542766
✉ mortimores@aol.com

Still Productions 3 Clifton Crescent, London, SE15 2RX, United Kingdom
☎ (07712) 791519/(07712) 791519 📠 (020) 7732 7165
✉ info@stillproductions.co.uk
🖥 www.stillproductions.co.uk

T Photographic 1 Heathgate Place, 75-83 Agincourt Road, London, London, NW3 2NU, United Kingdom
☎ (020) 7428 6070/ 📠 (020) 7428 6079
✉ peter@tphotographic.com
🖥 www.tphotographic.com

Tomo London Production Ltd Unit 305, Kingswharf, London, E8 4DS, United Kingdom
☎ (020) 7249 5707/(07958) 954901 📠 (020) 7249 6557
✉ info@tomolondon.com
🖥 www.tomolondon.com

Trish Appleton 4 Lysia Street, London, SW6 6NG, United Kingdom
☎ (07973) 909304
✉ trish@trishappleton.co.uk
🖥 www.trishappleton.co.uk

Unconventional Productions 3 Heber Road, London, NW2 6AB, United Kingdom
☎ **(020) 8450 6148/ 📠 (020) 8450 1574**
✉ **lou@unconventionalproductions.com**
🖥 **www.unconventionalproductions.com**
See ad in showcase

Caspar&Co
productions full service photo production
uk . europe . worldwide
020 7498 3663 info@casparco.com

www.casparco.com

Viaggi International Productions (VIP)
Athens, Greece
☎ 00 30 6944 757585
✎ filon@vip-prod.com
🖥 www.vip-prod.com

PROPS

980's Action Commercial Vehicles Unit 117, 22
Notting Hill Gate, London, W11 3JE, United Kingdom
☎ (07092) 221777/(07802) 825069/📠 (07092) 221888
✎ info@a2ecommercials.co.uk
🖥 www.a2ecommercials.co.uk

99 Cars Ltd Hyde Meadow Farm, Hyde Lane, Hemel
Hempstead, Hertfordshire, HP3 8SA, United Kingdom
☎ (01923) 266373/(07785) 382448 📠 (01923) 260852
✎ david@nineninecars.com
🖥 www.nineninecars.com

A & M Hire Ltd The Royals, Victoria Road, London,
NW10 6ND, United Kingdom
☎ (020) 8233 1500/📠 (020) 8233 1550
✎ mark@amhire.com
🖥 www.amhire.com

A D Modelmaking The Studio, 28 The Retreat, Frome,
Somerset, BA11 5JU, United Kingdom
☎ (01373) 455455/📠 (01373) 455455
🖥 www.admodelmaking.com

**AAA@Dream Cars 82 Holmethorpe Avenue, Redhill,
RH1 2NL, United Kingdom**
☎ **(01737) 765050/(07973) 400245 📠 (01737) 236179**
✎ **info@dreamcars.co.uk**
🖥 **www.dreamcars.co.uk**
See ad in showcase

Acre Jean Ltd Unit 7 The Kimber Centre, 54 Kimber
Road, London, SW18 4PP,
☎ 020 8877 3211/📠 020 8877 3213
✎ dan.hill@acrejean.com
🖥 www.acrejean.com

Action Cars Ltd Pinewood Studios, Pinewood Road, Iver
Heath, Iver, Buckinghamshire, SL0 0NH, United Kingdom
☎ (020) 8997 7771/📠 (020) 8997 1503
✎ info@actioncars.co.uk
🖥 www.actioncars.co.uk

Action Props Meikleriggs Farmhouse, Lochlibo Road,
Beith, Ayrshire, KA15 1IL, United Kingdom
☎ (0870) 0801977
✎ info@actionprops.co.uk
🖥 www.actionprops.co.uk

Alan Goodyear Classic Cars Engine Farm, 80 Cock
Bank, Whittlesey, PE7 2HN, United Kingdom
☎ (01733) 840553/(07779) 387673 📠 (01733) 840553
✎ alan@hotchkiss.to

Alpha 4 Ltd 24 Brunel Road, St. Leonards-on-Sea, East
Sussex, TN38 9RT, United Kingdom
☎ (01424) 854485/📠 (01424) 854402
✎ info@alpha-4.co.uk
🖥 www.alpha-4.co.uk

Angela Hallam Promotional Costumes 24 Clara
Street, Stoke, Coventry, CV2 4ET, United Kingdom
☎ (024) 7645 2508
✎ angelamhallam@hotmail.com

Art Squared The Hayloft Studio, Ditchford Farm,
Stretton on Fosse, Moreton-in-Marsh, Gloucestershire,
GL56 9RD, United Kingdom
☎ (01608) 664329/(07785) 302652 📠 (01608) 664329
✎ eva@art-squared.com
🖥 www.art-squared.com

Artem Ltd Perivale Park, Horsenden Lane South,
Perivale, Greenford, Middlesex, UB6 7RH, United
Kingdom
☎ (020) 8997 7771/📠 (020) 8997 1503
✎ info@artem.com
🖥 www.artem.com

Articole Studios, 9 Alexander Road, Stotfold, Hitchin,
Hertfordshire, SG5 4NA, United Kingdom
☎ (01462) 835640/📠 (01462) 834896
✎ steve@articolestudios.co.uk
🖥 www.articolestudios.co.uk

Artworkforbusiness 58 Alexandra Road, London, NW4
2RY, United Kingdom
☎ (020) 8203 1747/(07831) 378583 📠 (020) 8203 1064
✎ tano.rea@btopenworld.com

Autoprops 10 Harris Lane, Shenley, Hertfordshire, WD7
9EB, United Kingdom
☎ (01923) 853932/📠 (0871) 4335801
✎ info@autoprops.tv
🖥 www.autoprops.tv

B & T Antiques 47 Ledbury Road, London, W11 2AG,
United Kingdom
☎ (020) 7229 7001/📠 (020) 7229 2033
✎ bernadette@btantiques.freeserve.co.uk
🖥 www.bntantiques.co.uk

B N T Antiques 47 Ledbury Road, London, W11 2AA,
United Kingdom
☎ (020) 7229 7001/📠 (020) 7229 2033
✎ email@bntantiques.co.uk
🖥 www.bntantiques.co.uk

Backgrounds Surfaces & Tableware Unit 25,
Waterside, 44-48 Wharf Road, London, N1 7UX, United
Kingdom
☎ (020) 7490 1181/📠 (020) 7250 4104
🖥 www.backgroundsprophire.co.uk

Bakelite Museum Orchard Mill, Williton, Taunton,
Somerset, TA4 4NS, United Kingdom
☎ (01984) 632133/📠 (01984) 632322
✎ info@bakelitemuseum.co.uk
🖥 www.bakelitemuseum.co.uk

Bapty Ltd 1A Witley Gardens, Norwood Green, Southall,
Middlesex, UB2 4ES, United Kingdom
☎ (020) 8574 7700/📠 (020) 8571 5700
✎ hire@bapty.demon.co.uk

Beat About The Bush Unit 23, Enterprise Way, Triangle
Business Centre, Salter Street, London, NW10 6UG,
United Kingdom
☎ (020) 8960 2087/📠 (020) 8969 2281
✎ info@beataboutthebush.com
🖥 www.beataboutthebush.com

TOMOLONDON

PRODUCTION / CO-ORDINATION / CASTING / LOCATIONS

UNIT 305 KINGSWHARF / 301 KINGSLAND ROAD / LONDON / E8 4DS
T +44 (0)20 7249 5707 / F +44 (0)20 7249 6557
e-mail info@tomolondon.com / www.tomolondon.com

Becky John, 91 Middle Lane, London, N8 8NX, United Kingdom
✆ (020) 8341 2368/(07778) 518305
✉ beckyjohn15@btinternet.com

Bikes on Film 5 St. George's Court, 131 Putney Bridge Road, Putney, London, SW15 2PA, United Kingdom
✆ (020) 8877 9922/(07771) 595999 ✆ (020) 8870 5533
✉ mg@markgeorge.com
🖳 www.markgeorge.com

blueglassrabbit.com 53 Radstone Court, Woking, Surrey, GU22 7ND, United Kingdom
✆ (01483) 851879
✉ info@blueglassrabbit.com
🖳 www.blueglassrabbit.com

Bodomo Anvil House, Kingsingfield Road, West Kingsdown, Sevenoaks, Kent, TN15 6LJ, United Kingdom
✆ (01474) 854490
✉ info@bodomo.biz
🖳 www.bodomo.biz

Charles Pearce Ltd 26 Devonshire Road, London, W4 2HD, United Kingdom
✆ (020) 8995 3333
✉ ava@charlespearce.co.uk
🖳 www.charlespearce.co.uk

Charlotte Williams 48 Sandgate House, Pembury Road, London, E5 8JH, United Kingdom
✆ (07989) 206191
✉ stylist@charlottewilliams.co.uk
🖳 www.charlottewilliams.co.uk

China & Co. Props Hire 2 c/d Macfarlane Road, Shepherds Bush, London, W12 7JY, United Kingdom
✆ **(020) 8740 9588/**✆ **(020) 8740 8873**
✉ **info@chinaandco.com**
🖳 **www.chinaandco.com**
See ad in showcase

Cinebuild Ltd Studio House, 34 Rita Road, London, SW8 1JU, United Kingdom
✆ (020) 7582 8750/(07836) 220441 ✆ (020) 7793 0467
✉ cinebuild@btclick.com
🖳 www.cinebuild.com

Cole Hire Ltd Westar House, 690 Great West Road, Osterley, Isleworth, Middlesex, TW7 4PU, United Kingdom
✆ (020) 8568 0733
✉ colehire@demon.co.uk
🖳 www.colehire.co.uk

Cops On The Box BM Box 7301, London, WC1N 3XX, United Kingdom
✆ (07710) 065851
✉ info@tvcops.co.uk
🖳 www.cotb.co.uk

Crucible Theatre 55 Norfolk Street, Sheffield, S1 1DA, United Kingdom
✆ 0114-249 5999/✆ 0114-249 6003
✉ info@sheffieldtheatres.co.uk
🖳 www.sheffieldtheatres.co.uk

Custom Creations Unit 39, 26-28 Queensway, Enfield, Middlesex, EN3 4SA, United Kingdom
✆ (020) 8443 4444/(07715) 109208 ✆ (020) 8443 4444
✉ info@themodelmaker.co.uk
🖳 www.customcreations.cc

Dark Horse Graphics Yorkshire TV, Kirkstall Road, Leeds, LS3 1JS, United Kingdom
✆ 0113-222 8390/(07831) 729670 ✆ 0113-222 8391
✉ chaz@darkhorsegraphics.co.uk
🖳 www.darkhorsegraphics.co.uk

EFG - Expo Flora Ltd The Tree House, Charlecote, Warwick, CV35 9GZ, United Kingdom
✆ (01789) 470847/ ✆ (01789) 470897
✉ sales@efg-europe.com
🖳 www.efg-europe.com

Fab n Funky 1-4 Bethune Road, North Acton, London, NW10 6NJ, United Kingdom
✆ (020) 8453 3900/ ✆ (020) 8965 8107
✉ info@superhire.com
🖳 www.scene2hire.com

Fairgrounds Old & New Halstead, Fovant, Salisbury, SP3 5NL, United Kingdom
✆ (01722) 714786/(07710) 287251 ✆ (01722) 714786
✉ s-vpostlethwaite@forrins.fsnet.co.uk
🖳 www.pozzy.co.uk

Film Medical Services Units 5 & 7 Commercial Way, Park Royal, London, NW10 7XF, United Kingdom
✆ (020) 8961 3222/ ✆ (020) 8961 7427
✉ filmmed@aol.com
🖳 www.filmmedical.co.uk

Fishtail Neon 282 Madiera Drive Arches, Brighton, BN2 1PT, United Kingdom
✆ (01273) 694662/07808 761452 ✆ (01273) 694662
✉ info@fishtailneon.com
🖳 www.fishtailneon.com

Gorlick-King 59 Rutland Gate, London, SW7 1PJ, United Kingdom
✆ (020) 7584 2688/(07776) 192828 ✆ (020) 7584 2688
✉ gorlickking@hotmail.com
🖳 www.pensportobello.com

Kimberley Watson 16 Albion Square, London, E8 4ES, United Kingdom
✆ (020) 7241 4821/(07768) 737371 ✆ (020) 7241 4821
✉ watsonkimberley@mac.com

Lacquer Chest 75 Kensington Church Street, London, W8 4BG, United Kingdom
✆ (020) 7938 2070/ ✆ (020) 7376 0223
✉ info@lacquerchest.com
🖳 www.lacquerchest.com

Lancelyn Theatre Supplies Poulton Road, Bebbington, Wirral, Merseyside, CH63 9LN, United Kingdom
✆ 0151-334 3000/ ✆ 0151-334 4047
✉ northwest@lancelyn.co.uk
🖳 www.lancelyn.co.uk

Lewis & Kaye (Hire) Ltd 3B Brassie Avenue, London, W3 7DE, United Kingdom
✆ (020) 8749 2121/ ✆ (020) 8749 9455
✉ props@lewisandkaye.eclipse.co.uk
🖳 www.lewisandkaye.co.uk

London Cab Co. Ltd 49 Raymond Avenue, South Woodford, London, E18 2HF, United Kingdom
✆ (07885) 349994/ ✆ (020) 8530 1578
✉ gary@thelondoncabcompany.com
🖳 www.thelondoncabcompany.com

If we can't find the vehicle you require, then it probably doesn't exist

The **car, bike, boat** or **plane** to fit the era you visualize and the professionals with the skill to put it through the most demanding paces. Comprehensive facts and **technical advice** on the period of your shoot and the **wardrobe** and **props** you need for absoute authenticity as well as assistance in finding or booking **locations**.
All with the full back-up of the Ten Tenths team of experts.
To talk **shoots**, **editorials**, **promotions** or **exhibitions**, call

TEN TENTHS

106 GIFFORD STREET LONDON, N1 0DF
TEL: +44(0)1285 831 060 / +44(0)7721 420489   FAX: +44(0)1285 831188
www.tentenths.co.uk • Email: mike@tentenths.co.uk

London Taxidermy Hire 144a Bridge Road, East Molesey, Surrey, KT8 9HW, United Kingdom
(020) 3274 4014/(07770) 880 960
info@londontaxidermy.com
www.londontaxidermy.com

Mark Boyes Models & Props 14 Potter Street, Melbourne, Derby, DE73 1DW, United Kingdom
(01332) 864208/ (01332) 864208
mark1boyes@aol.com
www.mbmodelmaking.co.uk

Mexicolore 28 Warriner Gardens, London, SW11 4EB, United Kingdom
(020) 7622 9577/ (020) 7498 3643
ian.mursell@btinternet.com
www.mexicolore.co.uk

Michael Sinclair Modelmakers 29 Blenheim Gardens, 6 Blenheim Studios, London, SW2 5EU, United Kingdom
(020) 8671 5051/(07780) 737719 (020) 8671 5051
msinc7@yahoo.com

Mike & Rosi Compton 11 Woodstock Road, Croydon, CR0 1JS, United Kingdom
(020) 8680 4364/(07900) 258646 (020) 8681 3126
mikeandrosicompton@btopenworld.com

Naomi Sheppard Couture Jewellery Studio 723, The Big Peg, 120 Vyse Street, Hockley, Birmingham, B18 6NF, United Kingdom
(07736) 934075
info@naomisheppard.com
www.naomisheppard.com

Northern Prop Hire South Linton Farm, Linton Colliery, Morpeth, Northumberland, NE61 5SN, United Kingdom
(01670) 861010
deanna@northernprophire.co.uk
www.northernprophire.co.uk

Original Bookworks Ltd 1 Wilkinson Road, Cirencester, Gloucestershire, GL7 1YT, United Kingdom
(01285) 641664/ (01285) 641705
sales@originalbooks.net
www.originalbooks.net

Palmbrokers Ltd Cenacle Nursery, Taplow Common Rd, Burnham, Slough, SL1 8NW, United Kingdom
(01628) 663734/ (01628) 661047
matthew@palmbrokers.com
www.palmbrokers.com

Pictures Props Co. Ltd Brunel House, 12-16 Brunel Rd, London, W3 7XR, United Kingdom
(020) 8749 2433/ (020) 8740 5846
pictureprops@tiscali.co.uk
www.propascene.com

Pollocks Toy Museum Theatres & Toyshop 1 Scala Street, London, W1T 2HL, United Kingdom
(020) 7636 3452
pollocks@btconnect.com
www.pollockstoymuseum.com

Portobello Antique Dealers Association 223a Portabella Road, London, W11 1LU, United Kingdom
(020) 7229 8354/ (020) 7243 3419
info@portobelloroad.co.uk
www.portobelloroad.co.uk

Professor Patten's Punch & Judy 14 The Crest, Goffs Oak, Waltham Cross, Hertfordshire, EN7 5NP, United Kingdom
(01707) 873262
www.dennispatten.co.uk

Prop Solutions 91a Acton Lane, Harlesden, London, NW10 8UT, United Kingdom
(020) 8965 5152
info@propsolutions.co.uk
www.propsolutions.co.uk

Propaganda UK Ltd Unit 21 Rondin Road, Manchester, M12 6BF, United Kingdom
0161-273 6444/ 0161-273 6888
post@propagandauk.co.uk
www.propagandauk.co.uk

Props Galore 1-17 Brunel Road, London, W3 7XR, United Kingdom
(020) 8746 1222/ (020) 8354 1866
props@farley.co.uk
www.farley.co.uk

S2 Events Ltd 3-5 Valentine Place, London, SE1 8QH, United Kingdom
(020) 7928 5474/ (020) 7928 6082
info@s2events.co.uk
www.s2events.co.uk

Sanctuary Backcloths 32-36 Telford Way, London, W3 7XS, United Kingdom
(020) 8743 1563/ (020) 8743 8075
backcloths@sanctuarystudios.co.uk
www.sanctuarybackcloths.co.uk

Setbuild 66 Gordon Road, Harborne, Birmingham, B32 2JB, United Kingdom
0121-428 2822/(07973) 442750
setbuild@blueyonder.co.uk
www.setbuild.com

Soft Sculptures by PAB Soft Options, 10 Woodhead Road, Glossop, Derbyshire, SK13 7RH, United Kingdom
(01457) 855067
pennywillow@freenet.co.uk

Spur Creative Workshop 169b Davidson Road, Croydon, CR0 6DP, United Kingdom
(020) 8405 3436/07940 790580
phil@spurcreative.co.uk
www.spurcreative.co.uk

Steve Finch Graphic Art 23 St. Albans Crescent, Newcastle upon Tyne, NE6 5UQ, United Kingdom
(07903) 415533
s_a_finch@hotmail.com

Stuart Learmouth Unit 24, Acton Park Industrial Estate, The Vale, London, W3 7QE, United Kingdom
(020) 8749 3100/(07831) 626785 (020) 8749 3111

Studio & TV Hire 3 Ariel Way, Wood Lane, White City, London, W12 7SL, United Kingdom
(020) 8749 3445/ (020) 8740 9662
enquiries@stvhire.com
www.stvhire.com

Superhire 1-4 Bethune Road, North Acton, London, NW10 6NJ, United Kingdom
(020) 8965 9909/ (020) 8965 8107
info@superhire.com
www.superhire.com

5000 sq.ft. of the best props in London for food..drink..sets.. surfaces..backgrounds..textiles..cutlery..glass..china..etc..etc.

china & company
props hire

2 c/d/e Macfarlane Road
Shepherds Bush
London W12 7JY
phone: 020 8740 9588 fax: 020 8740 8873
web: http://www.chinaandco.com
email: info@chinaandco.com

Tables Laid Church Farm, Ashchurch Road, Ashchurch, Tewkesbury, Gloucestershire, GL20 8JU, United Kingdom
- (01684) 297999/ (01684) 291201
- www.tableslaid.co.uk

Ten Tenths Ltd 106 Gifford Street, London, N1 0DF, United Kingdom
- **(01285) 831060/(07721) 420489 (01285) 831188**
- **mike@tentenths.co.uk**
- **www.tentenths.co.uk**
- **See ad in showcase**

The Trading Post Ltd Witley Works, Witley Gardens, Norwood Green, Southall, Middlesex, UB2 4ES, United Kingdom
- (020) 8574 7017/ (020) 8571 7633
- info@tradingpostnhire.co.uk
- www.tradingposthire.co.uk

Theme Traders Ltd The Stadium, Oaklands Road, London, NW2 6DL, United Kingdom
- (020) 8452 8518/ (020) 8450 7322
- mailroom@themetraders.com
- www.themetraders.com

Thomas Fattorini Ltd Regent Street Works, Birmingham, B1 3HQ, United Kingdom
- 0121-236 1307/ 0121-200 1568
- sales@fattorini.co.uk
- www.fattorini.co.uk

Turk Film Services Ltd Turks Boat Yard, The Historic Dockyard, Chatham, Kent, ME4 2TZ, United Kingdom
- (01634) 400110/ (01634) 400237
- operations@turks.co.uk
- www.turks.co.uk

Twentytwentyone 18c River Street, London, EC1R 1XN, United Kingdom
- (020) 7837 1900/ (020) 7837 1908
- mail@twentytwentyone.com
- www.twentytwentyone.com

Van Der Graaf Perspex Productions 178A Glyn Road, London, E5 0JE, United Kingdom
- (020) 8510 9977/ (020) 8510 9977
- studio@van-der-graaf.co.uk
- www.van-der-graaf.co.uk

Ventriloquist's Dummy Hire 14 The Crest, Goffs Oak, Waltham Cross, Hertfordshire, EN7 5NP, United Kingdom
- (01707) 873262
- dennis.patten@btinternet.com
- www.dennispatten.co.uk

Vigi Sawdon 299 Lillie Road, London, SW6 7LL, United Kingdom
- (020) 7610 3233/(07859) 896383
- vigisawdon@yahoo.co.uk
- www.vigisawdon.co.uk

Vintage Carriages Trust The Railway Station, Haworth, Keighley, West Yorkshire, BD22 8NJ, United Kingdom
- (01535) 680425/(07979) 837180 (01535) 610796
- filming@vintagecarriagestrust.org
- www.vintagecarriagestrust.org

SET BUILDERS AND DESIGNERS

2Can Productions PO Box 668, Cardiff, CF11 1EZ,
- 0845 0545096/ 0845 0545097
- info@2canproductions.com
- www.2canproductions.com

2D:3D 263 Abbeydale Road, Wembley, Wembley, Middlesex, HA0 1TW, United Kingdom
- (020) 8998 3199/ (020) 8998 7767
- rob@2d3d.co.uk
- www.2d3d.co.uk

3D Studios 2 Bedlam Mews, off Walnut Tree Walk, London, SE11 6DF, United Kingdom
- (020) 7735 7932/(07710) 809692 (020) 7587 5105
- paul@3d-studios.co.uk
- www.3d-studios.co.uk

A Construction Production 9 Alpha Street, London, SE15 4NX, United Kingdom
- (07971) 009015
- ac.e@aconstructionproduction.com
- www.aconstructionproduction.com

Acre Jean Ltd Unit 7 The Kimber Centre, 54 Kimber Road, London, SW18 4PP,
- 020 8877 3211/ 020 8877 3213
- dan.hill@acrejean.com
- www.acrejean.com

Alan Martin 71 Edwin Road, Twickenham, TW2 6SP, United Kingdom
- (020) 8287 2784/(07752) 431316

Albatross The Coach House, St. Pauls Waudenbury, Hitchin, Hertfordshire, SG4 8BP, United Kingdom
- (01438) 871688/(07971) 849893 (01438) 871874
- enquiries@albatrossmodels.co.uk
- www.albatrossmodels.co.uk

All Handmade Unit 6-8, Stapley Manor Farm, Long Lane, Odiham, Hook, Hampshire, RG29 1JE, United Kingdom
- (01256) 862111

Andrew Newton-Cox 5 Poulton Cottages, Tinpit, Marlborough, Wiltshire, SN8 1BQ, United Kingdom
- (01672) 511973/(07976) 819638 (01672) 516531
- andrewnewton-cox@eclipse.co.uk

Andy Knight Ltd 2-6 Occupation Road, London, SE17 3BE, United Kingdom
- (020) 7252 5252/ (020) 7252 5111
- info@andyknight.co.uk
- www.andyknight.co.uk

Art Attack Exhibitions Ltd Unit 6, Temperance Street, Ardwick, Manchester, M12 6HR, United Kingdom
- 0161-273 7753/ 0161-273 1438
- info@artattackexhibitions.co.uk
- www.artattackexhibitions.co.uk

Artwiz 229 Hither Green Lane, London, SE13 6RS, United Kingdom
- (020) 8318 3224
- helena@artwiz.eclipse.co.uk
- www.artwiz.eclipse.co.uk

Backdrops 4 Bayer House, Golden Lane, London, EC1Y 0RN, United Kingdom
- (020) 7490 2635

AAA@DREAMCARS

We supply ANY 'On Screen'
or related vehicle

Contact us with your requirements

Tel: +44 (0)1737 765050
Fax: +44 (0)1737 236 179

Email: aaa@dreamcars.co.uk

www.dreamcars.co.uk

Tim Chapman Setbuilding

advertising / editorial / events
exhibitions / fashion / interiors

Tel: 020 7923 9909
email@tcsetbuild.com

www.tcsetbuild.com

Bullet Movies
Brighton, United Kingdom
✆ (01273) 301608/(07717) 400968
✉ info@bulletmovies.com
🖥 www.bulletmovies.com

Cameron Eccles 9 Alpha Street, London, SE15 4NX,
United Kingdom
✆ (07971) 009015
✉ ac.e@aconstructionproduction.com
🖥 www.aconstructionproduction.com

Carmel Said Unit 45, Stadium Business Centre, North
End Road, Wembley, Middlesex, HA9 0AT, United
Kingdom
✆ (020) 8795 3820/(07785) 770434 ✆ (020) 8795 3830
✉ carmellouissaid@aol.com

Cod Steaks Ltd 2 Cole Road, St. Philips, Bristol, BS2
0UG, United Kingdom
✆ 0117-980 3910/ ✆ 0117-972 8999
✉ mail@codsteaks.com
🖥 www.codsteaks.com

Crucible Theatre 55 Norfolk Street, Sheffield, S1 1DA,
United Kingdom
✆ 0114-249 5999/ ✆ 0114-249 6003
✉ info@sheffieldtheatres.co.uk
🖥 www.sheffieldtheatres.co.uk

Dawn Weller
London, NW6 7BE, United Kingdom
✆ (07966) 014 580
✉ dawn@dawnweller.com
🖥 www.dawnweller.com

Delb 6 The Croft, Hastings, East Sussex, TN34 3HH,
United Kingdom
✆ (01424) 446156/(07801) 866645
✉ design@delb.co.uk

Dramascope 35 Schofield Avenue, Witney, Oxfordshire,
OX28 1JR, United Kingdom
✆ (01993) 704820/(07710) 234112 ✆ (01993) 704820
✉ dramascope@btinternet.com
🖥 www.dramascope.co.uk

Einsteins Octopus 22 Clapton Square, London, E5 8HP,
United Kingdom
✆ (020) 8985 9850/(07976) 353676
✉ tony@einsteinsoctopus.co.uk
🖥 www.einsteinsoctopus.co.uk

Elsinore 44 Blurton Road, Flat b, Hackney, London, E5
0NL, United Kingdom
✆ (07875) 053066
✉ nicolai@hart.dk
🖥 www.nicolaiharthansen.blogspot.com

Folkcolor 431 Hall Road, Norwich, NR4 6ET, United
Kingdom
✆ (01603) 403534/ ✆ (01603) 618530

Gus Wookey 4 Forge Cottages, Pontuir Road, Caerleon,
Newport, NP18 3NX, United Kingdom
✆ (07775) 691889
✉ gus@wookey.biz
🖥 www.gus@barkingdragon.co.uk

Harry Metcalfe 129 Chapman Street, London, E1 2PH,
United Kingdom
✆ (020) 7739 2530/ ✆ (020) 7702 7334
✉ harry@harrymetcalfe.demon.co.uk

Houghton Wyatt 30 Woolpack Lane, Nottingham, NG1
1GA, United Kingdom
✆ 0115-958 2171/(07702) 104536 ✆ 0115-958 2171
✉ pete@houghtonwyatt.co.uk
🖥 www.houghtonwyatt.co.uk

Iain Richardson 171 Stapleton Hall Road, London, N4
4QS, United Kingdom
✆ (07817) 466361
✉ iainrichardson9@hotmail.com

James Henderson 136 Brookdale Road, Catford,
London, SE6 4JN, United Kingdom
✆ (07801) 544585
✉ leadcow@mac.com

John Ryan 88 Whitton Road, Hounslow, TW3 2DF,
United Kingdom
✆ (020) 8570 1513/(07836) 244321 ✆ (020) 8570 1513

Kate Thompson-Yates 36 Shirley Drive, Hove, East
Sussex, BN3 6UD, United Kingdom
✆ (01273) 556475

Keith Ryder Aylesbury House, Aylesbury Street,
Wolverton, Milton Keynes, MK12 5HY, United Kingdom
✆ (07962) 063438
✉ keithrryder@aol.com

Live Wire Polystyrene 299-300 Clare Street, Bethnal
Green, London, E2 9HD, United Kingdom
✆ (07960) 075522
✉ kevinblakenz@hotmail.com
🖥 www.livewirepoly.co.uk

Matthew Duguid/Bill Charles London Ltd. Unit 3E1,
Zetland House, 5-25 Scrutton Street, London, EC2A 4HJ,
United Kingdom
✆ 020 7033 9284/020 2033 9285
✉ london@billcharles.com
🖥 www.billcharles.com

Michael Howells/C L M Top Floor, 19 All Saints Road,
London, W11 1HE, United Kingdom
✆ (020) 7750 2999/ ✆ (020) 7792 8507
✉ clm@clmuk.com
🖥 www.clmuk.com

Mimesis 1 Bedlam Mews, London, SE11 6DF, United
Kingdom
✆ (020) 7582 4303/(07973) 615948 ✆ (020) 7820 1562
✉ martin@mimesis-models.com
🖥 www.mimesis-models.com

Paul Crimin 117 Marine Court, St. Leonards-on-Sea,
East Sussex, TN38 0DN, United Kingdom
✆ (07905) 096890
✉ likeudu2005@yahoo.co.uk

Peter Evans Studios Ltd 12-14 Tavistock Street,
Dunstable, Bedfordshire, LU6 1NE, United Kingdom
✆ (01582) 725730/ ✆ (01582) 481329
✉ sales@peterevansstudios.co.uk

R P F Scaffolding Ltd 284 High Road, North Weald,
Essex, CM16 6EG, United Kingdom
✆ (01992) 524411/(07974) 921140 ✆ (01992) 524298
✉ rpfscaffolding@ukonline.co.uk

Rachel Thomas/Big Active Ltd Unit 6.01, The Tea
Building, 56 Shoreditch High Street, London, E16 JJ,
United Kingdom
✆ (020) 7739 5601/ ✆ (020) 7739 7479
✉ contact@bigactive.com
🖥 www.bigactive.com

Roberta Holm/Tattersall Love 40 Langham Street,
London, W1W 7AS, United Kingdom
✆ (020) 7637 5737/ ✆ (020) 7637 5747
✉ mail@tattersall-love.com
🖥 www.tattersall-love.com

Rutters Unit 6, South Cambridgeshire Business Park,
Babraham Road, Sawston, CB2 4JH, United Kingdom
✆ (01223) 833522/ ✆ (01223) 833543
✉ info@ruttersuk.com
🖥 www.ruttersuk.com

S2 Events Ltd 3-5 Valentine Place, London, SE1 8QH,
United Kingdom
✆ (020) 7928 5474/ ✆ (020) 7928 6082
✉ info@s2events.co.uk
🖥 www.s2events.co.uk

Sarah Charles 143 Old Church Street, London, SW3
6EB, United Kingdom
✆ (020) 7370 6027/ ✆ (01424) 812756
✉ sarah@antcreative.com
🖥 www.antcreative.com

Sculpture Studios 3 Hornsby Square, Southfields
Industrial Park, Laindon, Basildon, Essex, SS15 6SD,
United Kingdom
✆ (01268) 418837/ ✆ (01268) 414118
✉ aden.hynes@virgin.net
🖥 www.sculpturestudios.co.uk

Set the Scene Home-Field-House, Burcott, Nr. Wing,
Leighton Buzzard, Bedfordshire, LU7 0JW, United
Kingdom
✆ (01296) 682344/(07970) 753142 ✆ (01296) 682197
✉ shargreaves@btinternet.com

Setbuild 66 Gordon Road, Harborne, Birmingham, B32
2JB, United Kingdom
✆ 0121-428 2822/(07973) 442750
✉ setbuild@blueyonder.co.uk
🖥 www.setbuild.com

Shona Heath/C L M Top Floor, 19 All Saints Road,
London, W11 1HE, United Kingdom
✆ (020) 7750 2999/ ✆ (020) 7792 8507
✉ clm@clmuk.com
🖥 www.clmuk.com

Simon Costin/C L M Top Floor, 19 All Saints Road,
London, W11 1HE, United Kingdom
✆ (020) 7750 2999/ ✆ (020) 7792 8507
✉ clm@clmuk.com
🖥 www.clmuk.com

Spur Creative Workshop 169b Davidson Road,
Croydon, CR0 6DP, United Kingdom
✆ (020) 8405 3436/07940 790580
✉ phil@spurcreative.com
🖥 www.spurcreative.co.uk

Steve Oakes/Shoot Production Ltd 23 Glebe Road,
London, N8 7DA, United Kingdom
✆ (020) 8442 9171/ ✆ (020) 8348 7404
✉ adele@shootgroup.com
🖥 www.shootgroup.com

Steve Smithwick Scenery 4 Burcote Road, London,
SW18 3LQ, United Kingdom
✆ (020) 8874 5383/(07836) 551730 ✆ (020) 8877 3701
✉ steve@smithwick.com
🖥 www.steve.smithwick.com

Tim Chapman Set Building 2 Dunston Street,
London, E8 4EB, United Kingdom
✆ **(020) 7923 9909**/ ✆ **(020) 4923 9744**
✉ email@tcsetbuild.com
🖥 www.tcsetbuild.com
See ad

Upstage Designs 125 Calton Road, Gloucester, GL1 5ES, United Kingdom
(01452) 503975/ (01452) 503975
Upstage-Designs@btconnect.com

Yvonne Toner Ltd 2 Ivy House, Ivy House Lane, Ross-on-Wye, Herefordshire, HR9 9SN, United Kingdom
(07970) 898933
yvonnetoner@ukonline.co.uk

SPECIAL EFFECTS AND CGI

2Can Productions PO Box 668, Cardiff, CF11 1EZ,
0845 0545096/ 0845 0545097
info@2canproductions.com
www.2canproductions.com

Act Two 3rd Floor, 16 Bishops Bridge Road, London, W2 6AA
0207 863 9570/0207 863 9571 info@acttwo.biz
www.acttwo.biz
See ad in showcase

Bold Endeavours Ltd 7 Manor Park, Staines, Middlesex, TW18 4XE,
01784 460 064
derek@boldendeavours.com
www.big-easy-footage-library-software.co.uk

Cinebuild Ltd Studio House, 34 Rita Road, London, SW8 1JU, United Kingdom
(020) 7582 8750/(07836) 220441 (020) 7793 0467
cinebuild@btclick.com
www.cinebuild.com

Dave Brown 55 Farringdon Road, London, EC1M 3JB, United Kingdom
(020) 7404 9888/ (020) 7404 9800
dave@davebrownstudio.co.uk
www.davebrownstudio.co.uk

Daydream Linton House, 164-180 Union Street, London, SE1 0LH,
+44 (0) 20 7096 1471/+44 (0) 20 7117 1636
ralph@daydream.co.uk
www.daydream.co.uk

In the Wings LLC 5 Rue Des Grands Augustins, St Michel, Paris, 75006, France
00 33 1 31 09 20 72 85
junis11@aol.com

James King Photographer Unit 19c Barton Hill Trading Estate, Maze Street, Bristol, BS5 9BD,
1179350839
james@jameskingphotographer.co.uk
www.jameskingphotographer.co.uk

JASPA Photography Holland Park Avenue, London, W11 3RA, United Kingdom
(07757) 324135
office@jaspaphoto.com
www.jaspaphoto.com

Joe Lyons Assoc The Studio, Saxon Street, St. Leonards-on-Sea, East Sussex, TN37 6AG, United Kingdom
(01424) 421850/ (01424) 713799
joe@joe58.wannadoo.co.uk

Limelight Design Limited
27 Bolingbroke Grove, London, SW11 6EJ,
7946582074
tom@limelight-design.co.uk
www.limelight-design.co.uk

Patrick Llewelyn-Davies 1 Dallington Street, London, EC1V 0BH, United Kingdom
(020) 7253 2838/(07866) 622478
patrick@llewelyn-davies.com
www.llewelyn-davies.com/indexchb.html

Peter Kidd 22 Vanbrugh Hill, London, SE3 7UF, United Kingdom
(07973) 315122
p.kidd7@ntlworld.com

Ray Massey Camden Park Studios, The Church Hall, Camden Park Road, London, NW1 9AY, United Kingdom
(020) 7267 9550/(07831) 606342 (020) 7267 5612
ray@raymassey.com
www.raymassey.com

Saddington Baynes Studio 3 , 21 Wren Street, London, WC1X 0HF
020 7833 3032/020 7837 1942
info@saddingtonbaynes.com
www.saddingtonbaynes.com
See ad in showcase

Simon Mackney Photography
Top Floor, 348 Caledonian Road, Islington, London, N1 1DU, United Kingdom
(07830) 131817
simon@simonmackney.co.uk
www.simonmackney.co.uk

Smutt Magazine 41 Kensington Road, Chichester, West Sussex, PO19 7XS,
70926368776
lou.marshall@hotmail.com
www.smuttmagazine.com

Stevie FX 81 Oxford Street, London, W1D 2EU, United Kingdom
(020) 7851 3575
info@steviefx.com
www.steviefx.com

Terry Payne Packshot & Food Photographer
First Floor, Building D, The Chocolate Factory, Clarendon Road, London, N22 6XJ,
020 8889 6609
terry.payne1@ntlworld.com
www.terrypaynephotog.co.uk

This Little Fish 14a Dufours Place, London, W1F 7SN
020 7534 0810/ info@thislittlefish.com
www.thislittlefish.com
See ad in showcase

Thomas Cochrane Associates
3/2 150 Butterbiggins Road, Glasgow, G42 7AF, United Kingdom
0141-585 8581
info@thomas-cochrane-associates.com
www.thomas-cochrane-associates.com

STUDIO HIRE

3 Mills Studios Three Mill Lane, Bromley By Bow, London, E3 3DU, United Kingdom
(020) 7363 3336/ (020) 8215 3499
info@3mills.com
www.3mills.com
See ad in showcase

A & M Studios The Royals, Victoria Road, London, NW10 6ND, United Kingdom
(020) 8233 1515/ (020) 8233 1550
studio@amhire.com
www.amhire.com

A Village Underground 52-54 Holywell Lane, Shoreditch, London, EC2A 3PQ, United Kingdom
(07886) 751205
info@villageunderground.co.uk
www.villageunderground.co.uk

Action Underwater Studios Ltd Archers Fields, Basildon, Essex, SS1 3DW, United Kingdom
(01268) 270171/ (01268) 270156
ausadmin@actionunderwaterstudios.co.uk
www.actionunderwaterstudios.co.uk

Adrian Houston Amberley Studio, 32A Goldney Road, London, W9 2AX, United Kingdom
(020) 7289 1419/(07850) 475105 (020) 7289 1419
adrian@adrianhouston.co.uk
www.adrianhouston.co.uk

Amber Room Digital Studios Studio 3, 2-18 Yelverton Road, London, SW11 3QG, United Kingdom
(020) 7228 0220/ (020) 7228 2090
jez@amberroom.net
www.amberroom.net

Amberley Studio 32A Goldney Road, London, W9 2AX, United Kingdom
(020) 7289 1122
susi.cobin@btinternet.com
www.amberleystudios.co.uk

Andy Knight Ltd 2-6 Occupation Road, London, SE17 3BE, United Kingdom
(020) 7252 5252/ (020) 7252 5111
info@andyknight.co.uk
www.andyknight.co.uk

Angelspace 27-28 St. Albans Place, London, N1 0NX, United Kingdom
(020) 7704 8803
greg@angelstudio.freeserve.co.uk
www.angelspace.co.uk

Arden Studios Shepley Lane, Hawk Green, Marple, Stockport, Cheshire, SK6 7JW, United Kingdom
0161-449 6607/ 0161- 449 9436
info@ardenstudios.co.uk
www.ardenstudios.co.uk

Ben Rector Photography 38 Longfield Road, Wickford, Essex, SS11 8PU, United Kingdom
(07770) 467791
ben@benrector.com
www.benrector.com

Big Sky London 29-31 Brewery Road, London, N7 9QH, United Kingdom
(0870) 1996699/ (0870) 1992299
them@bigskylondon.com
www.bigskylondon.com

Bladon Studios Ltd Studio 2, Lower Road, Long Hanborough, Oxfordshire, OX29 8LW, United Kingdom
(0845) 1082237
steve@rsimail.co.uk
www.bladonstudios.co.uk

Blank Space Studios 10A Belmont Street, Chalk Farm, London, NW1 8HH, United Kingdom
(020) 7482 0957/ (020) 7485 9283
www.blankspacestudios.com

Bleeding Heart Studio 2 Bleeding Heart Yard, London, EC1N 8SJ, United Kingdom
(020) 7430 1006
steve@bleedingheartstudio.co.uk
www.bleedingheartstudio.co.uk

Boardroom Productions 22b Iliffe Yard, London, SE17 3QA, United Kingdom
(020) 7228 0225/ (020) 7223 9740
jon.self@virgin.net
www.sunnyhill1.co.uk

Box Studios 15 Mandela Street, London, NW1 0DU, United Kingdom
(020) 7388 0020/ (020) 7387 4259
mail@boxstudios.co.uk
www.boxstudios.co.uk

Bray Management Ltd Bray Film Studios, Down Place, Water Oakley, Windsor, Berkshire, SL4 5UG, United Kingdom
(01628) 622111
bray.studios@btinternet.com

Calvert Studios Ltd Enterprise Way, Grovebury Road, Leighton Buzzard, Bedfordshire, LU7 4SZ, United Kingdom
(01525) 853700/(07831) 562152 (01525) 852111
kevin@calvertstudios.co.uk
www.calvertstudios.co.uk

Carroll & Brown Ltd 20 Lonsdale Road, Queens Park, London, NW6 6RD, United Kingdom
(020) 7372 0900/ (020) 7372 0460
mail@carrollandbrown.co.uk

Casting at Sweet Sweet Entertainments, 42 Theobalds Road, London, WC1X 8NW, United Kingdom
(020) 7404 6411/ (020) 7404 6412
info@sweet-uk.com
www.sweet-uk.com

Courtyard Studio 1st Floor, Unit 17a Perseverance Works, London, E2 8DD, United Kingdom
(020) 7729 3658/ (020) 7613 1198
perserverancestudio@btconnect.com
www.londonphotostudios.com

Crena Watson Unit 5, The Village, 101 Amies Street, London, SW11 2JW, United Kingdom
(020) 7738 2233/ (020) 7738 2244
crena@crenawatson.com
www.crenawatson.com

Curtain Road Studios Top Floor, 134-146 Curtain Road, London, EC2A 3AR, United Kingdom
(020) 7739 4510/(07733) 008539 (0870) 052 4242
nigel@crs.demon.co.uk
www.curtainroadstudios.com

Depot 14 33-39 Parsons Green Lane, Parsons Green, London, SW6 4HH, United Kingdom
(020) 7736 9933
jeremy@hudsonphoto.co.uk.
www.hudsonphoto.co.uk

Dufour's Place Studios 14a Dufours Place, London, W1F 7SN, United Kingdom
(020) 7434 3437
studio@dufoursplacestudios.com
www.dufoursplacestudios.com

Duthy Hall Studios Duthy Hall, Great Guildford Street, London, SE1 0ES, United Kingdom
(020) 7652 3322
www.duthyhall.com

Eastside Studios Ltd 40A River Road, Barking, Essex, IG11 0DW, United Kingdom
(020) 8507 7572/ (020) 8507 8550
info@eastsidestudios.com
www.eastsidestudios.com

Edinburgh Film Productions (PACT) Traquair House, Innerleithen, Peeblesshire, EH44 6PP, United Kingdom
✆ (01896) 831188/ (01896) 831199
✉ crichton.efp@virgin.nert

Edinburgh Film Studios West Marfield, Nine Mile Burn, Penicuik, Midlothian, EH26 9LT, United Kingdom
✆ (01968) 672131/(07956) 307381
✉ info@edinburghfilmstudios.co.uk
🖥 www.edinburghfilmstudios.co.uk

Expose Studios Unit 12, Parsons Green Depot, 33-39 Parsons Green Lane, London, SW6 4HH, United Kingdom
✆ (020) 7736 6444/ (020) 7751 0364
✉ enquiries@exposestudios.co.uk
🖥 www.exposestudios.co.uk

Eyelights Ltd Vision Studios, Old Mill Road, Portishead, Bristol, BS20 7BX, United Kingdom
✆ (01275) 847257/(07836) 349342 (01275) 814187
✉ colin_eyelights@yahoo.com
🖥 www.eyelights.co.uk

Farringdon Photo Studio Hire 2 Bleeding Heart Yard, Greville Street, London, EC1N 8SJ,
✆ 020 7242 7031
✉ bill@billburnett.co.uk
🖥 www.billburnett.co.uk

First Option Studio 11 Perseverance Works, 38 Kingsland Road, London, E2 8DD, United Kingdom
✆ (020) 7739 0132/ (020) 7729 7066
✉ studio@christinehanscomb.co.uk
🖥 www.christinehanscomb.co.uk

Focusing Ltd Unit 6, New Milton Bus. Center, Wick Drive, New Milton, Hampshire, BH25 6RQ,
✆ 01425 617800
✉ info@focusingltd.com
🖥 www.focusingltd.com

Garth Dale Studios 2 Phoenix Court, Finch Close, Nottingham, NG7 2PU, United Kingdom
✆ 0115-952 7107/(07889) 924038 0115-952 7107
✉ talk2us@garth.co.uk
🖥 www.garth.co.uk

Halliford Studios Manygate Lane, Shepperton, Middlesex, TW17 9EG, United Kingdom
✆ (01932) 226341/ (01932) 246336
✉ sales@hallifordstudios.co.uk
🖥 www.hallifordfilmstudios.co.uk

Hampton Hill Studios 73 High Street, Hampton Hill, Middlesex, TW12 1NH, United Kingdom
✆ (020) 8979 9484/(07966) 518310 (020) 8979 4942
✉ paul@hamptonhillstudios.co.uk
🖥 www.hamptonhillstudios.co.uk

Holborn Studios 49-50 Eagle Wharf Road, London, N1 7ED, United Kingdom
✆ (020) 7490 4099/ (020) 7253 8120
✉ reception@holborn-studios.co.uk
🖥 www.holbornstudios.com

House 62 Fortis Green, East Finchley, London, N2 9EN, United Kingdom
✆ (020) 8883 2091/ (020) 8883 8713
✉ sh@housestudio.co.uk
🖥 www.housestudio.co.uk

Hubert Grove Studios 157a Hubert Grove, Clapham, London, SW9 9NZ, United Kingdom
✆ (07956) 945417
✉ dadastudios@mac.com
🖥 www.dadastudios.co.uk

Hungry Tiger Unit 16, The Piper Building, Peterborough Road, London, SW6 3EF, United Kingdom
✆ (020) 7751 8600/ (020) 7751 8618
✉ studio@hungrytiger.co.uk
🖥 www.hungrytiger.co.uk

Imagesmith Studios Unit 46, Micro Business Park, 46-50 Greatorex Street, London, E1 5NP, United Kingdom
✆ (020) 7247 8544
✉ kath@imagesmith.co.uk
🖥 www.imagesmith.co.uk

Jam Studios Old School House, High Street, Stanford in the Vale, Faringdon, Oxfordshire, SN7 8LH, United Kingdom
✆ (01367) 710168/(07768) 000013
✉ jay@myrdal.com
🖥 www.myrdal.com

James King Photographer Unit 19c Barton Hill Trading Estate, Maze Street, Bristol, BS5 9BD,
✆ 1179350839
✉ james@jameskingphotographer.co.uk
🖥 www.jameskingphotographer.co.uk

John Bigglestone & Co. Wharf Studios, 13a The Wharf, Couch Lane, Devizes, Wiltshire, SN10 1EB, United Kingdom
✆ (01380) 720599
✉ upstarts@phototutor-online.com
🖥 www.thewharfstudio.com

Junction Eleven Ltd Unit 4 Jugglers Close, Off Wildmere Road, Banbury, Oxfordshire, OX16 3JU, United Kingdom
✆ 0121-627 5012/ 0121-627 5038
✉ dan.burman@junctioneleven.com
🖥 www.junctioneleven.com

Karma Studio 1 Park Hill, Clapham, London, SW4 9NS, United Kingdom
✆ (020) 7498 6888/ (020) 7498 7555
✉ studio@karma-productions.com
🖥 www.karma-productions.com

Kevin Calvert Enterprise Way, Grovebury Road, Leighton Buzzard, Bedfordshire, LU7 4SZ, United Kingdom
✆ (01525) 853700/(07831) 562152 (01525) 852111
✉ kevin@calvertstudios.com
🖥 www.calvertstudios.com

L H 2 142 Mildmay Road, London, N1 4NE, United Kingdom
✆ (020) 7275 7039/ (020) 7249 5376
✉ info@lh2.co.uk
🖥 www.lh2.co.uk

Lancashire Colour Laboratories 11 Towers Court, Duckworth Street, Blackburn, BB2 2JQ, United Kingdom
✆ (01254) 263500/ (01254) 699813
✉ sales@millersphotography.co.uk
🖥 www.millersphotography.co.uk

Lane End Studios High Street, Lane End, High Wycombe, Buckinghamshire, HP14 3JG, United Kingdom
✆ (01494) 882291/ (01494) 881826
✉ reflectons@clara.net
🖥 www.reflectionsphoto-graphics.co.uk

Lanterns Studios 1 William Blake House, The Lanterns, Bridge Lane, London, SW11 3AD, United Kingdom
✆ (020) 7978 4175/ (020) 7978 4176
✉ info@lanternsstudios.com
🖥 www.lanternsstudios.com

Lazy Dog Studios The Mews, Charlton Place, Manchester, M12 6HS, United Kingdom
✆ 0161-273 6989/(07831) 228219 0161-273 5432
✉ tim-h@btconnect.com
🖥 www.tim-h.com

LCA Studio's Studio 10, Cuba Street, Canary Wharf, London, E14 3RS, United Kingdom
✆ (07793) 081068
✉ studio10@lycos.co.uk
🖥 www.lcalondon.co.uk

Lettice Studio 18 Lettice Street, London, SW6 4EH, United Kingdom
✆ (020) 7731 1111/ (020) 7731 3500
✉ bookings@letticestudios.com
🖥 www.letticestudios.com

Locamotive Studio 12, The Waterside, 44-48 Wharf Road, London, N1 7UX, United Kingdom
✆ (020) 7490 8787/(07702) 233721 (020) 7490 1009
✉ info@markharwood.plus.com
🖥 www.locamotive.co.uk

Malcolm Ryan Studios Ltd Unit 48, Wimbledon Stadium Business Centre, London, SW17 0BA, United Kingdom
✆ (020) 8947 4766/ (020) 8947 9517
✉ info@mrstudios.co.uk
🖥 www.mrstudios.co.uk

Mel Grundy Oakbase House, Trafford Street, Chester, CH1 3HP, United Kingdom
✆ (01244) 391391/ (01244) 370237
✉ mel@oakbase.co.uk
🖥 www.oakbase.co.uk

Metro Studios 200 Hercules Road, London, SE1 7LD, United Kingdom
✆ (020) 7490 5965/ (020) 7490 0120
✉ studios@metroimaging.co.uk
🖥 www.metroimaging.co.uk

Mike Prior Photography 7 The Old Laundry, Hayden Way, London, SW11 1YF, United Kingdom
✆ (020) 7207 1964/(07721) 646464 (020) 7207 1965
✉ info@mikeprior.com
🖥 www.mikeprior.com

Millennium Studios 17 Marshall Street, Holbeck, Leeds, LS11 9YL, United Kingdom
✆ 0113 244 0931/070 50 093757 0113 242 0631
✉ info@millennium-studio.co.uk
🖥 www.millennium-studio.co.uk

Miloco Studios 36 Leroy Street, London, SE1 4SP, United Kingdom
✆ (020) 7232 0008/ (020) 7237 6109
✉ nick@miloco.co.uk
🖥 www.miloco.co.uk

Motoring Picture Library National Motor Museum, Beaulieu, Brockenhurst, Hampshire, SO42 7ZN, United Kingdom
✆ (01590) 614656/ (01590) 612655
✉ motoring.pictures@beaulieu.co.uk
🖥 www.motoringpicturelibrary.com

Moving Arts Base Syracusae, 134 Liverpool Road, London, N1 1LA, United Kingdom
✆ (020) 7609 6969
✉ info@movingartsbase.co.uk
🖥 www.movingartsbase.co.uk

Moy Williams Photography 10 Booth Street, Salford, Manchester, M3 5DG, United Kingdom
✆ 0161 839 6660/(07836) 770977 0161 839 8300
✉ moy@moyphotgraphy.com
🖥 www.moyphotgraphy.com

N1 Studios 1st Floor, 6-8 Vestry Street, London, N1 7RE, United Kingdom
✆ (020) 7251 3836/ (020) 7490 2392
✉ info@n1studios.co.uk
🖥 www.n1studios.co.uk

Nick Robinson 101A Anderton Street, Chorley, Lancashire, PR7 2AY, United Kingdom
✆ 078 89 294102/078 89 294102 (01257) 265039
✉ nick.robinson17@btinternet.com
🖥 www.nick-robinson-photography.co.uk

P P L (Photo Agency) Ltd Bookers Yard, The Street, Walberton, Arundel, West Sussex, BN18 0PF, United Kingdom
✆ (01243) 555561/(07768) 395719 (01243) 555562
✉ ppl@mistral.co.uk
🖥 www.pplmedia.com

Park Royal Studios 1 Barretts Green Road, London, NW10 7AE, United Kingdom
✆ **(020) 8453 3801,(07855) 779223 (020) 8963 1056**
✉ **francois@parkroyalstudios.com**
🖥 **www.parkroyalstudios.com**
See ad in showcase

Peartree Rental Ltd Lower Ground Floor, 53 Central Street, London, EC1V 8AD, United Kingdom
✆ (020) 7251 2044/078 41260777 (020) 7251 2455
✉ info@peartreerental.com
🖥 www.peartreerental.com

Perch 283 Camberwell New Road, London, SE5 0TF, United Kingdom
✆ (07767) 836221
✉ les@theperch.co.uk
🖥 www.theperch.co.uk

Perseverance Studio 2nd Floor, Unit 17, Perseverance Works, 25-27 Hackney Road, London, E2 8DD, United Kingdom
✆ (020) 7729 3658/ (020) 7613 1198
✉ perseverancestudio@btconnect.com
🖥 www.londonphotostudios.com

Peter MacKertich Invicta Works, 8 Graces Mews, London, SE5 8JF, United Kingdom
✆ (020) 7701 4989/(07973) 952071 (020) 7701 4989
✉ peter@petermackertich.com
🖥 www.petermackertich.com

Phil Cawley Photography The Mews, Charlton Place, Ardwick, Manchester, M12 6HS, United Kingdom
✆ 0161-273 7050/07973 186623
✉ studio@philcawley.com
🖥 www.philcawley.com

Photosphere Studios 12-14 Redbank Court, Redbank, Manchester, M4 4HF, United Kingdom
✆ 0161-833 4040/ 0161-832 8492
✉ studio@photosphere.co.uk
🖥 www.photosphere.co.uk

Picturebyte Ltd The Coppice, 384 Wilbraham Road, Chorlton-Cum-Hardy, Manchester, M21 0UW, United Kingdom
✆ (07007) 788346/07836 508884
✉ studio@picturebyte.co.uk
🖥 www.picturebyte.co.uk

Pixeleye Studio 73 St. John Street, London, EC1M 4AN, United Kingdom
(020) 7253 3202
studio@pixeleye.co.uk
www.pixeleye.co.uk

Plough Studios Ltd Unit 4, 9 Park Hill, Clapham, London, SW4 9NS, United Kingdom
(020) 7622 1939
cove@ploughstudios.com
www.ploughstudios.com

Re:fresh Suit 4, The Swans Centre, Fishers Lane, London, W4 1RX, United Kingdom
(020) 8747 8080/ (020) 8747 8228
info@refresh-agency.com
www.refresh-agency.com

Retna Pictures Ltd Unit 1A/1B, Farm Lane Trading Estate, 101 Farm Lane, London, SW6 1QJ, United Kingdom
(0845) 0340645/(07711) 608607 (0845) 0340646
ukinfo@retna.com
www.retna.com

River Studio 305 The Custard Factory, Gibb Street, Birmingham, B9 4AA, United Kingdom
0121-624 4777/(07860) 824101 0121-693 3993
info@riverstudio.co.uk
www.riverstudio.co.uk

Rob Mitchell Units 12 & 13, Enterprise Estate, Guildford, Surrey, GU1 1RB, United Kingdom
(020) 7823 9410/ (01483) 450773
rob@rob-mitchell.co.uk
www.rob-mitchell.co.uk

Robert Rebec Photography 26 Crowndale Road, London, NW1 1TT, United Kingdom
(07788) 598791
robert@robertrebec.com
www.robertrebec.com

Roof Studios 81 Rivington Street, London, EC2A 3AY, United Kingdom
(07831) 229489
studio@roofstudios.co.uk

Sanctuary Backcloths 32-36 Telford Way, London, W3 7XS, United Kingdom
(020) 8743 1563/ (020) 8743 8075
backcloths@sanctuarystudios.co.uk
www.sanctuarybackcloths.co.uk

Sanctuary Photographic 32-36 Telford Way, W3 7XS, United Kingdom
(020) 8743 1563/ (020) 8743 8075
photographic@sanctuarystudios.co.uk
www.sanctuaryphotographic.co.uk

Scene Studio 2 Marshall Street, London, W1F 9BB, United Kingdom
(020) 7734 6393/ (020) 7287 0178
jo@spirogroup.net
www.scenestudio.tv

Shed 16 Studios 16 Olga Road, Nottingham, NG3 2NW, United Kingdom
0115-941 9416
robin.culley.co.uk
www.robinculley.co.uk

Snap Productions 151-155 New North Road, N1 6TA, London, United Kingdom
(020) 7684 7555/ (020) 7684 7556
rich@snap-pro.com
www.snap-pro.com

South Manchester Studios Ltd Studio House, Battersea Road, Stockport, Cheshire, SK4 3EA, United Kingdom
0161-432 9000/ 0161-443 1325
enquiries@southmanchesterstudios.co.uk
www.southmanchesterstudios.co.uk

Space Photographic Film Location Loft 20, Haybridge House, 15 Mount Pleasant Hill, London, E5 9NB, United Kingdom
(07956) 326864/ (020) 8806 1273
www.spacelocationS.net

Space-2 Battersea Studios, 80 Silverthorne Road, London, SW8 3HE, United Kingdom
(07922) 224216
mark@space2online.com
www.space2online.com

Spaced Studios 90 De Beauvoir Road, London, N1 4EN, United Kingdom
(020) 7254 9900/ (020) 7254 9955
emma@spacedstudios.com
www.spacedstudios.com

Spot Daylight Studios Barcelona Calle Ramon Turró 23, s.at, Barcelona, 8005, Spain
69 038 0205/ 93 221 6083
barcelona@spot-lightservice.com
www.productionparadise.com/spot

Spot Lighting Palma de Mallorca Calle Tetuan 26, Palma de Mallorca, 7011, Spain
00 34 629 866 002/ 00 34 971 731 905
mallorca@spot-lightservice.com
www.spot-lightservice.com

SpotStudios Canonbury Yard, 202 New North Road, London, N1 7BJ, United Kingdom
(020) 7354 9955/ (020) 7354 8333
info@spot.co.uk
www.spotlightstudios.co.uk

Spring Studios Ltd 10 Spring Place, Kentish Town, London, NW5 3BH, United Kingdom
(020) 7267 8383/(07764) 331234 (020) 7267 8481
info@springstudios.com
www.springstudios.com

Stratford Studios Unit 122, Stratford Workshops, Burford Road, London, E15 2SP, United Kingdom
(020) 8503 0304/ (020) 8503 0709
info@stratfordstudios.co.uk
www.stratfordstudios.co.uk

Studio 12 12 Waterside Studios, 44-48 Wharf Road, London, N1 7SF, United Kingdom
(020) 7490 8787/(07702) 233721 (020) 7490 1009
mail@markharwood.plus.com
www.locamotive.co.uk

Studio 19 19 London Lane, London, E8 3PR, United Kingdom
(020) 8525 7976/ (020) 8525 7976

Studio 7 10 Jamestown Road, London, NW1 7BY, United Kingdom
(020) 7284 5700/ (020) 7284 5708
contact@studiosevenphotography.co.uk
www.studiosevenphotography.co.uk

Studio Boardroom 22b Iliffe Yard, off Amelia Street, Kennington, London, SE17 3QA, United Kingdom
(07774) 445695
jon.self@virgin.net
www.sunnyhill1.co.uk

Studio D Photography 234 Church Street, Blackpool, FY1 3PX, United Kingdom
(01253) 290191/ (01253) 290182
paul@studiodphotography.co.uk
www.studiodphotography.co.uk

Studio Exigent Unit F2 Roden House, Roden Street, Nottingham, NG3 1JH, United Kingdom
(07974) 818110
contact@at-exigent.co.uk
studio.at-exigent.co.uk

Studio Pictures Unit 3, Queensway Trading Estate, Birmingham, B5 5JU, United Kingdom
0121-666 6022/ 0121-233 2109
pictures@waverider.co.uk
www.rossvincent.co.uk

Studio-D 86 Greenfield Road, London, E1 1EJ, United Kingdom
(020) 7247 9842/ (020) 7247 9843
info@studio-d.co.uk
www.studio-d.co.uk

StudioTime Photography Studio 25, 10 Martello St, London Fields, London, E8 3PE,
020 7241 2816
info@studiotime.org
www.studiotimeadvertising.com

Sunbeam Studios Ladbroke Hall, 79 Barlby Road, London, W10 6AZ, United Kingdom
(020) 8962 8690/ (020) 8962 8687
info@sunbeamstudios.com
www.sunbeamstudios.com

The Dairy Studio 43 Bellenden Road, London, SE15 5BB, United Kingdom
(020) 7639 2712/ 020 7732 8235
info@thedairystudio.com
www.thedairystudio.com

The Other Studio The Old School, 1 Thirsk Street, Ardwick Green, Manchester, M12 6FW, United Kingdom
(0161) 273 7489/ (0161) 274 3449
hire@theotherstudio.co.uk
www.theotherstudio.co.uk

The ROOST 142 Sandringham Road, London, E8 2HJ, United Kingdom
/07767 836221 (020) 7703 7419
les@theroost.co.uk
www.theroost.co.uk

The Stone Studio of Petersfield 45 High Street, Petersfield, Hants, GU32 3JR,
01730 269966
mail@thestonestudio.co.uk
www.thestonestudio.co.uk

The Street Studios 2 Dunston Street, London, E8 4EB, United Kingdom
(020) 7923 9430/ (020) 7923 9429
mail@streetstudios.co.uk
www.streetstudios.co.uk
See ad in showcase

The Studio 21 Cabul Road, London, SW11 2PR, United Kingdom
(020) 7228 5228/07740 417278 (020) 7228 9975
thestudio@filmed.com the-studio.co.uk

The Village Studio Unit 5, The Village, 101 Amies Street, London, SW11 2JW, United Kingdom
(020) 7738 2233/ (020) 7738 2244
helen@thevillagestudio.net
www.thevillagestudio.net

The White Room 45 Morrish Road, London, SW2 4EE, United Kingdom
(020) 8678 1199/(07979) 964994
info@thewhiteroom-sw2.co.uk
www.whiteroomstudio.co.uk

The Worx UK Ltd 10 Heathmans Road, Parsons Green, London, SW6 4TJ, United Kingdom
(020) 7371 9777/ (020) 7371 9888
enquiries@theworx.co.uk
www.theworx.co.uk

Tim White 74 Burnfoot Avenue, London, SW6 5EA, United Kingdom
(020) 7736 8845
timwhitefoto@clara.co.uk

Touch Studios Unit 10, Waterside, 44-48 Wharf Road, London, N1 7UX, United Kingdom
(020) 7608 2345/(07702) 290931 (020) 7608 0017
viv@touchstudios.co.uk
www.touchstudios.co.uk

Urban Phtography Jack's Place, 6 Corbet Place, London, E1 6NH, United Kingdom
(08000) 811 877
sales@urbanphotography.co.uk
www.urbanphotography.co.uk

STYLISTS

34 Magazine Ibrahim Karaoglanoglu Cad. Yayincilar Sok., No: 10. Kat: 4 Seyrantepe, Levent, Istanbul, 75000, Turkey
00 90 212 325 16 53
tiara@34mag.com
www.34mag.com

A & R Photographic 16A Crane Grove, London, N7 8LE, United Kingdom
(020) 7607 3030/ (020) 7607 2190
info@aandrphotographic.co.uk
www.aandrphotographic.co.uk

Abi Boura/Tattersall Love 40 Langham Street, London, W1W 7AS, United Kingdom
(020) 7637 5737/ (020) 7637 5747
mail@tattersall-love.com
www.tattersall-love.com

Adam Howe/MAP 72 Rochester Place, London, NW1 9JX, United Kingdom
(020) 7424 9144/ (020) 7284 3274
info@mapltd.com
www.mapltd.com

Alex Kammerling Unit 1c 1st Floor, Zetland House, 5-25 Scrutton, London, EC2A 4HJ, United Kingdom
(07740) 701595
alex@akenterprises.eu
www.akenterprises.eu

Ali Moloney Brook Farm, Bath Road, Colnbrook, SL3 0LU, United Kingdom
(020) 73786411/(07831) 377711

Alison Nicholls 118 Eastcombe Avenue, Charlton, London, SE7 7LW, United Kingdom
(020) 8293 3776/(07970) 831163
alison.nicholls76@ntlworld.com

Allan Kennedy/The Katy Barker Agency Ltd 11 Mason's Arms Mews, Maddox Street, London, W1S 1NX, United Kingdom
✆ (020) 7493 3933/📠 (020) 7493 3311
✉ catherine@katybarker.com
🖥 www.katybarker.com

Angela Gusty 33 Kimberley Road, Cambridge, CB4 1HG, United Kingdom
✆ (01223) 316348/📠 (01223) 463180
✉ angelomassucco@yahoo.co.uk

Angela Marie Stephens Flat 7, 10 Walpole Gardens, London, W4 4HG, United Kingdom
✆ (07814) 218801
✉ angelamariestephens@hotmail.com

Annabel Hodin 12 Eaton Avenue, London, NW3 3EH, United Kingdom
✆ (020) 7431 8761/(07836) 754079 📠 (020) 7431 8761
✉ annabelhodin@aol.com

Annazbell.com PO Box 47726, London, NW10 8YF,
✆ 7910540311
✉ harriet@annazbell.com
🖥 www.annazbell.com

Areia London Studio1, 42 Theobalds Road, London, WC1X 8NW, United Kingdom
✆ (020) 7404 8600/📠 (020) 7404 8601
✉ info@areia.com
🖥 www.areia.com

Arianne Phillips/The Katy Barker Agency Ltd 11 Mason's Arms Mews, Maddox Street, London, W1S 1NX, United Kingdom
✆ (020) 7493 3933/📠 (020) 7493 3311
✉ catherine@katybarker.com
🖥 www.katybarker.com

Art Directions College Mansions, Winchester Avenue, London, NW6 7TY, United Kingdom
✆ (020) 7625 5939/(07971) 546057
✉ cornelius@hungryfish.com

Artistic Licence 5A Hillgate Place, 18-20 Balham Hill, London, SW12 9ER, United Kingdom
✆ (020) 8675 7555/📠 (020) 8675 6090
✉ info@artisticlicenceagency.com
🖥 www.artisticlicenceagency.com

Barbara Brady 216 Twickenham Road, London, E11 4BH, United Kingdom
✆ (020) 8556 6749/079 76 243008 📠 (020) 8556 6749

Becky John, 91 Middle Lane, London, N8 8NX, United Kingdom
✆ (020) 8341 2368/(07778) 518305
✉ beckyjohn15@btinternet.com

Belinda Green-Smith 480b Kingston Road, Wimbledon, London, SW20 8DX, United Kingdom
✆ (07967) 587235/📠 (020) 8540 3515
✉ belinda-greensmith@tiscali.co.uk
🖥 www.belindagreensmith.com

Beverly Toby Flat 8, 40-41 Whiskin Street, London, EC1 0BP, United Kingdom
✆ (07774) 834619
✉ btoby@btinternet.com

Black Cherry Productions 109 Britannia Walk, London, N1 7LU, United Kingdom
✆ (020) 7490 3498
✉ blackcherryproductions@yahoo.co.uk

Blake Minton 1 Elrington Road, London, E8 3BJ, United Kingdom
✆ (020) 7249 6332/(07770) 274303

Blunt Management The Courtyard Studio 2, Old Grammarphone Works, London, W10 5BZ, United Kingdom
✆ (020) 8960 2041/(07979) 900068 📠 (020) 8960 2039
✉ info@bluntlondon.com
🖥 www.bluntlondon.com

Bo Chapman/Mandy Coakley Represents 18 Mandeville Courtyard, Warriner Gardens, London, SW11 4NB, United Kingdom
✆ (020) 7720 6234/📠 (020) 7720 0199
✉ mandy@mandycoakley.co.uk
🖥 www.mandycoakley.co.uk

Bob Lea/Artist Partners Ltd 2e The Chandlery, 50 Westminster Bridge Road, London, SE1 7QY, United Kingdom
✆ (020) 7401 7904/📠 (020) 7401 3378
✉ chris@artistpartners.demon.co.uk
🖥 www.artistpartners.com

C L M Top Floor, 19 All Saints Road, London, W11 1HE, United Kingdom
✆ (020) 7750 2999/📠 (020) 7792 8507
✉ clm@clmuk.com
🖥 www.clmuk.com

C S B Management 40 Bowling Green Lane, London, EC1R 0NE, United Kingdom
✆ (020) 7415 7051/📠 (020) 7415 7059
✉ susie@csbmanagement.com
🖥 www.csbmanagement.com

Camilla Turner/Shoot Production Ltd 23 Glebe Road, London, N8 7DA, United Kingdom
✆ (020) 8442 9171/📠 (020) 8348 7404
✉ adele@shootgroup.com
🖥 www.shootgroup.com

Carol Hayes Management 1 Parkway, London, NW1 7PG, United Kingdom
✆ (020) 7482 1555/📠 (020) 7482 1666
✉ rebekah@fashion-stylist.net
🖥 www.fashion-stylist.net

Celia Topping/Adrenalin Management Temple Works, Brett Passage, London, E8 1JR, United Kingdom
✆ (020) 8986 3939/📠 (020) 8986 3665
✉ info@adrenalinmanagement.com
🖥 www.adrenalinmanagement.com

Charlie Varley North Cottage, Upper Sheriff Farmhouse, Hammingden Lane, Ardingly, Haywards Heath, West Sussex, RH17 6SR, United Kingdom
✆ (01444) 891340/(07836) 322227
✉ charlie.varley@tiscali.co.uk

Charlotte Melling/Tattersall Love 40 Langham Street, London, W1W 7AS, United Kingdom
✆ (020) 7637 5737/📠 (020) 7637 5747
✉ mail@tattersall-love.com
🖥 www.tattersall-love.com

Charlotte Pilcher/C L M Top Floor, 19 All Saints Road, London, W11 1HE, United Kingdom
✆ (020) 7750 2999/📠 (020) 7792 8507
✉ clm@clmuk.com
🖥 www.clmuk.com

Charlotte Stockdale/C L M Top Floor, 19 All Saints Road, London, W11 1HE, United Kingdom
✆ (020) 7750 2999/📠 (020) 7792 8507
✉ clm@clmuk.com
🖥 www.clmuk.com

Charlotte Taylor 18 Eleanor Grove, Barnes, London, SW13 0JN, United Kingdom
✆ (020) 8876 9085/(07836) 708904 📠 (020) 8876 9085
✉ charlotte-taylor@breathemail.net

Charlotte Williams 48 Sandgate House, Pembury Road, London, E5 8JH, United Kingdom
✆ (07989) 206191
✉ stylist@charlottewilliams.co.uk
🖥 www.charlottewilliams.co.uk

Charlyvia Cantave 1067 New York Avenue, Brooklyn, United States of America
✆ 00 1 347 678 6543
✉ charlyviacantave@aol.com

Chloe Brown
London, United Kingdom
✆ (07881) 827604

Chloe Richardson/Mandy Coakley Represents 18 Mandeville Courtyard, Warriner Gardens, London, SW11 4NB, United Kingdom
✆ (020) 7720 6234/📠 (020) 7720 0199
✉ mandy@mandycoakley.co.uk
🖥 www.mandycoakley.co.uk

Christina Wilson/Sarah Kaye Representation Ltd 38 Queen's Gate, London, SW7 5HR, United Kingdom
✆ (020) 7225 5005/📠 (020) 7225 0109
✉ sarah@sarahkaye.com
🖥 www.sarahkaye.com

Claire Durbridge/Ellison Lee 17 Quadrant Business Centre, 135 Salusbury Road, London, NW6 6RJ, United Kingdom
✆ (020) 7624 2345/📠 (020) 7624 1100
✉ info@ellisonlee.com
🖥 www.ellisonlee.com

Clare Harries 153 Huddlestone Road, London, N7 0EH, United Kingdom
✆ (07796) 173171
✉ clare@clareharries.com
🖥 www.clareharries.com

Clare Hunt/HERS Agency Ltd Cleaveside, Bickleigh, Tiverton, Devon, EX16 8RB, United Kingdom
✆ (0870) 429 6499/📠 (01884) 855855
✉ hers@hersagency.co.uk
🖥 www.hersagency.co.uk

Covert Set Design & Construction Unit 13 Cleve Studios, Cleve Studios, London, E2 7JP, United Kingdom
✆ 07788 921183
✉ wigglawood@hotmail.com
🖥 www.covertsdc.co.uk

Creative Styling Top Floor, 77 Fortess Road, Kentish Town, London, NW5 1AG, United Kingdom
✆ (020) 7428 0695/(07958) 437786
✉ bob_dare@yahoo.co.uk
🖥 www.creative-styling.com

Creative Talent (UK) Limited 78 York Street, London, W1H 1DP, United Kingdom
✆ (020) 7439 1877/📠 (020) 7434 1144
✉ info@creativetalentlimited.com
🖥 www.creativetalentlimited.com

Creative Talent UK Ltd 78 York Street, London, W1H 1DP, United Kingdom
✆ (020) 7439 1877/📠 (020) 7434 1144
✉ info@creativetalentlimited.com
🖥 www.creativetalentlimited.com

Crystal McClory/E S P Agency 1st Floor, 63 Charlotte Street, London, W1T 4PG, United Kingdom
✆ (020) 7209 1626/📠 (020) 7209 1627
✉ info@esp-agency.com
🖥 www.esp-agency.com

David Bradshaw/C L M Top Floor, 19 All Saints Road, London, W11 1HE, United Kingdom
✆ (020) 7750 2999/📠 (020) 7792 8507
✉ clm@clmuk.com
🖥 www.clmuk.com

Dawn Mead 69 Gower Road, Haywards Heath, West Sussex, RH16 4PW, United Kingdom
✆ (07900) 554532
✉ dawn@luxuk.co.uk
🖥 www.luxuk.co.uk

Dawn Stock 15 Woodland Drive, Thorpe End, Norwich, NR13 5BH, United Kingdom
✆ (01603) 433174
✉ dawn_doc@hotmail.com

Deborah Brett/A & R Photographic 16A Crane Grove, London, N7 8LE, United Kingdom
✆ (020) 7607 3030/📠 (020) 7607 2190
✉ info@aandrphotographic.co.uk
🖥 www.aandrphotographic.co.uk

Deco Chic Boutique Waterfront Farm, Biddisham Lane, Biddisham, Axbridge, Somerset, BS26 2RS, United Kingdom
✆ (01934) 750827
✉ alexi@decochicboutique.com
🖥 www.decochicboutique.com

Deena Beverley 5 Poulton Cottages, Tinpit, Marlborough, Wiltshire, SN8 1BQ, United Kingdom
✆ (01672) 511973/(07976) 958699 📠 (01672) 516531
✉ deenabeverley@eclipse.co.uk
🖥 www.deenabeverley.co.uk

Desiree Lederer 40a Cavendish Road, London, NW6 7XP, United Kingdom
✆ (07957) 364267
✉ info@desireelederer.com
🖥 www.desireelederer.com

DesirÈe Lederer/Mandy Coakley Represents 18 Mandeville Courtyard, Warriner Gardens, London, SW11 4NB, United Kingdom
✆ (020) 7720 6234/📠 (020) 7720 0199
✉ mandy@mandycoakley.co.uk
🖥 www.mandycoakley.co.uk

Diana Civil 18 Nightingale Road, Bushey, WD23 3NJ, United Kingdom
✆ (020) 8950 1052/📠 (020) 8950 1052
✉ diana.civil@virgin.net

Diane Edwards 12 Burlington Lodge Studios, Rigault Road, London, SW6 4JJ, United Kingdom
✆ (020) 7736 7966/📠 (020) 7736 7966
✉ styling@dianedwards.com

Dinedor Management 81 Oxford Street, London, W1D 2EU, United Kingdom
✆ (020) 7851 3575/📠 (020) 7851 3576
✉ info@dinedor.com
🖥 www.dinedor.com

Donna Gray Photographic & Casting Services 1 Bale Avenue, Southborough, Cambridgewells, Tonbridge, Kent, TN4 0QO, United Kingdom
✆ (07976) 244090/📠 01892 522 545
✉ donna@donnagray.co.uk
🖥 www.donnagray.co.uk

E S P Agency 1st Floor, 63 Charlotte Street, London, W1T 4PG, United Kingdom
☎ (020) 7209 1626/📠 (020) 7209 1627
✉ info@esp-agency.com
🖥 www.esp-agency.com

East Photographic Ltd 8 Iron Bridge House, 3 Bridge Approach, London, NW1 8BD, United Kingdom
☎ (020) 7722 3444/📠 (020) 7722 3544
✉ roger@eastphotographic.com
🖥 www.eastphotographic.com

Ellison Lee 17 Quadrant Business Centre, 135 Salusbury Road, London, NW6 6RJ, United Kingdom
☎ (020) 7624 2345/📠 (020) 7624 1100
✉ info@ellisonlee.com
🖥 www.ellisonlee.com

Emeline Watchorn/Creative Talent (UK) Limited 78 York Street, London, W1H 1DP, United Kingdom
☎ (020) 7439 1877/📠 (020) 7434 1144
✉ info@creativetalentlimited.com
🖥 www.creativetalentlimited.com

Emily Barnes/C L M Top Floor, 19 All Saints Road, London, W11 1HE, United Kingdom
☎ (020) 7750 2999/📠 (020) 7792 8507
✉ clm@clmuk.com
🖥 www.clmuk.com

Emily Chalmers Unit 1, 7a Plough Yard, London, EC2A 3LP, United Kingdom
☎ (020) 7247 0461/📠 (020) 7247 0461
✉ emily@emilychalmers.com

Emily Fitch/Ellison Lee 17 Quadrant Business Centre, 135 Salusbury Road, London, NW6 6RJ, United Kingdom
☎ (020) 7624 2345/📠 (020) 7624 1100
✉ info@ellisonlee.com
🖥 www.ellisonlee.com

Emily Jewsbury/Sarah Kaye Representation Ltd 38 Queen's Gate, London, SW7 5HR, United Kingdom
☎ (020) 7225 5005/📠 (020) 7225 0109
✉ sarah@sarahkaye.com
🖥 www.sarahkaye.com

Emily Sellers 26 Carlton Road, Friern Barnet, London, N11 3EX, United Kingdom
☎ (07944) 432 908
✉ emily_sellers@hotmail.com

Emma Bull 12 Crown Court, Horn Park Lane, London, SE12 9AA, United Kingdom
☎ (07855) 793643
✉ emmabull82@aol.com
🖥 www.emmabull.net

Emma Cassi/Sarah Kaye Representation Ltd 38 Queen's Gate, London, SW7 5HR, United Kingdom
☎ (020) 7225 5005/📠 (020) 7225 0109
✉ sarah@sarahkaye.com
🖥 www.sarahkaye.com

Emmanuelle Alt/The Katy Barker Agency Ltd 11 Mason's Arms Mews, Maddox Street, London, W1S 1NX, United Kingdom
☎ (020) 7493 3933/📠 (020) 7493 3311
✉ catherine@katybarker.com
🖥 www.katybarker.com

Fanny Ward/Creative Talent (UK) Limited 78 York Street, London, W1H 1DP, United Kingdom
☎ (020) 7439 1877/📠 (020) 7434 1144
✉ info@creativetalentlimited.com
🖥 www.creativetalentlimited.com

Fashion Styling 1 West Hill Road, Brighton, BN1 3RT, United Kingdom
☎ (07709) 861796
✉ jane_postlethwaite@hotmail.com

Fiona Rubie/A & R Photographic 16A Crane Grove, London, N7 8LE, United Kingdom
☎ (020) 7607 3030/📠 (020) 7607 2190
✉ info@aandrphotographic.co.uk
🖥 www.aandrphotographic.co.uk

Gabriel Feliciano /Bill Charles London Ltd. Unit 3E1, Zetland House, 5-25 Scrutton Street, London, EC2A 4HJ, United Kingdom
☎ 020 7033 9284/020 2033 9285
✉ london@billcharles.com
🖥 www.billcharles.com

Gaby Tubbs 14 Montpelier Villas, Brighton, BN1 3DG, United Kingdom
☎ (01273) 771488/(07802) 780210
✉ gabytubbs@aol.com
🖥 www.gabytubbs.com

Gaïle Paul/A & R Photographic 16A Crane Grove, London, N7 8LE, United Kingdom
☎ (020) 7607 3030/📠 (020) 7607 2190
✉ info@aandrphotographic.co.uk
🖥 www.aandrphotographic.co.uk

Gareth Scourfield/Areia London Studio1, 42 Theobalds Road, London, WC1X 8NW, United Kingdom
☎ (020) 7404 8600/📠 (020) 7404 8601
✉ info@areia.com
🖥 www.areia.com

Georgia Taliotis 24 Cholmeley Crescent, London, N6 5HA, United Kingdom
☎ (020) 8348 4921/(07957) 288376
✉ georgiataliotis@btinternet.com

Geriada Kefford/Blunt Management The Courtyard Studio 2, Old Grammarphone Works, London, W10 5BZ, United Kingdom
☎ (020) 8960 2041/(07979) 900068 📠 (020) 8960 2039
✉ info@bluntlondon.com
🖥 www.bluntlondon.com

Gianluca Longo/Terrie Tanaka Management 101 Talbot Road, London, W11 2AT, United Kingdom
☎ (020) 7792 3500/📠 (020) 7792 2600
✉ danni@terrietanaka.com
🖥 www.terrietanaka.com

Gill McCormick Forest Dene, 26 Little Forest Road, Bournemouth, BH4 9NW, United Kingdom
☎ (01202) 759311/(07956) 258309 📠 (01202) 759311

Gina Phillips Represents Ltd 6 Leverton Place, London, NW5 2PL, United Kingdom
☎ (020) 7284 2022/📠 (020) 7424 0272
✉ info@ginaphillips.co.uk
🖥 www.ginaphillips.co.uk

Glenbeigh Model & Promotion Agency 1-2 Elizabeth Court, Whimple Street, Plymouth, PL1 2DH, United Kingdom
☎ (01752) 201331/📠 (01752) 204140
✉ gmpa@glenbeigh.co.uk
🖥 www.glenbeigh.co.uk

Grace Cobb/MAP 72 Rochester Place, London, NW1 9JX, United Kingdom
☎ (020) 7424 9144/📠 (020) 7284 3274
✉ info@mapltd.com
🖥 www.mapltd.com

Everything you want from a hire studio.

See **www.junctioneleven.com** for the fuller picture.

junction eleven

State-of-the-art facilities | Huge & versatile spaces

Maximum privacy | Relaxation area

Off J11 M40 Jugglers Close Banbury Oxfordshire OX16 3JU
Tel 01295 700122 email info@junctioneleven.com

Grace Woodward/E S P Agency 1st Floor, 63 Charlotte Street, London, W1T 4PG, United Kingdom
☎ (020) 7209 1626/📠 (020) 7209 1627
✉ info@esp-agency.com
🖥 www.esp-agency.com

Graham Hollick/Tattersall Love 40 Langham Street, London, W1W 7AS, United Kingdom
☎ (020) 7637 5737/📠 (020) 7637 5747
✉ mail@tattersall-love.com
🖥 www.tattersall-love.com

Halo Duncan 92A Belsize Road, London, NW6 4TG, United Kingdom
☎ (020) 7624 7681/(07973) 828422

Harriet Cotterill/E S P Agency 1st Floor, 63 Charlotte Street, London, W1T 4PG, United Kingdom
☎ (020) 7209 1626/📠 (020) 7209 1627
✉ info@esp-agency.com
🖥 www.esp-agency.com

Harriet Porter 48 Elm Park, Brixton, London, SW2 2UB, United Kingdom
☎ (07831) 690673/📠 (020) 8678 7184
✉ mail@harrietporter.com
🖥 www.harrietporter.com

HERS Agency Ltd Cleaveside, Bickleigh, Tiverton, Devon, EX16 8RB, United Kingdom
☎ **(0870) 429 6499**/📠 **(01884) 855855**
✉ **hers@hersagency.co.uk**
🖥 **www.hersagency.co.uk**
See ad in showcase

Hilary Guy 78 Tollington Way, London, N7 6RP, United Kingdom
☎ (020) 7281 0620/(07831) 365946 📠 (020) 7281 0620
✉ hilaryguy@hjguy.demon.co.uk
🖥 www.hilaryguy.co.uk

Hirearchy Classic & Contemporary Costume 45-47 Palmerston Road, Boscombe, Bournemouth, BH1 4HW, United Kingdom
☎ (01202) 394465
✉ hirearchy1@aol.com
🖥 www.hirearchy.co.uk

Izzy King 22 Alder Lodge, 73 Stevenage Road, London, SW6 6NP, United Kingdom
☎ (07961) 168086/📠 (020) 7381 9726
✉ izzy@izzyking.co.uk
🖥 www.izzyking.co.uk

Jacqui Frye 4 Hounslow Avenue, Hounslow, TW3 2DX, United Kingdom
☎ (020) 8894 6573/(07766) 453205
✉ jacqui.frye@mac.com

James Sleaford/Ellison Lee 17 Quadrant Business Centre, 135 Salusbury Road, London, NW6 6RJ, United Kingdom
☎ (020) 7624 2345/📠 (020) 7624 1100
✉ info@ellisonlee.com
🖥 www.ellisonlee.com

Jane Dundas Top Floor Flat, 464 Kings road, London, SW10 0LG, United Kingdom
☎ (020) 7352 9597/(07850) 034404
✉ jane.dundas@zen.co.uk

Jason Hughes Flat E, 14 Coldharbour Lane, London, SE5 9PR, United Kingdom
☎ (07749) 010006
✉ jason_hughes@mail.com

Jayne Pickering/Terrie Tanaka Management 101 Talbot Road, London, W11 2AT, United Kingdom
☎ (020) 7792 3500/ 📠 (020) 7792 2600
✉ danni@terrietanaka.com
🖥 www.terrietanaka.com

Jeneffer Jones Rosen Styling 123 Dartmouth Road, London, NW2 4ES, United Kingdom
☎ (07969) 491911
✉ jenneferjones@yahoo.com
🖥 www.jenjonesrosen.com

Jennifer Beech Rose Cottage, High Street, Cavendish, Sudbury, Suffolk, CO10 8AW, United Kingdom
☎ (01787) 280973
✉ jenniferbeech@mac.com

Jenny Heel
London, United Kingdom
☎ (07740) 153361
✉ info@jennyheel.co.uk
🖥 www.jennyheel.co.uk

Jo Barker/John Parkinson Photographic Agent Unit 17, 1-10 Summer's Street, London, EC1R 5BD, United Kingdom
☎ (020) 7278 6882/ 📠 (020) 7278 1251
✉ johnparkinsonagency@btinternet.com
🖥 www.johnparkinsonagency.co.uk

Jo-Anne Pabst 53 Cheshire Street, London, E2 6EE, United Kingdom
☎ (07771) 770 369/ 📠 (020) 7739 7390
✉ joanne@joannepabst.com
🖥 www.tiggygee.com

Joanne Woollard 23 Parsons Green Lane, Fulham, London, SW6 4HH, United Kingdom
☎ (020) 7736 2717/(07774) 864290
✉ joanne.woollard2@btinternet.com

John Parkinson Photographic Agent Unit 17, 1-10 Summer's Street, London, EC1R 5BD, United Kingdom
☎ (020) 7278 6882/ 📠 (020) 7278 1251
✉ johnparkinsonagency@btinternet.com
🖥 www.johnparkinsonagency.co.uk

Jonathan Kaye/The Katy Barker Agency Ltd 11 Mason's Arms Mews, Maddox Street, London, W1S 1NX, United Kingdom
☎ (020) 7493 3933/ 📠 (020) 7493 3311
✉ catherine@katybarker.com
🖥 www.katybarker.com

Julia Griffiths/HERS Agency Ltd Cleaveside, Bickleigh, Tiverton, Devon, EX16 8RB, United Kingdom
☎ (0870) 429 6499/ 📠 (01884) 855855
✉ hers@hersagency.co.uk
🖥 www.hersagency.co.uk

Kandis Cook 109 Salcott Road, London, SW11 6DG, United Kingdom
☎ (020) 7924 1989/(07967) 505516
✉ kandis@kandiscook.com
🖥 www.kandiscook.com

Karen Foster/Gina Phillips Represents Ltd 6 Leverton Place, London, NW5 2PL, United Kingdom
☎ (020) 7284 2022/ 📠 (020) 7424 0272
✉ info@ginaphillips.co.uk
🖥 www.ginaphillips.co.uk

Karen Russell Styling Apartment 12, Connect House, The Express Building, 1 Henry Street, Manchester, M4 5DA, United Kingdom
☎ (07979) 818576
✉ info@karenrussellstyling.co.uk
🖥 www.karenrussellstyling.co.uk

Karin Otte 56 Goldney Road, London, W9 2AU, United Kingdom
☎ (020) 7286 6149/(07850) 271536 📠 (020) 7289 1213
✉ ko@karin-otte-stylist.com
🖥 www.karin-otte-stylist.com

Kasha Harmer/Sarah Kaye Representation Ltd 38 Queen's Gate, London, SW7 5HR, United Kingdom
☎ (020) 7225 5005/ 📠 (020) 7225 0109
✉ sarah@sarahkaye.com
🖥 www.sarahkaye.com

Kat Byrne 70 Antill Road, London, E3 5BP, United Kingdom
☎ (07980) 254137
✉ katbyrne@btinternet.com

Kate Abrahams 1A Roman Road, London, W4 1NA, United Kingdom
☎ (020) 8747 1082/(07850) 454094
✉ k8y123@aol.com

Kate Thompson-Yates 36 Shirley Drive, Hove, East Sussex, BN3 6UD, United Kingdom
☎ (01273) 556475

Kathy Chan/Ellison Lee 17 Quadrant Business Centre, 135 Salusbury Road, London, NW6 6RJ, United Kingdom
☎ (020) 7624 2345/ 📠 (020) 7624 1100
✉ info@ellisonlee.com
🖥 www.ellisonlee.com

Kay Mcglone Ltd 10 Mentmore Terrace, London, E8 3PN, United Kingdom
☎ (020) 8510 9180/ 📠 (020) 8510 9180
✉ kay.mcglone@virgin.net

Keely M 34 Morrish Road, London, SW2 4EH, United Kingdom
☎ (07855) 403172
✉ keelym@gmail.com

Kelly Russell/Sarah Kaye Representation Ltd 38 Queen's Gate, London, SW7 5HR, United Kingdom
☎ (020) 7225 5005/ 📠 (020) 7225 0109
✉ sarah@sarahkaye.com
🖥 www.sarahkaye.com

Kimberley Watson 16 Albion Square, London, E8 4ES, United Kingdom
☎ (020) 7241 4821/(07768) 737371 📠 (020) 7241 4821
✉ watsonkimberley@mac.com

Kit Lee Styling 51 Burleigh Gardens, London, N14 5AJ, United Kingdom
☎ (07731) 320304
✉ kitlee_fashion@hotmail.com
🖥 www.pressbook.com/kitlee

Kristin Peters/Tattersall Love 40 Langham Street, London, W1W 7AS, United Kingdom
☎ (020) 7637 5737/ 📠 (020) 7637 5747
✉ mail@tattersall-love.com
🖥 www.tattersall-love.com

Lee Staffords Salons 1231-1233 London Road, Leigh-on-Sea, Essex, SS9 3JA, United Kingdom
☎ (01702) 471954/ 📠 (01702) 470317
✉ reception@staffordshouseofhair.com
🖥 www.staffordshouseofhair.com

Leslie Lessin/The Katy Barker Agency Ltd 11 Mason's Arms Mews, Maddox Street, London, W1S 1NX, United Kingdom
☎ (020) 7493 3933/ 📠 (020) 7493 3311
✉ catherine@katybarker.com
🖥 www.katybarker.com

Lilia Toncheva O'Rourke 64 Acre Lane, London, SW2 5SP, United Kingdom
☎ (07769) 941968/ 📠 (020) 7738 4822
✉ liliabtoncheva@yahoo.co.uk
🖥 www.liliatonchevaorourke.com

Lisa Von Weise/The Katy Barker Agency Ltd 11 Mason's Arms Mews, Maddox Street, London, W1S 1NX, United Kingdom
☎ (020) 7493 3933/ 📠 (020) 7493 3311
✉ catherine@katybarker.com
🖥 www.katybarker.com

Liz Cocozza/Creative Talent (UK) Limited 78 York St, London, W1H 1DP, United Kingdom
☎ (020) 7439 1877/ 📠 (020) 7434 1144
✉ info@creativetalentlimited.com
🖥 www.creativetalentlimited.com

Liz Thody/A & R Photographic 16A Crane Grove, London, N7 8LE, United Kingdom
☎ (020) 7607 3030/ 📠 (020) 7607 2190
✉ info@aandrphotographic.co.uk
🖥 www.aandrphotographic.co.uk

Lorraine Kinman/Mandy Coakley Represents 18 Mandeville Courtyard, Warriner Gardens, London, SW11 4NB, United Kingdom
☎ (020) 7720 6234/ 📠 (020) 7720 0199
✉ mandy@mandycoakley.co.uk
🖥 www.mandycoakley.co.uk

Louise De Ville Morel 3 Heber Road, Cricklewood, London, NW2 6AB, United Kingdom
☎ (020) 8450 6148/(07966) 173913 📠 (020) 8450 1574
✉ lou@unconventionalproductions.com
🖥 www.unconventionalproductions.com

Lucinda Maydon/Re:fresh Suit 4, The Swans Centre, Fishers Lane, London, W4 1RX, United Kingdom
☎ (020) 8747 8080/ 📠 (020) 8747 8228
✉ info@refresh-agency.com
🖥 www.refresh-agency.com

Lucy Pinter/Terrie Tanaka Management 101 Talbot Road, London, W11 2AT, United Kingdom
☎ (020) 7792 3500/ 📠 (020) 7792 2600
✉ danni@terrietanaka.com
🖥 www.terrietanaka.com

Luke Moloney, Architect 24 Queen Street, Dumfries, Dumfriesshire, DG1 2JF,
☎ 01387 259338/ 📠 01387 259338
✉ info@lukemoloneyarchitect.co.uk
🖥 www.lukemoloneyarchitect.co.uk

Lynette Garland/East Photographic Ltd 8 Iron Bridge House, 3 Bridge Approach, London, NW1 8BD, United Kingdom
☎ (020) 7722 3444/ 📠 (020) 7722 3544
✉ roger@eastphotographic.com
🖥 www.eastphotographic.com

Madeleine Smith/Sarah Kaye Representation Ltd 38 Queen's Gate, London, SW7 5HR, United Kingdom
☎ (020) 7225 5005/ 📠 (020) 7225 0109
✉ sarah@sarahkaye.com
🖥 www.sarahkaye.com

Mandy Coakley Represents 18 Mandeville Courtyard, Warriner Gardens, London, SW11 4NB, United Kingdom
☎ (020) 7720 6234/ 📠 (020) 7720 0199
✉ mandy@mandycoakley.co.uk
🖥 www.mandycoakley.co.uk

Mark Anthony/E S P Agency 1st Floor, 63 Charlotte Street, London, W1T 4PG, United Kingdom
☎ (020) 7209 1626/ 📠 (020) 7209 1627
✉ info@esp-agency.com
🖥 www.esp-agency.com

Martina Luisetti/HERS Agency Ltd Cleaveside, Bickleigh, Tiverton, Devon, EX16 8RB, United Kingdom
☎ (0870) 429 6499/ 📠 (01884) 855855
✉ hers@hersagency.co.uk
🖥 www.hersagency.co.uk

Maureen Kane
London, W11 1JD, United Kingdom
☎ (07778) 157474
✉ maureen.kane@virgin.net

Megan Wright Basement Flat, 11 Camden Hill Road, London, SE19 1NX, United Kingdom
☎ (07903) 937221
✉ megwright@breathe.com

Merryn Watts 2 Princes Way, London, SW19 6QE, United Kingdom
☎ (07716) 957379
✉ makeup@merrynwatts.com
🖥 www.merrynwatts.com

Michaeljohn 25 Albemarle Street, London, W1S 4HU, United Kingdom
☎ (020) 7491 4401/ 📠 (020) 7495 0152
✉ info@michaeljohn.co.uk
🖥 www.michaeljohn.co.uk

Michelle Rafferty/E S P Agency 1st Floor, 63 Charlotte Street, London, W1T 4PG, United Kingdom
☎ (020) 7209 1626/ 📠 (020) 7209 1627
✉ info@esp-agency.com
🖥 www.esp-agency.com

Miguel Ordonez/Artist Partners Ltd 2e The Chandlery, 50 Westminster Bridge Road, London, SE1 7QY, United Kingdom
☎ (020) 7401 7904/ 📠 (020) 7401 3378
✉ chris@artistpartners.demon.co.uk
🖥 www.artistpartners.com

Millie McGhee Manor Farm Cottage, Fishpond Lane, Egginton, Derby, DE65 6HJ, United Kingdom
☎ (07866) 500835
✉ millie.mcghee@btopenworld.com

Monica Dolfini/C L M Top Floor, 19 All Saints Road, London, W11 1HE, United Kingdom
☎ (020) 7750 2999/ 📠 (020) 7792 8507
✉ clm@clmuk.com
🖥 www.clmuk.com

Neil Greer/Artist Partners Ltd 2e The Chandlery, 50 Westminster Bridge Road, London, SE1 7QY, United Kingdom
☎ (020) 7401 7904/ 📠 (020) 7401 3378
✉ chris@artistpartners.demon.co.uk
🖥 www.artistpartners.com

Nick Griffiths/Bill Charles London Ltd. Unit 3E1, Zetland House, 5-25 Scrutton Street, London, EC2A 4HJ, United Kingdom
☎ 020 7033 9284/020 2033 9285
✉ london@billcharles.com
🖥 www.billcharles.com

Nicky Clarke Salon 130 Mount Street, London, W1K 3NY, United Kingdom
📞 (020) 7491 4700/ 📠 (020) 7491 9564
✉ bookings@nickyclarke.com
🖥 www.nickyclarke.com

Nicola Formichetti/C L M Top Floor, 19 All Saints Road, London, W11 1HE, United Kingdom
📞 (020) 7750 2999/ 📠 (020) 7792 8507
✉ clm@clmuk.com
🖥 www.clmuk.com

Nikki Seymour 82 Princedale Road, Holland Park, London, W11,
📞 7788510878
✉ nikkiseymourfashion@yahoo.co.uk

Norman Young/Linda Rogers Associates 163 Half Moon Lane, London, SE24 9WB, United Kingdom
📞 (020) 7501 9106
✉ lr@lindarogers.net
🖥 www.lindarogers.net

Nuexcom Health & Medical 21 Wimpole Street, Chatteris, Cambridgeshire, PE16 6ND, United Kingdom
📞 (01354) 692059
✉ info@nuexcom.co.uk
🖥 www.nuexcom.co.uk

Onespaceman 24a York Road, North Berwick, East Lothian, EH39 4LX, United Kingdom
📞 (01620) 892024/(07976) 909506
✉ info@onespaceman.co.uk
🖥 www.onespacaceman.co.uk

Pat Crouch 47 Kings Avenue, Bromley, BR1 4HL, United Kingdom
📞 (020) 8460 3651/(07850) 456208 📠 (020) 8460 3651
✉ stylepat@btinternet.com

Paul Finn/Artist Partners Ltd 2e The Chandlery, 50 Westminster Bridge Road, London, SE1 7QY, United Kingdom
📞 (020) 7401 7904/ 📠 (020) 7401 3378
✉ chris@artistpartners.demon.co.uk
🖥 www.artistpartners.com

Paul Robinson/Artist Partners Ltd 2e The Chandlery, 50 Westminster Bridge Road, London, SE1 7QY, United Kingdom
📞 (020) 7401 7904/ 📠 (020) 7401 3378
✉ chris@artistpartners.demon.co.uk
🖥 www.artistpartners.com

Paula Lovell/HERS Agency Ltd Cleaveside, Bickleigh, Tiverton, Devon, EX16 8RB, United Kingdom
📞 (0870) 429 6499/ 📠 (01884) 855855
✉ hers@hersagency.co.uk
🖥 www.hersagency.co.uk

Paula McNamara Flat 6, 51 Tib Street, Manchester, M4 1LS, United Kingdom
📞 /(07957) 417775
✉ paulamcnamara@hotmail.com
🖥 www.paulamcnamara.net

Pearson Lyle Management 3rd Floor, 40 Bowling Green Lane, London, EC1R 0NE, United Kingdom
📞 (020) 7415 7061/ 📠 (020) 7415 7059
✉ contact@pearsonlyle.co.uk
🖥 www.pearsonlyle.co.uk

Peta Hunt/Creative Talent (UK) Limited 78 York St, London, W1H 1DP, United Kingdom
📞 (020) 7439 1877/ 📠 (020) 7434 1144
✉ info@creativetalentlimited.com
🖥 www.creativetalentlimited.com

Pippa Holt/A & R Photographic 16A Crane Grove, London, N7 8LE, United Kingdom
📞 (020) 7607 3030/ 📠 (020) 7607 2190
✉ info@aandrphotographic.co.uk
🖥 www.aandrphotographic.co.uk

Portland Mitchell/Sarah Kaye Representation Ltd 38 Queen's Gate, London, SW7 5HR, United Kingdom
📞 (020) 7225 5005/ 📠 (020) 7225 0109
✉ sarah@sarahkaye.com
🖥 www.sarahkaye.com

R V Interiors Old Manor Farm, Ashton Keynes, Swindon, SN6 6QR, United Kingdom
📞 (01285) 869520/ 📠 (01285) 869520
✉ rvinteriors@tiscali.co.uk

Re:fresh Suit 4, The Swans Centre, Fishers Lane, London, W4 1RX, United Kingdom
📞 (020) 8747 8080/ 📠 (020) 8747 8228
✉ info@refresh-agency.com
🖥 www.refresh-agency.com

Rebecca Gore 3 Rowhill Mansions, Rowhill Road, London, E5 8ED, United Kingdom
📞 (07977) 205196
✉ beckygorerocks@yahoo.co.uk

Rebekah Roy London, NW3 5DR, United Kingdom
📞 (07919) 994 2323
✉ rebekah@fashion-stylist.net
🖥 www.fashion-stylist.net

Rise Media 45 Summerrow, Birmingham, B3 1JJ, United Kingdom
📞 (07811) 400388/ 📠 0121-212 1144
✉ tess@risemedia.co.uk
🖥 www.risemedia.co.uk

Rita Furzey Flat A, Rembrandt House, 100 Great Portland Street, London, W1W 6PB, United Kingdom
📞 (020) 7637 0174/(07949) 851341

Roberta Holm 3 Doria Road, London, SW6 4UF, United Kingdom
📞 (07719) 769466
✉ roberta@robertaholm.co.uk
🖥 www.robertaholm.co.uk

Rose Hammick/Sarah Kaye Representation Ltd 38 Queen's Gate, London, SW7 5HR, United Kingdom
📞 (020) 7225 5005/ 📠 (020) 7225 0109
✉ sarah@sarahkaye.com
🖥 www.sarahkaye.com

S Management 15 Rocks Lane, London, SW13 0BD, United Kingdom
📞 (020) 8487 9655/ 📠 (020) 8487 9541
✉ fiona@smanagement.co.uk
🖥 www.smanagement.co.uk

Sally McEwan 4 Jennings Road, London, SE22 9JU, United Kingdom
📞 (07903) 019591/ 📠 (020) 8299 4295
✉ sallyjmcewan@hotmail.com

Samantha Grigg/Sarah Kaye Representation Ltd 38 Queen's Gate, London, SW7 5HR, United Kingdom
📞 (020) 7225 5005/ 📠 (020) 7225 0109
✉ sarah@sarahkaye.com
🖥 www.sarahkaye.com

Samuel FranÁois/The Katy Barker Agency Ltd 11 Mason's Arms Mews, Maddox Street, London, W1S 1NX, United Kingdom
📞 (020) 7493 3933/ 📠 (020) 7493 3311
✉ catherine@katybarker.com
🖥 www.katybarker.com

Sara Darling 18 Victoria Road, Brighton, BN1 3SS, United Kingdom
📞 (07974) 447593
✉ disorderfashion@yahoo.co.uk
🖥 www.saradarling.com

Sara Emslie/Creative Talent (UK) Limited 78 York Street, London, W1H 1DP, United Kingdom
📞 (020) 7439 1877/ 📠 (020) 7434 1144
✉ info@creativetalentlimited.com
🖥 www.creativetalentlimited.com

Sarah Broom/Sarah Kaye Representation Ltd 38 Queen's Gate, London, SW7 5HR, United Kingdom
📞 (020) 7225 5005/ 📠 (020) 7225 0109
✉ sarah@sarahkaye.com
🖥 www.sarahkaye.com

Sarah Brummitt Image Consulting 16 Beverley Path, London, SW13 0AL, United Kingdom
📞 (020) 8392 8242/ 📠 (020) 8392 8242
✉ sarah.brummitt@btinternet.com
🖥 www.sarahbrummitt.com

Sarah Charles 143 Old Church Street, London, SW3 6EB, United Kingdom
📞 (020) 7370 6027/ 📠 (01424) 812756
✉ sarah@antcreative.com
🖥 www.antcreative.com

Sarah Clark/Terrie Tanaka Management 101 Talbot Road, London, W11 2AT, United Kingdom
📞 (020) 7792 3500/ 📠 (020) 7792 2600
✉ danni@terrietanaka.com
🖥 www.terrietanaka.com

Sarah Kaye Representation Ltd 38 Queen's Gate, London, SW7 5HR, United Kingdom
📞 (020) 7225 5005/ 📠 (020) 7225 0109
✉ sarah@sarahkaye.com
🖥 www.sarahkaye.com

Sarah the Stylist London, United Kingdom
📞 (020) 8747 1957/(07971) 477224
✉ sarahthestylist@mac.com

Sarita Sharma 9 Cadogan Road, Surbiton, Surrey, KT6 4DQ, United Kingdom
📞 (020) 8715 6995/(07973) 115514
✉ saritasha@aol.com

Schumi Ltd suite 206, 18 Britten Street, Chelsea, London, SW3 3TU, United Kingdom
📞 (020) 7352 6504/ 📠 (020) 7581 4445

Sean Bennett/Artist Partners Ltd 2e The Chandlery, 50 Westminster Bridge Road, London, SE1 7QY, United Kingdom
📞 (020) 7401 7904/ 📠 (020) 7401 3378
✉ chris@artistpartners.demon.co.uk
🖥 www.artistpartners.com

Selena Middleton/Blunt Management The Courtyard Studio 2, Old Grammarphone Works, London, W10 5BZ, United Kingdom
📞 (020) 8960 2041/(07979) 900068 📠 (020) 8960 2039
✉ info@bluntlondon.com
🖥 www.bluntlondon.com

Ser Amada 87A Norbury Crescent, Norbury, London, SW16 4JT, United Kingdom
📞 (07939) 307347
✉ amanda@ser-amada.co.uk
🖥 www.ser-amada.co.uk

Sharron Daly The Studio, 44 York Road, London, W3 6TP, United Kingdom
📞 (07831) 766092/ 📠 (020) 8992 6021
✉ sharron@sharrondaly.com
🖥 www.sharrondaly.com

Sheena Stafford 83 Longlands Court, London, W11 2QG, United Kingdom
📞 (020) 7792 1150

Shireena Facey 26 Ivydale Road, London, SE15 3BS, United Kingdom
📞 (07944) 699310
✉ info@shireenafacey.com
🖥 www.shireenafacey.com

Shoot People 3rd Floor, 202 City Road, London, EC1V 2PH, United Kingdom
📞 (020) 7253 0009/(07767) 313007 📠 (020) 7253 0009
✉ victoria@shootpeople.com
🖥 www.shootpeople.com

Shoot Production Ltd 23 Glebe Road, London, N8 7DA, United Kingdom
📞 (020) 8442 9171/ 📠 (020) 8348 7404
✉ adele@shootgroup.com
🖥 www.shootgroup.com

Simon Foxton/The Katy Barker Agency Ltd 11 Mason's Arms Mews, Maddox Street, London, W1S 1NX, United Kingdom
📞 (020) 7493 3933/ 📠 (020) 7493 3311
✉ catherine@katybarker.com
🖥 www.katybarker.com

Sophia Neophitou/The Katy Barker Agency Ltd 11 Mason's Arms Mews, Maddox Street, London, W1S 1NX, United Kingdom
📞 (020) 7493 3933/ 📠 (020) 7493 3311
✉ catherine@katybarker.com
🖥 www.katybarker.com

Stephenie McMillan 62 Regents Park Road, London, NW1 7SX, United Kingdom
📞 (020) 7586 0926/(07831) 625068
✉ stepheniemcmillan@btinternet.com

Steve Oakes/Shoot Production Ltd 23 Glebe Road, London, N8 7DA, United Kingdom
📞 (020) 8442 9171/ 📠 (020) 8348 7404
✉ adele@shootgroup.com
🖥 www.shootgroup.com

Stilorama United Kingdom
📞 (020) 8728 2299/(07904) 504945 📠 (020) 8728 2299
✉ editor@stilorama.com
🖥 www.stilorama.com

Sue Leighton 17 Cedar Court, Sheen Lane, London, SW14 8LY, United Kingdom
📞 (020) 8876 8497/(07973) 321474 📠 (020) 8876 9755
✉ sueleighton@blueyonder.co.uk

Sue Odell 12 Bartholomew Villas, London, NW5 2LL, United Kingdom
📞 (020) 7267 5839/(07831) 811506 📠 (020) 7284 1562
✉ sue@sueodell.com
🖥 www.sueodell.com

Image retouchers to the top brands.

See www.junctioneleven.com for the fuller picture.

junction eleven

State-of-the-art technology & colour managed workflow

Highly experienced team | Tried and trusted

Off J11 M40 Jugglers Close Banbury Oxfordshire OX16 3JU
Tel 01295 700122 email info@junctioneleven.com

Sue Quimby 1 Holyoake Cottage, Castle Road, Studley, Warwickshire, B80 7AD, United Kingdom
✆ (01527) 857495/ (01527) 857465

Sue Rowlands 25 Wilkes Street, London, E1 6QF, United Kingdom
✆ (020) 7377 1170/(07836) 660365 (020) 7375 1956
✉ sue@suerowlands.co.uk

Susie Theodorou/Pearson Lyle Management 3rd Floor, 40 Bowling Green Lane, London, EC1R 0NE, United Kingdom
✆ (020) 7415 7061/ (020) 7415 7059
✉ contact@pearsonlyle.co.uk
🖳 www.pearsonlyle.co.uk

Suzie Finch/HERS Agency Ltd Cleaveside, Bickleigh, Tiverton, Devon, EX16 8RB, United Kingdom
✆ (0870) 429 6499/ (01884) 855855
✉ hers@hersagency.co.uk
🖳 www.hersagency.co.uk

Tano Rea 58 Alexandra Road, London, NW4 2RY, United Kingdom
✆ (020) 8203 1747/(07831) 378583 (020) 8203 1064
✉ tano.rea@btopenworld.com
🖳 www.tanorea-presents.com

Tattersall Love 40 Langham Street, London, W1W 7AS, United Kingdom
✆ (020) 7637 5737/ (020) 7637 5747
✉ mail@tattersall-love.com
🖳 www.tattersall-love.com

Terri Manduca The Basement, 11 Elvaston Place, London, SW7 5QG, United Kingdom
✆ (020) 7581 5844/ (020) 7581 5822
✉ terri@terrimanduca.co.uk
🖳 www.terrimanduca.co.uk

Terrie Tanaka Management 101 Talbot Road, London, W11 2AT, United Kingdom
✆ (020) 7792 3500/ (020) 7792 2600
✉ danni@terrietanaka.com
🖳 www.terrietanaka.com

The Katy Barker Agency Ltd 11 Mason's Arms Mews, Maddox Street, London, W1S 1NX, United Kingdom
✆ (020) 7493 3933/ (020) 7493 3311
✉ catherine@katybarker.com
🖳 www.katybarker.com

Timna Rose 12 Woodland Way, London, N21 3QA, United Kingdom
✆ (020) 8882 9448/(07860) 161627 (020) 8882 9448
✉ timna.rose@virgin.net

Tommy Swahn/Artist Partners Ltd 2e The Chandlery, 50 Westminster Bridge Road, London, SE1 7QY, United Kingdom
✆ (020) 7401 7904/ (020) 7401 3378
✉ chris@artistpartners.demon.co.uk
🖳 www.artistpartners.com

Trish Appleton 4 Lysia Street, London, SW6 6NG, United Kingdom
✆ (07973) 909304
✉ trish@trishappleton.co.uk
🖳 www.trishappleton.co.uk

Unconventional Productions 3 Heber Road, London, NW2 6AB, United Kingdom
✆ (020) 8450 6148/ (020) 8450 1574
✉ lou@unconventionalproductions.com
🖳 www.unconventionalproductions.com

Veronica McAuliffe Flat 7, Exeter Mansions, London, W1D 5EQ, United Kingdom
✆ (020) 7437 5488/(07831) 248398 (020) 7437 5488
✉ veronica@costume-design.fsbusiness.co.uk
🖳 www.costume-design.fsbusiness.co.uk

Vicky Firmston/HERS Agency Ltd Cleaveside, Bickleigh, Tiverton, Devon, EX16 8RB, United Kingdom
✆ (0870) 429 6499/ (01884) 855855
✉ hers@hersagency.co.uk
🖳 www.hersagency.co.uk

Victoria Lees Management (VLM) 2 Fairview Gardens, Woodford Green, Essex, IG8 7DJ, United Kingdom
✆ (07710) 287220/ (020) 8504 8125
✉ victoria@victorialeesmanagement.co.uk
🖳 www.victorialeesmanagement.co.uk

Victoria Metcalf Flat 2, 8 The Avenue, London, NW6 7YD, United Kingdom
✆ (07957) 433886/ (020) 8451 2465
✉ mail@victoriametcalf.com
🖳 www.victoriametcalf.com

Vidal Sassoon 56 Brook Street, London, W1K 5NE, United Kingdom
✆ (020) 7318 5200/ (020) 7318 5247
🖳 www.vidalsassoon.co.uk

Way Perry/Blunt Management The Courtyard Studio 2, Old Grammarphone Works, London, W10 5BZ, United Kingdom
✆ (020) 8960 2041/(07979) 900068 (020) 8960 2039
✉ info@bluntlondon.com
🖳 www.bluntlondon.com

Wood Associates 62 Bell Street, London, NW1 6SP, United Kingdom
✆ (020) 7723 6600
✉ info@wood-associates.co.uk
🖳 www.wood-associates.co.uk

Yvonne Toner Ltd 2 Ivy House, Ivy House Lane, Ross-on-Wye, Herefordshire, HR9 9SN, United Kingdom
✆ (07970) 898933
✉ yvonnetoner@ukonline.co.uk

Z Photographic The Mezzanine, 5 Dryden Street, Covent Garden, London, WC2E 9NW, United Kingdom
✆ (020) 7829 8455/(07917) 302 491 (020) 7240 5600
✉ zuk@zphotographic.com
🖳 www.zphotographic.com

Zoe Hill 59 Rosebery Road, Muswell Hill, London, N10 2LE, United Kingdom
✆ (020) 8444 0609/078 31 881122
✉ ezhill@onetel.net

Illustration

début **art** • Illustrators, Photographers and Fine Artists Agents

30 Tottenham Street, London, W1T 4RJ. United Kingdom

Tel: +44 (0) 20 7636 1064. Fax: +44 (0) 20 7580 7017

The Coningsby Gallery • Tel: +44 (0) 20 7636 7478

email: **info@debutart.com** • **www.debutart.com**

Vault49

Advertising showcase:
Illustration
03.

début **art** • Illustrators, Photographers and Fine Artists Agents
30 Tottenham Street, London, W1T 4RJ. United Kingdom
Tel: +44 (0) 20 7636 1064. Fax: +44 (0) 20 7580 7017
The Coningsby Gallery • Tel: +44 (0) 20 7636 7478
email: **info@debutart.com** • **www.debutart.com**

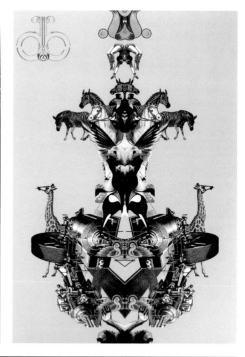

Hawaii

début **art** • Illustrators, Photographers and Fine Artists Agents
30 Tottenham Street, London, W1T 4RJ. United Kingdom
Tel: +44 (0) 20 7636 1064. Fax: +44 (0) 20 7580 7017
The Coningsby Gallery • Tel: +44 (0) 20 7636 7478
email: **info@debutart.com** • **www.debutart.com**

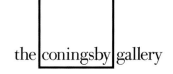

Since 1985, *début* **art** (based in London, England and now with offices in New York, Amsterdam and Sydney) has proactively sought out leading contemporary image-makers & clients who create original, progressive and commercially successful media material. Today, *début* **art** and the highly artistic illustrators it promotes, are widely regarded, both in the UK and around the world, as representing one of the finest and most contemporary talent groupings in the field of illustration.

début **art** and the illustrators it markets have successfully undertaken assignments worldwide for very many companies that are leaders in their fields including: Microsoft, Apple, Coca-Cola, Proctor and Gamble, Samsung, Levi's, Nokia, Rolls-Royce, BP, Shell, Nike, The Chicago Mercantile Exchange, The NYSE, The London Stock Exchange, Citibank, American Express, Barclaycard, HSBC, IBM, British Airways, Unilever, Harrods, Selfridges, Macy's (New York), Verizon, Target, Lucas Inc, The Royal Opera House (London), Universal Music, Sony, Miller, Burton, Harper Collins, The Wall Street Journal, The New York Times, The Times (London), Le Monde, The Economist, The Financial Times, Vogue, Cosmopolitan, Nature and National Geographic Magazine.

Full portfolios for every artist can be reviewed and requested via our web site at **www.debutart.com**

The Coningsby Gallery stages some 30 exhibitions per year by selected leading illustrators, photographers and fine artists. Review of previous exhibitions, a look at upcoming shows and a photo tour of the gallery itself can be accessed at **www.coningsbygallery.com**

Contact: Andrew Coningsby, Samuel Summerskill and Jonathan Hedley.

Joanna Agis	James Carey	Sarah Hanson	Neil Leslie	Chris Nurse	Bridget Strachan
Fusako Akimoto	Marina Caruso	Richard Hart	Lie-ins & Tigers	Sunil Pawar	Michel Streich
David Angel	Celyn	The Hejz	Rob MacDougall	Ali Pellatt	Tado
Nicola Antaki	Container	Matt Herring	Ric Machin	Pietari Posti	James Taylor
Arno	Sarah Coulston	Oliver Hibert	Daniel Mackie	Paul Price	The Studio
Tim Ashton	Matthew Cooper	Richard Holiday	Harry Malt	Peter Quinnell	Sophie Toulouse
Andrew Baker	Peter Crowther	Nanette Hoogslag	Stephane Manel	Steve Rawlings	Dominic Trevett
Greg Banning	Josie Da-Bank	Cathy Horton	Gary Marsh	Nick Reddyhoff	Alex Trochut
Gary Bates	Matthew Dartford	Sarah Howell	Sophie Marsham	Red	Jim Tsinganos
Glen Baxter	Carol del Angel	I Love Dust	Mauve	Redseal	Vault49
Sara Beazley	Barry Downard	Infomen	Bill McConkey	Kerry Roper	Neil Webb
Barbara Bellingham	Elita	Jacey	Kim McGillivray	Rouzbeh	Webbo
Jon Berkeley	Tim Ellis	Jaroslav	Vince McIndoe	Saeko	Jane Webster
Adrian Bradbury	Flatliner	Sarah Jones	Claire McMahon	Serge Seidlitz	Louise Weir
Norm Breyfogle	Flatliner V2	Alan Kitching	Pat Morgan	Seripop	Oscar Wilson
Jon Burgerman	Ewan Fraser	Ronald Kurniawan	Morten Morland	Craig Shuttlewood	Alex Williamson
Oliver Burston	Freya	Christina K	Huntley/Muir	Kid Spaniard	Tina Zellmer
Benedict Campbell	Peter Grundy	Adam Larson	David Newton	James Starr	Jurgen Ziewe

'Beauty is truth, truth beauty'
John Keats

début **art** • Illustrators, Photographers and Fine Artists Agents
30 Tottenham Street, London, W1T 4RJ. United Kingdom
Tel: +44 (0) 20 7636 1064. Fax: +44 (0) 20 7580 7017
The Coningsby Gallery • Tel: +44 (0) 20 7636 7478
email: **info@debutart.com** • **www.debutart.com**

Patrick Morgan

début **art** • Illustrators, Photographers and Fine Artists Agents

30 Tottenham Street, London, W1T 4RJ. United Kingdom

Tel: +44 (0) 20 7636 1064. Fax: +44 (0) 20 7580 7017

The Coningsby Gallery • Tel: +44 (0) 20 7636 7478

email: **info@debutart.com** • **www.debutart.com**

James Taylor

début **art** • Illustrators, Photographers and Fine Artists Agents

30 Tottenham Street, London, W1T 4RJ. United Kingdom

Tel: +44 (0) 20 7636 1064. Fax: +44 (0) 20 7580 7017

The Coningsby Gallery · Tel: +44 (0) 20 7636 7478

email: **info@debutart.com** • **www.debutart.com**

FIND OUT WHERE THE DESIGNERS IN OUR COVER STORY WILL BE SHOWING DURING LONDON'S DESIGN WEEK...

100%
100% Design
Earls Court Exhibition Centre
Warwick Road
London SW5 9TA

Matthew Hilton
LAUNCH OF OWN BRAND

Simon Pengelly
SLIDE SHELVING FOR MODUS,
BABAR STOOL FOR ARPER
AND HM88 FOR
HITCH MYLIUS

Pearson Lloyd
ALLEMUIR, MARTINEZ OTEREO

Mark Gabbertas
EBB & FLOW FOR NOMIQUE AND
TOM DICK HARRY FOR BOSS DESIGN

DG
Designer's Guild
267 King's Road
London SW3 5EN

Klauser & Carpenter
EASY CHAIR FOR ESTABLISHED & SONS

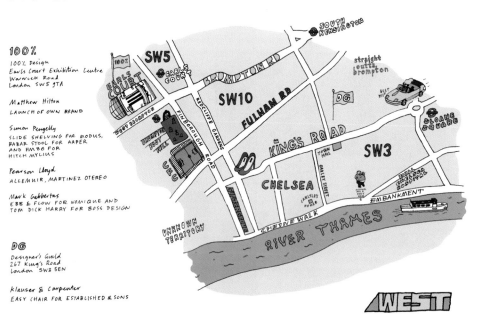

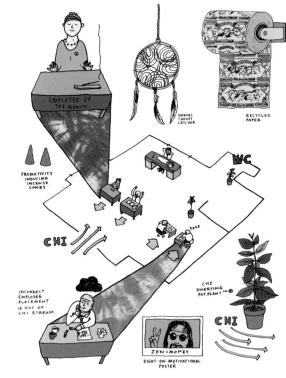

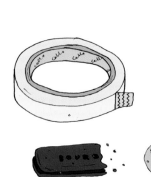

Harry Malt

début **art** • Illustrators, Photographers and Fine Artists Agents

30 Tottenham Street, London, W1T 4RJ. United Kingdom

Tel: +44 (0) 20 7636 1064. Fax: +44 (0) 20 7580 7017

The Coningsby Gallery • Tel: +44 (0) 20 7636 7478

email: **info@debutart.com** • **www.debutart.com**

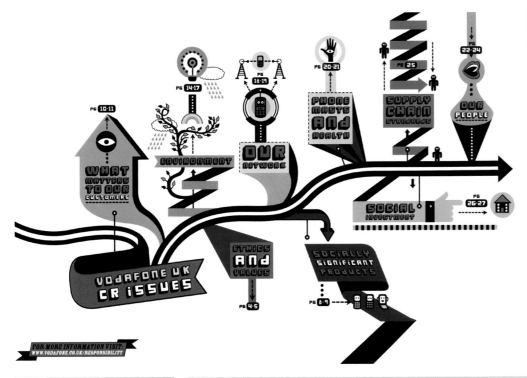

Serge Seidlitz

début **art** • Illustrators, Photographers and Fine Artists Agents

30 Tottenham Street, London, W1T 4RJ. United Kingdom

Tel: +44 (0) 20 7636 1064. Fax: +44 (0) 20 7580 7017

The Coningsby Gallery • Tel: +44 (0) 20 7636 7478

email: **info@debutart.com** • **www.debutart.com**

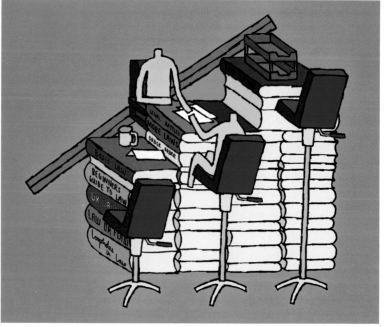

Tim Ellis

début **art** • Illustrators, Photographers and Fine Artists Agents

30 Tottenham Street, London, W1T 4RJ. United Kingdom

Tel: +44 (0) 20 7636 1064. Fax: +44 (0) 20 7580 7017

The Coningsby Gallery • Tel: +44 (0) 20 7636 7478

email: **info@debutart.com** • **www.debutart.com**

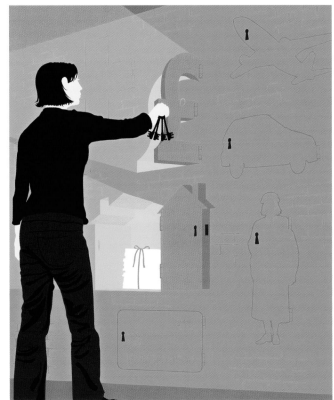

Neil Webb

début **art** • Illustrators, Photographers and Fine Artists Agents

30 Tottenham Street, London, W1T 4RJ. United Kingdom

Tel: +44 (0) 20 7636 1064. Fax: +44 (0) 20 7580 7017

The Coningsby Gallery • Tel: +44 (0) 20 7636 7478

email: **info@debutart.com** • **www.debutart.com**

Peter Crowther

Detail from 'Paparazzi' commissioned by Saatchi & Saatchi, New York

THREEblindmice

9-10 Charlotte Mews,
London W1T 4EF.

Tel: +44 (0) 20 7636 2502
Fax: +44 (0) 20 7636 2455

www.three-blind-mice.co.uk

jelly

illustration
motion graphics
animation
creative solutions

I'd like to move to a bigger home

9-10 charlotte mews, london w1t 4ef
t: 020 7323 3307   f: 020 7636 2455
www.jellylondon.com

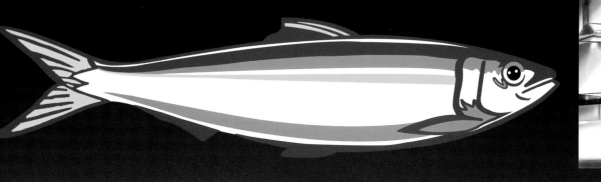

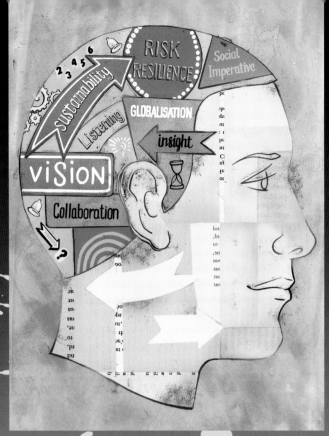

A3 Illustration

Shropshire House   179 Tottenham Court Road   London   W1T 7NZ
t. 020 7631 5398   f. 020 7436 4195   e. info@a3studios.com
www.a3studios.com

The Artworks

Ai Tatebayashi

Meilo So

Chris Wormell

Andrew Davidson

Izhar Cohen

Mary Woodin

Hanoch Piven

Ilene Winn Lederer

Miguel Gallardo

Rutu Modan

Salvatore Rubbino

www.theartworksinc.com   T. 020 7734 3333

Lisel Ashlock

Niroot Puttapipat

Lucy Davey

Charlotte Knox

Matthew Cook

Daniela Jaglenka Terrazzini

Heather Gatley

Paul Rogers

Marco Ventura

Olivier Kugler

THE ARTWORKS 40 Frith Street London W1D 5LN

Sarah Gibb

Peter Malone

Penny Dann

Joe Morse

James Majowski

Swan Park

Zed

Debbie Powell

Ed Parker

THE ARTWORKS 40 Frith Street London W1D 5LN

Beegee Tolpa

Rosie Scott

Tatsuro Kiuchi

Dennis Balogh

Marcin Baranski

Greg Clarke

Kathy Osborn

David Doyle

Sarah McMenemy

www.theartworksinc.com   T. 020 7734 3333

The Artworks

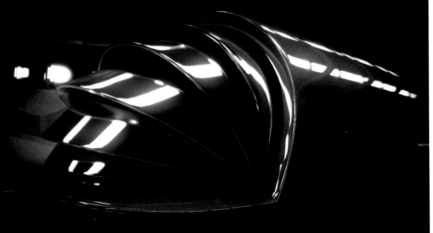

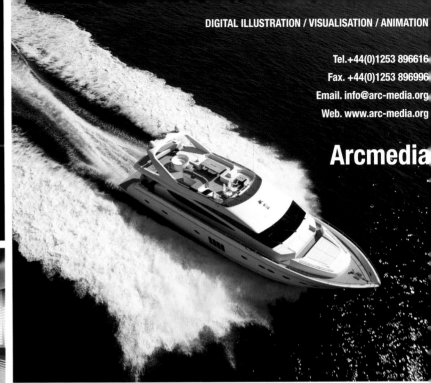

DIGITAL ILLUSTRATION / VISUALISATION / ANIMATION

Tel.+44(0)1253 896616
Fax. +44(0)1253 896996
Email. info@arc-media.org
Web. www.arc-media.org

Arcmedia

Fast responsive, offering top quality products. The Third Edge Studio can meet all your needs. From highly photorealistic 3D illustration to fast turn-around visuals. We house various styles of illustration, and our artwork service can take your ideas from concepts through to finished print. With the inclusion of large format printing, mockups and DVD editing to our name, Third Edge truly has all your creative needs covered.

Third Edge Ltd 17a Riding House Street London W1W 7DS
T: 020 7436 7930 E: info@the3rdedge.com
www.the3rdedge.com

neil duerden

owen rimington

arron lindsay

gabriel moreno

karl escritt

pablo pasadas

michael worthy

chellie carroll

a

advocate art

www.advocate-art.com mail@advocate-art.com
39 church road wimbledon village london sw19 5dq +44 (0) 20 8879 1166

Peepshow

www.peepshow.org.uk
Illustration / Design
Animation / Art Direction

The Association of Illustrators

Working together to protect, promote and inspire professional illustrators

AOI   the Association of Illustrators   www.theAOI.com

Illustration by Michael Kirkham   www.heartagency.com

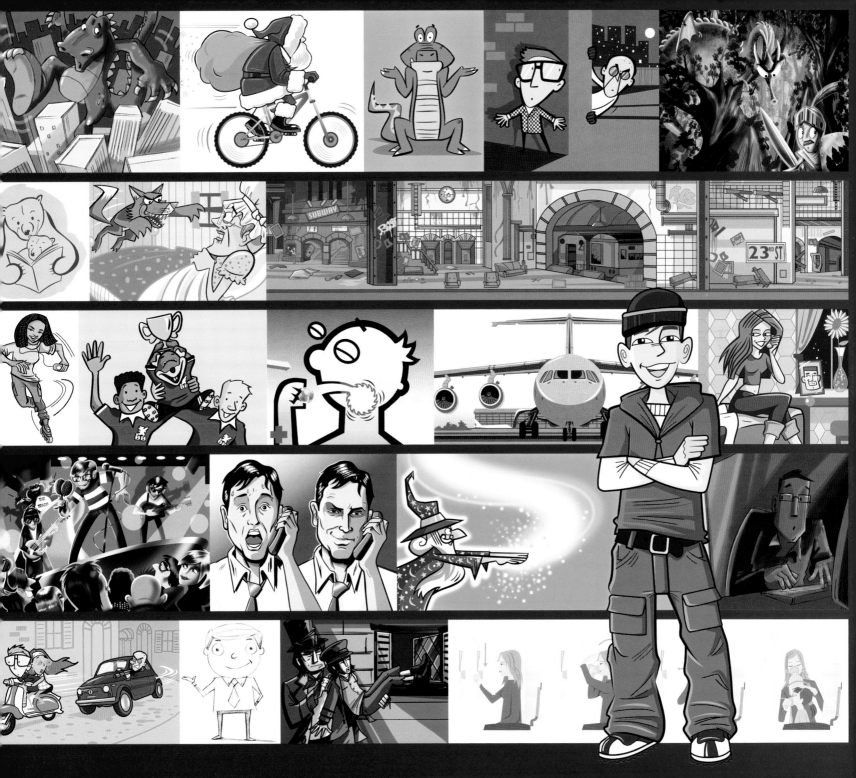

ANDREW HENNESSEY STUDIOS

Mobile: 07798 688 530
E-mail: andrewhennessey@blueyonder.co.uk
www.andrewhennessey.com

Illustration
Character Design
Storyboards
Visuals

At www.designweek.co.uk there's more than you might think.

You'll find over 20 stories a week that aren't in the magazine, the latest jobs, a 15 year archive and our events diary to plan your design year by.

So why not pay us a visit today, at www.designweek.co.uk

ILLUSTRATORS - GENERAL

1minus1 93-94 West Street, Farnham, Surrey, GU9 7EB, United Kingdom
(0870) 0501280
signup@1minus1.com
www.1minus1.com

3DA Ltd 16 Bond Close, Tadley, Hampshire, RG26 4EW, United Kingdom
0118-981 6328/(07810) 008671 0118-981 9320
damian@3-da.com
www.3-da.com

A. Kincaid@Bernard Thornton Artists The Penthouse, 4 Hamilton Mews, 310 Merton Road, London, SW18 5AB, United Kingdom
(020) 8874 9081/(07702) 554583 (020) 8877 1386
bernard@btartists.com
www.btartists.com

A3 Ltd 3rd Floor, Shropshire House, 2-10 Capper Street, London, WC1E 6JA, United Kingdom
(020) 7631 5398/ (020) 7436 4195
info@a3studios.com
www.a3studios.com
See ad in showcase

ABC Zone Studio Via Orobia, 3, Milan, 20139, Italy
00 39 02 5740 8447
barbarabongini@abcz1.it
www.abcz1.it

Abel Kesteven@Art Collection UK Ltd 7 Worsley Mill, 10 Blantyre Street, Castlefield, Manchester, M15 4LG, United Kingdom
(0870) 2405001/ (0870) 2405002
info@artcollection.co.uk
www.artcollection.co.uk

Adam Beer Storyboards 31 Westmoreland Road, London, SE17 2AX, United Kingdom
(07789) 027148
storyboards@gmail.com
www.adambeer.co.uk

Adam Errington@New Division 5 Risborough Street, London, SE1 0HF, United Kingdom
(020) 7593 0505/ (020) 7593 0501
info@newdivision.com
www.newdivision.com

Adam Hook@Linden Artists Ltd 41 Battersea Business Centre, 103 Lavender Hill, London, SW11 5QL, United Kingdom
(020) 7738 2505/ (020) 7738 2513
lindenartists@aol.com
www.lindenartists.co.uk

Adam Linley@Linda Rogers Associates 163 Half Moon Lane, London, SE24 9WB, United Kingdom
(020) 7501 9106
lr@lindarogers.net
www.lindarogers.net

Adam Stower@Arena 31 Eleanor Road, London, E15 4AB, United Kingdom
(08450) 507 600
info@arenaworks.com
www.arenaworks.com

Adam Willis@Artist Partners Ltd 2e The Chandlery, 50 Westminster Bridge Road, London, SE1 7QY, United Kingdom
(020) 7401 7904/ (020) 7401 3378
chris@artistpartners.demon.co.uk
www.artistpartners.com

addesign 53 Siward Road, Bromley, BR2 9JY, United Kingdom
(020) 8466 5570
johngovett.addesign@virgin.net

Adrian Barclay 30A College Green, Bristol, BS1 5TB, United Kingdom
0117-922 7444/ 0117-922 7444
mail@fruitcakeuk.com
www.fruitcakeuk.com

Adrian Chesterman@Art Collection UK Ltd 7 Worsley Mill, 10 Blantyre Street, Castlefield, Manchester, M15 4LG, United Kingdom
(0870) 2405001/ (0870) 2405002
info@artcollection.co.uk
www.artcollection.co.uk

Adrian Johnson@Central Illustration Agency 36 Wellington Street, London, WC2E 7BD, United Kingdom
(020) 7240 8925/ (020) 7836 1172
info@centralillustration.com
www.centralillustration.com

Adrian Reynolds@David Higham 5-8 Lower John Street, Golden Square, London, W1F 9HA, United Kingdom
(020) 7437 7888/ (020) 7437 1072
carolinewalsh@davidhigham.co.uk
www.davidhigham.co.uk

Adrian Valencia@Eastwing 99 Chase Side, Enfield, Middlesex, EN2 6NL, United Kingdom
(020) 8367 6760/ (020) 8367 6730
andrea@eastwing.co.uk
www.eastwing.co.uk

Adrienne Salgado Bellfield House, 9 Upper Bridge Street, Stirling, FK8 1ER, United Kingdom
(01786) 451324
adriennesalgado@f2s.com

Advocate Artists Agents 39 Church Road, Wimberlton Village, London, SW19 5DQ, United Kingdom
(020) 8877 0072/ (020) 879 3303
mail@advocate-art.com
www.advocate-art.com
See ad in showcase

Agent-Art Department Studio 5, 4 Clarendon Avenue, Altrincham, Cheshire, WA15 8HD, United Kingdom
(07811) 352322
paul@karalius.co.uk
www.karalius.co.uk

Agnieszka Jatkowska@Advocate Art 39 Church Road, London, SW19 5DQ, United Kingdom
020 8879 1166/020 8879 3303
lesley@advocate-art.com
www.advocate-art.com

Ai Tatebayashi@The Artworks 40 Frith Street, London, W1D 5LN, United Kingdom
(020) 7734 3333/ (020) 7734 3484
lucy@theartworksinc.com
www.theartworksinc.com

Ainslie Macleod@Art Collection UK Ltd 7 Worsley Mill, 10 Blantyre Street, Castlefield, Manchester, M15 4LG, United Kingdom
(0870) 2405001/ (0870) 2405002
info@artcollection.co.uk
www.artcollection.co.uk

Al Sacui@Thorogood Illustration Ltd 5 Dryden Street, Covent Garden, London, WC2E 9NW, United Kingdom
(020) 7829 8468
draw@thorogood.net
www.thorogood.net

Alan Aldridge@Central Illustration Agency 36 Wellington Street, London, WC2E 7BD, United Kingdom
(020) 7240 8925/ (020) 7836 1177
info@centralillustration.com
www.centralillustration.com

Alan Austin@Phosphor Art 41 The Pump House, Pump House Close, off Renforth Street, London, SE16 7HS, United Kingdom
(020) 7064 4666/ (020) 7064 4660
info@phosphorart.com
www.phosphorart.com

Alan Baker@Illustration Ltd 2 Brooks Court, Cringle Street, London, SW8 5BX, United Kingdom
(020) 7720 5202/ (020) 7720 5920
team@illustrationweb.com
www.illustrationweb.com

Alan Birch 49 Cobden Street, Stourbridge, West Midlands, DY8 3RT, United Kingdom
(01384) 396752/ (01384) 396752
alanbirch@blueyonder.co.uk
www.kartoonart.co.uk

Alan Cracknell@Meiklejohn Illustration 5 Risborough Street, London, SE1 0HF, United Kingdom
(020) 7593 0505/ (020) 7593 0501
info@meiklejohn.co.uk
www.meiklejohn.co.uk

Alan Kitching@Début Art & The Coningsby Gallery 30 Tottenham Street, London, W1T 4RJ, United Kingdom
(020) 7636 1064/ (020) 7580 7017
info@debutart.com
www.debutart.com

Alan Linsdell 87 Mersey Bank Avenue, Chorlton-Cum-Hardy, Manchester, M21 7NT, United Kingdom
0161-434 1016
alan.linsdell@excite.com

Alan Male@Linden Artists Ltd 41 Battersea Business Centre, 103 Lavender Hill, London, SW11 5QL, United Kingdom
(020) 7738 2505/ (020) 7738 2513
lindenartists@aol.com
www.lindenartists.co.uk

Alan Nanson 12 Southey Street, Keswick, Cumbria, CA12 4EF, United Kingdom
(01768) 772630
nansonalan@aol.com

Alan Rowe 17 Surrey Grove, Sutton, Surrey, SM1 3PW, United Kingdom
(020) 8643 1626/ (020) 8641 1528
bignose@alanrowe.com
www.alanrowe.com

Alasdair Bright@N B Illustration Ltd 40 Bowling Green Lane, London, EC1R 0NE, United Kingdom
(020) 7278 9131/ (020) 7278 9121
info@nbillustration.co.uk
www.nbillustration.co.uk

Alastair Graham Chapel End, Keys Lane, Priors Marston, Southam, Warwickshire, CV47 7SA, United Kingdom
(01327) 260655
alastairgraham1@ukgateway.net
www.alagram.co.uk

Alastair Taylor@Inkshed 99 Chase Side, Enfield, Middlesex, EN2 6NL, United Kingdom
(020) 8367 4545/ (020) 8367 6730
www.inkshed.co.uk

Albany Wiseman 1B Avenue Studios, Sydney Close, London, SW3 6HN, United Kingdom
(020) 7589 0478/ (020) 7589 0478
albanywiseman@hotmail.com

Alberto Sveso@Advocate Art 39 Church Road, London, SW19 5DQ, United Kingdom
020 8879 1166/020 8879 3303
lesley@advocate-art.com
www.advocate-art.com

Albino Igil 12 Grangeover Way, Derby, DE22 3QD, United Kingdom
(01332) 265618
creative@albino-igilco.uk
www.albino-igil.co.uk

Aldous Eveleigh@N B Illustration Ltd 40 Bowling Green Lane, London, EC1R 0NE, United Kingdom
(020) 7278 9131/ (020) 7278 9121
info@nbillustration.co.uk
www.nbillustration.co.uk

Alec MacDonald@Advocate Art 39 Church Road, London, SW19 5DQ, United Kingdom
020 8879 1166/020 8879 3303
lesley@advocate-art.com
www.advocate-art.com

Alex Green@Folio 10 Gate Street, Lincoln's Inn Fields, London, WC2A 3HP, United Kingdom
(020) 7242 9562/ (020) 7242 1816
all@folioart.co.uk
www.folioart.co.uk

Alex Higlett@Drawer Illustrators Agents 8 Belmont, Bath, BA1 5DZ, United Kingdom
(01225) 445262
enquiries@drawer.me.uk

Alex Orlov 47 Gravel Pit Lane, Spondon, Derby, DE21 7DB, United Kingdom
(07779) 794929
al_orlov@yahoo.co.uk
www.alexorlov.com

Alex Steele-Morgan@The Organisation The Basement, 69 Caledonian Road, London, N1 9BT, United Kingdom
(020) 7833 8268/(07973) 172902 (020) 7833 8269
organise@easynet.co.uk
www.organisart.co.uk

Alex Turvey @Advocate Art 39 Church Road, London, SW19 5DQ, United Kingdom
020 8879 1166/020 8879 3303
lesley@advocate-art.com
www.advocate-art.com

Alex Williamson@Début Art & The Coningsby Gallery 30 Tottenham Street, London, W1T 4RJ, United Kingdom
(020) 7636 1064/ (020) 7580 7017
info@debutart.com
www.debutart.com

Alexandra Burnett@Advocate Art 39 Church Road, London, SW19 5DQ, United Kingdom
020 8879 1166/020 8879 3303
lesley@advocate-art.com
www.advocate-art.com

Ali Pellatt@Début Art & The Coningsby Gallery 30 Tottenham Street, London, W1T 4RJ, United Kingdom
☎ (020) 7636 1064/ 📠 (020) 7580 7017
✉ info@debutart.com
🖥 www.debutart.com

Alison Barratt@Thorogood Illustration Ltd 5 Dryden Street, Covent Garden, London, WC2E 9NW, United Kingdom
☎ (020) 7829 8468
✉ draw@thorogood.net
🖥 www.thorogood.net

Alison Edgson@Advocate Art 39 Church Road, London, SW19 5DQ, United Kingdom
☎ 020 8879 1166/020 8879 3303
✉ lesley@advocate-art.com
🖥 www.advocate-art.com

Alison Hullyer Smallstone, Hall End, Milton, Cambridge, CB24 6AQ, United Kingdom
☎ (01223) 862974
✉ alison@hullyer.co.uk
🖥 www.hullyer.co.uk

Alison Jay@The Organisation The Basement, 69 Caledonian Road, London, N1 9BT, United Kingdom
☎ (020) 7833 8268/(07973) 172902 / 📠 (020) 7833 8269
✉ organise@easynet.co.uk
🖥 www.organisart.co.uk

Alison Lang@Phosphor Art 41 The Pump House, Pump House Close, off Renforth Street, London, SE16 7HS, United Kingdom
☎ (020) 7064 4666/ 📠 (020) 7064 4660
✉ info@phosphorart.com
🖥 www.phosphorart.com

All Handmade Unit 6-8, Stapley Manor Farm, Long Lane, Odiham, Hook, Hampshire, RG29 1JE, United Kingdom
☎ (01256) 862111

All Royalty Free 10 Old Bakery Gardens, Chichester, West Sussex, PO19 8AJ, United Kingdom
☎ (01243) 780385/ 📠 (01243) 780385
✉ sales@allroyaltyfree.co.uk
🖥 www.allroyaltyfree.co.uk

Allied Artists@ Artistic License The Gallery @ Richmond, 63 Sheen Road, Richmond, Surrey, TW9 1YJ, United Kingdom
☎ (020) 8334 1010/ 📠 (020) 8334 9900
✉ info@allied-artists.net
🖥 www.allied-artists.net

Alma Larroca@Advocate Art 39 Church Road, London, SW19 5DQ, United Kingdom
☎ 020 8879 1166/020 8879 3303
✉ lesley@advocate-art.com
🖥 www.advocate-art.com

Amanda Enright@Advocate Art 39 Church Road, London, SW19 5DQ, United Kingdom
☎ 020 8879 1166/020 8879 3303
✉ lesley@advocate-art.com
🖥 www.advocate-art.com

Amanda Hutt 7 Maria Terrace, London, E1 4NE, United Kingdom
☎ (020) 7702 8899/(07961) 144988 / 📠 (020) 7702 8899
✉ amandahutt@talktalk.net
🖥 www.amandahutt.com

Amanda Wood@Drawer Illustrators Agents 8 Belmont, Bath, BA1 5DZ, United Kingdom
☎ (01225) 445262
✉ enquiries@drawer.me.uk

Ami Plasse@Illustration Ltd 2 Brooks Court, Cringle Street, London, SW8 5BX, United Kingdom
☎ (020) 7720 5202/ 📠 (020) 7720 5920
✉ team@illustrationweb.com
🖥 www.illustrationweb.com

Andrew Beckett@Illustration Ltd 2 Brooks Court, Cringle Street, London, SW8 5BX, United Kingdom
☎ (020) 7720 5202/ 📠 (020) 7720 5920
✉ team@illustrationweb.com
🖥 www.illustrationweb.com

Andrew Bylo@Central Illustration Agency 36 Wellington Street, London, WC2E 7BD, United Kingdom
☎ (020) 7240 8925/ 📠 (020) 7836 1177
✉ info@centralillustration.com
🖥 www.centralillustration.com

Andrew Clark Illustration 191 High Street, Milton Regis, Sittingbourne, Kent, ME10 2BB, United Kingdom
☎ (01795) 470276/ 📠 (01795) 470276
✉ andrew.clark@tesco.net
🖥 www.andrewclarkillustration.co.uk

Andrew Davidson@The Artworks 40 Frith Street, London, W1D 5LN, United Kingdom
☎ (020) 7734 3333/ 📠 (020) 7734 3484
✉ lucy@theartworksinc.com
🖥 www.theartworksinc.com

Andrew Donaldson The Yews, Main Street, Bardsea, Ulverston, Cumbria, LA12 9QT, United Kingdom
☎ (01229) 869373/ 📠 (01229) 869373

Andrew Farley@Meiklejohn Illustration 5 Risborough Street, London, SE1 0HF, United Kingdom
☎ (020) 7593 0500/ 📠 (020) 7593 0501
✉ info@meiklejohn.co.uk
🖥 www.meiklejohn.co.uk

Andrew Foley Underhill Cottage, 98 Main Street, Leadhills, Biggar, Lanarkshire, ML12 6XR, United Kingdom
☎ (01659) 74323/(07974) 119557 / 📠 (01659) 74323
✉ andrew.foley@virgin.net
🖥 www.geocities.com/leafywonderillustration/

Andrew Foster@Central Illustration Agency 36 Wellington Street, London, WC2E 7BD, United Kingdom
☎ (020) 7240 8925/ 📠 (020) 7836 1177
✉ info@centralillustration.com
🖥 www.centralillustration.com

Andrew Hamilton@Meiklejohn Illustration 5 Risborough Street, London, SE1 0HF, United Kingdom
☎ (020) 7593 0500/ 📠 (020) 7593 0501
✉ info@meiklejohn.co.uk
🖥 www.meiklejohn.co.uk

Andrew Hennessey 24 Westfield Way, Ruislip, Middlesex, HA4 6HN, United Kingdom
☎ (020) 7323 1149/(07798) 688530 / 📠 (020) 7436 4195
✉ andrewhennessey@blueyonder.co.uk
🖥 **www.andrewhennessey.com**
See ad in showcase

Andrew Hutchinson@Illustration Ltd 2 Brooks Court, Cringle Street, London, SW8 5BX, United Kingdom
☎ (020) 7720 5202/ 📠 (020) 7720 5920
✉ team@illustrationweb.com
🖥 www.illustrationweb.com

Andrew Ingamells@Folio 10 Gate Street, Lincoln's Inn Fields, London, WC2A 3HP, United Kingdom
☎ (020) 7242 9562/ 📠 (020) 7242 1816
✉ all@folioart.co.uk
🖥 www.folioart.co.uk

Andrew Mockett 3 Lewes Crescent, Brighton, BN2 1FH, United Kingdom
☎ (01273) 601262/(07850) 440320 / 📠 (01273) 620170
✉ info@mockettandmoquette.co.uk
🖥 www.mockettandmoquette.co.uk

Andrew Morris 34 Big Wood Avenue, Hove, East Sussex, BN3 6FQ, United Kingdom
☎ (01273) 724903/(07870) 755182 / 📠 (01273) 724903
✉ mojo34@btinternet.com

Andrew Potter@Phosphor Art 41 The Pump House, Pump House Close, off Renforth Street, London, SE16 7HS, United Kingdom
☎ (020) 7064 4666/ 📠 (020) 7064 4660
✉ info@phosphorart.com
🖥 www.phosphorart.com

Andrew Rowland@Advocate Art 39 Church Road, London, SW19 5DQ, United Kingdom
☎ 020 8879 1166/020 8879 3303
✉ lesley@advocate-art.com
🖥 www.advocate-art.com

Andrew Selby@Illustration Ltd 2 Brooks Court, Cringle Street, London, SW8 5BX, United Kingdom
☎ (020) 7720 5202/ 📠 (020) 7720 5920
✉ team@illustrationweb.com
🖥 www.illustrationweb.com

Andrew Steward@The Organisation The Basement, 69 Caledonian Road, London, N1 9BT, United Kingdom
☎ (020) 7833 8268/(07973) 172902 / 📠 (020) 7833 8269
✉ organise@easynet.co.uk
🖥 www.organisart.co.uk

Andrew Whiteley@Inkshed 99 Chase Side, Enfield, Middlesex, EN2 6NL, United Kingdom
☎ (020) 8367 4545/ 📠 (020) 8367 6730
🖥 www.inkshed.co.uk

Andy Baker@Début Art & The Coningsby Gallery 30 Tottenham Street, London, W1T 4RJ, United Kingdom
☎ (020) 7636 1064/ 📠 (020) 7580 7017
✉ info@debutart.com
🖥 www.debutart.com

Andy Burton 388 Finchampstead Road, Wokingham, Berkshire, RG40 3LA, United Kingdom
☎ 0118-973 3294/(07808) 950255 / 📠 0118-973 3294
✉ andy.illo@talk21.com
🖥 www.contact-me.net/andyburton

Andy Catling@Advocate Art 39 Church Road, London, SW19 5DQ, United Kingdom
☎ 020 8879 1166/020 8879 3303
✉ lesley@advocate-art.com
🖥 www.advocate-art.com

Andy Council@Drawer Illustrators Agents 8 Belmont, Bath, BA1 5DZ, United Kingdom
☎ (01225) 445262
✉ enquiries@drawer.me.uk

Andy Everett Stewart@Advocate Art 39 Church Road, London, SW19 5DQ, United Kingdom
☎ 020 8879 1166/020 8879 3303
✉ lesley@advocate-art.com
🖥 www.advocate-art.com

Andy Hammond@Illustration Ltd 2 Brooks Court, Cringle Street, London, SW8 5BX, United Kingdom
☎ (020) 7720 5202/ 📠 (020) 7720 5920
✉ team@illustrationweb.com
🖥 www.illustrationweb.com

Andy Potts@Thorogood Illustration Ltd 5 Dryden Street, Covent Garden, London, WC2E 9NW, United Kingdom
☎ (020) 7829 8468
✉ draw@thorogood.net
🖥 www.thorogood.net

Andy Potts Illustration 15 Upper Bardsey Walk, London, N1 2RZ, United Kingdom
☎ (07817) 159049
✉ info@andy-potts.com
🖥 www.andy-potts.com

Andy Robb@Linden Artists Ltd 41 Battersea Business Centre, 103 Lavender Hill, London, SW11 5QL, United Kingdom
☎ (020) 7738 2505/ 📠 (020) 7738 2513
✉ lindenartists@aol.com
🖥 www.lindenartists.co.uk

Andy Smith 45 Hubert Road, London, E6 3EX, United Kingdom
☎ (01424) 871043/(07949) 997978 / 📠 (020) 8503 5959
✉ andy@asmithillustration.com
🖥 www.asmithillustration.com

Andy Ward@N B Illustration Ltd 40 Bowling Green Lane, London, EC1R 0NE, United Kingdom
☎ (020) 7278 9131/ 📠 (020) 7278 9121
✉ info@nbillustration.co.uk
🖥 www.nbillustration.co.uk

Andy Watt@Folio 10 Gate Street, Lincoln's Inn Fields, London, WC2A 3HP, United Kingdom
☎ (020) 7242 9562/ 📠 (020) 7242 1816
✉ all@folioart.co.uk
🖥 www.folioart.co.uk

Andy White 19 Ashbridge Road, Leytonstone, London, E11 1NH, United Kingdom
☎ (020) 8518 8350/(07973) 178613 / 📠
✉ f@tfish.co.uk
🖥 www.tfish.co.uk

Anette Isberg Rozijn@Linda Rogers Associates 163 Half Moon Lane, London, SE24 9WB, United Kingdom
☎ (020) 7501 9106
✉ lr@lindarogers.net
🖥 www.lindarogers.net

Angel David@Début Art & The Coningsby Gallery 30 Tottenham Street, London, W1T 4RJ, United Kingdom
☎ (020) 7636 1064/ 📠 (020) 7580 7017
✉ info@debutart.com
🖥 www.debutart.com

Angela Christie 14 West End Avenue, Pinner, Middlesex, HA5 1BJ, United Kingdom
☎ (020) 8868 5469/(07962) 027 921 / 📠 (020) 8868 5469
✉ angela@maet1.plus.com

Angelo Rinaldi@Artist Partners Ltd 2e The Chandlery, 50 Westminster Bridge Road, London, SE1 7QY, United Kingdom
☎ (020) 7401 7904/ 📠 (020) 7401 3378
✉ chris@artistpartners.demon.co.uk
🖥 www.artistpartners.com

Angus McBride@Linden Artists Ltd 41 Battersea Business Centre, 103 Lavender Hill, London, SW11 5QL, United Kingdom
☎ (020) 7738 2505/ 📠 (020) 7738 2513
✉ lindenartists@aol.com
🖥 www.lindenartists.co.uk

Animation-Boy Productions 31 Church Road, Watford, WD17 4PY, United Kingdom
- (07971) 713264
- ben@animation-boy.com
- www.animation-boy.com

Anita Romeo@Advocate Art 39 Church Road, London, SW19 5DQ, United Kingdom
- 020 8879 1166/020 8879 3303
- lesley@advocate-art.com
- www.advocate-art.com

Ann & Richard Bonson Rose Tree Cottage, Church Row, Mellis, Eye, Suffolk, IP23 8EE, United Kingdom
- (01379) 783783/ (01379) 783783
- annie.bonson@virgin.net

Ann Baum@Drawer Illustrators Agents 8 Belmont, Bath, BA1 5DZ, United Kingdom
- (01225) 445262
- enquiries@drawer.me.uk

Ann Biggs@Graham-Cameron Illustration The Studio, 23 Holt Road, Sheringham, Norfolk, NR26 8NB, United Kingdom
- (01263) 821333/ (01263) 821334
- enquiry@graham-cameron-illustration.com
- www.graham-cameron-illustration.com

Ann Elson@Drawer Illustrators Agents 8 Belmont, Bath, BA1 5DZ, United Kingdom
- (01225) 445262
- enquiries@drawer.me.uk

Anna Hymas@New Division 5 Risborough Street, London, SE1 0HF, United Kingdom
- (020) 7593 0505/ (020) 7593 0501
- info@newdivision.com
- www.newdivision.com

Anna Lubecka 77 Tyne Court, Hanway Road, Hanwell, London, W7 3RR, United Kingdom
- (07745) 639213
- alubecka@hotmail.com
- www.annalubecka.com

Anna Wadham@Advocate Art 39 Church Road, London, SW19 5DQ, United Kingdom
- 020 8879 1166/020 8879 3303
- lesley@advocate-art.com
- www.advocate-art.com

Annabel Hudson 66 Onslow Gardens, Muswell Hill, London, N10 3JX, United Kingdom
- (020) 8442 1638/(07812) 198110 / (020) 8442 1638
- annabelstudio@mac.com

Annabel Wright@Heart Top Floor, 100 de Beauvoir Road, London, N1 4EN, United Kingdom
- (020) 7254 5558/ (020) 7923 4791
- heartinfo@heartagency.com
- www.heartagency.com

Annabelle Verhoye@N B Illustration Ltd 40 Bowling Green Lane, London, EC1R 0NE, United Kingdom
- (020) 7278 9131/ (020) 7278 9121
- info@nbillustration.co.uk
- www.nbillustration.co.uk

Annalisa Papagna@Advocate Art 39 Church Road, London, SW19 5DQ, United Kingdom
- 020 8879 1166/020 8879 3303
- lesley@advocate-art.com
- www.advocate-art.com

Anne Cakebread@Art Market 51 Oxford Drive, London, SE1 2FB, United Kingdom
- (020) 7407 8111/ (020) 7407 8222
- info@artmarketillustration.com
- www.artmarketillustration.com

Anne Howeson 91 Cloudesley Road, London, N1 0EL, United Kingdom
- (020) 7837 2939/ (020) 7837 2939
- aehoweson@aol.com

Anne Kristin Hagesaether@Inkshed 99 Chase Side, Enfield, Middlesex, EN2 6NL, United Kingdom
- (020) 8367 4545/ (020) 8367 6730
- www.inkshed.co.uk

Anne Sharp@Folio 10 Gate Street, Lincoln's Inn Fields, London, WC2A 3HP, United Kingdom
- (020) 7242 9562/ (020) 7242 1816
- all@folioart.co.uk
- www.folioart.co.uk

Anne Wilson@Illustration Ltd 2 Brooks Court, Cringle Street, London, SW8 5BX, United Kingdom
- (020) 7720 5202/ (020) 7720 5920
- team@illustrationweb.com
- www.illustrationweb.com

Anne Yvonne Gilbert@Thorogood Illustration Ltd 5 Dryden Street, Covent Garden, London, WC2E 9NW, United Kingdom
- (020) 7829 8468
- draw@thorogood.net
- www.thorogood.net

Annette Isberg-Rozijn@Drawer Illustrators Agents 8 Belmont, Bath, BA1 5DZ, United Kingdom
- (01225) 445262
- enquiries@drawer.me.uk

Annick Poirier@Advocate Art 39 Church Road, London, SW19 5DQ, United Kingdom
- 020 8879 1166/020 8879 3303
- lesley@advocate-art.com
- www.advocate-art.com

Annie Boberg@The Organisation The Basement, 69 Caledonian Road, London, N1 9BT, United Kingdom
- (020) 7833 8268/(07973) 172902 / (020) 7833 8269
- organise@easynet.co.uk
- www.organisart.co.uk

Another-Fine-Mesh.com 33a Fossgate, York, YO1 9TA, United Kingdom
- (01904) 630721
- 3d@another-fine-mesh.com
- www.another-fine-mesh.com

Antena Boy@Meiklejohn Illustration 5 Risborough Street, London, SE1 0HF, United Kingdom
- (020) 7593 0500/ (020) 7593 0501
- info@meiklejohn.co.uk
- www.meiklejohn.co.uk

Anthony Atkinson@Phosphor Art 41 The Pump House, Pump House Close, off Renforth Street, SE16 7HS, United Kingdom
- (020) 7064 4666/ (020) 7064 4660
- info@phosphorart.com
- www.phosphorart.com

Anthony Burrill@Siobhan Squire 111 Shoreditch High Street, London, E1 6JN, United Kingdom
- (020) 7739 8985/ (020) 7729 5125
- siobhan@siobhansquire.com
- www.siobhansquire.com

Anthony Morris@Linda Rogers Associates 163 Half Moon Lane, London, SE24 9WB, United Kingdom
- (020) 7501 9106
- lr@lindarogers.net
- www.lindarogers.net

Anthony Robinson Farley Studios, London, W1A, United Kingdom
- (07780) 707092/ (020) 8850 1294
- digital@rtwork.co.uk
- www.anthony-robinson.com

Anthony Russo@The Artworks 40 Frith Street, London, W1D 5LN, United Kingdom
- (020) 7734 3333/ (020) 7734 3484
- lucy@theartworksinc.com
- www.theartworksinc.com

Anthony Seldon@Graham-Cameron Illustration The Studio, 23 Holt Road, Sheringham, Norfolk, NR26 8NB, United Kingdom
- (01263) 821333/ (01263) 821334
- enquiry@graham-cameron-illustration.com
- www.graham-cameron-illustration.com

Anthony Sidwell Jacques Cottage, Windmill Lane, Atherstone, Warwickshire, CV9 2HN, United Kingdom
- (01827) 713459
- as@anthonysidwell.com
- www.anthonysidwell.com

Anthony Sidwell Illustration Jacques Cottage, Windmill Lane, Baxterley, Atherstone, Warwickshire, CV9 2HN, United Kingdom
- (01827) 713459
- as@anthonysidwell.com
- www.anthonysidwell.com

Antonia Enthoven Foley Farmhouse, Lower Street, Leeds, Maidstone, Kent, ME17 1TL, United Kingdom
- (01622) 863776
- aenthoven@foleyfarm.freeserve.co.uk
- www.antoniaenthoven.com

Antony Bridge Flat 5, 55 Abbey Road, Malvern, Worcestershire, WR14 3HH, United Kingdom
- (01684) 563 744/(07736) 051944 /
- antony@antonybridge.co.uk
- www.antonybridge.com

Apple Agency Ltd Design House, Exmoor Avenue, Scunthorpe, North Lincolnshire, DN15 8NJ, United Kingdom
- (01724) 289081/ (01724) 289381
- simonb@appleagency.co.uk
- www.apple.co.uk

Arcmedia Ltd 5 Hardhorn Road, Poulton-le-Fylde, Lancashire, FY6 7SR, United Kingdom
- **(01253) 896616/ (01253) 896996**
- **info@arc-media.org**
- **www.arc-media.org**
- **See ad in showcase**

Arena 31 Eleanor Road, London, E15 4AB, United Kingdom
- (08450) 507 600
- info@arenaworks.com
- www.arenaworks.com

Arhiann Direct 22 Saville Road Industrial Estate, Peterborough, PE3 7PR, United Kingdom
- (01733) 346739
- rob@arhiann.com
- www.arhiann.com

Arlene Adams 61 Oxford Road, Moseley, Birmingham, B13 9ES, United Kingdom
- 0121-449 6190/(07833) 682916 / 0121-449 6190
- mail@arleneadams.com
- www.arleneadams.com

Arron Lindsay@Advocate Art 39 Church Road, London, SW19 5DQ, United Kingdom
- 020 8879 1166/020 8879 3303
- lesley@advocate-art.com
- www.advocate-art.com

Art Collection UK Ltd 7 Worsley Mill, 10 Blantyre Street, Castlefield, Manchester, M15 4LG, United Kingdom
- (0870) 2405001/ (0870) 2405002
- info@artcollection.co.uk
- www.artcollection.co.uk

Art Machine 15 Addingford Drive, Horbury, Wakefield, West Yorkshire, WF4 5BW, United Kingdom
- (01924) 278434
- artmachine@blueyonder.co.uk
- www.caricaturist.pwp.blueyonder.co.uk

Art Market 51 Oxford Drive, London, SE1 2FB, United Kingdom
- (020) 7407 8111/ (020) 7407 8222
- info@artmarketillustration.com
- www.artmarketillustration.com

art-cell.com 15 Cowper Road, Burbage, Hinckley, Leicestershire, LE10 2LW, United Kingdom
- (07743) 781943
- art-cell@hotmail.co.uk
- www.art-cell.com

Artery 17 Garden Terrace, Bradford, West Yorkshire, BD9 4AA, United Kingdom
- (01274) 482737/ (01274) 482737
- leslie.megson@btconnect.com
- www.lmegsonillustration.com

Arthur Phillips 38 Aragon Avenue, Thames Ditton, Surrey, KT7 0PX, United Kingdom
- (020) 8398 0077/ (020) 8398 0077
- arthur@computerillustration.co.uk
- www.computerillustration.co.uk

Arthur Reid Eastdale, 3 South Mains Cottages, Pitmeadden, Ellon, Aberdeenshire, AB41 7PB, United Kingdom
- (01651) 842479/ (01651) 842479

Arthur Wren 32 Ganghill, Guildford, Surrey, GU1 1XF, United Kingdom
- (01483) 533878
- ARTHUR.WREN1@btopenworld.com

Artist Partners Ltd 2e The Chandlery, 50 Westminster Bridge Road, London, SE1 7QY, United Kingdom
- (020) 7401 7904/ (020) 7401 3378
- chris@artistpartners.demon.co.uk
- www.artistpartners.com

Artistan Studio 6, 8 Clissold Road, London, N16 9EU, United Kingdom
- (020) 7249 5398/ (020) 7503 0465
- one@artistan.net
- www.artistan.net

ArtLaundry 8 Rosslyn Terrace, Glasgow, G12 9NB, United Kingdom
- 0141-357 0419
- contact@artlaundry.com
- www.artlaundry.com

Asa Andersson@N B Illustration Ltd 40 Bowling Green Lane, London, EC1R 0NE, United Kingdom
- (020) 7278 9131/ (020) 7278 9121
- info@nbillustration.co.uk
- www.nbillustration.co.uk

asmithillustration.com 45 Hubert Road, London, E6 3EX, United Kingdom
- (07949) 997978
- andy@asmithillustration.com
- www.asmithillustration.com

Aurore Colson@Advocate Art 39 Church Road, London, SW19 5DQ, United Kingdom
- 020 8879 1166/020 8879 3303
- lesley@advocate-art.com
- www.advocate-art.com

Avram Dumitrescu Illustrations 190 Colinmill, Dunmurry, Belfast, BT17 0AU, United Kingdom
- (028) 9062 5430
- avram@onlineavram.com
- www.onlineavram.com

Avril Turner@Drawer Illustrators Agents 8 Belmont, Bath, BA1 5DZ, United Kingdom
- (01225) 445262
- enquiries@drawer.me.uk

B.L. Kearley Ltd 16 Chiltern Street, London, W1U 7PZ, United Kingdom
- (020) 7935 9550/ (020) 7224 6879
- b.l.kearleyltd@btopenworld.com
- www.kearley.co.uk

Barbara Bellingham@Début Art & The Coningsby Gallery 30 Tottenham Street, London, W1T 4RJ, United Kingdom
- (020) 7636 1064/ (020) 7580 7017
- info@debutart.com
- www.debutart.com

Barbara Geradi@Advocate Art 39 Church Road, London, SW19 5DQ, United Kingdom
- 020 8879 1166/020 8879 3303
- lesley@advocate-art.com
- www.advocate-art.com

Barbara Lofthouse@Artist Partners Ltd 2e The Chandlery, 50 Westminster Bridge Road, London, SE1 7QY, United Kingdom
- (020) 7401 7904/ (020) 7401 3378
- chris@artistpartners.demon.co.uk
- www.artistpartners.com

Barbara Nascimbeni@Advocate Art 39 Church Road, London, SW19 5DQ, United Kingdom
- 020 8879 1166/020 8879 3303
- lesley@advocate-art.com
- www.advocate-art.com

Barbara Siedlecka 21 West Oak, The Avenue, Beckenham, Kent, BR3 5EZ, United Kingdom
- (020) 8650 9029/ (020) 8650 9029
- barbara-s@ntlworld.com

Barry Craddock 2 Rammell Mews, Frythe Way, Cranbrook, Kent, TN17 3BQ, United Kingdom
- (01580) 714893/ (01580) 714893
- barrycraddock@btinternet.com
- www.barrycraddock.com

Barry Downard@Début Art & The Coningsby Gallery 30 Tottenham Street, London, W1T 4RJ, United Kingdom
- (020) 7636 1064/ (020) 7580 7017
- info@debutart.com
- www.debutart.com

Barry Macey Ivy Cottage, Aylesbury Road, Princes Risborough, Buckinghamshire, HP27 0JW, United Kingdom
- (01844) 343075
- barrymaceystudio@aol.com

Barry Patterson@Illustration Ltd 2 Brooks Court, Cringle Street, London, SW8 5BX, United Kingdom
- (020) 7720 5202/ (020) 7720 5920
- team@illustrationweb.com
- www.illustrationweb.com

Barry Robson@Linden Artists Ltd 41 Battersea Business Centre, 103 Lavender Hill, London, SW11 5QL, United Kingdom
- (020) 7738 2505/ (020) 7738 2513
- lindenartists@aol.com
- www.lindenartists.co.uk

Basia Bogdanovicz@Drawer Illustrators Agents 8 Belmont, Bath, BA1 5DZ, United Kingdom
- (01225) 445262
- enquiries@drawer.me.uk

Basia Bogdanowicz@Linda Rogers Associates 163 Half Moon Lane, London, SE24 9WB, United Kingdom
- (020) 7501 9106
- lr@lindarogers.net
- www.lindarogers.net

Baz Pringle@Advocate Art 39 Church Road, London, SW19 5DQ, United Kingdom
- 020 8879 1166/020 8879 3303
- lesley@advocate-art.com
- www.advocate-art.com

Beard with Beef Flat 22, Alwyne Mansions, Alwyne Road, London, SW19 7AD, United Kingdom
- (020) 8715 1849
- info@kevspeck.com
- www.kevspeck.com

Becky Blair@Private View Artists Agency 17A Swan Hill, Shrewsbury, SY1 1NL, United Kingdom
- (01743) 350355/ (01743) 233923
- create@pvuk.com
- www.pvuk.com

Becky Cole@The Organisation The Basement, 69 Caledonian Road, London, N1 9BT, United Kingdom
- (020) 7833 8268/(07973) 172902 (020) 7833 8269
- organise@organisart.co.uk
- www.organisart.co.uk

Bee Willey@Illustration Ltd 2 Brooks Court, Cringle Street, London, SW8 5BX, United Kingdom
- (020) 7720 5202/ (020) 7720 5920
- team@illustrationweb.com
- www.illustrationweb.com

Beefy@Folio 10 Gate Street, Lincoln's Inn Fields, London, WC2A 3HP, United Kingdom
- (020) 7242 9562/ (020) 7242 1816
- all@folioart.co.uk
- www.folioart.co.uk

Beegee Tolpn@The Artworks 40 Frith Street, London, W1D 5LN, United Kingdom
- (020) 7734 3333/ (020) 7734 3484
- lucy@theartworksinc.com
- www.theartworksinc.com

Beehive Illustration 42A Cricklade Street, Cirencester, Gloucestershire, GL7 1JH, United Kingdom
- (01285) 885149/ (01285) 641291
- info@beehiveillustration.co.uk
- www.beehiveillustration.com

Belinda Lyon@Linden Artists Ltd 41 Battersea Business Centre, 103 Lavender Hill, London, SW11 5QL, United Kingdom
- (020) 7738 2505/ (020) 7738 2513
- lindenartists@aol.com
- www.lindenartists.co.uk

Belinda Pearce@New Division 5 Risborough Street, London, SE1 0HF, United Kingdom
- (020) 7593 0505/ (020) 7593 0501
- info@newdivision.com
- www.newdivision.com

Ben & Stephanie Manchipp 14 Evesham Road, Reigate, Surrey, RH2 9DF, United Kingdom
- (01737) 246061/ (01737) 246061
- stephanie@manchipp.com
- www.manchipp.com

Ben Croft@Art Collection UK Ltd 7 Worsley Mill, 10 Blantyre Street, Castlefield, Manchester, M15 4LG, United Kingdom
- (0870) 2405001/ (0870) 2405002
- info@artcollection.co.uk
- www.artcollection.co.uk

Ben Hasler@N B Illustration Ltd 40 Bowling Green Lane, London, EC1R 0NE, United Kingdom
- (020) 7278 9131/ (020) 7278 9121
- info@nbillustration.co.uk
- www.nbillustration.co.uk

Ben Hawkes@Art Market 51 Oxford Drive, SE1 2FB, United Kingdom
- (020) 7407 8111/ (020) 7407 8222
- info@artmarketillustration.com
- www.artmarketillustration.com

Ben Warner@Artist Partners Ltd 2e The Chandlery, 50 Westminster Bridge Road, London, SE1 7QY, United Kingdom
- (020) 7401 7904/ (020) 7401 3378
- chris@artistpartners.demon.co.uk
- www.artistpartners.com

Benedict Campbell@Début Art & The Coningsby Gallery 30 Tottenham Street, London, W1T 4RJ, United Kingdom
- (020) 7636 1064/ (020) 7580 7017
- info@debutart.com
- www.debutart.com

Benjamin Savignac@Advocate Art 39 Church Road, London, SW19 5DQ, United Kingdom
- 020 8879 1166/020 8879 3303
- lesley@advocate-art.com
- www.advocate-art.com

Benjamin Wachenje@Central Illustration Agency 36 Wellington Street, London, WC2E 7BD, United Kingdom
- (020) 7240 8925/ (020) 7836 1177
- info@centralillustration.com
- www.centralillustration.com

Benji Creates The Studio, 9 Lightfoot Street, Hoole, Chester, CH2 3AH, United Kingdom
- (07776) 055465
- bholroyd1@orange.net

Bernard Blatch@Central Illustration Agency 36 Wellington Street, London, WC2E 7BD, United Kingdom
- (020) 7240 8925/ (020) 7836 1177
- info@centralillustration.com
- www.centralillustration.com

Bernard Thornton Artists The Penthouse, 4 Hamilton Mews, 310 Merton Road, London, SW18 5AB, United Kingdom
- (020) 8874 9081/(07702) 554583 (020) 8877 1386
- bernard@btartists.com
- www.btartists.com

Bernice Lum@The Organisation The Basement, 69 Caledonian Road, London, N1 9BT, United Kingdom
- (020) 7833 8268/(07973) 172902 (020) 7833 8269
- organise@easynet.co.uk
- www.organisart.co.uk

Bert Jackson@Linden Artists Ltd 41 Battersea Business Centre, 103 Lavender Hill, London, SW11 5QL, United Kingdom
- (020) 7738 2505/ (020) 7738 2513
- lindenartists@aol.com
- www.lindenartists.co.uk

Bert Kitchen@David Higham 5-8 Lower John Street, Golden Square, London, W1F 9HA, United Kingdom
- (020) 7437 7888/ (020) 7437 1072
- carolinewalsh@davidhigham.co.uk
- www.davidhigham.com

Bertie Bibb@Central Illustration Agency 36 Wellington Street, London, WC2E 7BD, United Kingdom
- (020) 7240 8925/ (020) 7836 1177
- info@centralillustration.com
- www.centralillustration.com

Betty Bibb@Central Illustration Agency 36 Wellington Street, London, WC2E 7BD, United Kingdom
- (020) 7240 8925/ (020) 7836 1177
- info@centralillustration.com
- www.centralillustration.com

Beyond Design UK Ltd Stubbings House, Henley Road, Maidenhead, Berkshire, SL6 6QL, United Kingdom
- (01628) 823007
- mail@beyond-design.co.uk
- www.beyond-design.co.uk

Big Active Ltd Unit 6.01, The Tea Building, 56 Shoreditch High Street, London, E16 JJ, United Kingdom
- (020) 7739 5601/ (020) 7739 7479
- contact@bigactive.com
- www.bigactive.com

Big Orange Studios 2nd Floor, Back Building, 150 Curtain Road, London, EC2A 3AT, United Kingdom
- (020) 7739 7765/ (020) 7613 2341
- andrewpavitt@btconnect.com

Bigbadbond Productions 49 Goldstone Villas, Hove, East Sussex, BN3 3RT, United Kingdom
- (07966) 593294
- john@bigbadbond.co.uk
- www.bigbadbond.co.uk

Bill Asprey, London, NW11 6WS, United Kingdom
- (020) 8455 3906/ (020) 8455 3906
- bill@artfulaspreycartoons.co.uk
- www.artfulaspreycartoons.co.uk

Bill Bolton@Advocate Art 39 Church Road, London, SW19 5DQ, United Kingdom
- 020 8879 1166/020 8879 3303
- lesley@advocate-art.com
- www.advocate-art.com

Bill Butcher Flat 23, 1-10 Summers Street, London, EC1R 5BD, United Kingdom
- (020) 7336 6642/ (020) 7336 6642
- bbutcher@btinternet.com
- www.billbutcher.com

Bill Crews@Allied Artists@ Artistic License The Gallery @ Richmond, 63 Sheen Road, Richmond, Surrey, TW9 1YJ, United Kingdom
(020) 8334 1010/ (020) 8334 9900
info@allied-artists.net
www.allied-artists.net

Bill Dare@Thorogood Illustration Ltd 5 Dryden Street, Covent Garden, London, WC2E 9NW, United Kingdom
(020) 7829 8468
draw@thorogood.net
www.thorogood.net

Bill Greenhead@Illustration Ltd 2 Brooks Court, Cringle Street, London, SW8 5BX, United Kingdom
(020) 7720 5202/ (020) 7720 5920
team@illustrationweb.com
www.illustrationweb.com

Bill McConkey@Début Art & The Coningsby Gallery 30 Tottenham Street, London, W1T 4RJ, United Kingdom
(020) 7636 1064/ (020) 7580 7017
info@debutart.com
www.debutart.com

Bill Pinder Illustration Tyn-Y-Graig, Rhydycroesau, Oswestry, Shropshire, SY10 7JE, United Kingdom
(01691) 791280
pinderraybill@btconnect.com

Bill Sanderson Fernleigh, Huntingdon Road, Houghton, Cambridgeshire, PE28 2AU, United Kingdom
(01480) 461506

Biman Mullick 33 Stillness Road, London, SE23 1NG, United Kingdom
(020) 8690 4649
bimanmullick@lineone.net
www.geocities.com/bimanmullick

Biz Hull@Artist Partners Ltd 2e The Chandlery, 50 Westminster Bridge Road, London, SE1 7QY, United Kingdom
(020) 7401 7904/ (020) 7401 3378
chris@artistpartners.demon.co.uk
www.artistpartners.com

Black & Ginger 14 Colquitt Street, Liverpool, L1 4DE, United Kingdom
(07782) 201620
alex@blackandginger.com
www.blackandginger.com

Black Hat 1d Olivers Wharf, 64 Wapping High Street, London, E1W 2PJ, United Kingdom
(020) 7702 3152/(07711) 034890
art@blackhat.demon.co.uk

Blackberry Studio 53 Talbot Road, Highgate, London, N6 4QX, United Kingdom
(020) 8341 0442/(07767) 022659 (020) 8341 0442
b@authors.co.uk

Blink Studio Limited, United Kingdom
(0845) 009 7997/ (0845) 009 7998
matthew@blink.biz
www.blink.biz

Blood Group Illustrations 45 Queens Park Rise, Brighton, BN2 9ZF, United Kingdom
(01273) 700540
jackjackpatrick@gmail.com

Blue Dot 5 Paget Road, Wivenhoe, CO7 9DT, United Kingdom
(07941) 864545
jussi@bluedotdotdot.com
www.bluedotdotdot.com

Blueskystudio Bluebell Cottage, Steeple Lane, St. Ives, Cornwall, TR26 2GY, United Kingdom
(01736) 793740
kerry@blueskystudio.co.uk
www.blueskystudio.co.uk

Bob Bampton@Bernard Thornton Artists The Penthouse, 4 Hamilton Mews, 310 Merton Road, London, SW18 5AB, United Kingdom
(020) 8874 9081/(07702) 554583 (020) 8877 1386
bernard@btartists.com
www.btartists.com

Bob Farley@Graham-Cameron Illustration The Studio, 23 Holt Road, Sheringham, Norfolk, NR26 8NB, United Kingdom
(01263) 821333/ (01263) 821334
enquiry@graham-cameron-illustration.com
www.graham-cameron-illustration.com

Bob Haslett 16 Brafferton Road, Croydon, CR0 1AD, United Kingdom
(020) 8688 7965/ (020) 8688 7965

Bob Hersey@Bernard Thornton Artists The Penthouse, 4 Hamilton Mews, 310 Merton Road, London, SW18 5AB, United Kingdom
(020) 8874 9081/(07702) 554583 (020) 8877 1386
bernard@btartists.com
www.btartists.com

Bob Moulder@Graham-Cameron Illustration The Studio, 23 Holt Road, Sheringham, Norfolk, NR26 8NB, United Kingdom
(01263) 821333/ (01263) 821334
enquiry@graham-cameron-illustration.com
www.graham-cameron-illustration.com

Bob Venables@Thorogood Illustration Ltd 5 Dryden Street, Covent Garden, London, WC2E 9NW, United Kingdom
(020) 7829 8468
draw@thorogood.net
www.thorogood.net

Bob Wilson@Phosphor Art 41 The Pump House, Pump House Close, off Renforth Street, London, SE16 7HS, United Kingdom
(020) 7064 4666/ (020) 7064 4660
info@phosphorart.com
www.phosphorart.com

Bocchinelli Design Brookland Barn, Wallingford Road, Kingsbridge, Devon, TQ7 1NF, United Kingdom
(01548) 856200
info@bocchinelli.com
www.bocchinelli.com

Brendan Kelly@Folio 10 Gate Street, Lincoln's Inn Fields, London, WC2A 3HP, United Kingdom
(020) 7242 9562/ (020) 7242 1816
all@folioart.co.uk
www.folioart.co.uk

Brett Hudson@Graham-Cameron Illustration The Studio, 23 Holt Road, Sheringham, Norfolk, NR26 8NB, United Kingdom
(01263) 821333/ (01263) 821334
enquiry@graham-cameron-illustration.com
www.graham-cameron-illustration.com

Brett James@Art Market 51 Oxford Drive, London, SE1 2FB, United Kingdom
(020) 7407 8111/ (020) 7407 8222
info@artmarketillustration.com
www.artmarketillustration.com

Brever Web Design Edinburgh 60a Craigour Drive, Edinburgh, EH17 7NT, United Kingdom
(0845) 129 8534
info@breverwebdesign.com
www.breverwebdesign.com

Brian Froud@Artist Partners Ltd 2e The Chandlery, 50 Westminster Bridge Road, London, SE1 7QY, United Kingdom
(020) 7401 7904/ (020) 7401 3378
chris@artistpartners.demon.co.uk
www.artistpartners.com

Brian Grimwood@Central Illustration Agency 36 Wellington Street, London, WC2E 7BD, United Kingdom
(020) 7240 8925/ (020) 7836 1177
info@centralillustration.com
www.centralillustration.com

Brian James@Meiklejohn Illustration 5 Risborough Street, London, SE1 0HF, United Kingdom
(020) 7593 0500/ (020) 7593 0501
info@meiklejohn.co.uk
www.meiklejohn.co.uk

Brian Lee Ltd 338 Coniscliffe Road, Darlington, County Durham, DL3 8AG, United Kingdom
(01325) 468064/ (01325) 468064
bleeillustration@mac.com
www.bleeillustration.com

Brian McIntyre@Phosphor Art 41 The Pump House, Pump House Close, off Renforth Street, London, SE16 7HS, United Kingdom
(020) 7064 4666/ (020) 7064 4660
info@phosphorart.com
www.phosphorart.com

Brian Sanders@Artist Partners Ltd 2e The Chandlery, 50 Westminster Bridge Road, London, SE1 7QY, United Kingdom
(020) 7401 7904/ (020) 7401 3378
chris@artistpartners.demon.co.uk
www.artistpartners.com

Brian Sweet@Arena 31 Eleanor Road, London, E15 4AB, United Kingdom
(08450) 507 600
info@arenaworks.com
www.arenaworks.com

Brian Walker Church Cottage, Hinton Blewett, Bristol, BS39 5AN, United Kingdom
(01761) 452312/ (01761) 452312

Brian Williamson 11 Estreham Road, London, SW16 5NT, United Kingdom
(020) 8677 5724/ (0870) 1604571
info@brianwilliamson.co.uk
www.brianwilliamson.co.uk

Bridget Dowty@Graham-Cameron Illustration The Studio, 23 Holt Road, Sheringham, Norfolk, NR26 8NB, United Kingdom
(01263) 821333/ (01263) 821334
enquiry@graham-cameron-illustration.com
www.graham-cameron-illustration.com

Bridget Strachan@Début Art & The Coningsby Gallery 30 Tottenham Street, London, W1T 4RJ, United Kingdom
(020) 7636 1064/ (020) 7580 7017
info@debutart.com
www.debutart.com

Bright Idea Flat 31, Pavia Court, Graigwen Road, Pontypridd, Mid Glamorgan, CF37 2TW, United Kingdom
(07952) 663680
info@brightidea.org.uk
www.brightidea.org.uk

Brigid Collins@Arena 31 Eleanor Road, London, E15 4AB, United Kingdom
(08450) 507 600
info@arenaworks.com
www.arenaworks.com

Brihton Illustration Agency 77A Lower Richmond Road, Putney, London, SW15 1ET, United Kingdom
(020) 8780 2535/ (020) 8780 0471
john@brihton.com
www.brihton.com

Brock Books & Illustrations 43 High Street, Catterick Village, Richmond, North Yorkshire, DL10 7LL, United Kingdom
(01748) 818729/(07789) 776783
judehaslam@btopenworld.com
www.brockbooks.com

Bruce Emmett@Folio 10 Gate Street, Lincoln's Inn Fields, London, WC2A 3HP, United Kingdom
(020) 7242 9562/ (020) 7242 1816
all@folioart.co.uk
www.folioart.co.uk

Bryan Poole 30 Wilton Way, London, E8 3EE, United Kingdom
(020) 7254 1213/ (020) 7923 1616
bryan@etchart.co.uk
www.etchart.co.uk

Business Cartoons 4 Reyntiens View, Odiham, Hampshire, RG29 1AF, United Kingdom
(01256) 703004
flantoons@btinternet.com
www.sensible.screaming.net

Cadmium Systems Ltd Church House, Castle Frome, Ledbury, Herefordshire, HR8 1HQ, United Kingdom
(0800) 436867/ (01531) 641101
sales@cadmium.co.uk
www.cadmium.co.uk

Carl Melegari 23 Priory Court Road, Westbury-on-Trym, Bristol, BS9 4DB, United Kingdom
0117-962 2125/(07816) 131045 0117-962 2125
carlmelegari@tantraweb.co.uk
www.carlmelegari.com

Carlo Molinari@Advocate Art 39 Church Road, London, SW19 5DQ, United Kingdom
020 8879 1166/020 8879 3303
lesley@advocate-art.com
www.advocate-art.com

Carol Del Angel@Début Art & The Coningsby Gallery 30 Tottenham Street, London, W1T 4RJ, United Kingdom
(020) 7636 1064/ (020) 7580 7017
info@debutart.com
www.debutart.com

Carol Kemp Little Mephams, Little London Road, Heathfield, East Sussex, TN21 0BD, United Kingdom
(01435) 812235/ (01435) 813305
www.carolkemp.com

Carol Morley@Thorogood Illustration Ltd 5 Dryden Street, Covent Garden, London, WC2E 9NW, United Kingdom
(020) 7829 8468
draw@thorogood.net
www.thorogood.net

Carole Verbyst@N B Illustration Ltd 40 Bowling Green Lane, London, EC1R 0NE, United Kingdom
(020) 7278 9131/ (020) 7278 9121
info@nbillustration.co.uk
www.nbillustration.co.uk

Carole Vincer 408 London Road, North Cheam, Sutton, Surrey, SM3 8JF, United Kingdom
(020) 8644 4271/ (020) 8644 4271
cvincerdesign@onetel.com

Caroline Anstey Sods Farm, Lurgashall, Petworth, West Sussex, GU28 9EX, United Kingdom
(01798) 861561
ansteycaroline@aol.com

Caroline Binch 1-2 Bojewyan Stennack, Pendeen, Penzance, Cornwall, TR19 7TN, United Kingdom
(01736) 786100
ceebee.info@carolinebinch.co.uk
www.carolinebinch.co.uk

Caroline Church@Illustration Ltd 2 Brooks Court, Cringle Street, London, SW8 5BX, United Kingdom
(020) 7720 5202/ (020) 7720 5920
team@illustrationweb.com
www.illustrationweb.com

Caroline Holden Flat 1, 53-55 Navarino Road, London, E8 1AG, United Kingdom
(020) 7241 5406
carolinehotopf@aol.com
www.contact-me.net/carolineholden

Caroline Jayne Church 100c West Street, Farnham, Surrey, GU9 7EN, United Kingdom
(01252) 820036/(07932) 605855
carolinejayne@lineone.net
www.carolinejaynechurch.com

Caroline Pedler@Advocate Art 39 Church Road, London, SW19 5DQ, United Kingdom
020 8879 1166/020 8879 3303
lesley@advocate-art.com
www.advocate-art.com

Caroline Thomson@Arena 31 Eleanor Road, London, E15 4AB, United Kingdom
(08450) 507 600
info@arenaworks.com
www.arenaworks.com

Caroline Uff@David Higham 5-8 Lower John Street, Golden Square, London, W1F 9HA, United Kingdom
(020) 7437 7888/ (020) 7437 1072
carolinewalsh@davidhigham.co.uk
www.davidhigham.co.uk

Carolyn Gowdy 2C Maynard Close, London, SW6 2EN, United Kingdom
(020) 7731 5380
cgowdy@attglobal.net

Cartoon Studio 29 Lake View Avenue, Walton, Chesterfield, Derbyshire, S40 3DR, United Kingdom
(01246) 209034/(07904) 064072 (01246) 209034
rd@cartoonstudio.co.uk
www.cartoonstudio.co.uk

Catalina Estrada@Folio 10 Gate Street, Lincoln's Inn Fields, London, WC2A 3HP, United Kingdom
(020) 7242 9562/ (020) 7242 1816
all@folioart.co.uk
www.folioart.co.uk

Cath Mason@Advocate Art 39 Church Road, London, SW19 5DQ, United Kingdom
020 8879 1166/020 8879 3303
lesley@advocate-art.com
www.advocate-art.com

Catherine Collins The Power Station, Coronet Street, London, N1 6HD, United Kingdom
(020) 7739 8678/(07785) 571187 (020) 7739 8489
catherine@catherinecollins.co.uk
www.catherinecollins.co.uk

Catherine Marche 27 Foxbourne Road, London, SW17 8EN, United Kingdom
(07941) 893072
cmarche@onetel.com
www.catherinemarche.com

Catherine Riley@Début Art & The Coningsby Gallery 30 Tottenham Street, London, W1T 4RJ, United Kingdom
(020) 7636 1064/ (020) 7580 7017
info@debutart.com
www.debutart.com

Cecilia Eales 14 High Road, Ickenham, Middlesex, UB10 8LJ, United Kingdom
(01895) 634941/(07957) 541095 (01895) 634941
ceciliaeales@btinternet.co.uk

Cecilia Fitzsimons Woodstock Lodge, 25 Hazel Grove, Waterlooville, Hampshire, PO8 0LE, United Kingdom
(023) 9259 7076
fitz.art@btopenworld.com

Celia Canning@Linda Rogers Associates 163 Half Moon Lane, London, SE24 9WB, United Kingdom
(020) 7501 9106
lr@lindarogers.net
www.lindarogers.net

Celia Witchard 24 Freemantle Square, Kingsdown, Bristol, BS6 5TN, United Kingdom
0117-949 4885

Central Illustration Agency 36 Wellington Street, London, WC2E 7BD, United Kingdom
(020) 7240 8925/ (020) 7836 1177
info@centralillustration.com
www.centralillustration.com

Channel Zero Production 242 Empire Road, Perivale, Greenford, Middlesex, UB6 7EB, United Kingdom
(07941) 575 971
michaelfiamanya@netscape.net

Charles Bell@Meiklejohn Illustration 5 Risborough Street, London, SE1 0HF, United Kingdom
(020) 7593 0500/ (020) 7593 0501
info@meiklejohn.co.uk
www.meiklejohn.co.uk

Charlie Fowkes@Advocate Art 39 Church Road, London, SW19 5DQ, United Kingdom
020 8879 1166/020 8879 3303
lesley@advocate-art.com
www.advocate-art.com

Charlie Hill@Meiklejohn Illustration 5 Risborough Street, London, SE1 0HF, United Kingdom
(020) 7593 0500/ (020) 7593 0501
info@meiklejohn.co.uk
www.meiklejohn.co.uk

Charlie-Anne Turner@Graham-Cameron Illustration The Studio, 23 Holt Road, Sheringham, Norfolk, NR26 8NB, United Kingdom
(01263) 821333/ (01263) 821334
enquiry@graham-cameron-illustration.com
www.graham-cameron-illustration.com

Charlotte Knox@The Artworks 40 Frith Street, London, W1D 5LN, United Kingdom
(020) 7734 3333/ (020) 7734 3484
lucy@theartworksinc.com
www.theartworksinc.com

Chellie Caroll@Advocate Art 39 Church Road, London, SW19 5DQ, United Kingdom
020 8879 1166/020 8879 3303
lesley@advocate-art.com
www.advocate-art.com

Chevron Artists Rodley Lane, Rodley, Leeds, LS13 1LJ, United Kingdom
0113-256 8526/(07944) 885421 0113-256 1246
chevronartists@hotmail.co.uk

childrensillustrators.com 5 Dryden Street, Covent Garden, London, WC2E 9NW, United Kingdom
(020) 8265 6847
tom@childrensillustrators.com
www.childrensillustrators.com

Chirs Chapman@N B Illustration Ltd 40 Bowling Green Lane, London, EC1R 0NE, United Kingdom
(020) 7278 9131/ (020) 7278 9121
info@nbillustration.co.uk
www.nbillustration.co.uk

Chloe Talbot Kelly 22 St Philips Road, Leicester, LE2 5TQ, United Kingdom
0116-273 9786

Chris Andrews@Eastwing 99 Chase Side, Enfield, Middlesex, EN2 6NL, United Kingdom
(020) 8367 6760/ (020) 8367 6730
andrea@eastwing.co.uk
www.eastwing.co.uk

Chris Burke 17 Upper Grosvenor Road, Tunbridge Wells, Kent, TN1 2DU, United Kingdom
(01892) 531329
christopher.burke@btclick.com
www.chrisburke.org.uk

Chris Chapman Ste 5, Pine Court, Bournemouth, BH1 3DH, United Kingdom
(01202) 780390/079 90 736873 (01202) 780390

Chris Coady@N B Illustration Ltd 40 Bowling Green Lane, London, EC1R 0NE, United Kingdom
(020) 7278 9131/ (020) 7278 9121
info@nbillustration.co.uk
www.nbillustration.co.uk

Chris Davidson@The Organisation The Basement, 69 Caledonian Road, London, N1 9BT, United Kingdom
(020) 7833 8268/(07973) 172902 (020) 7833 8269
organise@easynet.co.uk
www.organisart.co.uk

Chris Duggan 10 Hilly Field Crescent, London, SE4 1QA, United Kingdom
(020) 8691 3725/ (020) 8691 3725
dugganillustration@dsl.pipex.com
www.dugganillustration.dsl.pipex.com

Chris Embleton@Advocate Art 39 Church Road, London, SW19 5DQ, United Kingdom
020 8879 1166/020 8879 3303
lesley@advocate-art.com
www.advocate-art.com

Chris Garbutt@Arena 31 Eleanor Road, London, E15 4AB, United Kingdom
(08450) 507 600
info@arenaworks.com
www.arenaworks.com

Chris Gilvan-Cartwright@Central Illustration Agency 36 Wellington Street, London, WC2E 7BD, United Kingdom
(020) 7240 8925/ (020) 7836 1177
info@centralillustration.com
www.centralillustration.com

Chris Howell@Inkshed 99 Chase Side, Enfield, Middlesex, EN2 6NL, United Kingdom
(020) 8367 4545/ (020) 8367 6730
www.inkshed.co.uk

Chris Judge@Folio 10 Gate Street, Lincoln's Inn Fields, London, WC2A 3HP, United Kingdom
(020) 7242 9562/ (020) 7242 1816
all@folioart.co.uk
www.folioart.co.uk

Chris Kasch@Central Illustration Agency 36 Wellington Street, London, WC2E 7BD, United Kingdom
(020) 7240 8925/ (020) 7836 1177
info@centralillustration.com
www.centralillustration.com

Chris Madden 41 Clyde Road, London, N22 7AD, United Kingdom
(020) 8889 8775/ (020) 8889 8775
chris@chrismadden.co.uk
www.chrismadden.co.uk

Chris Masters 27 Meadowbank, Oxhey, Watford, WD19 4NP, United Kingdom
(01923) 233169/ (01923) 233169
ericthepenguin@hotmail.com

Chris Mitchell Epic Icons, Long Reach, Down Street, West Ashling, Chichester, West Sussex, PO18 8DP, United Kingdom
(01243) 572099/(07802) 874349 (01243) 572099
chris@epicicons.com
www.epicicons.com

Chris Moore@Artist Partners Ltd 2e The Chandlery, 50 Westminster Bridge Road, London, SE1 7QY, United Kingdom
(020) 7401 7904/ (020) 7401 3378
chris@artistpartners.demon.co.uk
www.artistpartners.com

Chris Mould Ink 12 Church Street, Hightown, Liversedge, West Yorkshire, WF15 8HR, United Kingdom
(01274) 873503/07748 417308
chris@chrismouldink.com
www.chrismouldink.com

Chris Nurse@Début Art & The Coningsby Gallery 30 Tottenham Street, London, W1T 4RJ, United Kingdom
(020) 7636 1064/ (020) 7580 7017
info@debutart.com
www.debutart.com

Chris Petty@Graham-Cameron Illustration The Studio, 23 Holt Road, Sheringham, Norfolk, NR26 8NB, United Kingdom
(01263) 821333/ (01263) 821334
enquiry@graham-cameron-illustration.com
www.graham-cameron-illustration.com

Chris Riddell@Artist Partners Ltd 2e The Chandlery, 50 Westminster Bridge Road, London, SE1 7QY, United Kingdom
(020) 7401 7904/ (020) 7401 3378
chris@artistpartners.demon.co.uk
www.artistpartners.com

Chris Robson@Meiklejohn Illustration 5 Risborough Street, London, SE1 0HF, United Kingdom
(020) 7593 0500/ (020) 7593 0501
info@meiklejohn.co.uk
www.meiklejohn.co.uk

Chris Rothero@Linden Artists Ltd 41 Battersea Business Centre, 103 Lavender Hill, London, SW11 5QL, United Kingdom
(020) 7738 2505/ (020) 7738 2513
lindenartists@aol.com
www.lindenartists.co.uk

Chris Stonehill@Phosphor Art 41 The Pump House, Pump House Close, off Renforth Street, London, SE16 7HS, United Kingdom
(020) 7064 4666/ (020) 7064 4660
info@phosphorart.com
www.phosphorart.com

Chris Swee@The Organisation The Basement, 69 Caledonian Road, London, N1 9BT, United Kingdom
(020) 7833 8268/(07973) 172902 (020) 7833 8269
organise@easynet.co.uk
www.organisart.co.uk

Christa Hook@Linden Artists Ltd 41 Battersea Business Centre, 103 Lavender Hill, London, SW11 5QL, United Kingdom
(020) 7738 2505/ (020) 7738 2513
lindenartists@aol.com
www.lindenartists.co.uk

Christiane Engel@Thorogood Illustration Ltd 5 Dryden Street, Covent Garden, London, WC2E 9NW, United Kingdom
(020) 7829 8468
draw@thorogood.net
www.thorogood.net

Christina Koutsospyrou@Début Art & The Coningsby Gallery 30 Tottenham Street, London, W1T 4RJ, United Kingdom
(020) 7636 1064/ (020) 7580 7017
info@debutart.com
www.debutart.com

Christine Berrington@Meiklejohn Illustration 5 Risborough Street, London, SE1 0HF, United Kingdom
(020) 7593 0500/ (020) 7593 0501
info@meiklejohn.co.uk
www.meiklejohn.co.uk

Christine Fitzmaurice Flat 2, 3 Westbourne Villas, Hove, East Sussex, BN3 4GQ, United Kingdom
(01273) 723378
nimmala@tavatimsa.co.uk

Christine Sheldon@Advocate Art 39 Church Road, London, SW19 5DQ, United Kingdom
020 8879 1166/020 8879 3303
lesley@advocate-art.com
www.advocate-art.com

Christopher Brown@Central Illustration Agency 36 Wellington Street, London, WC2E 7BD, United Kingdom
(020) 7240 8925/ (020) 7836 1177
info@centralillustration.com
www.centralillustration.com

Christopher Corr@Illustration Ltd 2 Brooks Court, Cringle Street, London, SW8 5BX, United Kingdom
(020) 7720 5202/ (020) 7720 5920
team@illustrationweb.com
www.illustrationweb.com

Christopher Douglas White 3 Rannoch Road, London, W6 9SS, United Kingdom
(020) 7381 6529/ (020) 7385 4992
chriswhiteart@aol.com
www.chris-white.co.uk

Christopher Gibbs@Arena 31 Eleanor Road, London, E15 4AB, United Kingdom
(08450) 507 600
info@arenaworks.com
www.arenaworks.com

Christopher Nielsen@Phosphor Art 41 The Pump House, Pump House Close, off Renforth Street, London, SE16 7HS, United Kingdom
(020) 7064 4666/ (020) 7064 4660
info@phosphorart.com
www.phosphorart.com

Christopher Radley 433 Liverpool Road, Islington, London, N7 8PR, United Kingdom
(020) 7609 2993
radders@radders.fsnet.co.uk

Christopher Wormell@The Artworks 40 Frith Street, London, W1D 5LN, United Kingdom
(020) 7734 3333/ (020) 7734 3484
lucy@theartworksinc.com
www.theartworksinc.com

Christos Magganas@Private View Artists Agency 17A Swan Hill, Shrewsbury, SY1 1NL, United Kingdom
(01743) 350355/ (01743) 233923
create@pvuk.com
www.pvuk.com

Chubbs@Début Art & The Coningsby Gallery 30 Tottenham Street, London, W1T 4RJ, United Kingdom
(020) 7636 1064/ (020) 7580 7017
info@debutart.com
www.debutart.com

Claire Caddy@Advocate Art 39 Church Road, London, SW19 5DQ, United Kingdom
020 8879 1166/020 8879 3303
lesley@advocate-art.com
www.advocate-art.com

Claire Chrystall@Art Collection UK Ltd 7 Worsley Mill, 10 Blantyre Street, Castlefield, Manchester, M15 4LG, United Kingdom
(0870) 2405001/ (0870) 2405002
info@artcollection.co.uk
www.artcollection.co.uk

Claire Clements@Meiklejohn Illustration 5 Risborough Street, London, SE1 0HF, United Kingdom
(020) 7593 0500/ (020) 7593 0501
info@meiklejohn.co.uk
www.meiklejohn.co.uk

Claire Fletcher@Phosphor Art 41 The Pump House, Pump House Close, off Renforth Street, London, SE16 7HS, United Kingdom
(020) 7064 4666/ (020) 7064 4660
info@phosphorart.com
www.phosphorart.com

Claire Mcmahon Illustration The Willows, Guildford Lodge Drive, East Horsley, Leatherhead, Surrey, KT24 6RJ, United Kingdom
(01483) 283771
claire_e_mcmahon@yahoo.co.uk
www.clairemcmahon.com

Claire Parsons Furzy Cottage, Pound Lane, Upottery, Honiton, Devon, EX14 9QB, United Kingdom
(07779) 586309
clairey_star76@yahoo.co.uk

Claire Prince 2 Stone House, Manthrig Lane, Caersws, Powys, SY17 5EY, United Kingdom
(01686) 688132
c.prince@rdplus.net

Claire Tindall@Graham-Cameron Illustration The Studio, 23 Holt Road, Sheringham, Norfolk, NR26 8NB, United Kingdom
(01263) 821333/ (01263) 821334
enquiry@graham-cameron-illustration.com
www.graham-cameron-illustration.com

Clare Hewitt 15 Meadow Place, Edinburgh, EH9 1JR, United Kingdom
0131-229 8345/ 0131-229 8345

Clare Melinsky@Central Illustration Agency 36 Wellington Street, London, WC2E 7BD, United Kingdom
(020) 7240 8925/ (020) 7836 1177
info@centralillustration.com
www.centralillustration.com

Clare Mumford@Drawer Illustrators Agents 8 Belmont, Bath, BA1 5DZ, United Kingdom
(01225) 445262
enquiries@drawer.me.uk

Clare Nicholas@New Division 5 Risborough Street, London, SE1 0HF, United Kingdom
(020) 7593 0505/ (020) 7593 0501
info@newdivision.com
www.newdivision.com

Claudio Parentela Via Milano n.10, Cantanzaro, 88100, Italy
00 39 9 6174 4087
c_parentela@libero.it
www.furtherfield.org/cparentela/docs/index.htm

Clement Graphics 21 John Tofts House, Leicester Row, Coventry, CV1 4LY, United Kingdom
(07958) 009133
jeanette@clementgraphics.com
www.clementgraphics.com

Clementine Hope@N B Illustration Ltd 40 Bowling Green Lane, London, EC1R 0NE, United Kingdom
(020) 7278 9131/ (020) 7278 9121
info@nbillustration.co.uk
www.nbillustration.co.uk

Clinton Banbury Old Chapel, Carnyorth Hill, St. Just-in-Penwith, Penzance, Cornwall, TR19 7QD, United Kingdom
(01736) 786076/ (01736) 786076
clint@clintonbanbury.com
www.clintonbanbury.com

Clive Armitage 45 Gould Road, Twickenham, TW2 6RN, United Kingdom
(020) 8894 4794/(07808) 346616 / (020) 8894 4794
cliveart2003@yahoo.co.uk
www.clivearmitage.com

Clive Spong@Linden Artists Ltd 41 Battersea Business Centre, 103 Lavender Hill, London, SW11 5QL, United Kingdom
(020) 7738 2505/ (020) 7738 2513
lindenartists@aol.com
www.lindenartists.co.uk

Clockwork Craven House, 121 Kings Way, London, WC2B 6PA, United Kingdom
(020) 7436 9696/ (020) 7953 8083
admin@clockwork.tm

Coburn@Meiklejohn Illustration 5 Risborough Street, London, SE1 0HF, United Kingdom
(020) 7593 0500/ (020) 7593 0501
info@meiklejohn.co.uk
www.meiklejohn.co.uk

Codi Design@Advocate Art 39 Church Road, London, SW19 5DQ, United Kingdom
020 8879 1166/020 8879 3303
lesley@advocate-art.com
www.advocate-art.com

Colin Backhouse@Arena 31 Eleanor Road, London, E15 4AB, United Kingdom
(08450) 507 600
info@arenaworks.com
www.arenaworks.com

Colin Bidgood The Rest, Berrys Hill, Westerham, Kent, TN16 3AE, United Kingdom
(01959) 571692/ (01959) 571692

Colin Elgie@Illustration Ltd 2 Brooks Court, Cringle Street, London, SW8 5BX, United Kingdom
(020) 7720 5202/ (020) 7720 5920
team@illustrationweb.com
www.illustrationweb.com

Colin Howard@Advocate Art 39 Church Road, London, SW19 5DQ, United Kingdom
020 8879 1166/020 8879 3303
lesley@advocate-art.com
www.advocate-art.com

Colin King@Drawer Illustrators Agents 8 Belmont, Bath, BA1 5DZ, United Kingdom
(01225) 445262
enquiries@drawer.me.uk

Colin Mier 21 Balmuir Gardens, Putney, London, SW15 6NG, United Kingdom
(020) 8789 7556/(07050) 153929 (020) 8789 7556
colinmier@talk21.com

Colin Shelbourn Cartoonists & Illustrators Pine Howe, Helm Road, Windermere, Cumbria, LA23 2NL, United Kingdom
(01539) 442052/ (01539) 442052
colin@shelbourn.com
www.shelbourn.com

Colm Dunne 43 Dufferin Avenue, S.C.R, Dublin 8, Ireland, Republic of
87 911 7461
cdunne77@yahoo.com
www.colmdunnegrafix.com

Commission a Portrait Unit 18, Lagare Apartments, 51 Surrey Row, London, SE1 0BZ, United Kingdom
(020) 7921 9704/ (020) 3267 1066
greg@commissionaportrait.com
www.commissionaportrait.com

Concept & Storyboard Artist Flat 3, Europa House, 11 Marsham Way, Gerrards Cross, Buckinghamshire, SL9 8BQ, United Kingdom
(01753) 899352
kimberly.pope@virgin.net
www.musecube.com/kimpope/84879

Coneyl Jay Po Box 65, Llandysul, Dyfed, SA44 5WS, United Kingdom
(01239) 654 550
coneyl@coneyljay.com
www.coneyljay.com

Conny Jude@Début Art & The Coningsby Gallery 30 Tottenham Street, London, W1T 4RJ, United Kingdom
(020) 7636 1064/ (020) 7580 7017
info@debutart.com
www.debutart.com

Conor Langton Illustration 510 East 20th Street, New York, 10009, United States of America
917 547 5754
conor@conorlangton.com
www.conorlangton.com

Cosei Kawa@Advocate Art 39 Church Road, London, SW19 5DQ, United Kingdom
020 8879 1166/020 8879 3303
lesley@advocate-art.com
www.advocate-art.com

Craig Cameron@Art Collection UK Ltd 7 Worsley Mill, 10 Blantyre Street, Castlefield, Manchester, M15 4LG, United Kingdom
(0870) 2405001/ (0870) 2405002
info@artcollection.co.uk
www.artcollection.co.uk

Craig Frazier@Folio 10 Gate Street, Lincoln's Inn Fields, London, WC2A 3HP, United Kingdom
(020) 7242 9562/ (020) 7242 1816
all@folioart.co.uk
www.folioart.co.uk

Craig Shuttlewood@Début Art & The Coningsby Gallery 30 Tottenham Street, London, W1T 4RJ, United Kingdom
(020) 7636 1064/ (020) 7580 7017
info@debutart.com
www.debutart.com

Craig Warwick@Linden Artists Ltd 41 Battersea Business Centre, 103 Lavender Hill, London, SW11 5QL, United Kingdom
(020) 7738 2505/ (020) 7738 2513
lindenartists@aol.com
www.lindenartists.co.uk

Cream Rises 1 Denman Cottages, California Road, Mistley, Manningtree, Essex, CO11 1JE, United Kingdom
(01206) 390167
kseville101@hotmail.com

Creative Eye Illustrations The Old Bakehouse, 3 Church View, Bampton, Oxfordshire, OX18 2NE, United Kingdom
(01993) 851408/ (01993) 851408
info@creativeeye.net
www.creativeeye.net

Creative Sponge 1 Netherconesford, King Street, Norwich, NR1 1PH, United Kingdom
(01603) 622766/ (01603) 622347
info@creativesponge.co.uk
www.creativesponge.co.uk

Cressida Cowell@David Higham 5-8 Lower John Street, Golden Square, London, W1F 9HA, United Kingdom
(020) 7437 7888/ (020) 7437 1072
carolinewalsh@davidhigham.co.uk
www.davidhigham.co.uk

Cristina Stan 16a Humberstone Road, Cambridge, CB4 1JF, United Kingdom
(07800) 745121
cristina_stan_ficu@yahoo.co.uk
www.cristina.stan.home.

Cube@Illustration Ltd 2 Brooks Court, Cringle Street, London, SW8 5BX, United Kingdom
(020) 7720 5202/ (020) 7720 5920
team@illustrationweb.com
www.illustrationweb.com

Dale Designs 7 Tayside Place, Glencarse, Perth, PH2 7UB, United Kingdom
(01738) 860427
dale@dalesimpson.co.uk
www.dalesimpson.co.uk

Damian Gascoigne@Eastwing 99 Chase Side, Enfield, Middlesex, EN2 6NL, United Kingdom
(020) 8367 6760/ (020) 8367 6730
andrea@eastwing.co.uk
www.eastwing.co.uk

Damijan Stepancic@Advocate Art 39 Church Road, London, SW19 5DQ, United Kingdom
020 8879 1166/020 8879 3303
lesley@advocate-art.com
www.advocate-art.com

Dan Alexander@Advocate Art 39 Church Road, London, SW19 5DQ, United Kingdom
020 8879 1166/020 8879 3303
lesley@advocate-art.com
www.advocate-art.com

Dan Crisp@Art Collection UK Ltd 7 Worsley Mill, 10 Blantyre Street, Castlefield, Manchester, M15 4LG, United Kingdom
(0870) 2405001/ (0870) 2405002
info@artcollection.co.uk
www.artcollection.co.uk

Dan Hambe@Thorogood Illustration Ltd 5 Dryden Street, Covent Garden, London, WC2E 9NW, United Kingdom
(020) 7829 8468
draw@thorogood.net
www.thorogood.net

Dan Taylor@N B Illustration Ltd 40 Bowling Green Lane, London, EC1R 0NE, United Kingdom
(020) 7278 9131/ (020) 7278 9121
info@nbillustration.co.uk
www.nbillustration.co.uk

Dandi Palmer, Folkestone, Kent, United Kingdom
dandipalmer@tiscali.co.uk
www.dandi.me.uk/folio

Daniel Alexander@Advocate Artists Agents 39 Church Road, Wimberlton Village, London, SW19 5DQ, United Kingdom
(020) 8877 0072/ (020) 879 3303
mail@advocate-art.com
www.advocate-art.com

Daniel Egneus@Thorogood Illustration Ltd 5 Dryden Street, Covent Garden, London, WC2E 9NW, United Kingdom
(020) 7829 8468
draw@thorogood.net
www.thorogood.net

Daniel Howarth@Advocate Art 39 Church Road, London, SW19 5DQ, United Kingdom
020 8879 1166/020 8879 3303
lesley@advocate-art.com
www.advocate-art.com

Daniel Mackie@Début Art & The Coningsby Gallery 30 Tottenham Street, London, W1T 4RJ, United Kingdom
(020) 7636 1064/ (020) 7580 7017
info@debutart.com
www.debutart.com

Daniela Jaglenka Terrazzini@The Artworks 40 Frith Street, London, W1D 5LN, United Kingdom
(020) 7734 3333/ (020) 7734 3484
lucy@theartworksinc.com
www.theartworksinc.com

Dardanele Boguslawskiego, Cracow, 31-048, Poland
0048 888 44 22 42
mail@dardanele.com
www.dardanele.com

Darren Diss@Art Market 51 Oxford Drive, London, SE1 2FB, United Kingdom
(020) 7407 8111/ (020) 7407 8222
info@artmarketillustration.com
www.artmarketillustration.com

Darren Hopes@Début Art & The Coningsby Gallery 30 Tottenham Street, London, W1T 4RJ, United Kingdom
(020) 7636 1064/ (020) 7580 7017
info@debutart.com
www.debutart.com

Darren Lock@The Organisation The Basement, 69 Caledonian Road, London, N1 9BT, United Kingdom
(020) 7833 8268/(07973) 172902 (020) 7833 8269
organise@easynet.co.uk
www.organisart.co.uk

Darren Whittington@Phosphor Art 41 The Pump House, Pump House Close, off Renforth Street, London, SE16 7HS, United Kingdom
(020) 7064 4666/ (020) 7064 4660
info@phosphorart.com
www.phosphorart.com

Dave Burroughs@Linda Rogers Associates 163 Half Moon Lane, London, SE24 9WB, United Kingdom
(020) 7501 9106
lr@lindarogers.net
www.lindarogers.net

Dave Cockburn's Squeaky Pictures 40 Onslow Gardens, Wallington, Surrey, SM6 9QN, United Kingdom
(020) 8773 0024/ (020) 8773 9963
dave@squeakypics.co.uk
www.squeakypics.co.uk

Dave Hills Art 28 Deanstone Walk, Coatbridge, Lanarkshire, ML5 4AZ, United Kingdom
✆ (01236) 436467
✉ dave@davehillsart.co.uk
🖥 www.davehillsart.co.uk

Dave Hopkins@Phosphor Art 41 The Pump House, Pump House Close, off Renforth Street, London, SE16 7HS, United Kingdom
✆ (020) 7064 4666/✆ (020) 7064 4660
✉ info@phosphorart.com
🖥 www.phosphorart.com

Dave Lynx@The Organisation The Basement, 69 Caledonian Road, London, N1 9BT, United Kingdom
✆ (020) 7833 8268/(07973) 172902 ✆ (020) 7833 8269
✉ organise@easynet.co.uk
🖥 www.organisart.co.uk

Dave Needham@Central Illustration Agency 36 Wellington Street, London, WC2E 7BD, United Kingdom
✆ (020) 7240 8925/✆ (020) 7836 1177
✉ info@centralillustration.com
🖥 www.centralillustration.com

Dave Orchard@Drawer Illustrators Agents 8 Belmont, Bath, BA1 5DZ, United Kingdom
✆ (01225) 445262
✉ enquiries@drawer.me.uk

Dave Parkinson Murals 21 Hanbury Road, Pontypool, Gwent, NP4 6QN, United Kingdom
✆ (01495) 751288
🖥 www.daveparkinsonmural.co.uk

Dave Pratt@Advocate Art 39 Church Road, London, SW19 5DQ, United Kingdom
✆ 020 8879 1166/020 8879 3303
✉ lesley@advocate-art.com
🖥 www.advocate-art.com

David Astin@Linden Artists Ltd 41 Battersea Business Centre, 103 Lavender Hill, London, SW11 5QL, United Kingdom
✆ (020) 7738 2505/✆ (020) 7738 2513
✉ lindenartists@aol.com
🖥 www.lindenartists.co.uk

David Atkinson@N B Illustration Ltd 40 Bowling Green Lane, London, EC1R 0NE, United Kingdom
✆ (020) 7278 9131/✆ (020) 7278 9121
✉ info@nbillustration.co.uk
🖥 www.nbillustration.co.uk

David Barnett 41 Hidcote Road, Oadby, Leicester, LE2 5PG, United Kingdom
✆ 0116-271 7658/✆ 0116-271 7658
🖥 www.contact-me.net/davidbarnett

David Benham@Graham-Cameron Illustration The Studio, 23 Holt Road, Sheringham, Norfolk, NR26 8NB, United Kingdom
✆ (01263) 821333/✆ (01263) 821334
✉ enquiry@graham-cameron-illustration.com
🖥 www.graham-cameron-illustration.com

David Bray@Private View Artists Agency 17A Swan Hill, Shrewsbury, SY1 1NL, United Kingdom
✆ (01743) 350355/✆ (01743) 233923
✉ create@pvuk.com
🖥 www.pvuk.com

David Brindley Rowan House, 31 Reevers Road, Newent, Gloucestershire, GL18 1TN, United Kingdom
✆ (01531) 822213
✉ brindley.illustrator@newentbb.co.uk
🖥 www.brindleyillustrations.com

David Broadbent@Eastwing 99 Chase Side, Enfield, Middlesex, EN2 6NL, United Kingdom
✆ (020) 8367 6760/✆ (020) 8367 6730
✉ andrea@eastwing.co.uk
🖥 www.eastwing.co.uk

David Bromley@Thorogood Illustration Ltd 5 Dryden Street, Covent Garden, London, WC2E 9NW, United Kingdom
✆ (020) 7829 8468
✉ draw@thorogood.net
🖥 www.thorogood.net

David Bull 197 Chiswick High Road, Chiswick, London, W4 2DR, United Kingdom
✆ (020) 8995 1924

David Burroughs@Drawer Illustrators Agents 8 Belmont, Bath, BA1 5DZ, United Kingdom
✆ (01225) 445262
✉ enquiries@drawer.me.uk

David Cockcroft 52 Derwent Road, London, N13 4PU, United Kingdom
✆ (020) 8882 0150/✆ (020) 8882 0150
✉ cockroftnet@blueyonder.co.uk

David Crossley@Linden Artists Ltd 41 Battersea Business Centre, 103 Lavender Hill, London, SW11 5QL, United Kingdom
✆ (020) 7738 2505/✆ (020) 7738 2513
✉ lindenartists@aol.com
🖥 www.lindenartists.co.uk

David Cutter@Folio 10 Gate Street, Lincoln's Inn Fields, London, WC2A 3HP, United Kingdom
✆ (020) 7242 9562/✆ (020) 7242 1816
✉ all@folioart.co.uk
🖥 www.folioart.co.uk

David Dean@The Organisation The Basement, 69 Caledonian Road, London, N1 9BT, United Kingdom
✆ (020) 7833 8268/(07973) 172902 ✆ (020) 7833 8269
✉ organise@easynet.co.uk
🖥 www.organisart.co.uk

David Eaton@The Organisation The Basement, 69 Caledonian Road, London, N1 9BT, United Kingdom
✆ (020) 7833 8268/(07973) 172902 ✆ (020) 7833 8269
✉ organise@easynet.co.uk
🖥 www.organisart.co.uk

David Faithfull 20 Cumberland Street, Edinburgh, EH3 6SA, United Kingdom
✆ 0131-556 6063/✆ 0131-556 6063
✉ david.faithfull@btinternet.com
🖥 www.davidfaithfull.com

David Febland@Meiklejohn Illustration 5 Risborough Street, London, SE1 0HF, United Kingdom
✆ (020) 7593 0500/✆ (020) 7593 0501
✉ info@meiklejohn.co.uk
🖥 www.meiklejohn.co.uk

David Foldvari@Big Active Ltd Unit 6.01, The Tea Building, 56 Shoreditch High Street, London, E16 JJ, United Kingdom
✆ (020) 7739 5601/✆ (020) 7739 7479
✉ contact@bigactive.com
🖥 www.bigactive.com

David Frankland@Artist Partners Ltd 2e The Chandlery, 50 Westminster Bridge Road, London, SE1 7QY, United Kingdom
✆ (020) 7401 7904/✆ (020) 7401 3378
✉ chris@artistpartners.demon.co.uk
🖥 www.artistpartners.com

Leading the way
FROM 2D LINEWORK TO 3D PHOTOREALISM
Standard Chartered
ALL DELIVERED ON TIME & WITHIN BUDGET
PAUL **WOOTTON** ASSOCIATES
info@graphicnet.co.uk
+44 (0) 207 252 8555
www.graphicnet.co.uk
DIGITAL ILLUSTRATION & GRAPHICS
BANK OF ENGLAND

David Gifford 69 Latchmere Road, Kingston upon Thames, Surrey, KT2 5TS, United Kingdom
✆ (020) 8546 3462/(07715) 569671 ✆ (020) 8549 0113
✉ david@davidgifford.co.uk
🖥 www.davidgifford.co.uk

David Gray 11 Ceres Gardens, Bishopbriggs, Glasgow, G64 1LP, United Kingdom
✆ 0141-586 1210/(07790) 092182 ✆ 0141-586 1210
✉ dgray11@hotmail.com

David Higham 5-8 Lower John Street, Golden Square, London, W1F 9HA, United Kingdom
✆ (020) 7437 7888/✆ (020) 7437 1072
✉ carolinewalsh@davidhigham.co.uk
🖥 www.davidhigham.co.uk

David Hitch@Arena 31 Eleanor Road, London, E15 4AB, United Kingdom
✆ (08450) 507 600
✉ info@arenaworks.com
🖥 www.arenaworks.com

David Holmes@Central Illustration Agency 36 Wellington Street, London, WC2E 7BD, United Kingdom
✆ (020) 7240 8925/✆ (020) 7836 1177
✉ info@centralillustration.com
🖥 www.centralillustration.com

David Hughes@Central Illustration Agency 36 Wellington Street, London, WC2E 7BD, United Kingdom
✆ (020) 7240 8925/✆ (020) 7836 1177
✉ info@centralillustration.com
🖥 www.centralillustration.com

David Juniper@Folio 10 Gate Street, Lincoln's Inn Fields, London, WC2A 3HP, United Kingdom
✆ (020) 7242 9562/✆ (020) 7242 1816
✉ all@folioart.co.uk
🖥 www.folioart.co.uk

David Kearney@Artist Partners Ltd 2e The Chandlery, 50 Westminster Bridge Road, London, SE1 7QY, United Kingdom
✆ (020) 7401 7904/✆ (020) 7401 3378
✉ chris@artistpartners.demon.co.uk
🖥 www.artistpartners.co.uk

David Lloyd 1st Floor, 9 Portland Place, Brighton, BN2 1DG, United Kingdom
✆ (01273) 600173
✉ lforlloyd@aol.com
🖥 www.lforlloyd.com

David Lock Cartoons 67 East Street, Wareham, Dorset, BH20 4NW, United Kingdom
✆ (01929) 553 834/✆ (01929) 553 834
✉ david.lock1@tesco.net

David Lupton@Advocate Art 39 Church Road, London, SW19 5DQ, United Kingdom
✆ 020 8879 1166/020 8879 3303
✉ lesley@advocate-art.com
🖥 www.advocate-art.com

David Macallister@N B Illustration Ltd 40 Bowling Green Lane, London, EC1R 0NE, United Kingdom
✆ (020) 7278 9131/✆ (020) 7278 9121
✉ info@nbillustration.co.uk
🖥 www.nbillustration.co.uk

David McDougall@Artist Partners Ltd 2e The Chandlery, 50 Westminster Bridge Road, London, SE1 7QY, United Kingdom
☎ (020) 7401 7904/✆ (020) 7401 3378
✉ chris@artistpartners.demon.co.uk
🖥 www.artistpartners.com

David McKay@Début Art & The Coningsby Gallery 30 Tottenham Street, London, W1T 4RJ, United Kingdom
☎ (020) 7636 1064/✆ (020) 7580 7017
✉ info@debutart.com
🖥 www.debutart.com

David Mostyn@Artist Partners Ltd 2e The Chandlery, 50 Westminster Bridge Road, London, SE1 7QY, United Kingdom
☎ (020) 7401 7904/✆ (020) 7401 3378
✉ chris@artistpartners.demon.co.uk
🖥 www.artistpartners.com

David Newton@Début Art & The Coningsby Gallery 30 Tottenham Street, London, W1T 4RJ, United Kingdom
☎ (020) 7636 1064/✆ (020) 7580 7017
✉ info@debutart.com
🖥 www.debutart.com

David Newton Scanography@Début Art & The Coningsby Gallery 30 Tottenham Street, London, W1T 4RJ, United Kingdom
☎ (020) 7636 1064/✆ (020) 7580 7017
✉ info@debutart.com
🖥 www.debutart.com

David Nichols@Phosphor Art 41 The Pump House, Pump House Close, off Renforth Street, London, SE16 7HS, United Kingdom
☎ (020) 7064 4666/✆ (020) 7064 4660
✉ info@phosphorart.com
🖥 www.phosphorart.com

David O'Connor The Annexe, Belmont Street, Brighton, BN1 4HN, United Kingdom
☎ (01273) 623667
✉ david.designs@mistral.co.uk

David Powell Illustration 40 Barratt Street, Easton, Bristol, BS5 6DF, United Kingdom
☎ 0117-952 2250
✉ gwatkin65@btinternet.co.uk

David Pugh 10 Gadlys Terrace, Aberdare, Mid Glamorgan, CF44 8AN, United Kingdom
☎ (01685) 884108
✉ lastplanet@boltblue.com

David Roberts@Artist Partners Ltd 2e The Chandlery, 50 Westminster Bridge Road, London, SE1 7QY, United Kingdom
☎ (020) 7401 7904/✆ (020) 7401 3378
✉ chris@artistpartners.demon.co.uk
🖥 www.artistpartners.com

David Russell@Folio 10 Gate Street, Lincoln's Inn Fields, London, WC2A 3HP, United Kingdom
☎ (020) 7242 9562/✆ (020) 7242 1816
✉ all@folioart.co.uk
🖥 www.folioart.co.uk

David S. Blanco@Private View Artists Agency 17A Swan Hill, Shrewsbury, SY1 1NL, United Kingdom
☎ (01743) 350355/✆ (01743) 233923
✉ create@pvuk.com
🖥 www.pvuk.com

David Shephard@Illustration Ltd 2 Brooks Court, Cringle Street, London, SW8 5BX, United Kingdom
☎ (020) 7720 5202/✆ (020) 7720 5920
✉ team@illustrationweb.com
🖥 www.illustrationweb.com

David Sim@The Organisation The Basement, 69 Caledonian Road, London, N1 9BT, United Kingdom
☎ (020) 7833 8268/(07973) 172902 ✆ (020) 7833 8269
✉ organise@easynet.co.uk
🖥 www.organisart.co.uk

David Tazzyman@Private View Artists Agency 17A Swan Hill, Shrewsbury, SY1 1NL, United Kingdom
☎ (01743) 350355/✆ (01743) 233923
✉ create@pvuk.com
🖥 www.pvuk.com

David Thelwell@Bernard Thornton Artists The Penthouse, 4 Hamilton Mews, 310 Merton Road, London, SW18 5AB, United Kingdom
☎ (020) 8874 9081/(07702) 554583 ✆ (020) 8877 1386
✉ bernard@btartists.com
🖥 www.btartists.com

David Whittle@The Organisation The Basement, 69 Caledonian Road, London, N1 9BT, United Kingdom
☎ (020) 7833 8268/(07973) 172902 ✆ (020) 7833 8269
✉ organise@easynet.co.uk
🖥 www.organisart.co.uk

David Wiggs Suite 1, Magenta House, 21 Horace Road, Ilford, Essex, IG6 2BG, United Kingdom
☎ 020 8551 2054
✉ david.wiggs@ntlworld.com
🖥 www.davefranks.com

David Williams 35 Magnolia Drive, Rendlesham, Woodbridge, Suffolk, IP12 2GB, United Kingdom
☎ (01394) 421084

David Wise 26 Norman Avenue, St. Margarets, Twickenham, TW1 2LY, United Kingdom
☎ (020) 8892 3817/✆ (020) 8892 3817
✉ irenejuliawise@aol.com

David Wojtowycz@David Higham 5-8 Lower John Street, Golden Square, London, W1F 9HA, United Kingdom
☎ (020) 7437 7888/✆ (020) 7437 1072
✉ carolinewalsh@davidhigham.co.uk
🖥 www.davidhigham.co.uk

David Wyatt@Sarah Brown Agency 10 The Avenue, Ealing, London, W13 8PH, United Kingdom
☎ (020) 8998 0390/(07778) 177102 ✆ (020) 8843 1175
✉ sbagency@dsl.pipex.com
🖥 www.sbagency.com

David Young@N B Illustration Ltd 40 Bowling Green Lane, London, EC1R 0NE, United Kingdom
☎ (020) 7278 9131/✆ (020) 7278 9121
✉ info@nbillustration.co.uk
🖥 www.nbillustration.co.uk

Davies 30 The Causeway, Fareham, Hampshire, PO16 8RW, United Kingdom
☎ (07766) 282616
✉ steven.davies@chn.co.uk

Dawn Austin@Artist Partners Ltd 2e The Chandlery, 50 Westminster Bridge Road, London, SE1 7QY, United Kingdom
☎ (020) 7401 7904/✆ (020) 7401 3378
✉ chris@artistpartners.demon.co.uk
🖥 www.artistpartners.com

Daydream Linton House, 164-180 Union Street, London, SE1 0LH,
☎ +44 (0) 20 7096 1471/+44 (0) 7117 1636
✉ ralph@daydream.co.uk
🖥 www.daydream.co.uk

Debbie Boon@Artist Partners Ltd 2e The Chandlery, 50 Westminster Bridge Road, London, SE1 7QY, United Kingdom
☎ (020) 7401 7904/✆ (020) 7401 3378
✉ chris@artistpartners.demon.co.uk
🖥 www.artistpartners.com

Debbie Cook 9 Leverton Street, London, NW5 2PH, United Kingdom
☎ (020) 7482 2958/(07957) 124123 ✆ (020) 7284 1731
✉ deb@debbiecook.co.uk
🖥 www.debbiecook.co.uk

Debbie Hinks 96 Stanmer Park Road, Brighton, BN1 7JH, United Kingdom
☎ (01273) 553392
✉ d.hinks@virgin.net
🖥 www.illustrator.org.uk/big/illustrat/hinks

Debora Burr Illustration & Design 39 Corsham Road, Lacock, Chippenham, Wiltshire, SN15 2NA, United Kingdom
☎ (01249) 730983/(07950) 256093 ✆
✉ debora@deboraburr.com
🖥 www.deboraburr.com

Deborah Jones@Advocate Art 39 Church Road, London, SW19 5DQ, United Kingdom
☎ 020 8879 1166/020 8879 3303
✉ lesley@advocate-art.com
🖥 www.advocate-art.com

Deborah Kindred@Linden Artists Ltd 41 Battersea Business Centre, 103 Lavender Hill, London, SW11 5QL, United Kingdom
☎ (020) 7738 2505/✆ (020) 7738 2513
✉ lindenartists@aol.com
🖥 www.lindenartists.co.uk

Deborah King@David Higham 5-8 Lower John Street, Golden Square, London, W1F 9HA, United Kingdom
☎ (020) 7437 7888/✆ (020) 7437 1072
✉ carolinewalsh@davidhigham.co.uk
🖥 www.davidhigham.co.uk

Deborah Van Der Leijgraff@The Organisation The Basement, 69 Caledonian Road, London, N1 9BT, United Kingdom
☎ (020) 7833 8268/(07973) 172902 ✆ (020) 7833 8269
✉ organise@easynet.co.uk
🖥 www.organisart.co.uk

Dee McLean@Linden Artists Ltd 41 Battersea Business Centre, 103 Lavender Hill, London, SW11 5QL, United Kingdom
☎ (020) 7738 2505/✆ (020) 7738 2513
✉ lindenartists@aol.com
🖥 www.lindenartists.co.uk

Delphine Thomas@Linda Rogers Associates 163 Half Moon Lane, London, SE24 9WB, United Kingdom
☎ (020) 7501 9106
✉ lr@lindarogers.net
🖥 www.lindarogers.net

Dennis Balogh@The Artworks 40 Frith Street, London, W1D 5LN, United Kingdom
☎ (020) 7734 3333/✆ (020) 7734 3484
✉ lucy@theartworksinc.com
🖥 www.theartworksinc.com

Derek Allwood Units 6 & 7, Highgate Square Craft Centre, Birmingham, B12 0DU, United Kingdom
☎ 0121-440 4004/✆ 0121-440 4004

Derek Bacon@Illustration Ltd 2 Brooks Court, Cringle Street, London, SW8 5BX, United Kingdom
☎ (020) 7720 5202/✆ (020) 7720 5920
✉ team@illustrationweb.com
🖥 www.illustrationweb.com

Derek Brazell@Artist Partners Ltd 2e The Chandlery, 50 Westminster Bridge Road, London, SE1 7QY, United Kingdom
☎ (020) 7401 7904/✆ (020) 7401 3378
✉ chris@artistpartners.demon.co.uk
🖥 www.artistpartners.com

Derek Gray 25 Beechtree Terrace, Milton of Campsie, Glasgow, G66 8DA, United Kingdom
☎ (01360) 312861/✆ (01360) 312861
✉ gray@tesco.net

Derek Matthews Langhurst Cottage, Prestwick Lane, Chiddingfold, Surrey, GU8 4XP, United Kingdom
☎ (01428) 684580/✆ (01428) 685591
✉ derekmatthews@btinternet.com
🖥 www.derekmatthews.co.uk

Derick Bown@Linden Artists Ltd 41 Battersea Business Centre, 103 Lavender Hill, London, SW11 5QL, United Kingdom
☎ (020) 7738 2505/✆ (020) 7738 2513
✉ lindenartists@aol.com
🖥 www.lindenartists.co.uk

Des Lynch 55 Carlton House, Canterbury Terrace, London, NW6 5DX, United Kingdom
☎ (020) 7328 1091

Des Taylor@Private View Artists Agency 17A Swan Hill, Shrewsbury, SY1 1NL, United Kingdom
☎ (01743) 350355/✆ (01743) 233923
✉ create@pvuk.com
🖥 www.pvuk.com

design@djhunter 133 Ravensbourne Avenue, Bromley, BR2 0AZ, United Kingdom
☎ (020) 8466 7196/✆ (020) 8466 7196
✉ design@djhunter.co.uk

Design73 26 Kingswear Road, Ruislip, Middlesex, HA4 6AY, United Kingdom
☎ (01895) 460942/✆ (01895) 460942
✉ martin@design73.co.uk
🖥 www.design73.co.uk

Device 2 Blake Mews, Richmond, Surrey, TW9 3WA, United Kingdom
☎ (020) 8896 0626/(07979) 602272 ✆ (020) 8439 9080
✉ rianhughes@aol.com
🖥 www.devicefonts.co.uk

Dez Pop@Advocate Art 39 Church Road, London, SW19 5DQ, United Kingdom
☎ 020 8879 1166/020 8879 3303
✉ lesley@advocate-art.com
🖥 www.advocate-art.com

Diana Catchpole@Drawer Illustrators Agents 8 Belmont, Bath, BA1 5DZ, United Kingdom
☎ (01225) 445262
✉ enquiries@drawer.me.uk

Diana Defries, Wood Green, London, Middlesex, N22 5DS, United Kingdom
- (07989) 346853/ (020) 8881 0052
- scribbler@scribbler.org
- www.scribbler.org

Diane Broadley Centre Space, 6 Leonard Lane, Bristol, BS1 1EA, United Kingdom
- 0117-904 1106/(07815) 206658
- d@dianebroadley.com
- www.dianebroadley.co.uk

Dick Twinney@Bernard Thornton Artists The Penthouse, 4 Hamilton Mews, 310 Merton Road, London, SW18 5AB, United Kingdom
- (020) 8874 9081/(07702) 554583 / (020) 8877 1386
- bernard@btartists.com
- www.btartists.com

Die For Love 13 Felton Street, London, N1 5AN, United Kingdom
- (07866) 249663
- info@dieforlove.co.uk

Dieckmann GmbH Heinrich-Heine-Allee 41, Düsseldorf, 40213, Germany
- 00 49 211 32 20 46/ 00 49 211 32 20 48
- ines.dieckmann@dieckmann-gmbh.com
- www.dieckmann-gmbh.com

Dionne Sievewright Dunvegan, Wern-Y-Cwrt, Raglan, Monmouthshire, NP15 2JG, United Kingdom
- (01291) 690299/ (01291) 690158
- dionne@sievewright.freeserve.co.uk
- www.dionnesievewright.com

Dirty Ego Creative 93 Southwell Road East, Rainworth, Mansfield, Nottinghamshire, NG21 0DE, United Kingdom
- (07981) 056208
- info@dirtyegocreative.co.uk
- www.dirtyegocreative.co.uk

Diz Wallis@Folio 10 Gate Street, Lincoln's Inn Fields, London, WC2A 3HP, United Kingdom
- (020) 7242 9562/ (020) 7242 1816
- all@folioart.co.uk
- www.folioart.co.uk

Doffy Weir 116 Rushmore Road, London, E5 0EX, United Kingdom
- (020) 8986 1059
- doffy.weir@virgin.net

Dolby Gallery The Design Factory, The Old Surgery, 30 West Street, Oundle, Peterborough, PE8 4EF, United Kingdom
- (01832) 273801
- dolbygallery@design-factory.co.uk
- www.dolbygallery.com

Dolby Gallery at Design Factory The Old Surgery, 30 West Street, Oundle, PE8 4EF, United Kingdom
- (01832) 273801/(07713) 960117
- designfactory@btinternet.com
- www.watercolours-uk.com

Dom Mimms@Phosphor Art 41 The Pump House, Pump House Close, off Renforth Street, London, SE16 7HS, United Kingdom
- (020) 7064 4666/ (020) 7064 4660
- info@phosphorart.com
- www.phosphorart.com

Dominic Harman@Arena 31 Eleanor Road, London, E15 4AB, United Kingdom
- (08450) 507 600
- info@arenaworks.com
- www.arenaworks.com

Dominic Li@The Organisation The Basement, 69 Caledonian Road, London, N1 9BT, United Kingdom
- (020) 7833 8268/(07973) 172902 / (020) 7833 8269
- organise@easynet.co.uk
- www.organisart.co.uk

Don Seed 33 Culverden Park Road, Tunbridge Wells, Kent, TN4 9RB, United Kingdom
- (01892) 616300/(07792) 314072 / (01892) 616300
- seedart@globalnet.co.uk
- www.seedart.co.uk

Dorothea King@Linden Artists Ltd 41 Battersea Business Centre, 103 Lavender Hill, London, SW11 5QL, United Kingdom
- (020) 7738 2505/ (020) 7738 2513
- lindenartists@aol.com
- www.lindenartists.co.uk

Douglas Carrel@Sarah Brown Agency 10 The Avenue, Ealing, London, W13 8PH, United Kingdom
- (020) 8998 0390/(07778) 177102 / (020) 8843 1175
- sbagency@dsl.pipex.com
- www.sbagency.com

Douglas Fraser@Catherine Collins The Power Station, Coronet Street, London, N1 6HD, United Kingdom
- (020) 7739 8678/(07785) 571187 / (020) 7739 8489
- catherine@catherinecollins.co.uk
- www.catherinecollins.co.uk

Douglas Ingram 15 Uplands Park Road, Enfield, Middlesex, EN2 7PU, United Kingdom
- (020) 8367 4646/(07721) 011331 / (020) 8367 4646
- ingram1@btconnect.com
- www.storyboardsingram.co.uk

Douglas Pledger@Bernard Thornton Artists The Penthouse, 4 Hamilton Mews, 310 Merton Road, London, SW18 5AB, United Kingdom
- (020) 8874 9081/(07702) 554583 / (020) 8877 1386
- bernard@btartists.com
- www.btartists.com

Douglas Watson 80 Blackford Avenue, Edinburgh, EH9 3ER, United Kingdom
- 0131-667 5975
- ddd.doug@lineone.net
- www.scottishillustrators.com

Dragonfly Media 3 Berkeley Crescent, Clifton, Bristol, Avon, BS8 1HA,
- 0845 6520 888/ 0845 6520 808
- jon@dragonfly-media.co.uk
- www.dragonfly-media.co.uk

Drawer Illustrators Agents 8 Belmont, Bath, BA1 5DZ, United Kingdom
- (01225) 445262
- enquiries@drawer.me.uk

Drawing Attention 4 Stagenhoe Bottom Cottages, Lilley Bottom Road, Hitchin, Hertfordshire, SG4 8JN, United Kingdom
- (01438) 871627

Dreamtree Ltd Unit 3/4, Mellington Work Shops, Church Stoke, Montgomery, Powys, SY15 6TQ, United Kingdom
- (01588) 620552/(07957) 733830 / (01588) 620632
- colin@dreamtree.co.uk
- www.dreamtree.co.uk

Duncan Gutteridge@Artist Partners Ltd 2e The Chandlery, 50 Westminster Bridge Road, London, SE1 7QY, United Kingdom
- (020) 7401 7904/ (020) 7401 3378
- chris@artistpartners.demon.co.uk
- www.artistpartners.com

Duncan Smith 21 Dellwood Gardens, Clayhall, Ilford, Essex, IG5 0EH, United Kingdom
- (020) 8550 0907/(07939) 508705 / (020) 8550 0907
- duncansmithillustrations@ntlworld.com
- www.childrensillustrators.com/illustrator.cgi/duncan

E-kit.co.uk Field Cottage, Main Street, Goadby Marwood, Melton Mowbray, Leicestershire, LE14 4LN, United Kingdom
- (01664) 464713
- edward@e-kit.co.uk
- www.e-kit.co.uk

Eastwing 99 Chase Side, Enfield, Middlesex, EN2 6NL, United Kingdom
- (020) 8367 6760/ (020) 8367 6730
- andrea@eastwing.co.uk
- www.eastwing.co.uk

Ed McLachlan@Folio 10 Gate Street, Lincoln's Inn Fields, London, WC2A 3HP, United Kingdom
- (020) 7242 9562/ (020) 7242 1816
- all@folioart.co.uk
- www.folioart.co.uk

Ed Parker@The Artworks 40 Frith Street, London, W1D 5LN, United Kingdom
- (020) 7734 3333/ (020) 7734 3484
- lucy@theartworksinc.com
- www.theartworksinc.com

Edmond Davies@Meiklejohn Illustration 5 Risborough Street, London, SE1 0HF, United Kingdom
- (020) 7593 0500/ (020) 7593 0501
- info@meiklejohn.co.uk
- www.meiklejohn.co.uk

Edmond Davis 144 Laburnum Road, Redcar, Cleveland, TS10 3LS, United Kingdom
- (01642) 473448

Eelco van den Berg@Advocate Art 39 Church Road, London, SW19 5DQ, United Kingdom
- 020 8879 1166/020 8879 3303
- lesley@advocate-art.com
- www.advocate-art.com

Eikon Ltd The Gasworks, Aylestone Road, Leicester, LE2 7LZ, United Kingdom
- 0116-233 0500/ 0116-233 0600
- mail@eikonillustration.co.uk
- www.eikonillustration.co.uk

Eileen Ogg@The Artworks 40 Frith Street, London, W1D 5LN, United Kingdom
- (020) 7734 3333/ (020) 7734 3484
- lucy@theartworksinc.com
- www.theartworksinc.com

Eleanor Clark@Folio 10 Gate Street, Lincoln's Inn Fields, London, WC2A 3HP, United Kingdom
- (020) 7242 9562/ (020) 7242 1816
- all@folioart.co.uk
- www.folioart.co.uk

Elios Spinola@Sarah Lane Represents 56 Bidwell Gardens, London, N11 2AU, United Kingdom
- (07901) 552520/ (020) 8292 4001
- sarah@sarahlanerepresents.com
- www.sarahlanerepresents.com

Elizabet Zeilon@Début Art & The Coningsby Gallery 30 Tottenham Street, London, W1T 4RJ, United Kingdom
- (020) 7636 1064/ (020) 7580 7017
- info@debutart.com
- www.debutart.com

Elke Counsell@Drawer Illustrators Agents 8 Belmont, Bath, BA1 5DZ, United Kingdom
- (01225) 445262
- enquiries@drawer.me.uk

Ella Okstad@The Organisation The Basement, 69 Caledonian Road, London, N1 9BT, United Kingdom
- (020) 7833 8268/(07973) 172902 / (020) 7833 8269
- organise@easynet.co.uk
- www.organisart.co.uk

Ella Tjader@Illustration Ltd 2 Brooks Court, Cringle Street, London, SW8 5BX, United Kingdom
- (020) 7720 5202/ (020) 7720 5920
- team@illustrationweb.com
- www.illustrationweb.com

Elliott Golden@Thorogood Illustration Ltd 5 Dryden Street, Covent Garden, London, WC2E 9NW, United Kingdom
- (020) 7829 8468
- draw@thorogood.net
- www.thorogood.net

Emak Mafu First Floor, 388 Old Street, London, EC1V 9LT, United Kingdom
- (020) 7168 8241
- studio@emakmafu.com
- www.emakmafu.com

Ember Design 88a Thicket Road, London, SE20 8DR, United Kingdom
- (020) 8659 9560
- info@emberdesign.net
- www.emberdesign.net

Emil Nair 42 Kenwyn Road, Clapham, London, SW4 7LH, United Kingdom
- (020) 7627 5215
- emil@podesta.demon.co.uk
- www.contact-me.net/emilnair

Emily Smith@Allied Artists@ Artistic License The Gallery @ Richmond, 63 Sheen Road, Richmond, Surrey, TW9 1YJ, United Kingdom
- (020) 8334 1010/ (020) 8334 9900
- info@allied-artists.net
- www.allied-artists.net

Emma Griffin@Début Art & The Coningsby Gallery 30 Tottenham Street, London, W1T 4RJ, United Kingdom
- (020) 7636 1064/ (020) 7580 7017
- info@debutart.com
- www.debutart.com

Entity Studios 9 Old School House, Brittania Road, Kingswood, Bristol, BS15 8DB, United Kingdom
- (0845) 8904430
- info@entitystudios.com
- www.entitystudios.com

Eric Hanson Illustration 4444 Upton Avenue S, Minneapolis, 55410, United States of America
- 612 927 9054
- erichanson@er-h.com
- www.er-h.com/

Eric Rowe@Linden Artists Ltd 41 Battersea Business Centre, 103 Lavender Hill, London, SW11 5QL, United Kingdom
- (020) 7738 2505/ (020) 7738 2513
- lindenartists@aol.com
- www.lindenartists.co.uk

Eric Smith 124 Kennel Lane, Fetcham, Leatherhead, Surrey, KT22 9PW, United Kingdom
(01372) 456378
erics@zoom.co.uk
www.ericsmithillustrator.co.uk

Eva Muszynski@Advocate Art 39 Church Road, London, SW19 5DQ, United Kingdom
020 8879 1166/020 8879 3303
lesley@advocate-art.com
www.advocate-art.com

Eva Thimgren@The Organisation The Basement, 69 Caledonian Road, London, N1 9BT, United Kingdom
(020) 7833 8268/(07973) 172902 (020) 7833 8269
organise@easynet.co.uk
www.organisart.co.uk

Event Communications Ltd India House, 45 Curlew Street, London, SE1 2ND, United Kingdom
(020) 7378 9900/ (020) 7378 9911
info@eventcomm.com
www.eventcomm.com

Evie Safarewicz@John Hodgson Illustrators Agency 38 Westminster Palace Gardens, Artillery Row, London, SW1P 1RR, United Kingdom
(020) 7222 4468/ (020) 7222 4468

Ewan Fraser@Début Art & The Coningsby Gallery 30 Tottenham Street, London, W1T 4RJ, United Kingdom
(020) 7636 1064/ (020) 7580 7017
info@debutart.com
www.debutart.com

Exwyzee Communication House, Hillhouse Business Park, Thornton-Cleveleys, Lancashire, FY5 4QD, United Kingdom
(01253) 856000/ (01253) 682208
lee@exwyzee.com
www.exwyzee.com

Eyeball 114 Pentonville Road, London, N1 9JB, United Kingdom
(020) 7713 6261
eyeball@eyeball.co.uk
www.eyeball.co.uk

Fabian Negrin@Central Illustration Agency 36 Wellington Street, London, WC2E 7BD, United Kingdom
(020) 7240 8925/ (020) 7836 1177
info@centralillustration.com
www.centralillustration.com

Faranak@Arena 31 Eleanor Road, London, E15 4AB, United Kingdom
(08450) 507 600
info@arenaworks.com
www.arenaworks.com

Fashion Executives Via Monte, Di Pieta, Milan, Italy, 20121,
7717366567/ 8700625674
riz@fashionexecutives.com
www.fashionexecutives.com

Felicia Atanasiu@Advocate Art 39 Church Road, London, SW19 5DQ, United Kingdom
020 8879 1166/020 8879 3303
lesley@advocate-art.com
www.advocate-art.com

Felicity House@Graham-Cameron Illustration The Studio, 23 Holt Road, Sheringham, Norfolk, NR26 8NB, United Kingdom
(01263) 821333/ (01263) 821334
enquiry@graham-cameron-illustration.com
www.graham-cameron-illustration.com

Fernanda Cohen@The Artworks 40 Frith Street, London, W1D 5LN, United Kingdom
(020) 7734 3333/ (020) 7734 3484
lucy@theartworksinc.com
www.theartworksinc.com

Fernando Juarez@Illustration Ltd 2 Brooks Court, Cringle Street, London, SW8 5BX, United Kingdom
(020) 7720 5202/ (020) 7720 5920
team@illustrationweb.com
www.illustrationweb.com

Fhiona Galloway Illustration 10 Howard Street, Kilmarnock, Ayrshire, KA1 2BP, United Kingdom
(01563) 544704/ (01563) 544704
mail@fgalloway.co.uk
www.fgalloway.co.uk

Filipe Alcada@Art Market 51 Oxford Drive, London, SE1 2FB, United Kingdom
(020) 7407 8111/ (020) 7407 8222
info@artmarketillustration.com
www.artmarketillustration.com

Fine & Dandy@Central Illustration Agency 36 Wellington Street, London, WC2E 7BD, United Kingdom
(020) 7240 8925/ (020) 7836 1177
info@centralillustration.com
www.centralillustration.com

Finn Neary@Advocate Art 39 Church Road, London, SW19 5DQ, United Kingdom
020 8879 1166/020 8879 3303
lesley@advocate-art.com
www.advocate-art.com

Fiona Bell Currie 9 Belmont Grove, Lewisham, London, SE13 5DW, United Kingdom
(020) 8318 6074
fiona.bellcurrie@btinternet.com

Fiona Hamilton Clifton Arcade, Boyces Avenue, Bristol, BS8 4AA, United Kingdom
(0117) 973 9838
fiona@fiona-hamilton.co.uk
www.fiona-hamilton.co.uk

Fiona McIntyre Designs Ltd Ampney Mill Cottages, Ampney Crucis, Cirencester, Gloucestershire, GL7 5RS, United Kingdom
(07977) 675891
fiona@mcintyredesigns.co.uk

Fiona McVicar@Advocate Art 39 Church Road, London, SW19 5DQ, United Kingdom
020 8879 1166/020 8879 3303
lesley@advocate-art.com
www.advocate-art.com

Fiona White@Central Illustration Agency 36 Wellington Street, London, WC2E 7BD, United Kingdom
(020) 7240 8925/ (020) 7836 1177
info@centralillustration.com
www.centralillustration.com

Fiona Wylie@Début Art & The Coningsby Gallery 30 Tottenham Street, London, W1T 4RJ, United Kingdom
(020) 7636 1064/ (020) 7580 7017
info@debutart.com
www.debutart.com

Firebrand Pictures.com 47 Firhill Road, London, SE6 3SA, United Kingdom
(07799) 458419
keith@firebrandpictures.com
www.firebrandpictures.com

Firespit 45 Myrtle Avenue, Bingly, BD16 1EW,
7968505946
firespitdesign@yahoo.com

Flatliner@Début Art & The Coningsby Gallery 30 Tottenham Street, London, W1T 4RJ, United Kingdom
(020) 7636 1064/ (020) 7580 7017
info@debutart.com
www.debutart.com

Flavin Illustration 77 Hanson Street, Glasgow, G31 2HF, United Kingdom
0141-556 5555/ 0141-556 5555
teresa@teresaflavin.com
www.teresaflavin.com

Fleming Associates 41 The Pump House, Pump House Close, London, SE16 7HS, United Kingdom
(020) 7064 4666/ (020) 7064 4660
info@phosphorart.com
www.phosphorart.com

Fliss Cary@Graham-Cameron Illustration The Studio, 23 Holt Road, Sheringham, Norfolk, NR26 8NB, United Kingdom
(01263) 821333/ (01263) 821334
enquiry@graham-cameron-illustration.com
www.graham-cameron-illustration.com

fluidics 12 Athelney Street, Bellingham, Catford, London, SE6 3LE, United Kingdom
(07939) 221010
equaakum@btinternet.com

Folio 10 Gate Street, Lincoln's Inn Fields, London, WC2A 3HP, United Kingdom
(020) 7242 9562/ (020) 7242 1816
all@folioart.co.uk
www.folioart.co.uk

FR3Y Turu 13, Tartu, 51004, Estonia
737 1062/506 9654
carl@fr3y.com
www.fr3y.com

Fran Jordan 142 Curly Hill, Ilkley, West Yorkshire, LS29 0DS, United Kingdom
(01943) 600230/ (01943) 600230
jordan.fran@btopenworld.com
www.contact-me.net/franjordan

Frances Castle@Arena 31 Eleanor Road, London, E15 4AB, United Kingdom
(08450) 507 600
info@arenaworks.com
www.arenaworks.com

Frances Cony 21 Tyndalls Park Road, Clifton, Bristol, BS8 1PQ, United Kingdom
0117-973 0022/ 0117-973 0022
francony2@yahoo.co.uk
www.francescony.co.uk

Francis Phillipps@Linden Artists Ltd 41 Battersea Business Centre, 103 Lavender Hill, London, SW11 5QL, United Kingdom
(020) 7738 2505/ (020) 7738 2513
lindenartists@aol.com
www.lindenartists.co.uk

Frank Love@Eastwing 99 Chase Side, Enfield, Middlesex, EN2 6NL, United Kingdom
(020) 8367 6760/ (020) 8367 6730
andrea@eastwing.co.uk
www.eastwing.co.uk

Frazer Hudson@Central Illustration Agency 36 Wellington Street, London, WC2E 7BD, United Kingdom
(020) 7240 8925/ (020) 7836 1177
info@centralillustration.com
www.centralillustration.com

Fred Blunt@Meiklejohn Illustration 5 Risborough Street, London, SE1 0HF, United Kingdom
(020) 7593 0500/ (020) 7593 0501
info@meiklejohn.co.uk
www.meiklejohn.co.uk

Fred Gambino 89 Muswell Hill Road, London, N10 3HT, United Kingdom
(020) 8444 9553/(07712) 592155
alisoneldred@gmail.com
www.alisoneldred.com

Fred Van Deelen@The Organisation The Basement, 69 Caledonian Road, London, N1 9BT, United Kingdom
(020) 7833 8268/(07973) 172902 (020) 7833 8269
organise@easynet.co.uk
www.organisart.co.uk

Frederique Vayssieres@Illustration Ltd 2 Brooks Court, Cringle Street, London, SW8 5BX, United Kingdom
(020) 7720 5202/ (020) 7720 5920
team@illustrationweb.com
www.illustrationweb.com

Freelance 6 Clareways, Lady Margaret Road, Sunningdale, Berks, SL5 9QH,
mehrdokht1976@yahoo.com
www.myart2c.com

Freelance Illustrators Fall Head Farm, Fall Head Lane, Silkstone, Barnsley, South Yorkshire, S75 4LB, United Kingdom
(01226) 790508/(07860) 517287 (01226) 790508
mail@freelanceillustrators.co.uk
www.freelanceillustrators.co.uk

Freire Wright 28 Brondesbury Villas, London, NW6 6AA, United Kingdom
(07768) 760168
freire.wright@virgin.net

Freya@Début Art & The Coningsby Gallery 30 Tottenham Street, London, W1T 4RJ, United Kingdom
(020) 7636 1064/ (020) 7580 7017
info@debutart.com
www.debutart.com

Funky Concepts 5 Lansdowne Close, Coseley, Bilston, West Midlands, WV14 9TR, United Kingdom
(01902) 651239/ (01902) 651239
info@funkyconecpts.co.uk
www.funkyconcepts.co.uk

Fusako Akimoto@Début Art & The Coningsby Gallery 30 Tottenham Street, London, W1T 4RJ, United Kingdom
(020) 7636 1064/ (020) 7580 7017
info@debutart.com
www.debutart.com

G. Roland Smith Collard House, School Lane Hadlow, Tonbridge, Kent, TN11 0EH, United Kingdom
(01732) 850850

Gabriel Moreno@Advocate Art 39 Church Road, London, SW19 5DQ, United Kingdom
020 8879 1166/020 8879 3303
lesley@advocate-art.com
www.advocate-art.com

Gabriele Antonini@Advocate Art 39 Church Road, London, SW19 5DQ, United Kingdom
020 8879 1166/020 8879 3303
lesley@advocate-art.com
www.advocate-art.com

Gaby Swiatkowsica@Advocate Art 39 Church Road, London, SW19 5DQ, United Kingdom
020 8879 1166/020 8879 3303
lesley@advocate-art.com
www.advocate-art.com

Gail Armstrong@Illustration Ltd 2 Brooks Court, Cringle Street, London, SW8 5BX, United Kingdom
(020) 7720 5202/ (020) 7720 5920
team@illustrationweb.com
www.illustrationweb.com

Gail Glaser@Advocate Art 39 Church Road, London, SW19 5DQ, United Kingdom
020 8879 1166/020 8879 3303
lesley@advocate-art.com
www.advocate-art.com

Gail Newey@Phosphor Art 41 The Pump House, Pump House Close, off Renforth Street, London, SE16 7HS, United Kingdom
(020) 7064 4666/ (020) 7064 4660
info@phosphorart.com
www.phosphorart.com

Gareth Lucas@Art Market 51 Oxford Drive, London, SE1 2FB, United Kingdom
(020) 7407 8111/ (020) 7407 8222
info@artmarketillustration.com
www.artmarketillustration.com

Garry Davies Grove House, 5 Grove Road, Fareham, Hampshire, PO16 7TF, United Kingdom
(01329) 236219/ (01329) 236219

Garry Parsons@Meiklejohn Illustration 5 Risborough Street, London, SE1 0HF, United Kingdom
(020) 7593 0500/ (020) 7593 0501
info@meiklejohn.co.uk
www.meiklejohn.co.uk

Garry Walton@Meiklejohn Illustration 5 Risborough Street, London, SE1 0HF, United Kingdom
(020) 7593 0500/ (020) 7593 0501
info@meiklejohn.co.uk
www.meiklejohn.co.uk

Gary A. Newman, London, United Kingdom
/(07903) 584937
gary@garynewman.co.uk
www.garynewman.co.uk

Gary Bates@Début Art & The Coningsby Gallery 30 Tottenham Street, London, W1T 4RJ, United Kingdom
(020) 7636 1064/ (020) 7580 7017
info@debutart.com
www.debutart.com

Gary Blythe@Artist Partners Ltd 2e The Chandlery, 50 Westminster Bridge Road, London, SE1 7QY, United Kingdom
(020) 7401 7904/ (020) 7401 3378
chris@artistpartners.demon.co.uk
www.artistpartners.com

Gary Dunn Oakwood House, 70 Inkerman Drive, Hazlemere, Buckinghamshire, HP15 7JJ, United Kingdom
(01494) 714993/(07970) 855958
mrdunn236@hotmail.com
www.mr-dunn.com

Gary Embury@Inkshed 99 Chase Side, Enfield, Middlesex, EN2 6NL, United Kingdom
(020) 8367 4545/ (020) 8367 6730
www.inkshed.co.uk

Gary Keane@Artist Partners Ltd 2e The Chandlery, 50 Westminster Bridge Road, London, SE1 7QY, United Kingdom
(020) 7401 7904/ (020) 7401 3378
chris@artistpartners.demon.co.uk
www.artistpartners.com

Gary Kempston@New Division 5 Risborough Street, London, SE1 0HF, United Kingdom
(020) 7593 0505/ (020) 7593 0501
info@newdivision.com
www.newdivision.com

Gary Neill@Central Illustration Agency 36 Wellington Street, London, WC2E 7BD, United Kingdom
(020) 7240 8925/ (020) 7836 1177
info@centralillustration.com
www.centralillustration.com

Gary Rees@Drawer Illustrators Agents 8 Belmont, Bath, BA1 5DZ, United Kingdom
(01225) 445262
enquiries@drawer.me.uk

Gary Sawyer@Eastwing 99 Chase Side, Enfield, Middlesex, EN2 6NL, United Kingdom
(020) 8367 6760/ (020) 8367 6730
andrea@eastwing.co.uk
www.eastwing.co.uk

Gary Swift Fieldhouse Studios, 8 Hague Park Lane, South Kirkby, Pontefract, West Yorkshire, WF9 3SS, United Kingdom
(01977) 646431/ (01977) 646431
gary@garyswift.com
www.garyswift.com

Gary West@Meiklejohn Illustration 5 Risborough Street, London, SE1 0HF, United Kingdom
(020) 7593 0500/ (020) 7593 0501
info@meiklejohn.co.uk
www.meiklejohn.co.uk

Gary Wing 2 Coghill, Bletchingdon, Kidlington, Oxfordshire, OX5 3BY, United Kingdom
(01869) 350925/(07770) 671658 (01869) 350925
garywing1@btinternet.com

Gaunt Faces Windsor Court, East Grinstead House, East Grinstead, West Sussex, RH19 1XA, United Kingdom
/ (01342) 336113
phewson@reedinfo.co.uk

Gavin Reece@New Division 5 Risborough Street, London, SE1 0HF, United Kingdom
(020) 7593 0505/ (020) 7593 0501
info@newdivision.com
www.newdivision.com

Gecko Studios Ltd 20 Norton Road, Roundhay, Leeds, LS8 2DE, United Kingdom
0113-393 0011/ (07092) 106705
info@gecko-studios.com
www.gecko-studios.com

Geo Parkin Ltd 21 Lauriston Road, Brighton, BN1 6SN, United Kingdom
(01273) 562269/ (01273) 239292
geo@geoparkin.com
www.geoparkin.com

Geoff Hardie@Thorogood Illustration Ltd 5 Dryden Street, Covent Garden, London, WC2E 9NW, United Kingdom
(020) 7829 8468
draw@thorogood.net
www.thorogood.net

Geoff Hunt@Artist Partners Ltd 2e The Chandlery, 50 Westminster Bridge Road, London, SE1 7QY, United Kingdom
(020) 7401 7904/ (020) 7401 3378
chris@artistpartners.demon.co.uk
www.artistpartners.com

Geoff Jones 38 Wimborne Close, Up Hatherley, Cheltenham, Gloucestershire, GL51 3QP, United Kingdom
(01242) 517256/ (01242) 517256
wimborne38@blueyonder.co.uk
www.chelt.clara.net

Geoffrey Appleton@Art Collection UK Ltd 7 Worsley Mill, 10 Blantyre Street, Castlefield, Manchester, M15 4LG, United Kingdom
(0870) 2405001/ (0870) 2405002
info@artcollection.co.uk
www.artcollection.co.uk

George Downes Decorative Artist 21A Farleigh Road, London, N16 7TB, United Kingdom
(020) 7249 8747/(07929) 025104

George Hardie Coopers Cottage, White Chimney Row, Emsworth, Hampshire, PO10 8RS, United Kingdom
(01243) 377528
hardie.drounces@virgin.net

George Robinson 36 Grove Street, Edinburgh, EH3 8AZ, United Kingdom
0131-229 1524
george.e.robinson@btinternet.com

George Underwood@Début Art & The Coningsby Gallery 30 Tottenham Street, London, W1T 4RJ, United Kingdom
(020) 7636 1064/ (020) 7580 7017
info@debutart.com
www.debutart.com

Georges Panis@Art Collection UK Ltd 7 Worsley Mill, 10 Blantyre Street, Castlefield, Manchester, M15 4LG, United Kingdom
(0870) 2405001/ (0870) 2405002
info@artcollection.co.uk
www.artcollection.co.uk

Georgie Ripper@David Higham 5-8 Lower John Street, Golden Square, London, W1F 9HA, United Kingdom
(020) 7437 7888/ (020) 7437 1072
carolinewalsh@davidhigham.co.uk
www.davidhigham.co.uk

Georgios Manoli, London, United Kingdom
(0870) 6091249
info@manoli.co.uk
www.manoli.co.uk

Gerald Green 211 Hinckley Road, Nuneaton, Warwickshire, CV11 6LL, United Kingdom
(024) 7632 5059/ (024) 7632 5059
gerald@ggarts.demon.co.uk
www.ggarts.demon.co.uk

Gerard Graphics Ground Floor Studio, 52B Upper Lewes Road, Brighton, BN2 3FH, United Kingdom
(01273) 604984/ (01273) 887604
illustrator@worldonline.co.uk
www.gerardgraphics.co.uk

Gerry Baptist@Phosphor Art 41 The Pump House, Pump House Close, off Renforth Street, London, SE16 7HS, United Kingdom
(020) 7064 4666/ (020) 7064 4660
info@phosphorart.com
www.phosphorart.com

Gerry Murray@Advocate Art 39 Church Road, London, SW19 5DQ, United Kingdom
020 8879 1166/020 8879 3303
lesley@advocate-art.com
www.advocate-art.com

Gery Lebecq@Folio 10 Gate Street, Lincoln's Inn Fields, London, WC2A 3HP, United Kingdom
(020) 7242 9562/ (020) 7242 1816
all@folioart.co.uk
www.folioart.co.uk

Gez Fry@Folio 10 Gate Street, Lincoln's Inn Fields, London, WC2A 3HP, United Kingdom
(020) 7242 9562/ (020) 7242 1816
all@folioart.co.uk
www.folioart.co.uk

Giannelli@Meiklejohn Illustration 5 Risborough Street, London, SE1 0HF, United Kingdom
(020) 7593 0500/ (020) 7593 0501
info@meiklejohn.co.uk
www.meiklejohn.co.uk

Gilad Soffer@Advocate Art 39 Church Road, London, SW19 5DQ, United Kingdom
020 8879 1166/020 8879 3303
lesley@advocate-art.com
www.advocate-art.com

Giles Hargreaves@Phosphor Art 41 The Pump House, Pump House Close, off Renforth Street, London, SE16 7HS, United Kingdom
(020) 7064 4666/ (020) 7064 4660
info@phosphorart.com
www.phosphorart.com

Gill Button Illustration 54 Bethel Road, Sevenoaks, Kent, TN13 3UE, United Kingdom
(07973) 402885
illustration@gillbutton.com
www.gillbutton.com

Gilles Boogaerts@Art Market 51 Oxford Drive, London, SE1 2FB, United Kingdom
(020) 7407 8111/ (020) 7407 8222
info@artmarketillustration.com
www.artmarketillustration.com

Gillian Carr 20 Meadowside, Sandford, Crediton, Devon, EX17 4NN, United Kingdom
(01363) 774679

Gillian Chapman@Linden Artists Ltd 41 Battersea Business Centre, 103 Lavender Hill, London, SW11 5QL, United Kingdom
(020) 7738 2505/ (020) 7738 2513
lindenartists@aol.com
www.lindenartists.co.uk

Gillian Martin@Art Market 51 Oxford Drive, London, SE1 2FB, United Kingdom
(020) 7407 8111/ (020) 7407 8222
info@artmarketillustration.com
www.artmarketillustration.com

Gina Birch, Godalming, Surrey, United Kingdom
(07866) 847523
info@ginabirch.co.uk
www.whatsinthebox.co.uk

Gini Wade Plas Tylwch, Tylwch, Llanidloes, Powys, SY18 6JN, United Kingdom
(01597) 870627
gini_wade@lineone.net
www.contact-me.net/giniwade

Gino D'Achille@Artist Partners Ltd 2e The Chandlery, 50 Westminster Bridge Road, London, SE1 7QY, United Kingdom
(020) 7401 7904/ (020) 7401 3378
chris@artistpartners.demon.co.uk
www.artistpartners.com

Giuliana Gregori@Advocate Art 39 Church Road, London, SW19 5DQ, United Kingdom
020 8879 1166/020 8879 3303
lesley@advocate-art.com
www.advocate-art.com

Glen Baxter@Thorogood Illustration Ltd 5 Dryden Street, Covent Garden, London, WC2E 9NW, United Kingdom
(020) 7829 8468
draw@thorogood.net
www.thorogood.net

Glen McBeth 4 Abbey Mains Cottages, Haddington, East Lothian, EH41 3SB, United Kingdom
(01602) 824025/(0771) 359 0498
email@glenmcbeth.co.uk
www.glenmcbeth.co.uk

Glyn Brewerton@New Division 5 Risborough Street, London, SE1 0HF, United Kingdom
(020) 7593 0505/ (020) 7593 0501
info@newdivision.com
www.newdivision.com

Goatpix Ltd 105 High Street, Maldon, Essex, CM9 5EP, United Kingdom
(01621) 850528
alas@goatpix.com
www.goatpix.com

Gone Loco@Début Art & The Coningsby Gallery 30 Tottenham Street, London, W1T 4RJ, United Kingdom
(020) 7636 1064/ (020) 7580 7017
info@debutart.com
www.debutart.com

Gordon Crabb 89 Muswell Hill Road, London, N10 3HT, United Kingdom
(020) 8444 9553/(07712) 592155 / (020) 8883 4235
alisoneldred@gmail.com
www.alisoneldred.com

Gordon Fraser Illustrations 48 Lynmouth Close, Hemlington, Middlesbrough, Cleveland, TS8 9NH, United Kingdom
(01642) 270529
gothtwinz@hotmail.com
www.freewebs.com/gordonfraser

Graeme Puckett Hellzapoppin, 26 Malvern Buildings, Bath, BA1 6JX, United Kingdom
(01225) 332942
www.hoppinmad.co.uk

Graham Allen@Linden Artists Ltd 41 Battersea Business Centre, 103 Lavender Hill, London, SW11 5QL, United Kingdom
(020) 7738 2505/ (020) 7738 2513
lindenartists@aol.com
www.lindenartists.co.uk

Graham Byfield@Artist Partners Ltd 2e The Chandlery, 50 Westminster Bridge Road, London, SE1 7QY, United Kingdom
(020) 7401 7904/ (020) 7401 3378
chris@artistpartners.demon.co.uk
www.artistpartners.com

Graham Carter@Private View Artists Agency 17A Swan Hill, Shrewsbury, SY1 1NL, United Kingdom
(01743) 350355/ (01743) 233923
create@pvuk.com
www.pvuk.com

Graham Evernden@The Organisation The Basement, 69 Caledonian Road, London, N1 9BT, United Kingdom
(020) 7833 8268/(07973) 172902 / (020) 7833 8269
organise@easynet.co.uk
www.organisart.co.uk

Graham Higgins 38 Prospect Road, Moseley, Birmingham, B13 9TB, United Kingdom
0121-449 0571/ 0121-449 0571
g@pokkettz.demon.co.uk
www.pokkettz.demon.co.uk

Graham Humphreys@Art Market 51 Oxford Drive, London, SE1 2FB, United Kingdom
(020) 7407 8111/ (020) 7407 8222
info@artmarketillustration.com
www.artmarketillustration.com

Graham Philpot 21 Rosemont Road, Acton, London, W3 9LU, United Kingdom
(020) 8992 2544/(07870) 420599 / (020) 8932 4569
grahamcphilpot@aol.com

Graham Rawle 2nd Floor, 111 Shoreditch High Street, London, E1 6JN, United Kingdom
(020) 7739 8292/(07774) 938129 /
questions@grahamrawle.com
www.grahamrawle.com

Graham Round@Drawer Illustrators Agents 8 Belmont, Bath, BA1 5DZ, United Kingdom
(01225) 445262
enquiries@drawer.me.uk

Graham Thompson 1A Admirals Walk, St. Albans, Hertfordshire, AL1 5SH, United Kingdom
(01727) 857505/ (01727) 857505
graham@grahamthompsonillustration.co.uk
www.grahamthompsonillustration.co.uk

Graham White@N B Illustration Ltd 40 Bowling Green Lane, London, EC1R 0NE, United Kingdom
(020) 7278 9131/ (020) 7278 9121
info@nbillustration.co.uk
www.nbillustration.co.uk

Graham-Cameron Illustration The Studio, 23 Holt Road, Sheringham, Norfolk, NR26 8NB, United Kingdom
(01263) 821333/ (01263) 821334
enquiry@graham-cameron-illustration.com
www.graham-cameron-illustration.com

Grasshopper Design Unit 103A, The Mayford Centre, Mayford Green, Woking, Surrey, GU22 0PP, United Kingdom
(01483) 751255
doug@grasshopperdesign.co.uk
www.grasshopperdesign.co.uk

Gray Jolliffe@Illustration Ltd 2 Brooks Court, Cringle Street, London, SW8 5BX, United Kingdom
(020) 7720 5202/ (020) 7720 5920
team@illustrationweb.com
www.illustrationweb.com

Greg Banning@Début Art & The Coningsby Gallery 30 Tottenham Street, London, W1T 4RJ, United Kingdom
(020) 7636 1064/ (020) 7580 7017
info@debutart.com
www.debutart.com

Greg Becker@Illustration Ltd 2 Brooks Court, Cringle Street, London, SW8 5BX, United Kingdom
(020) 7720 5202/ (020) 7720 5920
team@illustrationweb.com
www.illustrationweb.com

Greg Bridges@Sarah Brown Agency 10 The Avenue, Ealing, London, W13 8PH, United Kingdom
(020) 8998 0390/(07778) 177102 / (020) 8843 1175
sbagency@dsl.pipex.com
www.sbagency.com

Greg Clarke@The Artworks 40 Frith Street, London, W1D 5LN, United Kingdom
(020) 7734 3333/ (020) 7734 3484
lucy@theartworksinc.com
www.theartworksinc.com

Grizelda Holderness@Illustration Ltd 2 Brooks Court, Cringle Street, London, SW8 5BX, United Kingdom
(020) 7720 5202/ (020) 7720 5920
team@illustrationweb.com
www.illustrationweb.com

Guy Boucault@Advocate Art 39 Church Road, London, SW19 5DQ, United Kingdom
020 8879 1166/020 8879 3303
lesley@advocate-art.com
www.advocate-art.com

Guy Carter, London, E17, United Kingdom
(020) 8523 3465/(07773) 603239 /
guycarter@bushinternet.com
www.humour.co.uk

Gwen Millward@David Higham 5-8 Lower John Street, Golden Square, London, W1F 9HA, United Kingdom
(020) 7437 7888/ (020) 7437 1072
carolinewalsh@davidhigham.co.uk
www.davidhigham.co.uk

Gwyneth Jones@Artist Partners Ltd 2e The Chandlery, 50 Westminster Bridge Road, London, SE1 7QY, United Kingdom
(020) 7401 7904/ (020) 7401 3378
chris@artistpartners.demon.co.uk
www.artistpartners.com

Hag@Début Art & The Coningsby Gallery 30 Tottenham Street, London, W1T 4RJ, United Kingdom
(020) 7636 1064/ (020) 7580 7017
info@debutart.com
www.debutart.com

Hand Colouring Helena Zakrzewska-Rucinska Invicta Works, 8 Graces Mews, London, SE5 8JF, United Kingdom
(020) 7701 4865/7920042865 /
helena@helenazr.com
www.helenazr.com

Hanna Melin@Private View Artists Agency 17A Swan Hill, Shrewsbury, SY1 1NL, United Kingdom
(01743) 350355/ (01743) 233923
create@pvuk.com
www.pvuk.com

Hannah Carty@Eastwing 99 Chase Side, Enfield, Middlesex, EN2 6NL, United Kingdom
(020) 8367 6760/ (020) 8367 6730
andrea@eastwing.co.uk
www.eastwing.co.uk

Hannah Firmin@Illustration Ltd 2 Brooks Court, Cringle Street, London, SW8 5BX, United Kingdom
(020) 7720 5202/ (020) 7720 5920
team@illustrationweb.com
www.illustrationweb.com

Hannah Giffard@David Higham 5-8 Lower John Street, Golden Square, London, W1F 9HA, United Kingdom
(020) 7437 7888/ (020) 7437 1072
carolinewalsh@davidhigham.co.uk
www.davidhigham.co.uk

Hannah Wood@Advocate Art 39 Church Road, London, SW19 5DQ, United Kingdom
020 8879 1166/020 8879 3303
lesley@advocate-art.com
www.advocate-art.com

Hanoch Piven@The Artworks 40 Frith Street, London, W1D 5LN, United Kingdom
(020) 7734 3333/ (020) 7734 3484
lucy@theartworksinc.com
www.theartworksinc.com

Harriet Russell@Central Illustration Agency 36 Wellington Street, London, WC2E 7BD, United Kingdom
(020) 7240 8925/ (020) 7836 1177
info@centralillustration.com
www.centralillustration.com

Harry Malt@Début Art & The Coningsby Gallery 30 Tottenham Street, London, W1T 4RJ, United Kingdom
(020) 7636 1064/ (020) 7580 7017
info@debutart.com
www.debutart.com

Hartoons 37 Beach Priory Gardens, Southport, Merseyside, PR8 2SA, United Kingdom
(01704) 543981/ (01704) 501238
mail@hartoons.co.uk
www.hartoons.co.uk

Hashim Akib@Thorogood Illustration Ltd 5 Dryden Street, Covent Garden, London, WC2E 9NW, United Kingdom
(020) 7829 8468
draw@thorogood.net
www.thorogood.net

Haydn Cornner@Central Illustration Agency 36 Wellington Street, London, WC2E 7BD, United Kingdom
(020) 7240 8925/ (020) 7836 1177
info@centralillustration.com
www.centralillustration.com

Heart Top Floor, 100 de Beauvoir Road, London, N1 4EN, United Kingdom
(020) 7254 5558/ (020) 7923 4791
heartinfo@heartagency.com
www.heartagency.com

Heather Gatley@The Artworks 40 Frith Street, London, W1D 5LN, United Kingdom
(020) 7734 3333/ (020) 7734 3484
lucy@theartworksinc.com
www.theartworksinc.com

Heather Mitchell@Advocate Art 39 Church Road,
London, SW19 5DQ, United Kingdom
✆ 020 8879 1166/020 8879 3303
✉ lesley@advocate-art.com
🖥 www.advocate-art.com

Heather Taylor 6 War Memorial Homes, Castle Lane,
Bournemouth, BH8 9TP, United Kingdom
✆ (01202) 397986
✉ heather4red@aol.com

Helen Cowcher 30 Telford Avenue, London, SW2 4XF,
United Kingdom
✆ (020) 8674 3986/📠 (020) 8674 3986
✉ helen@helencowcher.com
🖥 www.helencowcher.com

Helen James@New Division 5 Risborough Street,
London, SE1 0HF, United Kingdom
✆ (020) 7593 0505/📠 (020) 7593 0501
✉ info@newdivision.com
🖥 www.newdivision.com

Helen Jones Studio 310, 3rd Floor, 5 Torrens Street,
London, EC1V 1NQ, United Kingdom
✆ (020) 7837 0509/📠 (020) 7837 0509
✉ helenjonesstudio@hotmail.com
🖥 www.helenjonesonline.com

Helena Greene 22 Sleaford Street, Cambridge, CB1
2PW, United Kingdom
✆ (01223) 350857
✉ h.greene@virgin.net
🖥 www.helenagreene.co.uk

Helene Burrow 21 Risingside, Barrow-in-Furness,
Cumbria, LA13 9ES, United Kingdom
✆ (01229) 821023/(07808) 762149 📠 (01229) 836580
✉ helene.bdda@btconnect.com
🖥 www.heleneburrow.co.uk

Heli Hieta@Arena 31 Eleanor Road, London, E15 4AB,
United Kingdom
✆ (08450) 507 600
✉ info@arenaworks.com
🖥 www.arenaworks.com

Helicopter Grafix Ltd Evelyn House, 142 -144 New
Cavendish Street, London, W1W 6YF, United Kingdom
✆ (020) 7612 2757/(07814) 362714 📠 (020) 7612 2789
✉ info@missioncontrol-fx.co.uk
🖥 www.helicoptergrafix.com

Helzbelzart 201 The Street, Rustington, Littlehampton,
West Sussex, BN16 3DN, United Kingdom
✆ (07709) 270014
✉ helzbelzart@yahoo.co.uk
🖥 www.helzbelzart.co.uk

Henry Gardiner 21 Merrivale, Camden Street, London,
NW1 0LH, United Kingdom
✆ (020) 7387 6381

Heretakis@hotmail.com 54 Sina Street, Athens,
Greece
✆ 00 30 694 2250 836/📠 00 30 210 33615 055
✉ heretakis@hotmail.com
🖥 www.heretakis.com

High Pitch Graphics 1st Floor, 51 Prestonville Road,
Brighton, BN1 3TJ, United Kingdom
✆ (01273) 710466
✉ info@high-pitch.co.uk
🖥 www.high-pitch.co.uk

Hollyhead Bush, London/Newcastle, United Kingdom
✆ /(07973) 185392 📠
✉ bushhollyhead@hotmail.com

Hoodwinked.biz 19 Lyngilzenn Court, Nottingham, NG3
3JF, United Kingdom
✆ (07748) 551110/📠 0115-925 2978
✉ melvenleavy@hotmil.com
🖥 www.hoodwinked.biz

Hot Frog Graphics Stanmore, 4 Moorland Avenue,
Barnsley, South Yorkshire, S70 6PQ, United Kingdom
✆ (01226) 242777/📠 (01226) 242777
✉ hotfroggraphics@blueyonder.co.uk
🖥 www.hotfroggraphics.com

Howard Cartoons 8 Belle Vue Street, York, YO10 5AY,
United Kingdom
✆ (01904) 656702
✉ graemejhoward@aol.com
🖥 www.howardcartoons.co.uk

Howard Gerrard 11 Oaks Road, Tenterden, Kent, TN30
6RD, United Kingdom
✆ (01580) 765748/📠 (01580) 765748
✉ howard.gerrard@virgin.net

Howard Levitt Illustration Ltd 24 Overdale Road,
Newtown, Disley, Stockport, Cheshire, SK12 2RJ, United
Kingdom
✆ (01663) 746 882/📠 (01663) 746 882
✉ howard@howardlevittillustration.co.uk
🖥 www.howardlevittillustration.co.uk

Howard Read@Inkshed 99 Chase Side, Enfield,
Middlesex, EN2 6NL, United Kingdom
✆ (020) 8367 4545/📠 (020) 8367 6730
🖥 www.inkshed.co.uk

Howard Tangye 1 Campsbourne Road, Hornsey, London,
N8 7PT, United Kingdom
✆ (020) 8341 1929/📠 (020) 8341 1929

I Like Drawing 166 Forest Hill Road, London, SE23
3QR, United Kingdom
✆ (07903) 271938
🖥 www.ianstevenson.co.uk

I T E A Ltd The Old Chapel, Llanishen, Chepstow, Gwent,
NP16 6QT, United Kingdom
✆ (01600) 869084
✉ edgson@lineone.net
🖥 www.alisonedgson.com

Ian Bilbey@Central Illustration Agency 36
Wellington Street, London, WC2E 7BD, United Kingdom
✆ (020) 7240 8925/📠 (020) 7836 1177
✉ info@centralillustration.com
🖥 www.centralillustration.com

Ian Fraser Jackson 44 Coniston Road, Muswell Hill,
London, N10 2BP, United Kingdom
✆ (020) 8374 8281/(07957) 257365 📠 (020) 8374 8281
✉ jaxxi@blueyonder.co.uk

Ian Keltie@Art Market 51 Oxford Drive, London, SE1
2FB, United Kingdom
✆ (020) 7407 8111/📠 (020) 7407 8222
✉ info@artmarketillustration.com
🖥 www.artmarketillustration.com

Ian Naylor 90 Milnthorpe Road, Kendal, Cumbria, LA9
5HP, United Kingdom
✆ (01539) 733103
✉ ian.aircrew@clara.net
🖥 www.aircrew.co.uk

Ian Phillips@N B Illustration Ltd 40 Bowling Green
Lane, London, EC1R 0NE, United Kingdom
✆ (020) 7278 9131/📠 (020) 7278 9121
✉ info@nbillustration.com
🖥 www.nbillustration.co.uk

01226 242777
Hot Frog Graphics
Paul Morton • hotfroggraphics@blueyonder.co.uk
www.hotfroggraphics.com • www.hotfroggraphics.blogspot.com

Ian Pollock@Inkshed 99 Chase Side, Enfield,
Middlesex, EN2 6NL, United Kingdom
✆ (020) 8367 4545/📠 (020) 8367 6730
🖥 www.inkshed.co.uk

Ian Purdie 43 Bankfield Lane, Rochdale, Lancashire,
OL11 5RS, United Kingdom
✆ (01706) 633617

Ian Whadcock@Eastwing 99 Chase Side, Enfield,
Middlesex, EN2 6NL, United Kingdom
✆ (020) 8367 6760/📠 (020) 8367 6730
✉ andrea@eastwing.co.uk
🖥 www.eastwing.co.uk

iD2 Country House, Sea End Road, Benington, Boston,
Lincolnshire, PE22 0DQ, United Kingdom
✆ (01205) 761793/(07801) 766863 📠
✉ vincentwakerley@btinternet.com
🖥 www.id2-studio.com

Ilene Winn-Lederer@The Artworks 40 Frith Street,
London, W1D 5LN, United Kingdom
✆ (020) 7734 3333/📠 (020) 7734 3484
✉ lucy@theartworksinc.com
🖥 www.theartworksinc.com

Illustration Ltd 2 Brooks Court, Cringle Street, London,
SW8 5BX, United Kingdom
✆ (020) 7720 5202/📠 (020) 7720 5920
✉ team@illustrationweb.com
🖥 www.illustrationweb.com

Illustration Reps Inc 1234 SilverLake, SilverLake,
Hollywood, Los Angeles, 90039, United States of America
✆ 323 667 1234
✉ illustrationreps@hotmail.com
🖥 www.illustrationreps.com

Illustratorsmith 36 Woolley Street, Bradford-on-Avon,
Wiltshire, BA15 1AG, United Kingdom
✆ (01225) 868248
✉ dfs@illustratorsmith.com
🖥 www.illustratorsmith.com

Imageri Haverhill, Church Street, Whitchurch,
Hampshire, RG28 7AS, United Kingdom
✆ (01256) 895600
✉ info@imageri.com
🖥 www.imageri.com

Immersive Media Ltd 56 Frederick Road, Sutton,
Surrey, SM1 2HU, United Kingdom
✆ 020 84011278
✉ seo@immersivemedia.co.uk
🖥 www.immersivemedia.co.uk

Industrial Art Studio Consols, St. Ives, Cornwall, TR26
2HW, United Kingdom
✆ (01736) 797651/📠 (01736) 797651
✉ roger@ind-art.co.uk
🖥 www.ind-art.co.uk

Ingela Peterson@The Organisation The Basement, 69
Caledonian Road, London, N1 9BT, United Kingdom
✆ (020) 7833 8268/(07973) 172902 📠 (020) 7833 8269
✉ organise@easynet.co.uk
🖥 www.organisart.co.uk

Ingenious Beacon House, Brambleside, Bellbrook
Industrial Estate, Uckfield, East Sussex, TN22 1PL,
United Kingdom
✆ (01825) 768 811/📠 (01825) 768 062
✉ maria@ingeniousdesign.co.uk
🖥 www.ingeniousdesign.co.uk

15

Ingram Pinn 33 Alexandra Road, Chiswick, London, W4 1AX, United Kingdom
✆ (020) 8994 5311/✆ (020) 8747 8200
✉ ingram@pinn33.freeserve.co.uk

Ink & Colors Ltd 27 Old Gloucester Street, London, WC1N 3XX, United Kingdom
✆ (020) 7558 8374
✉ info@inkandcolors.com
🖳 www.inkandcolors.com

Inkshed 99 Chase Side, Enfield, Middlesex, EN2 6NL, United Kingdom
✆ (020) 8367 4545/✆ (020) 8367 6730
🖳 www.inkshed.co.uk

Inspired Design 6 Poulton Close, Washington, Tyne and Wear, NE38 9DG, United Kingdom
✆ 0191-417 6000
✉ andrew@inspireddesign.co.uk
🖳 www.inspireddesign.co.uk

Iola Rosa@Allied Artists@ Artistic License The Gallery @ Richmond, 63 Sheen Road, Richmond, Surrey, TW9 1YJ, United Kingdom
✆ (020) 8334 1010/✆ (020) 8334 9900
✉ info@allied-artists.net
🖳 www.allied-artists.net

Ionna Maria Antoniadi 2 Batavia Mews, New Cross, London, SE14 6EA, United Kingdom
✆ (020) 8691 9590
✉ i_antoniade@yahoo.gr

Ironcoast Ltd 5/26 The Common, London, W5 3JB, United Kingdom
✆ (07725) 186394/✆ (020) 8328 9042

Ivan Allen@Inkshed 99 Chase Side, Enfield, Middlesex, EN2 6NL, United Kingdom
✆ (020) 8367 4545/✆ (020) 8367 6730
🖳 www.inkshed.co.uk

Ivan Gillett@N B Illustration Ltd 40 Bowling Green Lane, London, EC1R 0NE, United Kingdom
✆ (020) 7278 9131/✆ (020) 7278 9121
✉ info@nbillustration.co.uk
🖳 www.nbillustration.co.uk

Izhar Cohen@The Artworks 40 Frith Street, London, W1D 5LN, United Kingdom
✆ (020) 7734 3333/✆ (020) 7734 3484
✉ lucy@theartworksinc.com
🖳 www.theartworksinc.com

J F Wegner 14 Swains Lane, London, N6 6QS, United Kingdom
✆ (020) 7485 6430/✆ (020) 7485 6430

J K Illo 17 Montreal Street, Currock, Carlisle, CA2 4EE, United Kingdom
✆ (01228) 403312/(07789) 361605 ✆
✉ jkillo@jkillo.co.uk
🖳 www.jkillo.co.uk

J T Creative 3 Fieldhouse Road, London, SW12 0HL, United Kingdom
✆ (020) 8673 0641
✉ james@jtcreative.co.uk
🖳 www.jtcreative.co.uk

J.A. Stubbs 39 Westminster Mansions, Great Smith Street, London, SW1P 3BP, United Kingdom
✆ (020) 7222 2449

Jacey@Début Art & The Coningsby Gallery 30 Tottenham Street, London, W1T 4RJ, United Kingdom
✆ (020) 7636 1064/✆ (020) 7580 7017
✉ info@debutart.com
🖳 www.debutart.com

Jacey Abram@Drawer Illustrators Agents 8 Belmont, Bath, BA1 5DZ, United Kingdom
✆ (01225) 445262
✉ enquiries@drawer.me.uk

Jackie Parsons@Central Illustration Agency 36 Wellington Street, London, WC2E 7BD, United Kingdom
✆ (020) 7240 8925/✆ (020) 7836 1177
✉ info@centralillustration.com
🖳 www.centralillustration.com

Jackie Sinnott 112 Addiscombe Road, Croydon, CR0 5PQ, United Kingdom
✆ (020) 8654 3017

Jacqueline Stevenson 11 Priestfield Avenue, Edinburgh, EH16 5JL, United Kingdom
✆ 0131-667 4777/✆ 0131-667 4777
✉ jacquie.stevenson@btinternet.ocm

Jacques Fabre@N B Illustration Ltd 40 Bowling Green Lane, London, EC1R 0NE, United Kingdom
✆ (020) 7278 9131/✆ (020) 7278 9121
✉ info@nbillustration.co.uk
🖳 www.nbillustration.co.uk

Jacqui Grantford@Advocate Art 39 Church Road, London, SW19 5DQ, United Kingdom
✆ 020 8879 1166/020 8879 3303
✉ lesley@advocate-art.com
🖳 www.advocate-art.com

Jacqui Paull Melegari@Private View Artists Agency 17A Swan Hill, Shrewsbury, SY1 1NL, United Kingdom
✆ (01743) 350355/✆ (01743) 233923
✉ create@pvuk.com
🖳 www.pvuk.com

Jaknife Creations 34 Barnet Drive, Bromley, BR2 8PQ, United Kingdom
✆ (07952) 300276
✉ jaknifecreations@hotmail.com

Jakob Lunden@Art Market 51 Oxford Drive, London, SE1 2FB, United Kingdom
✆ (020) 7407 8111/✆ (020) 7407 8222
✉ info@artmarketillustration.com
🖳 www.artmarketillustration.com

Jamel Akib@Illustration Ltd 2 Brooks Court, Cringle Street, London, SW8 5BX, United Kingdom
✆ (020) 7720 5202/✆ (020) 7720 5920
✉ team@illustrationweb.com
🖳 www.illustrationweb.com

James Bourne@Drawer Illustrators Agents 8 Belmont, Bath, BA1 5DZ, United Kingdom
✆ (01225) 445262
✉ enquiries@drawer.me.uk

James Brown@New Division 5 Risborough Street, London, SE1 0HF, United Kingdom
✆ (020) 7593 0505/✆ (020) 7593 0501
✉ info@newdivision.com
🖳 www.newdivision.com

James Croft@Arena 31 Eleanor Road, London, E15 4AB, United Kingdom
✆ (08450) 507 600
✉ info@arenaworks.com
🖳 www.arenaworks.com

James Kirkwood 224 Sangley Road, Catford, London, SE6 2JS, United Kingdom
✆ (020) 8461 0794
✉ kirkle77@hotmail.com
🖳 www.jameskirkwood.com

James Macfarlane@Meiklejohn Illustration 5 Risborough Street, London, SE1 0HF, United Kingdom
✆ (020) 7593 0500/✆ (020) 7593 0501
✉ info@meiklejohn.co.uk
🖳 www.meiklejohn.co.uk

James Mackay@Central Illustration Agency 36 Wellington Street, London, WC2E 7BD, United Kingdom
✆ (020) 7240 8925/✆ (020) 7836 1177
✉ info@centralillustration.com
🖳 www.centralillustration.com

James McGairy@Advocate Art 39 Church Road, London, SW19 5DQ, United Kingdom
✆ 020 8879 1166/020 8879 3303
✉ lesley@advocate-art.com
🖳 www.advocate-art.com

James Starr@Début Art & The Coningsby Gallery 30 Tottenham Street, London, W1T 4RJ, United Kingdom
✆ (020) 7636 1064/✆ (020) 7580 7017
✉ info@debutart.com
🖳 www.debutart.com

James Taylor@Début Art & The Coningsby Gallery 30 Tottenham Street, London, W1T 4RJ, United Kingdom
✆ (020) 7636 1064/✆ (020) 7580 7017
✉ info@debutart.com
🖳 www.debutart.com

Jamie Jay@Folio 10 Gate Street, Lincoln's Inn Fields, London, WC2A 3HP, United Kingdom
✆ (020) 7242 9562/✆ (020) 7242 1816
✉ all@folioart.co.uk
🖳 www.folioart.co.uk

Jan Lewis 1 Coombe End, Whitchurch Hill, Reading, RG8 7PD, United Kingdom
✆ 0118-984 2590/(07712) 893355 ✆ 0118-984 2590
✉ jan.lewis1@btinternet.com

Jan McCafferty@Arena 31 Eleanor Road, London, E15 4AB, United Kingdom
✆ (08450) 507 600
✉ info@arenaworks.com
🖳 www.arenaworks.com

Jan Smith@Advocate Art 39 Church Road, London, SW19 5DQ, United Kingdom
✆ 020 8879 1166/020 8879 3303
✉ lesley@advocate-art.com
🖳 www.advocate-art.com

Jane Cope@Drawer Illustrators Agents 8 Belmont, Bath, BA1 5DZ, United Kingdom
✆ (01225) 445262
✉ enquiries@drawer.me.uk

Jane E. Williamson Hydaway, 12 Manor Road, Pitsford, Northampton, NN6 9AR, United Kingdom
✆ (01604) 880115/(07763) 798774 ✆

Jane Gerwitz 13 Plevna Terrace, Bingley, West Yorkshire, BD16 4BX, United Kingdom
✆ (01274) 560190
✉ janegerwitz@aol.com
🖳 www.janegerwitz.com

Jane Heyes@Advocate Art 39 Church Road, London, SW19 5DQ, United Kingdom
✆ 020 8879 1166/020 8879 3303
✉ lesley@advocate-art.com
🖳 www.advocate-art.com

Jane Hughes Cromer House, 41 Belle Vue Road, Wivenhoe, CO7 9LD, United Kingdom
✆ (01206) 822723/✆ (01206) 822723
✉ jane@skyfield.co.uk

Jane McCracken 3 Prima Road, Ground Floor Flat, London, SW9 0NA, United Kingdom
✆ (020) 7735 5519

Jane Pickering@Linden Artists Ltd 41 Battersea Business Centre, 103 Lavender Hill, London, SW11 5QL, United Kingdom
✆ (020) 7738 2505/✆ (020) 7738 2513
✉ lindenartists@aol.com
🖳 www.lindenartists.co.uk

Jane Spencer@Thorogood Illustration Ltd 5 Dryden Street, Covent Garden, London, WC2E 9NW, United Kingdom
✆ (020) 7829 8468
✉ draw@thorogood.net
🖳 www.thorogood.net

Jane Spencer Illustration 17 Brigden Street, Brighton, BN1 5DP, United Kingdom
✆ (01273) 231755
✉ jane@janespencer.com
🖳 www.janespencer.com

Jane Webster@Début Art & The Coningsby Gallery 30 Tottenham Street, London, W1T 4RJ, United Kingdom
✆ (020) 7636 1064/✆ (020) 7580 7017
✉ info@debutart.com
🖳 www.debutart.com

Janet Lees Copywriter 29 Malew Street, Castletown, Isle of Man, IM9 1AD, United Kingdom
✆ (01624) 823253/✆ (01624) 825779
✉ jpx10@mac.com

Janet R. Woolley 34 Stanhope Road, London, N6 5NG, United Kingdom
✆ (020) 8341 3651
✉ janetrwoolley@aol.com

Janet Woolley@Arena 31 Eleanor Road, London, E15 4AB, United Kingdom
✆ (08450) 507 600
✉ info@arenaworks.com
🖳 www.arenaworks.com

Jannat Messenger Church View, Causeway, Redmarley, Glouceste, GL19 3JS, United Kingdom
✆ (01531) 650367

Jaqueline Bissett@Pearce Stoner Associates 12B Links Yard, Spelman Street, London, E1 5LX, United Kingdom
✆ (020) 7247 7100/✆ (020) 7247 7144
✉ info@pearcestoner.com
🖳 www.pearcestoner.com

Jaroslav@Début Art & The Coningsby Gallery 30 Tottenham Street, London, W1T 4RJ, United Kingdom
✆ (020) 7636 1064/✆ (020) 7580 7017
✉ info@debutart.com
🖳 www.debutart.com

Jason Brooks@Folio 10 Gate Street, Lincoln's Inn Fields, London, WC2A 3HP, United Kingdom
(020) 7242 9562/ (020) 7242 1816
all@folioart.co.uk
www.folioart.co.uk

Jasper Goodall@Big Active Ltd Unit 6.01, The Tea Building, 56 Shoreditch High Street, London, E16 JJ, United Kingdom
(020) 7739 5601/ (020) 7739 7479
contact@bigactive.com
www.bigactive.com

Javier Joaquin@The Organisation The Basement, 69 Caledonian Road, London, N1 9BT, United Kingdom
(020) 7833 8268/(07973) 172902 (020) 7833 8269
organise@easynet.co.uk
www.organisart.co.uk

Jawabrand 45-46 Charlotte Road, London, EC2A 3PD, United Kingdom
(07790) 527006
nils@jawabrand.co.uk
www.jawabrand.co.uk

Jean de Lemos@Graham-Cameron Illustration The Studio, 23 Holt Road, Sheringham, Norfolk, NR26 8NB, United Kingdom
(01263) 821333/ (01263) 821334
enquiry@graham-cameron-illustration.com
www.graham-cameron-illustration.com

Jean-Manuel Duvivier@Inkshed 99 Chase Side, Enfield, Middlesex, EN2 6NL, United Kingdom
(020) 8367 4545/ (020) 8367 6730
www.inkshed.co.uk

Jean-Sebastien Guiliani@Advocate Art 39 Church Road, London, SW19 5DQ, United Kingdom
020 8879 1166/020 8879 3303
lesley@advocate-art.com
www.advocate-art.com

Jeff Fisher@Central Illustration Agency 36 Wellington Street, London, WC2E 7BD, United Kingdom
(020) 7240 8925/ (020) 7836 1177
info@centralillustration.com
www.centralillustration.com

Jelly London 9-10 Charlotte mews, London, W11 4EF, United Kingdom
(020) 7323 3307/ (020) 7636 2455
info@jellylondon.com
www.jellylondon.com
See ad in showcase

Jellybird Illustration 111 Carholme Road, Lincoln, Lincolnshire, LN1 1RT,
7821412516
jellybirdillustration@dsl.pipex.com
jellybirdillustration.dsl.pipex.com

Jenni Johnson Risistrasse 11c, Birmensdorf, 8903, Switzerland
00 41 44 77 77 689
jenni@jennijohnson.com
www.jennijohnson.com

Jennie@Phosphor Art 41 The Pump House, Pump House Close, off Renforth Street, London, SE16 7HS, United Kingdom
(020) 7064 4666/ (020) 7064 4660
info@phosphorart.com
www.phosphorart.com

Jenny Fionda@Graham-Cameron Illustration The Studio, 23 Holt Road, Sheringham, Norfolk, NR26 8NB, United Kingdom
(01263) 821333/ (01263) 821334
enquiry@graham-cameron-illustration.com
www.graham-cameron-illustration.com

Jenny Gregory@Drawer Illustrators Agents 8 Belmont, Bath, BA1 5DZ, United Kingdom
(01225) 445262
enquiries@drawer.me.uk

Jenny Samuels@David Higham 5-8 Lower John Street, Golden Square, London, W1F 9HA, United Kingdom
(020) 7437 7888/ (020) 7437 1072
carolinewalsh@davidhigham.co.uk
www.davidhigham.co.uk

Jenny Thorne@Linda Rogers Associates 163 Half Moon Lane, London, SE24 9WB, United Kingdom
(020) 7501 9106
lr@lindarogers.net
www.lindarogers.net

Jennyariane.co.uk 44 New Road, Ilford, Essex, IG3 8AR, United Kingdom
(020) 8590 5802
jennyariane@hotmail.com
www.jennyariane.co.uk

Jeremy Bays@Graham-Cameron Illustration The Studio, 23 Holt Road, Sheringham, Norfolk, NR26 8NB, United Kingdom
(01263) 821333/ (01263) 821334
enquiry@graham-cameron-illustration.com
www.graham-cameron-illustration.com

Jeremy Mallard The Tree House, 5 Station Road, Kidderminster, Worcestershire, DY14 8TT, United Kingdom
(01746) 718697/ (01746) 718717
jtmallard@aol.com
www.penandthink.biz

Jeremy Sancha@Central Illustration Agency 36 Wellington Street, London, WC2E 7BD, United Kingdom
(020) 7240 8925/ (020) 7836 1177
info@centralillustration.com
www.centralillustration.com

Jerry Hoare@Meiklejohn Illustration 5 Risborough Street, London, SE1 0HF, United Kingdom
(020) 7593 0500/ (020) 7593 0501
info@meiklejohn.co.uk
www.meiklejohn.co.uk

Jerry Malone 37B Fonnereau Road, Ipswich, IP1 3JH, United Kingdom
(01473) 288668/(07981) 899050 (01473) 288668
jerrymaloneart@yahoo.co.uk
www.creative-freelance.org.uk

Jesse Lindley@Advocate Art 39 Church Road, London, SW19 5DQ, United Kingdom
020 8879 1166/020 8879 3303
lesley@advocate-art.com
www.advocate-art.com

Jessie Eckel@New Division 5 Risborough Street, London, SE1 0HF, United Kingdom
(020) 7593 0505/ (020) 7593 0501
info@newdivision.com
www.newdivision.com

Jessie Ford@Central Illustration Agency 36 Wellington Street, London, WC2E 7BD, United Kingdom
(020) 7240 8925/ (020) 7836 1177
info@centralillustration.com
www.centralillustration.com

Jill Barthorpe@Folio 10 Gate Street, Lincoln's Inn Fields, London, WC2A 3HP, United Kingdom
(020) 7242 9562/ (020) 7242 1816
all@folioart.co.uk
www.folioart.co.uk

Jill Moore 73 Cromwell Avenue, Highgate, London, N6 5HS, United Kingdom
(020) 8340 9402/ (020) 8340 9402
jillmoore@macunlimited.net

Jill Wadsworth@Linden Artists Ltd 41 Battersea Business Centre, 103 Lavender Hill, London, SW11 5QL, United Kingdom
(020) 7738 2505/ (020) 7738 2513
lindenartists@aol.com
www.lindenartists.co.uk

Jim Brown 7 Fordhams Close, Stanton, Bury St. Edmunds, Suffolk, IP31 2EE, United Kingdom
(01359) 251766/ (01359) 251766
j.brown27@btinternet.com

Jim Burns 89 Muswell Hill Road, London, N10 3HT, United Kingdom
(020) 8444 9553/ (020) 8883 4235
alisoneldred@gmail.com
www.alisoneldred.com

Jim Friedman@Début Art & The Coningsby Gallery 30 Tottenham Street, London, W1T 4RJ, United Kingdom
(020) 7636 1064/ (020) 7580 7017
info@debutart.com
www.debutart.com

Jim Laurance@New Division 5 Risborough Street, London, SE1 0HF, United Kingdom
(020) 7593 0505/ (020) 7593 0501
info@newdivision.com
www.newdivision.com

Jim Mitchell@Advocate Art 39 Church Road, London, SW19 5DQ, United Kingdom
020 8879 1166/020 8879 3303
lesley@advocate-art.com
www.advocate-art.com

Jitesh Patel@Central Illustration Agency 36 Wellington Street, London, WC2E 7BD, United Kingdom
(020) 7240 8925/ (020) 7836 1177
info@centralillustration.com
www.centralillustration.com

Jo Banner@Allied Artists@ Artistic License The Gallery @ Richmond, 63 Sheen Road, Richmond, Surrey, TW9 1YJ, United Kingdom
(020) 8334 1010/ (020) 8334 9900
info@allied-artists.net
www.allied-artists.net

Jo Bird@Meiklejohn Illustration 5 Risborough Street, London, SE1 0HF, United Kingdom
(020) 7593 0500/ (020) 7593 0501
info@meiklejohn.co.uk
www.meiklejohn.co.uk

Jo Goodberry@N B Illustration Ltd 40 Bowling Green Lane, London, EC1R 0NE, United Kingdom
(020) 7278 9131/ (020) 7278 9121
info@nbillustration.co.uk
www.nbillustration.co.uk

Jo Hayman@Eastwing 99 Chase Side, Enfield, Middlesex, EN2 6NL, United Kingdom
(020) 8367 6760/ (020) 8367 6730
andrea@eastwing.co.uk
www.eastwing.co.uk

Jo Parry@Advocate Art 39 Church Road, London, SW19 5DQ, United Kingdom
020 8879 1166/020 8879 3303
lesley@advocate-art.com
www.advocate-art.com

Jo Quinn@Inkshed 99 Chase Side, Enfield, Middlesex, EN2 6NL, United Kingdom
(020) 8367 4545/ (020) 8367 6730
www.inkshed.co.uk

Joanna Agis@Début Art & The Coningsby Gallery 30 Tottenham Street, London, W1T 4RJ, United Kingdom
(020) 7636 1064/ (020) 7580 7017
info@debutart.com
www.debutart.com

Joanna Cameron (Medical Artist) 1 Heath Cottages, 58 Little Heath Lane, Cobham, Surrey, KT11 2QN, United Kingdom
(01372) 843817/ (01372) 843817
fineartjo.cameron@virgin.net

Joanna Kerr@New Division 5 Risborough Street, London, SE1 0HF, United Kingdom
(020) 7593 0505/ (020) 7593 0501
info@newdivision.com
www.newdivision.com

Joanna Venus 16 Brafferton Road, Croydon, CR0 1AD, United Kingdom
(020) 8688 7965/ (020) 8688 7965

Joanne Nelson@Advocate Art 39 Church Road, London, SW19 5DQ, United Kingdom
020 8879 1166/020 8879 3303
lesley@advocate-art.com
www.advocate-art.com

Joaquin Gonzalez@New Division 5 Risborough Street, London, SE1 0HF, United Kingdom
(020) 7593 0505/ (020) 7593 0501
info@newdivision.com
www.newdivision.com

Jody Barton@Big Active Ltd Unit 6.01, The Tea Building, 56 Shoreditch High Street, London, E16 JJ, United Kingdom
(020) 7739 5601/ (020) 7739 7479
contact@bigactive.com
www.bigactive.com

Joe Morse@The Artworks 40 Frith Street, London, W1D 5LN, United Kingdom
(020) 7734 3333/ (020) 7734 3484
lucy@theartworksinc.com
www.theartworksinc.com

Joe Petagno@Folio 10 Gate Street, Lincoln's Inn Fields, London, WC2A 3HP, United Kingdom
(020) 7242 9562/ (020) 7242 1816
all@folioart.co.uk
www.folioart.co.uk

John Adams@Illustration Ltd 2 Brooks Court, Cringle Street, London, SW8 5BX, United Kingdom
(020) 7720 5202/ (020) 7720 5920
team@illustrationweb.com
www.illustrationweb.com

John Batchelor Pentle Ridge, Northleigh Lane, Wimborne, Dorset, BH21 2PN, United Kingdom
✆ (01202) 889372/✆ (01202) 889372

John Batten 51 Stondon Park, London, SE23 1LB, United Kingdom
✆ (020) 8291 3365/✆ (020) 8291 3365
✉ jp.batten@btopenworld.com
⌨ www.johnbatten.net

John Burns St Mabyn, Trethevy, Tintagel, Cornwall, PL34 0BE, United Kingdom
✆ (01840) 770270

John Campbell 46A Goldhurst Terrace, London, NW6 3HT, United Kingdom
✆ (020) 7625 4674/✆ (020) 7625 4674
✉ j.o.h.n@ntlworld.com

John Chamberlain 14 Telston Close, Bourne End, Buckinghamshire, SL8 5TY, United Kingdom
✆ (01628) 521941

John Cooper 43 Saint Hilda Street, Bridlington, East Yorkshire, YO15 3EE, United Kingdom
✆ (01262) 676337/(07960) 841711 ✆ (01262) 676337
✉ coops@coopart.com

John Dronsfield 1 Park Drive, Norris Bank, Stockport, Cheshire, SK4 2HJ, United Kingdom
✆ 0161-432 6430
✉ thedroneys@aol.com

John Dunne Illustration No. 1 The Lake, Ampney Crucis, Cirencester, Gloucestershire, GL7 5SE, United Kingdom
✆ (01285) 851195/(07813) 813733 ✆
✉ john@thepencils.com
⌨ www.thepencils.com

John Erasmus (NPA) 213 Petersham Road, Richmond, Surrey, TW10 7AW, United Kingdom
✆ (020) 8948 2378/(07811) 433184 ✆ (020) 8948 2378
✉ lightsource@btinternet.com

John Fowler@The Organisation The Basement, 69 Caledonian Road, London, N1 9BT, United Kingdom
✆ (020) 7833 8268/(07973) 172902 ✆ (020) 7833 8269
✉ organise@easynet.co.uk
⌨ www.organisart.co.uk

John Francis@Bernard Thornton Artists The Penthouse, 4 Hamilton Mews, 310 Merton Road, London, SW18 5AB, United Kingdom
✆ (020) 8874 9081/(07702) 554583 ✆ (020) 8877 1386
✉ bernard@btartists.com
⌨ www.btartists.com

John Green The Lodge, Victoria Road, Weybridge, Surrey, KT13 9QH, United Kingdom
✆ (01932) 854443/✆ (01932) 854443

John Harris 89 Muswell Hill Road, London, N10 3HT, United Kingdom
✆ (020) 8444 9553/(07712) 592155 ✆ (020) 8883 4235
✉ alisoneldred@gmail.com
⌨ www.alisoneldred.com

John Hodgson Illustrators Agency 38 Westminster Palace Gardens, Artillery Row, London, SW1P 1RR, United Kingdom
✆ (020) 7222 4468/✆ (020) 7222 4468

John Holder@Illustration Ltd 2 Brooks Court, Cringle Street, London, SW8 5BX, United Kingdom
✆ (020) 7720 5202/✆ (020) 7720 5920
✉ team@illustrationweb.com
⌨ www.illustrationweb.com

John Howe@Arena 31 Eleanor Road, London, E15 4AB, United Kingdom
✆ (08450) 507 600
✉ info@arenaworks.com
⌨ www.arenaworks.com

John Lee@Advocate Art 39 Church Road, London, SW19 5DQ, United Kingdom
✆ 020 8879 1166/020 8879 3303
✉ lesley@advocate-art.com
⌨ www.advocate-art.com

John Paul Early@Illustration Ltd 2 Brooks Court, Cringle Street, London, SW8 5BX, United Kingdom
✆ (020) 7720 5202/✆ (020) 7720 5920
✉ team@illustrationweb.com
⌨ www.illustrationweb.com

John Reilly@Meiklejohn Illustration 5 Risborough Street, London, SE1 0HF, United Kingdom
✆ (020) 7593 0500/✆ (020) 7593 0501
✉ info@meiklejohn.co.uk
⌨ www.meiklejohn.co.uk

John Richardson@Illustration Ltd 2 Brooks Court, Cringle Street, London, SW8 5BX, United Kingdom
✆ (020) 7720 5202/✆ (020) 7720 5920
✉ team@illustrationweb.com
⌨ www.illustrationweb.com

John Smyth 63 Ashridge Crescent, Shooters Hill, London, SE18 3EA, United Kingdom
✆ (020) 8855 0270/✆ (020) 8855 0270

John Woodcock@Thorogood Illustration Ltd 5 Dryden Street, Covent Garden, London, WC2E 9NW, United Kingdom
✆ (020) 7829 8468
✉ draw@thorogood.net
⌨ www.thorogood.net

John Young Sherwood House, 186 White Hill, Chesham, Buckinghamshire, HP5 1AZ, United Kingdom
✆ (01494) 782589

Johnny Ring@Art Market 51 Oxford Drive, London, SE1 2FB, United Kingdom
✆ (020) 7407 8111/✆ (020) 7407 8222
✉ info@artmarketillustration.com
⌨ www.artmarketillustration.com

Jolanta Damski Freelance Design Flat 1, 40 Ewelme Road, London, SE23 3BH, United Kingdom
✆ (020) 8291 6023
✉ jolantadamski@btinternet.com
⌨ www.jolantadamski.co.uk

Jolyne Knox 33 The Plantation, London, SE3 0AB, United Kingdom
✆ (020) 8852 9602

Jon Berkeley@Début Art & The Coningsby Gallery 30 Tottenham Street, London, W1T 4RJ, United Kingdom
✆ (020) 7636 1064/✆ (020) 7580 7017
✉ info@debutart.com
⌨ www.debutart.com

Jon Davis@Linden Artists Ltd 41 Battersea Business Centre, 103 Lavender Hill, London, SW11 5QL, United Kingdom
✆ (020) 7738 2505/✆ (020) 7738 2513
✉ lindenartists@aol.com
⌨ www.lindenartists.co.uk

Jon Rogers@Phosphor Art 41 The Pump House, Pump House Close, off Renforth Street, London, SE16 7HS, United Kingdom
✆ (020) 7064 4666/✆ (020) 7064 4660
✉ info@phosphorart.com
⌨ www.phosphorart.com

Jon Sayer@Illustration Ltd 2 Brooks Court, Cringle Street, London, SW8 5BX, United Kingdom
✆ (020) 7720 5202/✆ (020) 7720 5920
✉ team@illustrationweb.com
⌨ www.illustrationweb.com

Jonas Bergstrand@Central Illustration Agency 36 Wellington Street, London, WC2E 7BD, United Kingdom
✆ (020) 7240 8925/✆ (020) 7836 1177
✉ info@centralillustration.com
⌨ www.centralillustration.com

Jonathan Burton@N B Illustration Ltd 40 Bowling Green Lane, London, EC1R 0NE, United Kingdom
✆ (020) 7278 9131/✆ (020) 7278 9121
✉ info@nbillustration.co.uk
⌨ www.nbillustration.co.uk

Jonathan Cusick 10 Wynyates, Sageside, Tamworth, Staffordshire, B79 7UP, United Kingdom
✆ (01827) 50003/✆ (01827) 50003
✉ theboss@jonathancusick.com
⌨ www.jonathancusick.com

Jonathan Emmett@David Higham 5-8 Lower John Street, Golden Square, London, W1F 9HA, United Kingdom
✆ (020) 7437 7888/✆ (020) 7437 1072
✉ carolinewalsh@davidhigham.co.uk
⌨ www.davidhigham.co.uk

Jonathan Gibbs@Central Illustration Agency 36 Wellington Street, London, WC2E 7BD, United Kingdom
✆ (020) 7240 8925/✆ (020) 7836 1177
✉ info@centralillustration.com
⌨ www.centralillustration.com

Jonathan Grimwood@Meiklejohn Illustration 5 Risborough Street, London, SE1 0HF, United Kingdom
✆ (020) 7593 0500/✆ (020) 7593 0501
✉ info@meiklejohn.co.uk
⌨ www.meiklejohn.co.uk

Jonathan Harker@New Division 5 Risborough Street, London, SE1 0HF, United Kingdom
✆ (020) 7593 0505/✆ (020) 7593 0501
✉ info@newdivision.com
⌨ www.newdivision.com

Jonathan Langley@John Hodgson Illustrators Agency 38 Westminster Palace Gardens, Artillery Row, London, SW1P 1RR, United Kingdom
✆ (020) 7222 4468/✆ (020) 7222 4468

Jonathan Milne@Folio 10 Gate Street, Lincoln's Inn Fields, London, WC2A 3HP, United Kingdom
✆ (020) 7242 9562/✆ (020) 7242 1816
✉ all@folioart.co.uk
⌨ www.folioart.co.uk

Jonathan Schofield@Advocate Art 39 Church Road, London, SW19 5DQ, United Kingdom
✆ 020 8879 1166/020 8879 3303
✉ lesley@advocate-art.com
⌨ www.advocate-art.com

Jonathan Tran@Private View Artists Agency 17A Swan Hill, Shrewsbury, SY1 1NL, United Kingdom
✆ (01743) 350355/✆ (01743) 233923
✉ create@pvuk.com
⌨ www.pvuk.com

Jonathan Williams West Backhill of Lethenty, Fyvie, Turriff, Aberdeenshire, AB53 8NL, United Kingdom
✆ (0560) 0479886/(07867) 526477 ✆ (01651) 891876
✉ jon@blazingfruit.com
⌨ www.blazingfruit.com

Jonathan Wright@Phosphor Art 41 The Pump House, Pump House Close, off Renforth Street, London, SE16 7HS, United Kingdom
✆ (020) 7064 4666/✆ (020) 7064 4660
✉ info@phosphorart.com
⌨ www.phosphorart.com

Jonny Mendelsson@Eastwing 99 Chase Side, Enfield, Middlesex, EN2 6NL, United Kingdom
✆ (020) 8367 6760/✆ (020) 8367 6730
✉ andrea@eastwing.co.uk
⌨ www.eastwing.co.uk

Josie@Folio 10 Gate Street, Lincoln's Inn Fields, London, WC2A 3HP, United Kingdom
✆ (020) 7242 9562/✆ (020) 7242 1816
✉ all@folioart.co.uk
⌨ www.folioart.co.uk

Jovan Djordjevic 18 Elm Grove, Wivenhoe, CO7 9AY, United Kingdom
✆ (01206) 822118/(07788) 778296 ✆
✉ jovan@jovan.demon.co.uk
⌨ www.jovandjordjevic.com

Juan Gonzalez Illustration Flat 19, Gwynne House, Lloyd Baker Street, London, WC1X 9BG, United Kingdom
✆ (07985) 620974
✉ juanillustrator@msn.com

Judith Johnston@Advocate Art 39 Church Road, London, SW19 5DQ, United Kingdom
✆ 020 8879 1166/020 8879 3303
✉ lesley@advocate-art.com
⌨ www.advocate-art.com

Judith Katz 105 Philbeach Gardens, London, SW5 9ET, United Kingdom
✆ (020) 7385 4613/✆ (020) 7385 4613
✉ judith.katz@tiscali.co.uk

Judy Brown & Alan Rowe 17 Surrey Grove, Sutton, Surrey, SM1 3PW, United Kingdom
✆ (020) 8643 1626/(07050) 131455 ✆ (020) 8641 1528
✉ judy@judybrown.co.uk
⌨ www.alanrowe.com

Judy Stevens@Linda Rogers Associates 163 Half Moon Lane, London, SE24 9WB, United Kingdom
✆ (020) 7501 9106
✉ lr@lindarogers.net
⌨ www.lindarogers.net

Julia Barber@Meiklejohn Illustration 5 Risborough Street, London, SE1 0HF, United Kingdom
✆ (020) 7593 0500/✆ (020) 7593 0501
✉ info@meiklejohn.co.uk
⌨ www.meiklejohn.co.uk

Julia Barber Illustrations, Wroxham, Norwich, United Kingdom
✆ (01603) 784434
✉ illustration@juliabarber.co.uk
⌨ www.juliabarber.co.uk

Julia Pewsey@Linden Artists Ltd 41 Battersea Business Centre, 103 Lavender Hill, London, SW11 5QL, United Kingdom
✆ (020) 7738 2505/✆ (020) 7738 2513
✉ lindenartists@aol.com
⌨ www.lindenartists.co.uk

Julia Staite@Private View Artists Agency 17A Swan Hill, Shrewsbury, SY1 1NL, United Kingdom
(01743) 350355/ (01743) 233923
create@pvuk.com
www.pvuk.com

Julie Downing@Linda Rogers Associates 163 Half Moon Lane, London, SE24 9WB, United Kingdom
(020) 7501 9106
lr@lindarogers.net
www.lindarogers.net

Julie Smith Moat Cottage, 67A Summer Road, East Molesey, Surrey, KT8 9LX, United Kingdom
(020) 8398 5358/(07768) 302414
smirkysmith1@hotmail.com

Julie Verhoeven@C L M Top Floor, 19 All Saints Road, London, W11 1HE, United Kingdom
(020) 7750 2999/ (020) 7792 8507
clm@clmuk.com
www.clmuk.com

Julien Tainmont-Pierrat@Advocate Art 39 Church Road, London, SW19 5DQ, United Kingdom
020 8879 1166/020 8879 3303
lesley@advocate-art.com
www.advocate-art.com

Juliet Dallas Conte@Thorogood Illustration Ltd 5 Dryden Street, Covent Garden, London, WC2E 9NW, United Kingdom
(020) 7829 8468
draw@thorogood.net
www.thorogood.net

Juliette Borda@Eastwing 99 Chase Side, Enfield, Middlesex, EN2 6NL, United Kingdom
(020) 8367 6760/ (020) 8367 6730
andrea@eastwing.co.uk
www.eastwing.co.uk

June Armstrong@Art Collection UK Ltd 7 Worsley Mill, 10 Blantyre Street, Castlefield, Manchester, M15 4LG, United Kingdom
(0870) 2405001/ (0870) 2405002
info@artcollection.co.uk
www.artcollection.co.uk

Junkyard Puppy 94 Brondesbury Road, Queens Park, London, NW6 6RX, United Kingdom
(020) 7604 3467
woof@junkyardpuppy.com
www.junkyardpuppy.com

Jurgen Ziewe@Début Art & The Coningsby Gallery 30 Tottenham Street, London, W1T 4RJ, United Kingdom
(020) 7636 1064/ (020) 7580 7017
info@debutart.com
www.debutart.com

Just For Laffs 7 Worsley Mill, 10 Blantyre Street, Castlefield, Manchester, M15 4LG, United Kingdom
(0870) 1225003/ (0870) 2405002
info@justforlaffs.co.uk
www.justforlaffs.co.uk

Justine Beckett@Private View Artists Agency 17A Swan Hill, Shrewsbury, SY1 1NL, United Kingdom
(01743) 350355/ (01743) 233923
create@pvuk.com
www.pvuk.com

Justine Capelle Illustrator Milo Road, East Dulwich, London, SE22, United Kingdom
(07973) 323709
justine.capelle@infamie.com
www.justinecapelle.com

Justine Formentelli@Art Market 51 Oxford Drive, London, SE1 2FB, United Kingdom
(020) 7407 8111/ (020) 7407 8222
info@artmarketillustration.com
www.artmarketillustration.com

Kady Macdonald Denton@David Higham 5-8 Lower John Street, Golden Square, London, W1F 9HA, United Kingdom
(020) 7437 7888/ (020) 7437 1072
carolinewalsh@davidhigham.co.uk
www.davidhigham.co.uk

Kai & Sunny@Central Illustration Agency 36 Wellington Street, London, WC2E 7BD, United Kingdom
(020) 7240 8925/ (020) 7836 1177
info@centralillustration.com
www.centralillustration.com

Kam Tang@Big Active Ltd Unit 6.01, The Tea Building, 56 Shoreditch High Street, London, E16 JJ, United Kingdom
(020) 7739 5601/ (020) 7739 7479
contact@bigactive.com
www.bigactive.com

Kanako@Thorogood Illustration Ltd 5 Dryden Street, Covent Garden, London, WC2E 9NW, United Kingdom
(020) 7829 8468
draw@thorogood.net
www.thorogood.net

Kannebell 172 Archway Road, Highgate, London, N6 5BB, United Kingdom
(020) 8341 0590
peenakoladas@hotmail.com

Karen Bentley@Advocate Art 39 Church Road, London, SW19 5DQ, United Kingdom
020 8879 1166/020 8879 3303
lesley@advocate-art.com
www.advocate-art.com

Karen Donnelly 94 Southover Street, Brighton, BN2 9UD, United Kingdom
(01273) 673747/ (01273) 673747

Karen Perrins 123 Aston Road, Willenhall, West Midlands, WV13 3DA, United Kingdom
(01902) 637542
kperrins@karenperrins.fsnet.co.uk
www.karenperrins.co.uk

Karen Selby@Shirley Hart Creative Consultants 19 Ulundi Road, London, SE3 7UQ, United Kingdom
(020) 8853 2987/(07867) 806250
shirleyhart@btinternet.com
www.shirleyhart.com

Karin Akesson 144 Commercial Street, London, E1 6NU, United Kingdom
(07766) 476 569
k@karinakesson.com
www.karinakesson.com

Karl Escritt@Advocate Art 39 Church Road, London, SW19 5DQ, United Kingdom
020 8879 1166/020 8879 3303
lesley@advocate-art.com
www.advocate-art.com

Karol Kreations 25 Lower Bartons, Fordingbridge, Hampshire, SP6 1JB, United Kingdom
(07919) 094523
ianmabb1971@hotmail.com

Katarzyna Klein@Eastwing 99 Chase Side, Enfield, Middlesex, EN2 6NL, United Kingdom
(020) 8367 6760/ (020) 8367 6730
andrea@eastwing.co.uk
www.eastwing.co.uk

Kate Gibb@Big Active Ltd Unit 6.01, The Tea Building, 56 Shoreditch High Street, London, E16 JJ, United Kingdom
(020) 7739 5601/ (020) 7739 7479
contact@bigactive.com
www.bigactive.com

Kate Miller@Central Illustration Agency 36 Wellington Street, London, WC2E 7BD, United Kingdom
(020) 7240 8925/ (020) 7836 1177
info@centralillustration.com
www.centralillustration.com

Kate Mockford@The Organisation The Basement, 69 Caledonian Road, London, N1 9BT, United Kingdom
(020) 7833 8268/(07973) 172902 (020) 7833 8269
organise@easynet.co.uk
www.organisart.com

Kate Simpson@John Hodgson Illustrators Agency 38 Westminster Palace Gardens, Artillery Row, London, SW1P 1RR, United Kingdom
(020) 7222 4468/ (020) 7222 4468

Kate Taylor 355 Whitehall Road, Wyke, Bradford, West Yorkshire, BD12 9DP, United Kingdom
(01274) 676870/ (01274) 676870
kate@yorkshiregirl.freeserve.co.uk
www.contact-me.net/KateTaylor

Kath Lucas@The Organisation The Basement, 69 Caledonian Road, London, N1 9BT, United Kingdom
(020) 7833 8268/(07973) 172902 (020) 7833 8269
organise@easynet.co.uk
www.organisart.com

Katherine Baxter@Folio 10 Gate Street, Lincoln's Inn Fields, London, WC2A 3HP, United Kingdom
(020) 7242 9562/ (020) 7242 1816
all@folioart.co.uk
www.folioart.co.uk

Katherine Brozenich@Sarah Lane Represents 56 Bidwell Gardens, London, N11 2AU, United Kingdom
(07901) 552520/ (020) 8292 4001
sarah@sarahlanerepresents.com
www.sarahlanerepresents.com

Kathy Osborn@The Artworks 40 Frith Street, London, W1D 5LN, United Kingdom
(020) 7734 3333/ (020) 7734 3484
lucy@theartworksinc.com
www.theartworksinc.com

Kathy Wyatt 52 Egerton Road, Bishopston, Bristol, BS7 8HL, United Kingdom
0117-924 3929/ 0117-924 3929
kathy@kathywyatt.com
www.kathywyatt.com

Katie Cusack Illustration 1330 Barlow Road, Hudson, 44236, United States of America
00 1 912 844 1608
katie@katiecusack.com
www.katiecusack.com

Katie Mac@N B Illustration Ltd 40 Bowling Green Lane, London, EC1R 0NE, United Kingdom
(020) 7278 9131/ (020) 7278 9121
info@nbillustration.co.uk
www.nbillustration.co.uk

Katie Saunders@Advocate Art 39 Church Road, London, SW19 5DQ, United Kingdom
020 8879 1166/020 8879 3303
lesley@advocate-art.com
www.advocate-art.com

Katie Wood@New Division 5 Risborough Street, London, SE1 0HF, United Kingdom
(020) 7593 0505/ (020) 7593 0501
info@newdivision.com
www.newdivision.com

Katja Rosenberg@Art Market 51 Oxford Drive, London, SE1 2FB, United Kingdom
(020) 7407 8111/ (020) 7407 8222
info@artmarketillustration.com
www.artmarketillustration.com

Katmo@Illustration Ltd 2 Brooks Court, Cringle Street, London, SW8 5BX, United Kingdom
(020) 7720 5202/ (020) 7720 5920
team@illustrationweb.com
www.illustrationweb.com

Katriona Chapman@Advocate Art 39 Church Road, London, SW19 5DQ, United Kingdom
020 8879 1166/020 8879 3303
lesley@advocate-art.com
www.advocate-art.com

Kay Dixey@Linda Rogers Associates 163 Half Moon Lane, London, SE24 9WB, United Kingdom
(020) 7501 9106
lr@lindarogers.net
www.lindarogers.net

Kay Smith 751 Woodbridge Road, Ipswich, IP4 4NB, United Kingdom
(01473) 718143

Keith Hagan@Phosphor Art 41 The Pump House, Pump House Close, off Renforth Street, London, SE16 7HS, United Kingdom
(020) 7064 4666/ (020) 7064 4660
info@phosphorart.com
www.phosphorart.com

Keith Howard@Linda Rogers Associates 163 Half Moon Lane, London, SE24 9WB, United Kingdom
(020) 7501 9106
lr@lindarogers.net
www.lindarogers.net

Keith Robinson@Illustration Ltd 2 Brooks Court, Cringle Street, London, SW8 5BX, United Kingdom
(020) 7720 5202/ (020) 7720 5920
team@illustrationweb.com
www.illustrationweb.com

Keith Scaife@Sarah Brown Agency 10 The Avenue, Ealing, London, W13 8PH, United Kingdom
(020) 8998 0390/(07778) 177102 (020) 8843 1175
sbagency@dsl.pipex.com
www.sbagency.com

Keith Watts@Phosphor Art 41 The Pump House, Pump House Close, off Renforth Street, London, SE16 7HS, United Kingdom
(020) 7064 4666/ (020) 7064 4660
info@phosphorart.com
www.phosphorart.com

Kelly Waldek@The Organisation The Basement, 69 Caledonian Road, London, N1 9BT, United Kingdom
(020) 7833 8268/(07973) 172902 (020) 7833 8269
organise@easynet.co.uk
www.organisart.co.uk

Ken Reilly Design Associates 11 Chiswick Staithe, Hartington Road, Grove Park, London, W4 3TP, United Kingdom
(020) 8994 2228/(020) 8994 2238
ken.reilly@btconnect.com
www.kenreilly.co.uk

Kenny McKendry@Artist Partners Ltd 2e The Chandlery, 50 Westminster Bridge Road, London, SE1 7QY, United Kingdom
(020) 7401 7904/(020) 7401 3378
chris@artistpartners.demon.co.uk
www.artistpartners.com

Kevin February@Meiklejohn Illustration 5 Risborough Street, London, SE1 0HF, United Kingdom
(020) 7593 0500/(020) 7593 0501
info@meiklejohn.co.uk
www.meiklejohn.co.uk

Kevin Jenkins@Folio 10 Gate Street, Lincoln's Inn Fields, London, WC2A 3HP, United Kingdom
(020) 7242 9562/(020) 7242 1816
all@folioart.co.uk
www.folioart.co.uk

Kevin Jones Associates 12 Marriott Road, Barnet, Hertfordshire, EN5 4NJ, United Kingdom
(020) 8449 2831
info@kja-artists.com
www.kja-artists.com

Kevin Kimber@Drawer Illustrators Agents 8 Belmont, Bath, BA1 5DZ, United Kingdom
(01225) 445262
enquiries@drawer.me.uk

Kevin Lyles Hill View, 38 Boswick Lane, Berkhamsted, Hertfordshire, HP4 3TE, United Kingdom
(01442) 865763
kevinlyles@freezone.co.uk

Kevin Tweddell@Artist Partners Ltd 2e The Chandlery, 50 Westminster Bridge Road, London, SE1 7QY, United Kingdom
(020) 7401 7904/(020) 7401 3378
chris@artistpartners.demon.co.uk
www.artistpartners.com

Kevin White Inglenook Cottage, 2 Albion Road, Marden, Kent, TN12 9EF, United Kingdom
(01622) 831252/(07050) 157906 (01622) 831252
kevin@kwillustrations.co.uk
www.kwillustrations.co.uk

Kid Acne@Blunt Management The Courtyard Studio 2, Old Grammarphone Works, London, W10 5BZ, United Kingdom
(020) 8960 2041/(07979) 900068 (020) 8960 2039
info@bluntlondon.com
www.bluntlondon.com

Kid Spaniard@Début Art & The Coningsby Gallery 30 Tottenham Street, London, W1T 4RJ, United Kingdom
(020) 7636 1064/(020) 7580 7017
info@debutart.com
www.debutart.com

Kim Anderson 139 Braeside Avenue, Brighton, BN1 8SQ, United Kingdom
(01273) 509881
ksa74@hotmail.com
www.contactacreative.com

Kim McGillivray@Début Art & The Coningsby Gallery 30 Tottenham Street, London, W1T 4RJ, United Kingdom
(020) 7636 1064/(020) 7580 7017
info@debutart.com
www.debutart.com

Kim Smith@Eastwing 99 Chase Side, Enfield, Middlesex, EN2 6NL, United Kingdom
(020) 8367 6760/(020) 8367 6730
andrea@eastwing.co.uk
www.eastwing.co.uk

Kiosk Design & Print No 2, 43 High Street, Leamington Spa, Warwickshire, CV31 1NL, United Kingdom
(01926) 776282/(01926) 776282
info@kioskgraphics.co.uk
www.kioskgraphics.co.uk

Kipper Williams 6 Windmill Street, London, W1P 1HF, United Kingdom
(020) 7636 0911

Kira Josey@Illustration Ltd 2 Brooks Court, Cringle Street, London, SW8 5BX, United Kingdom
(020) 7720 5202/(020) 7720 5920
team@illustrationweb.com
www.illustrationweb.com

Kirsty Wilson@Graham-Cameron Illustration The Studio, 23 Holt Road, Sheringham, Norfolk, NR26 8NB, United Kingdom
(01263) 821333/(01263) 821334
enquiry@graham-cameron-illustration.com
www.graham-cameron-illustration.com

KJA-artists.com 12 Marriott Road, Barnet, Hertfordshire, EN5 4NJ, United Kingdom
(020) 8449 2831
info@kja-artists.com
www.kja-artists.com

Kristel Steenbergen@Advocate Art 39 Church Road, London, SW19 5DQ, United Kingdom
020 8879 1166/020 8879 3303
lesley@advocate-art.com
www.advocate-art.com

Krister Flodin Tranarövägen 22, Ingarö, SE-134 64, Sweden
0046 70 847 52 44
krister@flodin.biz
www.flodin.biz

Kristian Olson@Central Illustration Agency 36 Wellington Street, London, WC2E 7BD, United Kingdom
(020) 7240 8925/(020) 7836 1177
info@centralillustration.com
www.centralillustration.com

Kristian Russell@Big Active Ltd Unit 6.01, The Tea Building, 56 Shoreditch High Street, London, E16 JJ, United Kingdom
(020) 7739 5601/(020) 7739 7479
contact@bigactive.com
www.bigactive.com

Kristina Krinn@Advocate Art 39 Church Road, London, SW19 5DQ, United Kingdom
020 8879 1166/020 8879 3303
lesley@advocate-art.com
www.advocate-art.com

Kyle Deltella@Advocate Art 39 Church Road, London, SW19 5DQ, United Kingdom
020 8879 1166/020 8879 3303
lesley@advocate-art.com
www.advocate-art.com

LairdSquared Wrenswood, Chope Road, Northam, Bideford, Devon, EX39 3QE, United Kingdom
(01237) 479397
tim@lairdsquared.co.uk
www.lairdsquared.co.uk

Lara Ede@Advocate Art 39 Church Road, London, SW19 5DQ, United Kingdom
020 8879 1166/020 8879 3303
lesley@advocate-art.com
www.advocate-art.com

Larry Rostant@Artist Partners Ltd 2e The Chandlery, 50 Westminster Bridge Road, London, SE1 7QY, United Kingdom
(020) 7401 7904/(020) 7401 3378
chris@artistpartners.demon.co.uk
www.artistpartners.com

Lars Rehnberg@Art Market 51 Oxford Drive, London, SE1 2FB, United Kingdom
(020) 7407 8111/(020) 7407 8222
info@artmarketillustration.com
www.artmarketillustration.com

Laura Ellison@The Organisation The Basement, 69 Caledonian Road, London, N1 9BT, United Kingdom
(020) 7833 8268/(07973) 172902 (020) 7833 8269
organise@easynet.co.uk
www.organisart.co.uk

Laura Scott 8 Belmont, Bath, BA1 5DZ, United Kingdom
(01225) 445262

Lauren Bishop Illustration Hove Street, Hove, East Sussex, BN3 2TS, United Kingdom
(07753) 743800
lauren17483@hotmail.com
www.laurenbishopillustration.co.uk

Lauren Child@David Higham 5-8 Lower John Street, Golden Square, London, W1F 9HA, United Kingdom
(020) 7437 7888/(020) 7437 1072
carolinewalsh@davidhigham.co.uk
www.davidhigham.co.uk

Laurence Clevet-Merle@Illustration Ltd 2 Brooks Court, Cringle Street, London, SW8 5BX, United Kingdom
(020) 7720 5202/(020) 7720 5920
team@illustrationweb.com
www.illustrationweb.com

Laurence Whilteley@N B Illustration Ltd 40 Bowling Green Lane, London, EC1R 0NE, United Kingdom
(020) 7278 9131/(020) 7278 9121
info@nbillustration.co.uk
www.nbillustration.co.uk

Laurie Rosenwald@Début Art & The Coningsby Gallery 30 Tottenham Street, London, W1T 4RJ, United Kingdom
(020) 7636 1064/(020) 7580 7017
info@debutart.com
www.debutart.com

Lavapepper 38 Weir Road, London, SW12 0NA, United Kingdom
(07050) 192354/(07050) 286044
its@lavapepper.com
www.lavapepper.com

Lawrie Taylor@Bernard Thornton Artists The Penthouse, 4 Hamilton Mews, 310 Merton Road, London, SW18 5AB, United Kingdom
(020) 8874 9081/(07702) 554583 (020) 8877 1386
bernard@btartists.com
www.btartists.com

Lee John Rouse 404 St. Albans Road, Watford, WD24 6PJ, United Kingdom
(01923) 247538/(07968) 196914
studio@leejohnrouse.co.uk
www.leejohnrouse.co.uk

Lee Montgomery@Illustration Ltd 2 Brooks Court, Cringle Street, London, SW8 5BX, United Kingdom
(020) 7720 5202/(020) 7720 5920
team@illustrationweb.com
www.illustrationweb.com

Lee Stannard 38 St. Dunstan Road, London, W6 8RB, United Kingdom
(020) 8846 9252/(07980) 958726 (020) 8846 9252
art@leestannard.demon.co.uk
www.leestanard.com

Leighton Noyes@Graham-Cameron Illustration The Studio, 23 Holt Road, Sheringham, Norfolk, NR26 8NB, United Kingdom
(01263) 821333/(01263) 821334
enquiry@graham-cameron-illustration.com
www.graham-cameron-illustration.com

Leming Design Studio, Kharkiv, 61000, Ukraine
00 380 50 2240450
admin@lemingdesign.com
lemingdesign.com

Lemonade Illustration Agency Hill House, Suite 231, 210 Upper Richmond Road, London, SW15 6NP, United Kingdom
(07891) 390750
info@lemonadeillustration.com
www.lemonadeillustration.com

Lena Sjoberg@The Organisation The Basement, 69 Caledonian Road, London, N1 9BT, United Kingdom
(020) 7833 8268/(07973) 172902 (020) 7833 8269
organise@easynet.co.uk
www.organisart.co.uk

Leo Duff Osborne Villa, 29 Bellevue Road, Kingston upon Thames, Surrey, KT1 2UD, United Kingdom
(020) 8549 3598/(020) 8287 7614
l.duff@kingston.ac.uk

Leo Hillier Illustration, Huntingdon, Cambridgeshire, PE29 2HR, United Kingdom
leo@leohillier.com
www.leohillier.com

Leo Stevenson@Folio 10 Gate Street, Lincoln's Inn Fields, London, WC2A 3HP, United Kingdom
(020) 7242 9562/(020) 7242 1816
all@folioart.co.uk
www.folioart.co.uk

Leo Timmers@Thorogood Illustration Ltd 5 Dryden Street, Covent Garden, London, WC2E 9NW, United Kingdom
(020) 7829 8468
draw@thorogood.net
www.thorogood.net

Leonardo Meschini@Advocate Art 39 Church Road, London, SW19 5DQ, United Kingdom
020 8879 1166/020 8879 3303
lesley@advocate-art.com
www.advocate-art.com

Leonello Calvetti@Central Illustration Agency 36 Wellington Street, London, WC2E 7BD, United Kingdom
(020) 7240 8925/(020) 7836 1177
info@centralillustration.com
www.centralillustration.com

Leonie Lord@Inkshed 99 Chase Side, Enfield, Middlesex, EN2 6NL, United Kingdom
☎ (020) 8367 4545/ (020) 8367 6730
🖵 www.inkshed.co.uk

Lesley Buckingham@Central Illustration Agency 36 Wellington Street, London, WC2E 7BD, United Kingdom
☎ (020) 7240 8925/ (020) 7836 1177
✎ info@centralillustration.com
🖵 www.centralillustration.com

Lesley Champkins 104 Glennie Road, London, SE27 0LU, United Kingdom
☎ (020) 8670 6903

Lewis Evans 90 Kennedy Court, Stonehouse Drive, St. Leonards-on-Sea, East Sussex, TN38 9DH, United Kingdom
☎ (01424) 202992

Liane Payne@N B Illustration Ltd 40 Bowling Green Lane, London, EC1R 0NE, United Kingdom
☎ (020) 7278 9131/ (020) 7278 9121
✎ info@nbillustration.co.uk
🖵 www.nbillustration.co.uk

Liesl Wilson@Advocate Art 39 Church Road, London, SW19 5DQ, United Kingdom
☎ 020 8879 1166/020 8879 3303
✎ lesley@advocate-art.com
🖵 www.advocate-art.com

Linda Boddy Plantivel, Allemans, Riberac, 24600, France
☎ 5 53 91 22 69/6 74 23 31 55

Linda Bronson@Illustration Ltd 2 Brooks Court, Cringle Street, London, SW8 5BX, United Kingdom
☎ (020) 7720 5202/ (020) 7720 5920
✎ team@illustrationweb.com
🖵 www.illustrationweb.com

Linda Clark@Phosphor Art 41 The Pump House, Pump House Close, off Renforth Street, London, SE16 7HS, United Kingdom
☎ (020) 7064 4666/ (020) 7064 4660
✎ info@phosphorart.com
🖵 www.phosphorart.com

Linda Combi 17 Albemarle Road, York, YO23 1EW, United Kingdom
☎ (01904) 623036
✎ linda@combi.wanadoo.co.uk
🖵 www.contact-me.net/lindacombi

Linda Herd 70A Ferry Road, Leith, Edinburgh, EH6 4AH, United Kingdom
☎ 0131-554 5633
✎ gardenerherd@blueyonder.co.uk

Linda M. Farquharson Borelick Farm House, Dunkeld, Perthshire, PH8 0BX, United Kingdom
☎ 01350-723 330/(07890) 833937
✎ linda@linocut.co.uk
🖵 www.linocut.co.uk

Linda Rogers Associates 163 Half Moon Lane, London, SE24 9WB, United Kingdom
☎ (020) 7501 9106
✎ lr@lindarogers.net
🖵 www.lindarogers.net

Linda Smith 21 Upper Camden Place, Bath, BA1 5HX, United Kingdom
☎ (01225) 333492/ (01225) 333492

Linden Artists Ltd 41 Battersea Business Centre, 103 Lavender Hill, London, SW11 5QL, United Kingdom
☎ (020) 7738 2505/ (020) 7738 2513
✎ lindenartists@aol.com
🖵 www.lindenartists.co.uk

Lindsay Graham@Linden Artists Ltd 41 Battersea Business Centre, 103 Lavender Hill, London, SW11 5QL, United Kingdom
☎ (020) 7738 2505/ (020) 7738 2513
✎ lindenartists@aol.com
🖵 www.lindenartists.co.uk

Lindy Norton@The Organisation The Basement, 69 Caledonian Road, London, N1 9BT, United Kingdom
☎ (020) 7833 8268/(07973) 172902/ (020) 7833 8269
✎ organise@easynet.co.uk
🖵 www.organisart.co.uk

Linzi Henry 5 Ashfurlong Close, Dore, Sheffield, S17 3NN, United Kingdom
☎ 0114-236 7481

Lisa Alderson@Advocate Art 39 Church Road, London, SW19 5DQ, United Kingdom
☎ 020 8879 1166/020 8879 3303
✎ lesley@advocate-art.com
🖵 www.advocate-art.com

Lisa Evans@Folio 10 Gate Street, Lincoln's Inn Fields, London, WC2A 3HP, United Kingdom
☎ (020) 7242 9562/ (020) 7242 1816
✎ all@folioart.co.uk
🖵 www.folioart.co.uk

Lisa Kopper Acton Court, Latteridge Road, Bristol, BS37 9TL, United Kingdom
☎ (01454) 227257/ (01454) 227256
✎ lisak@dircon.co.uk

Liz Butler 33 Alexandra Road, Chiswick, London, W4 1AX, United Kingdom
☎ (020) 8994 5311/ (020) 8747 8200
✎ lizbutler@pinn33.freeserve.co.uk

Liz Clements@Advocate Art 39 Church Road, London, SW19 5DQ, United Kingdom
☎ 020 8879 1166/020 8879 3303
✎ lesley@advocate-art.com
🖵 www.advocate-art.com

Liz Couldwell@Début Art & The Coningsby Gallery 30 Tottenham Street, London, W1T 4RJ, United Kingdom
☎ (020) 7636 1064/ (020) 7580 7017
✎ info@debutart.com
🖵 www.debutart.com

Liz Pepperell@Illustration Ltd 2 Brooks Court, Cringle Street, London, SW8 5BX, United Kingdom
☎ (020) 7720 5202/ (020) 7720 5920
✎ team@illustrationweb.com
🖵 www.illustrationweb.com

Liz Pichon Oakwood Lodge, 259 Preston Road, Brighton, BN1 6SE, United Kingdom
☎ (01273) 690605/(07899) 013681/ (01273) 690605
✎ liz.pichon@mistral.co.uk
🖵 www.lizpichon.co.uk

Lizze Gardiner@Inkshed 99 Chase Side, Enfield, Middlesex, EN2 6NL, United Kingdom
☎ (020) 8367 4545/ (020) 8367 6730
🖵 www.inkshed.co.uk

Lizzie Collcutt@N B Illustration Ltd 40 Bowling Green Lane, London, EC1R 0NE, United Kingdom
☎ (020) 7278 9131/ (020) 7278 9121
✎ info@nbillustration.co.uk
🖵 www.nbillustration.co.uk

Lizzie Robinson@Advocate Art 39 Church Road, London, SW19 5DQ, United Kingdom
☎ 020 8879 1166/020 8879 3303
✎ lesley@advocate-art.com
🖵 www.advocate-art.com

Lizzie Sanders@Artist Partners Ltd 2e The Chandlery, 50 Westminster Bridge Road, London, SE1 7QY, United Kingdom
☎ (020) 7401 7904/ (020) 7401 3378
✎ chris@artistpartners.demon.co.uk
🖵 www.artistpartners.com

Lo Cole@Inkshed 99 Chase Side, Enfield, Middlesex, EN2 6NL, United Kingdom
☎ (020) 8367 4545/ (020) 8367 6730
🖵 www.inkshed.co.uk

Lola & Rosanas@Folio 10 Gate Street, Lincoln's Inn Fields, London, WC2A 3HP, United Kingdom
☎ (020) 7242 9562/ (020) 7242 1816
✎ all@folioart.co.uk
🖵 www.folioart.co.uk

Longneck Afgan Road 27, Battersea, London, SW11 2QD,
☎ 7506018062
✎ vlad@longneck.ro
🖵 www.longneck.ro

Lord John Vernon 4 Orchard Lane, Ditchling, Hassocks, West Sussex, BN6 8TH, United Kingdom
☎ (01273) 844718

Lorna Siviter@The Organisation The Basement, 69 Caledonian Road, London, N1 9BT, United Kingdom
☎ (020) 7833 8268/(07973) 172902/ (020) 7833 8269
✎ organise@easynet.co.uk
🖵 www.organisart.co.uk

Louisa St Pierre@Central Illustration Agency 36 Wellington Street, London, WC2E 7BD, United Kingdom
☎ (020) 7240 8925/ (020) 7836 1177
✎ info@centralillustration.com
🖵 www.centralillustration.com

Louise Alexander@Drawer Illustrators Agents 8 Belmont, Bath, BA1 5DZ, United Kingdom
☎ (01225) 445262
✎ enquiries@drawer.me.uk

Louise Anglicas@Advocate Art 39 Church Road, London, SW19 5DQ, United Kingdom
☎ 020 8879 1166/020 8879 3303
✎ lesley@advocate-art.com
🖵 www.advocate-art.com

Louise Brierley@Central Illustration Agency 36 Wellington Street, London, WC2E 7BD, United Kingdom
☎ (020) 7240 8925/ (020) 7836 1177
✎ info@centralillustration.com
🖵 www.centralillustration.com

Louise Daykin@Graham-Cameron Illustration The Studio, 23 Holt Road, Sheringham, Norfolk, NR26 8NB, United Kingdom
☎ (01263) 821333/ (01263) 821334
✎ enquiry@graham-cameron-illustration.com
🖵 www.graham-cameron-illustration.com

Louise Ellis@The Organisation The Basement, 69 Caledonian Road, London, N1 9BT, United Kingdom
☎ (020) 7833 8268/(07973) 172902/ (020) 7833 8269
✎ organise@easynet.co.uk
🖵 www.organisart.co.uk

Louise Hilton@N B Illustration Ltd 40 Bowling Green Lane, London, EC1R 0NE, United Kingdom
☎ (020) 7278 9131/ (020) 7278 9121
✎ info@nbillustration.co.uk
🖵 www.nbillustration.co.uk

Louise Maxwell 30 Morland House, Marsham Street, London, SW1P 4JH, United Kingdom
☎ (020) 7821 0340/(07957) 377479

Louise Morgan@Art Market 51 Oxford Drive, London, SE1 2FB, United Kingdom
☎ (020) 7407 8111/ (020) 7407 8222
✎ info@artmarketillustration.com
🖵 www.artmarketillustration.com

Louise Wallace@Inkshed 99 Chase Side, Enfield, Middlesex, EN2 6NL, United Kingdom
☎ (020) 8367 4545/ (020) 8367 6730
🖵 www.inkshed.co.uk

Louise Weir@Début Art & The Coningsby Gallery 30 Tottenham Street, London, W1T 4RJ, United Kingdom
☎ (020) 7636 1064/ (020) 7580 7017
✎ info@debutart.com
🖵 www.debutart.com

Loupe Images 20-21 Jockey's Fields, London, WC1R 4BW United Kingdom
☎ (020) 7025 2249
✎ info@loupeimages.com
🖵 www.loupeimages.com

LSD | Brand Designer L Martinez 983, (Martinez), Buenos Aires, 1460,
☎ 54 11 4798 1760/ 54 11 4798 1760
✎ luzsoldano@sion.com
🖵 www.luzsoldano.com

Luc Janin@Phosphor Art 41 The Pump House, Pump House Close, off Renforth Street, London, SE16 7HS, United Kingdom
☎ (020) 7064 4666/ (020) 7064 4660
✎ info@phosphorart.com
🖵 www.phosphorart.com

Lucian Marin, Bucharest, 61079, Romania
☎ 721 230 631
✎ lucian.marin@gmail.com
🖵 www.lucianmarin.ro

Lucy Barnard@Advocate Art 39 Church Road, London, SW19 5DQ, United Kingdom
☎ 020 8879 1166/020 8879 3303
✎ lesley@advocate-art.com
🖵 www.advocate-art.com

Lucy Davey@The Artworks 40 Frith Street, London, W1D 5LN, United Kingdom
☎ (020) 7734 3333/ (020) 7734 3484
✎ lucy@theartworksinc.com
🖵 www.theartworksinc.com

Lucy Macleod@Private View Artists Agency 17A Swan Hill, Shrewsbury, SY1 1NL, United Kingdom
☎ (01743) 350355/ (01743) 233923
✎ create@pvuk.com
🖵 www.pvuk.com

Lucy Maddison 11 Estreham Road, London, SW16 5NT, United Kingdom
- (020) 8677 5724/ (0870) 1604571
- info@lucymaddison.com
- www.lucymaddison.com

Lucy Truman@New Division 5 Risborough Street, London, SE1 0HF, United Kingdom
- (020) 7593 0505/ (020) 7593 0501
- info@newdivision.com
- www.newdivision.com

Lucy Weller@Début Art & The Coningsby Gallery 30 Tottenham Street, London, W1T 4RJ, United Kingdom
- (020) 7636 1064/ (020) 7580 7017
- info@debutart.com
- www.debutart.com

Luella Wright@Advocate Art 39 Church Road, London, SW19 5DQ, United Kingdom
- 020 8879 1166/020 8879 3303
- lesley@advocate-art.com
- www.advocate-art.com

Luisa Bucciero@Sarah Lane Represents 56 Bidwell Gardens, London, N11 2AU, United Kingdom
- (07901) 552520/ (020) 8292 4001
- sarah@sarahlanerepresents.com
- www.sarahlanerepresents.com

Luke Feldman@Advocate Art 39 Church Road, London, SW19 5DQ, United Kingdom
- 020 8879 1166/020 8879 3303
- lesley@advocate-art.com
- www.advocate-art.com

Luke Finlayson@Advocate Art 39 Church Road, London, SW19 5DQ, United Kingdom
- 020 8879 1166/020 8879 3303
- lesley@advocate-art.com
- www.advocate-art.com

Luke Moloney, Architect 24 Queen Street, Dumfries, Dumfriesshire, DG1 2JF,
- 01387 259338/ 01387 259338
- info@lukemoloneyarchitect.co.uk
- www.lukemoloneyarchitect.co.uk

Lyn Gray@Graham-Cameron Illustration The Studio, 23 Holt Road, Sheringham, Norfolk, NR26 8NB, United Kingdom
- (01263) 821333/ (01263) 821334
- enquiry@graham-cameron-illustration.com
- www.graham-cameron-illustration.com

Lynn Breeze@Linden Artists Ltd 41 Battersea Business Centre, 103 Lavender Hill, London, SW11 5QL, United Kingdom
- (020) 7738 2505/ (020) 7738 2513
- lindenartists@aol.com
- www.lindenartists.co.uk

Lynn Horrabin@Advocate Art 39 Church Road, London, SW19 5DQ, United Kingdom
- 020 8879 1166/020 8879 3303
- lesley@advocate-art.com
- www.advocate-art.com

M R 2 Design West Barn, Great Whittington, Newcastle upon Tyne, NE19 2HA, United Kingdom
- (01434) 672461
- mr2web@ndirect.co.uk
- www.contact-me.net/MikeRitchie

M.H. Jeeves@Central Illustration Agency 36 Wellington Street, London, WC2E 7BD, United Kingdom
- (020) 7240 8925/ (020) 7836 1177
- info@centralillustration.com
- www.centralillustration.com

M.P. Robertson@Arena 31 Eleanor Road, London, E15 4AB, United Kingdom
- (08450) 507 600
- info@arenaworks.com
- www.arenaworks.com

M&M Creative High Trees, Bishops Down Park Road, Tunbridge Wells, Kent, TN4 8XU,
- 01892 533103
- mike@mandmcreative.co.uk
- www.mandmcreative.co.uk

Mac McIntosh 5 Worley Road, St. Albans, Hertfordshire, AL3 5NR, United Kingdom
- (01727) 844839/ (01727) 844839
- lesmacs@btinternet.com

Maik Wolfram@Graham-Cameron Illustration The Studio, 23 Holt Road, Sheringham, Norfolk, NR26 8NB, United Kingdom
- (01263) 821333/ (01263) 821334
- enquiry@graham-cameron-illustration.com
- www.graham-cameron-illustration.com

Malcolm Bird Oaker Glen, Sowerby Road, Cumbria, CA4 0QG, United Kingdom
- (01697) 476123
- birdanddart@aol.com
- www.malcolm-bird.co.uk

Malcolm Stokes@Linden Artists Ltd 41 Battersea Business Centre, 103 Lavender Hill, London, SW11 5QL, United Kingdom
- (020) 7738 2505/ (020) 7738 2513
- lindenartists@aol.com
- www.lindenartists.co.uk

Malcolm Tween@Meiklejohn Illustration 5 Risborough Street, London, SE1 0HF, United Kingdom
- (020) 7593 0500/ (020) 7593 0501
- info@meiklejohn.co.uk
- www.meiklejohn.co.uk

Mandy Field@Phosphor Art 41 The Pump House, Pump House Close, off Renforth Street, London, SE16 7HS, United Kingdom
- (020) 7064 4666/ (020) 7064 4660
- info@phosphorart.com
- www.phosphorart.com

Manic Illustrations 2 Rose Cottages, Spring Lane, Thrupp, Stroud, Gloucestershire, GL5 2DS, United Kingdom
- (07708) 018651
- dianeyoung@hotmail.com
- www.manicillustrators.com

Manny Curtis 10 Datchworth Court, Village Road, Enfield, Middlesex, EN1 2DS, United Kingdom
- (020) 8366 5389/ (020) 8342 1996
- manecurtis@aol.com
- www.cartooningcurtis.co.uk

MAP 72 Rochester Place, London, NW1 9JX, United Kingdom
- (020) 7424 9144/ (020) 7284 3274
- info@mapltd.com
- www.mapltd.com

MAPgrafix Westcroft, Northchurch Common, Berkhamsted, Hertfordshire, HP4 1LR, United Kingdom
- (01442) 863 745/(07743) 942727/ (0870) 0515410
- jluff@mapgrafix.com
- www.mapgrafix.com

Maran@Advocate Art 39 Church Road, London, SW19 5DQ, United Kingdom
- 020 8879 1166/020 8879 3303
- lesley@advocate-art.com
- www.advocate-art.com

Marc Arundale@Meiklejohn Illustration 5 Risborough Street, London, SE1 0HF, United Kingdom
- (020) 7593 0500/ (020) 7593 0501
- info@meiklejohn.co.uk
- www.meiklejohn.co.uk

Marc Vyvyan-Jones 1 Cross Cottage, 2 St Andrews Road, Stogursey, Bridgwater, Somerset, TA5 1TE, United Kingdom
- (01278) 733377

Marcelo Corti@Advocate Art 39 Church Road, London, SW19 5DQ, United Kingdom
- 020 8879 1166/020 8879 3303
- lesley@advocate-art.com
- www.advocate-art.com

Marcin Baranski@The Artworks 40 Frith Street, London, W1D 5LN, United Kingdom
- (020) 7734 3333/ (020) 7734 3484
- lucy@theartworksinc.com
- www.theartworksinc.com

Marco Schaaf@N B Illustration Ltd 40 Bowling Green Lane, London, EC1R 0NE, United Kingdom
- (020) 7278 9131/ (020) 7278 9121
- info@nbillustration.co.uk
- www.nbillustration.co.uk

Marco Ventura@The Artworks 40 Frith Street, London, W1D 5LN, United Kingdom
- (020) 7734 3333/ (020) 7734 3484
- lucy@theartworksinc.com
- www.theartworksinc.com

Margaret Anne Suggs@Graham-Cameron Illustration The Studio, 23 Holt Road, Sheringham, Norfolk, NR26 8NB, United Kingdom
- (01263) 821333/ (01263) 821334
- enquiry@graham-cameron-illustration.com
- www.graham-cameron-illustration.com

Margaret Wellbank@Drawer Illustrators Agents 8 Belmont, Bath, BA1 5DZ, United Kingdom
- (01225) 445262
- enquiries@drawer.me.uk

Maria Cardelli@Illustration Ltd 2 Brooks Court, Cringle Street, London, SW8 5BX, United Kingdom
- (020) 7720 5202/ (020) 7720 5920
- team@illustrationweb.com
- www.illustrationweb.com

Maria Colino@Folio 10 Gate Street, Lincoln's Inn Fields, London, WC2A 3HP, United Kingdom
- (020) 7242 9562/ (020) 7242 1816
- all@folioart.co.uk
- www.folioart.co.uk

Maria Maddocks@The Organisation The Basement, 69 Caledonian Road, London, N1 9BT, United Kingdom
- (020) 7833 8268/(07973) 172902/ (020) 7833 8269
- organise@easynet.co.uk
- www.organisart.co.uk

Maria Raymondsdotter@Central Illustration Agency 36 Wellington Street, London, WC2E 7BD, United Kingdom
- (020) 7240 8925/ (020) 7836 1177
- info@centralillustration.com
- www.centralillustration.com

Maria Woods@Advocate Art 39 Church Road, London, SW19 5DQ, United Kingdom
- 020 8879 1166/020 8879 3303
- lesley@advocate-art.com
- www.advocate-art.com

Marian Hill@Inkshed 99 Chase Side, Enfield, Middlesex, EN2 6NL, United Kingdom
- (020) 8367 4545/ (020) 8367 6730
- www.inkshed.co.uk

Mariano Pérez Clemente@Advocate Art 39 Church Road, London, SW19 5DQ, United Kingdom
- 020 8879 1166/020 8879 3303
- lesley@advocate-art.com
- www.advocate-art.com

Marie Allen@Advocate Art 39 Church Road, London, SW19 5DQ, United Kingdom
- 020 8879 1166/020 8879 3303
- lesley@advocate-art.com
- www.advocate-art.com

Marie Bastille 47 Rue de Douai, Paris, 75009, France
- 00 33 14 52 67 00 9
- marie@mariebastille.com
- www.mariebastillle.com

Marijan Ramljak@Advocate Art 39 Church Road, London, SW19 5DQ, United Kingdom
- 020 8879 1166/020 8879 3303
- lesley@advocate-art.com
- www.advocate-art.com

Marina Fedotova@Advocate Art 39 Church Road, London, SW19 5DQ, United Kingdom
- 020 8879 1166/020 8879 3303
- lesley@advocate-art.com
- www.advocate-art.com

Marina Le Ray @Advocate Art 39 Church Road, London, SW19 5DQ, United Kingdom
- 020 8879 1166/020 8879 3303
- lesley@advocate-art.com
- www.advocate-art.com

Mario Belem@Début Art & The Coningsby Gallery 30 Tottenham Street, London, W1T 4RJ, United Kingdom
- (020) 7636 1064/ (020) 7580 7017
- info@debutart.com
- www.debutart.com

Marius Shafer 19 Queensway, Frimley Green, Camberley, Surrey, GU16 6QB, United Kingdom
- (01252) 835749/(07811) 946981/ (01252) 836032
- shafer@ntlworld.com
- www.marius-shafer.com

Mark Blade@New Division 5 Risborough Street, London, SE1 0HF, United Kingdom
- (020) 7593 0505/ (020) 7593 0501
- info@newdivision.com
- www.newdivision.com

Mark Di Meo@Linda Rogers Associates 163 Half Moon Lane, London, SE24 9WB, United Kingdom
- (020) 7501 9106
- lr@lindarogers.net
- www.lindarogers.net

Mark Dickson@Folio 10 Gate Street, Lincoln's Inn Fields, London, WC2A 3HP, United Kingdom
- (020) 7242 9562/ (020) 7242 1816
- all@folioart.co.uk
- www.folioart.co.uk

Mark Edwards@Artist Partners Ltd 2e The Chandlery, 50 Westminster Bridge Road, London, SE1 7QY, United Kingdom
- (020) 7401 7904/ (020) 7401 3378
- chris@artistpartners.demon.co.uk
- www.artistpartners.com

Mark Franklin 41 Borwick Avenue, London, E17 6RA, United Kingdom
- (07793) 753173
- mail@markfranklinarts.co.uk
- www.markfranklinarts.co.uk

Mark Hackett 9 Fairfield Terrace, Bath, BA1 6HN, United Kingdom
- (01225) 337401/(07752) 522845 / (01225) 337401
- hackettmarcus@yahoo.co.uk
- www.markhackett.co.uk

Mark Hooley@Drawer Illustrators Agents 8 Belmont, Bath, BA1 5DZ, United Kingdom
- (01225) 445262
- enquiries@drawer.me.uk

Mark Marella@Phosphor Art 41 The Pump House, Pump House Close, off Renforth Street, London, SE16 7HS, United Kingdom
- (020) 7064 4666/ (020) 7064 4660
- info@phosphorart.com
- www.phosphorart.com

Mark Moran@Inkshed 99 Chase Side, Enfield, Middlesex, EN2 6NL, United Kingdom
- (020) 8367 4545/ (020) 8367 6730
- www.inkshed.co.uk

Mark Oldroyd@Arena 31 Eleanor Road, London, E15 4AB, United Kingdom
- (08450) 507 600
- info@arenaworks.com
- www.arenaworks.com

Mark Oliver@Illustration Ltd 2 Brooks Court, Cringle Street, London, SW8 5BX, United Kingdom
- (020) 7720 5202/ (020) 7720 5920
- team@illustrationweb.com
- www.illustrationweb.com

Mark Pacan 25 Windmill Road, Irthlingborough, Wellingborough, Northamptonshire, NN9 5RJ, United Kingdom
- (01933) 652062
- mark@pacan.com
- www.pacan.com

Mark Thomas@Central Illustration Agency 36 Wellington Street, London, WC2E 7BD, United Kingdom
- (020) 7240 8925/ (020) 7836 1177
- info@centralillustration.com
- www.centralillustration.com

Mark Watkinson@Illustration Ltd 2 Brooks Court, Cringle Street, London, SW8 5BX, United Kingdom
- (020) 7720 5202/ (020) 7720 5920
- team@illustrationweb.com
- www.illustrationweb.com

Mark Wood Cartoonist 22 Standen Street, Tunbridge Wells, Kent, TN4 9RJ, United Kingdom
- (01892) 539332
- mark@markwoodcartoonist.co.uk
- www.markwoodcartoonist.co.uk

Marsela Hajdinjak-Krec@Advocate Art 39 Church Road, London, SW19 5DQ, United Kingdom
- 020 8879 1166/020 8879 3303
- lesley@advocate-art.com
- www.advocate-art.com

Martha Hardy@Graham-Cameron Illustration The Studio, 23 Holt Road, Sheringham, Norfolk, NR26 8NB, United Kingdom
- (01263) 821333/ (01263) 821334
- enquiry@graham-cameron-illustration.com
- www.graham-cameron-illustration.com

Martin Ash Paintings Holmsley House, Holtye, Cowden, Kent, TN8 7ED, United Kingdom
- (01342) 850366/(07759) 925087 /
- ash_martin@tiscali.co.uk

Martin Chatterton@Inkshed 99 Chase Side, Enfield, Middlesex, EN2 6NL, United Kingdom
- (020) 8367 4545/ (020) 8367 6730
- www.inkshed.co.uk

Martin Goneau@Advocate Art 39 Church Road, London, SW19 5DQ, United Kingdom
- 020 8879 1166/020 8879 3303
- lesley@advocate-art.com
- www.advocate-art.com

Martin Haake@Central Illustration Agency 36 Wellington Street, London, WC2E 7BD, United Kingdom
- (020) 7240 8925/ (020) 7836 1177
- info@centralillustration.com
- www.centralillustration.com

Martin Hargreaves@Illustration Ltd 2 Brooks Court, Cringle Street, London, SW8 5BX, United Kingdom
- (020) 7720 5202/ (020) 7720 5920
- team@illustrationweb.com
- www.illustrationweb.com

Martin Honeysett 13 West Street, Hastings, East Sussex, TN34 3AN, United Kingdom
- (01424) 440249/ (01424) 440249
- martin.honeysett@kirion.net
- www.martinhoneysett.com

Martin Irish@Advocate Art 39 Church Road, London, SW19 5DQ, United Kingdom
- 020 8879 1166/020 8879 3303
- lesley@advocate-art.com
- www.advocate-art.com

Martin James McGuire 219 Kingspark Avenue, Glasgow, G44 4hz, United Kingdom
- 0141-649 2382/ 0141-649 2382
- mjmjmcguire@aol.com

Martin Jones Brabant, 11A Ward Road, Blundel Sands, Liverpool, L23 8TB, United Kingdom
- 0151-924 5160/(07891) 437072 / 0151-924 5160

Martin Macrae@N B Illustration Ltd 40 Bowling Green Lane, London, EC1R 0NE, United Kingdom
- (020) 7278 9131/ (020) 7278 9121
- info@nbillustration.co.uk
- www.nbillustration.co.uk

Martin McKenna@Sarah Brown Agency 10 The Avenue, Ealing, London, W13 8PH, United Kingdom
- (020) 8998 0390/(07778) 177102 / (020) 8843 1175
- sbagency@dsl.pipex.com
- www.sbagency.com

Martin O'Neill@Début Art & The Coningsby Gallery 30 Tottenham Street, London, W1T 4RJ, United Kingdom
- (020) 7636 1064/ (020) 7580 7017
- info@debutart.com
- www.debutart.com

Martin Remphry@Advocate Art 39 Church Road, London, SW19 5DQ, United Kingdom
- 020 8879 1166/020 8879 3303
- lesley@advocate-art.com
- www.advocate-art.com

Martin Salisbury@Linda Rogers Associates 163 Half Moon Lane, London, SE24 9WB, United Kingdom
- (020) 7501 9106
- lr@lindarogers.net
- www.lindarogers.net

Martin Shovel 13 Lancaster Road, Brighton, BN1 5DG, United Kingdom
- (01273) 249 813/ (0870) 169 6025
- info@shovel.co.uk
- www.shovel.co.uk

Martin Woodward 28 Dean Close, Rushden, Northamptonshire, NN10 9EH, United Kingdom
- (01933) 411966/ (01933) 411966
- tecmedi@ntlweld.com
- www.tecmedi.co.uk

Martina Farrow@New Division 5 Risborough Street, London, SE1 0HF, United Kingdom
- (020) 7593 0505/ (020) 7593 0501
- info@newdivision.com
- www.newdivision.com

Martine Blaney@Drawer Illustrators Agents 8 Belmont, Bath, BA1 5DZ, United Kingdom
- (01225) 445262
- enquiries@drawer.me.uk

Mary Hall@Linden Artists Ltd 41 Battersea Business Centre, 103 Lavender Hill, London, SW11 5QL, United Kingdom
- (020) 7738 2505/ (020) 7738 2513
- lindenartists@aol.com
- www.lindenartists.co.uk

Mary Kilvert@New Division 5 Risborough Street, London, SE1 0HF, United Kingdom
- (020) 7593 0505/ (020) 7593 0501
- info@newdivision.com
- www.newdivision.com

Mary Woodin@The Artworks 40 Frith Street, London, W1D 5LN, United Kingdom
- (020) 7734 3333/ (020) 7734 3484
- lucy@theartworksinc.com
- www.theartworksinc.com

Mass Technology (UK) Ltd 36b Evington Road, Leicester, Leicestershire, LE2 1HG,
- 0116 25 44 171
- masstechnology@hotmail.com
- www.masstechnologyonline.com

Mathew Russell@The Organisation The Basement, 69 Caledonian Road, London, N1 9BT, United Kingdom
- (020) 7833 8268/(07973) 172902 / (020) 7833 8269
- organise@easynet.co.uk
- www.organisart.co.uk

Matilda Harrison@Arena 31 Eleanor Road, London, E15 4AB, United Kingdom
- (08450) 507 600
- info@arenaworks.com
- www.arenaworks.com

Matt Buckingham@Arena 31 Eleanor Road, London, E15 4AB, United Kingdom
- (08450) 507 600
- info@arenaworks.com
- www.arenaworks.com

Matt Ferres@Advocate Art 39 Church Road, London, SW19 5DQ, United Kingdom
- 020 8879 1166/020 8879 3303
- lesley@advocate-art.com
- www.advocate-art.com

Matt Latchford@Advocate Art 39 Church Road, London, SW19 5DQ, United Kingdom
- 020 8879 1166/020 8879 3303
- lesley@advocate-art.com
- www.advocate-art.com

Matt Taylor@Private View Artists Agency 17A Swan Hill, Shrewsbury, SY1 1NL, United Kingdom
- (01743) 350355/ (01743) 233923
- create@pvuk.com
- www.pvuk.com

Matthew Cook@The Artworks 40 Frith Street, London, W1D 5LN, United Kingdom
- (020) 7734 3333/ (020) 7734 3484
- lucy@theartworksinc.com
- www.theartworksinc.com

Matthew Cooper@Début Art & The Coningsby Gallery 30 Tottenham Street, London, W1T 4RJ, United Kingdom
- (020) 7636 1064/ (020) 7580 7017
- info@debutart.com
- www.debutart.com

Matthew Herring@Début Art & The Coningsby Gallery 30 Tottenham Street, London, W1T 4RJ, United Kingdom
- (020) 7636 1064/ (020) 7580 7017
- info@debutart.com
- www.debutart.com

Matthew Howard 10 Lanercost Road, London, SW2 3DN, United Kingdom
- (07799) 416915
- mattychowee@yahoo.com
- www.matt-howard.com

Matthew Richardson@Eastwing 99 Chase Side, Enfield, Middlesex, EN2 6NL, United Kingdom
- (020) 8367 6760/ (020) 8367 6730
- andrea@eastwing.co.uk
- www.eastwing.co.uk

Matthew Robson@Illustration Ltd 2 Brooks Court, Cringle Street, London, SW8 5BX, United Kingdom
- (020) 7720 5202/ (020) 7720 5920
- team@illustrationweb.com
- www.illustrationweb.com

Matthew White 10 Dent De Lion Court, Garlinge, Margate, Kent, CT9 5LL, United Kingdom
- (01843) 833300/(07767) 457665 / (01843) 833300
- matthew@white-art.co.uk
- www.white-art.co.uk

Matthew Williams@The Organisation The Basement, 69 Caledonian Road, London, N1 9BT, United Kingdom
- (020) 7833 8268/(07973) 172902 / (020) 7833 8269
- organise@easynet.co.uk
- www.organisart.co.uk

Maureen Galvani@Linden Artists Ltd 41 Battersea Business Centre, 103 Lavender Hill, London, SW11 5QL, United Kingdom
(020) 7738 2505/ (020) 7738 2513
lindenartists@aol.com
www.lindenartists.co.uk

Maurice Pledger@Bernard Thornton Artists The Penthouse, 4 Hamilton Mews, 310 Merton Road, London, SW18 5AB, United Kingdom
(020) 8874 9081/(07702) 554583 (020) 8877 1386
bernard@btartists.com
www.btartists.com

Mauro Evangelista@Advocate Art 39 Church Road, London, SW19 5DQ, United Kingdom
020 8879 1166/020 8879 3303
lesley@advocate-art.com
www.advocate-art.com

Mauve@Début Art & The Coningsby Gallery 30 Tottenham Street, London, W1T 4RJ, United Kingdom
(020) 7636 1064/ (020) 7580 7017
info@debutart.com
www.debutart.com

Max Ellis@Central Illustration Agency 36 Wellington Street, London, WC2E 7BD, United Kingdom
(020) 7240 8925/ (020) 7836 1177
info@centralillustration.com
www.centralillustration.com

Max Schindler@Artist Partners Ltd 2e The Chandlery, 50 Westminster Bridge Road, London, SE1 7QY, United Kingdom
(020) 7401 7904/ (020) 7401 3378
chris@artistpartners.demon.co.uk
www.artistpartners.com

McFaul@Central Illustration Agency 36 Wellington Street, London, WC2E 7BD, United Kingdom
(020) 7240 8925/ (020) 7836 1177
info@centralillustration.com
www.centralillustration.com

Mdi-Digital 130 Mansfield Lane, Norwich, NR1 2LT, United Kingdom
(01603) 632005/ (01603) 632005
info@mdi-digital.com
www.mdi-digital.com

Meave Fitzsimons@Advocate Art 39 Church Road, London, SW19 5DQ, United Kingdom
020 8879 1166/020 8879 3303
lesley@advocate-art.com
www.advocate-art.com

Meiklejohn Illustration 5 Risborough Street, London, SE1 0HF, United Kingdom
(020) 7593 0500/ (020) 7593 0501
info@meiklejohn.co.uk
www.meiklejohn.co.uk

Meilo So@The Artworks 40 Frith Street, London, W1D 5LN, United Kingdom
(020) 7734 3333/ (020) 7734 3484
lucy@theartworksinc.com
www.theartworksinc.com

Melanie Lawrence@Advocate Art 39 Church Road, London, SW19 5DQ, United Kingdom
020 8879 1166/020 8879 3303
lesley@advocate-art.com
www.advocate-art.com

Melanie Mitchell@Advocate Art 39 Church Road, London, SW19 5DQ, United Kingdom
020 8879 1166/020 8879 3303
lesley@advocate-art.com
www.advocate-art.com

Melisande Luthringer@Advocate Art 39 Church Road, London, SW19 5DQ, United Kingdom
020 8879 1166/020 8879 3303
lesley@advocate-art.com
www.advocate-art.com

Melissa Evans Illustration Ltd 2b St. Johns Crescent, Canton, Cardiff, CF5 1NX, United Kingdom
(07780) 987540
melissajevans@hotmail.com

Melvyn Evans@New Division 5 Risborough Street, London, SE1 0HF, United Kingdom
(020) 7593 0505/ (020) 7593 0501
info@newdivision.com
www.newdivision.com

Melvyn Grant@Artist Partners Ltd 2e The Chandlery, 50 Westminster Bridge Road, London, SE1 7QY, United Kingdom
(020) 7401 7904/ (020) 7401 3378
chris@artistpartners.demon.co.uk
www.artistpartners.com

Michael Bramman 104 Dudley Court, Upper Berkeley Street, London, W1H 5QB, United Kingdom
(020) 7723 3564
michaelbramman@globalnet.co.uk
www.michaelbramman-illustration.co.uk

Michael Cartwright Flat 4, Tuttle House, Aylesford Street, London, SW1V 3RW, United Kingdom
(020) 7821 5573
mike@modernarts.freeserve.co.uk
mysite.wanadoo-members.co.uk/modernarts

Michael Cheung@Advocate Art 39 Church Road, London, SW19 5DQ, United Kingdom
020 8879 1166/020 8879 3303
lesley@advocate-art.com
www.advocate-art.com

Michael Crampton@Meiklejohn Illustration 5 Risborough Street, London, SE1 0HF, United Kingdom
(020) 7593 0500/ (020) 7593 0501
info@meiklejohn.co.uk
www.meiklejohn.co.uk

Michael Daley 15 Capel Road, East Barnet, Barnet, Hertfordshire, EN4 8JD, United Kingdom
(020) 8449 6351/ (020) 8440 9440
michael.daley8@btinternet.com

Michael Emmerson@Advocate Art 39 Church Road, London, SW19 5DQ, United Kingdom
020 8879 1166/020 8879 3303
lesley@advocate-art.com
www.advocate-art.com

Michael Frith@Illustration Ltd 2 Brooks Court, Cringle Street, London, SW8 5BX, United Kingdom
(020) 7720 5202/ (020) 7720 5920
team@illustrationweb.com
www.illustrationweb.com

Michael Halycz 25A Whitehorse Street, Baldock, Hertfordshire, SG7 6QB, United Kingdom
(01462) 892537/ (01462) 894247

Michael Munday@Inkshed 99 Chase Side, Enfield, Middlesex, EN2 6NL, United Kingdom
(020) 8367 4545/ (020) 8367 6730
www.inkshed.co.uk

Michael Worthy@Advocate Art 39 Church Road, London, SW19 5DQ, United Kingdom
020 8879 1166/020 8879 3303
lesley@advocate-art.com
www.advocate-art.com

Michaela Bloomfield 2 Hill Side Road, Reydon, Southwold, Suffolk, IP18 6RH, United Kingdom
(07850) 941256
michaelabloomfield@hotmail.com
www.contact-me.net/michaelabloomfield

Michel Streich@Début Art & The Coningsby Gallery 30 Tottenham Street, London, W1T 4RJ, United Kingdom
(020) 7636 1064/ (020) 7580 7017
info@debutart.com
www.debutart.com

Michela Galassi@Advocate Art 39 Church Road, London, SW19 5DQ, United Kingdom
020 8879 1166/020 8879 3303
lesley@advocate-art.com
www.advocate-art.com

Michelle Ives@Graham-Cameron Illustration The Studio, 23 Holt Road, Sheringham, Norfolk, NR26 8NB, United Kingdom
(01263) 821333/ (01263) 821334
enquiry@graham-cameron-illustration.com
www.graham-cameron-illustration.com

Michelle Mathers@Advocate Art 39 Church Road, London, SW19 5DQ, United Kingdom
020 8879 1166/020 8879 3303
lesley@advocate-art.com
www.advocate-art.com

Michelle Ross c/o 2 Gainford Avenue, Middlesbrough, Cleveland, TS5 7RF, United Kingdom
(01287) 669019
michelle.ross2@ntlworld.com
mysite.wanadoo-members.co.uk/MichelleRoss

Michelle Thompson@Inkshed 99 Chase Side, Enfield, Middlesex, EN2 6NL, United Kingdom
(020) 8367 4545/ (020) 8367 6730
www.inkshed.co.uk

Mick Brownfield@Central Illustration Agency 36 Wellington Street, London, WC2E 7BD, United Kingdom
(020) 7240 8925/ (020) 7836 1177
info@centralillustration.com
www.centralillustration.com

Mick Loates@Linden Artists Ltd 41 Battersea Business Centre, 103 Lavender Hill, London, SW11 5QL, United Kingdom
(020) 7738 2505/ (020) 7738 2513
lindenartists@aol.com
www.lindenartists.co.uk

Mick Marston@Central Illustration Agency 36 Wellington Street, London, WC2E 7BD, United Kingdom
(020) 7240 8925/ (020) 7836 1177
info@centralillustration.com
www.centralillustration.com

Mick Van Houten@Sarah Brown Agency 10 The Avenue, Ealing, London, W13 8PH, United Kingdom
(020) 8998 0390/(07778) 177102 (020) 8843 1175
sbagency@dsl.pipex.com
www.sbagency.com

Mignel Gallardo@The Artworks 40 Frith Street, London, W1D 5LN, United Kingdom
(020) 7734 3333/ (020) 7734 3484
lucy@theartworksinc.com
www.theartworksinc.com

Mijn Schatje 15 Rue Feutrier, Paris, 75018, France
00 33 06 71 92 39 07
marieisnotdead@hotmail.com
www.fotolog.net/mijnschatje

Mik Brown@Meiklejohn Illustration 5 Risborough Street, London, SE1 0HF, United Kingdom
(020) 7593 0500/ (020) 7593 0501
info@meiklejohn.co.uk
www.meiklejohn.co.uk

Mike Bell@Phosphor Art 41 The Pump House, Pump House Close, off Renforth Street, London, SE16 7HS, United Kingdom
(020) 7064 4666/ (020) 7064 4660
info@phosphorart.com
www.phosphorart.com

Mike Brownlow@David Higham 5-8 Lower John Street, Golden Square, London, W1F 9HA, United Kingdom
(020) 7437 7888/ (020) 7437 1072
carolinewalsh@davidhigham.co.uk
www.davidhigham.co.uk

Mike Gibbie@The Organisation The Basement, 69 Caledonian Road, London, N1 9BT, United Kingdom
(020) 7833 8268/(07973) 172902 (020) 7833 8269
organise@easynet.co.uk
www.organisart.co.uk

Mike Lye The Old Parsonage, Beaford, Winkleigh, Devon, EX19 8AQ, United Kingdom
(01805) 603306/ (01805) 603306
illustration@mikelye.co.uk

Mike Moran 44 St. Lukes Crescent, Totterdown, Bristol, BS3 4SD, United Kingdom
0117-971 9389/(07876) 193697 0117-971 9389
mike.moran@blueyonder.co.uk
www.mmoran.co.uk

Mike Posen@Sarah Brown Agency 10 The Avenue, Ealing, London, W13 8PH, United Kingdom
(020) 8998 0390/(07778) 177102 (020) 8843 1175
sbagency@dsl.pipex.com
www.sbagency.com

Mike Shepherd@Début Art & The Coningsby Gallery 30 Tottenham Street, London, W1T 4RJ, United Kingdom
(020) 7636 1064/ (020) 7580 7017
info@debutart.com
www.debutart.com

Mike Stones@Illustration Ltd 2 Brooks Court, Cringle Street, London, SW8 5BX, United Kingdom
(020) 7720 5202/ (020) 7720 5920
team@illustrationweb.com
www.illustrationweb.com

Mike Wilks@Central Illustration Agency 36 Wellington Street, London, WC2E 7BD, United Kingdom
(020) 7240 8925/ (020) 7836 1177
info@centralillustration.com
www.centralillustration.com

Mikki Rain@Thorogood Illustration Ltd 5 Dryden Street, Covent Garden, London, WC2E 9NW, United Kingdom
✆ (020) 7829 8468
✉ draw@thorogood.net
🖥 www.thorogood.net

Miko Flat 2, 202a Denmark Hill, London, SE5 8EE, United Kingdom
✆ (020) 7978 9440
✉ mik.brown@btopenworld.com
🖥 www.mikbrown-miko.com

Milkhouse.co.uk Fernhill Farm, Kingswells, Aberdeen, AB15 8PR, United Kingdom
✆ (07790) 729836
✉ marie@milkhouse.co.uk
🖥 www.milkhouse.co.uk

Ming Chow Designs 5 Portland Close, Worcester Park, Surrey, KT4 8BW, United Kingdom
✆ (07817) 022632
✉ faine@mingchow.co.uk
🖥 www.mingchow.co.uk

Minuca Sostres 44 Conduit Mews, London, W2 3RE, United Kingdom
✆ (020) 7402 5244
✉ minuca.sustres@talk21.com
🖥 www.minucasostres.com

Mique Moriuchi@Arena 31 Eleanor Road, London, E15 4AB, United Kingdom
✆ (08450) 507 600
✉ info@arenaworks.com
🖥 www.arenaworks.com

Mnich Design Associates Beulah House, 18a West Street, Rottingdean, Brighton, BN2 7HP, United Kingdom
✆ (01273) 301213/(07906) 363520
✉ info@mnich-design.co.uk
🖥 www.mnich-design.co.uk

Moira Kemp 40B Denton Road, Twickenham, TW1 2HQ, United Kingdom
✆ (020) 8892 0519
✉ mail@moirakemp.plus.com

Moira Maclean@Linden Artists Ltd 41 Battersea Business Centre, 103 Lavender Hill, London, SW11 5QL, United Kingdom
✆ (020) 7738 2505/✆ (020) 7738 2513
✉ lindenartists@aol.com
🖥 www.lindenartists.co.uk

Moira Millman@New Division 5 Risborough Street, London, SE1 0HF, United Kingdom
✆ (020) 7593 0505/✆ (020) 7593 0501
✉ info@newdivision.com
🖥 www.newdivision.com

Mokko Blue 21 Arncott Hall, 13 Poole Road, Bournemouth, BH2 5QR, United Kingdom
✆ 01202 269 257/✆ 01202 269 257
✉ info@mokko-blue.com
🖥 www.mokko-blue.com

Molly Molloy@Pearce Stoner Associates 12B Links Yard, Spelman Street, London, E1 5LX, United Kingdom
✆ (020) 7247 7100/✆ (020) 7247 7144
✉ info@pearcestoner.com
🖥 www.pearcestoner.com

Molly Sage 15 Lytton Road, Chadwell-St-Mary, Grays, Essex, RM16 4EU, United Kingdom
✆ (01375) 856572
✉ molly.sage@btopenworld.com

Monica Laita@New Division 5 Risborough Street, London, SE1 0HF, United Kingdom
✆ (020) 7593 0505/✆ (020) 7593 0501
✉ info@newdivision.com
🖥 www.newdivision.com

Morphic-Art 22 Litchfield Avenue, London, E15 4LN, United Kingdom
✆ (07729) 328750/✆ (020) 8221 1106
✉ info@morphic-art.com
🖥 www.morphic-art.com
www.warmtoastcafe.com/art/beenieman

Murilo Maciel@Advocate Art 39 Church Road, London, SW19 5DQ, United Kingdom
✆ 020 8879 1166/020 8879 3303
✉ lesley@advocate-art.com
🖥 www.advocate-art.com

My Beady Eye 48 Priestfield Crescent, Edinburgh, EH16 5JG,
✆ /07979 861532
✉ mybeadyeye@mac.com
🖥 www.mybeadyeye.co.uk

Myles Talbot 3 Sunny Dale Park, East Morton, Keighley, West Yorkshire, BD20 5UF, United Kingdom
✆ (01274) 510338/(07710) 831288 ✆ (01274) 510338
✉ myles@mylestalbot.com
🖥 www.mylestalbot.com

N B Illustration Ltd 40 Bowling Green Lane, London, EC1R 0NE, United Kingdom
✆ (020) 7278 9131/✆ (020) 7278 9121
✉ info@nbillustration.co.uk
🖥 www.nbillustration.co.uk

N G S Art & Design 10 Loch Striven, East Kilbride, Glasgow, G74 2EQ, United Kingdom
✆ (01355) 266558
✉ neil.smith40@virgin.net
🖥 www.arttoon.co.uk

Nancy Anderson 8A Birdhurst Rise, Croydon, CR2 7ED, United Kingdom
✆ (020) 8681 0310/✆ (020) 8681 0310
✉ n.anderson@btinternet.com
🖥 www.nancyanderson.co.uk

Nanette Hoogslag@Début Art & The Coningsby Gallery 30 Tottenham Street, London, W1T 4RJ, United Kingdom
✆ (020) 7636 1064/✆ (020) 7580 7017
✉ info@debutart.com
🖥 www.debutart.com

Natacha Ledwidge@The Organisation The Basement, 69 Caledonian Road, London, N1 9BT, United Kingdom
✆ (020) 7833 8268/(07973) 172902 ✆ (020) 7833 8269
✉ organise@easynet.co.uk
🖥 www.organisart.co.uk

Natalie Ferstendik@New Division 5 Risborough Street, London, SE1 0HF, United Kingdom
✆ (020) 7593 0505/✆ (020) 7593 0501
✉ info@newdivision.com
🖥 www.newdivision.com

Natalie Hinrichsen@Advocate Art 39 Church Road, London, SW19 5DQ, United Kingdom
✆ 020 8879 1166/020 8879 3303
✉ lesley@advocate-art.com
🖥 www.advocate-art.com

Natasha Law@Pearce Stoner Associates 12B Links Yard, Spelman Street, London, E1 5LX, United Kingdom
✆ (020) 7247 7100/✆ (020) 7247 7144
✉ info@pearcestoner.com
🖥 www.pearcestoner.com

Nathan Jurivicius@Phosphor Art 41 The Pump House, Pump House Close, off Renforth Street, London, SE16 7HS, United Kingdom
✆ (020) 7064 4666/✆ (020) 7064 4660
✉ info@phosphorart.com
🖥 www.phosphorart.com

Neal Layton@Arena 31 Eleanor Road, London, E15 4AB, United Kingdom
✆ (08450) 507 600
✉ info@arenaworks.com
🖥 www.arenaworks.com

Neil Boyce@Graham-Cameron Illustration The Studio, 23 Holt Road, Sheringham, Norfolk, NR26 8NB, United Kingdom
✆ (01263) 821333/✆ (01263) 821334
✉ enquiry@graham-cameron-illustration.com
🖥 www.graham-cameron-illustration.com

Neil Duerden@Advocate Art 39 Church Road, London, SW19 5DQ, United Kingdom
✆ 020 8879 1166/020 8879 3303
✉ lesley@advocate-art.com
🖥 www.advocate-art.com

Neil Leslie@Début Art & The Coningsby Gallery 30 Tottenham Street, London, W1T 4RJ, United Kingdom
✆ (020) 7636 1064/✆ (020) 7580 7017
✉ info@debutart.com
🖥 www.debutart.com

Neil Webb@Début Art & The Coningsby Gallery 30 Tottenham Street, London, W1T 4RJ, United Kingdom
✆ (020) 7636 1064/✆ (020) 7580 7017
✉ info@debutart.com
🖥 www.debutart.com

Neils Art 3/1 46 Thornwood Avenue, Glasgow, G11 7PQ, United Kingdom
✆ (07967) 910388
✉ neilthomson@ntdesign.co.uk
🖥 www.neilart.co.uk

Nelly Dimitranova@Eastwing 99 Chase Side, Enfield, Middlesex, EN2 6NL, United Kingdom
✆ (020) 8367 6760/✆ (020) 8367 6730
✉ andrea@eastwing.co.uk
🖥 www.eastwing.co.uk

New Division 5 Risborough Street, London, SE1 0HF, United Kingdom
✆ (020) 7593 0505/✆ (020) 7593 0501
✉ info@newdivision.com
🖥 www.newdivision.com

Nicholas Carn@The Organisation The Basement, 69 Caledonian Road, London, N1 9BT, United Kingdom
✆ (020) 7833 8268/(07973) 172902 ✆ (020) 7833 8269
✉ organise@easynet.co.uk
🖥 www.organisart.co.uk

Nicholls & Nicholls 27 Abbots Park, Chester, CH1 4AW, United Kingdom
✆ (01244) 383116/(07971) 193006 ✆ (01244) 382102
✉ info@n-n.co.uk
🖥 www.n-n.co.uk

Nick Cronin@Eastwing 99 Chase Side, Enfield, Middlesex, EN2 6NL, United Kingdom
✆ (020) 8367 6760/✆ (020) 8367 6730
✉ andrea@eastwing.co.uk
🖥 www.eastwing.co.uk

Nick Dewar@Eastwing 99 Chase Side, Enfield, Middlesex, EN2 6NL, United Kingdom
✆ (020) 8367 6760/✆ (020) 8367 6730
✉ andrea@eastwing.co.uk
🖥 www.eastwing.co.uk

Nick Diggory@Illustration Ltd 2 Brooks Court, Cringle Street, London, SW8 5BX, United Kingdom
✆ (020) 7720 5202/✆ (020) 7720 5920
✉ team@illustrationweb.com
🖥 www.illustrationweb.com

Nick Hawken Higher Trethake, Darite, Liskeard, Cornwall, PL14 5JT, United Kingdom
✆ (01579) 343276
✉ hawken@macace.net
🖥 www.contact-uk.com/nickhawken

Nick Kobyluch@New Division 5 Risborough Street, London, SE1 0HF, United Kingdom
✆ (020) 7593 0505/✆ (020) 7593 0501
✉ info@newdivision.com
🖥 www.newdivision.com

Nick Lowndes@Eastwing 99 Chase Side, Enfield, Middlesex, EN2 6NL, United Kingdom
✆ (020) 8367 6760/✆ (020) 8367 6730
✉ andrea@eastwing.co.uk
🖥 www.eastwing.co.uk

Nick Price@Illustration Ltd 2 Brooks Court, Cringle Street, London, SW8 5BX, United Kingdom
✆ (020) 7720 5202/✆ (020) 7720 5920
✉ team@illustrationweb.com
🖥 www.illustrationweb.com

Nick Reddyhoff@Début Art & The Coningsby Gallery 30 Tottenham Street, London, W1T 4RJ, United Kingdom
✆ (020) 7636 1064/✆ (020) 7580 7017
✉ info@debutart.com
🖥 www.debutart.com

Nick Schon@Folio 10 Gate Street, Lincoln's Inn Fields, London, WC2A 3HP, United Kingdom
✆ (020) 7242 9562/✆ (020) 7242 1816
✉ all@folioart.co.uk
🖥 www.folioart.co.uk

Nick Spender@Advocate Art 39 Church Road, London, SW19 5DQ, United Kingdom
✆ 020 8879 1166/020 8879 3303
✉ lesley@advocate-art.com
🖥 www.advocate-art.com

nickstreet.co.uk 192 Sunnyhill Road, London, SW16 2UN, United Kingdom
✆ (07814) 684 552
✉ contact@nickstreet.co.uk
🖥 www.nickstreet.co.uk

Nicky Dupays@Thorogood Illustration Ltd 5 Dryden Street, Covent Garden, London, WC2E 9NW, United Kingdom
✆ (020) 7829 8468
✉ draw@thorogood.net
🖥 www.thorogood.net

Nicky Gissing@Début Art & The Coningsby Gallery 30 Tottenham Street, London, W1T 4RJ, United Kingdom
(020) 7636 1064/ (020) 7580 7017
info@debutart.com
www.debutart.com

Nicola Cramp@New Division 5 Risborough Street, London, SE1 0HF, United Kingdom
(020) 7593 0505/ (020) 7593 0501
info@newdivision.com
www.newdivision.com

Nicola Gregory@Art Collection UK Ltd 7 Worsley Mill, 10 Blantyre Street, Castlefield, Manchester, M15 4LG, United Kingdom
(0870) 2405001/ (0870) 2405002
info@artcollection.co.uk
www.artcollection.co.uk

Nicola L Robinson Mynachdy, Cardiff, Glamorgan, CF14 3AG,
nlrobinson@thesurrealdemon.co.uk
www.thesurrealdemon.co.uk

Nicola Slater@Thorogood Illustration Ltd 5 Dryden Street, Covent Garden, London, WC2E 9NW, United Kingdom
(020) 7829 8468
draw@thorogood.net
www.thorogood.net

Nicola Storr@Advocate Art 39 Church Road, London, SW19 5DQ, United Kingdom
020 8879 1166/020 8879 3303
lesley@advocate-art.com
www.advocate-art.com

Nicola Taylor@N B Illustration Ltd 40 Bowling Green Lane, London, EC1R 0NE, United Kingdom
(020) 7278 9131/ (020) 7278 9121
info@nbillustration.co.uk
www.nbillustration.co.uk

Nicole De Rueda 149 Rue du Jardin Public, Bordeaux, 33300, France
00 33 5 5787 0302
n.derni@wanadoo.fr
www.nicole-is-online.net

Nicoletta Pagano@Advocate Art 39 Church Road, London, SW19 5DQ, United Kingdom
020 8879 1166/020 8879 3303
lesley@advocate-art.com
www.advocate-art.com

Nigel Chamberlain 89 Muswell Hill Road, London, N10 3HT, United Kingdom
(020) 8444 9553/(07712) 592155
alisoneldred@gmail.com
www.alisoneldred.com

Nigel Kitching Old Hall Cottage, Sexhow, Hutton Rudby, Yarm, Cleveland, TS15 0ER, United Kingdom
(01642) 701402
nigel@nigelkitching.plus.com

Nigel Owen@Central Illustration Agency 36 Wellington Street, London, WC2E 7BD, United Kingdom
(020) 7240 8925/ (020) 7836 1177
info@centralillustration.com
www.centralillustration.com

Nigel Priddey 184 Quinton Road, Harborne, Birmingham, B17 0RP, United Kingdom
0121-427 6091

Nik Holmes@Private View Artists Agency 17A Swan Hill, Shrewsbury, SY1 1NL, United Kingdom
(01743) 350355/ (01743) 233923
create@pvuk.com
www.pvuk.com

Nikolai Bird@Allied Artists@ Artistic License The Gallery @ Richmond, 63 Sheen Road, Richmond, Surrey, TW9 1YJ, United Kingdom
(020) 8334 1010/ (020) 8334 9900
info@allied-artists.net
www.allied-artists.net

Nila Aye@New Division 5 Risborough Street, London, SE1 0HF, United Kingdom
(020) 7593 0505/ (020) 7593 0501
info@newdivision.com
www.newdivision.com

Nina Davis@N B Illustration Ltd 40 Bowling Green Lane, London, EC1R 0NE, United Kingdom
(020) 7278 9131/ (020) 7278 9121
info@nbillustration.co.uk
www.nbillustration.co.uk

Ning-i Yen@Private View Artists Agency 17A Swan Hill, Shrewsbury, SY1 1NL, United Kingdom
(01743) 350355/ (01743) 233923
create@pvuk.com
www.pvuk.com

Niroot Puttapipat@The Artworks 40 Frith Street, London, W1D 5LN, United Kingdom
(020) 7734 3333/ (020) 7734 3484
lucy@theartworksinc.com
www.theartworksinc.com

Noel Ford Ty Rhyd, Ystrad Meurig, Ceredigion, SY25 6AX, United Kingdom
(01974) 831468/ (08700) 518267
noel@fordcartoon.com
www.fordcartoon.com

Norman Johnson 17 Beaumont Terrace, Jarrow, Tyne & Wear, NE32 5SG, United Kingdom
0191-489 1078

Norman Young@Drawer Illustrators Agents 8 Belmont, Bath, BA1 5DZ, United Kingdom
(01225) 445262
enquiries@drawer.me.uk

Nuno Da Costa@Advocate Art 39 Church Road, London, SW19 5DQ, United Kingdom
020 8879 1166/020 8879 3303
lesley@advocate-art.com
www.advocate-art.com

Ofra Amit@The Organisation The Basement, 69 Caledonian Road, London, N1 9BT, United Kingdom
(020) 7833 8268/(07973) 172902 (020) 7833 8269
organise@easynet.co.uk
www.organisart.co.uk

Olaf Hajek@Central Illustration Agency 36 Wellington Street, London, WC2E 7BD, United Kingdom
(020) 7240 8925/ (020) 7836 1177
info@centralillustration.com
www.centralillustration.com

Olga Isaeva@Advocate Art 39 Church Road, London, SW19 5DQ, United Kingdom
020 8879 1166/020 8879 3303
lesley@advocate-art.com
www.advocate-art.com

Oliver Burston@Début Art & The Coningsby Gallery 30 Tottenham Street, London, W1T 4RJ, United Kingdom
(020) 7636 1064/ (020) 7580 7017
info@debutart.com
www.debutart.com

Oliver Hurst@Advocate Art 39 Church Road, London, SW19 5DQ, United Kingdom
020 8879 1166/020 8879 3303
lesley@advocate-art.com
www.advocate-art.com

Olivier Duamas@Advocate Art 39 Church Road, London, SW19 5DQ, United Kingdom
020 8879 1166/020 8879 3303
lesley@advocate-art.com
www.advocate-art.com

Olivier Kugler@The Artworks 40 Frith Street, London, W1D 5LN, United Kingdom
(020) 7734 3333/ (020) 7734 3484
lucy@theartworksinc.com
www.theartworksinc.com

Olivier Latyk@Thorogood Illustration Ltd 5 Dryden Street, Covent Garden, London, WC2E 9NW, United Kingdom
(020) 7829 8468
draw@thorogood.net
www.thorogood.net

Omri Stephenson@Allied Artists@ Artistic License The Gallery @ Richmond, 63 Sheen Road, Richmond, Surrey, TW9 1YJ, United Kingdom
(020) 8334 1010/ (020) 8334 9900
info@allied-artists.net
www.allied-artists.net

Oviart Ltd Ravensburger Ring 69, Munich, Bayern, 81243, Germany
0049 89 82 00 00 49/ 0049 89 82 00 00 49
hondru@t-online.de
www.oviart.com

Owen Phillips@Advocate Art 39 Church Road, London, SW19 5DQ, United Kingdom
020 8879 1166/020 8879 3303
lesley@advocate-art.com
www.advocate-art.com

Owen Rimmington@Advocate Art 39 Church Road, London, SW19 5DQ, United Kingdom
020 8879 1166/020 8879 3303
lesley@advocate-art.com
www.advocate-art.com

P W A International 4 Brightfield Road, London, SE12 8QF, United Kingdom
(020) 8297 3434
pwaint@dircon.co.uk
www.pwainternational.com

Pablo Bernasconi@Début Art & The Coningsby Gallery 30 Tottenham Street, London, W1T 4RJ, United Kingdom
(020) 7636 1064/ (020) 7580 7017
info@debutart.com
www.debutart.com

Pablo Pasadas@Advocate Art 39 Church Road, London, SW19 5DQ, United Kingdom
020 8879 1166/020 8879 3303
lesley@advocate-art.com
www.advocate-art.com

Paco Krijnen@Advocate Art 39 Church Road, London, SW19 5DQ, United Kingdom
020 8879 1166/020 8879 3303
lesley@advocate-art.com
www.advocate-art.com

Pamela Venus Whin Brow Cottage, Hood Lane, Cloughton, Scarborough, North Yorkshire, YO13 0AT, United Kingdom
(01723) 870873/ (01723) 870873

Panteli Illustration, London, United Kingdom
(020) 7272 9940/(07961) 878346 (020) 7272 9940
imaging@panteli.net
www.panteli.net

Paper Alligator Ltd 67 Wood End Lane, Northolt, Middlesex, UB5 4JW, United Kingdom
(07751) 310303
louisecunningham133@hotmail.com
www.louisecunningham.com

Parra@Big Active Ltd Unit 6.01, The Tea Building, 56 Shoreditch High Street, London, E16 JJ, United Kingdom
(020) 7739 5601/ (020) 7739 7479
contact@bigactive.com
www.bigactive.com

Pascal Lafond@Advocate Art 39 Church Road, London, SW19 5DQ, United Kingdom
020 8879 1166/020 8879 3303
lesley@advocate-art.com
www.advocate-art.com

Pat Lee Boro Fen, 81 Osbaldwick Lane, York, YO10 3AY, United Kingdom
(01904) 411855

Pat Murray@Graham-Cameron Illustration The Studio, 23 Holt Road, Sheringham, Norfolk, NR26 8NB, United Kingdom
(01263) 821333/ (01263) 821334
enquiry@graham-cameron-illustration.com
www.graham-cameron-illustration.com

Pat Walker@Central Illustration Agency 36 Wellington Street, London, WC2E 7BD, United Kingdom
(020) 7240 8925/ (020) 7836 1177
info@centralillustration.com
www.centralillustration.com

Patricia Andrade 6 William Bonney Estate, London, SW4 7JG, United Kingdom
(020) 7627 1064
lady_arryeinne@hotmail.com
www.lotr.home.sapo.pt

Patricia Harrison Moss Cottage, South Downs Road, Bowdon, Altrincham, Cheshire, WA14 3DR, United Kingdom
0161-928 1835/ 0161-928 1835
triciadesign3@hotmail.com

Patricia Ludlow@Linden Artists Ltd 41 Battersea Business Centre, 103 Lavender Hill, London, SW11 5QL, United Kingdom
(020) 7738 2505/ (020) 7738 2513
lindenartists@aol.com
www.lindenartists.co.uk

Patrick Morgan@Début Art & The Coningsby Gallery 30 Tottenham Street, London, W1T 4RJ, United Kingdom
(020) 7636 1064/ (020) 7580 7017
info@debutart.com
www.debutart.com

Patrick O'Callaghan Design 10 Barley Mow Passage, London, W4 4PH, United Kingdom
(020) 8994 6477/ (020) 8400 6162
pat.design@vylan.com
www.pat.design.com

Patrik Washburn@Advocate Art 39 Church Road, London, SW19 5DQ, United Kingdom
020 8879 1166/020 8879 3303
lesley@advocate-art.com
www.advocate-art.com

Patriozio Spadoni@Advocate Art 39 Church Road, London, SW19 5DQ, United Kingdom
020 8879 1166/020 8879 3303
lesley@advocate-art.com
www.advocate-art.com

Paul Blow@Eastwing 99 Chase Side, Enfield, Middlesex, EN2 6NL, United Kingdom
(020) 8367 6760/ (020) 8367 6730
andrea@eastwing.co.uk
www.eastwing.co.uk

Paul Boston@Meiklejohn Illustration 5 Risborough Street, London, SE1 0HF, United Kingdom
(020) 7593 0500/ (020) 7593 0501
info@meiklejohn.co.uk
www.meiklejohn.co.uk

Paul Catherall@Art Market 51 Oxford Drive, London, SE1 2FB, United Kingdom
(020) 7407 8111/ (020) 7407 8222
info@artmarketillustration.com
www.artmarketillustration.com

Paul Cemmick@The Organisation The Basement, 69 Caledonian Road, London, N1 9BT, United Kingdom
(020) 7833 8268/(07973) 172902 (020) 7833 8269
organise@easynet.co.uk
www.organisart.co.uk

Paul Chappell 44 Beechwood Close, Little Chalfont, Buckinghamshire, HP6 6QX, United Kingdom
(01494) 762484/(07977) 298433
paulc@vizualeye.com
www.vizualeye.com

Paul Clewley 142 Chester Road, Streetly, Sutton Coldfield, West Midlands, B74 2HS, United Kingdom
0121-353 4221/(07922) 293160 0121-353 4221
paul@paulclewley.com
www.paulclewley.com

Paul Collicutt The Annexe, Belmont Street, Brighton, BN1 4HN, United Kingdom
(01273) 628405/ (01273) 628405
paul.collicutt@virgin.net
www.contact-me.net/paulcollicutt

Paul Davis@MAP 72 Rochester Place, London, NW1 9JX, United Kingdom
(020) 7424 9144/ (020) 7284 3274
info@mapltd.com
www.mapltd.com

Paul Daviz@Illustration Ltd 2 Brooks Court, Cringle Street, London, SW8 5BX, United Kingdom
(020) 7720 5202/ (020) 7720 5920
team@illustrationweb.com
www.illustrationweb.com

Paul E. Sheldon Riverview, 18 Mill Green, Lyme Regis, Dorset, DT7 3PH, United Kingdom
(01297) 444644/(07867) 911225 (01297) 444644
paulesheldon@btopenworld.com

Paul Gibbs@Drawer Illustrators Agents 8 Belmont, Bath, BA1 5DZ, United Kingdom
(01225) 445262
enquiries@drawer.me.uk

Paul Gregory@Sarah Brown Agency 10 The Avenue, Ealing, London, W13 8PH, United Kingdom
(020) 8998 0390/(07778) 177102 (020) 8843 1175
sbagency@dsl.pipex.com
www.sbagency.com

Paul Hess@Arena 31 Eleanor Road, London, E15 4AB, United Kingdom
(08450) 507 600
info@arenaworks.com
www.arenaworks.com

Paul Higgens@Phosphor Art 41 The Pump House, Pump House Close, off Renforth Street, London, SE16 7HS, United Kingdom
(020) 7064 4666/ (020) 7064 4660
info@phosphorart.com
www.phosphorart.com

Paul Nicholls@Advocate Art 39 Church Road, London, SW19 5DQ, United Kingdom
020 8879 1166/020 8879 3303
lesley@advocate-art.com
www.advocate-art.com

Paul Oakley@Central Illustration Agency 36 Wellington Street, London, WC2E 7BD, United Kingdom
(020) 7240 8925/ (020) 7836 1177
info@centralillustration.com
www.centralillustration.com

Paul Price@Début Art & The Coningsby Gallery 30 Tottenham Street, London, W1T 4RJ, United Kingdom
(020) 7636 1064/ (020) 7580 7017
info@debutart.com
www.debutart.com

Paul Rigby 28 Normanton Lane, Derby, DE23 6GP, United Kingdom
(07939) 034612/(07939) 034612
paul@paulrigby.co.uk
www.paulrigby.co.uk

Paul Rogers@The Artworks 40 Frith Street, London, W1D 5LN, United Kingdom
(020) 7734 3333/ (020) 7734 3484
lucy@theartworksinc.com
www.theartworksinc.com

Paul Sample@Meiklejohn Illustration 5 Risborough Street, London, SE1 0HF, United Kingdom
(020) 7593 0500/ (020) 7593 0501
info@meiklejohn.co.uk
www.meiklejohn.co.uk

Paul Shorrock 80 Knowsley Road, Wilpshire, Blackburn, BB1 9PN, United Kingdom
(01282) 605071
shorrock@dircon.co.uk
www.paulshorrock.com

Paul Slater@Central Illustration Agency 36 Wellington Street, London, WC2E 7BD, United Kingdom
(020) 7240 8925/ (020) 7836 1177
info@centralillustration.com
www.centralillustration.com

Paul Stickland Mill Court, Milborne Wick, Sherborne, Dorset, DT9 4PW, United Kingdom
(01963) 250900
paul@ruggedbears.co.uk
www.ruggedbears.co.uk

Paul Tucker 15 Roman Rise, London, SE19 1JG, United Kingdom
(020) 8670 5549/(07932) 140730 (020) 8670 5549
paul.@tuckerportrates.com
www.tuckerillustration.com

Paul Wootton Associates 138 Erlanger Road, London, SE14 5TJ, United Kingdom
(020) 7252 8555/ (020) 7252 8777
paul@graphicnet.co.uk
www.graphicnet.co.uk
See ad in showcase

Paul Young@Artist Partners Ltd 2e The Chandlery, 50 Westminster Bridge Road, London, SE1 7QY, United Kingdom
(020) 7401 7904/ (020) 7401 3378
chris@artistpartners.demon.co.uk
www.artistpartners.com

Paula Bowles, Oxfordshire, United Kingdom
(01608) 641050/(07763) 214858
pybowles@hotmail.com
www.paulabowles.co.uk

Paula Doherty@Advocate Art 39 Church Road, London, SW19 5DQ, United Kingdom
020 8879 1166/020 8879 3303
lesley@advocate-art.com
www.advocate-art.com

Paula Martyr@Linden Artists Ltd 41 Battersea Business Centre, 103 Lavender Hill, London, SW11 5QL, United Kingdom
(020) 7738 2505/ (020) 7738 2513
lindenartists@aol.com
www.lindenartists.co.uk

Paula McNamara Flat 6, 51 Tib Street, Manchester, M4 1LS, United Kingdom
/(07957) 417775
paulamcnamara@hotmail.com
www.paulamcnamara.net

Pearce Stoner Associates 12B Links Yard, Spelman Street, London, E1 5LX, United Kingdom
(020) 7247 7100/ (020) 7247 7144
info@pearcestoner.com
www.pearcestoner.com

Pennant Illustration 16 Littleton Street, London, SW18 3SY, United Kingdom
(020) 8947 4002/(07850) 865591 (020) 8946 7667
matt@pennantinc.co.uk
www.pennantinc.co.uk

Penny Dann@The Artworks 40 Frith Street, London, W1D 5LN, United Kingdom
(020) 7734 3333/ (020) 7734 3484
lucy@theartworksinc.com
www.theartworksinc.com

Penny Sobr 1 New Court, Flask Walk, London, NW3 1HD, United Kingdom
(07814) 807723
penny@pennysobr.com
www.pennysobr.com

Per Karlen@Art Market 51 Oxford Drive, London, SE1 2FB, United Kingdom
(020) 7407 8111/ (020) 7407 8222
info@artmarketillustration.com
www.artmarketillustration.com

Perspective 77a Hutton Grove, North Finchley, London, N12 8DS, United Kingdom
(020) 8445 0628/(07803) 464836
stephen@perspective.wanadoo.co.uk

Pete Viccars@Phosphor Art 41 The Pump House, Pump House Close, off Renforth Street, London, SE16 7HS, United Kingdom
(020) 7064 4666/ (020) 7064 4660
info@phosphorart.com
www.phosphorart.com

Peter Andrew Jones Picture Library Woodcote Edge, Church Stretton, Shropshire, SY6 6DF, United Kingdom
(01694) 724584/ (01694) 724584
licensing@peterandrewjones.net
www.peterandrewjones.net

Peter Beddoe Castle Hill House, Castle Donington, Derby, DE74 2LD, United Kingdom
(01332) 810537/ (01332) 810537

Peter Campbell 2 Prebend Mansion, Chiswick High Road, London, W4 2LU, United Kingdom
(020) 8995 5812/(07941) 049862 (020) 8995 5812
peter@petercampbell.demon.co.uk
www.petercampbellstudios.co.uk

Peter Collington@David Higham 5-8 Lower John Street, Golden Square, London, W1F 9HA, United Kingdom
(020) 7437 7888/ (020) 7437 1072
carolinewalsh@davidhigham.co.uk
www.davidhigham.co.uk

Peter Crowther Associates@Début Art & The Coningsby Gallery 30 Tottenham Street, London, W1T 4RJ, United Kingdom
(020) 7636 1064/ (020) 7580 7017
info@debutart.com
www.debutart.com

Peter Davies 175 Henry Doulton Drive, Tooting Bec, London, SW17 6DH, United Kingdom
(07956) 247630
petee_d@hotmail.com
www.alldrawn.com/pete/index.htm

Peter Dennis@Linda Rogers Associates 163 Half Moon Lane, London, SE24 9WB, United Kingdom
(020) 7501 9106
lr@lindarogers.net
www.lindarogers.net

Peter Dobbin Flat 23, Tudor House, Tudor Grove, London, E9 7QJ, United Kingdom
(07814) 855218
peter@peterdobbin.co.uk
www.peterdobbin.co.uk

Peter Ellis@Meiklejohn Illustration 5 Risborough Street, London, SE1 0HF, United Kingdom
(020) 7593 0500/ (020) 7593 0501
info@meiklejohn.co.uk
www.meiklejohn.co.uk

Peter Greenwood@Advocate Art 39 Church Road, London, SW19 5DQ, United Kingdom
020 8879 1166/020 8879 3303
lesley@advocate-art.com
www.advocate-art.com

Peter Grundy@Début Art & The Coningsby Gallery 30 Tottenham Street, London, W1T 4RJ, United Kingdom
(020) 7636 1064/ (020) 7580 7017
info@debutart.com
www.debutart.com

Peter Horridge@Central Illustration Agency 36 Wellington Street, London, WC2E 7BD, United Kingdom
(020) 7240 8925/ (020) 7836 1177
info@centralillustration.com
www.centralillustration.com

Peter Jaques 4 Stourvale Gardens, Chandler's Ford, Eastleigh, Hampshire, SO53 3NE, United Kingdom
- (023) 8027 0513
- peter@peterjaques.co.uk
- www.peterjaques.co.uk

Peter John Brown 16 Richmond Avenue, Islington, London, N1 0NF, United Kingdom
- (020) 7713 5603/ (020) 7713 5603

Peter Kent@Graham-Cameron Illustration The Studio, 23 Holt Road, Sheringham, Norfolk, NR26 8NB, United Kingdom
- (01263) 821333/ (01263) 821334
- enquiry@graham-cameron-illustration.com
- www.graham-cameron-illustration.com

Peter Kyprianou@Illustration Ltd 2 Brooks Court, Cringle Street, London, SW8 5BX, United Kingdom
- (020) 7720 5202/ (020) 7720 5920
- team@illustrationweb.com
- www.illustrationweb.com

Peter Malone@The Artworks 40 Frith Street, London, W1D 5LN, United Kingdom
- (020) 7734 3333/ (020) 7734 3484
- lucy@theartworksinc.com
- www.theartworksinc.com

Peter Meszaros@Illustration Ltd 2 Brooks Court, Cringle Street, London, SW8 5BX, United Kingdom
- (020) 7720 5202/ (020) 7720 5920
- team@illustrationweb.com
- www.illustrationweb.com

Peter North 185 Brecknock Road, London, N19 5AB, United Kingdom
- (020) 7485 7270/ (020) 7482 4797
- lamming@dircon.co.uk

Peter Quinnell@Début Art & The Coningsby Gallery 30 Tottenham Street, London, W1T 4RJ, United Kingdom
- (020) 7636 1064/ (020) 7580 7017
- info@debutart.com
- www.debutart.com

Peter Ruane Treetops, Lynden Chase, Uckfield, East Sussex, TN22 1EE, United Kingdom
- (07768) 390824
- info@peterruane.com
- www.peterruane.com

Peter Scholey Partnership 73 Old Park Avenue, Sheffield, S8 7DQ, United Kingdom
- 0114-274 7662
- www.peterscholey.co.uk

Peter Spence@Phosphor Art 41 The Pump House, Pump House Close, off Renforth Street, London, SE16 7HS, United Kingdom
- (020) 7064 4666/ (020) 7064 4660
- info@phosphorart.com
- www.phosphorart.com

Peter Stevenson@Linden Artists Ltd 41 Battersea Business Centre, 103 Lavender Hill, London, SW11 5QL, United Kingdom
- (020) 7738 2505/ (020) 7738 2513
- lindenartists@aol.com
- www.lindenartists.co.uk

Peter Tillmann 20 Crouch Hall Road, London, N8 8HU, United Kingdom
- (020) 8341 0497/ (020) 8341 0497
- peter@tillmann.co.uk

Peter Ward Design 7 Stanford Way, Broadbridge Heath, Horsham, West Sussex, RH12 3LH, United Kingdom
- (01403) 276570
- peter@wardacolour.fsnet.co.uk (pw@peterward.info)
- www.peterward.info

Petula Stone@Illustration Ltd 2 Brooks Court, Cringle Street, London, SW8 5BX, United Kingdom
- (020) 7720 5202/ (020) 7720 5920
- team@illustrationweb.com
- www.illustrationweb.com

Phil Dobson 24 Buxton Road, Brighton, BN1 5DE, United Kingdom
- (01273) 626241
- info@magicpen.co.uk
- www.magicpen.co.uk

Phil Gascoine 23 Elm Close, Waltham Abbey, Essex, EN9 1SQ, United Kingdom
- (01992) 711671/ (01992) 711671
- pegascoine@aol.com

Phil Schramm@Meiklejohn Illustration 5 Risborough Street, London, SE1 0HF, United Kingdom
- (020) 7593 0500/ (020) 7593 0501
- info@meiklejohn.co.uk
- www.meiklejohn.co.uk

Phil Wheeler@Thorogood Illustration Ltd 5 Dryden Street, Covent Garden, London, WC2E 9NW, United Kingdom
- (020) 7829 8468
- draw@thorogood.net
- www.thorogood.net

Phil Wrigglesworth 7 Standroyd Drive, Colne, Lancashire, BB8 7BG, United Kingdom
- (07939) 794267
- phil@phillwigg[?]worth.com
- www.phillwiggles worth.com

Philip Bannister@Illustration Ltd 2 Brooks Court, Cringle Street, London, SW8 5BX, United Kingdom
- (020) 7720 5202/ (020) 7720 5920
- team@illustrationweb.com
- www.illustrationweb.com

Philip Bishop@Illustration Ltd 2 Brooks Court, Cringle Street, London, SW8 5BX, United Kingdom
- (020) 7720 5202/ (020) 7720 5920
- team@illustrationweb.com
- www.illustrationweb.com

Philip Castle 56 Burnfoot Avenue, London, SW6 5EA, United Kingdom
- (020) 7736 0735/(07981) 045022

Philip Disley 7 Parkgate Close, Aigburth, Liverpool, L17 6EH, United Kingdom
- 0151-494 1604/07779 783414 0151-494 1604
- phill@philldisley.com
- www.phildisley.com

Philip Dunn Window Gallery, 59 Ship Street, Brighton, BN1 1AE, United Kingdom
- (01273) 726190
- windowgallery@btconnect.com
- www.windowgallery.co.uk

Philip Hood@Arena 31 Eleanor Road, London, E15 4AB, United Kingdom
- (08450) 507 600
- info@arenaworks.com
- www.arenaworks.com

Philip Nicholson@Thorogood Illustration Ltd 5 Dryden Street, Covent Garden, London, WC2E 9NW, United Kingdom
- (020) 7829 8468
- draw@thorogood.net
- www.thorogood.net

Philip Thompson 35 Elgin Crescent, London, W11 2JD, United Kingdom
- (020) 7221 1925/ (020) 7243 0868
- phil@jotom.demon.co.uk
- www.contact-me.net/philipthomson

Phill Burrows 16A Bolton Cresent, Windsor, Berkshire, SL4 3JQ, United Kingdom
- (01753) 869686
- phillip.burrows@btinternet.com
- www.phillburrows.co.uk

Phosphor Art 41 The Pump House, Pump House Close, off Renforth Street, London, SE16 7HS, United Kingdom
- (020) 7064 4666/ (020) 7064 4660
- info@phosphorart.com
- www.phosphorart.com

Phosphor Art Ltd 41 The Pump House, Pump House Close, London, SE16 7HS, United Kingdom
- (020) 7064 4666/ (020) 7064 4660
- info@phosphorart.com
- www.phosporart.com

Photo Fiction 14 Tremes Close, Marshfield, Chippenham, Wiltshire, SN14 8TB, United Kingdom
- (07973) 631185
- mail@photofiction.co.uk
- www.photofiction.co.uk

Pickled_Jo Studios 15 Garden Street, Eccles, Manchester, M30 0EZ, United Kingdom
- (077430) 073338
- jo.blakeley@gmail.com
- www.design-inc.com/jo/

Piero Corvo@Folio 10 Gate Street, Lincoln's Inn Fields, London, WC2A 3HP, United Kingdom
- (020) 7242 9562/ (020) 7242 1816
- all@folioart.co.uk
- www.folioart.co.uk

Pierre Paul Pariseau@The Organisation The Basement, 69 Caledonian Road, London, N1 9BT, United Kingdom
- (020) 7833 8268/(07973) 172902 (020) 7833 8269
- organise@easynet.co.uk
- www.organisart.co.uk

Pierre-Paul Pariseau@Advocate Art 39 Church Road, London, SW19 5DQ, United Kingdom
- 020 8879 1166/020 8879 3303
- lesley@advocate-art.com
- www.advocate-art.com

Piers Baker Saxton, Parklands, Railton Road, Guildford, Surrey, GU2 9JX, United Kingdom
- (01483) 238267/(07889) 128331
- pbaker@piersbaker.co.uk
- www.piersbaker.co.uk

Piers Sanford@Meiklejohn Illustration 5 Risborough Street, London, SE1 0HF, United Kingdom
- (020) 7593 0500/ (020) 7593 0501
- info@meiklejohn.co.uk
- www.meiklejohn.co.uk

Pietari Posti@Début Art & The Coningsby Gallery 30 Tottenham Street, London, W1T 4RJ, United Kingdom
- (020) 7636 1064/ (020) 7580 7017
- info@debutart.com
- www.debutart.com

Pigeon Press 21 Gardenfield, Skellingthorpe, Lincoln, LN6 5SP, United Kingdom
- (07796) 141355
- david_md_thompson@hotmail.com
- www.pigeonpress.co.uk

Pinglet@Private View Artists Agency 17A Swan Hill, Shrewsbury, SY1 1NL, United Kingdom
- (01743) 350355/ (01743) 233923
- create@pvuk.com
- www.pvuk.com

Piotr Lesniak@Thorogood Illustration Ltd 5 Dryden Street, Covent Garden, London, WC2E 9NW, United Kingdom
- (020) 7829 8468
- draw@thorogood.net
- www.thorogood.net

Pip Sampson@Graham-Cameron Illustration The Studio, 23 Holt Road, Sheringham, Norfolk, NR26 8NB, United Kingdom
- (01263) 821333/ (01263) 821334
- enquiry@graham-cameron-illustration.com
- www.graham-cameron-illustration.com

Pippa Sterne Flat 4, 62 Chesterton Road, London, W10 6ER, United Kingdom
- (07956) 158474
- pippasterne@ntlworld.com
- www.dreamgenies.com

Pixel Perfect The White House, Copse Road, Haslemere, Surrey, GU27 3QQ, United Kingdom
- (01428) 643500/ (0871) 7502375
- jason@pixelperfect.co.uk
- www.pixelperfect.co.uk

Plum Illustration Hedges House, 153-155 Regent Street, London, W1B 4JE, United Kingdom
- (020) 7494 9664/ (020) 7494 9641
- phil@plum-illustration.com

Pocko People Unit 214, 24-28 Hatton Wall, London, EC1N 8JH, United Kingdom
- (020) 7404 9210/ (020) 7404 9210
- people@pocko.com
- www.pocko.com/pockopeople/

Polona Lovsin@Advocate Art 39 Church Road, London, SW19 5DQ, United Kingdom
- 020 8879 1166/020 8879 3303
- lesley@advocate-art.com
- www.advocate-art.com

Pope Twins@Advocate Art 39 Church Road, London, SW19 5DQ, United Kingdom
- 020 8879 1166/020 8879 3303
- lesley@advocate-art.com
- www.advocate-art.com

Portland 2 58 St Mary's Road, Oatlands Village, Weybridge, Surrey, KT13 9PZ, United Kingdom
- (01932) 843546/(07831) 599405 (01932) 821854
- doloresportlands3@aol.com

Portraits.Org.Uk UK 27 Floral Avenue, Chapel Allerton, Leeds, LS7 3DP, United Kingdom
- 0113-262 6123
- david@portraits.org.uk
- www.portraits.org.uk

Prescott & Co. 232 Southport Road, Scarsbrick, Southport, Merseyside, PR8 5LF, United Kingdom
- (01704) 880881
- david@prescott.co.uk
- www.prescott.co.uk

Priscilla Barrett Jack of Clubs, Fen Road, Lode, Cambridge, CB25 9HE, United Kingdom
- (01223) 812229

Private View Artists Agency 17A Swan Hill, Shrewsbury, SY1 1NL, United Kingdom
- (01743) 350355/ (01743) 233923
- create@pvuk.com
- www.pvuk.com

Projekt Alpha 58 Cedar Avenue, Hazlemere, High Wycombe, Buckinghamshire, HP15 7EE, United Kingdom
- (07818) 813959
- info@projektalpha.com
- www.projektalpha.com

Punch NMC Fern House, 53 Padbrook, Limpsfield, Surrey, RH8 0DZ,
- (01883) 730073
- andrew.richardson@thinkpunch.co.uk
- www.thinkpunch.co.uk

Quantum Leap Design Studio BVBA St-Truidensteenweg 81, Hasselt, 3500, Belgium
- 4 97 57 82 75
- kristof@quantum-leap.be
- www.quantum-leap.be

Rachel Ross@Inkshed 99 Chase Side, Enfield, Middlesex, EN2 6NL, United Kingdom
- (020) 8367 4545/ (020) 8367 6730
- www.inkshed.co.uk

Raymond Ore 9 Jesmond Road, Croydon, CR0 6JR, United Kingdom
- (020) 8654 2014/(07941) 692235 / (020) 8654 2014
- rore@raymation.co.uk
- www.raymation.co.uk

Reality 3D 17 St Clements Road, Parkstone, Poole, Dorset, BH15 3PB, United Kingdom
- (07973) 534171
- Steve@reality3d.co.uk
- www.reality3d.co.uk

Realtime UK Willows Farm Studios, Ballam Road, Westby, Preston, PR4 3PN, United Kingdom
- (01772) 682363/ (01772) 683592
- info@realtimeuk.com
- www.realtimeuk.com

Rebecca Gibbon@Inkshed 99 Chase Side, Enfield, Middlesex, EN2 6NL, United Kingdom
- (020) 8367 4545/ (020) 8367 6730
- www.inkshed.co.uk

Rebecca Halls@The Organisation The Basement, 69 Caledonian Road, London, N1 9BT, United Kingdom
- (020) 7833 8268/(07973) 172902 / (020) 7833 8269
- organise@easynet.co.uk
- www.organisart.co.uk

Rebecca Terborg@Advocate Art 39 Church Road, London, SW19 5DQ, United Kingdom
- 020 8879 1166/020 8879 3303
- lesley@advocate-art.com
- www.advocate-art.com

Red@Début Art & The Coningsby Gallery 30 Tottenham Street, London, W1T 4RJ, United Kingdom
- (020) 7636 1064/ (020) 7580 7017
- info@debutart.com
- www.debutart.com

Red Giraffe Ltd 2nd Floor, 5 Church Street, Aylesbury, Buckinghamshire, HP20 2QP, United Kingdom
- (01296) 334466/ (01296) 334467
- karen@redgiraffe.co.uk
- www.redgiraffe.co.uk

Redseal@Début Art & The Coningsby Gallery 30 Tottenham Street, London, W1T 4RJ, United Kingdom
- (020) 7636 1064/ (020) 7580 7017
- info@debutart.com
- www.debutart.com

Reed Wilson@Art Market 51 Oxford Drive, London, SE1 2FB, United Kingdom
- (020) 7407 8111/ (020) 7407 8222
- info@artmarketillustration.com
- www.artmarketillustration.com

Reggie Pedro@Folio 10 Gate Street, Lincoln's Inn Fields, London, WC2A 3HP, United Kingdom
- (020) 7242 9562/ (020) 7242 1816
- all@folioart.co.uk
- www.folioart.co.uk

Reluctant Hero 3rd Floor Bolbec Hall, Westgate Road, Newcastle upon Tyne, NE1 1SE, United Kingdom
- 0191-230 3030/ 0191-230 3097
- sheilen@reluctanthero.co.uk
- www.reluctanthero.co.uk

Renate Decker-Berry- Europe Unlimited 59 Lambeth Walk, London, SE11 6DX, United Kingdom
- (020) 7735 6623/(07768) 251626 / (0707) 5009648
- renate@europeunlimited.com
- www.europeunlimited.com

Rhona Garvin@Eastwing 99 Chase Side, Enfield, Middlesex, EN2 6NL, United Kingdom
- (020) 8367 6760/ (020) 8367 6730
- andrea@eastwing.co.uk
- www.eastwing.co.uk

Ric Machin@Début Art & The Coningsby Gallery 30 Tottenham Street, London, W1T 4RJ, United Kingdom
- (020) 7636 1064/ (020) 7580 7017
- info@debutart.com
- www.debutart.com

Richard Draper Little Woolpit, Town Cross Avenue, Bognor Regis, West Sussex, P021 2DN, United Kingdom
- (01243) 820806/(07799) 310728 / (01243) 820806
- richarddraper@webnet2000.net
- www.richarddraper.com

Richard Duckett@N B Illustration Ltd 40 Bowling Green Lane, London, EC1R 0NE, United Kingdom
- (020) 7278 9131/ (020) 7278 9121
- info@nbillustration.co.uk
- www.nbillustration.co.uk

Richard Duckett Illustration 5 Torrems Street, London, EC1Z 1NQ, United Kingdom
- (07718) 580249
- richard.duckett@virgin.net
- www.richardduckett.com

Richard Elton@Graham-Cameron Illustration The Studio, 23 Holt Road, Sheringham, Norfolk, NR26 8NB, United Kingdom
- (01263) 821333/ (01263) 821334
- enquiry@graham-cameron-illustration.com
- www.graham-cameron-illustration.com

Richard Gregory The Folly, 61-62 Norton Lane, Durweston, Blandford Forum, Dorset, DT11 0QF, United Kingdom
- (01258) 452001/(07956) 507802
- info@richardgregorydesign.com
- www.richardgregorydesign.com

Richard Hall 18 Nicolas Road, Chorlton cum Hardy, Manchester, M21 9LR, United Kingdom
- 0161-862 9260
- richard@fiveleg.co.uk
- www.fiveleg.co.uk

Richard Hart@Début Art & The Coningsby Gallery 30 Tottenham Street, London, W1T 4RJ, United Kingdom
- (020) 7636 1064/ (020) 7580 7017
- info@debutart.com
- www.debutart.com

Richard Hook@Linden Artists Ltd 41 Battersea Business Centre, 103 Lavender Hill, London, SW11 5QL, United Kingdom
- (020) 7738 2505/ (020) 7738 2513
- lindenartists@aol.com
- www.lindenartists.co.uk

Richard J. Duszczak 29 Lake View Avenue, Walton, Chesterfield, Derbyshire, S40 3DR, United Kingdom
- (01246) 209034/ (01246) 209034
- rd@cartoonstudio.co.uk
- www.cartoonstudio.co.uk

Richard Johnson@The Organisation The Basement, 69 Caledonian Road, London, N1 9BT, United Kingdom
- (020) 7833 8268/(07973) 172902 / (020) 7833 8269
- organise@easynet.co.uk
- www.organisart.co.uk

Richard Jones@Artist Partners Ltd 2e The Chandlery, 50 Westminster Bridge Road, London, SE1 7QY, United Kingdom
- (020) 7401 7904/ (020) 7401 3378
- chris@artistpartners.demon.co.uk
- www.artistpartners.com

Richard Levesley@Art Market 51 Oxford Drive, London, SE1 2FB, United Kingdom
- (020) 7407 8111/ (020) 7407 8222
- info@artmarketillustration.com
- www.artmarketillustration.com

Richard Osley@N B Illustration Ltd 40 Bowling Green Lane, London, EC1R 0NE, United Kingdom
- (020) 7278 9131/ (020) 7278 9121
- info@nbillustration.co.uk
- www.nbillustration.co.uk

Richard Phipps@Illustration Ltd 2 Brooks Court, Cringle Street, London, SW8 5BX, United Kingdom
- (020) 7720 5202/ (020) 7720 5920
- team@illustrationweb.com
- www.illustrationweb.com

Richard Wetherill@Phosphor Art 41 The Pump House, Pump House Close, off Renforth Street, London, SE16 7HS, United Kingdom
- (020) 7064 4666/ (020) 7064 4660
- info@phosphorart.com
- www.phosphorart.com

Richard Williams@Eastwing 99 Chase Side, Enfield, Middlesex, EN2 6NL, United Kingdom
- (020) 8367 6760/ (020) 8367 6730
- andrea@eastwing.co.uk
- www.eastwing.co.uk

Richard Willson Shepherds Hill, Peaslake, Guildford, Surrey, GU5 9TB, United Kingdom
- (01306) 730570

Richardson Studio 41 Kirkleathen Lane, Redcar, Cleveland, TS10 1NT, United Kingdom
- (01642) 477119/ (01642) 477732
- richardsonstudio@btconnect.com
- www.cartoonist-illustrator.com

Rikki O'Neil@Bernard Thornton Artists The Penthouse, 4 Hamilton Mews, 310 Merton Road, London, SW18 5AB, United Kingdom
- (020) 8874 9081/(07702) 554583 / (020) 8877 1386
- bernard@btartists.com
- www.btartists.com

Riyaz@Art Collection UK Ltd 7 Worsley Mill, 10 Blantyre Street, Castlefield, Manchester, M15 4LG, United Kingdom
- (0870) 2405001/ (0870) 2405002
- info@artcollection.co.uk
- www.artcollection.co.uk

Rob Chapman@Linden Artists Ltd 41 Battersea Business Centre, 103 Lavender Hill, London, SW11 5QL, United Kingdom
- (020) 7738 2505/ (020) 7738 2513
- lindenartists@aol.com
- www.lindenartists.co.uk

Rob Dyke@Bernard Thornton Artists The Penthouse, 4 Hamilton Mews, 310 Merton Road, London, SW18 5AB, United Kingdom
- (020) 8874 9081/(07702) 554583 / (020) 8877 1386
- bernard@btartists.com
- www.btartists.com

Rob Heesom Wyatts Rectory Drive, Bidborough, Tunbridge Wells, Kent, TN3 0UL, United Kingdom
- (01892) 549084/ (01892) 549084
- robheesom@aol.com
- www.robheesom.com

Robert Davies Chestnut Lodge, Cathole Lane, Uplyme, Lyme Regis, Dorset, DT7 3SJ, United Kingdom
- (01297) 445014/ (01297) 445014
- robert@chestnut-lodge.org.uk
- www.chestnut-lodge.org.uk

Robert Drake 218-220 Lowerhouse Lane, Burnley, Lancashire, BB12 6LP, United Kingdom
- (01282) 426008/ (01282) 426008

Robert Holder Twin Oaks, 14 Darren View, Bridgend, Mid Glamorgan, CF34 9SG, United Kingdom
- (01656) 732944/(07796) 172129 / (01656) 733895
- rholder@freeuk.com

Robert Littleford 7 Upper Gardner Street, Brighton, BN1 4AN, United Kingdom
- (01273) 621 372
- robert_littleford@yahoo
- www.robertlittleford.co.uk

Robert Morton@Bernard Thornton Artists The Penthouse, 4 Hamilton Mews, 310 Merton Road, London, SW18 5AB, United Kingdom
- (020) 8874 9081/(07702) 554583 / (020) 8877 1386
- bernard@btartists.com
- www.btartists.com

Robert Nelmes@The Organisation The Basement, 69 Caledonian Road, London, N1 9BT, United Kingdom
- (020) 7833 8268/(07973) 172902 / (020) 7833 8269
- organise@easynet.co.uk
- www.organisart.co.uk

Robert Tilleard Pythouse Farm Cottage, Tisbury, Salisbury, SP3 6NY, United Kingdom
☏ (01747) 870801
✉ tilleard@madasafish.com
🖥 www.tilleard.co.uk

Robin Budden@Drawer Illustrators Agents 8 Belmont, Bath, BA1 5DZ, United Kingdom
☏ (01225) 445262
✉ enquiries@drawer.me.uk

Robin Carter 33 High Field Close, Thorpe, St. Andrew, Norwich, NR7 0RQ, United Kingdom
☏ (01603) 701555/(07776) 221345/☏ (01603) 701555
✉ bellae@ntlworld.com
🖥 www.carterwongtomlin.com/robincarter

Robin Chevalier@Eastwing 99 Chase Side, Enfield, Middlesex, EN2 6NL, United Kingdom
☏ (020) 8367 6760/☏ (020) 8367 6730
✉ andrea@eastwing.co.uk
🖥 www.eastwing.co.uk

Robin Edmonds@Just For Laffs 7 Worsley Mill, 10 Blantyre Street, Castlefield, Manchester, M15 4LG, United Kingdom
☏ (0870) 1225003/☏ (0870) 2405002
✉ info@justforlaffs.co.uk
🖥 www.justforlaffs.co.uk

Robin Harris 60 Weltje Road, Hammersmith, London, W6 9LT, United Kingdom
☏ (020) 8748 5998
✉ thestars@twilight.ndo.co.uk

Robin Heighway-Bury@Thorogood Illustration Ltd 5 Dryden Street, Covent Garden, London, WC2E 9NW, United Kingdom
☏ (020) 7829 8468
✉ draw@thorogood.net
🖥 www.thorogood.net

Rockwood Flat 40, 216 Kennington Road, London, SE11 6HR, United Kingdom
☏ (020) 7582 9308
✉ richardrockwood@mac.com

Rod Clark@Art Market 51 Oxford Drive, London, SE1 2FB, United Kingdom
☏ (020) 7407 8111/☏ (020) 7407 8222
✉ info@artmarketillustration.com
🖥 www.artmarketillustration.com

Rod Holt@Artist Partners Ltd 2e The Chandlery, 50 Westminster Bridge Road, London, SE1 7QY, United Kingdom
☏ (020) 7401 7904/☏ (020) 7401 3378
✉ chris@artistpartners.demon.co.uk
🖥 www.artistpartners.com

Rod Josey@Illustration Ltd 2 Brooks Court, Cringle Street, London, SW8 5BX, United Kingdom
☏ (020) 7720 5202/☏ (020) 7720 5920
✉ team@illustrationweb.com
🖥 www.illustrationweb.com

Roger Farr 68 Station Road, Lawley Bank, Telford, Shropshire, TF4 2LH, United Kingdom
☏ (01952) 403670/(07879) 241242 ☏
✉ rogerfarr@msn.com
🖥 www.rogerfarr.net

Roger Fereday@Linda Rogers Associates 163 Half Moon Lane, London, SE24 9WB, United Kingdom
☏ (020) 7501 9106
✉ lr@lindarogers.net
🖥 www.lindarogers.net

Roger Gorringe@Illustration Ltd 2 Brooks Court, Cringle Street, London, SW8 5BX, United Kingdom
☏ (020) 7720 5202/☏ (020) 7720 5920
✉ team@illustrationweb.com
🖥 www.illustrationweb.com

Roger Harris@N B Illustration Ltd 40 Bowling Green Lane, London, EC1R 0NE, United Kingdom
☏ (020) 7278 9131/☏ (020) 7278 9121
✉ info@nbillustration.co.uk
🖥 www.nbillustration.co.uk

Roger Kent@Illustration Ltd 2 Brooks Court, Cringle Street, London, SW8 5BX, United Kingdom
☏ (020) 7720 5202/☏ (020) 7720 5920
✉ team@illustrationweb.com
🖥 www.illustrationweb.com

Roger Norris Tir Bach, Libanus, Brecon, Powys, LD3 8NE, United Kingdom
☏ (01874) 625675/☏ (01874) 611198
✉ roger_norris@btconnect.com

Roger Payne@Linden Artists Ltd 41 Battersea Business Centre, 103 Lavender Hill, London, SW11 5QL, United Kingdom
☏ (020) 7738 2505/☏ (020) 7738 2513
✉ lindenartists@aol.com
🖥 www.lindenartists.co.uk

Roger Penwill 6 Marcle Orchard, Brimfield, Ludlow, Shropshire, SY8 4PD, United Kingdom
☏ (01584) 711854/(07840) 659522 ☏ (01584) 711854
✉ roger@penwill.com
🖥 www.penwillcartoons.com

Roger Sanderson Bucklers Lodge, 32 Ringwood Road, St. Ives, Ringwood, Hampshire, BH24 2NY, United Kingdom
☏ (01425) 474242

Roger Stewart 54 Ashurst Road, West Moors, Ferndown, Dorset, BH22 0LS, United Kingdom
☏ (01202) 890119/(07778) 876594 ☏ (01202) 890106
✉ roger@rmstewart.demon.co.uk
🖥 www.rogerstewart.co.uk

Roger Watt@Folio 10 Gate Street, Lincoln's Inn Fields, London, WC2A 3HP, United Kingdom
☏ (020) 7242 9562/☏ (020) 7242 1816
✉ all@folioart.co.uk
🖥 www.folioart.co.uk

Roman Grey@Inkshed 99 Chase Side, Enfield, Middlesex, EN2 6NL, United Kingdom
☏ (020) 8367 4545/☏ (020) 8367 6730
🖥 www.inkshed.co.uk

Ron Hopkins 38 Sandy Lane South, Wallington, Surrey, SM6 9QZ, United Kingdom
☏ (020) 8773 0826

Ronald Maddox 21 New Road, Digswell, Welwyn, Hertfordshire, AL6 0AQ, United Kingdom
☏ (01438) 714884

Roofs 16f Grand Parade, Green Lanes, London, N4 1LA, United Kingdom
☏ (020) 8482 1167
✉ mail@garofeanu.com
🖥 www.garofeanu.com/design

Ros Baron 34 Trinder Road, London, N19 4QU, United Kingdom
☏ (020) 7263 2705
✉ ros.baron@virgin.net
🖥 www.rosbaron.co.uk

Rosamund Fowler@Artist Partners Ltd 2e The Chandlery, 50 Westminster Bridge Road, London, SE1 7QY, United Kingdom
☏ (020) 7401 7904/☏ (020) 7401 3378
✉ chris@artistpartners.demon.co.uk
🖥 www.artistpartners.com

Rosendorf 117 Northen Avenue, No 4, Decatur, 30030, United States of America
☏ 00 1 404 229 7445
✉ studio@rosendorf.us
🖥 rosendorf.us

Rosie Brooks Illustration, London, United Kingdom
☏ (07909) 924384
✉ rosie@rosiebrooks.co.uk
🖥 www.rosiebrooks.co.uk

Rosie Sanders@Illustration Ltd 2 Brooks Court, Cringle Street, London, SW8 5BX, United Kingdom
☏ (020) 7720 5202/☏ (020) 7720 5920
✉ team@illustrationweb.com
🖥 www.illustrationweb.com

Rosie Scott@The Artworks 40 Frith Street, London, W1D 5LN, United Kingdom
☏ (020) 7734 3333/☏ (020) 7734 3484
✉ lucy@theartworksinc.com
🖥 www.theartworksinc.com

Ross Simmons Illustration & Design 43 Crossways, Three Bridges, Crawley, West Sussex, RH10 1QT, United Kingdom
☏ 07876 203171/☏ 01293 571102
✉ rosssimmons77@hotmail.com

Ross Thomson@Graham-Cameron Illustration The Studio, 23 Holt Road, Sheringham, Norfolk, NR26 8NB, United Kingdom
☏ (01263) 821333/☏ (01263) 821334
✉ enquiry@graham-cameron-illustration.com
🖥 www.graham-cameron-illustration.com

Rowena Dugdale@Début Art & The Coningsby Gallery 30 Tottenham Street, London, W1T 4RJ, United Kingdom
☏ (020) 7636 1064/☏ (020) 7580 7017
✉ info@debutart.com
🖥 www.debutart.com

Rox Hsiao@Advocate Art 39 Church Road, London, SW19 5DQ, United Kingdom
☏ 020 8879 1166/020 8879 3303
✉ lesley@advocate-art.com
🖥 www.advocate-art.com

Roy Avis@Advocate Art 39 Church Road, London, SW19 5DQ, United Kingdom
☏ 020 8879 1166/020 8879 3303
✉ lesley@advocate-art.com
🖥 www.advocate-art.com

Roy Knipe@Thorogood Illustration Ltd 5 Dryden Street, Covent Garden, London, WC2E 9NW, United Kingdom
☏ (020) 7829 8468
✉ draw@thorogood.net
🖥 www.thorogood.net

Royston Robertson 20 Upton Road, Broadstairs, Kent, CT10 2AS, United Kingdom
☏ (01843) 871241/(07787) 303974 ☏
✉ royston@dircon.co.uk
🖥 www.roystonrobertson.co.uk

Rozart 132 Knavesmire Crescent, York, YO23 1EU, United Kingdom
☏ (01904) 653983

Rubens@Advocate Art 39 Church Road, London, SW19 5DQ, United Kingdom
☏ 020 8879 1166/020 8879 3303
✉ lesley@advocate-art.com
🖥 www.advocate-art.com

Ruffle Brothers Ltd Sycamore Cottage, Bussage, Stroud, Gloucestershire, GL6 8AX, United Kingdom
☏ (01453) 885953/☏ (01453) 885953
✉ mark@rufflebrothers.com
🖥 www.rufflebrothers.com

Rui Ricardo@Folio 10 Gate Street, Lincoln's Inn Fields, London, WC2A 3HP, United Kingdom
☏ (020) 7242 9562/☏ (020) 7242 1816
✉ all@folioart.co.uk
🖥 www.folioart.co.uk

Rupert Besley 26 College Road, Newport, Isle of Wight, PO30 1HB, United Kingdom
☏ (01983) 528943/☏ (01983) 528943
✉ cartoons@rbesley.freeserve.co.uk
🖥 www.besleycartoons.com

Russ Tudor 2 Hathaway Drive, Astley Bridge, Bolton, BL1 7RY, United Kingdom
☏ (01204) 597795/☏ (01204) 597795
✉ cartoons@russtudor.wanadoo.co.uk
🖥 www.russtudor.com

Russ Widstrand@Début Art & The Coningsby Gallery 30 Tottenham Street, London, W1T 4RJ, United Kingdom
☏ (020) 7636 1064/☏ (020) 7580 7017
✉ info@debutart.com
🖥 www.debutart.com

Russell Becker 16a Crockwell Street, Bodmin, Cornwall, PL31 2DS, United Kingdom
☏ (01208) 76086/077 76 045023 ☏ (01208) 76086
✉ russ@russellbecker.com
🖥 www.russellbecker.com

Russell Cobb@The Artworks 40 Frith Street, London, W1D 5LN, United Kingdom
☏ (020) 7734 3333/☏ (020) 7734 3484
✉ lucy@theartworksinc.com
🖥 www.theartworksinc.com

Russell Rukin@Private View Artists Agency 17A Swan Hill, Shrewsbury, SY1 1NL, United Kingdom
☏ (01743) 350355/☏ (01743) 233923
✉ create@pvuk.com
🖥 www.pvuk.com

Russell Walker@Central Illustration Agency 36 Wellington Street, London, WC2E 7BD, United Kingdom
☏ (020) 7240 8925/☏ (020) 7836 1177
✉ info@centralillustration.com
🖥 www.centralillustration.com

Ruth Galloway@Advocate Art 39 Church Road, London, SW19 5DQ, United Kingdom
☏ 020 8879 1166/020 8879 3303
✉ lesley@advocate-art.com
🖥 www.advocate-art.com

Ruth Palmer Halshayne, Widworthy, Honiton, Devon, EX14 9JS, United Kingdom
☏ (01404) 831705/(07905) 951453 ☏ (01404) 831705
✉ ruth.palmer@btinternet.com
🖥 www.ruth.palmer.btinternet.co.uk

Ruth Rivers@The Organisation The Basement, 69 Caledonian Road, London, N1 9BT, United Kingdom
☏ (020) 7833 8268/(07973) 172902 ☏ (020) 7833 8269
✉ organise@easynet.co.uk
🖥 www.organisart.co.uk

Ruth Thornlevold@N B Illustration Ltd 40 Bowling Green Lane, London, EC1R 0NE, United Kingdom
- (020) 7278 9131/ (020) 7278 9121
- info@nbillustration.co.uk
- www.nbillustration.co.uk

Rutu Modan@The Artworks 40 Frith Street, London, W1D 5LN, United Kingdom
- (020) 7734 3333/ (020) 7734 3484
- lucy@theartworksinc.com
- www.theartworksinc.com

S Sigma Creative Illustration 72 Langhorn Road, Swaythling, Southampton, SO16 3TN, United Kingdom
- (023) 8055 3666/ (023) 8055 3666
- blake.ssigma@virgin.net

S.P. Ashmore 41 Blunts Way, Horsham, West Sussex, RH12 2BJ, United Kingdom
- (01403) 267269/ (01403) 267269

Sabine Vittinghoff@Phosphor Art 41 The Pump House, Pump House Close, off Renforth Street, London, SE16 7HS, United Kingdom
- (020) 7064 4666/ (020) 7064 4660
- info@phosphorart.com
- www.phosphorart.com

Saeko Ilustration First Floor Flat, Warrior Square, St. Leonards-on-Sea, East Sussex, TN37 6BG, United Kingdom
- (07939) 582808
- info@saekoillustration.com
- www.saekoillustration.com

Sailesh Thakprar@Advocate Art 39 Church Road, London, SW19 5DQ, United Kingdom
- 020 8879 1166/020 8879 3303
- lesley@advocate-art.com
- www.advocate-art.com

Sally Barton@Linden Artists Ltd 41 Battersea Business Centre, 103 Lavender Hill, London, SW11 5QL, United Kingdom
- (020) 7738 2505/ (020) 7738 2513
- lindenartists@aol.com
- www.lindenartists.co.uk

Sally Kember 137 Acorn Avenue, Cowfold, West Sussex, RH13 8RT, United Kingdom
- (01403) 864432
- sally.kember@virgin.net
- www.kember.com/sally

Sally Kindberg 126A Gloucester Avenue, London, NW1 8JA, United Kingdom
- (020) 7722 6600
- k@sallykindberg.co.uk
- www.sallykindberg.co.uk

Sally Launder@Drawer Illustrators Agents 8 Belmont, Bath, BA1 5DZ, United Kingdom
- (01225) 445262
- enquiries@drawer.me.uk

Sally Taylor@Artist Partners Ltd 2e The Chandlery, 50 Westminster Bridge Road, London, SE1 7QY, United Kingdom
- (020) 7401 7904/ (020) 7401 3378
- chris@artistpartners.demon.co.uk
- www.artistpartners.com

Salvatore Rubbino@The Artworks 40 Frith Street, London, W1D 5LN, United Kingdom
- (020) 7734 3333/ (020) 7734 3484
- lucy@theartworksinc.com
- www.theartworksinc.com

Sam Hadley@Artist Partners Ltd 2e The Chandlery, 50 Westminster Bridge Road, London, SE1 7QY, United Kingdom
- (020) 7401 7904/ (020) 7401 3378
- chris@artistpartners.demon.co.uk
- www.artistpartners.com

Samara Bryan@Art Market 51 Oxford Drive, London, SE1 2FB, United Kingdom
- (020) 7407 8111/ (020) 7407 8222
- info@artmarketillustration.com
- www.artmarketillustration.com

Sandra Isaksson@Phosphor Art 41 The Pump House, Pump House Close, off Renforth Street, London, SE16 7HS, United Kingdom
- (020) 7064 4666/ (020) 7064 4660
- info@phosphorart.com
- www.phosphorart.com

Sandy Nightingale@Artist Partners Ltd 2e The Chandlery, 50 Westminster Bridge Road, London, SE1 7QY, United Kingdom
- (020) 7401 7904/ (020) 7401 3378
- chris@artistpartners.demon.co.uk
- www.artistpartners.com

Sara Baker@Graham-Cameron Illustration The Studio, 23 Holt Road, Sheringham, Norfolk, NR26 8NB, United Kingdom
- (01263) 821333/ (01263) 821334
- enquiry@graham-cameron-illustration.com
- www.graham-cameron-illustration.com

Sara Beazley@Début Art & The Coningsby Gallery 30 Tottenham Street, London, W1T 4RJ, United Kingdom
- (020) 7636 1064/ (020) 7580 7017
- info@debutart.com
- www.debutart.com

Sara Gancho@Advocate Art 39 Church Road, London, SW19 5DQ, United Kingdom
- 020 8879 1166/020 8879 3303
- lesley@advocate-art.com
- www.advocate-art.com

Sara Hayward@Central Illustration Agency 36 Wellington Street, London, WC2E 7BD, United Kingdom
- (020) 7240 8925/ (020) 7836 1177
- info@centralillustration.com
- www.centralillustration.com

Sara Ruano@Advocate Art 39 Church Road, London, SW19 5DQ, United Kingdom
- 020 8879 1166/020 8879 3303
- lesley@advocate-art.com
- www.advocate-art.com

Sara Silcock@Linda Rogers Associates 163 Half Moon Lane, London, SE24 9WB, United Kingdom
- (020) 7501 9106
- lr@lindarogers.net
- www.lindarogers.net

Sarah Ashton Illustration Flat 2, 165 Loughborough Road, West Bridgford, Nottingham, NG2 7JS, United Kingdom
- (07841) 104606
- sashton56@gmail.com
- www.sarahhashton.co.uk

Sarah Barrett Design Church View, Dodford, Northampton, NN7 4SX, United Kingdom
- (01327) 341826

Sarah Beetson@Illustration Ltd 2 Brooks Court, Cringle Street, London, SW8 5BX, United Kingdom
- (020) 7720 5202/ (020) 7720 5920
- team@illustrationweb.com
- www.illustrationweb.com

Sarah Brown Agency 10 The Avenue, Ealing, London, W13 8PH, United Kingdom
- (020) 8998 0390/(07778) 177102 (020) 8843 1175
- sbagency@dsl.pipex.com
- www.sbagency.com

Sarah Fawkes Graphic Design 79 Grooms Lane, Silver End, Witham, Essex, CM8 3SH, United Kingdom
- (07759) 125598
- sarahfawkes@btinternet.com

Sarah Gibb@The Artworks 40 Frith Street, London, W1D 5LN, United Kingdom
- (020) 7734 3333/ (020) 7734 3484
- lucy@theartworksinc.com
- www.theartworksinc.com

Sarah Horne@Advocate Art 39 Church Road, London, SW19 5DQ, United Kingdom
- 020 8879 1166/020 8879 3303
- lesley@advocate-art.com
- www.advocate-art.com

Sarah Jones@Début Art & The Coningsby Gallery 30 Tottenham Street, London, W1T 4RJ, United Kingdom
- (020) 7636 1064/ (020) 7580 7017
- info@debutart.com
- www.debutart.com

Sarah Kelly@Art Collection UK Ltd 7 Worsley Mill, 10 Blantyre Street, Castlefield, Manchester, M15 4LG, United Kingdom
- (0870) 2405001/ (0870) 2405002
- info@artcollection.co.uk
- www.artcollection.co.uk

Sarah Kranz@Allied Artists@ Artistic License The Gallery @ Richmond, 63 Sheen Road, Richmond, Surrey, TW9 1YJ, United Kingdom
- (020) 8334 1010/ (020) 8334 9900
- info@allied-artists.net
- www.allied-artists.net

Sarah Lane Represents 56 Bidwell Gardens, London, N11 2AU, United Kingdom
- (07901) 552520/ (020) 8292 4001
- sarah@sarahlanerepresents.com
- www.sarahlanerepresents.com

Sarah McMenemy@The Artworks 40 Frith Street, London, W1D 5LN, United Kingdom
- (020) 7734 3333/ (020) 7734 3484
- lucy@theartworksinc.com
- www.theartworksinc.com

Sarah Nayler@N B Illustration Ltd 40 Bowling Green Lane, London, EC1R 0NE, United Kingdom
- (020) 7278 9131/ (020) 7278 9121
- info@nbillustration.co.uk
- www.nbillustration.co.uk

Sarah Perkins@Inkshed 99 Chase Side, Enfield, Middlesex, EN2 6NL, United Kingdom
- (020) 8367 4545/ (020) 8367 6730
- www.inkshed.co.uk

Sarah Roe 32 Granville Road, Poole, Dorset, BH12 3BG, United Kingdom
- (01202) 731793/(07815) 076693
- sarah9000@ntlworld.com
- www.sarahroe.co.uk

Sarah Smith@Linden Artists Ltd 41 Battersea Business Centre, 103 Lavender Hill, London, SW11 5QL, United Kingdom
- (020) 7738 2505/ (020) 7738 2513
- lindenartists@aol.com
- www.lindenartists.co.uk

Sarah Venus Whin Brow Cottage, Hood Lane, Cloughton, Scarborough, North Yorkshire, YO13 0AT, United Kingdom
- (01723) 871051/ (01723) 871051
- sarah.venus@virgin.net
- www.sarahjvenus.co.uk

Sarah Wade@Advocate Art 39 Church Road, London, SW19 5DQ, United Kingdom
- 020 8879 1166/020 8879 3303
- lesley@advocate-art.com
- www.advocate-art.com

Sarah Wimperis@Graham-Cameron Illustration The Studio, 23 Holt Road, Sheringham, Norfolk, NR26 8NB, United Kingdom
- (01263) 821333/ (01263) 821334
- enquiry@graham-cameron-illustration.com
- www.graham-cameron-illustration.com

Satoshi Kambayashi@Phosphor Art 41 The Pump House, Pump House Close, off Renforth Street, London, SE16 7HS, United Kingdom
- (020) 7064 4666/ (020) 7064 4660
- info@phosphorart.com
- www.phosphorart.com

Scott & Antony Evans@Advocate Art 39 Church Road, London, SW19 5DQ, United Kingdom
- 020 8879 1166/020 8879 3303
- lesley@advocate-art.com
- www.advocate-art.com

Scott Jessop@Advocate Art 39 Church Road, London, SW19 5DQ, United Kingdom
- 020 8879 1166/020 8879 3303
- lesley@advocate-art.com
- www.advocate-art.com

Scott Wilson@Advocate Art 39 Church Road, London, SW19 5DQ, United Kingdom
- 020 8879 1166/020 8879 3303
- lesley@advocate-art.com
- www.advocate-art.com

Sean Rodwell@Advocate Art 39 Church Road, London, SW19 5DQ, United Kingdom
- 020 8879 1166/020 8879 3303
- lesley@advocate-art.com
- www.advocate-art.com

Sean Sims@New Division 5 Risborough Street, London, SE1 0HF, United Kingdom
- (020) 7593 0505/ (020) 7593 0501
- info@newdivision.com
- www.newdivision.com

Sebastian Quigley@Linden Artists Ltd 41 Battersea Business Centre, 103 Lavender Hill, London, SW11 5QL, United Kingdom
- (020) 7738 2505/ (020) 7738 2513
- lindenartists@aol.com
- www.lindenartists.co.uk

Sensible Pencil 6 Chantry Mead Road, Bath, BA2 2DA, United Kingdom
- (07974) 910667
- chrissy@sensiblepencil.com
- www.sensiblepencil.com

Serge Seldlitz@Début Art & The Coningsby Gallery
30 Tottenham Street, London, W1T 4RJ, United Kingdom
(020) 7636 1064/ (020) 7580 7017
info@debutart.com
www.debutart.com

Sergey Shinjaev@Advocate Art 39 Church Road,
London, SW19 5DQ, United Kingdom
020 8879 1166/020 8879 3303
lesley@advocate-art.com
www.advocate-art.com

Seripop@Début Art & The Coningsby Gallery 30
Tottenham Street, London, W1T 4RJ, United Kingdom
(020) 7636 1064/ (020) 7580 7017
info@debutart.com
www.debutart.com

Shane Marsh@Linden Artists Ltd 41 Battersea
Business Centre, 103 Lavender Hill, London, SW11 5QL,
United Kingdom
(020) 7738 2505/ (020) 7738 2513
lindenartists@aol.com
www.lindenartists.co.uk

Shani Bean@Allied Artists@ Artistic License The
Gallery @ Richmond, 63 Sheen Road, Richmond, Surrey,
TW9 1YJ, United Kingdom
(020) 8334 1010/ (020) 8334 9900
info@allied-artists.net
www.allied-artists.net

Sharif Tarabay@Illustration Ltd 2 Brooks Court,
Cringle Street, London, SW8 5BX, United Kingdom
(020) 7720 5202/ (020) 7720 5920
team@illustrationweb.com
www.illustrationweb.com

Sharon Harmer@Advocate Art 39 Church Road,
London, SW19 5DQ, United Kingdom
020 8879 1166/020 8879 3303
lesley@advocate-art.com
www.advocate-art.com

Sharon Pinsker@Artist Partners Ltd 2e The
Chandlery, 50 Westminster Bridge Road, London, SE1
7QY, United Kingdom
(020) 7401 7904/ (020) 7401 3378
chris@artistpartners.demon.co.uk
www.artistpartners.com

Sharon Williams@Advocate Art 39 Church Road,
London, SW19 5DQ, United Kingdom
020 8879 1166/020 8879 3303
lesley@advocate-art.com
www.advocate-art.com

Shaun Askew Illustrator Animator, Third Floor, 3-11
Westland Place, London, N1 7LP, United Kingdom
(020) 7490 3769/ (020) 7490 3769
shaun@holistic-hamster.com
www.holistic-hamster.com

Shaunna Peterson@Thorogood Illustration Ltd 5
Dryden Street, Covent Garden, London, WC2E 9NW,
United Kingdom
(020) 7829 8468
draw@thorogood.net
www.thorogood.net

Sheena Dawson@Linda Rogers Associates 163 Half
Moon Lane, London, SE24 9WB, United Kingdom
(020) 7501 9106
lr@lindarogers.net
www.lindarogers.net

Sheila MacLean Hillend House, Lothianburn, Edinburgh,
EH10 7DX, United Kingdom
0131-445 2767
sheilarmaclean@hotmail.com

Sheridan Art Works 29 Lynnhurst, Uddingston, Glasgow,
G71 6SA, United Kingdom
(07791) 201985
paulsheridan24@yahoo.co.uk
www.freewebs.com/sheridanartworks

Shirley Curzon Birch Glade, 60 The Grove, Biggin Hill,
Westerham, Kent, TN16 3TD, United Kingdom
(01959) 573407

Shirley Hart Creative Consultants 19 Ulundi Road,
London, SE3 7UQ, United Kingdom
(020) 8853 2987/(07867) 806250
shirleyhart@btinternet.com
www.shirleyhart.com

Sholto Walker@Illustration Ltd 2 Brooks Court,
Cringle Street, London, SW8 5BX, United Kingdom
(020) 7720 5202/ (020) 7720 5920
team@illustrationweb.com
www.illustrationweb.com

Siku@Folio 10 Gate Street, Lincoln's Inn Fields, London,
WC2A 3HP, United Kingdom
(020) 7242 9562/ (020) 7242 1816
all@folioart.co.uk
www.folioart.co.uk

Silvia Rocha Campos@Advocate Art 39 Church Road,
London, SW19 5DQ, United Kingdom
020 8879 1166/020 8879 3303
lesley@advocate-art.com
www.advocate-art.com

Simon Abbott@Advocate Art 39 Church Road,
London, SW19 5DQ, United Kingdom
020 8879 1166/020 8879 3303
lesley@advocate-art.com
www.advocate-art.com

Simon Bartram@Arena 31 Eleanor Road, London, E15
4AB, United Kingdom
(08450) 507 600
info@arenaworks.com
www.arenaworks.com

Simon Clare Creative Workshop Little Leydens, Stick
Hill, Edenbridge, Kent, TN8 5NH, United Kingdom
(01732) 862672
simonc.creative@btinternet.com
www.contact-me.net/SimonClare

Simon Dolby The Design Factory, The Old Surgery, 30
West Street, Oundle, Peterborough, PE8 4EF, United
Kingdom
(01832) 273801/(07713) 960117
dolbygallery@design-factory.co.uk
www.dolbygallery.com

Simon Godsell@Advocate Art 39 Church Road,
London, SW19 5DQ, United Kingdom
020 8879 1166/020 8879 3303
lesley@advocate-art.com
www.advocate-art.com

Simon Henshaw 86 Cariocca Business Park, Manchester,
M12 4AH, United Kingdom
0161-272 7712/ 0161-272 7712
art.henshaw@btopenworld.com

Simon Henwood@Big Active Ltd Unit 6.01, The Tea
Building, 56 Shoreditch High Street, London, E16 JJ,
United Kingdom
(020) 7739 5601/ (020) 7739 7479
contact@bigactive.com
www.bigactive.com

Simon Mendez@Advocate Art 39 Church Road,
London, SW19 5DQ, United Kingdom
020 8879 1166/020 8879 3303
lesley@advocate-art.com
www.advocate-art.com

Simon Paulson@Art Collection UK Ltd 7 Worsley
Mill, 10 Blantyre Street, Castlefield, Manchester, M15
4LG, United Kingdom
(0870) 2405001/ (0870) 2405002
info@artcollection.co.uk
www.artcollection.co.uk

Simon Roberts Illustration Ltd 8 Springfield House,
Cotham Road, Bristol, BS6 6DQ, United Kingdom
0117-973 7179/(07968) 556568
simon@sr-illustration.com
www.sr-illustration.com

Simon Spilsbury@Central Illustration Agency 36
Wellington Street, London, WC2E 7BD, United Kingdom
(020) 7240 8925/ (020) 7836 1177
info@centralillustration.com
www.centralillustration.com

Simon Stephenson@N B Illustration Ltd 40 Bowling
Green Lane, London, EC1R 0NE, United Kingdom
(020) 7278 9131/ (020) 7278 9121
info@nbillustration.co.uk
www.nbillustration.co.uk

Simon Stern@Inkshed 99 Chase Side, Enfield,
Middlesex, EN2 6NL, United Kingdom
(020) 8367 4545/ (020) 8367 6730
www.inkshed.co.uk

Simon Williams@Illustration Ltd 2 Brooks Court,
Cringle Street, London, SW8 5BX, United Kingdom
(020) 7720 5202/ (020) 7720 5920
team@illustrationweb.com
www.illustrationweb.com

Sir Peter Blake@Central Illustration Agency 36
Wellington Street, London, WC2E 7BD, United Kingdom
(020) 7240 8925/ (020) 7836 1177
info@centralillustration.com
www.centralillustration.com

Small Moon Valley Finsbury Park Road, London, N4
2JY, United Kingdom
(020) 7288 1271
frances.castle@btinternet.com
www.smallmoonvalley.com

Smutt Magazine 41 Kensington Road, Chichester, West
Sussex, PO19 7XS,
70926368776
lou.marshall@hotmail.com
www.smuttmagazine.com

Social Fabric UK Ltd William Blake House, 8 Marshall
Street, London, W1F 7EJ, United Kingdom
(020) 7788 7876
us@thesocialfabric.com
www.thesocialfabric.com

Sohie Tilley@Artist Partners Ltd 2e The Chandlery, 50
Westminster Bridge Road, London, SE1 7QY, United
Kingdom
(020) 7401 7904/ (020) 7401 3378
chris@artistpartners.demon.co.uk
www.artistpartners.com

Sonia Canals, Brighton, United Kingdom
(01273) 626241/ (01273) 507130
info@magicpen.co.uk
www.magicpen.co.uk

Sophie Allsopp@Thorogood Illustration Ltd 5
Dryden Street, Covent Garden, London, WC2E 9NW,
United Kingdom
(020) 7829 8468
draw@thorogood.net
www.thorogood.net

Sophie Fatus@Advocate Art 39 Church Road, London,
SW19 5DQ, United Kingdom
020 8879 1166/020 8879 3303
lesley@advocate-art.com
www.advocate-art.com

Sophie Grillet 20 Greyladies Gardens, Wat Tyler Road,
London, SE10 8AU, United Kingdom
(020) 8691 0153/ (020) 8691 0153
sophie@sophiescartoons.com
www.sophiescartoons.com

Sophie Hanton@Advocate Art 39 Church Road,
London, SW19 5DQ, United Kingdom
020 8879 1166/020 8879 3303
lesley@advocate-art.com
www.advocate-art.com

Sophie Keen@The Organisation The Basement, 69
Caledonian Road, London, N1 9BT, United Kingdom
(020) 7833 8268/(07973) 172902 (020) 7833 8269
organise@easynet.co.uk
www.organisart.co.uk

Sophie Klerk@Début Art & The Coningsby Gallery
30 Tottenham Street, London, W1T 4RJ, United Kingdom
(020) 7636 1064/ (020) 7580 7017
info@debutart.com
www.debutart.com

**Sophie Marsham@Début Art & The Coningsby
Gallery** 30 Tottenham Street, London, W1T 4RJ, United
Kingdom
(020) 7636 1064/ (020) 7580 7017
info@debutart.com
www.debutart.com

Sparq 17 Kennington Lane, London, SE11 5LQ, United
Kingdom
(07944) 457171
info@sparq1.co.uk
www.sparq1.co.uk

Specs Art 93 London Road, Cheltenham, Gloucestershire,
GL52 6HL, United Kingdom
(01242) 515951
roland@specsart.com
www.specsart.com

Stage One Storyboards 2nd Floor, 14-19 Great Chapel
Street, London, W1F 8FN, United Kingdom
(020) 7494 3222/ (020) 7494 3220
studio@stageonestoryboards.co.uk
www.stageonestoryboards.co.uk

Stan Chow@Central Illustration Agency 36 Wellington Street, London, WC2E 7BD, United Kingdom
(020) 7240 8925/ (020) 7836 1177
info@centralillustration.com
www.centralillustration.com

Stefan Chabluk@Steiner Lund@Illustration Ltd 2 Brooks Court, Cringle Street, London, SW8 5BX, United Kingdom
(020) 7720 5202/ (020) 7720 5920
team@illustrationweb.com
www.illustrationweb.com

Stem Agency Top Floor, 23 Charlotte Road, London, EC2A 3PB, United Kingdom
(07790) 026628
will@stemagency.com
www.stemagency.com

Steph Dix@Graham-Cameron Illustration The Studio, 23 Holt Road, Sheringham, Norfolk, NR26 8NB, United Kingdom
(01263) 821333/ (01263) 821334
enquiry@graham-cameron-illustration.com
www.graham-cameron-illustration.com

Stephane Gamain@N B Illustration Ltd 40 Bowling Green Lane, London, EC1R 0NE, United Kingdom
(020) 7278 9131/ (020) 7278 9121
info@nbillustration.co.uk
www.nbillustration.co.uk

Stephanie Boey@Drawer Illustrators Agents 8 Belmont, Bath, BA1 5DZ, United Kingdom
(01225) 445262
enquiries@drawer.me.uk

Stephanie Longfoot@Bernard Thornton Artists The Penthouse, 4 Hamilton Mews, 310 Merton Road, London, SW18 5AB, United Kingdom
(020) 8874 9081/(07702) 554583 (020) 8877 1386
bernard@btartists.com
www.btartists.com

Stephen Biesty Church Path Cottage, Kingsdon, Somerton, Somerset, TA11 7JU, United Kingdom
(01935) 841789/ (01935) 841789
sbsd@aol.com

Stephen Bliss@Central Illustration Agency 36 Wellington Street, London, WC2E 7BD, United Kingdom
(020) 7240 8925/ (020) 7836 1177
info@centralillustration.com
www.centralillustration.com

Stephen Butler@Art Market 51 Oxford Drive, London, SE1 2FB, United Kingdom
(020) 7407 8111/ (020) 7407 8222
info@artmarketillustration.com
www.artmarketillustration.com

Stephen Cooper 4 Coltsfoot Close, Wednesfield, Wolverhampton, WV11 3UF, United Kingdom
(01902) 637153
stevesee@btinternet.com
www.originall.co.uk

Stephen Dell@The Organisation The Basement, 69 Caledonian Road, London, N1 9BT, United Kingdom
(020) 7833 8268/(07973) 172902 (020) 7833 8269
organise@easynet.co.uk
www.organisart.co.uk

Stephen Dumayne@Meiklejohn Illustration 5 Risborough Street, London, SE1 0HF, United Kingdom
(020) 7593 0500/ (020) 7593 0501
info@meiklejohn.co.uk
www.meiklejohn.co.uk

Stephen Hall 28 Cable Road, Whitehead, Carrickfergus, County Antrim, BT38 9PX, United Kingdom
(028) 9337 8583/(07910) 355794
theweebear@hotmail.com
www.earthnativeart.co.uk

Stephen Knowles@Private View Artists Agency 17A Swan Hill, Shrewsbury, SY1 1NL, United Kingdom
(01743) 350355/ (01743) 233923
create@pvuk.com
www.pvuk.com

Stephen Lee@N B Illustration Ltd 40 Bowling Green Lane, London, EC1R 0NE, United Kingdom
(020) 7278 9131/ (020) 7278 9121
info@nbillustration.co.uk
www.nbillustration.co.uk

Stephen Lewis@Graham-Cameron Illustration The Studio, 23 Holt Road, Sheringham, Norfolk, NR26 8NB, United Kingdom
(01263) 821333/ (01263) 821334
enquiry@graham-cameron-illustration.com
www.graham-cameron-illustration.com

Stephen Lings@Linden Artists Ltd 41 Battersea Business Centre, 103 Lavender Hill, London, SW11 5QL, United Kingdom
(020) 7738 2505/ (020) 7738 2513
lindenartists@aol.com
www.lindenartists.co.uk

Stephen May Graphics 36 The Oval, Sidcup, Kent, DA15 9ES, United Kingdom
(020) 8306 5948
info@stephenmaygraphics.co.uk
www.stephenmaygraphics.co.uk

Stephen Parkes@Catherine Collins The Power Station, Coronet Street, London, N1 6HD, United Kingdom
(020) 7739 8678/(07785) 571187 (020) 7739 8489
catherine@catherinecollins.co.uk
www.catherinecollins.co.uk

Stephen Player@Artist Partners Ltd 2e The Chandlery, 50 Westminster Bridge Road, London, SE1 7QY, United Kingdom
(020) 7401 7904/ (020) 7401 3378
chris@artistpartners.demon.co.uk
www.artistpartners.com

Stephen Seal@Début Art & The Coningsby Gallery 30 Tottenham Street, London, W1T 4RJ, United Kingdom
(020) 7636 1064/ (020) 7580 7017
info@debutart.com
www.debutart.com

Steve Barkess@Allied Artists@ Artistic License The Gallery @ Richmond, 63 Sheen Road, Richmond, Surrey, TW9 1YJ, United Kingdom
(020) 8334 1010/ (020) 8334 9900
info@allied-artists.net
www.allied-artists.net

Steve Fricker@Folio 10 Gate Street, Lincoln's Inn Fields, London, WC2A 3HP, United Kingdom
(020) 7242 9562/ (020) 7242 1816
all@folioart.co.uk
www.folioart.co.uk

Steve May@Arena 31 Eleanor Road, London, E15 4AB, United Kingdom
(08450) 507 600
info@arenaworks.com
www.arenaworks.com

Steve McGarry Cartoons & Illustration 19911 Rothert Lane, Huntington Beach, 92646, United States of America
00 1 714 593 0514/ 00 1 714 593 0504
mac@stevemcgarry.com
www.stevemcgarry.com

Steve Rawlings@Début Art & The Coningsby Gallery 30 Tottenham Street, London, W1T 4RJ, United Kingdom
(020) 7636 1064/ (020) 7580 7017
info@debutart.com
www.debutart.com

Steve Read@Meiklejohn Illustration 5 Risborough Street, London, SE1 0HF, United Kingdom
(020) 7593 0500/ (020) 7593 0501
info@meiklejohn.co.uk
www.meiklejohn.co.uk

Steve Stone@Artist Partners Ltd 2e The Chandlery, 50 Westminster Bridge Road, London, SE1 7QY, United Kingdom
(020) 7401 7904/ (020) 7401 3378
chris@artistpartners.demon.co.uk
www.artistpartners.com

Steve Weston@Linden Artists Ltd 41 Battersea Business Centre, 103 Lavender Hill, London, SW11 5QL, United Kingdom
(020) 7738 2505/ (020) 7738 2513
lindenartists@aol.com
www.lindenartists.co.uk

Steven Jones Gallery Ltd Bulkeley Hotel, Castle Street, Beaumaris, Isle of Anglesey, LL58 8AW, United Kingdom
(01248) 810081
steven@stevenjonesart.freeuk.com
www.stevenjonesart.freeuk.com

Steven Ratcliffe Artist@Illustrator 26 Shelley Road, Swinton, Manchester, M27 0PA, United Kingdom
(07950) 854590
info@artist-illustrator.net
www.artist-illustrator.net

Steven Wilson@Pearce Stoner Associates 12B Links Yard, Spelman Street, London, E1 5LX, United Kingdom
(020) 7247 7100/ (020) 7247 7144
info@pearcestoner.com
www.pearcestoner.com

Stevie Gee@Stem Agency Top Floor, 23 Charlotte Road, London, EC2A 3PB, United Kingdom
(07790) 026628
will@stemagency.com
www.stemagency.com

Stevie Hale Jones@Advocate Art 39 Church Road, London, SW19 5DQ, United Kingdom
020 8879 1166/020 8879 3303
lesley@advocate-art.com
www.advocate-art.com

Stewart Lees@Folio 10 Gate Street, Lincoln's Inn Fields, London, WC2A 3HP, United Kingdom
(020) 7242 9562/ (020) 7242 1816
all@folioart.co.uk
www.folioart.co.uk

Storyboards Ltd 18 Greek Street, London, W1D 4JD, United Kingdom
(020) 7734 1437/ (020) 7760 7713
info@storyboards.co.uk
www.storyboards.co.uk

Stretchmark 22 Laburnum Lane, Newhey, Rochdale, Lancashire, OL16 4LP, United Kingdom
(07980) 224261
mark_hoolaham_554@hotmail.com

Stuart Harrison 126 Hampton Road, Southport, Merseyside, PR8 5DZ, United Kingdom
(01704) 532655/(07956) 370037
stuart.harrison2@virgin.net
www.stu-art.biz

Stuart Haygarth@Début Art & The Coningsby Gallery 30 Tottenham Street, London, W1T 4RJ, United Kingdom
(020) 7636 1064/ (020) 7580 7017
info@debutart.com
www.debutart.com

Stuart Holmes@Illustration Ltd 2 Brooks Court, Cringle Street, London, SW8 5BX, United Kingdom
(020) 7720 5202/ (020) 7720 5920
team@illustrationweb.com
www.illustrationweb.com

Stuart Lafford@Linden Artists Ltd 41 Battersea Business Centre, 103 Lavender Hill, London, SW11 5QL, United Kingdom
(020) 7738 2505/ (020) 7738 2513
lindenartists@aol.com
www.lindenartists.co.uk

Stuart Williams@The Organisation The Basement, 69 Caledonian Road, London, N1 9BT, United Kingdom
(020) 7833 8268/(07973) 172902 (020) 7833 8269
organise@easynet.co.uk
www.organisart.co.uk

Studio 17-18 The Royal Victoria Patriotic Building, Trinity Road, London, SW18 3SX, United Kingdom
(020) 8870 8743/ (020) 8877 1151
john@adcreative.co.uk
www.adcreative.co.uk

Substance Design Ltd The Business Village, 3-9 Broomhill Road, London, SW18 4JQ, United Kingdom
(020) 8871 5230
glan@gotsubstance.co.uk
www.substance-design.com

Sue Clarke@Eastwing 99 Chase Side, Enfield, Middlesex, EN2 6NL, United Kingdom
(020) 8367 6760/ (020) 8367 6730
andrea@eastwing.co.uk
www.eastwing.co.uk

Sue Hillwood-Harris 22 Scutari Road, London, SE22 0NN, United Kingdom
(020) 8693 3710/ (020) 8693 5701
sue.hillwood@btinternet.com

Sue Lines 8 Westville Road, Thames Ditton, Surrey, KT7 0UJ, United Kingdom
(020) 8398 5808/(07977) 127091
s_lines@talk21.com

Sue Scullard Beech Hill Cottage, Glassenbury Road, Cranbrook, Kent, TN17 2QJ, United Kingdom
(01580) 714340/ (01580) 714340
sue@suescullard.co.uk
www.suescullard.co.uk

Sue Williams@Folio 10 Gate Street, Lincoln's Inn Fields, London, WC2A 3HP, United Kingdom
(020) 7242 9562/ (020) 7242 1816
all@folioart.co.uk
www.folioart.co.uk

Sue Woollatt@Graham-Cameron Illustration The Studio, 23 Holt Road, Sheringham, Norfolk, NR26 8NB, United Kingdom
- (01263) 821333/ (01263) 821334
- enquiry@graham-cameron-illustration.com
- www.graham-cameron-illustration.com

Sumiko Davies@Advocate Art 39 Church Road, London, SW19 5DQ, United Kingdom
- 020 8879 1166/020 8879 3303
- lesley@advocate-art.com
- www.advocate-art.com

Superdead@Private View Artists Agency 17A Swan Hill, Shrewsbury, SY1 1NL, United Kingdom
- (01743) 350355/ (01743) 233923
- create@pvuk.com
- www.pvuk.com

Susan Everett 18 Moorgate Drive, Kippax, Leeds, LS25 7QT, United Kingdom
- 0113-286 5001/ 0113-286 5001
- Susan.Everett@ukgateway.net

Susan Hellard@Arena 31 Eleanor Road, London, E15 4AB, United Kingdom
- (08450) 507 600
- info@arenaworks.com
- www.arenaworks.com

Susanna Lockheart@Advocate Art 39 Church Road, London, SW19 5DQ, United Kingdom
- 020 8879 1166/020 8879 3303
- lesley@advocate-art.com
- www.advocate-art.com

Suzanna Hubbard@David Higham 5-8 Lower John Street, Golden Square, London, W1F 9HA, United Kingdom
- (020) 7437 7888/ (020) 7437 1072
- carolinewalsh@davidhigham.co.uk
- www.davidhigham.co.uk

Suzanne Carpenter@Artist Partners Ltd 2e The Chandlery, 50 Westminster Bridge Road, London, SE1 7QY, United Kingdom
- (020) 7401 7904/ (020) 7401 3378
- chris@artistpartners.demon.co.uk
- www.artistpartners.com

Suzanne Sales@New Division 5 Risborough Street, London, SE1 0HF, United Kingdom
- (020) 7593 0505/ (020) 7593 0501
- info@newdivision.com
- www.newdivision.com

Swan Park@The Artworks 40 Frith Street, London, W1D 5LN, United Kingdom
- (020) 7734 3333/ (020) 7734 3484
- lucy@theartworksinc.com
- www.theartworksinc.com

Swee Illustration 54 Clyde Road, Brighton, BN1 4NP, United Kingdom
- (01273) 570623
- chris@swee.co.uk
- www.swee.co.uk

Syd Brak@Folio 10 Gate Street, Lincoln's Inn Fields, London, WC2A 3HP, United Kingdom
- (020) 7242 9562/ (020) 7242 1816
- all@folioart.co.uk
- www.folioart.co.uk

Sydney Couldridge@Folio 10 Gate Street, Lincoln's Inn Fields, London, WC2A 3HP, United Kingdom
- (020) 7242 9562/ (020) 7242 1816
- all@folioart.co.uk
- www.folioart.co.uk

Symbolon@Central Illustration Agency 36 Wellington Street, London, WC2E 7BD, United Kingdom
- (020) 7240 8925/ (020) 7836 1177
- info@centralillustration.com
- www.centralillustration.com

Syrah Jade Arnold 44 Tithe Road, Chatteris, Cambridgeshire, PE16 6SL, United Kingdom
- (01354) 696245/ (01354) 696245
- artist@syrahjade.com
- www.syrahjade.com

Tamsin Cook@Graham-Cameron Illustration The Studio, 23 Holt Road, Sheringham, Norfolk, NR26 8NB, United Kingdom
- (01263) 821333/ (01263) 821334
- enquiry@graham-cameron-illustration.com
- www.graham-cameron-illustration.com

Tamsin Hinrichsen@Advocate Art 39 Church Road, London, SW19 5DQ, United Kingdom
- 020 8879 1166/020 8879 3303
- lesley@advocate-art.com
- www.advocate-art.com

Tartan Baffies 51 Forfar Road, Dundee, Tayside, DD4 7BE,
- 01382 461484
- john@tartanbaffies.fsnet.co.uk
- www.tartanbaffies.co.uk

Tatjana Reksc@Advocate Art 39 Church Road, London, SW19 5DQ, United Kingdom
- 020 8879 1166/020 8879 3303
- lesley@advocate-art.com
- www.advocate-art.com

Tatsuro Kiuchi@The Artworks 40 Frith Street, London, W1D 5LN, United Kingdom
- (020) 7734 3333/ (020) 7734 3484
- lucy@theartworksinc.com
- www.theartworksinc.com

Temple Clark 48 Underhill Road, London, SE22 0QT, United Kingdom
- (020) 8299 2015/(07931) 991949 (020) 8299 2015
- templeclark@btinternet.com

Terence Lawlor@Meiklejohn Illustration 5 Risborough Street, London, SE1 0HF, United Kingdom
- (020) 7593 0500/ (020) 7593 0501
- info@meiklejohn.co.uk
- www.meiklejohn.co.uk

Teresa Murfin@Arena 31 Eleanor Road, London, E15 4AB, United Kingdom
- (08450) 507 600
- info@arenaworks.com
- www.arenaworks.com

Terry Burton@Bernard Thornton Artists The Penthouse, 4 Hamilton Mews, 310 Merton Road, London, SW18 5AB, United Kingdom
- (020) 8874 9081/(07702) 554583 (020) 8877 1386
- bernard@btartists.com
- www.btartists.com

Terry Hand@Art Collection UK Ltd 7 Worsley Mill, 10 Blantyre Street, Castlefield, Manchester, M15 4LG, United Kingdom
- (0870) 2405001/ (0870) 2405002
- info@artcollection.co.uk
- www.artcollection.co.uk

Terry Kennett@Art Market 51 Oxford Drive, London, SE1 2FB, United Kingdom
- (020) 7407 8111/ (020) 7407 8222
- info@artmarketillustration.com
- www.artmarketillustration.com

The Anna Su Agency Flat G12, The School House, Pages Walk, London, SE1 4HG, United Kingdom
- (020) 7064 9350
- info@theannasuagency.com
- www.theannasuagency.com

The Art Agency The Lodge, Cargate Lane, Saxlingham Thorpe, Norwich, NR15 1TU, United Kingdom
- (01508) 471500/ (01508) 470391
- info@the-art-agency.co.uk
- www.the-art-agency.co.uk

The Artworks 40 Frith Street, London, W1D 5LN
- 020 7734 3333/020 7734 3484
- info@theartworksinc.com
- www.theartworksinc.com
- See ad in showcase

The Boy Fitz Hammond Studio 74, 196 Rose Street, Edinburgh, EH2 4AT, United Kingdom
- (07766) 716318
- theboy@tbfh.com
- www.tbfh.com

The Drawer Artist Agency, Bath, United Kingdom
- (01225) 462940/ (01225) 462940
- www.drawer.me.uk

The Illustration Library 2 Brooks Court, Cringle Street, London, SW8 5BX, United Kingdom
- (020) 7720 5202/ (020) 7720 5920
- team@illustrationweb.com
- www.illustrationweb.com

The Marmalade Cat 2 Oberon Close, Bilton, Rugby, Warwickshire, CV22 6LZ, United Kingdom
- (01788) 811232
- jo@themarmaladecat.co.uk
- www.themarmaladecat.co.uk

The Mozzarella Legion 12 Doyle Gardens, London, NW10 3DA, United Kingdom
- (07787) 588219
- rosapopulos@yahoo.com

The Organisation The Basement, 69 Caledonian Road, London, N1 9BT, United Kingdom
- (020) 7833 8268/(07973) 172902 (020) 7833 8269
- organise@easynet.co.uk
- www.organisart.com

The Pesky Kids@Stem Agency Top Floor, 23 Charlotte Road, London, EC2A 3PB, United Kingdom
- (07790) 026628
- will@stemagency.com
- www.stemagency.com

The Rough Idea Ltd 5 Glen View, St Austell, Cornwall, PL25 5HR
- 01726 67101/07814 413351/ sim@theroughidea.co.uk
- www.theroughidea.co.uk
- See ad in showcase

The Scribbler 43 Ferme Park Road, London, N4 4EB, United Kingdom
- (07815) 310436
- dan@danbramall.co.uk
- www.thescribbler.co.uk

The Wax Mill Parternship The Raylor Centre, James Street, York, YO24 4BP, United Kingdom
- (01904) 422114

Third Edge 17a Ridinghouse Street, London, W1 7DS
- 020 7436 7930/ info@the3rdedge.com
- www.the3rdedge.com
- See ad in showcase

Thomas Denbigh@Advocate Art 39 Church Road, London, SW19 5DQ, United Kingdom
- 020 8879 1166/020 8879 3303
- lesley@advocate-art.com
- www.advocate-art.com

Thomas Moon@Advocate Art 39 Church Road, London, SW19 5DQ, United Kingdom
- 020 8879 1166/020 8879 3303
- lesley@advocate-art.com
- www.advocate-art.com

Thorbjorn Ingasson@Central Illustration Agency 36 Wellington Street, London, WC2E 7BD, United Kingdom
- (020) 7240 8925/ (020) 7836 1177
- info@centralillustration.com
- www.centralillustration.com

Thorogood Illustration Ltd 5 Dryden Street, Covent Garden, London, WC2E 9NW, United Kingdom
- (020) 7829 8468
- draw@thorogood.net
- www.thorogood.net

Three Blind Mice 9-10 Charlotte Mews, London, W1T 4EF, United Kingdom
- (020) 7636 2502/ (020) 7636 2455
- andy@three-blind-mice.co.uk
- www.three-blind-mice.co.uk
- See ad in showcase

Tiffany Lynch@New Division 5 Risborough Street, London, SE1 0HF, United Kingdom
- (020) 7593 0505/ (020) 7593 0501
- info@newdivision.com
- www.newdivision.com

Tilly Northedge@Début Art & The Coningsby Gallery 30 Tottenham Street, London, W1T 4RJ, United Kingdom
- (020) 7636 1064/ (020) 7580 7017
- info@debutart.com
- www.debutart.com

Tim Archbold@Graham-Cameron Illustration The Studio, 23 Holt Road, Sheringham, Norfolk, NR26 8NB, United Kingdom
- (01263) 821333/ (01263) 821334
- enquiry@graham-cameron-illustration.com
- www.graham-cameron-illustration.com

Tim Ashton@Début Art & The Coningsby Gallery 30 Tottenham Street, London, W1T 4RJ, United Kingdom
- (020) 7636 1064/ (020) 7580 7017
- info@debutart.com
- www.debutart.com

Tim Benton@Linda Rogers Associates 163 Half Moon Lane, London, SE24 9WB, United Kingdom
- (020) 7501 9106
- lr@lindarogers.net
- www.lindarogers.net

Tim Clarey@Artist Partners Ltd 2e The Chandlery, 50 Westminster Bridge Road, London, SE1 7QY, United Kingdom
(020) 7401 7904/ (020) 7401 3378
chris@artistpartners.demon.co.uk
www.artistpartners.com

Tim Ellis@Début Art & The Coningsby Gallery 30 Tottenham Street, London, W1T 4RJ, United Kingdom
(020) 7636 1064/ (020) 7580 7017
info@debutart.com
www.debutart.com

Tim Kahane Lavender Cottage, Brome Avenue, Eye, Suffolk, IP23 7HW, United Kingdom
(01379) 871358
tim@kahane.co.uk
www.kahane.co.uk

Tim Marrs@Central Illustration Agency 36 Wellington Street, London, WC2E 7BD, United Kingdom
(020) 7240 8925/ (020) 7836 1177
info@centralillustration.com
www.centralillustration.com
See ad in showcase

Tim Pestridge Photography@Design 11 Walnut Close, Exminster, Exeter, EX6 8SZ, United Kingdom
(01392) 825718
studio@timpestridge.co.uk
www.timpestridge.co.uk

Tina Mansuwan@Central Illustration Agency 36 Wellington Street, London, WC2E 7BD, United Kingdom
(020) 7240 8925/ (020) 7836 1177
info@centralillustration.com
www.centralillustration.com

Tina Zellmer@Début Art & The Coningsby Gallery 30 Tottenham Street, London, W1T 4RJ, United Kingdom
(020) 7636 1064/ (020) 7580 7017
info@debutart.com
www.debutart.com

Tinder 2 Manor Farm Close, Bishopstoke, Eastleigh, Hampshire, SO50 6LG, United Kingdom
(023) 8065 3860
info@tinderdesign.co.uk
www.tinderdesign.co.uk

Tobatron@Folio 10 Gate Street, Lincoln's Inn Fields, London, WC2A 3HP, United Kingdom
(020) 7242 9562/ (020) 7242 1816
all@folioart.co.uk
www.folioart.co.uk

Toby Leigh@Folio 10 Gate Street, Lincoln's Inn Fields, London, WC2A 3HP, United Kingdom
(020) 7242 9562/ (020) 7242 1816
all@folioart.co.uk
www.folioart.co.uk

Tom Connell 57 Pemberton Gardens, Calcot, Reading, RG31 7DY, United Kingdom
0118-941 8832/ 0118-941 8832
dart@connell7001.fsnet.co.uk
www.tomconnellstudio.com

Tom Connell@Advocate Art 39 Church Road, London, SW19 5DQ, United Kingdom
020 8879 1166/020 8879 3303
lesley@advocate-art.com
www.advocate-art.com

Tom Croft@Advocate Art 39 Church Road, London, SW19 5DQ, United Kingdom
020 8879 1166/020 8879 3303
lesley@advocate-art.com
www.advocate-art.com

Tom Frost@Art Market 51 Oxford Drive, London, SE1 2FB, United Kingdom
(020) 7407 8111/ (020) 7407 8222
info@artmarketillustration.com
www.artmarketillustration.com

Tom Gravestock@N B Illustration Ltd 40 Bowling Green Lane, London, EC1R 0NE, United Kingdom
(020) 7278 9131/ (020) 7278 9121
info@nbillustration.co.uk
www.nbillustration.co.uk

Tom Lane @Advocate Art 39 Church Road, London, SW19 5DQ, United Kingdom
020 8879 1166/020 8879 3303
lesley@advocate-art.com
www.advocate-art.com

Tom Percival@Advocate Art 39 Church Road, London, SW19 5DQ, United Kingdom
020 8879 1166/020 8879 3303
lesley@advocate-art.com
www.advocate-art.com

Tom Steyer@Illustration Ltd 2 Brooks Court, Cringle Street, London, SW8 5BX, United Kingdom
(020) 7720 5202/ (020) 7720 5920
team@illustrationweb.com
www.illustrationweb.com

Tommy Penton@Sarah Lane Represents 56 Bidwell Gardens, London, N11 2AU, United Kingdom
(07901) 552520/ (020) 8292 4001
sarah@sarahlanerepresents.com
www.sarahlanerepresents.com

Toni Goffe@Linda Rogers Associates 163 Half Moon Lane, London, SE24 9WB, United Kingdom
(020) 7501 9106
lr@lindarogers.net
www.lindarogers.net

Tony Campbell@Private View Artists Agency 17A Swan Hill, Shrewsbury, SY1 1NL, United Kingdom
(01743) 350355/ (01743) 233923
create@pvuk.com
www.pvuk.com

Tony Escott 29 Peterborough Road, Parsons Green, London, SW6 3BT, United Kingdom
(020) 7731 0158/ (020) 7731 0158

Tony Gibbons@Bernard Thornton Artists The Penthouse, 4 Hamilton Mews, 310 Merton Road, London, SW18 5AB, United Kingdom
(020) 8874 9081/(07702) 554583 / (020) 8877 1386
bernard@btartists.com
www.btartists.com

Tony Healey@Art Collection UK Ltd 7 Worsley Mill, 10 Blantyre Street, Castlefield, Manchester, M15 4LG, United Kingdom
(0870) 2405001/ (0870) 2405002
info@artcollection.co.uk
www.artcollection.co.uk

Tony Hinchliffe@Advocate Art 39 Church Road, London, SW19 5DQ, United Kingdom
020 8879 1166/020 8879 3303
lesley@advocate-art.com
www.advocate-art.com

Tony McSweeney 4 Water Lane, Richmond, Surrey, TW9 1TJ, United Kingdom
(020) 8940 2425/(07779) 061050 / (020) 8940 2425
mcsweeneyrichmond@yahoo.co.uk

Tony Meeuwissen@Folio 10 Gate Street, Lincoln's Inn Fields, London, WC2A 3HP, United Kingdom
(020) 7242 9562/ (020) 7242 1816
all@folioart.co.uk
www.folioart.co.uk

Tony Neat 22 Westcliffe Road, Westbrook, Margate, Kent, CT9 5DN, United Kingdom
(01843) 292903
tonyneat@cartoons65.fsnet.co.uk

Tony Randell 58 Viking Way, Pilgrims Hatch, Brentwood, Essex, CM15 9HY, United Kingdom
(01277) 260488
tony.randell@btopenworld.com

Tony Roberts@Arena 31 Eleanor Road, London, E15 4AB, United Kingdom
(08450) 507 600
info@arenaworks.com
www.arenaworks.com

Tony Simpson 26 Berkley House, Wellington Road, Brighton, BN2 3BE, United Kingdom
(01273) 621624/ (01273) 621624
info@tony-simpson.co.uk
www.tony-simpson.co.uk

Tony Todd Fine Art 65 New Road, Chilworth, Guildford, Surrey, GU4 8LP, United Kingdom
(01483) 533851/ (01483) 533851
sales@tony-todd.co.uk
www.tony-todd.co.uk

Tony Wilson@Shirley Hart Creative Consultants 19 Ulundi Road, London, SE3 7UQ, United Kingdom
(020) 8853 2987/(07867) 806250 /
shirleyhart@btinternet.com
www.shirleyhart.com

Tortoy 43c Quaker Street, London, E1 6SN, United Kingdom
(020) 7426 0866/077867 20020 /
hector@tortoy.com
www.tortoy.com

Tracey Knight 56 Thackeray Road, Bradford, West Yorkshire, BD10 0JR, United Kingdom
(01274) 410743/ (01274) 410743
tracey@misato.co.uk
www.traceyknight.com

Tracy McGuiness Kelly@Advocate Art 39 Church Road, London, SW19 5DQ, United Kingdom
020 8879 1166/020 8879 3303
lesley@advocate-art.com
www.advocate-art.com

Trainwreck Impression 4 Auckland Close, Maidenhead, Berkshire, SL6 8QB, United Kingdom
(07816) 391256
trainwreck_impression@hotmail.co.uk
www.thedefeated.deviantart.com

Trevor Laidler 10 Delver Road, Worthing, West Sussex, BN11 5NR, United Kingdom
(07719) 401997 /
trevorlaidler@supernet.com
www.trevorlaidler.co.uk

Trevor Neal Fossdale Towers, 23 Fossdale Road, Sheffield, S7 2DA, United Kingdom
0114-258 8112/(07940) 179520 /
painter@trevorneal.co.uk
www.trevorneal.co.uk

Tricksey Pixie Ltd 35 Basil Street, Stockport, Cheshire, SK4 1QL, United Kingdom
0161-477 3772
linz@tricksypixie.com
www.tricksypixie.com

Trina Dalziel@New Division 5 Risborough Street, London, SE1 0HF, United Kingdom
(020) 7593 0505/ (020) 7593 0501
info@newdivision.com
www.newdivision.com

Tristan Eaton@Central Illustration Agency 36 Wellington Street, London, WC2E 7BD, United Kingdom
(020) 7240 8925/ (020) 7836 1177
info@centralillustration.com
www.centralillustration.com

Tulip Illustrations Ltd 26 Pennington Drive, Oatlands Chase, Weybridge, Surrey, KT13 9RU, United Kingdom
(01932) 240801/ (01932) 240801
jenny.tulip@btopenworld.com
www.contact-me.net/JennyTulip

Turinna Gren@Inkshed 99 Chase Side, Enfield, Middlesex, EN2 6NL, United Kingdom
(020) 8367 4545/ (020) 8367 6730
www.inkshed.co.uk

Ulla Puggaard@Central Illustration Agency 36 Wellington Street, London, WC2E 7BD, United Kingdom
(020) 7240 8925/ (020) 7836 1177
info@centralillustration.com
www.centralillustration.com

Ute Simon@Advocate Art 39 Church Road, London, SW19 5DQ, United Kingdom
020 8879 1166/020 8879 3303
lesley@advocate-art.com
www.advocate-art.com

Vanessa Bell@N B Illustration Ltd 40 Bowling Green Lane, London, EC1R 0NE, United Kingdom
(020) 7278 9131/ (020) 7278 9121
info@nbillustration.co.uk
www.nbillustration.co.uk

Vanessa Card 56 Ulster Road, Bowerham, Lancaster, LA1 4AH, United Kingdom
(01524) 596 219/ (01524) 596 219
vanessa.card@good.co.uk
www.vanessacard.co.uk

Vault49@Début Art & The Coningsby Gallery 30 Tottenham Street, London, W1T 4RJ, United Kingdom
(020) 7636 1064/ (020) 7580 7017
info@debutart.com
www.debutart.com

Veronica Palmieri@Folio 10 Gate Street, Lincoln's Inn Fields, London, WC2A 3HP, United Kingdom
(020) 7242 9562/ (020) 7242 1816
all@folioart.co.uk
www.folioart.co.uk

Veronica Vasylenko@Advocate Art 39 Church Road, London, SW19 5DQ, United Kingdom
020 8879 1166/020 8879 3303
lesley@advocate-art.com
www.advocate-art.com

Vicki Mitchell@Advocate Art 39 Church Road, London, SW19 5DQ, United Kingdom
020 8879 1166/020 8879 3303
lesley@advocate-art.com
www.advocate-art.com

Vicky Emptage 31 Landells Road, London, SE22 9PG, United Kingdom
(020) 8693 4303/ (020) 8693 4303
vicky.emptage@btinternet.com

Vicky Newman@Advocate Art 39 Church Road, London, SW19 5DQ, United Kingdom
020 8879 1166/020 8879 3303
lesley@advocate-art.com
www.advocate-art.com

Vicky Newman Illustrations 34 Mill Court, Ashford, Kent, TN24 8DN, United Kingdom
(07989) 449835
v_newman@yahoo.com
www.vickynewman.com

Victoria Baker@Advocate Art 39 Church Road, London, SW19 5DQ, United Kingdom
020 8879 1166/020 8879 3303
lesley@advocate-art.com
www.advocate-art.com

Victoria Ball@Illustration Ltd 2 Brooks Court, Cringle Street, London, SW8 5BX, United Kingdom
(020) 7720 5202/ (020) 7720 5920
team@illustrationweb.com
www.illustrationweb.com

Vince McIndoe@Début Art & The Coningsby Gallery 30 Tottenham Street, London, W1T 4RJ, United Kingdom
(020) 7636 1064/ (020) 7580 7017
info@debutart.com
www.debutart.com

Vincent Creatives 49 Vinery Road, Cambridge, CB1 3DN, United Kingdom
(01223) 240996
trevor@vincent-creatives.com
www.vincent-creatives.com

Vincent Vigla@Illustration Ltd 2 Brooks Court, Cringle Street, London, SW8 5BX, United Kingdom
(020) 7720 5202/ (020) 7720 5920
team@illustrationweb.com
www.illustrationweb.com

Virginia Gray@Graham-Cameron Illustration The Studio, 23 Holt Road, Sheringham, Norfolk, NR26 8NB, United Kingdom
(01263) 821333/ (01263) 821334
enquiry@graham-cameron-illustration.com
www.graham-cameron-illustration.com

Virginia Mayo@Graham-Cameron Illustration The Studio, 23 Holt Road, Sheringham, Norfolk, NR26 8NB, United Kingdom
(01263) 821333/ (01263) 821334
enquiry@graham-cameron-illustration.com
www.graham-cameron-illustration.com

Vivid Carlton Mills, Pickering Street, Leeds, LS12 2QG, United Kingdom
0113-224 4800/ 0113-224 4801
lindsay.kemp@logistik.co.uk
www.logistik-vivid.co.uk

Vivienne Roberts@Advocate Art 39 Church Road, London, SW19 5DQ, United Kingdom
020 8879 1166/020 8879 3303
lesley@advocate-art.com
www.advocate-art.com

Vizual Eye 44 Beechwood Close, Little Chalfont, Amersham, Buckinghamshire, HP6 6QX, United Kingdom
020 7071 2392/07977 298 433
paulc@vizualeye.com
www.vizualeye.com

Wai@Illustration Ltd 2 Brooks Court, Cringle Street, London, SW8 5BX, United Kingdom
(020) 7720 5202/ (020) 7720 5920
team@illustrationweb.com
www.illustrationweb.com

Walshworks@Eastwing 99 Chase Side, Enfield, Middlesex, EN2 6NL, United Kingdom
(020) 8367 6760/ (020) 8367 6730
andrea@eastwing.co.uk
www.eastwing.co.uk

Warren Madill@Meiklejohn Illustration 5 Risborough Street, London, SE1 0HF, United Kingdom
(020) 7593 0500/ (020) 7593 0501
info@meiklejohn.co.uk
www.meiklejohn.co.uk

Warwick Johnson-Cadwell@Eastwing 99 Chase Side, Enfield, Middlesex, EN2 6NL, United Kingdom
(020) 8367 6760/ (020) 8367 6730
andrea@eastwing.co.uk
www.eastwing.co.uk

Wendy Brett 10 Sandfield Road, St. Albans, Hertfordshire, AL1 4LA, United Kingdom
(01727) 837881/(07751) 516635
wendybrett2004@yahoo.co.uk

West End House Gallery West End House, Water Lane, Smarden, Kent, TN27 8QB, United Kingdom
(01233) 770261/ (01233) 770261
art@west-end-house-gallery.co.uk
www.west-end-house-gallery.co.uk

Will Ainley@Private View Artists Agency 17A Swan Hill, Shrewsbury, SY1 1NL, United Kingdom
(01743) 350355/ (01743) 233923
create@pvuk.com
www.pvuk.com

Will Barras@Art Collection UK Ltd 7 Worsley Mill, 10 Blantyre Street, Castlefield, Manchester, M15 4LG, United Kingdom
(0870) 2405001/ (0870) 2405002
info@artcollection.co.uk
www.artcollection.co.uk

Will Parker@Sarah Lane Represents 56 Bidwell Gardens, London, N11 2AU, United Kingdom
(07901) 552520/ (020) 8292 4001
sarah@sarahlanerepresents.com
www.sarahlanerepresents.com

Will Sweeney@Big Active Ltd Unit 6.01, The Tea Building, 56 Shoreditch High Street, London, E16 JJ, United Kingdom
(020) 7739 5601/ (020) 7739 7479
contact@bigactive.com
www.bigactive.com

William Ings@Folio 10 Gate Street, Lincoln's Inn Fields, London, WC2A 3HP, United Kingdom
(020) 7242 9562/ (020) 7242 1816
all@folioart.co.uk
www.folioart.co.uk

William Rudling 6 The Close, Alwoodley, Leeds, LS17 7RD, United Kingdom
0113-267 5696/(07792) 023009 0113-267 5662
william@williamrudling.com
www.williamrudling.com

Willie Ryan@Illustration Ltd 2 Brooks Court, Cringle Street, London, SW8 5BX, United Kingdom
(020) 7720 5202/ (020) 7720 5920
team@illustrationweb.com
www.illustrationweb.com

Willowbank House Willowbank House, 84 Station Road, Marlow, Buckinghamshire, SL7 1NX, United Kingdom
(0845) 6445656/ (0845) 6445646
steve@stickee.co.uk
www.stickee.co.uk

Wingnut Designs Waterfront Farm, Biddisham Lane, Biddisham, Axbridge, Somerset, BS26 2RS, United Kingdom
(01934) 750827
chris@wingnutdesigns.co.uk
www.wingnutdesigns.co.uk

Winter of Excellence 58 Gloucester Drive, London, N4 2LN, United Kingdom
(07732) 552 745
hello@benpearce.com
www.benpearce.com

Wonderfuel 118 Hatherley Gardens, London, E6 3HQ, United Kingdom
020 8548 1358
info@wonderfuel.co.uk
www.wonderfuel.co.uk

workbygee, London, SE1, United Kingdom
(07753) 302765
georgehurst86@hotmail.com
www.workbygee.co.uk

Writersworld Limited 9 Manor Close, Enstone, Chipping Norton, Oxfordshire, OX7 4LU, United Kingdom
(01608) 677393
enquiries@writersworld.co.uk
www.writersworld.co.uk

www.angelicillustrations.com 29 Buntingbridge Road, Newbury Park, Ilford, Essex, IG2 7LW, United Kingdom
(07939) 506557
andrea@angelicillustrations.com
www.angelicillustrations.com

www.emmadibben.com 12a York Road, Bristol, BS6 5QE, United Kingdom
(07814) 881386
emma@emmadibben.com
www.emmadibben.com

Yannick Robert@N B Illustration Ltd 40 Bowling Green Lane, London, EC1R 0NE, United Kingdom
(020) 7278 9131/ (020) 7278 9121
info@nbillustration.co.uk
www.nbillustration.co.uk

Yorgus Sgouros@Advocate Art 39 Church Road, London, SW19 5DQ, United Kingdom
020 8879 1166/020 8879 3303
lesley@advocate-art.com
www.advocate-art.com

Yuzuru@Thorogood Illustration Ltd 5 Dryden Street, Covent Garden, London, WC2E 9NW, United Kingdom
(020) 7829 8468
draw@thorogood.net
www.thorogood.net

Yvonne Howard@Advocate Art 39 Church Road, London, SW19 5DQ, United Kingdom
020 8879 1166/020 8879 3303
lesley@advocate-art.com
www.advocate-art.com

Zan Pearce 63 Sherrick Green Road, London, NW10 1LB, United Kingdom
(020) 8452 0681/ (020) 7603 1744
zanpearce@m-tag.net

Zap Art@N B Illustration Ltd 40 Bowling Green Lane, London, EC1R 0NE, United Kingdom
(020) 7278 9131/ (020) 7278 9121
info@nbillustration.co.uk
www.nbillustration.co.uk

Zara Slattery@Graham-Cameron Illustration The Studio, 23 Holt Road, Sheringham, Norfolk, NR26 8NB, United Kingdom
(01263) 821333/ (01263) 821334
enquiry@graham-cameron-illustration.com
www.graham-cameron-illustration.com

Zed@The Artworks 40 Frith Street, London, W1D 5LN, United Kingdom
(020) 7734 3333/ (020) 7734 3484
lucy@theartworksinc.com
www.theartworksinc.com

Zoe Connery@Advocate Art 39 Church Road, London, SW19 5DQ, United Kingdom
020 8879 1166/020 8879 3303
lesley@advocate-art.com
www.advocate-art.com

Zoran Perdi Luka evi @Advocate Art 39 Church Road, London, SW19 5DQ, United Kingdom
020 8879 1166/020 8879 3303
lesley@advocate-art.com
www.advocate-art.com

Zuzanna Lipinska Smith 28 Buckingham Road, London, E11 2EB, United Kingdom
(020) 8989 8667/ (020) 8530 7940
zuzka@asmith.demon.co.uk

Début Art & The Coningsby Gallery 30 Tottenham Street, London, W1T 4RJ, United Kingdom
(020) 7636 1064/ (020) 7580 7017
info@debutart.com
www.debutart.com

Peter Campbell 2 Prebend Mansion, Chiswick High Road, London, W4 2LU, United Kingdom
(020) 8995 5812/(07941) 049862 (020) 8995 5812
peter@petercampbell.demon.co.uk
www.petercampbellstudios.co.uk

Wonderfuel 118 Hatherley Gardens, London, E6 3HQ, United Kingdom
020 8548 1358
info@wonderfuel.co.uk
www.wonderfuel.co.uk

CARTOONS

Adam Linley@Linda Rogers Associates 163 Half Moon Lane, London, SE24 9WB, United Kingdom
(020) 7501 9106
lr@lindarogers.net
www.lindarogers.net

addesign 53 Siward Road, Bromley, BR2 9JY, United Kingdom
✆ (020) 8466 5570
✉ johngovett.addesign@virgin.net

Alan Birch 49 Cobden Street, Stourbridge, West Midlands, DY8 3RT, United Kingdom
✆ (01384) 396752/✆ (01384) 396752
✉ alanbirch@blueyonder.co.uk
🖥 www.kartoonart.co.uk

Alan Linsdell 87 Mersey Bank Avenue, Chorlton-Cum-Hardy, Manchester, M21 7NT, United Kingdom
✆ 0161-434 1016
✉ alan.linsdell@excite.com

Alan Rowe 17 Surrey Grove, Sutton, Surrey, SM1 3PW, United Kingdom
✆ (020) 8643 1626/✆ (020) 8641 1528
✉ bignose@alanrowe.com
🖥 www.alanrowe.com

Alastair Graham Chapel End, Keys Lane, Priors Marston, Southam, Warwickshire, CV47 7SA, United Kingdom
✆ (01327) 260655
✉ alastairgraham1@ukgateway.net
🖥 www.alagram.co.uk

All Handmade Unit 6-8, Stapley Manor Farm, Long Lane, Odiham, Hook, Hampshire, RG29 1JE, United Kingdom
✆ (01256) 862111

Andrew Hennessey 24 Westfield Way, Ruislip, Middlesex, HA4 6HN, United Kingdom
✆ (020) 7323 1149/(07798) 688530 / ✆ (020) 7436 4195
✉ andrewhennessey@blueyonder.co.uk
🖥 www.andrewhennessey.com

Andy Hammond@Illustration Ltd 2 Brooks Court, Cringle Street, London, SW8 5BX, United Kingdom
✆ (020) 7720 5202/✆ (020) 7720 5920
✉ team@illustrationweb.com
🖥 www.illustrationweb.com

Animation-Boy Productions 31 Church Road, Watford, WD17 4PY, United Kingdom
✆ (07971) 713264
✉ ben@animation-boy.com
🖥 www.animation-boy.com

Annabel Hudson 66 Onslow Gardens, Muswell Hill, London, N10 3JX, United Kingdom
✆ (020) 8442 1638/(07812) 198110 / ✆ (020) 8442 1638
✉ annabelstudio@mac.com

Anthony Seldon@Graham-Cameron Illustration The Studio, 23 Holt Road, Sheringham, Norfolk, NR26 8NB, United Kingdom
✆ (01263) 821333/ ✆ (01263) 821334
✉ enquiry@graham-cameron-illustration.com
🖥 www.graham-cameron-illustration.com

Art Collection UK Ltd 7 Worsley Mill, 10 Blantyre St, Castlefield, Manchester, M15 4LG, United Kingdom
✆ (0870) 2405001/✆ (0870) 2405002
✉ info@artcollection.co.uk
🖥 www.artcollection.co.uk

Arthur Reid Eastdale, 3 South Mains Cottages, Pitmeadden, Ellon, Aberdeenshire, AB41 7PB, United Kingdom
✆ (01651) 842479/✆ (01651) 842479

Arthur Wren 32 Ganghill, Guildford, Surrey, GU1 1XF, United Kingdom
✆ (01483) 533878
✉ ARTHUR.WREN1@btopenworld.com

Avril Turner@Linda Rogers Associates 163 Half Moon Lane, London, SE24 9WB, United Kingdom
✆ (020) 7501 9106
✉ lr@lindarogers.net
🖥 www.lindarogers.net

B.L. Kearley Ltd 16 Chiltern Street, London, W1U 7PZ, United Kingdom
✆ (020) 7935 9550/✆ (020) 7224 6879
✉ b.l.kearleyltd@btopenworld.com
🖥 www.kearley.co.uk

Barry Macey Ivy Cottage, Aylesbury Road, Princes Risborough, Buckinghamshire, HP27 0JW, United Kingdom
✆ (01844) 343075
✉ barrymaceystudio@aol.com

Basia Bogdanowicz@Linda Rogers Associates 163 Half Moon Lane, London, SE24 9WB, United Kingdom
✆ (020) 7501 9106
✉ lr@lindarogers.net
🖥 www.lindarogers.net

Bennett Illustration 80 Waterside, Chesham, Buckinghamshire, HP5 1PE, United Kingdom
✆ (01494) 775481
✉ bennettillusrtion@hotmail.com
🖥 www.bennettillustration.com

Bill Asprey, London, NW11 6WS, United Kingdom
✆ (020) 8455 3906/✆ (020) 8455 3906
✉ bill@artfulaspreycartoons.co.uk
🖥 www.artfulaspreycartoons.co.uk

Bill Greenhead@Illustration Ltd 2 Brooks Court, Cringle Street, London, SW8 5BX, United Kingdom
✆ (020) 7720 5202/✆ (020) 7720 5920
✉ team@illustrationweb.com
🖥 www.illustrationweb.com

Bill Pinder Illustration Tyn-Y-Graig, Rhydycroesau, Oswestry, Shropshire, SY10 7JE, United Kingdom
✆ (01691) 791280
✉ pinderraybill@btconnect.com

Blood Group Illustrations 45 Queens Park Rise, Brighton, BN2 9ZF, United Kingdom
✆ (01273) 700540
✉ jackjackpatrick@gmail.com

Brett Hudson@Graham-Cameron Illustration The Studio, 23 Holt Road, Sheringham, Norfolk, NR26 8NB, United Kingdom
✆ (01263) 821333/ ✆ (01263) 821334
✉ enquiry@graham-cameron-illustration.com
🖥 www.graham-cameron-illustration.com

Brian Lee Ltd 338 Coniscliffe Road, Darlington, County Durham, DL3 8AG, United Kingdom
✆ (01325) 468064/✆ (01325) 468064
✉ bleeillustration@mac.com
🖥 www.bleeillustration.com

Brian Walker Church Cottage, Hinton Blewett, Bristol, BS39 5AN, United Kingdom
✆ (01761) 452312/✆ (01761) 452312

Brian Williamson 11 Estreham Road, London, SW16 5NT, United Kingdom
✆ (020) 8677 5724/✆ (0870) 1604571
✉ info@brianwilliamson.co.uk
🖥 www.brianwilliamson.co.uk

Business Cartoons 4 Reyntiens View, Odiham, Hampshire, RG29 1AF, United Kingdom
✆ (01256) 703004
✉ flantoons@btinternet.com
🖥 www.sensible.screaming.net

Caroline Holden Flat 1, 53-55 Navarino Road, London, E8 1AG, United Kingdom
✆ (020) 7241 5406
✉ carolinehotopf@aol.com
🖥 www.contact-me.net/carolineholden

Cartoon Studio 29 Lake View Avenue, Walton, Chesterfield, Derbyshire, S40 3DR, United Kingdom
✆ (01246) 209034/(07904) 064072 / ✆ (01246) 209034
✉ rd@cartoonstudio.co.uk
🖥 www.cartoonstudio.co.uk

Cartoonists' Club of Great Britain 46 Strawberry Vale, Twickenham, TW1 4SE, United Kingdom
✆ 020 8892 3621/✆ 020 8891 5946
✉ terry@cartoonology.com
🖥 www.ccgb.org.uk

Cartoonstock Unit 2, Lansdowne Mews, Bath, BA1 5DY, United Kingdom
✆ (01225) 789600/ ✆ (01225) 789642
✉ admin@cartoonstock.com
🖥 www.cartoonstock.com

Celia Canning@Linda Rogers Associates 163 Half Moon Lane, London, SE24 9WB, United Kingdom
✆ (020) 7501 9106
✉ lr@lindarogers.net
🖥 www.lindarogers.net

Celia Witchard 24 Freemantle Square, Kingsdown, Bristol, BS6 5TN, United Kingdom
✆ 0117-949 4885

Charles Yorke Flat 4, 3 Vicarage Gate, London, W8 4HH, United Kingdom
✆ (020) 7937 4500

Chris Burke 17 Upper Grosvenor Road, Tunbridge Wells, Kent, TN1 2DU, United Kingdom
✆ (01892) 531329
✉ christopher.burke@btclick.com
🖥 www.chrisburke.org.uk

Chris Madden 41 Clyde Road, London, N22 7AD, United Kingdom
✆ (020) 8889 8775/ ✆ (020) 8889 8775
✉ chris@chrismadden.co.uk
🖥 www.chrismadden.co.uk

Chris Masters 27 Meadowbank, Oxhey, Watford, WD19 4NP, United Kingdom
✆ (01923) 233169/ ✆ (01923) 233169
✉ ericthepenguin@hotmail.com

Chris Mould Ink 12 Church Street, Hightown, Liversedge, West Yorkshire, WF15 8HR, United Kingdom
✆ (01274) 873503/07748 417308 /
✉ chris@chrismouldink.com
🖥 www.chrismouldink.com

Christopher Douglas White 3 Rannoch Road, London, W6 9SS, United Kingdom
✆ (020) 7381 6529/ ✆ (020) 7385 4992
✉ chriswhiteart@aol.com
🖥 www.chris-white.co.uk

Colin Mier 21 Balmuir Gardens, Putney, London, SW15 6NG, United Kingdom
✆ (020) 8789 7556/(07050) 153929 / ✆ (020) 8789 7556
✉ colinmier@talk21.com

Colin Shelbourn Cartoonists & Illustrators Pine Howe, Helm Road, Windermere, Cumbria, LA23 2NL, United Kingdom
✆ (01539) 442052/ ✆ (01539) 442052
✉ colin@shelbourn.com
🖥 www.shelbourn.com

Cowlin Cartoons 21 Wye Close, Barry, South Glamorgan, CF62 7TF, United Kingdom
✆ (01446) 743194
✉ cowlincartoons@aol.com

Cream Rises 1 Denman Cottages, California Road, Mistley, Manningtree, Essex, CO11 1JE, United Kingdom
✆ (01206) 390167
✉ kseville101@hotmail.com

Dardanele Boguslawskiego, Cracow, 31-048, Poland
✆ 0048 888 44 22 42
✉ mail@dardanele.com
🖥 www.dardanele.com

David Benham@Graham-Cameron Illustration The Studio, 23 Holt Road, Sheringham, Norfolk, NR26 8NB, United Kingdom
✆ (01263) 821333/ ✆ (01263) 821334
✉ enquiry@graham-cameron-illustration.com
🖥 www.graham-cameron-illustration.com

David Cockcroft 52 Derwent Road, London, N13 4PU, United Kingdom
✆ (020) 8882 0150/ ✆ (020) 8882 0150
✉ cockroftnet@blueyonder.co.uk

David Frankland@Artist Partners Ltd 2e The Chandlery, 50 Westminster Bridge Road, London, SE1 7QY, United Kingdom
✆ (020) 7401 7904/ ✆ (020) 7401 3378
✉ chris@artistpartners.demon.co.uk
🖥 www.artistpartners.com

David Gifford 69 Latchmere Road, Kingston upon Thames, Surrey, KT2 5TS, United Kingdom
✆ (020) 8546 3462/(07715) 569671 / ✆ (020) 8549 0113
✉ david@davidgifford.co.uk
🖥 www.davidgifford.co.uk

David Lloyd 1st Floor, 9 Portland Place, Brighton, BN2 1DG, United Kingdom
✆ (01273) 600173
✉ lforlloyd@aol.com
🖥 www.lforlloyd.com

David Lock Cartoons 67 East Street, Wareham, Dorset, BH20 4NW, United Kingdom
✆ (01929) 553 834/ ✆ (01929) 553 834
✉ david.lock1@tesco.net

Deadringer Cartoons 120 Babylon Lane, Adlington, Chorley, Lancashire, PR6 9NP, United Kingdom
✆ (01257) 483719
✉ info@deadringercartoons.com
🖥 www.deadringercartoons.com

Derek Matthews Langhurst Cottage, Prestwick Lane, Chiddingfold, Surrey, GU8 4XP, United Kingdom
✆ (01428) 684580/ ✆ (01428) 685591
✉ derekmatthews@btinternet.com
🖥 www.derekmatthews.com

Derek Quint Crossways, Sampford Brett, Taunton, Somerset, TA4 4JT, United Kingdom
✆ (01984) 632592/ ✆ (01984) 632592

design@djhunter 133 Ravensbourne Avenue, Bromley, BR2 0AZ, United Kingdom
✆ (020) 8466 7196/ ✆ (020) 8466 7196
✉ design@djhunter.co.uk

Diana Defries, Wood Green, London, Middlesex, N22 5DS, United Kingdom
✆ (07989) 346853/✆ (020) 8881 0052
✉ scribbler@scribbler.org
🖳 www.scribbler.org

Don Seed 33 Culverden Park Road, Tunbridge Wells, Kent, TN4 9RB, United Kingdom
✆ (01892) 616300/(07792) 314072 ✆ (01892) 616300
✉ seedart@globalnet.co.uk
🖳 www.seedart.co.uk

Douglas Ingram 15 Uplands Park Road, Enfield, Middlesex, EN2 7PU, United Kingdom
✆ (020) 8367 4646/(07721) 011331 ✆ (020) 8367 4646
✉ ingram1@btconnect.com
🖳 www.storyboardsingram.co.uk

Dreamtree Ltd Unit 3/4, Mellington Work Shops, Church Stoke, Montgomery, Powys, SY15 6TQ, United Kingdom
✆ (01588) 620552/(07957) 733830 ✆ (01588) 620632
✉ colin@dreamtree.co.uk
🖳 www.dreamtree.co.uk

Duncan Scott Cartoons Flat 6, 23 Park Road, Moseley, Birmingham, B13 8AB, United Kingdom
✆ 0121-449 0798
✉ duncan.scott2@btopenworld.com
🖳 www.cartoonsandthat.com

Ed McHenry 63 Fortis Green, East Finchley, London, N2 9JJ, United Kingdom
✆ (020) 8444 8994

Ed McLachlan@Folio 10 Gate Street, Lincoln's Inn Fields, London, WC2A 3HP, United Kingdom
✆ (020) 7242 9562/✆ (020) 7242 1816
✉ all@folioart.co.uk
🖳 www.folioart.co.uk

Elke Counsell@Linda Rogers Associates 163 Half Moon Lane, London, SE24 9WB, United Kingdom
✆ (020) 7501 9106
✉ lr@lindarogers.net
🖳 www.lindarogers.net

Fijit Ltd 5 Great James Street, London, WC1N 3DB, United Kingdom
✆ (08702) 418053
✉ admin@fijit-design.co.uk
🖳 www.fijit-design.co.uk

Firespit 45 Myrtle Avenue, Bingly, BD16 1EW,
✆ 7968505946
✉ firespitdesign@yahoo.com

Garry Davies Grove House, 5 Grove Road, Fareham, Hampshire, PO16 7TF, United Kingdom
✆ (01329) 236219/✆ (01329) 236219

Gary Rees@Linda Rogers Associates 163 Half Moon Lane, London, SE24 9WB, United Kingdom
✆ (020) 7501 9106
✉ lr@lindarogers.net
🖳 www.lindarogers.net

Gary Swift Fieldhouse Studios, 8 Hague Park Lane, South Kirkby, Pontefract, West Yorkshire, WF9 3SS, United Kingdom
✆ (01977) 646431/✆ (01977) 646431
✉ gary@garyswift.com
🖳 www.garyswift.com

Geo Parkin Ltd 21 Lauriston Road, Brighton, BN1 6SN, United Kingdom
✆ (01273) 562269/✆ (01273) 239292
✉ geo@geoparkin.com
🖳 www.geoparkin.com

Geoff Jones 38 Wimborne Close, Up Hatherley, Cheltenham, Gloucestershire, GL51 3QP, United Kingdom
✆ (01242) 517256/✆ (01242) 517256
✉ wimborne38@blueyonder.co.uk
🖳 www.chelt.clara.net

George Robinson 36 Grove Street, Edinburgh, EH3 8AZ, United Kingdom
✆ 0131-229 1524
✉ george.e.robinson@btinternet.com

GJB World 37 Cambridge Road, West Molesey, Surrey, KT8 2AU, United Kingdom
✆ (07812) 669159
✉ garry.beckett@ntlworld.com
🖳 www.gjbworld.co,

Gordon Fraser Illustrations 48 Lynmouth Close, Hemlington, Middlesbrough, Cleveland, TS8 9NH, United Kingdom
✆ (01642) 270529
✉ gothtwinz@hotmail.com
🖳 www.freewebs.com/gordonfraser

Gouty Foot 47 Culvers, South Harting, Petersfield, Hampshire, GU31 5LE, United Kingdom
✆ (01730) 826850/(07901) 582677 ✆
✉ gary@goutyfoot.com
🖳 www.goutyfoot.com

Graeme Puckett Hellzapoppin, 26 Malvern Buildings, Bath, BA1 6JX, United Kingdom
✆ (01225) 332942
🖳 www.hoppinmad.co.uk

Graham Higgins 38 Prospect Road, Moseley, Birmingham, B13 9TB, United Kingdom
✆ 0121-449 0571/✆ 0121-449 0571
✉ g@pokkettz.demon.co.uk
🖳 www.pokkettz.demon.co.uk

Graham Thompson 1A Admirals Walk, St. Albans, Hertfordshire, AL1 5SH, United Kingdom
✆ (01727) 857505/✆ (01727) 857505
✉ graham@grahamthompsonillustration.co.uk
🖳 www.grahamthompsonillustration.co.uk

Gray Jolliffe@Illustration Ltd 2 Brooks Court, Cringle Street, London, SW8 5BX, United Kingdom
✆ (020) 7720 5202/✆ (020) 7720 5920
✉ team@illustrationweb.com
🖳 www.illustrationweb.com

Guy Carter, London, E17, United Kingdom
✆ (020) 8523 3465/(07773) 603239 ✆
✉ guycarter@bushinternet.com
🖳 www.humour.co.uk

Hartoons 37 Beach Priory Gardens, Southport, Merseyside, PR8 2SA, United Kingdom
✆ (01704) 543981/✆ (01704) 501238
✉ mail@hartoons.co.uk
🖳 www.hartoons.co.uk

Henry Gardiner 21 Merrivale, Camden Street, London, NW1 0LH, United Kingdom
✆ (020) 7387 6381

Hens-Teeth 34 Marsden Lane, Marsden, Huddersfield, HD7 6AF, United Kingdom
✆ (01484) 841 076
✉ howard@hens-teeth.com
🖳 www.hens-teeth.com

Howard Cartoons 8 Belle Vue Street, York, YO10 5AY, United Kingdom
✆ (01904) 656702
✉ graemejhoward@aol.com
🖳 www.howardcartoons.co.uk

Ian Fraser Jackson 44 Coniston Road, Muswell Hill, London, N10 2BP, United Kingdom
✆ (020) 8374 8281/(07957) 257365 ✆ (020) 8374 8281
✉ jaxxi@blueyonder.co.uk

Ian Purdie 43 Bankfield Lane, Rochdale, Lancashire, OL11 5RS, United Kingdom
✆ (01706) 633617

Illustratorsmith 36 Woolley Street, Bradford-on-Avon, Wiltshire, BA15 1AG, United Kingdom
✆ (01225) 868248
✉ dfs@illustratorsmith.com
🖳 www.illustratorsmith.com

Ink & Colors Ltd 27 Old Gloucester Street, London, WC1N 3XX, United Kingdom
✆ (020) 7558 8374
✉ info@inkandcolors.com
🖳 www.inkandcolors.com

Jack Kirkbride New Inn Farm, Highmoor, Oldham, OL4 3RX, United Kingdom
✆ (01457) 874658/✆ (01457) 874658
✉ smileyman@tiscali.co.uk

Jackie Sinnott 112 Addiscombe Road, Croydon, CR0 5PQ, United Kingdom
✆ (020) 8654 3017

Jane Cope@Linda Rogers Associates 163 Half Moon Lane, London, SE24 9WB, United Kingdom
✆ (020) 7501 9106
✉ lr@lindarogers.net
🖳 www.lindarogers.net

Jane Gerwitz 13 Plevna Terrace, Bingley, West Yorkshire, BD16 4BX, United Kingdom
✆ (01274) 560190
✉ janegerwitz@aol.com
🖳 www.janegerwitz.com

Jean de Lemos@Graham-Cameron Illustration The Studio, 23 Holt Road, Sheringham, Norfolk, NR26 8NB, United Kingdom
✆ (01263) 821333/✆ (01263) 821334
✉ enquiry@graham-cameron-illustration.com
🖳 www.graham-cameron-illustration.com

Jenni Johnson Risistrasse 11c, Birmensdorf, 8903, Switzerland
✆ 00 41 44 77 77 689
✉ jenni@jennijohnson.com
🖳 www.jennijohnson.com

Jo Bird@Meiklejohn Illustration 5 Risborough Street, London, SE1 0HF, United Kingdom
✆ (020) 7593 0500/✆ (020) 7593 0501
✉ info@meiklejohn.co.uk
🖳 www.meiklejohn.co.uk

John Adams@Illustration Ltd 2 Brooks Court, Cringle Street, London, SW8 5BX, United Kingdom
✆ (020) 7720 5202/✆ (020) 7720 5920
✉ team@illustrationweb.com
🖳 www.illustrationweb.com

John Batten 51 Stondon Park, London, SE23 1LB, United Kingdom
✆ (020) 8291 3365/✆ (020) 8291 3365
✉ jp.batten@btopenworld.com
🖳 www.johnbatten.net

John Cooper 43 Saint Hilda Street, Bridlington, East Yorkshire, YO15 3EE, United Kingdom
✆ (01262) 676337/(07960) 841711 ✆ (01262) 676337
✉ coops@coopart.co.uk

John Erasmus (NPA) 213 Petersham Road, Richmond, Surrey, TW10 7AW, United Kingdom
✆ (020) 8948 2378/(07811) 433184 ✆ (020) 8948 2378
✉ lightsource@btinternet.com

John Hodgson Illustrators Agency 38 Westminster Palace Gardens, Artillery Row, London, SW1P 1RR, United Kingdom
✆ (020) 7222 4468/✆ (020) 7222 4468

John Richardson@Illustration Ltd 2 Brooks Court, Cringle Street, London, SW8 5BX, United Kingdom
✆ (020) 7720 5202/✆ (020) 7720 5920
✉ team@illustrationweb.com
🖳 www.illustrationweb.com

John Smyth 63 Ashridge Crescent, Shooters Hill, London, SE18 3EA, United Kingdom
✆ (020) 8855 0270/✆ (020) 8855 0270

Jonathan Cusick 10 Wynyates, Sageside, Tamworth, Staffordshire, B79 7UP, United Kingdom
✆ (01827) 50003/✆ (01827) 50003
✉ theboss@jonathancusick.com
🖳 www.jonathancusick.com

Judy Brown & Alan Rowe 17 Surrey Grove, Sutton, Surrey, SM1 3PW, United Kingdom
✆ (020) 8643 1626/(07050) 131455 ✆ (020) 8641 1528
✉ judy@judybrown.co.uk
🖳 www.alanrowe.com

Just For Laffs 7 Worsley Mill, 10 Blantyre Street, Castlefield, Manchester, M15 4LG, United Kingdom
✆ (0870) 1225003/✆ (0870) 2405002
✉ info@justforlaffs.co.uk
🖳 www.justforlaffs.co.uk

Karol Kreations 25 Lower Bartons, Fordingbridge, Hampshire, SP6 1JB, United Kingdom
✆ (07919) 094523
✉ ianmabb1971@hotmail.com

Katie Cusack Illustration 1330 Barlow Road, Hudson, 44236, United States of America
✆ 00 1 912 844 1608
✉ katie@katiecusack.com
🖳 www.katiecusack.com

Kipper Williams 6 Windmill Street, London, W1P 1HF, United Kingdom
✆ (020) 7636 0911

Kokoro Design 80 Warwick Road, Solihull, West Midlands, B92 7JJ, United Kingdom
✆ 0121-707 8635
✉ botmatt@yahoo.co.uk

Lee Healey Cartoonist 64 Barry Road, London, SE22 0HP, United Kingdom
✆ (020) 7564 5309/✆ (020) 7564 5309
✉ leehealey@ntlworld.com
🖳 www.leehealey.com

Leighton Noyes@Graham-Cameron Illustration The Studio, 23 Holt Road, Sheringham, Norfolk, NR26 8NB, United Kingdom
✆ (01263) 821333/✆ (01263) 821334
✉ enquiry@graham-cameron-illustration.com
🖳 www.graham-cameron-illustration.com

Linda Combi 17 Albemarle Road, York, YO23 1EW, United Kingdom
✆ (01904) 623036
✎ linda@combi.wanadoo.co.uk
🖥 www.contact-me.net/lindacombi

Linzi Henry 5 Ashfurlong Close, Dore, Sheffield, S17 3NN, United Kingdom
✆ 0114-236 7481

Lucy Maddison 11 Estreham Road, London, SW16 5NT, United Kingdom
✆ (020) 8677 5724/✍ (0870) 1604571
✎ info@lucymaddison.com
🖥 www.lucymaddison.com

Lyn Davies Cartoons & Illustrations 467 Trewyddfa Road, Morriston, Swansea, SA6 7QH, United Kingdom
✆ (01792) 428358
✎ creepbags@msn.com
🖥 www.lyndavies.com

Manny Curtis 10 Datchworth Court, Village Road, Enfield, Middlesex, EN1 2DS, United Kingdom
✆ (020) 8366 5389/✍ (020) 8342 1996
✎ manecurtis@aol.com
🖥 www.cartooningcurtis.co.uk

Margaret Wellbank@Linda Rogers Associates 163 Half Moon Lane, London, SE24 9WB, United Kingdom
✆ (020) 7501 9106
✎ lr@lindarogers.net
🖥 www.lindarogers.net

Mark Hackett 9 Fairfield Terrace, Bath, BA1 6HN, United Kingdom
✆ (01225) 337401/(07752) 522845 ✍ (01225) 337401
✎ hackettmarcus@yahoo.co.uk
🖥 www.markhackett.co.uk

Mark Lovell Design The Old Stables, Wood End, Saffron Walden, Essex, CB11 3SN, United Kingdom
✆ (01799) 542668/(07941) 019647 ✍ (01799) 542668
✎ mk.lovell@virgin.net

Mark Tabbener 12 Sheridan Close, Aldershot, Hampshire, GU11 3DS, United Kingdom
✆ (01252) 319127/✍ (01252) 319127
✎ m.tabbener@ntlworld.com
🖥 www.caricaturist.tv

Mark Wilson Cartoons 219 Bedford Street, Crewe, CW2 6JL, United Kingdom
✆ (07786) 431327
✎ mark@mwartist.co.uk
🖥 www.mwartist.co.uk

Mark Wood Cartoonist 22 Standen Street, Tunbridge Wells, Kent, TN4 9RJ, United Kingdom
✆ (01892) 539332
✎ mark@markwoodcartoonist.co.uk
🖥 www.markwoodcartoonist.co.uk

Martin Honeysett 13 West Street, Hastings, East Sussex, TN34 3AN, United Kingdom
✆ (01424) 440249/✍ (01424) 440249
✎ martin.honeysett@kirion.net
🖥 www.martinhoneysett.com

Martin Shovel 13 Lancaster Road, Brighton, BN1 5DG, United Kingdom
✆ (01273) 249 813/✍ (0870) 169 6025
✎ info@shovel.co.uk
🖥 www.shovel.co.uk

Michelle Ross c/o 2 Gainford Avenue, Middlesbrough, Cleveland, TS5 7RF, United Kingdom
✆ (01287) 669019
✎ michelle.ross2@ntlworld.com
🖥 mysite.wanadoo-members.co.uk/MichelleRoss

Mike Argent 5 Woodside Road, Clevedon, Somerset, BS21 7JY, United Kingdom
✆ (01275) 872690
✎ mgargent@waitrose.com

Mike Mosedale Wellbrook Hill Cottage, Mayfield, East Sussex, TN20 6EA, United Kingdom
✆ (01435) 872133/✍ (01435) 872133
✎ mike@londoncartoonists.co.uk
🖥 www.londoncartoonists.co.uk

Mr Creighton Global Enterprises 54/2 Willowbrae Road, Edinburgh, EH8 7HA, United Kingdom
✆ (07786) 478866
✎ mrcreighton@mrcreighton.com
🖥 www.mrcreighton.com

My Hands 24 Montpelier Road, Ealing, London, W5 2QT, United Kingdom
✆ 7810004911/020 8991 5920
✎ louise.flockhart@ntlworld.com

Neil Bradley Linden House, 73 Upper Marehay, Ripley, Derbyshire, DE5 8JF, United Kingdom
✆ (01773) 741555/✍ (01773) 741555
✎ bradcart@aol.com
🖥 www.cartoonists.co.uk/neilbradley/neilbradleyintroduction.html

Neils Art 3/1 46 Thornwood Avenue, Glasgow, G11 7PQ, United Kingdom
✆ (07967) 910388
✎ neilthomson@ntdesign.co.uk
🖥 www.neilart.co.uk

Nick Davies 2 Dol Helyg, Pembrey, Burry Port, Carmarthenshire, SA16 0EH, United Kingdom
✆ (01554) 832758/(07835) 696477 ✍
✎ nickdaviescartoons@hotmail.com

Nick Diggory@Illustration Ltd 2 Brooks Court, Cringle Street, London, SW8 5BX, United Kingdom
✆ (020) 7720 5202/✍ (020) 7720 5920
✎ team@illustrationweb.com
🖥 www.illustrationweb.com

Nicola L Robinson Mynachdy, Cardiff, Glamorgan, CF14 3AG,
✆
✎ nlrobinson@thesurrealdemon.co.uk
🖥 www.thesurrealdemon.co.uk

Nigel Kitching Old Hall Cottage, Sexhow, Hutton Rudby, Yarm, Cleveland, TS15 0ER, United Kingdom
✆ (01642) 701402
✎ nigel@nigelkitching.plus.com

Noel Ford Ty Rhyd, Ystrad Meurig, Ceredigion, SY25 6AX, United Kingdom
✆ (01974) 831468/✍ (08700) 518267
✎ noel@fordcartoon.com
🖥 www.fordcartoon.com

Norman Young@Linda Rogers Associates 163 Half Moon Lane, London, SE24 9WB, United Kingdom
✆ (020) 7501 9106
✎ lr@lindarogers.net
🖥 www.lindarogers.net

OneBrightSpark 10 Matthews Court, Harrington Lane, Exeter, EX4 8NX, United Kingdom
✆ (01392) 460294/(07778) 510437 ✍
✎ ideas@onebrightspark.co.uk
🖥 www.onebrightspark.co.uk

Paul Beattie 3 Bacons Lane, Pinchbeck, Spalding, Lincolnshire, PE11 3XS, United Kingdom
✆ (01775) 680193
✎ paul@beattiep68.freeserve.co.uk

Paul Chappell 44 Beechwood Close, Little Chalfont, Buckinghamshire, HP6 6QX, United Kingdom
✆ (01494) 762484/(07977) 298433 ✍
✎ paulc@vizualeye.com
🖥 www.vizualeye.com

Paul Daviz@Illustration Ltd 2 Brooks Court, Cringle Street, London, SW8 5BX, United Kingdom
✆ (020) 7720 5202/✍ (020) 7720 5920
✎ team@illustrationweb.com
🖥 www.illustrationweb.com

Paul Rigby 28 Normanton Lane, Derby, DE23 6GP, United Kingdom
✆ (07939) 034612/(07939) 034612 ✍
✎ paul@paulrigby.co.uk
🖥 www.paulrigby.co.uk

Paul Tucker 15 Roman Rise, London, SE19 1JG, United Kingdom
✆ (020) 8670 5549/(07932) 140730 ✍ (020) 8670 5549
✎ paul.@tuckerportrates.com
🖥 www.tuckerillustration.com

Pear Tree Studio Bisterne Close, Burley, Hampshire, BH24 4AZ, United Kingdom
✆ 0142-540-2115/07860-346-787 ✍
✎ paul@paulhampson.co.uk
🖥 www.paulhampson.co.uk

Pennant Illustration 16 Littleton Street, London, SW18 3SY, United Kingdom
✆ (020) 8947 4002/(07850) 865591 ✍ (020) 8946 7667
✎ matt@pennantinc.co.uk
🖥 www.pennantinc.co.uk

Peter Plant Oakfield, Love Lane, Petersfield, Hampshire, GU31 4BW, United Kingdom
✆ (01730) 264608
✎ peterplant@ntlworld.com
🖥 www.peterplant.net

Philip Disley 7 Parkgate Close, Aigburth, Liverpool, L17 6EH, United Kingdom
✆ 0151-494 1604/07779 783414 ✍ 0151-494 1604
✎ phill@philldisley.com
🖥 www.philldisley.com

Philip Thompson 35 Elgin Crescent, London, W11 2JD, United Kingdom
✆ (020) 7221 1925/✍ (020) 7243 0868
✎ phil@jotom.demon.co.uk
🖥 www.contact-me.net/philipthomson

Phill Burrows 16A Bolton Cresent, Windsor, Berkshire, SL4 3JQ, United Kingdom
✆ (01753) 869686
✎ phillip.burrows@btinternet.com
🖥 www.phillburrows.co.uk

Piers Baker Saxton, Parklands, Railton Road, Guildford, Surrey, GU2 9JX, United Kingdom
✆ (01483) 238267/(07889) 128331 ✍
✎ pbaker@piersbaker.co.uk
🖥 www.piersbaker.co.uk

Portland 2 58 St Mary's Road, Oatlands Village, Weybridge, Surrey, KT13 9PZ, United Kingdom
✆ (01932) 843546/(07831) 599405 ✍ (01932) 821854
✎ doloresportlands3@aol.com

radimus.co.uk Suite 4, Putney Bridge Road, London, SW15 2PX, United Kingdom
✆ (07711) 049227/✍ (020) 8871 2261
✎ mail@radimus.co.uk
🖥 www.radimus.co.uk

Richard J. Duszczak 29 Lake View Avenue, Walton, Chesterfield, Derbyshire, S40 3DR, United Kingdom
✆ (01246) 209034/✍ (01246) 209034
✎ rd@cartoonstudio.co.uk
🖥 www.cartoonstudio.co.uk

Richard Willson Shepherds Hill, Peaslake, Guildford, Surrey, GU5 9TB, United Kingdom
✆ (01306) 730570

Richardson Studio 41 Kirkleathen Lane, Redcar, Cleveland, TS10 1NT, United Kingdom
✆ (01642) 477119/✍ (01642) 477732
✎ richardsonstudio@btconnect.com
🖥 www.cartoonist-illustrator.com

Robert Duncan The Old Forge, Frogmore Lane, Long Crendon, Aylesbury, Buckinghamshire, HP18 9DZ, United Kingdom
✆ (01844) 201803/(07830) 183241 ✍ (01844) 201751
🖥 www.duncancartoons.com

Robin Carter 33 High Field Close, Thorpe, St. Andrew, Norwich, NR7 0RQ, United Kingdom
✆ (01603) 701555/(07776) 221345 ✍ (01603) 701555
✎ bellae@ntworld.com
🖥 www.carterwongtomlin.com/robincarter

Robin Edmonds@Just For Laffs 7 Worsley Mill, 10 Blantyre Street, Castlefield, Manchester, M15 4LG, United Kingdom
✆ (0870) 1225003/✍ (0870) 2405002
✎ info@justforlaffs.co.uk
🖥 www.justforlaffs.co.uk

Roger Fereday@Linda Rogers Associates 163 Half Moon Lane, London, SE24 9WB, United Kingdom
✆ (020) 7501 9106
✎ lr@lindarogers.net
🖥 www.lindarogers.net

Roger Penwill 6 Marcle Orchard, Brimfield, Ludlow, Shropshire, SY8 4PD, United Kingdom
✆ (01584) 711854/(07840) 659522 ✍ (01584) 711854
✎ roger@penwill.co.uk
🖥 www.penwillcartoons.com

Roger Sanderson Bucklers Lodge, 32 Ringwood Road, St. Ives, Ringwood, Hampshire, BH24 2NY, United Kingdom
✆ (01425) 474242

Ron Tiner 24 Thornton Hill, Exeter, EX4 4NS, United Kingdom
✆ (01392) 213066
✎ rontiner@blueyonder.co.uk
🖥 www.rontiner.com

Ross Simmons Illustration & Design 43 Crossways, Three Bridges, Crawley, West Sussex, RH10 1QT, United Kingdom
✆ 07876 203171/✍ 01293 571102
✎ rosssimmons77@hotmail.com

Ross Thomson@Graham-Cameron Illustration The Studio, 23 Holt Road, Sheringham, Norfolk, NR26 8NB, United Kingdom
- (01263) 821333/ (01263) 821334
- enquiry@graham-cameron-illustration.com
- www.graham-cameron-illustration.com

Royston Robertson 20 Upton Road, Broadstairs, Kent, CT10 2AS, United Kingdom
- (01843) 871241/(07787) 303974
- royston@dircon.co.uk
- www.roystonrobertson.co.uk

Rupert Besley 26 College Road, Newport, Isle of Wight, PO30 1HB, United Kingdom
- (01983) 528943/ (01983) 528943
- cartoons@rbesley.freeserve.co.uk
- www.besleycartoons.com

Russ Tudor 2 Hathaway Drive, Astley Bridge, Bolton, BL1 7RY, United Kingdom
- (01204) 597795/ (01204) 597795
- cartoons@russtudor.wanadoo.co.uk
- www.russtudor.com

Sheridan Art Works 29 Lynnhurst, Uddingston, Glasgow, G71 6SA, United Kingdom
- (07791) 201985
- paulsheridan24@yahoo.co.uk
- www.freewebs.com/sheridanartworks

Sholto Walker@Illustration Ltd 2 Brooks Court, Cringle Street, London, SW8 5BX, United Kingdom
- (020) 7720 5202/ (020) 7720 5920
- team@illustrationweb.com
- www.illustrationweb.com

Simon Clare Creative Workshop Little Leydens, Stick Hill, Edenbridge, Kent, TN8 5NH, United Kingdom
- (01732) 862672
- simonc.creative@btinternet.com
- www.contact-me.net/SimonClare

Simon Jenkins Associates 14 Hillcrest Road, London, W3 9RZ, United Kingdom
- (020) 8993 3936/7808297146
- simon@shipoffools.com
- www.shipoffools.com

Smutt Magazine 41 Kensington Road, Chichester, West Sussex, PO19 7XS,
- 70926368776
- lou.marshall@hotmail.com
- www.smuttmagazine.com

Sophie Grillet 20 Greyladies Gardens, Wat Tyler Road, London, SE10 8AU, United Kingdom
- (020) 8691 0153/ (020) 8691 0153
- sophie@sophiescartoons.com
- www.sophiescartoons.com

Spark & Zoom Productions The Stables, Luttrell House, Brockencote, Chaddesley Corbett, Kidderminster, Worcestershire, DY10 4PZ, United Kingdom
- (01562) 777424
- mail@sparkandzoom.com
- www.sparkandzoom.com

Sparq 17 Kennington Lane, London, SE11 5LQ, United Kingdom
- (07944) 457171
- info@sparq1.co.uk
- www.sparq1.co.uk

Stephen Hall 28 Cable Road, Whitehead, Carrickfergus, County Antrim, BT38 9PX, United Kingdom
- (028) 9337 8583/(07910) 355794
- theweebear@hotmail.com
- www.earthnativeart.co.uk

Stuart Harrison 126 Hampton Road, Southport, Merseyside, PR8 5DZ, United Kingdom
- (01704) 532655/(07956) 370037
- stuart.harrison2@virgin.net
- www.stu-art.biz

Sue Woollatt@Graham-Cameron Illustration The Studio, 23 Holt Road, Sheringham, Norfolk, NR26 8NB, United Kingdom
- (01263) 821333/ (01263) 821334
- enquiry@graham-cameron-illustration.com
- www.graham-cameron-illustration.com

Tamsin Cook@Graham-Cameron Illustration The Studio, 23 Holt Road, Sheringham, Norfolk, NR26 8NB, United Kingdom
- (01263) 821333/ (01263) 821334
- enquiry@graham-cameron-illustration.com
- www.graham-cameron-illustration.com

Terry Christien Cartoonology 46 Strawberry Vale, Twickenham, TW1 4SE, United Kingdom
- (020) 8892 3621/(07956) 897783 (020) 8891 5946
- terry@cartoonology.com
- www.cartoonology.com

Tim Archbold@Graham-Cameron Illustration The Studio, 23 Holt Road, Sheringham, Norfolk, NR26 8NB, United Kingdom
- (01263) 821333/ (01263) 821334
- enquiry@graham-cameron-illustration.com
- www.graham-cameron-illustration.com

Tim Benton@Linda Rogers Associates 163 Half Moon Lane, London, SE24 9WB, United Kingdom
- (020) 7501 9106
- lr@lindarogers.net
- www.lindarogers.net

Timothy Donaldson Domus, Crossheads, Colwich, Stafford, ST18 0UG, United Kingdom
- (01889) 882043/ (01889) 882043
- e@timothydonaldson.com
- www.timothydonaldson.com

Toni Goffe@Linda Rogers Associates 163 Half Moon Lane, London, SE24 9WB, United Kingdom
- (020) 7501 9106
- lr@lindarogers.net
- www.lindarogers.net

Tony Escott 29 Peterborough Road, Parsons Green, London, SW6 3BT, United Kingdom
- (020) 7731 0158/ (020) 7731 0158

Tony Neat 22 Westcliffe Road, Westbrook, Margate, Kent, CT9 5DN, United Kingdom
- (01843) 292903
- tonyneat@cartoons65.fsnet.co.uk

Touchpoint 14th Floor, Oakland House, Talbot Road, Manchester, M16 0PQ, United Kingdom
- (0161) 888 5747/ (0161) 888 5741
- info@touchpointuk.com
- www.touchpointuk.com

Visual Humour 5 Greymouth Close, Stockton-on-Tees, Cleveland, TS18 5LF, United Kingdom
- (01642) 581847
- peterdodsworth@btclick.com
- www.businesscartoons.co.uk

Vizual Eye 44 Beechwood Close, Little Chalfont, Amersham, Buckinghamshire, HP6 6QX, United Kingdom
- (020) 7071 2392/07977 298 433
- paulc@vizualeye.com
- www.vizualeye.com

Weef 4 Trinity Close, The Pavement, London, SW4 0JD, United Kingdom
- (020) 7622 9868/(07788) 944071 (020) 7622 9868
- weef@lineone.net
- www.weef.co.uk

William Rudling 6 The Close, Alwoodley, Leeds, LS17 7RD, United Kingdom
- 0113-267 5696/(07792) 023009 0113-267 5662
- william@williamrudling.com
- www.williamrudling.com

Wingnut Designs Waterfront Farm, Biddisham Lane, Biddisham, Axbridge, Somerset, BS26 2RS, United Kingdom
- (01934) 750827
- chris@wingnutdesigns.co.uk
- www.wingnutdesigns.co.uk

Zan Pearce Illustration, London, W14 0QH, United Kingdom
- (07799) 795756/ (020) 7603 1744
- zanpearce@hotmail.com

EDITORIAL

Début Art & The Coningsby Gallery 30 Tottenham Street, London, W1T 4RJ, United Kingdom
- (020) 7636 1064/ (020) 7580 7017
- info@debutart.com
- www.debutart.com

Peter Campbell 2 Prebend Mansion, Chiswick High Road, London, W4 2LU, United Kingdom
- (020) 8995 5812/(07941) 049862 (020) 8995 5812
- peter@petercampbell.demon.co.uk
- www.petercampbellstudios.co.uk

Phill Burrows 16A Bolton Cresent, Windsor, Berkshire, SL4 3JQ, United Kingdom
- (01753) 869686
- phillip.burrows@btinternet.com
- www.phillburrows.co.uk

FASHION

Début Art & The Coningsby Gallery 30 Tottenham Street, London, W1T 4RJ, United Kingdom
- (020) 7636 1064/ (020) 7580 7017
- info@debutart.com
- www.debutart.com

Ken Reilly Design Associates 11 Chiswick Staithe, Hartington Road, Grove Park, London, W4 3TP, UK
- (020) 8994 2228/ (020) 8994 2238
- ken.reilly@btconnect.com
- www.kenreilly.co.uk

FOOD

Hot Frog Graphics Stanmore, 4 Moorland Avenue, Barnsley, South Yorkshire, S70 6PQ, United Kingdom
- (01226) 242777/ (01226) 242777
- hotfroggraphics@blueyonder.co.uk
- www.hotfroggraphics.com

Ken Reilly Design Associates 11 Chiswick Staithe, Hartington Road, Grove Park, London, W4 3TP, United Kingdom
- (020) 8994 2228/ (020) 8994 2238
- ken.reilly@btconnect.com
- www.kenreilly.co.uk

Phill Burrows 16A Bolton Cresent, Windsor, Berkshire, SL4 3JQ, United Kingdom
- (01753) 869686
- phillip.burrows@btinternet.com
- www.phillburrows.co.uk

LIFESTYLE

Début Art & The Coningsby Gallery 30 Tottenham Street, London, W1T 4RJ, United Kingdom
- (020) 7636 1064/ (020) 7580 7017
- info@debutart.com
- www.debutart.com

Phill Burrows 16A Bolton Cresent, Windsor, Berkshire, SL4 3JQ, United Kingdom
- (01753) 869686
- phillip.burrows@btinternet.com
- www.phillburrows.co.uk

PACKAGING

Ken Reilly Design Associates 11 Chiswick Staithe, Hartington Road, Grove Park, London, W4 3TP, United Kingdom
- (020) 8994 2228/ (020) 8994 2238
- ken.reilly@btconnect.com
- www.kenreilly.co.uk

PEOPLE

David Barnett 41 Hidcote Road, Oadby, Leicester, LE2 5PG, United Kingdom
- 0116-271 7658/ 0116-271 7658
- www.contact-me.net/davidbarnett

Début Art & The Coningsby Gallery 30 Tottenham Street, London, W1T 4RJ, United Kingdom
- (020) 7636 1064/ (020) 7580 7017
- info@debutart.com
- www.debutart.com

Irene Wise 26 Norman Avenue, St. Margarets, Twickenham, TW1 2LY, United Kingdom
- (020) 8892 3817/ (020) 8892 3817
- irenejuliawise@aol.com

Marius Shafer 19 Queensway, Frimley Green, Camberley, Surrey, GU16 6QB, United Kingdom
- (01252) 835749/(07811) 946981 (01252) 836032
- shafer@ntlworld.com
- www.marius-shafer.com

Martin Ash Paintings Holmsley House, Holtye, Cowden, Kent, TN8 7ED, United Kingdom
- (01342) 850366/(07759) 925087
- ash_martin@tiscali.co.uk

Phill Burrows 16A Bolton Cresent, Windsor, Berkshire, SL4 3JQ, United Kingdom
- (01753) 869686
- phillip.burrows@btinternet.com
- www.phillburrows.co.uk

SCENIC

David Barnett 41 Hidcote Road, Oadby, Leicester, LE2 5PG, United Kingdom
☎ 0116-271 7658/✆ 0116-271 7658
🖥 www.contact-me.net/davidbarnett

Irene Wise 26 Norman Avenue, St. Margarets, Twickenham, TW1 2LY, United Kingdom
☎ (020) 8892 3817/✆ (020) 8892 3817
✉ irenejuliawise@aol.com

STILL LIFE

Ken Reilly Design Associates 11 Chiswick Staithe, Hartington Road, Grove Park, London, W4 3TP, United Kingdom
☎ (020) 8994 2228/✆ (020) 8994 2238
✉ ken.reilly@btconnect.com
🖥 www.kenreilly.co.uk

Phill Burrows 16A Bolton Cresent, Windsor, Berkshire, SL4 3JQ, United Kingdom
☎ (01753) 869686
✉ phillip.burrows@btinternet.com
🖥 www.phillburrows.co.uk

Wonderfuel 118 Hatherley Gardens, London, E6 3HQ, United Kingdom
☎ 020 8548 1358
✉ info@wonderfuel.co.uk
🖥 www.wonderfuel.co.uk

STORYBOARDS

A3 Ltd 3rd Floor, Shropshire House, 2-10 Capper Street, London, WC1E 6JA, United Kingdom
☎ (020) 7631 5398/✆ (020) 7436 4195
✉ info@a3studios.com
🖥 www.a3studios.com

Marius Shafer 19 Queensway, Frimley Green, Camberley, Surrey, GU16 6QB, United Kingdom
☎ (01252) 835749/(07811) 946981 ✆ (01252) 836032
✉ shafer@ntlworld.com
🖥 www.marius-shafer.com

Phill Burrows 16A Bolton Cresent, Windsor, Berkshire, SL4 3JQ, United Kingdom
☎ (01753) 869686
✉ phillip.burrows@btinternet.com
🖥 www.phillburrows.co.uk

Robert Butler, London, United Kingdom
☎ (07903) 365688
✉ robert@constructivelines.com
🖥 www.constructivelines.com

Storyboards Ltd 18 Greek Street, London, W1D 4JD, United Kingdom
☎ (020) 7734 1437/✆ (020) 7760 7713
✉ info@storyboards.co.uk
🖥 www.storyboards.co.uk

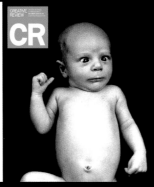

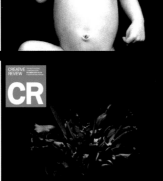
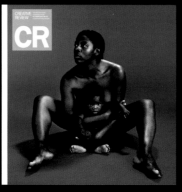

SUBSCRIBE TO
CREATIVE REVIEW
TODAY FOR JUST £64

BY PHONE
0207 292 3703
ONLINE
CREATIVEREVIEW.CO.UK/SUBSCRIBE.PHP

PEEPSHOW.ORG.UK

Picture Libraries

OUR IMAGE. YOUR STORY.

iStockphoto.com | Provocative royalty-free stock images as low as $1

iStockphoto

Advertising showcase:
Picture libraries
04.

Showcasing the best of contemporary food and drink photography

food&drink
photos.com

t: +44 (0)20 8740 6610
e: info@foodanddrinkphotos.com

photography you can feel®
www.4cornersimages.com

4COR
NERS
images

The Lightbox, 111 Power Road, London W4 5PY
Tel +44 20 8811 1010

The Réunion des Musées Nationaux's **photo agency**

**Photographic agency
of the Réunion des
Musées Nationaux**

10, rue de l'Abbaye
75006 Paris - France
Tel.: 33 (0)1 40 13 49 00
Fax: 33 (0)1 40 13 46 01
e-mail : photo@rmn.fr

www.photo.rmn.fr

RMN

Louvre   Orsay   Versailles   Picasso Museum   Georges Pompido

New
Open
Discover
Astonish
Admire
Save

Import Art images...

Magazine
Fine Books
Advertisement
Packaging
Publishing
Mult

100%   Page : 1

Mise en page 1

158,397 mr

Y :   42   H :   137,583 mr   0°   XX   100%

Graphic design: Pierre Finot - © Photo RMN - C. Jean - La belle ferronnière,
Léonard de Vinci, Musée du Louvre et ©Photo RMN - ©Droits réservés
Dragon marin crachant de l'eau, 1702, Jean Hardy (1653-1737)
Versailles, Jardin du Grand Trianon, châteaux de Versailles et de Trianon.

The Réunion des Musées Nationaux's **photo agency**

**Photographic agency
of the Réunion des
Musées Nationaux**

10, rue de l'Abbaye
75006 Paris - France
Tel.: 33 (0)1 40 13 49 00
Fax: 33 (0)1 40 13 46 01
e-mail : photo@rmn.fr

www.photo.rmn.fr

Versailles   Picasso Museum   Georges Pompidou

Graphic design: Pierre Bardet. Conception RMN - C. Jean - La belle ferronnière,
Léonard de Vinci, Musée du Louvre et ©Photo RMN - ©Droits réservés
La Garonne, figure de vieillard-fleuve allongé sur une urne et appuyé sur un gouvernail
fiché dans le socle, à ses pieds un amour tenant une corne d'abondance, 1686,
Antoine Coysevox (1640-1720) - Versailles, châteaux de Versailles et de Trianon.

CHOOSE 25 HI-RES DOWNLOADS A DAY FROM 2.5 MILLION PHOTOGRAPHS AND VECTOR IMAGES
www.shutterstock.com | 001.646.257.4529 | SAVE 10% WITH THIS CODE: CHB10

700-00182541 © Dave Robertson / masterfile.com

Get your pictures here!

Masterfile.com

Which programme? 🔲 SimSearch is better than zapping,
it gets you straight to where you want to go.

masterfile.com: the right images for every kind
of project from £39 to exclusive.

www.doverbooks.co.uk

Copyright Free Image sourcebooks and CDs. Our Pictorial Archive range represents the largest collection of permission, royalty and copyright free images and illustration references in the world. Specialists in historical graphic and commercial art and illustration. All titles are available to browse and select at our Covent Garden shop.

The Dover Bookshop

18 Earlham Street
London WC2H 9LG

Telephone: +44 (0)20 7836 2111
Fax: +44 (0)20 7836 1603

Email: sales@doverbooks.co.uk

THE DOVER

BOOKSHOP

Looking for a Picture Researcher in the UK?

The PRA Freelance Register has
highly-experienced personnel available

Contact Ruth Smith
Tel: +44 (0)1727 833 676
Email: freelance.reg@picture-research.org.uk

Founded in 1977 the PRA is a professional organization for
picture researchers, picture editors and anyone specifically
involved in the research, management and supply of visual
material to the media industry.

Benefits of membership include meetings, our magazine
Montage, a newsletter, social events, and job opportunities

THE PICTURE RESEARCH ASSOCIATION

Join us!

Contact Veneta Bullen – PRA Chair

Tel: +44 (0)20 7739 8544
Fax: +44 (0)20 7782 0011

Or apply online
www.picture-research.org.uk
Email: **chair@picture-research.org.uk**

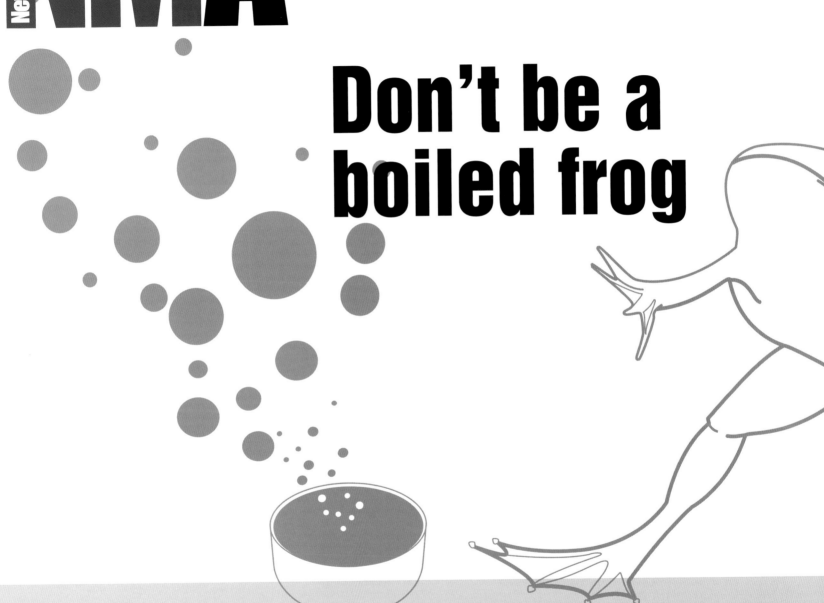

Don't be a boiled frog

NMA NewMediaAge

If you drop a frog into boiling water, it'll leap out. If you put it in cold water and heat it up slowly, it will eventually boil. Don't be a boiled frog. NMA covers the newest innovations in the digital market place, to help you see the bigger picture and avoid complacency.

So stay one leap ahead. Visit www.nma.co.uk to subscribe or call 0207 292 3717.

PHOTOLIBRARIES - GENERAL

1dpi Ltd Headwall Green Farm, Golcar, Huddersfield, HD7 4LE, United Kingdom
(0870) 9905197
enquiries@1dpi.com
www.1dpi.com

4Corners Images Ltd The Lightbox, 111 Power Road, London, W4 5PY, United Kingdom
(020) 8811 1010
info@4cornersimages.com
www.4cornersimages.com
See ad in showcase

72 Point PR Media Centre, Abbey Wood Business Park, Emma Chris Way, Filton, Bristol, BS34 7JU, United Kingdom
0117-906 6524/ 0117-906 6501
jay@72point.com
www.72point.com

A A Publishing 13th Floor, Fanum House, Basing View, Basingstoke, Hampshire, RG21 4EA, United Kingdom
(01256) 491588/ (01256) 492440
chris.butler@theaa.com

A A World Travel Library 13th Floor, Fanum House, Basingstoke, Hampshire, RG21 4EA, United Kingdom
(01256) 491588/ (01256) 323575
travel.images@theaa.com
www.aaworldtravellibrary.com

A T M Images 35 Elmhurst Road, Langley, Slough, SL3 8LT, United Kingdom
/(07721) 641708 / (01753) 592176
atimages@tinyworld.co.uk
www.transportpics.com

A1PIX 40 Bowling Green Lane, The Finsbury Business Centre, London, EC1R 0NE, United Kingdom
(020) 7415 7045/ (020) 7415 7111
london@a1pix.com
www.a1pix.com

Abode Interiors Picture Library Ltd Albion Court, 1 Pierce Street, Macclesfield, Cheshire, SK11 6ER, United Kingdom
(01625) 500070/ (01625) 500910
info@abodepix.co.uk
www.abodepix.co.uk

Absolutely Wild Visuals PO Box 48694, London, NW8 1BG,
2076044998
kate@wildvisuals.com.au
www.absolutelywildvisuals.com

Ace Stock Ltd Satellite House, 2 Salisbury Road, London, SW19 4EZ, United Kingdom
(020) 8944 9944
info@acestock.com
www.acestock.com

Action Images Plc Image House, Station Road, London, N17 9LR, United Kingdom
(020) 8885 3000/ (020) 8267 2067
info@actionimages.com
www.actionimages.com

Action Plus Sports Images 54-58 Tanner Street, London, SE1 3PH, United Kingdom
(020) 7403 1558/ (020) 7403 1526
pictures@actionplus.co.uk
www.actionplus.co.uk

Adams Picture Library Studio 1, Canalot Production Studios, London, W10 5BN, United Kingdom
(020) 8964 8007/ 0208 960 8609
mail@adamspicturelibrary.com
www.adamspicturelibrary.com

Adventure Archive Fudge Cottage, Dalditch Lane, Budleigh Salterton, Devon, EX9 7AH, United Kingdom
(01395) 446242/(07711) 787737
leo@adventurearchive.com
www.adventurearchive.com

Agripicture Images 1 Bowdens Lane, Shillingford, Tiverton, Devon, EX16 9DG, United Kingdom
(01398) 331598
info@agripicture.com
www.agripicture.com

Aircraft Picture Services 42 Sunningvale Avenue, Biggin Hill, Kent, TN16 3BX, United Kingdom
(01959) 574872
norman.rivett@virgin.net

Airsport Photo Library Noredelph, Downham Market, Norfolk, PE38 0BG, United Kingdom
(01366) 324346
library@airsport-photo.co.uk
www.airsport-photo.co.uk

akg-images Ltd The Arts and History Picture Library, 5 Melbray Mews, 158 Hurlingham Road, London, SW6 3NS, United Kingdom
(020) 7610 6103/ (020) 7610 6125
enquiries@akg-images.co.uk
www.akg-images.co.uk

Alamy Images 127 Milton Park, Milton, Abingdon, Oxfordshire, OX14 4SA, United Kingdom
(01235) 844600/ (01235) 844650
sales@alamy.com
www.alamy.com

Alan Copson City Pictures 84 Rucklidge Avenue, London, NW10 4PR, United Kingdom
(020) 8961 3480
contact@alancopsonpictures.co.uk
www.alancopsonpictures.com

Allstar & Sportsphoto Ltd 20 Clifton Street, Scarborough, North Yorkshire, YO12 7SR, United Kingdom
(01723) 367264/ (01723) 500117
stewart@sportsphoto.co.uk
www.allstarpl.com

Alpha Ltd 63 Gee Street, London, EC1V 3RS, United Kingdom
(020) 7251 1003/ (020) 7553 4040
alpha.library@alphapress.com
www.alphapress.com

Alpine Club Photo Library 55 Charlotte Road, London, EC2A 3QF, United Kingdom
(020) 7033 0203
photos@alpine-club.org.uk
www.alpine-club.org.uk

Alvey & Towers The Springboard Centre, Mantle Lane, Coalville, Leicestershire, LE67 3DW, United Kingdom
01530 450011/ 01530 450011
office@alveyandtowers.com
www.alveyandtowers.com

Ancient Art & Architecture Collection Ltd Suite 1, 410-420 Rayners Lane, Pinner, Middlesex, HA5 5DY, United Kingdom
(020) 8429 3131/ (020) 8429 4646
library@aaacollection.co.uk
www.aaacollection.com

Ancient Egypt Picture Library 6 Branden Drive, Knutsford, Cheshire, WA16 8EJ, United Kingdom
(01565) 633106/ (01565) 633106
bobegyptpl@aol.com

Andes Press Agency 26 Padbury Court, London, London, E2 7EH, United Kingdom
(020) 7613 5417
apa@andespressagency.com
www.andespressagency.com

Andrew Lawson Photography Noahs Ark, Market Street, Charlbury, Oxfordshire, OX7 3PL, United Kingdom
(01608) 810654/ (01608) 811251
photos@andrewlawson.com
www.andrewlawson.com

Andrew N. Gagg's PHOTO FLORA Town House Two, Fordbank Court, Henwick Road, Worcester, WR2 5PF, United Kingdom
0190-574-8515
info@photoflora.co.uk
www.photoflora.co.uk

Andy Williams Photo Library 3 Levylsdene, Merrow, Guildford, Surrey, GU1 2RS, United Kingdom
(01483) 572778
andy_williams@amserve.net

Angelo Hornak Library 17 Alwyne Villas, London, N1 2HG, United Kingdom
(020) 7354 1790
angelohornak@mac.com
www.angelohornak.co.uk

Anglian Images Harmer's End, Chapel Road, Southrepps, Norwich, NR11 8UW, United Kingdom
(01263) 833753/ (01263) 833753
worrall@supanet.com
www.anglianimages.co.uk

Animal Photography 4 Marylebone Mews, New Cavendish Street, London, W1G 8PY, United Kingdom
(020) 7935 0503
stephen@animal-photography.co.uk
www.animal-photography.co.uk

Ann & Bury Peerless 22 Kings Avenue, Minnis Bay, Birchington, Kent, CT7 9QL, United Kingdom
(01843) 841428/ (01843) 848321
ann@peerlessmail.com

Annabel Ossel 12 Northill Road, Cople, Bedford, MK44 3TU, United Kingdom
(01234) 838415/ (01234) 838415
aossel@aol.com

Anthony Blake Photo Library 20 Blades Court, Deodar Road, London, SW15 2NU, United Kingdom
(020) 8877 1123/ (020) 8877 9787
info@abpl.co.uk
www.abpl.co.uk

Antiquarian Images , Chislehurst, Kent, BR7 5SZ, United Kingdom
(020) 8467 6297/ (020) 8467 6297
enquiries@antiquarianimages.co.uk
www.antiquarianimages.com

Anwar Hussein Royal Picture Library Scotts Mill Farm, Tytherton Lucas, Chippenham, Wiltshire, SN15 3RH, United Kingdom
(01249) 740242/(07836) 709436 / (01249) 740242
anwar@anwarhussein.com
www.anwarhussein.com

Aquarius Library , Hastings, East Sussex, TN34 1HR, United Kingdom
(01424) 721196/ (01424) 717704
aquarius.lib@clara.net
www.aquariuscollection.com

ArabianEye , Dubai, United Arab Emirates
00 971 50 425 9174/ 00 971 4 3455 226
info@arabianeye.com
www.arabianeye.com

Arcaid Picture Library Parc House, 25-37 Cowleaze Road, Kingston upon Thames, Surrey, KT2 6DZ, United Kingdom
(020) 8546 4352/ (020) 8541 5230
arcaid@arcaid.co.uk
www.arcaid.co.uk

Arcblue 93 Gainsborough Road, Richmond, Surrey, TW9 2ET, United Kingdom
(020) 8940 2227/ (020) 8940 6570
info@arcblue.com
www.arcblue.com

Archie Miles Photographer Hill House Farm, Stoke Lacy, Bromyard, Herefordshire, HR7 4RE, United Kingdom
(01432) 820588/07891 513045
archiemiles@btinternet.com
www.archiemiles.co.uk

Archie Miles Photography Hill House Farm, Stoke Lacy, Bromyard, Herefordshire, HR7 4RE, United Kingdom
(01432) 820588/ (01432) 520588
hfdarchiemiles@aol.com
www.archiemiles.co.uk

Architectural Association Photo Library 36 Bedford Square, London, WC1B 3ES, United Kingdom
(020) 7887 4078/ (020) 7414 0782
valerie@aaschool.ac.uk/photolib
www.aaschool.ac.uk

Arctic Camera 66 Ashburnham Grove, Greenwich, London, SE10 8UJ, United Kingdom
(020) 8692 7651/(07798) 606350
derek.fordham@btinternet.com

ARDEA Wildlife Pets Environment 35 Brodrick Road, Wandsworth Common, London, SW17 7DX, United Kingdom
(020) 8672 2067/ (020) 8672 8787
ardea@ardea.com
www.ardea.com

Arena PAL 1st Floor, 55 Southwark Street, London, SE1 1RU, United Kingdom
(020) 7403 8542/ (020) 7403 8561
enquiries@arenapal.com
www.arenapal.com

Aroomwithviews The Barn, Duncastle Farm, Main Road, Alvington, Lydney, Gloucestershire, GL15 6AT, United Kingdom
(01594) 529111/(07836) 216909
steph@molyneuxassociates.com
www.molyneuxassociates.com

www.rspcaphotolibrary.com
Tel: 0300 123 0150
email: pictures@rspcaphotolibrary.com
PETS | WILDLIFE | FARM ANIMALS

Art Directors & Trip 57 Burdon Lane, Cheam, Surrey, SM2 7BY, United Kingdom
(020) 8642 3593/ (020) 8395 7230
images@artdirectors.co.uk
www.arkreligion.com

Art Edit 16 Lake Street, Oxford, OX1 4RN, United Kingdom
(07813) 183482/ (0870) 1694700
pierre@artedit.co.uk
www.artedit.co.uk

Artdesign 52 Salmons Lane, Whyteleafe, Surrey, CR3 0AN, United Kingdom
(020) 8660 3552
vanessajacynth@aol.com
www.artdesign-vjwagstaff.com

Artseens Images The Hub, 123 Star Lane, London, E16 4PZ, United Kingdom
(020) 7055 0005/ (020) 7055 0005
info@artseens.com
www.artseens.com

Aspect Picture Library 40 Rostrevor Road, London, SW6 5AD, United Kingdom
(020) 7736 1998/ (020) 7731 7362
aspect.ldn@btinternet.com
www.aspect-picture-library.co.uk

Associated Press Photo Archive Associated Press House, 12 Norwich Street, London, EC4A 1BP, United Kingdom
(020) 7427 4333/ (020) 7427 4269
london_photolibrary@ap.org
http/apimages.ap.org

Atmosphere Willis Vean, Mullion, Helston, Cornwall, TR12 7DF, United Kingdom
(01326) 240180/ (01326) 240900
pix@atmosphere.co.uk
www.atmosphere.co.uk

Australian Picture Library Flat 2, Auriol Mansions, Edith Road, London, W14 0ST, United Kingdom
(020) 7602 1989/ (020) 7602 1989
equilibrium.films@virgin.net
www.facesandplacespix.com

Auto Express Picture Library 30 Cleveland Street, London, W1T 4JD, United Kingdom
(020) 7907 6132/ (020) 7907 6139
pictures@dennis.co.uk
www.autoexpressimages.co.uk

Aviation Picture Library 30 Wyndham Road, London, W13 9TE, United Kingdom
(07860) 670073
avpix@aol.com
www.aviationpictures.com

Aviation-Images.com 42 Queens Road, Wimbledon, London, SW19 8LR, United Kingdom
(020) 8944 5225/(07764) 194388 (020) 8944 5335
library@aviation-images.com
www.aviation-images.com

Axel Poignant Archive 115 Bedford Court Mansions, Bedford Avenue, London, WC1B 3AG, United Kingdom
(020) 7636 2555/ (020) 7636 2555
rpoignant@aol.com

B F I Stills, Posters & Designs 21 Stephen Street, London, W1T 1LN, United Kingdom
(020) 7957 4797/ (020) 7323 9260
stills.films@bfi.org.uk
www.bfi.org.uk

B M Totterdell Photography (Volleyball) Constable Cottage, Burlings Lane, Knockholt, Sevenoaks, Kent, TN14 7PE, United Kingdom
(01959) 532001/ (01959) 532001
btrial@btinternet.com
www.whatvolleyball.co.uk

BAA Aviation Photo Library Green Dragon Vaults, Parliament Square, Hertford, SG14 1PT, United Kingdom
(01992) 501134/ (01992) 501174
sales@in-press.co.uk
www.baa.com/photolibrary

Bandphoto Agency 29-31 Saffron Hill, London, EC1N 8SW, United Kingdom
(020) 7421 6000/ (020) 7421 6006
charles@uppa.co.uk
www.uppa.co.uk

Barnardos Film & Photographic Archive Tanners Lane, Barkingside, Ilford, Essex, IG6 1QG, United Kingdom
(020) 8498 7345/ (020) 8498 7090
stephen.pover@barnardos.org.uk
www.barnardos.org.uk

Barrie Watts Photographer Gelli Studio, Crafnant Road, Trefriw, Conwy, LL27 0JZ, United Kingdom
(01492) 642264
barrie@barriewatts.co.uk
www.barriewatts.co.uk

Barry Pickthall Bookers Yard, The Street, Walberton, Arundel, West Sussex, BN18 0PF, United Kingdom
(01243) 555561/(07768) 395719 (01243) 555562
ppl@mistral.com
www.pplmedia.com

BBC Photo Library B116, BBC Television Centre, Wood Lane, London, W12 7RJ, United Kingdom
(020) 8225 7193/ (020) 8576 7020
research-central@bbc.co.uk

BDI Images Ltd 56 Five Ash Down, Uckfield, East Sussex, TN22 3AL, United Kingdom
(01825) 732006/ (01825) 732009
info@bdi-images.com
www.bdi-images.com

Beachfeature.com Hobart House, 41 Trebarwith Crescent, Newquay, Cornwall, TR7 1DX, United Kingdom
(01637) 870 430
info@beachfeature.com
www.beachfeature.com

Beckham Books Ltd Chilton Mount, Newton Road, Sudbury, Suffolk, CO10 2RS, United Kingdom
(01787) 373683/ (01787) 375441
beckhambooks1@btconnect.com
www.beckhambooks.com

Beken Ltd 16 Birmingham Road, Cowes, Isle of Wight, PO31 7BH, United Kingdom
(01983) 297311/ (01983) 291059
beken@beken.co.uk
www.beken.co.uk

Bert Neale Collection/Popperfoto.com The Old Mill, Overstone Farm, Northampton, NN6 0AB, United Kingdom
(01604) 670670/ (01604) 670635
ian.blackwell@popperfoto.com
www.popperfoto.com

Big Pictures 50-54 Clerkenwell Road, London, EC1M 5PS, United Kingdom
(020) 7250 3555/ (020) 7250 0033
info@bigpictures.co.uk
www.bigpicturesphoto.com

Bigg World Photography 114b Chiswick High Road, London, W4 1PU, United Kingdom
(020) 8995 3129
philipjbigg@biggworldphotography.com
www.biggworldphotography.com

Billie Love Historical Collection Reflections, 3 Winton Street, Ryde, Isle of Wight, PO33 2BX, United Kingdom
(01983) 812572/ (01983) 616565
info@billielovehistoricalcollection.co.uk
www.billielovehistoricalcollection.co.uk

Birmingham Central Library Chamberlain Square, Birmingham, B3 3HQ, United Kingdom
0121-303 4439
pete.james@birmingham.gov.uk
www.birmingham.gov.uk/libraries

Birmingham Museums and Art Gallery Picture Library Chamberlain Square, Birmingham, B3 3DH, United Kingdom
0121-303 3155/ 0121-303 1394
picture_library@birmingham.gov.uk
www.bmag.org.uk

Birmingham Picture Library 14 St Bernard Road, Solihull, West Midlands, B92 7BB, United Kingdom
0121-765 4114/(07973) 379050 0121-765 4224
office@bplphoto.co.uk
www.bplphoto.co.uk

Blayz Images , London, United Kingdom
(07768) 797 553
post@blayz.co.uk
www.blayz.co.uk

Blue Green Picture 11 Bath Road, Cowes, Isle of Wight, PO31 7QN, United Kingdom
(01983) 282233/ (01983) 282244
info@bluegreenpictures.com
www.bluegreenpictures.com

Boating Images Foxes Studio, Foxes, Ramsden Heath, Billericay, Essex, CM11 1HR, United Kingdom
(01268) 710454
info@boating-images.com
www.boating-images.com

Bob Thomas Sports Photography/Popperfoto.com The Old Mill, Overstone Farm, Northampton, NN6 0AB, United Kingdom
(01604) 670670/ (01604) 670635
ian.blackwell@popperfoto.com
www.popperfoto.com

Bodleian Library University of Oxford, Broad Street, Oxford, OX1 3BG, United Kingdom
(01865) 277626/ (01865) 287127
repro@bodley.ox.ac.uk
www.bodley.ox.ac.uk/imaging

Bold Endeavours Ltd 7 Manor Park, Staines, Middlesex, TW18 4XE,
☎ 01784 460 064
✉ derek@boldendeavours.com
💻 www.big-easy-footage-library-software.co.uk

Bookart Architecture Picture Library 1 Woodcock Lodge, Epping Green, Hertford, SG13 8ND, United Kingdom
☎ (01707) 875253/(07710) 207404 📠 (01707) 875286
✉ mail@sharparchitects.co.uk
💻 www.sharparchitects.co.uk

Bridgeman Art Library (FOCAL) BAPLA 17-19 Garway Road, London, W2 4PH, United Kingdom
☎ **(020) 7727 4065/** 📠 **(020) 7792 8509**
✉ **london@bridgeman.co.uk**
💻 **www.bridgemanart.com**
See ad

Britain on View, Visit Britain Thames Tower, Blacks Road, London, W6 9EL, United Kingdom
☎ (020) 8563 3120/ 📠 (020) 8563 3130
✉ britainonview@visitbritain.org
💻 www.britainonview.com

British Antarctic Survey High Cross, Madingley Road, Cambridge, CB3 0ET, United Kingdom
☎ (01223) 221400/ 📠 (01223) 362616
✉ information@bas.ac.uk
💻 www.antarctica.ac.uk

British Assoc of Picture Libraries & Agencies 18 Vine Hill, London, EC1R 5DZ, United Kingdom
☎ (020) 7713 1780/ 📠 (020) 7713 1211
✉ enquiries@bapla.org.uk
💻 www.bapla.org

British Library - Picture Library/ Images Online British Library, 96 Euston Road, London, NW1 2DB, United Kingdom
☎ (020) 7412 7614/ 📠 (020) 7412 7771
✉ imagesonline@bl.uk
💻 www.bl.uk/imagesonline

British Motor Industry Heritage Trust Heritage Motor Centre, Banbury Road, Gaydon, Warwick, CV35 0BJ, United Kingdom
☎ (01926) 645073/ 📠 (01926) 641555
✉ bmiht@tiscali.co.uk
💻 www.heritage.org.uk

British Museum Photography and Imaging Great Russell Street, London, WC1B 3DG, United Kingdom
☎ (020) 7323 8231/ 📠 (020) 7323 8630
✉ photography@thebritishmuseum.ac.uk
💻 www.thebritishmuseum.ac.uk/compass

Broad Daylight Ltd 18a Albany Street, Edinburgh, EH1 3QB, United Kingdom
☎ 0131-477 9571
✉ info@broaddaylightltd.co.uk
💻 www.broaddaylightltd.co.uk

Brooklands Museum The Clubhouse, Brooklands Road, Weybridge, Surrey, KT13 0QN, United Kingdom
☎ (01932) 857381/ 📠 (01932) 855465
✉ info@brooklandsmuseum.com
💻 www.brooklandsmuseum.com

Bruce Coleman Ltd Chalfont House, Hampden Road, Chalfont St. Peter, Gerrards Cross, Buckinghamshire, SL9 9RY, United Kingdom
☎ (0870) 4204186/ 📠 (0870) 4204187
✉ library@brucecoleman.co.uk
💻 www.brucecoleman.co.uk

Brunswick Films Ltd 26 Macroom Road, London, W9 3HY, United Kingdom
☎ (020) 8960 0066/ 📠 (020) 8960 4997
✉ info@brunswickfilms.com
💻 www.brunswickfilms.com

Bryan & Cherry Alexander Arctic Photo Photography Higher Cottage, Manston, Sturminster Newton, Dorset, DT10 1EZ, United Kingdom
☎ (01258) 473006/ 📠 (01258) 473333
✉ alexander@arcticphoto.co.uk
💻 www.arcticphoto.com

Bryn Colton/Popperfoto.com The Old Mill, Overstone Farm, Northampton, NN6 0AB, United Kingdom
☎ (01604) 670670/ 📠 (01604) 670635
✉ ian.blackwell@popperfoto.com
💻 www.popperfoto.com

Bubbles Photo Library 3 Rose Lane, Ipswich, IP1 1XE, United Kingdom
☎ (01473) 288 605/ 📠 (01473) 288 247
✉ info@bubblesphotolibrary.co.uk
💻 www.bubblesphotolibrary.co.uk

Built Vision 49 Lucknow Drive, Nottingham, NG3 5EU, United Kingdom
☎ 0115-962 1112/ 📠 0115-962 1112
✉ office@builtvision.co.uk
💻 www.builtvision.co.uk

Burall Floraprint Ltd Oldfield Lane, Wisbech, Cambridgeshire, PE13 2TH, United Kingdom
☎ (0870) 7287222/ 📠 (0870) 7287277
✉ floraprint@burall.com
💻 www.bflora.com

Cache Lower Ground Studio, 12 St. John's Road, Tunbridge Wells, Kent, TN4 9NP, United Kingdom
☎ (01892) 539816/(07710) 352189 📠 (01892) 512903
✉ chris@cache-photofinder.com
💻 www.cache-photofinder.com

Cadmium Systems Ltd Church House, Castle Frome, Ledbury, Herefordshire, HR8 1HQ, United Kingdom
☎ (0800) 436867/ 📠 (01531) 641101
✉ sales@cadmium.co.uk
💻 www.cadmium.co.uk

Camera Press 21 Queen Elizabeth Street, London, SE1 2PD, United Kingdom
☎ (020) 7378 1300/ 📠 (020) 7278 5126
✉ info@camerapress.com
💻 www.camerapress.com

Capital Pictures 85 Randolph Avenue, London, W9 1DL, United Kingdom
☎ (020) 7286 2212
✉ sales@capitalpictures.com
💻 www.capitalpictures.com

Car Photo Library 28 Fernside Road, Talbot Park, Bournemouth, BH9 2LB, United Kingdom
☎ **(01202) 528849/(07785) 537928**
✉ **davidkimber@carphoto.co.uk**
💻 **www.carphoto.co.uk**
See ad in showcase

Next time your campaign needs a tweak...

Classic images with a contemporary twist – culture • fine art • history

THE BRIDGEMAN ART LIBRARY
www.bridgemanart.com

Cartoonstock Unit 2, Lansdowne Mews, Bath, BA1 5DY, United Kingdom
✆ (01225) 789600/ 🖷 (01225) 789642
✉ admin@cartoonstock.com
🖥 www.cartoonstock.com

Celebrity Pictures 98 De Beauvoir Road, London, London, N1 4EN, United Kingdom
✆ (020) 7275 2700/ 🖷 (020) 7275 2701
✉ info@celebritypictures.co.uk
🖥 www.celebritypictures.co.uk

Central Images Picture Library 10 Stoneleigh Road, Solihull, West Midlands, B91 1DG, United Kingdom
✆ 0121-711 2626
✉ images@cipl.co.uk
🖥 www.cipl.co.uk

Cephas Picture Library Unit A1, Kingsway Business Park, Oldfield Road, Hampton, Middlesex, TW12 2HD, United Kingdom
✆ (020) 8979 8647/ 🖷 (020) 8224 8095
✉ pictures@cephas.co.uk
🖥 www.cephas.com

Channel Island Pictures 6 La Chasse Brunet, St. Saviour, Jersey, JE2 7YE, United Kingdom
✆ (01534) 858751/(07797) 739426
✉ mail@cipictures.com
🖥 www.cipictures.com

Charles Tait Photographic Ltd Kelton, St. Ola, Kirkwall, Orkney, KW15 1TR, United Kingdom
✆ (01856) 873738/(07785) 220269 / 🖷 (01856) 875313
✉ charles.tait@zetnet.co.uk
🖥 www.charles-tait.co.uk

Chris Bonington Picture Library Badger Hill, Nether Row, Hesket Newmarket, Wigton, Cumbria, CA7 8LA, United Kingdom
✆ (01697) 478286/ 🖷 (01697) 478238
✉ frances@bonington.com
🖥 www.bonington.com

Chris Close , London, N4 4RR, United Kingdom
✆ (020) 8341 9880/(07740) 870579 / 🖷 (020) 8341 9880
✉ cc@chrisclose.co.uk
🖥 www.chrisclose.co.uk

Chris Close Photography 21 Kirkhill Road, Edinburgh, EH16 5DE, United Kingdom
✆ 0131-662 9999/(07740) 870579 / 🖷 0131-662 9999
✉ cc@chrisclose.co.uk
🖥 www.chrisclose.co.uk

Christie's Images 1 Langley Lane, Vauxhall, London, SW8 1TJ, United Kingdom
✆ (020) 7582 1282/ 🖷 (020) 7582 5632
✉ imageslondon@christies.com
🖥 www.christiesimages.com

Christine Hanscomb/The Producers 11 Perseverance Works, 38 Kingsland Road, London, E2 8DD, United Kingdom
✆ (020) 7739 0132/(07050) 039992 / 🖷 (020) 7729 7066
✉ mail@christinehanscomb.co.uk
🖥 www.christinehanscomb.co.uk

Christopher Hill Photographic Library 17 Clarence Street, Belfast, BT2 8DY, United Kingdom
✆ (028) 9024 5038/(07836) 361916 / 🖷 (028) 9023 1942
✉ chrishillphotographic@btclick.com
🖥 www.scenicireland.com

Christopher Moore Studio Unit 2, Butler House, 51 Curtain Road, London, EC2A 3PT, United Kingdom
✆ (020) 7012 1133/ 🖷 (020) 7012 1144
✉ catwalk@chrismoore.co.uk
🖥 www.catwalking.com

CIRCA RELIGION Photo Library 39 Beech Grove, Sale, Cheshire, M33 6RT, United Kingdom
✆ 0161-969 2483
✉ info@circalibrary.com
🖥 www.circalibrary.com

Clive Johnson 3 Norman House, Hardwick Mount, Buxton, Derbyshire, SK17 6PP, United Kingdom
✆ (01298) 25405/(07950) 760962 / 🖷 (01298) 25405
✉ clive@clive-johnson.com
🖥 www.clive-johnson.com

Clive Nichols Garden Pictures Rickyard Barn, Castle Farm, Chacombe, Banbury, Oxfordshire, OX17 2EN, United Kingdom
✆ (01295) 712288/ 🖷 (01295) 713672
✉ enquiries@clivenichols.com
🖥 www.clivenichols.com

Colin Bell Photography Unit E, Purdon Street, Glasgow, G11 6AF, United Kingdom
✆ 0141-334 8008/(07787) 573155 / 🖷 0141-334 8008
✉ colin@colinbellphotography.com
🖥 www.colinbellphotography.com

Colin Varndell The Happy Return, Whitecross, Bridport, Dorset, DT6 5NH, United Kingdom
✆ (01308) 488341/(07779) 941844
✉ colin_varndell@hotmail.com

Collections 13 Woodberry Crescent, London, N10 1PJ, United Kingdom
✆ (020) 8883 0083/ 🖷 (020) 8883 9215
✉ collections@btinternet.com
🖥 www.collectionspicturelibrary.co.uk

Colorsport Colorsport, The Old Tool Mill, Ruper Road, Capel, Capel, Surrey, RH5 5HF, United Kingdom
✆ (01306) 712233/ 🖷 (01306) 712260
✉ info@colorsport.co.uk
🖥 www.colorsport.co.uk

Construction Photography 2 Whitacre Mews, 26-34 Stannary Street, London, SE11 4AB, United Kingdom
✆ (020) 7820 6200/(07946) 705650
✉ lucy@constructionphotography.com
🖥 www.constructionphotography.com

Corbis Images UK Ltd 111 Salusbury Road, London, NW6 6RG, United Kingdom
✆ (020) 7644 7644/ 🖷 (020) 7644 7646
✉ ukcs@corbis.com
🖥 www.corbis.com

Cornish Picture Library Trelawney Lodge, Keveral Lane, Seaton, Torpoint, Cornwall, PL11 3JJ, United Kingdom
✆ (01503) 250673/ 🖷 (01503) 250383
✉ info@imageclick.co.uk
🖥 www.imageclick.co.uk

Country Life Picture Library Country Life Picture Library, The Blue Fin Building IPC Media, London, SE1 9LS, United Kingdom
✆ (020) 3148 4474
✉ camilla_costello@ipcmedia.com
🖥 www.countrylifelibrary.co.uk

Creative Image Library , Weald, Sevenoaks, Kent, TN14 6ZN, United Kingdom
✆ (01892) 723388/ 🖷 (01892) 723388
✉ sales@creativeimagelibrary.com
🖥 www.creativeimagelibrary.com

Culture Archive 193 Ditchling Road, Brighton, BN1 6JB, United Kingdom
✆ (01273) 552929/ 🖷 (01273) 885969
✉ info@culturearchive.demon.co.uk
🖥 www.culturearchive.demon.co.uk

Customimages.co.uk 12 Mill Brow, Armathwaite, Carlisle, CA4 9PJ, United Kingdom
✆ (01697) 472522/ 🖷 (01697) 472522
✉ info@customimages.co.uk
🖥 www.customimages.co.uk

Dance Picture Library & Circus Images 4 Ongar Place, Addlestone, Surrey, KT15 1JF, United Kingdom
✆ (07956) 319362/ 🖷 (01932) 848829
✉ linda-rich@dancepicturelibrary.com
🖥 www.dancepicturelibrary.com

Dat's Jazz 38 Kings Way, Harrow, Middlesex, HA1 1XU, United Kingdom
✆ (020) 8427 7384/ 🖷 (0870) 4581698
✉ datsjazz@macunlimited.net
🖥 www.datsjazz.co.uk

David Burton Photography/ Picture Library 23 Old Grove Court, Norwich, NR3 3NL, United Kingdom
✆ (01603) 411222/(07774) 843573 / 🖷 (01603) 411234
✉ sales@dbphoto.com
🖥 www.dbphoto.com

David Hoffman Photo Library c/o BAPLA, 18 Vine Hill, London, EC1R 5DZ, United Kingdom
✆ (020) 8981 5041
✉ libch@hoffmanphotos.com
🖥 www.hoffmanphotos.com

David Horwell 79 Maltings Place, 169 Tower Bridge Road, London, SE1 3LJ, United Kingdom
✆ (020) 7407 1478/ 🖷 (020) 7407 0397
✉ david@selectlatinamerica.co.uk
🖥 www.selectlatinamerica.co.uk

David King Collection 90 St. Pauls Road, London, N1 2QP, United Kingdom
✆ (020) 7226 0149/ 🖷 (020) 7354 8264
✉ davidkingcollection@btopenworld.com
🖥 www.davidkingcollection.com

David M. Grossman 211 E 7th Street, Brooklyn, 11218, United States of America
✆ 00 1 718 438 5021/ 🖷 00 1 718 438 5060
✉ david@grossmanphotos.com
🖥 www.grossmanphotos.com

David Noble Photolibrary Longleigh, 28 Coolinge Lane, Folkestone, Kent, CT20 3QT, United Kingdom
✆ (01303) 254263/ 🖷 (01303) 254263
✉ djn@noblepics.co.uk
🖥 www.noblepics.co.uk

David Noton Photography Clark House, Higher Kingsbury, Sherborne, Dorset, DT9 5EB, United Kingdom
✆ (01963) 250061/(07968) 850960
✉ info@davidnoton.com
🖥 www.davidnoton.com

David Williams Picture Library 50 Burlington Avenue, Glasgow, G12 0LH, United Kingdom
✆ 0141-339 7823/ 🖷 0141-337 3031
✉ david@scotland-guide.co.uk

Daydream Linton House, 164-180 Union Street, London, SE1 0LH,
✆ +44 (0) 20 7096 1471/+44 (0) 20 7117 1636
✉ ralph@daydream.co.uk
🖥 www.daydream.co.uk

Dee Conway Ballet & Dance Picture Library 110 Sussex Way, London, N7 6RR, United Kingdom
✆ (020) 7272 7845
✉ library@ddance.co.uk
🖥 www.ddance.co.uk

Defence Picture Library 14 Mary Seacole Road, Plymouth, PL1 3GY, United Kingdom
✆ (01752) 312061/ 🖷 (01752) 312063
✉ dpl@defencepictures.com
🖥 www.defencepictures.com

Demon Imaging 8C Raleigh Gardens, London, SW2 1 AD, United Kingdom
✆ (020) 8674 9548
✉ info@demonagency.com
🖥 www.demonagency.com

Derek St. Romaine Photography 239a Hook Road, Chessington, Surrey, KT9 1EQ, United Kingdom
✆ (020) 8397 3761/ 🖷 (020) 8397 3960
✉ derek@gardenphotolibrary.com
🖥 www.gardenphotolibrary.com

Diana Korchien 61 Forest Drive East, Leytonstone, London, E11 1JX, United Kingdom
✆ (020) 8539 8547/(07747) 014235
✉ diana@flipsidevision.com
🖥 www.flipsidevision.com

Digital Vision India House, 45 Curlew Street, London, SE1 2ND, United Kingdom
✆ (020) 7378 5555/ 🖷 (020) 7378 5533
✉ uk.sales@digitalvision.com
🖥 www.digitalvision.com

DK images 80 The Strand, London, WC2R 0RL, United Kingdom
✆ (020) 7010 4523/ 🖷 (020) 7010 6685
✉ philipahern@dkimages.com
🖥 www.dkimages.com

Dobson Agency.co.uk 20 Seafield Avenue, Osgodby, Scarborough, North Yorkshire, YO11 3QG, United Kingdom
✆ (01723) 585141/ 🖷 (0871) 433 8973
✉ pix@dobsonagency.co.uk
🖥 www.dobsonagency.co.uk

Dominic Photography 4B Moore Park Road, London, SW6 2JT, United Kingdom
✆ (020) 7381 0007/ 🖷 (020) 7381 0008
✉ office@catherineashmore.co.uk

Donaghue Photography 280A Cowley Road, Oxford, OX4 1UR, United Kingdom
✆ (01865) 251996/ 🖷 (01865) 251767
✉ chris@oxford-photo-library.co.uk
🖥 www.oxford-photo-library.co.uk

Double Red Photographic The Old School, Thorn Lane, Goxhill, Barrow-upon-Humber, North Lincolnshire, DN19 7JE, United Kingdom
✆ (01469) 531416/ 🖷 (01469) 531888
✉ s.ward@doublered.co.uk
🖥 www.doublered.co.uk

Downtown Darkroom Ltd Little Britain House, 12 Valentine Place, London, SE1 8QH, United Kingdom
✆ (020) 7620 0911
✉ darkroom@silverprint.co.uk

Dragon News & Picture Agency 21 Walter Road, Swansea, SA1 5NQ, United Kingdom
✆ (01792) 464800/(07810) 773929 / 🖷 (01792) 475264
✉ mail@dragon-pictures.com
🖥 www.dragon-pictures.com

Duncan Caratacus Clark 43a Gunter Grove, London, SW10 0UN, United Kingdom
☎ (020) 7376 5843/ ✆ (020) 7751 5845
✉ duncan@fotografique.com
⌨ www.fotografique.com

E M A P Gardening Picture Library Bretton Court, Peterborough, PE3 8DZ, United Kingdom
☎ (01733) 264666/ ✆ (01733) 282695
✉ jane.cutteridge@emap.com

E W A Stock 70 Mornington Street, London, NW1 7QE, United Kingdom
☎ (020) 7388 2828
✉ info@ewastock.com
⌨ www.ewastock.com

Ecclesiastical & Eccentricities Beggars Roost, Woolpack Hill, Ashford, Kent, TN25 6RR, United Kingdom
☎ (01303) 812 608/ ✆ (01303) 812 608
✉ info@picture-library.freeserve.co.uk
⌨ www.eeimages.co.uk

Edifice Cutterne Mill, Evercreech, Shepton Mallet, Somerset, BA4 6LY, United Kingdom
☎ (01749) 831400
✉ info@edificephoto.com
⌨ www.edificephoto.com

Edmund Nagele F.R.P.S. Parkgate, West Approach Drive, Cheltenham, Gloucestershire, GL52 3AD, United Kingdom
☎ (01242) 242952/ ✆ (01242) 575358
✉ look@nagelestock.com
⌨ www.nagelestock.com

Education Photos 8 Whitemore Road, Guildford, Surrey, GU1 1QT, United Kingdom
☎ (01483) 511 666
✉ johnwalmsley@educationphotos.co.uk
⌨ www.educationphotos.co.uk

Elizabeth Whiting & Associates 70 Mornington Street, Camden Town, London, NW1 7QE, United Kingdom
☎ (020) 7388 2828
✉ ewa@elizabethwhiting.com
⌨ www.ewastock.com

Emap Esprit Greater London House, Hampstead Road, London, NW1 7EJ, United Kingdom
☎ (020) 7347 1847/ ✆ (020) 7347 1852
⌨ www.emap.com

Emma Greig 6 Eastern Terrace Mews, Brighton, BN2 1EP, United Kingdom
☎ (07976) 607255
✉ info@tigerfoot.net
⌨ www.tigerfoot.net

Emma Wood 24 St. Lawrence Terrace, London, W10 5SX, United Kingdom
☎ (020) 8960 1977/(07918) 112048

EMPICS Sports Photo Agency Pavilion House, 16 Castle Boulevard, Nottingham, NG7 1FL, United Kingdom
☎ 0115-844 7447/ ✆ 0115-844 7448
✉ info@empics.com
⌨ www.empics.com

Emric Images 64 Union Street, Barnet, Hertfordshire, EN5 4HZ, United Kingdom
☎ (020) 8364 9506
⌨ www.emric-images.com

Encore Images Ltd Surrey House, 31 Church Street, Leatherhead, Surrey, KT22 8EF, United Kingdom
☎ (020) 7580 4717/ ✆ (020) 7580 7017
✉ sales@en-core.net
⌨ www.en-core.net

English Heritage 23 Saville Row, London, W1S 2ET, United Kingdom
☎ (020) 7973 3000/ ✆ (020) 7973 3001
✉ customer@english-heritage.org.uk
⌨ www.english-heritage.org.uk

Epcot Images 5 Charles Street, Epping, Essex, CM16 7AU, United Kingdom
☎ (01992) 574291/(07710) 783271
✉ jprice@epcotimages.com
⌨ www.epcotimages.com

ePicsScotland.com Unit 5 Hathaway Business Centre, 21/29 Hathaway Street, Glasgow, G20 8TD, United Kingdom
☎ 0141-945 0000
✉ info@epicscotland.com
⌨ www.epicscotland.com

Eric Crichton Longthorns, Blandford Forum, Dorset, DT11 0HT, United Kingdom
☎ (01258) 837990/ ✆ (01258) 837996
✉ eric@ecrichton.fsnet.co.uk

Eric Hepworth Golf Course Picture Library 72 Apley Road, Hyde Park, Doncaster, South Yorkshire, DN1 2AY, United Kingdom
☎ (01302) 322674/(07887) 594850 ✆ (01302) 343610
✉ eric@hepworthgolfphotography.com
⌨ www.hepworthgolfphotography.com

Eric Whitehead Photography 10 Brow Close, Windermere, Cumbria, LA23 2HA, United Kingdom
☎ (01539) 448894/(07768) 808249 ✆ (01539) 448294
✉ snooker@snookerimages.co.uk
⌨ www.snookerimages.co.uk

Everynight Images Top Floor Studio, 127 Strathleven Road, London, SW2 5JS, United Kingdom
☎ (020) 7738 7297/ ✆ (020) 7738 7297
✉ info@everynight.co.uk
⌨ www.everynight.co.uk

Exclusive News Agency/Popperfoto.com The Old Mill, Overstone Farm, Northampton, NN6 0AB, United Kingdom
☎ (01604) 670670/ ✆ (01604) 670635
✉ ian.blackwell@popperfoto.com
⌨ www.popperfoto.com

Exile Images 1 Mill Row, West Hill Road, Brighton, BN1 3SU, United Kingdom
☎ (01273) 208741
✉ pics@exileimages.co.uk
⌨ www.exileimages.co.uk

Express Newspapers Syndication Ludgate House, 245 Blackfriars Road, London, SE1 9UX, United Kingdom
☎ (020) 7922 7884/ ✆ (020) 7922 7871
✉ adam.williams@express.co.uk
⌨ www.expresspictures.com

Eye Ubiquitous 65 Brighton Road, Shoreham-by-Sea, West Sussex, BN43 6RE, United Kingdom
☎ (01273) 440113/ ✆ (01273) 440116
✉ library@eyeubiquitous.com
⌨ www.eyeubiquitous.com

F L P A Images of Nature Pages Green House, Wetheringsett, Stowmarket, Suffolk, IP14 5QA, United Kingdom
☎ (01728) 860789/ ✆ (01728) 860222
✉ pictures@flpa-images.co.uk
⌨ www.flpa-images.co.uk

F.V. Blackburn Countryside Images 15 Dolley's Hill, Normandy, Guildford, Surrey, GU3 2AJ, United Kingdom
☎ (01483) 811569
✉ frank.blackburn@btinternet.com

Faces & Places Pix Flat 2, Auriol Mansions, Edith Road, London, W14 0ST, United Kingdom
☎ (020) 7602 1989/(07930) 622964 ✆ (020) 7602 1989
✉ john@facesandplacespix.com
⌨ www.facesandplacespix.com

Faces from the Past 60A Priory Road, London, N8 7EX, United Kingdom
☎ (020) 8341 6999/ ✆ (020) 8341 6996
✉ michael.nicholson@onetel.net

FAMOUS Pictures & Features Agency 13 Harwood Road, London, SW6 4QP, United Kingdom
☎ (020) 7731 9333/ ✆ (020) 7731 9330
✉ info@famous.uk.com
⌨ www.famous.uk.com

Feature Press International 38 Rosedene Avenue, London, SW16 2LT, United Kingdom
☎ (020) 8769 4040/(07774) 151432 ✆ (020) 8769 4040
✉ richardgillard@atlas.co.uk

Felix Rosenstiel's Widow & Son Ltd 33-35 Markham Street, Chelsea Green, London, SW3 3NR, United Kingdom
☎ (020) 7352 3551/ ✆ (020) 7351 5300
✉ sales@felixr.com
⌨ www.felixr.com

Ffotograff 10 Kyveilog Street, Cardiff, CF11 9JA, United Kingdom
☎ (029) 2023 6879
✉ ffotograff@easynet.co.uk
⌨ www.ffotograff.com

Financial Times Picture Library 1 Southwark Bridge, London, SE1 9HL, United Kingdom
☎ (020) 7873 3671/ ✆ (020) 7873 4606
✉ photosynd@ft.com
⌨ www.ft.com

Fine Art Photographic Library Rawlings House, 2A Milner Street, London, SW3 2PU, United Kingdom
☎ (020) 7589 3127/ ✆ (020) 7584 1944
✉ mail@fineartphotolibrary.com
⌨ www.fineartphotolibrary.com

FirePix International 68 Arkles Lane, Anfield, Liverpool, L4 2SP, United Kingdom
☎ 0151-260 0111/(07775) 930419
✉ info@firepix.co.uk
⌨ www.firepix.com

Flight Collection Quadrant House, The Quadrant, Sutton, Surrey, SM2 5AS, United Kingdom
☎ (020) 8652 8888/ ✆ (020) 8652 8933
✉ qpl@rbi.co.uk
⌨ www.theflightcollection.com

Floragraphics 7 The Old School, 30 Church Lane, London, SW19 3HQ, United Kingdom
☎ (020) 8540 8910/ ✆ (020) 8540 8910

Flowerphotos Picture Library 71 Leonard Street, London, London, EC2A 4QU, United Kingdom
☎ (020) 7684 5668/ ✆ (020) 7729 7909
✉ sales@flowerphotos.com
⌨ www.flowerphotos.com

Food Features Stream House, West Flexford Lane, Wanborough, Guildford, Surrey, GU3 2JW, United Kingdom
☎ (01483) 810840/ ✆ (01483) 811587
✉ frontdesk@foodpix.co.uk
⌨ www.foodpix.co.uk

foodanddrinkphotos.ltd Studio 4, Sun Studios, 30 Warple Way, London, W3 0RX, United Kingdom
☎ **(020) 8740 6610**/ ✆ **(020) 8762 9994**
✉ **info@foodanddrinkphotos.com**
⌨ **www.foodanddrinkphotos.com**
See ad in showcase

Forest Life Picture Library Forestry Commission, 231 Corstorphine Road, Edinburgh, EH12 7AT, United Kingdom
☎ 0131-314 6411
✉ neill.campbell@forestry.gsi.gov.uk
⌨ www.forestry.gov.uk/pictures

Formula One Pictures Buzavirag U.6, Pomaz, 2013, Hungary, Republic of
☎ 00 36 2 632 2826/00 36 70 776 9682
✉ jt@f1pictures.com
⌨ www.f1pictures.com

Fortean Picture Library Henblas, Mwrog Street, Ruthin, Clwyd, LL15 1LG, United Kingdom
☎ (01824) 707278/ ✆ (01824) 705324
✉ janet.bord@forteanpix.demon.co.uk
⌨ www.forteanpix.demon.co.uk

fotoLibra 22 Mount View Road, London, N4 4HX, United Kingdom
☎ (020) 8348 1234
✉ professionals@fotolibra.com
⌨ www.fotolibra.com

Fotomas Index 12 Pickhurst Rise, West Wickham, Kent, BR4 0AL, United Kingdom
☎ (020) 8776 2772/ ✆ (020) 8776 2236
✉ fotomasindex@btconnect.com

Frances Topp 29 St. Leonards Court, St. Leonards Road, London, SW14 7NG, United Kingdom
☎ (020) 8876 8315/(07956) 370369 ✆ (020) 8487 9948
✉ ftpictures@blueyonder.co.uk

Francis Frith Collection Frith Barn, Teffont, Salisbury, SP3 5QP, United Kingdom
☎ (01722) 716376/ ✆ (01722) 716881
✉ sales@francisfrith.co.uk
⌨ www.francisfrith.com

Freelance Focus 39 Scottsgarth Close, Tickton, Beverley, East Yorkshire, HU17 9RQ, United Kingdom
☎ (01964) 501729/ ✆ (01964) 501729
✉ freelancefocus@hull24.com

French Picture Library 26A Denbigh Place, London, SW1V 2HA, United Kingdom
☎ (020) 7834 3007
✉ barrie@frenchpix.com
⌨ www.frenchpix.com

Galaxy Picture Library 34 Fennels Way, Flackwell Heath, High Wycombe, Buckinghamshire, HP10 9BY, United Kingdom
☎ (01628) 521338/(07941) 110968 ✆ (01628) 520132
✉ robin@galaxypix.com
⌨ www.galaxypix.com

Garden and Wildlife Matters Photo Library
Marlham, Watermill Lane, Battle, East Sussex, TN33
9BN, United Kingdom
✆ (01424) 830566/ (01424) 830224
✉ gardens@gmpix.com
🖳 www.gardenmatters.uk.com

Garden Exposures Photo Library 316 Kew Road, Kew
Gardens, Richmond, Surrey, TW9 3DU, United Kingdom
✆ (020) 8287 0600/ (020) 8287 0606
✉ pictures@gardenexposures.co.uk
🖳 www.gardenexposures.co.uk

Garden Photo Library 239a Hook Road, Chessington,
Surrey, KT9 1EQ, United Kingdom
✆ (020) 8397 3761/ (020) 8397 3960
✉ derek@gardenphotolibrary.com
🖳 www.gardenphotolibrary.com

Garden Picture Library Unit 12 Ransome's Dock, 35
Parkgate Road, London, SW11 4NP, United Kingdom
✆ (020) 7228 4332/ (020) 7924 3267
✉ info@gardenpicture.com
🖳 www.gardenpicture.com

Garden World Images Grange Studio, Woodham Road,
Wickford, Essex, SS11 7QU, United Kingdom
✆ (01245) 325725/ (01245) 429198
✉ info@gardenworldimages.com
🖳 www.gardenworldimages.com

gather:no:moss Foxes Studio, Heath Road, Ramsden
Heath, Billericay, Essex, CM11 1HR, United Kingdom
✆ (01268) 711620/ (01268) 710353
✉ info@abstractimages.co.uk
🖳 www.abstractimages.co.uk

Genius Loci 15 Primrose Close, Goldsithney, Penzance,
Cornwall, TR20 9JL, United Kingdom
✆ (01736) 719342
✉ sue.aston@geniusloci.co.uk
🖳 www.geniusloci.co.uk

GeoScience Features 6 Orchard Drive, Wye, Ashford,
Kent, TN25 5AU, United Kingdom
✆ (01233) 812707
🖳 www.geoscience.uk.com

Geoslides/Geo Aerial Photography 4 Christian Fields,
London, SW16 3JZ, United Kingdom
✆ 0115-981 9418/ 0115-981 9418
✉ geoslides@geo-group.co.uk
🖳 www.geo-group.co.uk

Gerry Cranham's Colour Library 80 Fairdene Road,
Coulsdon, Surrey, CR5 1RE, United Kingdom
✆ (01737) 553688/ (01737) 553688
✉ cranhamphoto@btinternet.com

Getty Images 101 Bayham Street, London, NW1 0AG,
United Kingdom
✆ (0800) 376 7977/ (020) 7544 3334
✉ sales@gettyimages.com
🖳 www.gettyimages.co.uk

Glasgow Museums Photolibrary The Burrell Collection,
Pollok Country Park, 2060 Pollokshaws Road, Glasgow,
G43 1AT, United Kingdom
✆ 0141-287 2595/ 0141-287 2585
✉ photolibrary@cls.glasgow.gov.uk
🖳 www.glasgowmuseums.com

Golf Course Photography 72 Apley Road, Hyde Park,
Doncaster, South Yorkshire, DN1 2AY, United Kingdom
✆ (01302) 322674/(07887) 594850/ (01302) 343610
✉ eric@hepworthgolfphotography.com
🖳 www.hepworthgolfphotography.com

Graciela Preece Images 1 Golden Lion Lane, Harwich,
Essex, CO12 3NG, United Kingdom
✆ (01255) 551443/(07818) 461833
✉ photo@graciela.info
🖳 www.gracielapreeceimages.com

Greenpeace Canonbury Villas, London, N1 2PN, United
Kingdom
✆ (020) 7865 8294/ (020) 7865 8203
✉ pix@uk.greenpeace.org
🖳 www.greenpeace.org.uk

Greg Evans International ICS House, 32 Crossways,
Ascot, Berkshire, SL5 0PL, United Kingdom
✆ (01344) 875430/ (01344) 291107
✉ greg@gregevans.net
🖳 www.gregevans.net

Gullachsen Productions 9 Wimpstone, Stratford-upon-
Avon, Warwickshire, CV37 8NS, United Kingdom
✆ (01789) 450080/ (01789) 450098
✉ lorentz@gullachsen.com
🖳 www.gullachsen.com

Guzelian Ltd 5 Victoria Road, Saltaire, Shipley, West
Yorkshire, BD18 3LA, United Kingdom
✆ (01274) 512012/ (01274) 532880
✉ pictures@guzelian.co.uk
🖳 www.guzelian.co.uk

Hali Archive / Hali Publications Ltd Saint Giles House,
50 Poland Street, London, W1F 7AX, United Kingdom
✆ (020) 7970 4600/ (020) 7578 7222
✉ hali@centaur.co.uk
🖳 www.hali.com

Harpur Garden Images 44 Roxwell Road, Chelmsford,
CM1 2NB, United Kingdom
✆ (01245) 257527/(07961) 934226 (01245) 344101
✉ info@harpurgardenimages.com
🖳 www.harpurgardenimages.com

Harry Ormesher Collection/Popperfoto.com The Old
Mill, Overstone Farm, Northampton, NN6 0AB, United
Kingdom
✆ (01604) 670670/ (01604) 670635
✉ ian.blackwell@popperfoto.com
🖳 www.popperfoto.com

HAT Archive HAT House, 12 Raveningham Centre,
Norwich, NR14 6NU, United Kingdom
✆ (01508) 548623/ (01508) 548478
✉ enquiries@hatads.org.uk
🖳 www.hatads.org.uk

Heather Angel / Natural Visions 6 Vicarage Hill,
Farnham, Surrey, GU9 8HG, United Kingdom
✆ (01252) 716700/ (01252) 727464
✉ hangel@naturalvisions.co.uk
🖳 www.naturalvisions.co.uk

Helene Rogers 57 Burdon Lane, Cheam, Surrey, SM2
7BY, United Kingdom
✆ (020) 8642 3593/ (020) 8395 7230
✉ images@artdirectors.co.uk
🖳 www.artdirectors.co.uk

**Henry Mayson & Luke Bagshaw
Collections/Popperfoto.com** The Old Mill, Overstone
Farm, Northampton, NN6 0AB, United Kingdom
✆ (01604) 670670/ (01604) 670635
✉ ian.blackwell@popperfoto.com
🖳 www.popperfoto.com

Herbert Ponting Collection/Popperfoto.com The Old
Mill, Overstone Farm, Northampton, NN6 0AB, United
Kingdom
✆ (01604) 670670/ (01604) 670635
✉ ian.blackwell@popperfoto.com
🖳 www.popperfoto.com

Heritage Image Partnership 18-20 St. John Street,
burningham, London, EC1M 4NX, United Kingdom
✆ (020) 7251 5091/ (020) 7608 0114
✉ info@heritage-images.com
🖳 www.heritage-images.com

Heseltine Archive The Old Mill Studio, Frogmarsh Mills,
South Woodchester, Stroud, Gloucestershire, GL5 5ET,
United Kingdom
✆ (01453) 873792/(07932) 160664
✉ john@heseltine.co.uk
🖳 www.heseltine.co.uk

Hewson Pictures St James House, 150 London Road,
East Grinstead, West Sussex, RH19 1HB, United Kingdom
✆ / (01342) 332037
✉ phewson@reedinfo.co.uk
🖳 www.kftv.co.uk

Historystore Ltd 29 Churton Street, Pimlico, London,
SW1V 2LY, United Kingdom
✆ (020) 7976 6040/ (020) 7976 6040
✉ claire@historystore.ltd.uk
🖳 www.historystore.ltd.uk

Hobbs Golf Collection 5 Winston Way, New Ridley,
Stocksfield, Northumberland, NE43 7RF, United Kingdom
✆ (01661) 842933/(07941) 445993 (01661) 842933
✉ info@hobbsgolfcollection.com
🖳 www.hobbsgolfcollection.com

Holt Studios Photograph Library Coxes Farm,
Branscombe, Seaton, Devon, EX12 3BJ, United Kingdom
✆ (01297) 680569/ (01297) 680478
✉ library@holt-studios.co.uk
🖳 www.holt-studios.co.uk

Horizon International Images Ltd Horizon House,
Route de Picaterre, Alderney, Guernsey, GY9 3UP, United
Kingdom
✆ (01481) 822587/ (01481) 823880
✉ mail@hrzn.com
🖳 www.hrzn.com

Houghton's Horses Radlet Cottage, Spaxton, Bridgwater,
Somerset, TA5 1DE, United Kingdom
✆ (01278) 671362/ (01278) 671739
✉ kit@enterprise.net
🖳 www.houghtonshorses.com

Hutchison Picture Library 65 Brighton Road,
Shoreham-by-Sea, West Sussex, BN43 6RE, United
Kingdom
✆ (01273) 440113/ (01273) 440116
✉ library@eyeubiquitous.com
🖳 www.eyeubiquitous.com

I C C E Photolibrary Burcott House, Wing, Leighton
Buzzard, Bedfordshire, LU7 0JU, United Kingdom
✆ (01296) 688245/(07802) 749932 (01296) 688245
✉ jacolyn@iccephotolibrary.co.uk
🖳 www.iccephotolibrary.co.uk

Ian Bruce Houldsworth Business & Arts Centre, 3rd Floor,
Houldsworth Street, Stockport, Cheshire, SK5 6DA, United
Kingdom
✆ 0161-975 6020/ 0161-975 6030
✉ clickon@ianbrucephoto.com
🖳 www.ianbrucephoto.com

Idols Licensing & Publicity Ltd 593-599 Fulham Road,
London, SW6 5UA, United Kingdom
✆ (020) 7385 5121/ (020) 7385 5110
✉ info@idols.co.uk
🖳 www.idols.co.uk

If Images Unit 4, Walpole Court, Ealing Green, London,
W5 5ED, United Kingdom
✆ (0870) 0119066/ (0870) 0115411
✉ info@ifimages.com
🖳 www.ifimages.com

Illustrated London News Picture Library 20 Upper
Ground, London, SE1 9PF, United Kingdom
✆ (020) 7805 5585/ (020) 7805 5905
✉ research@ilnpictures.co.uk
🖳 www.ilnpictures.co.uk

ILN Picture Library 20 Upper Ground, London, SE1
9PF, United Kingdom
✆ (020) 7805 5585/ (020) 7805 5905
✉ research@ilnpictures.co.uk
🖳 www.ilng.co.uk

Image Quest Marine The Moos, Poffley End, Witney,
Oxfordshire, OX29 9UW, United Kingdom
✆ (01993) 704050/ (01993) 779203
✉ info@imagequestmarine.com
🖳 www.imagequestmarine.com

Image Source Ltd 41 Great Pulteney Street, London,
W1F 9NZ, United Kingdom
✆ (020) 7851 5700/ (020) 7851 5601
✉ info@imagesource.com
🖳 www.imagesource.com

Image100 111 Salusbury Road, London, NW6 6RG,
United Kingdom
✆ (020) 7644 7400/ (020) 7644 7401
✉ info@corbis.com
🖳 www.corbis.com

Images of Africa Photobank 11 The Windings,
Lichfield, Staffordshire, WS13 7EX, United Kingdom
✆ (01543) 262898/ (01543) 417154
✉ info@imagesofafrica.co.uk
🖳 www.imagesofafrica.co.uk

Images of Birmingham.co.uk 20 Dorchester Drive,
Muxton, Telford, Shropshire, TF2 8SR, United Kingdom
✆ (01925) 603038
✉ pics@imagesofbirmingham.co.uk
🖳 www.imagesofbirmingham.co.uk

Images of Empire British Empire & Commonwealth
Museum, Clock Tower Yard, Temple Meads, Bristol, BS1
6QH, United Kingdom
✆ 0117-929 3851/ 0117-929 3852
✉ info@imagesofempire.com
🖳 www.imagesofempire.com

Imagestate 1st Floor, 18/20 St John Street, London,
EC1M 4NX, United Kingdom
✆ (020) 7734 7344/ (020) 7434 0673
✉ info@imagestate.co.uk
🖳 www.imagestate.com

Imogen Graham The Old Rectory, Village Road, Taunton,
Somerset, TA3 6SG, United Kingdom
✆ (01823) 480088/ (01823) 481170

Impact Photos 18-20 St John Street, London, EC1M
4NX, United Kingdom
✆ (020) 7251 5091/ (020) 7608 0114
✉ nathan.grainger@heritage-images.com
🖳 www.impactphotos.com

Infoterra Ltd Atlas House, 41 Wembley Road, Leicester, LE3 1UT, United Kingdom
☎ 0116-273 2391/(07901) 655438 ✆ 0116-273 2400
✉ info@infoterra-global.com
🖥 www.infoterra.co.uk

Ink & Colors Ltd 27 Old Gloucester Street, London, WC1N 3XX, United Kingdom
☎ (020) 7558 8374
✉ info@inkandcolors.com
🖥 www.inkandcolors.com

Institution of Mechanical Engineers 1 Birdcage Walk, London, SW1H 9JJ, United Kingdom
☎ (020) 7304 6836/✆ (020) 7222 8762
✉ m_claxton@imeche.org
🖥 www.imeche.org

Intersport Photographic 58 South Avenue, Egham, Surrey, TW20 8HQ, United Kingdom
☎ (07973) 819551
✉ images@intersport-images.com
🖥 www.intersport-images.com

Isphotos 353 West, New York, 10018, United States of America
☎ 212 658 9865
✉ info@isphotos.com
🖥 www.isphotos.com

ITN Source 200 Grays Inn Road, London, WC1X 8XZ, United Kingdom
☎ (020) 7430 4480/✆ (020) 7430 4453
✉ uksales@itnsource.com
🖥 www.itnsource.com/en

Ivan J. Belcher Colour Picture Library 57 Gibson Close, Abingdon, Oxfordshire, OX14 1XS, United Kingdom
☎ (01235) 521524/✆ (01235) 521524
✉ ivan.belcher@tiscali.co.uk

J Brightmore 2 Victoria Grove Mews, London, W2 4LN, United Kingdom
☎ (020) 7229 6967

J S Library International 101A Brondesbury Park, London, NW2 5JL, United Kingdom
☎ (020) 8451 2668/(07802) 170937 ✆ (020) 8459 0223
✉ js@online24.co.uk
🖥 www.jslibrary.com

Jacqui Hurst 66 Richford Street, London, W6 7HP, United Kingdom
☎ (020) 8743 2315/(07970) 781336
✉ jacquihurst@yahoo.co.uk
🖥 www.jacquihurstphotography.co.uk

Jaguar Daimler Photographic Library Jaguar Daimler Heritage Trust, B/1/002/B, Browns Lane, Allesley, Coventry, CV5 9DR, UK
☎ (024) 7620 2743/✆ (024) 7620 2777
✉ kram4@jaguar.com
🖥 www.jdht.com

Jason Shenai 48 Belsize Square, London, NW3 4HN, United Kingdom
☎ (020) 7794 9194/(07767) 756534 ✆ (020) 7435 0133
✉ jason@milim.com
🖥 www.milim.com

Jayawardene Travel Photo Library 7a Napier Road, Wembley, Middlesex, HA0 4UA, United Kingdom
☎ (020) 8795 3581/✆ (020) 8795 4083

Jazz Index 26 Fosse Way, London, W13 0BZ, United Kingdom
☎ (020) 8998 1232/✆ (020) 8998 1232
✉ christianhim@jazzindex.co.uk
🖥 www.jazzindex.co.uk

Jim Henderson Photography Crooktree, Kincardine O'Neil, Aboyne, Aberdeenshire, AB34 4JD, United Kingdom
☎ (01339) 882149/✆ (01339) 882149
✉ JHende7868@aol.com
🖥 www.jimhendersonphotography.com

Jo Carlill Picture Research , London, United Kingdom
☎ (07769) 701932
✉ jo@carlillj.freeserve.co.uk

Joanne Forrest-Smith 187 Magdalene Road, Oldfield, London, SW18 3PB, United Kingdom
☎ (07736) 405034
✉ work@lightbox11.demon.co.uk

John Birdsall Social Issues Photo Library 89 Zulu Road, New Basford, Nottingham, NG7 7DR, United Kingdom
☎ 0115-978 2645/✆ 0115-978 5546
✉ photos@johnbirdsall.co.uk
🖥 www.johnbirdsall.co.uk

John Brown Citrus Publishing Ltd The New Boathouse, 136-142 Bramley Road, London, W10 6SR, United Kingdom
☎ (020) 7565 3000/✆ (020) 7565 3050
✉ graham.harper@jbcp.co.uk
🖥 www.jbcp.co.uk

John Cleare Hill Cottage, Fonthill Gifford, Salisbury, SP3 6QW, United Kingdom
☎ (01747) 820320/✆ (01747) 820320
✉ cleare@btinternet.com
🖥 www.mountaincamera.com

John Cooper Collection East Chase, Bowerchalke, Salisbury, SP5 5RB, United Kingdom
☎ (01722) 780076/✆ (01722) 780076
✉ info@johncoopercollection.co.uk
🖥 www.johncoopercollection.co.uk

John Ferro Sims 11 Parkhill Road, London, NW3 2YH, United Kingdom
☎ (020) 7586 0780/✆ (020) 7586 3790
✉ john@henrymoorestudio.co.uk
🖥 simspix.co.uk

John Glover Photography The Oast Houses, Headley Lane, Liphook, Hampshire, GU30 7RN, United Kingdom
☎ (01428) 751925/(07973) 307078 ✆ (01428) 751191
✉ john@johnglover.co.uk
🖥 www.johnglover.co.uk

John Robert Young Collection 16 Green Acres Drive, Ringmer, Lewes, East Sussex, BN8 5LZ, United Kingdom
☎ (01273) 814172/✆ (01273) 814172
✉ johnrobert@paxvobiscum.fsnet.co.uk

John Shelley / JS Library International 101A Brondesbury Park, London, NW2 5JL, United Kingdom
☎ (020) 8451 2668/✆ (020) 8459 8517
✉ js@online24.co.uk
🖥 www.jslibrary.com www.jslibraryprints.com

John Vickers Theatre Collection 1938-1968 27 Shorrolds Road, London, SW6 7TR, United Kingdom
☎ (020) 7385 5774

John Walmsley Education Photos 8 Whitemore Road, Delmore, Guildford, Surrey, GU1 1QT, United Kingdom
☎ (01483) 511 666
✉ johnwalmsley@educationphotos.co.uk
🖥 www.educationphotos.co.uk

John Warburton-Lee Photography The Grange, Walcott, Sleaford, Lincolnshire, NG34 0ST, United Kingdom
☎ (01529) 497223/✆ (01529) 497223
✉ info@johnwarburtonlee.com
🖥 www.johnwarburtonlee.com

Jolanta Damski Freelance Design Flat 1, 40 Ewelme Road, London, SE23 3BH, United Kingdom
☎ (020) 8291 6023
✉ jolantadamski@btinternet.com
🖥 www.jolantadamski.co.uk

Jon Arnold Images Ltd 7 Rydes Avenue, Guildford, Surrey, GU2 9SR, United Kingdom
☎ (01483) 451245
✉ info@jonarnoldimages.com
🖥 www.jonarnoldimages.com

K Books Ltd Waplington Hall, Waplington, York, YO42 4RS, United Kingdom
☎ (01759) 302142/✆ (01759) 305891
✉ kaye@kbooks.uk.com
🖥 www.kbooks.uk.com

Kay Rowley 56 Stade Street, Hythe, Kent, CT21 6BD, United Kingdom
☎ (01303) 237867/(07967) 133621
✉ kayrowley@kaypix.demon.co.uk

Kennel Club Picture Library 1-5 Clarges Street, Piccadilly, London, W1J 8AB, United Kingdom
☎ (020) 7518 1035/✆ (020) 7518 1045
✉ picturelibrary@the-kennel-club.org.uk
🖥 www.the-kennel-club.org.uk/picturelibrary

Knudsens Fotosenter AS Sondrevegen 30, Oslo, 378, Norway
☎ 22 42 28 31/90 75 95 38 ✆ 22 20 21 38
✉ fotodesk@online.no
🖥 www.knudsensfotosenter.com

Kobi Israel Flat 27, Centre Point House, 15A St Giles High Street, London, WC2H 8LW, United Kingdom
☎ (07815) 100598
✉ kobi@kobiisrael.com
🖥 www.kobiisrael.com

Kos Picture Source Ltd P O Box 52854, 7 Spice Court, London, SW11 3UU, United Kingdom
☎ **(020) 7801 0044/** ✆ **(020) 7801 0055**
✉ **images@kospictures.com**
🖥 **www.kospictures.com**
See ad in showcase

L A T Photographic Somerset House, Somerset Road, Teddington, Middlesex, TW11 8RU, United Kingdom
☎ (020) 8251 3000/✆ (020) 8251 3001
✉ digital@latphoto.co.uk
🖥 www.latphoto.co.uk

Lakeland Life Picture Library Langsett, Lyndene Drive, Grange-over-Sands, Cumbria, LA11 6QP, United Kingdom
☎ (01539) 533565
✉ davidwdjones@ktdinternet.com
🖥 www.lakelandlifepicturelibrary.co.uk

Last Resort Picture Library Manvers Studios, 12 Ollerton Road, Tuxford, Newark, Nottinghamshire, NG22 0LF, United Kingdom
☎ (01777) 870166/(07771) 961217 ✆ (01777) 871739
✉ dick@dmimaging.co.uk
🖥 www.dmimaging.co.uk

Lebrecht Music & Arts Photo Library 58B Carlton Hill, London, NW8 0ES, United Kingdom
☎ (020) 7625 5341/✆ (020) 7625 5341
✉ pictures@lebrecht.co.uk
🖥 www.lebrecht.co.uk

Lee Miller Archives Farley Farmhouse, Muddles Green, Lewes, East Sussex, BN8 6HW, United Kingdom
☎ (01825) 872691/✆ (01825) 872733
✉ archives@leemiller.co.uk
🖥 www.leemiller.co.uk

Leslie Garland Picture Library High Pasture, Yarrow, Falstone, Hexham, Northumberland, NE48 1BG, United Kingdom
☎ (01434) 240324
✉ pictures@lesliegarland.co.uk
🖥 www.lesliegarland.co.uk

Leslie Turtle PO Box 6275, Wareham, Dorset, BH20 9AG, United Kingdom
☎ (020) 7731 6076/(07976) 855880
✉ picturebusiness@easynet.co.uk
🖥 www.picturebusiness.co.uk

Lindley Library Royal Horticultural Society, 80 Vincent Square, London, SW1P 2PE, United Kingdom
☎ (020) 7821 3050/✆ (020) 7828 3022
✉ library.london@rhs.org.uk
🖥 www.rhs.org.uk

Link India 41a The Downs, London, SW20 8HG, United Kingdom
☎ (020) 8944 6933/(07947) 884517
✉ library@linkpicturelibrary.com
🖥 www.linkpicturelibrary.com

Link Picture Library 41a The Downs, London, SW20 8HG, United Kingdom
☎ (020) 8944 6933/(07947) 884517
✉ library@linkpicturelibrary.com
🖥 www.linkpicturelibrary.com

Liz Heasman (Focal) 8 Lansdowne House, Lansdowne Road, London, W11 3LP, United Kingdom
☎ (020) 7229 9770
✉ LizHeasman2@aol.com

London Aerial Photo Library Studio D1, Fairoaks Airport, Chobham, Surrey, GU24 8HU, United Kingdom
☎ (01276) 855997/✆ (01276) 855455
✉ info@londonaerial.co.uk
🖥 www.londonaerial.co.uk

London Features International Ltd 3 Boscobel Street, London, NW8 8PS, United Kingdom
☎ (020) 7723 4204/✆ (020) 7723 9201
✉ sales@lfi.co.uk
🖥 www.lfi.co.uk

Londonstills 5 Keswick Road, London, SW15 2HL, United Kingdom
☎ (020) 8874 4905/✆ (020) 8870 9864
✉ ricky@londonstills.com
🖥 www.londonstills.com

Lonely Planet Images 72-82 Rosebery Avenue, London, EC1R 4RW, United Kingdom
☎ (020) 7841 9062/✆ (020) 7841 9001
✉ lpi@lonelyplanet.co.uk
🖥 www.lonelyplanetimages.com

At www.designweek.co.uk there's more than you might think.

You'll find over 20 stories a week that aren't in the magazine, the latest jobs, a 15 year archive and our events diary to plan your design year by.

So why not pay us a visit today, at www.designweek.co.uk

design WEEK.co.uk

Loupe Images 20-21 Jockey's Fields, London, WC1R 4BW
United Kingdom
(020) 7025 2249
info@loupeimages.com
www.loupeimages.com

Lucy Barden Photography Dillies Farm Lodge, Stow Road, Cirencester, Gloucestershire, GL7 5EX, United Kingdom
(07951) 180125
info@lucybarden.co.uk
www.lucybarden.co.uk

Ludvigsen Library Scoles Gate, Hawkedon, Bury St. Edmunds, Suffolk, IP29 4AU, United Kingdom
(01284) 789246/ (01284) 789246
library@ludvigsen.com
www.ludvigsen.com

M-Dash Tower House, 25 Wallaton Road, Nottingham, NG9 2NG, United Kingdom
0115-925 8802/ 0115-925 6979
info@m-dash.com
www.m-dash.com

MacQuitty International Collection 7 Elm Lodge, River Gardens, London, SW6 6NZ, United Kingdom
(020) 7385 5606/ (020) 7385 5606
miranda.macquitty@btinternet.com

Manchester Art Gallery Mosley Street, Manchester, M2 3JL, United Kingdom
0161-235 8863/ 0161-235 8805
t.walker@manchester.gov.uk
www.manchestergalleries.org

Mander & Mitchenson Theatre Collection Jerwood Library of the Performing Arts, Trinity College of Music, King Charles Court, Old Royal Naval College, London, SE10 9JF, United Kingdom
(020) 8305 4426/ (020) 8305 9426
rmangan@tcm.ac.uk

Mapstock Ltd 5 Albemarle Way, London, EC1V 4JB, United Kingdom
(020) 7490 3233/ (020) 7490 3323
j.lee@mapstock.com
www.mapstock.com

Marian Pullen 53 Lisbon Avenue, Twickenham, TW2 5HR, United Kingdom
(020) 8894 4363
marian_pullen@yahoo.co.uk

Marius Alexander Photo Library Wasps Studios, 2 West Park Place, Edinburgh, EH11 2DP, United Kingdom
0131-539 9100/(07889) 913485 / 0131-539 9100
marius@mariusalexander.com
www.mariusalexander.com

Marshall Cavendish 119 Wardour Street, London, W1F 0UW, United Kingdom
(020) 7565 6000/ (020) 7734 6221
www.marshallcavendish.co.uk

Marx Memorial Library Pictures 37a Clerkenwell Green, London, EC1R 0DU, United Kingdom
(020) 7253 1485/ (020) 7251 6039
marx.library@britishlibrary.net
www.marx-memorial-library.org

Mary Evans Picture Library - History 59 Tranquil Vale, Blackheath, London, SE3 0BS, United Kingdom
(020) 8318 0034/ (020) 8852 7211
mark.bezodis@maryevans.com
www.maryevans.com

Masterfile UK Ltd 1 Quality Court, Chancery Lane, London, WC2A 1HR
0870 351 7928/0870 351 7929 london@masterfile.com
www.masterfile.com
See ad in showcase

Matton Images UK Ltd 2 Western Avenue Business Park, Mansfield Road, London, W3 0BZ, United Kingdom
(020) 8753 7000/ (020) 8753 7001
info@mattonimages.co.uk
www.mattonimages.co.uk

Maureen Elliott 57 Selby Road, London, SE20 8ST, United Kingdom
(020) 8659 7811/(07974) 430369

Maureen Kane , London, W11 1JD, United Kingdom
(07778) 157474
maureen.kane@virgin.net

Mediscan 2nd Floor, Patman House, 23-27 Electric Parade, George Lane, South Woodward, London, E18 2LS, United Kingdom
(0871) 2205256/ (020) 8989 7795
info@mediscan.co.uk
www.mediscan.co.uk

Megapress Images Suite 2205, 1751 Richardson, Montreal, H3K 1G6, Canada
514 279 9859/ 514 279 9859
info@megapress.ca
www.megapress.ca

Merseyside Photo Library Suite 6, Egerton House, Tower Road, Birkenhead, Merseyside, CH41 1FN, United Kingdom
0151-650 6975/ 0151-650 6976
ron@rja-mpl.com
www.merseysidephotolibrary.com

Mia Stewart-Wilson 16 Ursula Street, London, SW11 3DW, United Kingdom
(020) 7228 1028/(07950) 636234
miastewartwilson@aol.com

Michael Busselle's Photo Library , Crouch, Kent, United Kingdom
(01732) 455607
mikebuss@btinternet.com
www.michael-busselle.com

Michael Cole Camerawork The Coach House, 27 The Avenue, Beckenham, Kent, BR3 2DP, United Kingdom
(020) 8658 6120/ (020) 8658 6120
mikecole@dircon.co.uk
www.tennisphotos.com

Mike Watson Images 52 Lime Street, London, EC3M 7NL, United Kingdom
(020) 7469 6946
sarah.mcnab@mikewatsonimages.com
www.mikewatsonimages.com

Millennium Images 48 Belsize Square, London, NW3 4HN, United Kingdom
(020) 7794 9194/(07767) 756534 (020) 7435 0133
jason@milim.com
www.milim.com

Mirrorpix 21 Bruton Street, Mayfair, London, London, W1J 6QD, United Kingdom
(020) 7293 3700/(07747) 790364 (020) 7491 0357
desk@mirrorpix.com
www.mirrorpix.com

Mitchell-McGree Garden Design 3 Poppyhills Road, Camberley, Surrey, GU15 4ES, United Kingdom
(01276) 469141
mitchell@lifeworld.wanadoo.co.uk
www.mitchell-mcgree.com

Molyneux Associates The Barn, Castle Farm, Alvington, Lydney, Gloucestershire, GL15 6AT, United Kingdom
(01594) 529111/(07836) 216909
helen@molyneuxassociates.com
www.molyneuxassociates.com

Monitor Picture Library The Forge, Roydon, Harlow, Essex, CM19 5HH, United Kingdom
(01279) 792 700/ (01279) 792 600
sales@monitorpicturelibrary.com
www.monitorpicturelibrary.com

Mooney Photo Ltd 25 Armitage Bridge Mills, Armitage Bridge, Huddersfield, HD4 7NR, United Kingdom
(020) 7193 6637/ (01484) 660575
admin@mooneyphoto.com
www.mooneyphoto.com

Mother & Baby Picture Library Greater London House, London, NW1 7EJ, United Kingdom
(020) 7347 1867/ (020) 7347 1888
mother.baby.pl@emap.com
www.motherandbabypicturelibrary.com

Motoring Picture Library National Motor Museum, Beaulieu, Brockenhurst, Hampshire, SO42 7ZN, United Kingdom
(01590) 614656/ (01590) 612655
motoring.pictures@beaulieu.co.uk
www.motoringpicturelibrary.com

Movie Store Collection 2nd Floor North, 61-65 Paulet Road, Chartwell House, London, SE5 9HW, United Kingdom
(020) 7733 9990/ (020) 7733 9858
sales@moviestorecollection.com
www.moviestorecollection.com

Museum of London London Wall, London, EC2Y 5HN, United Kingdom
(0870) 444 3852
info@museumoflondon.org.uk
www.museumoflondon.org.uk

N I Syndication 1 Virginia Street, London, E98 1SY, United Kingdom
(020) 7711 7888/ (020) 7782 5353
enquiries@nisyndication.com
www.nisyndication.com

nagelestock.com Parkgate, West Approach Drive, Cheltenham, Gloucestershire, GL52 3AD, United Kingdom
(01242) 242952/ (01242) 575358
look@nagelestock.com
www.nagelestock.com

Narratives 11 Gibraltar Walk, London, London, E2 7LH, United Kingdom
(020) 7366 6658/ (020) 7366 6658
pictures@narratives.co.uk
www.narratives.co.uk

Natalie Jones 6 Mount Pleasant, Biggin Hill, Westerham, Kent, TN16 3TR, United Kingdom
(07787) 310581
nat90mins@hotmail.com

National Archive of Geological Photographs (N.A.G.P.) Murchison House, Edinburgh, EH9 3LA, United Kingdom
☎ 0131-667 1000/📠 0131-668 2683
✉ nagp@bgs.ac.uk
🖥 www.bgs.ac.uk

National Army Museum Royal Hospital Road, Chelsea, London, SW3 4HT, United Kingdom
☎ (020) 7730 0717/📠 (020) 7823 6573
✉ photo@national-army-museum.ac.uk
🖥 www.national-army-museum.ac.uk

National Centre for Voulnteering Image Bank Regents Wharf, 8 All Saints Street, London, N1 9RL, United Kingdom
☎ (020) 7520 8900/📠 (020) 7520 8910
✉ membership@volunteeringengland.org
🖥 www.volunteering.org.uk

National Galleries of Scotland Picture Libary Dean Gallery 75 Belford Road, Edinburgh, EH4 3DR, United Kingdom
☎ 0131-624 6260/📠 0131-623 7135
✉ picture.library@nationalgalleries.org
🖥 www.nationalgalleries.org

National Gallery Picture Library 30 Orange Street, Vincent House, London, WC2H 7HH, United Kingdom
☎ (020) 7747 5994/📠 (020) 7747 5999
✉ picture.library@nationalgallery.co.uk
🖥 www.nationalgalleryimages.co.uk

National History Museum Picture Library Cromwell Road, South Kensington, London, SW7 5BD, United Kingdom
☎ (020) 7942 5401/📠 (020) 7942 5212
✉ nhmpl@nhm.ac.uk
🖥 www.nhm.ac.uk/piclib

National Maritime Museum Park Row, Greenwich, London, London, SE10 9NF, United Kingdom
☎ (020) 8312 6565/📠 (020) 8312 6632
✉ picturelibrary@nmm.ac.uk
🖥 www.nmm.ac.uk

National Museums Liverpool 127 Dale Street, Liverpool, L2 2JH, United Kingdom
☎ 0151-478 4657/📠 0151-478 4028
✉ photography@liverpoolmuseums.org.uk
🖥 www.liverpoolmuseums.org.uk

National Portrait Gallery Picture Library St Martin's Place, London, WC2H 0HE, United Kingdom
☎ (020) 7312 2474/📠 (020) 7312 2464
✉ picturelibrary@npg.org.uk
🖥 www.npg.org.uk/picturelibrary

National Trust for Scotland Wemyss House, 28 Charlotte Square, Edinburgh, EH2 4ET, United Kingdom
☎ 0131-243 9315/📠 0131-243 9301
✉ irobertson@nts.org.uk
🖥 www.nts.org.uk

National Trust Photographic Library Heelis, Kemble Drive, Swindon, SN2 2NA, United Kingdom
☎ (01793) 817700/📠 (01793) 817401
✉ photo.library@nationaltrust.org.uk
🖥 www.ntpl.org.uk

Nature Photographers Ltd West Wit, New Road, Little London, Tadley, Hampshire, RG26 5EU, United Kingdom
☎ (01256) 850661/(07771) 861566
✉ paul@naturephotographers.co.uk
🖥 www.naturephotographers.co.uk

Nature Picture Library Broadcasting House, Whiteladies Road, Bristol, BS8 2LR, United Kingdom
☎ 0117-974 6720/📠 0117-923 8166
✉ info@naturepl.com
🖥 www.naturepl.com
See ad

Neill Bruce's Automobile Photo Library Grange Cottage, Harts Lane, Burghclere, Newbury, Berkshire, RG20 9JN, United Kingdom
☎ (01635) 278342/📠 (01635) 278565
✉ neillb@brucephoto.co.uk
🖥 www.brucephoto.co.uk

News Quest Media Group Ltd 200 Renfield Street, Glasgow, G2 3QB, United Kingdom
☎ 0141-302 7361
✉ rights@glasgow.newsquest.co.uk
🖥 www.theherald.co.uk

News Team International Ltd 35 Gas Street, Birmingham, B2 5JT, United Kingdom
☎ 0121-246 5511/(07977) 041186 📠 0121-246 2201
✉ picture.desk@newsteam.co.uk
🖥 www.newsteam.co.uk

NewsCast 4 Cannon Hill, London, London, N14 7HG, United Kingdom
☎ (020) 8886 5895/📠 (020) 8882 8334
✉ photo@newscast.co.uk
🖥 www.newscast.co.uk

NHPA Ltd 29-31 Saffron Hill, Farringdon, London, EC1N 8SW, United Kingdom
☎ (020) 7421 6003/📠 (020) 7421 6006
✉ nhpa@nhpa.co.uk
🖥 www.nhpa.co.uk

No Image 15 Charlotte Place, London, W1T 1SP, United Kingdom
☎ (07751) 670489
✉ nobody@noimage.com
🖥 www.noimage.com

Novosti Photo Library 3 Rosary Gardens, London, SW7 4NW, United Kingdom
☎ (020) 7370 1873/📠 (020) 7244 7875
✉ photos@novosti.co.uk
🖥 www.rian.ru

Nunn Syndication Ltd 13a Shad Thames, Butlers Wharf, London, SE1 2PU, United Kingdom
☎ (020) 7357 9000/📠 (020) 7357 9000
✉ enquiries@nunn-syndication.com
🖥 www.nunn-syndication.com

Octopus Publishing Group 2-4 Heron Quays, London, E14 4JP, United Kingdom
☎ (020) 7531 8400/📠 (020) 7531 8650
🖥 www.theoctopus-publishing.co.uk

Offside Sports Photography Ltd 271-273 City Road, London, EC1V 1LA, United Kingdom
☎ (020) 7253 3344/📠 (020) 7253 2923
✉ mail@welloffside.com
🖥 www.welloffside.com

the best nature images online

NATURE PICTURE LIBRARY
www.naturepl.com

PHOTO LIBRARIES

Olympic Television Archive Bureau (OTAB) McCormack House, Burlington Lane, London, W4 2TH, United Kingdom
📞 (020) 8233 5353/📠 (020) 8233 5354
✉ webmaster@otab.com
💻 www.otab.com

Only Horses Picture Agency 27 Greenway Gardens, Greenford, Middlesex, UB6 9TU, United Kingdom
📞 (020) 8578 9047/📠 (020) 8575 7244
✉ onlyhorsespics@aol.com
💻 www.onlyhorsespictures.com

Organic Picture Library 18 Vine Hill, London, EC1R 5DZ, United Kingdom
📞 (020) 7278 6989/📠 (020) 7696 0973
✉ www.rexfeatures.com
💻 www.rexinterstock.com/opl

Organics Image Library The Studios, 27 Hogarth Road, Hove, East Sussex, BN3 5RH, United Kingdom
📞 (01273) 701557
✉ info@organicsimagelibrary.com
💻 www.organicsimagelibrary.com

Oxford Photo Library 280A Cowley Road, Oxford, OX4 1UR, United Kingdom
📞 (01865) 251996/📠 (01865) 251767
✉ chris@oxford-photo-library.co.uk
💻 www.oxford-photo-library.co.uk

Oxford Picture Library 15 Curtis Yd, North Hinksey Ln, Oxford, OX2 0LX, United Kingdom
📞 (01865) 723404/📠 (01865) 725294
✉ chris.andrews1@btclick.com
💻 www.oxfordpicturelibrary.co.uk

Oxford Scientific Films (OSF) Network House, Station Yard, Thame, Oxfordshire, OX9 3UH, United Kingdom
📞 (01844) 262370/📠 (01844) 262380
✉ uksales@osf.co.uk
💻 www.osf.co.uk

P P L (Photo Agency) Ltd Bookers Yard, The Street, Walberton, Arundel, West Sussex, BN18 0PF, United Kingdom
📞 (01243) 555561/07768 395719 📠 (01243) 555562
✉ ppl@mistral.co.uk
💻 www.pplmedia.com

P R A 1-3 Willow Court, London, EC2A 4QB, United Kingdom
📞 (020) 7739 8544/📠 (020) 7782 0011
✉ chair@picture-research.org.uk
💻 www.picture-research.org.uk

P Y M C A 43 Clerkenwell Road, London, London, EC1M 5RS, United Kingdom
📞 (020) 7251 8338
✉ info@pymca.com
💻 www.pymca.com

Palestine Exploration Fund Photographic Archive 2 Hinde Mews, Marylebone Lane, London, W1U 2AA, United Kingdom
📞 (020) 7935 5379/📠 (020) 7486 7438
✉ curator@pef.org.uk
💻 www.pef.org.uk

Panoptika Bourguerault, Chevannes, Billy Chevannes, 58270, France
📞 00 33 3 86 60 20 53
✉ photo@panoptika.net
💻 www.panoptika.net

Panos Pictures 1 Honduras Street, London, EC1Y 0TH, United Kingdom
📞 (020) 7253 1424/📠 (020) 7253 2752
✉ pics@panos.co.uk
💻 www.panos.co.uk

Papilio Natural History & Travel Library 155 Station Road, Herne Bay, Kent, CT6 5QA, United Kingdom
📞 (01227) 360996
✉ library@papiliophotos.com
💻 www.papiliophotos.com

Pat Hodgson Historical Picture Library Jasmine Cottage, Spring Grove Road, Richmond, Surrey, TW10 6EH, United Kingdom
📞 (020) 8940 5986
✉ pat.hodgpix@virgin.net

Patrick Eagar 1 Queensberry Place, Friars Lane, Richmond, Surrey, TW9 1NW, United Kingdom
📞 (020) 8940 9269/📠 (020) 8332 1229
✉ patrick@patrickeagar.com
💻 www.patrickeagar.com

Paul Beard Photo Agency PBPA House, 33 Sanctuary Close, Worcester, WR2 5PY, United Kingdom
📞 (01905) 749959
✉ pbphotography@btconnect.com
💻 http://home.btconnect.com/pbphotography

Paul Felix Hornbeam House, Robinson Lane, Cirencester, Gloucestershire, GL7 7EN, United Kingdom
📞 (01285) 831703/📠 (01285) 831045
✉ photos@paulfelix.co.uk
💻 www.paulfelix.co.uk

Perfect Pictures 49 Alexandra Road, Denton, Gravesend, Kent, DA12 2QG, United Kingdom
📞 (01474) 327742
✉ sales@perfect-pictures.net
💻 www.perfect-pictures.net

Pete Fontaine Photography 30 Southwark Close, Yateley, Hampshire, GU46 6QG, United Kingdom
📞 (07971) 299640
✉ petefontaine@mindspring.com
💻 www.petefontaine.com

Peter Andrew Jones Picture Library Woodcote Edge, Church Stretton, Shropshire, SY6 6DF, United Kingdom
📞 (01694) 724584/📠 (01694) 724584
✉ licensing@peterandrewjones.net
💻 www.peterandrewjones.net

Peter Phipp Longfield Cottage, 3B Uplands Close, London, SW14 7AS, United Kingdom
📞 (020) 8878 2226/📠 (020) 8392 2920
✉ photography@peterphipp.co.uk
💻 www.peterphipp.co.uk

Phil Sheldon Golf Picture Library 40 Manor Road, Barnet, Hertfordshire, EN5 2JQ, United Kingdom
📞 (020) 8440 1986/📠 (020) 8440 9348
✉ info@philsheldongolfpics.co.uk
💻 www.philsheldongolfpics.co.uk

Photo Archive News Unit G, Smarden Business Estate, Smarden, Ashford, Kent, TN27 8QL, United Kingdom
📞 (07802) 437827
✉ will@photoarchivenews.com
💻 www.photoarchivenews.com

 ...a world of difference

tel : 01622 609809
picturescolourlibrary.co.uk

Photo-Stock Library Intl 14 Neville Avenue, Thornton-Cleveleys, Blackpool, FY5 3BG, United Kingdom
☎ (01253) 864598
✉ wayne@photo-stock.co.uk
🖥 www.photo-stock.co.uk

Photo4.net Galleries 83 Lilliput Road, Poole, Dorset, BH14 8JX, United Kingdom
☎ (01202) 706565/(07973) 229283
✉ info@photo4.net
🖥 www.photo4.net

Photobyte Image Library - online travel pictures 11 Hammersmith Terrace, London, W6 9TS, United Kingdom
☎ (020) 8741 2462
✉ images@photobyte.co.uk
🖥 www.photobyte.co.uk

Photofusion Picture Library 17A Electric Lane, London, SW9 8LA, United Kingdom
☎ (020) 7733 3500/ ☏ (020) 7738 5509
✉ library@photofusion.org
🖥 www.photofusionpictures.org

Photolibrary.com Fourth floor, 83-84 Long Acre, London, WC2E 9NG, United Kingdom
☎ (020) 7836 5591/ ☏ (020) 7379 4650
✉ uksales@photolibrary.com
🖥 www.photolibrary.com

Photonica 10 Regents Wharf, All Saints Street, London, N1 9RL, United Kingdom
☎ (020) 7278 4117/ ☏ (020) 7278 4118
✉ info@photonica.co.uk
🖥 www.photonica.com

Photos 12 20 Rue Lalande, Paris, 75014, France
☎ 1 56 80 14 40/ ☏ 1 56 80 14 41
✉ meurin@photo12.com
🖥 www.photo12.com

Photos Horticultural Picture Library , Ipswich, IP1 4PR, United Kingdom
☎ (01473) 257329/ ☏ (01473) 233974
✉ library@photos-horticultural.com
🖥 www.photos-horticultural.com

Photoshot Holdings 29-31 Saffron Hill, London, EC1N 8SW, United Kingdom
☎ (020) 7421 6003/ ☏ (020) 7421 6006
✉ ctaylor@uppa.co.uk
🖥 www.uppa.co.uk

Photostage Shenley Lodge, Milton Keynes, MK5 7YT, United Kingdom
☎ (01908) 262324/ ☏ (01908) 262082
✉ info@photostage.co.uk

Photostore Ltd 23 Lammas Park Road, London, W5 5JD, United Kingdom
☎ (020) 8579 5823/ ☏ (020) 8840 3257
✉ support@photostore.co.uk
🖥 www.photostore.co.uk

Pictorial Press Photo Library Unit 1, Market Yard Mews, London, SE1 3TQ, United Kingdom
☎ (020) 7378 7211/ ☏ (020) 7378 7194
✉ tony@pictorialpress.com
🖥 www.pictorialpress.com

Picture Bank Photo Library Ltd Parman House, 30-36 Fife Road, Kingston upon Thames, Surrey, KT1 1SY, United Kingdom
☎ (020) 8547 2344/ ☏ (020) 8974 5652
✉ info@picturebank.co.uk
🖥 www.picturebank.co.uk

Picture Business PO Box 6275, Wareham, Dorset, BH20 9AG, United Kingdom
☎ (020) 7731 6076/(07976) 855880
✉ picturebusiness@easynet.co.uk
🖥 www.picturebusiness.co.uk

Picture Research 11c Falkland Road, London, NW5 2PS, United Kingdom
☎ (020) 7482 6455/ ☏ (020) 7482 6455
✉ diana@picture-research.co.uk

Picture Research & Authorship , London, United Kingdom
☎ (07947) 036054
✉ sara.waterson@britishlibrary.net

Picture Research Consultancy 266 St. Pauls Road, Islington, London, N1 2LJ, United Kingdom
☎ (020) 7226 0727/ ☏ (020) 7226 0727
✉ jenny.silkstone@blueyonder.co.uk

Pictures Colour Library Ltd 10 James Whatman Court, Turkey Mill, Maidstone, Kent, ME14 5SS, United Kingdom
☎ **(01622) 609809/ ☏ (01622) 609806**
✉ **enquiries@picturescolourlibrary.co.uk**
🖥 **www.picturescolourlibrary.com**
See ad in showcase

Pictures of Britain Alma House, 73 Rodney Road, Cheltenham, Gloucestershire, GL50 1HT, United Kingdom
☎ (01242) 537923/ ☏ (01242) 537901
✉ info@picturesofbritain.co.uk
🖥 www.picturesofbritain.co.uk

Pictures of Manchester 13 Alan Road, Whitington, Manchester, M20 4NQ, United Kingdom
☎ 0161-448 2034/ ☏ 0161-291 1586
✉ info@picturesofmanchester.com
🖥 www.picturesofmanchester.com

Picturesmiths Manor Farm Cottage, Main Road, Curbridge, Witney, Oxfordshire, OX29 7NT, United Kingdom
☎ (01993) 771907
✉ picturesmiths@btinternet.com
🖥 www.picturesmiths.co.uk

Pitkin Publishing Ltd Healey House, Dene Road, Andover, Hampshire, SP10 2AA, United Kingdom
☎ (01264) 409200/ ☏ (01264) 334110
✉ heritagesales@jarrold-publishing.co.uk
🖥 www.britguide.com

Planet News/Popperfoto.com The Old Mill, Overstone Farm, Northampton, NN6 0AB, United Kingdom
☎ (01604) 670670/ ☏ (01604) 670635
✉ ian.blackwell@popperfoto.com
🖥 www.popperfoto.com

Planet Syndication 15 Blackheath Road, West Greenwich, London, SE10 8PE, United Kingdom
☎ (020) 8694 7110/ ☏ (020) 8469 4260
✉ sales@planetsyndication.com
🖥 www.planetsyndication.com

Popperfoto.com The Old Mill, Overstone Farm, Northampton, NN6 0AB, United Kingdom
☎ (01604) 670670/ ☏ (01604) 670635
✉ ian.blackwell@popperfoto.com
🖥 www.popperfoto.com

Premaphotos Wildlife Amberstone, 1 Kirland Road, Bodmin, Cornwall, PL30 5JQ, United Kingdom
☎ (01208) 78258/ ☏ (01208) 72302
✉ enquiries@premaphotos.com
🖥 www.premaphotos.com

Prodeepta Das 80 Clavering Road, Wanstead, London, E12 5EX, United Kingdom
☎ (020) 8530 3906/(07775) 578489
✉ prodeeptadas@hotmail.com

Professional Sport UK Ltd 18-19 Shaftesbury Quay, Hertford, SG14 1SF, United Kingdom
☎ (01992) 505000/ ☏ (01992) 505020
✉ pictures@prosport.co.uk
🖥 www.professionalsport.com

Professionally Different 16 Sandore Road, Seaford, East Sussex, BN25 3PR, United Kingdom
☎ (01323) 892429/ ☏ (01323) 897347
✉ chef@colin-capon.fsworld.co.uk

Prudence Waller 19 Vanbrugh Park, Blackheath, London, SE3 7AF, United Kingdom
☎ (020) 8858 4383

Pulse Picture Library Ludgate House, 245 Blackfriars Road, London, SE1 9UY, United Kingdom
☎ (020) 7921 8099/ ☏ (020) 7921 8133
✉ mcollard@cmpmedica.com
🖥 www.cmpimages.com

Punch Cartoon Library 87-135 Brompton Road, London, London, SW1X 7XL, United Kingdom
☎ (020) 7225 6710/ ☏ (020) 7225 6712
✉ punch.library@harrods.com
🖥 www.punch.co.uk

Punchstock Sherwood House, Forest Road, Richmond, Kew, Surrey, TW9 3BY, United Kingdom
☎ (0800) 073 0760/ ☏ (020) 8406 4805
✉ sales@punchstock.co.uk
🖥 www.punchstock.co.uk

Q A Photos Ltd La Rosiere, 24620 Les Eyzies, Les Eyzies, 24620, France
☎ (01303) 894141 (diverted from UK)
✉ pix@qaphotos.com
🖥 www.qaphotos.com

Rago & Waring The Chapel, Chapel Lane, Normanby-by-Spital, Market Rasen, Lincolnshire, LN8 2HG, United Kingdom
☎ (01673) 878615/ ☏ (01673) 878615
✉ protoangel@btinternet.com
🖥 www.protoangelwebdesign.com

Rail Images 5 Sandhurst Crescent, Leigh-on-Sea, Essex, SS9 4AL, United Kingdom
☎ (01702) 525059/(07713) 245640 ☏ (01702) 525059
✉ info@railimages.co.uk
🖥 www.railimages.co.uk

Railways - Milepost 92Ω Milepost 92 Ω, Newton Harcourt, Leicestershire, LE8 9FH, United Kingdom
☎ 0116-259 2068/ ☏ 0116-259 3001
✉ studio@railphotolibrary.com
🖥 www.railphotolibrary.com

Raleigh International Image Library Raleigh House, 27 Parsons Green Lane, London, SW6 4HZ, United Kingdom
☎ (020) 7371 8585/ ☏ (020) 7371 5852
✉ imagelibrary@raleigh.org.uk
🖥 www.raleighinternational.org

Ray Green Collection/Popperfoto.com The Old Mill, Overstone Farm, Northampton, NN6 0AB, United Kingdom
☎ (01604) 670670/ ☏ (01604) 670635
✉ ian.blackwell@popperfoto.com
🖥 www.popperfoto.com

Raymond Irons 35 Langbourne Mansions, Holly Lodge Estate, London, N6 6PR, United Kingdom
☎ (020) 8348 1805/ ☏ (020) 8348 3210
✉ info@rayirons.com
🖥 www.rayirons.com

Realistic Photo Graphics (Ariel Photo) Ltd Stafford Studios, 129A Stafford Road, Wallington, Surrey, SM6 9BN, United Kingdom
☎ (020) 8669 4900/ ☏ (020) 8773 0129
✉ info@realistic-digital.com
🖥 www.realistic-digital.com

Red Cover 7 Aura House, 53 Oldridge Road, London, SW12 8PP, United Kingdom
☎ (020) 8772 1110/ ☏ (020) 8772 3113
✉ info@redcover.com
🖥 www.redcover.com

Redferns Music Picture Library 7 Bramley Road, London, W10 6SZ, United Kingdom
☎ (020) 7792 9914/ ☏ (020) 7792 0921
✉ info@redferns.com
🖥 www.redferns.com

Refresh Images , Burton Overy, Leicestershire, United Kingdom
☎ (07867) 574316/(07870) 606958
✉ info@refreshimages.com
🖥 www.refreshimages.com

Religions Picture Library Beggars Roost, Woolpack Hill, Smeeth, Ashford, Kent, TN25 6RR, United Kingdom
☎ (01303) 812608/ ☏ (01303) 812608
✉ isobel@picture-library.freeserve.co.uk
🖥 www.picture-library.freeserve.co.uk

Repfoto 74 Creffield Road, London, W3 9PS, United Kingdom
☎ (020) 8995 3632/ ☏ (020) 8992 9641
✉ repfoto@btinternet.com
🖥 www.repfoto.com

reportdigital.co.uk 4 Clarence Road, Stratford-upon-Avon, Warwickshire, CV37 9DL, United Kingdom
☎ (01789) 262151/(07831) 121483
✉ info@reportdigital.co.uk
🖥 www.reportdigital.co.uk

Reportphotos.com Chocolate Factory, 4 Coburg Road, London, N22 6UJ, United Kingdom
☎ (07973) 219201
✉ andrew@reportphotos.com
🖥 www.reportphotos.com

Retna Pictures Ltd Unit 1A/1B, Farm Lane Trading Estate, 101 Farm Lane, London, SW6 1QJ, United Kingdom
☎ (0845) 0340645/(07711) 608607 ☏ (0845) 0340646
✉ ukinfo@retna.com
🖥 www.retna.com

Reunion Images 236 Westbourne Park Road, London, W11 1EL, United Kingdom
☎ (020) 7221 3489/ ☏ (020) 7792 9112
✉ info@reunion-images.com
🖥 www.reunion-images.com

Reuters 85 Fleet Street, London, EC4P 4AJ, United Kingdom
☎ (020) 7542 5050/ ☏ (020) 7542 2999
✉ uki.media@reuters.com
🖥 www.reuters.com/pictures

Rex Features Ltd 18 Vine Hill, London, EC1R 5DZ, United Kingdom
📞 (020) 7278 7294/📠 (020) 7837 4812
✉ library@rexfeatures.com
🖥 www.rexfeatures.com

Rick Tomlinson Photography 10 Birmingham Road, Cowes, Isle of Wight, PO31 7BH, United Kingdom
📞 (01983) 248512
✉ photos@rick-tomlinson.com
🖥 www.rick-tomlinson.com

Riley Research 190 Ladbroke Grove, London, W10 5LZ, United Kingdom
📞 (020) 8968 7236/(07793) 818819 📠 (020) 8960 1678
✉ rileyresearch.uk@virgin.net

RMN Photo Agency 10 Rue de L'Abbaye, Paris, 75006, France
📞 1 4013 4900/📠 1 4013 4601
✉ photo@rmn.fr
🖥 www.photo.rmn.fr
See ad in showcase

Robbie Jack Photography 45 Church Road, Hanwell, London, W7 3BD, United Kingdom
📞 (020) 8567 9616/(07774) 235533
✉ robbie@robbiejack.com
🖥 www.robbiejack.com

Robert Estall Photo Agency 12-14 Swan Street, Boxford, Sudbury, Suffolk, CO10 5NZ, United Kingdom
📞 (01787) 210111/📠 (01787) 211440
✉ robertestall@mac.com
🖥 www.africanceremonies.com

Robert Harding World Imagery 58-59 Great Marlborough Street, London, W1F 7JY, United Kingdom
📞 (020) 7478 4000/📠 (020) 7478 4161
✉ info@robertharding.com
🖥 www.robertharding.com

Robert Opie Collection 120 Gordon Road, London, W13 8PJ, United Kingdom
📞 (020) 8997 6419

Ron Evans Garden Images 31 High Meadow, Cannock Wood, Rugeley, Staffordshire, WS15 4RJ, United Kingdom
📞 (01543) 676343/(07941) 822361
✉ ron@evans01543.freeserve.co.uk
🖥 www.ronevans.co.uk

Ronald Grant Archive The Masters House, The Old Lambeth Workhouse, 2 Dugard Way, off Renfrew Road, London, SE11 4TH, United Kingdom
📞 (020) 7840 2200/📠 (020) 7840 2299
✉ pixdesk@rgapix.com
🖥 www.ronaldgrantarchive.com

Rotherhithe Picture Research Library 82 St. Mary Church Street, London, SE16 4HZ, United Kingdom
📞 (020) 7231 2209/📠 (020) 7231 2119
✉ ostockman@sandsfilms.co.uk
🖥 www.sandsfilms.co.uk

Royal Collection Enterprises Ltd Photographic Services, St James's Palace, London, SW1A 1JR, United Kingdom
📞 (020) 7839 1377/📠 (020) 7024 5643
✉ photoservices@royalcollection.org.uk
🖥 www.royalcollection.org.uk

Royal Geographical Society 1 Kensington Gore, London, SW7 2AR, United Kingdom
📞 (020) 7591 3060/📠 (020) 7591 3001
✉ images@rgs.org
🖥 www.rgs.org/images

Royal Mail Film Archive , Sittingbourne, Kent, ME10 1NH, United Kingdom
📞 (01795) 426465/📠 (01795) 437988
✉ info@edist.co.uk

RSPB Images The Old Dairy, Broadfield Road, Sheffield, S8 0XQ, United Kingdom
📞 **0114-258 0001/📠 0114-258 0101**
✉ **sales@rspb-images.com**
🖥 **www.rspb-images.com**

RSPCA Photolibrary Wilberforce Way, Southwater, Horsham, West Sussex, RH13 9RS, United Kingdom
📞 **(0870) 7540150/📠 (0870) 7530150**
✉ **pictures@rspcaphotolibrary.com**
🖥 **www.rspcaphotolibrary.com**

Russia & Eastern Images Sonning, Cheapside Lane, Denham, Uxbridge, Middlesex, UB9 5AE, United Kingdom
📞 (01895) 833508
✉ easteuropix@btinternet.com
🖥 www.easteuropix.com

Sally & Richard Greenhill 357 Liverpool Road, London, N1 1NL, United Kingdom
📞 (020) 7607 8549
✉ sr.greenhill@virgin.net
🖥 www.srgreenhill.co.uk

SARL Roger Moss Balandiere, Linazay, France
📞 00 33 549871721
✉ contact@picturefrance.com
🖥 www.picturefrance.com

Scala Group SPA Via Chiantigiana 62, Antella, Florence, 50011, Italy
📞 00 39 055 6233 216/📠 00 39 055 6411 24
✉ firenze@scalarchives.it
🖥 www.scalarchives.it

Scenic Ireland 17 Clarence Street, Belfast, BT2 8DY, United Kingdom
📞 (028) 9024 5038/📠 (028) 9023 1942
✉ chrishillphotographic@btclick.com
🖥 www.scenicireland.com

Science & Society Picture Library Science Museum, Exhibition Road, London, SW7 2DD, United Kingdom
📞 020 7942 4400/📠 020 7942 4401
✉ piclib@nmsi.ac.uk
🖥 www.scienceandsociety.co.uk

Science Photo Library 327-329 Harrow Road, London, W9 3RB, United Kingdom
📞 (020) 7432 1100/📠 (020) 7286 8668
✉ info@sciencephoto.com
🖥 www.sciencephoto.com

Science Photo Library Ltd 327-329 Harrow Road, London, W9 3RB, United Kingdom
📞 (020) 7432 1100/📠 (020) 7286 8668
✉ info@sciencephoto.com
🖥 www.sciencephoto.com

Scope Beauty 26-29 St Cross Street, Hatton Garden, London, EC1N 8UH, United Kingdom
📞 (020) 7405 2997/📠 (020) 7831 4549
✉ images@scopefeatures.com
🖥 www.scopefeatures.com

Scope Features 26-29 St Cross Street, Hatton Garden, London, EC1N 8UH, United Kingdom
📞 (020) 7405 2997/📠 (0207) 7831 4549
✉ larryandrew@scopefeatures.com
🖥 www.scopefeatures.com

Scott Polar Research Institute Picture Library University of Cambridge, Lensfield Road, Cambridge, CB2 1ER, United Kingdom
📞 (01223) 336547/📠 (01223) 336549
✉ picture.library@spri.cam.ac.uk
🖥 www.spri.cam.ac.uk

Scottish Viewpoint 64 Polwarth Gardens, Edinburgh, EH11 1LL, United Kingdom
📞 0131-622 7174
✉ info@scottishviewpoint.com
🖥 www.scottishviewpoint.com

SCRAN 17 Kittle Yards, Edinburgh, EH9 1PJ, United Kingdom
📞 0131-662 1211/📠 0131-662 1511
✉ scran@scran.ac.uk
🖥 www.scran.ac.uk

Sea Spring Photos Lyme View, West Bexington, Dorchester, Dorset, DT2 9DD, United Kingdom
📞 (01308) 897766/📠 (01308) 897735
✉ sales@seaspringphotos.com
🖥 www.seaspringphotos.com

Seaco Picture Library Sea Containers House, 20 Upper Ground, London, SE1 9PF, United Kingdom
📞 (020) 7805 5831/📠 (020) 7805 5905
✉ research@ilnpictures.co.uk

Sealand Aerial Photography Ltd Pitlands Farm, Up Marden, Chichester, West Sussex, PO18 9JP, UK
📞 (023) 9263 1468/📠 (023) 9263 1890
✉ sales@sealandap.co.uk
🖥 www.sealandap.co.uk

Sheila Corr 77 Hemingford Road, London, N1 1BY, United Kingdom
📞 (020) 7607 7864/📠 (020) 7607 7864

Shell Photographic Services and Library Shell International Ltd, Shell Centre, London, SE1 7NA, United Kingdom
📞 (020) 7934 4817/📠 (020) 7934 7490
✉ photographicservices@shell.com
🖥 www.shell.com

Silvestris Fotoservice/F L P A Images of Nature Pages Green House, Wetheringsett, Stowmarket, Suffolk, IP14 5QA, United Kingdom
📞 (01728) 860789/📠 (01728) 860222
✉ pictures@flpa-images.co.uk
🖥 www.flpa-images.co.uk

Simmons Aerofilms Ltd 32-34 Station Close, Potters Bar, Hertfordshire, EN6 1TL, United Kingdom
📞 (01707) 648390/📠 (01707) 648399
✉ library@aerofilms.com
🖥 www.simmonsaerofilms.com

Simon Booth Photography 13 Blackburn Brow, Chorley, Lancashire, PR6 9AG, United Kingdom
📞 (01257) 234838
✉ info@simonboothphotography.com
🖥 www.simonboothphotography.com

Skies 19 Chippenham Mews, London, W9 2AN, United Kingdom
📞 (020) 7286 3688/(07767) 860504 📠 (020) 7266 3920

Skishoot Offshoot Hall Place, Upper Woodcott, Whitchurch, Hampshire, RG28 7PY, United Kingdom
📞 (01635) 255527/📠 (01635) 255528
✉ pictures@skishoot.co.uk
🖥 www.skishoot.co.uk

Skyscan Photolibrary Oak House, Toddington, Cheltenham, Gloucestershire, GL54 5BY, United Kingdom
📞 (01242) 621357/📠 (01242) 621343
✉ info@skyscan.co.uk
🖥 www.skyscan.co.uk

Snookerimages 10 Brow Close, Windermere, Cumbria, LA23 2HA, United Kingdom
📞 (01539) 448894/(07768) 808249
✉ snooker@snookerimages.co.uk
🖥 www.snookerimages.co.uk

Sonia Halliday Photographs 22 Bates Lane, Aylesbury, Buckinghamshire, HP22 5SL, United Kingdom
📞 (01296) 612266/📠 (01296) 612266
✉ info@soniahalliday.com
🖥 www.soniahalliday.com

Sophia Gibb Picture Research 9 Archel Road, Barons Court, London, W14 9QJ, United Kingdom
📞 (020) 7385 7585
✉ sophia.gibb@btinternet.com

Sotheby's Picture Library Level 2, Olympia 2, Hammersmith Road, London, W14 8UX, United Kingdom
📞 (020) 7293 5383/📠 (020) 7293 5062
✉ piclib@sothebys.com
🖥 www.sothebys.com

South American Pictures 48 Station Road, Woodbridge, Suffolk, IP12 4AT, United Kingdom
📞 (01394) 383963/📠 (01394) 380176
✉ morrison@southamericanpictures.com
🖥 www.southamericanpictures.com

Stay Still Ltd 29-31 Saffron Hill, London, EC1N 8SW, United Kingdom
📞 (020) 7421 6008/📠 (020) 7421 6006
✉ info@staystill.com
🖥 www.staystill.com

Steam Museum of the GWR Kemble Drive, Swindon, SN2 2TA, United Kingdom
📞 (01793) 466607/📠 (01793) 466615
✉ steamlibrary@swindon.gov.uk
🖥 www.swindon.gov.uk/steam

Steve Bloom Images Middlefield House, Olantigh Road, Wye, Ashford, Kent, TN25 5EP, United Kingdom
📞 (01233) 813777/📠 (01233) 813887
✉ sales@stevebloom.com
🖥 www.stevebloom.com

Steve Bond Photography 3 Stone Cottages, Furnace Lane, Lamberhurst, Tunbridge Wells, Kent, TN3 8LF, United Kingdom
📞 (01892) 891690/(07778) 177 690
✉ steve@stevebond.co.uk
🖥 www.stevebond.co.uk

Steven Behr Bearsden, Bourneside, Virginia Water, Surrey, GU25 4LZ, United Kingdom
📞 (01344) 844428/(07973) 719060
✉ info@stockfile.co.uk
🖥 www.stockfile.co.uk

Steven Morris Photography London, United Kingdom
📞 (07973) 523160
✉ steven@stevenmorris.com
🖥 www.stevenmorris.com

Still Pictures 199 Shooters Hill Road, Blackheath, London, SE3 8UL, United Kingdom
📞 (020) 8858 8307/📠 (020) 8858 2049
✉ info@stillpictures.com
🖥 www.stillpictures.com

Stockfile Bearsden, Bourneside, Virginia Water, Surrey, GU25 4LZ, United Kingdom
📞 (01344) 844428/(07973) 719060
✉ info@stockfile.co.uk
🖥 www.stockfile.co.uk

Stockscotland The Croft Studio, Croft Roy, Tain, Ross-shire, IV19 1JG, United Kingdom
📞 (01862) 892298/(07739) 795051 / 📠 (01862) 892298
✉ info@stockscotland.com
🖥 www.stockscotland.com

Stockshot 2B St. Vincent Street, Edinburgh, EH3 6SH, United Kingdom
📞 0131-557 6688/ 📠 0131-556 8282
✉ pictures@stockshot.co.uk
🖥 www.stockshot.co.uk

Sue Cunningham 56 Chatham Road, Kingston upon Thames, Surrey, KT1 3AA, United Kingdom
📞 (020) 8541 3024/ 📠 (020) 8541 5388
✉ pictures@scphotographic.com
🖥 www.scphotographic.com

Sutton Motor Sport Images The Chapel, 61 Watling Street, Towcester, Northamptonshire, NN12 6AG, United Kingdom
📞 (01327) 352188/ 📠 (01327) 359355
✉ customerservices@sutton-images.com
🖥 www.sutton-images.com

Sylvia Cordaiy Photo Library 45 Rotherstone, Devizes, Wiltshire, SN10 2DD, United Kingdom
📞 (01380) 728327/ 📠 (01380) 728328
✉ info@sylvia-cordaiy.com
🖥 www.sylvia-cordaiy.com

Sylvia Cordaiy Photo Library Ltd 45 Rotherstone, Devizes, Wiltshire, SN10 2DD, United Kingdom
📞 (01380) 728327/ 📠 (01380) 728328
✉ info@sylvia-cordaiy.com
🖥 www.sylvia-cordaiy.com

Sylvia Pitcher Photo Library 75 Bristol Road, Forest Gate, London, E7 8HG, United Kingdom
📞 (020) 8552 8308/ 📠 (020) 8552 8308
✉ spphotolibrary@aol.com
🖥 www.sylviapitcherphotos.com

T R H Pictures Ltd 2 Reform Street, Beith, Ayrshire, KA15 2AE, United Kingdom
📞 (0845) 2235451/ 📠 (0845) 2235452
🖥 www.codyimages.com

Tate Picture Library 21 John Islip Street, London, SW1P 4LL, United Kingdom
📞 (020) 7887 8867/ 📠 (020) 7887 8805
✉ picture.library@tate.org.uk
🖥 www.tate.org.uk

Telegraph Syndication 111 Buckingham Palace Road, London, SW1W 0DT, United Kingdom
📞 (020) 7931 2925/ 📠 (020) 7931 2867
✉ syndication@telegraph.co.uk
🖥 www.syndication.telegraph.co.uk

Tessa Traeger Picture Library 7 Rossetti Studios, 72 Flood Street, London, SW3 5TF, United Kingdom
📞 (020) 7352 3641/ 📠 (020) 7352 4846
✉ info@tessatraeger.com
🖥 www.tessatraeger.com

Thats Good Foxes Studio, Heath Road, Ramsden Heath, Billericay, Essex, CM11 1HR, United Kingdom
📞 (01268) 711611/ 📠 (01268) 710353
✉ claire@thatsgood.biz
🖥 www.thatsgood.biz

The Advertising Archives 45 Lyndale Avenue, London, NW2 2QB, United Kingdom
📞 (020) 7435 6540/ 📠 (020) 7794 6584
✉ library@advertisingarchives.co.uk
🖥 www.advertisingarchives.co.uk

The Garden Collection 6 Dorset Road, Harrow, Middlesex, HA1 4JG, United Kingdom
📞 (020) 2263 8298/ 📠 (020) 8863 6383
✉ info@garden-collection.com
🖥 www.garden-collection.com

The Garden Collection Garden Photography 6 Dorset Road, Harrow, Middlesex, HA1 4JG, United Kingdom
📞 (020) 8863 8236/ 📠 (020) 8863 6383
✉ liz@garden-collection.com
🖥 www.garden-collection.com

The Illustrated Magazine/Popperfoto.com The Old Mill, Overstone Farm, Northampton, NN6 0AB, United Kingdom
📞 (01604) 670670/ 📠 (01604) 670635
✉ ian.blackwell@popperfoto.com
🖥 www.popperfoto.com

The Illustration Library 2 Brooks Court, Cringle Street, London, SW8 5BX, United Kingdom
📞 (020) 7720 5202/ 📠 (020) 7720 5920
✉ team@illustrationweb.com
🖥 www.illustrationweb.com

The Image Barn Ltd The Barn Studio, Hatches, Sandlecopse, Sandle Heath, Fordingbridge, Hampshire, SP6 1DX, United Kingdom
📞 (01425) 656657
✉ mike@theimagebarn.co.uk
🖥 www.theimagebarn.co.uk

The Image Store The Studio, West Hill, St. Helier, Jersey, JE2 3HB, United Kingdom
📞 (01534) 769933/(07797) 715489 / 📠 (01534) 789191
✉ peter-trenchard@jerseymail.co.uk
🖥 www.peter-trenchard.com

The Interior Archive 1 Ruston Mews, London, W11 1RB, United Kingdom
📞 (020) 7221 9922/ 📠 (020) 7221 9933
✉ karen@interior-archive.netkonect.co.uk
🖥 www.interiorarchive.com

The Irish Image Collection Unit 507, Clerkenwell Workshops, 31 Clerkenwell Close, London, EC1R 0AT, United Kingdom
📞 (020) 7014 3404
✉ info@theirishimagecollection.com

The Kobal Collection 2 The Quadrant, 135 Salusbury Road, London, NW6 6RJ, United Kingdom
📞 (020) 7624 3500/ 📠 (020) 7624 3355
✉ info@picture-desk.com
🖥 www.picture-desk.com

The Library of Sealand Aerial Photography Meadows Unit, 51 Stean Street, Halnaker, Chichester, West Sussex, PO18 0NF, United Kingdom
📞 (01243) 781551/(07722) 115212
✉ info@sealandaerial.co.uk
🖥 www.sealandaerial.co.uk

The Marsden Archive The Presbytery, Hainton, Market Rasen, Lincolnshire, LN8 6LR, United Kingdom
📞 (01507) 313646/ 📠 (01507) 313646
✉ info@marsdenarchive.com
🖥 www.marsdenarchive.com

RSPB**IMAGES**
British Wildlife & Nature

Take a closer look at
www.rspb-images.com
0114 258 0001 sales@rspb-images.com

The Museum of English Rural Life University of Reading, Redlands Road, Reading, RG1 5EX, United Kingdom
📞 0118-378 8668/ 📠 0118-378-5632
✉ merl@reading.ac.uk
🖥 www.merl.org.uk

The National Archives Kew, Richmond, Surrey, TW9 4DU, United Kingdom
📞 (020) 8392 5225/ 📠 (020) 8487 1974
✉ image-library@nationalarchives.gov.uk
🖥 www.nationalarchives.gov.uk/imagelibrary

The Neil Williams Classical Collection 22 Avon, Hockley, Tamworth, Staffordshire, B77 5QA, United Kingdom
📞 (01827) 286086/07963 194921 / 📠 (01827) 286086
✉ neil@classicalcollection.co.uk

The Photo Library Wales 2 Bro-Nant, Church Road, Pentyrch, Cardiff, CF15 9QG, United Kingdom
📞 (029) 2089 0311
✉ info@photolibrarywales.com
🖥 www.photolibrarywales.com

The Picture Desk 2 The Quadrant, 135 Salusbury Road, London, London, NW6 6RJ, United Kingdom
📞 (020) 7624 3300/ 📠 (020) 7624 3355
✉ info@picture-desk.com
🖥 www.picture-desk.com

The Picture Library Ltd 16 Crescent Road, London, N22 7RS, United Kingdom
📞 (020) 8365 8389
✉ joanne@thepicturelibraryltd.net
🖥 www.alandavidson.net

The Picture Research Association 1st Floor, 1 Willow Court, London, EC2A 4QB, United Kingdom
📞 020 7739 8544/ 📠 020 7782 0011
✉ chair@picture-research.org.uk
🖥 www.picture-research.org.uk
See ad in showcase

The Sky Library 8 Ancaster Road, West Park, Leeds, LS16 5HH, United Kingdom
📞 0113-230 2590/ 📠 0113-275 0202
✉ jane@theskylibrary.com
🖥 www.theskylibrary.com

The Tinsley Lockhart Group 44 West Preston Street, Edinburgh, EH8 9PY, United Kingdom
📞 0131-466 7767
✉ creative@tinsleylockhart.com
🖥 www.tinsleylockhart.com

The Travel Library Unit 7, The Kiln Workshops, Pilcot Road, Crookham Village, Fleet, Hampshire, GU51 5RY, United Kingdom
📞 (01252) 627233/ 📠 (01252) 812399
✉ info@travel-library.co.uk
🖥 www.travel-library.co.uk

This Life Pictures Chytresor, 18 Pauls Row, Truro, Cornwall, TR1 1HH, United Kingdom
📞 (01872) 240260
✉ find@thislifepictures.com

Thoroughbred Photography Ltd The Hornbeams, 2 The Street, Worlington, Bury St. Edmunds, Suffolk, IP28 8RU, United Kingdom
📞 (01638) 713944/ 📠 (01638) 713945
✉ mail@thoroughbredphoto.com
🖥 www.thoroughbredphoto.com

Tim Graham Picture Library 30 Bracknell Gardens, London, NW3 7ED, United Kingdom
☎ (020) 7435 7693/📠 (020) 7431 4312
✉ mail@timgraham.co.uk
🖥 www.royalphotographs.com

Tony Nathan The Little Cottage, 31 High Street, Cranley, Guildford, Surrey, GU6 8AS, United Kingdom
☎ (01483) 275149
✉ nathanstudio@hotmail.com
🖥 www.nathan-weddings-photographers.com

Topham Picturepoint House of Jaques, 1 Fircroft Way, Edenbridge, Kent, TN8 6EL, United Kingdom
☎ (01732) 863939/📠 (01732) 860215
✉ requests@topfoto.co.uk
🖥 www.topfoto.co.uk

Travel Ink Photo & Feature Library The Old Coach House, 14 High Street, Goring on Thames, Reading, RG8 9AR, United Kingdom
☎ (01491) 873011/📠 (01491) 875558
✉ info@travel-ink.co.uk
🖥 www.travel-ink.co.uk

Travelshots.com Longfield Cottage, 3B Uplands Close, London, SW14 7AS, United Kingdom
☎ (020) 8878 2226/📠 (020) 8392 2920
✉ sales@travelshots.com
🖥 www.travelshots.com

Trevillion Images 75 Jeddo Road, London, W12 9ED, United Kingdom
☎ (020) 8740 9005
✉ info@trevillion.com
🖥 www.trevillion.com

Trevor Jones Thoroughbred Photography The Hornbeams, 2 The Street, Worlington, Bury St. Edmunds, Suffolk, IP28 8RU, United Kingdom
☎ (01638) 713944
✉ mail@throroughbredphoto.com
🖥 www.thoroughbredphoto.com

Ulster Folk & Transport Museum 153 Bangor Road, Cultra, Holywood, County Down, BT18 0EU, United Kingdom
☎ (028) 9042 8428/📠 (028) 9042 8728
✉ ken.anderson@magni.org.uk
🖥 www.magni.org.uk

Ulster Museum Picture Library, National Museums Northern Ireland, Cultra, Holywood BT18 0EU, United Kingdom
☎ **(028) 9039 5109**/📠 **(028) 9039 5004**
✉ michelle.ashmore@magni.org.uk
🖥 **www.ulstermuseum.org.uk**
See ad

Untitled Radar Studio, Coldblow Lane, Thurnham, Maidstone, Kent, ME14 3LR, United Kingdom
☎ (01622) 737722/📠 (01622) 738644
✉ info@untitled.co.uk
🖥 www.untitled.co.uk

V & A Images Cromwell Road, South Kensington, London, SW7 2RL, United Kingdom
☎ (020) 7942 2483/📠 (020) 7942 2482
✉ vanda.images@vam.ac.uk
🖥 www.vandaimages.com

Vaughan Williams Memorial Library (EFDSS) Cecil Sharp House, 2 Regents Park Road, London, NW1 7AY, United Kingdom
☎ (020) 7485 2206/📠 (020) 7284 0523
✉ library@efdss.org
🖥 www.efdss.org

Veneta Bullen c/o Scala Art Resource, 1 Willow Court, London, EC2A 4QB, United Kingdom
☎ (020) 7739 8544/📠 (020) 7782 0011
✉ v.bullen@btinternet.com

Venturepix Ltd 29 London Road, Sawbridgeworth, Hertfordshire, CM21 9EH, United Kingdom
☎ (020) 8150 9120/(07970) 262505
✉ pictures@kumaraimages.com
🖥 www.kumaraimages.com

VIEW Pictures Ltd 14 The Dove Centre, 109 Bartholomew Road, London, NW5 2BJ, United Kingdom
☎ (020) 7284 2928/📠 (020) 7284 3617
✉ info@viewpictures.co.uk
🖥 www.viewpictures.co.uk

Viewing Medicine 24 Craigwell Avenue, Radlett, Hertfordshire, WD7 7EX, United Kingdom
☎ (01923) 857308/(07771) 534450
✉ mikewyndham@btinternet.com
🖥 www.viewingmedicine.com

Vin Mag Archive Ltd Vinmag House, 84-90 Digby Road, London, E9 6HX, United Kingdom
☎ (020) 8533 7588/📠 (020) 8533 7283
✉ piclib@vinmag.com
🖥 www.vinmagarchive.com

Visions in Golf The Barn, 6 Wood End Court, Dodworth, Barnsley, South Yorkshire, S75 3UA, United Kingdom
☎ (01226) 286111/(07894) 050908
✉ info@visionsingolf.com
🖥 www.visionsingolf.com

W W F UK Panda House, Weyside Park, Godalming, Surrey, GU7 1XR, United Kingdom
☎ (01483) 426444/📠 (01483) 426409
✉ garmfield@wwf.org.uk
🖥 www.wwf.org.uk

Waterways Photo Library 39 Manor Court Road, Hanwell, London, W7 3EJ, United Kingdom
☎ (020) 8840 1659/(07721) 329950/📠 (020) 8567 0605
✉ watphot39@aol.com
🖥 www.waterwaysphotolibrary.com

Wellcome Images 183 Euston Road, London, NW1 2BE, United Kingdom
☎ (020) 7611 8348/📠 (020) 7611 8577
✉ images@wellcome.ac.uk
🖥 www.images.wellcome.ac.uk

West Country Pictures 10 Headon Gardens, Exeter, EX2 6LE, United Kingdom
☎ (01392) 426640/(07763) 367639
✉ peter@cooperphotography.co.uk
🖥 www.cooperphotography.co.uk

Wiener Library 4 Devonshire Street, London, W1W 5BH, United Kingdom
☎ (020) 7636 7247/📠 (020) 7436 6428
✉ info@wienerlibrary.co.uk
🖥 www.wienerlibrary.co.uk

art
archaeology
world cultures
natural history
historical photographs

www.ulstermuseum.org.uk

national **museums** northern ireland

ULSTER MUSEUM PICTURE LIBRARY

Wild Images Ltd 4 Leigh Road, Clifton, Bristol, BS8 2DA, United Kingdom
📞 0117-970 6026/📠 0117-973 6866
✉ samantha@zebrafilms.co.uk
🖥 www.rspcaphotolibrary.com

Wilderness Photographic Library 4 Kings Court, Kirkby Lonsdale, Cumbria, LA6 2BP, United Kingdom
📞 (01524) 272149/📠 (01524) 272149
✉ wildernessphoto@btinternet.com
🖥 www.wildernessphoto.co.uk

Window on the World Picture Library 124 Cornwall Road, London, SE1 8TQ, United Kingdom
📞 (020) 7928 3448/📠 (020) 7620 0350
✉ usill@winworld.co.uk
🖥 www.winworld.co.uk

Wireimage UK Mission Studios, 145 Marlborough Road, London, N19 4AN, United Kingdom
📞 (020) 7281 5599/📠 (020) 7281 7744
✉ james@wireimage.com
🖥 www.wireimage.com

Woodfall Wild Images 17 Bull Lane, Denbigh, LL16 3SN, United Kingdom
📞 (01745) 815903/📠 (01745) 814581
✉ wwimages@woodfall.com
🖥 www.woodfall.com

World Aerospace Series 33 Oakhurst Avenue, East Barnet, Barnet, Hertfordshire, EN4 8DN, United Kingdom
📞 (020) 8368 4997/📠 (020) 8368 4997
✉ info@intercarb.org

World Pictures 29-31 Saffron Hill, London, EC1N 8SW, United Kingdom
📞 (020) 7421 6004/📠 (020) 7421 6006
✉ worldpictures@btinternet.com
🖥 www.worldpictures.co.uk

World Religions Photo Library/ Christine Osborne Pictures 53A Crimsworth Road, London, SW8 4RJ, United Kingdom
📞 (020) 7720 6951/📠 (020) 7720 6951
✉ co@worldreligions.co.uk
🖥 www.worldreligions.co.uk

Worldwide Picture Library Unit 2, Telford Road, Basingstoke, Hampshire, RG21 6YU, United Kingdom
📞 (01256) 814 070/📠 (01256) 814 643
✉ info@worldwidepicturelibrary.com
🖥 www.worldwidepicturelibrary.com

York Archaeological Trust for Excavation & Research Ltd 47 Old Walk, York, YO1 7BX, United Kingdom
📞 (01904) 663000/📠 (01904) 663024
✉ enquiries@yorkarchaeology.co.uk
🖥 www.yorkarchaeology.co.uk

Zefa Visual Media UK Ltd Threeways House, 40 - 44 Clipstone Street, London, W1W 5DW, United Kingdom
📞 (020) 7644 7490/079 77 570427 📠 (020) 7079 0541
✉ info@zefa.co.uk
🖥 www.zefa.co.uk

Zooid Pictures Ltd 66 Alexander Road, London, N19 3PQ, United Kingdom
📞 (020) 7281 2407/📠 (020) 7281 2404
✉ pictures@zooid.co.uk
🖥 www.zooid.co.uk

Zoological Society of London Zoological Society of London, Photo Library, Regent's Park, London, NW1 4RY, United Kingdom
📞 (020) 7449 6293/📠 (020) 7586 5743
✉ laurie.sherwood@zsl.org
🖥 www.zsl.org

ARCHITECTURE AND INTERIORS

Arcblue 93 Gainsborough Road, Richmond, Surrey, TW9 2ET, United Kingdom
📞 (020) 8940 2227/📠 (020) 8940 6570
✉ info@arcblue.com
🖥 www.arcblue.com

Bridgeman Art Library (FOCAL) BAPLA 17-19 Garway Road, London, W2 4PH, United Kingdom
📞 **(020) 7727 4065**/📠 **(020) 7792 8509**
✉ london@bridgeman.co.uk
🖥 **www.bridgemanart.com**
See ad

Lonely Planet Images 72-82 Rosebery Avenue, London, EC1R 4RW, United Kingdom
📞 (020) 7841 9062/📠 (020) 7841 9001
✉ lpi@lonelyplanet.co.uk
🖥 www.lonelyplanetimages.com

Robert Harding World Imagery 58-59 Great Marlborough Street, London, W1F 7JY, United Kingdom
📞 (020) 7478 4000/📠 (020) 7478 4161
✉ info@robertharding.com
🖥 www.robertharding.com

ARTS AND ENTERTAINMENT

Bridgeman Art Library (FOCAL) BAPLA 17-19 Garway Road, London, W2 4PH, United Kingdom
📞 **(020) 7727 4065**/📠 **(020) 7792 8509**
✉ london@bridgeman.co.uk
🖥 **www.bridgemanart.com**
See ad

EDITORIAL FEATURES

foodanddrinkphotos.ltd Studio 4, Sun Studios, 30 Warple Way, London, W3 0RX, United Kingdom
📞 (020) 8740 6610/📠 (020) 8762 9994
✉ info@foodanddrinkphotos.com
🖥 www.foodanddrinkphotos.com

Robert Harding World Imagery 58-59 Great Marlborough Street, London, W1F 7JY, United Kingdom
📞 (020) 7478 4000/📠 (020) 7478 4161
✉ info@robertharding.com
🖥 www.robertharding.com

Royal Geographical Society 1 Kensington Gore, London, SW7 2AR, United Kingdom
📞 (020) 7591 3060/📠 (020) 7591 3001
✉ images@rgs.org
🖥 www.rgs.org/images

Wonderfuel 118 Hatherley Gardens, London, E6 3HQ, United Kingdom
📞 020 8548 1358
✉ info@wonderfuel.co.uk
🖥 www.wonderfuel.co.uk

Next time your campaign needs to hit the target...

Classic images with a contemporary twist – culture • fine art • history

THE BRIDGEMAN ART LIBRARY
www.bridgemanart.com

TRAVEL GEOGRAPHY AND CULTURE

Wonderfuel 118 Hatherley Gardens, London, E6 3HQ, United Kingdom
☎ 020 8548 1358
✉ info@wonderfuel.co.uk
🖳 www.wonderfuel.co.uk

HISTORY

Bridgeman Art Library (FOCAL) BAPLA 17-19 Garway Road, London, W2 4PH, United Kingdom
☎ **(020) 7727 4065**/✆ **(020) 7792 8509**
✉ **london@bridgeman.co.uk**
🖳 **www.bridgemanart.com**
See ad in showcase

Mary Evans Picture Library - History 59 Tranquil Vale, Blackheath, London, SE3 0BS, United Kingdom
☎ (020) 8318 0034/✆ (020) 8852 7211
✉ mark.bezodis@maryevans.com
🖳 www.maryevans.com

Palestine Exploration Fund Photographic Archive 2 Hinde Mews, Marylebone Lane, London, W1U 2AA, United Kingdom
☎ (020) 7935 5379/✆ (020) 7486 7438
✉ curator@pef.org.uk
🖳 www.pef.org.uk

Robert Harding World Imagery 58-59 Great Marlborough Street, London, W1F 7JY, United Kingdom
☎ (020) 7478 4000/✆ (020) 7478 4161
✉ info@robertharding.com
🖳 www.robertharding.com

Royal Geographical Society 1 Kensington Gore, London, SW7 2AR, United Kingdom
☎ (020) 7591 3060/✆ (020) 7591 3001
✉ images@rgs.org
🖳 www.rgs.org/images

INDUSTRY AND COMMERCE

Image Source Ltd 41 Great Pulteney Street, London, W1F 9NZ, United Kingdom
☎ (020) 7851 5700/✆ (020) 7851 5601
✉ info@imagesource.com
🖳 www.imagesource.com

Matton Images UK Ltd 2 Western Avenue Business Park, Mansfield Road, London, W3 0BZ, United Kingdom
☎ (020) 8753 7000/✆ (020) 8753 7001
✉ info@mattonimages.co.uk
🖳 www.mattonimages.co.uk

NATURAL WORLD

Absolutely Wild Visuals PO Box 48694, London, NW8 1BG,
☎ 2076044998
✉ kate@wildvisuals.com.au
🖳 www.absolutelywildvisuals.com

Arcblue 93 Gainsborough Road, Richmond, Surrey, TW9 2ET, United Kingdom
☎ (020) 8940 2227/✆ (020) 8940 6570
✉ info@arcblue.com
🖳 www.arcblue.com

ARDEA Wildlife Pets Environment 35 Brodrick Road, Wandsworth Common, London, SW17 7DX, United Kingdom
☎ (020) 8672 2067/✆ (020) 8672 8787
✉ ardea@ardea.com
🖳 www.ardea.com

BAA Aviation Photo Library Green Dragon Vaults, Parliament Square, Hertford, SG14 1PT, United Kingdom
☎ (01992) 501134/✆ (01992) 501174
✉ sales@in-press.co.uk
🖳 www.baa.com/photolibrary

foodanddrinkphotos.ltd Studio 4, Sun Studios, 30 Warple Way, London, W3 0RX, United Kingdom
☎ (020) 8740 6610/✆ (020) 8762 9994
✉ info@foodanddrinkphotos.com
🖳 www.foodanddrinkphotos.com

Kos Picture Source Ltd P O Box 52854, 7 Spice Court, London, SW11 3UU, United Kingdom
☎ (020) 7801 0044/✆ (020) 7801 0055
✉ images@kospictures.com
🖳 www.kospictures.com

Lonely Planet Images 72-82 Rosebery Avenue, London, EC1R 4RW, United Kingdom
☎ (020) 7841 9062/✆ (020) 7841 9001
✉ lpi@lonelyplanet.co.uk
🖳 www.lonelyplanetimages.com

Mary Evans Picture Library - History 59 Tranquil Vale, Blackheath, London, SE3 0BS, United Kingdom
☎ (020) 8318 0034/✆ (020) 8852 7211
✉ mark.bezodis@maryevans.com
🖳 www.maryevans.com

Nature Picture Library Broadcasting House, Whiteladies Road, Bristol, BS8 2LR, United Kingdom
☎ 0117-974 6720/✆ 0117-923 8166
✉ info@naturepl.com
🖳 www.naturepl.com

P S P 49 Palmerston Avenue, Goring-by-Sea, Worthing, West Sussex, BN12 4RN, United Kingdom
☎ (01903) 503147/✆ (01903) 503147
✉ info@peterstiles.com
🖳 www.peterstiles.com

Pictures Colour Library Ltd 10 James Whatman Court, Turkey Mill, Maidstone, Kent, ME14 5SS, United Kingdom
☎ **(01622) 609809**/✆ **(01622) 609806**
✉ **enquiries@picturescolourlibrary.co.uk**
🖳 **www.picturescolourlibrary.com**
See ad in showcase

Robert Harding World Imagery 58-59 Great Marlborough Street, London, W1F 7JY, United Kingdom
☎ (020) 7478 4000/✆ (020) 7478 4161
✉ info@robertharding.com
🖳 www.robertharding.com

Royal Geographical Society 1 Kensington Gore, London, SW7 2AR, United Kingdom
☎ (020) 7591 3060/✆ (020) 7591 3001
✉ images@rgs.org
🖳 www.rgs.org/images

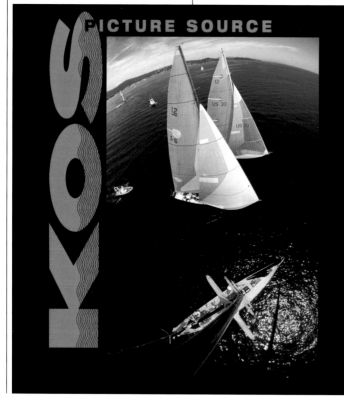

KOS PICTURE SOURCE

SAILING
CLASSIC
RACING
DINGHIES
WATERSPORTS
POWER
TEAMWORK
TIMING

AQUA
COMMERCIAL
LIFESTYLE
CRUISING
EXTRAVAGANCE
TEXTURE
SEASCAPES
TRAVEL

KOS PICTURE SOURCE
Featuring New Video Library
TEL: +44 (0) 207 801 0044 FAX: +44 (0) 207 801 0055
images@kospictures.com
www.kospictures.com

RSPCA Photolibrary Wilberforce Way, Southwater, Horsham, West Sussex, RH13 9RS, United Kingdom
✆ (0870) 7540150/ (0870) 7530150
✉ pictures@rspcaphotolibrary.com
🖥 www.rspcaphotolibrary.com

Science Photo Library Ltd 327-329 Harrow Road, London, W9 3RB, United Kingdom
✆ (020) 7432 1100/ (020) 7286 8668
✉ info@sciencephoto.com
🖥 www.sciencephoto.com

Steve Bloom Images Middlefield House, Olantigh Road, Wye, Ashford, Kent, TN25 5EP, United Kingdom
✆ (01233) 813777/ (01233) 813887
✉ sales@stevebloom.com
🖥 www.stevebloom.com

The Image Barn Ltd The Barn Studio, Hatches, Sandlecopse, Sandle Heath, Fordingbridge, Hampshire, SP6 1DX, United Kingdom
✆ (01425) 656657
✉ mike@theimagebarn.co.uk
🖥 www.theimagebarn.co.uk

Thoroughbred Photography Ltd The Hornbeams, 2 The Street, Worlington, Bury St. Edmunds, Suffolk, IP28 8RU, United Kingdom
✆ (01638) 713944/ (01638) 713945
✉ mail@thoroughbredphoto.com
🖥 www.thoroughbredphoto.com

PEOPLE AND CULTURE/LIFESTYLE

Absolutely Wild Visuals PO Box 48694, London, NW8 1BG,
✆ 2076044998
✉ kate@wildvisuals.com.au
🖥 www.absolutelywildvisuals.com

Artseens Images The Hub, 123 Star Lane, London, E16 4PZ, United Kingdom
✆ (020) 7055 0005/ (020) 7055 0005
✉ info@artseens.com
🖥 www.artseens.com

Bridgeman Art Library (FOCAL) BAPLA 17-19 Garway Road, London, W2 4PH, United Kingdom
✆ **(020) 7727 4065/ (020) 7792 8509**
✉ **london@bridgeman.co.uk**
🖥 **www.bridgemanart.com**
See ad in showcase

foodanddrinkphotos.ltd Studio 4, Sun Studios, 30 Warple Way, London, W3 0RX, United Kingdom
✆ (020) 8740 6610/ (020) 8762 9994
✉ info@foodanddrinkphotos.com
🖥 www.foodanddrinkphotos.com

Image Source Ltd 41 Great Pulteney Street, London, W1F 9NZ, United Kingdom
✆ (020) 7851 5700/ (020) 7851 5601
✉ info@imagesource.com
🖥 www.imagesource.com

Kos Picture Source Ltd P O Box 52854, 7 Spice Court, London, SW11 3UU, United Kingdom
✆ (020) 7801 0044/ (020) 7801 0055
✉ images@kospictures.com
🖥 www.kospictures.com

Lonely Planet Images 72-82 Rosebery Avenue, London, EC1R 4RW, United Kingdom
✆ (020) 7841 9062/ (020) 7841 9001
✉ lpi@lonelyplanet.co.uk
🖥 www.lonelyplanetimages.com

Mary Evans Picture Library - History 59 Tranquil Vale, Blackheath, London, SE3 0BS, United Kingdom
✆ (020) 8318 0034/ (020) 8852 7211
✉ mark.bezodis@maryevans.com
🖥 www.maryevans.com

Matton Images UK Ltd 2 Western Avenue Business Park, Mansfield Road, London, W3 0BZ, United Kingdom
✆ (020) 8753 7000/ (020) 8753 7001
✉ info@mattonimages.co.uk
🖥 www.mattonimages.co.uk

Mother & Baby Picture Library Greater London House, London, NW1 7EJ, United Kingdom
✆ (020) 7347 1867/ (020) 7347 1888
✉ mother.baby.pl@emap.com
🖥 www.motherandbabypicturelibrary.com

Palestine Exploration Fund Photographic Archive 2 Hinde Mews, Marylebone Lane, London, W1U 2AA, United Kingdom
✆ (020) 7935 5379/ (020) 7486 7438
✉ curator@pef.org.uk
🖥 www.pef.org.uk

Pictures Colour Library Ltd 10 James Whatman Court, Turkey Mill, Maidstone, Kent, ME14 5SS, United Kingdom
✆ (01622) 609809/ (01622) 609806
✉ enquiries@picturescolourlibrary.co.uk
🖥 www.picturescolourlibrary.com

Robert Harding World Imagery 58-59 Great Marlborough Street, London, W1F 7JY, United Kingdom
✆ (020) 7478 4000/ (020) 7478 4161
✉ info@robertharding.com
🖥 www.robertharding.com

Science Photo Library Ltd 327-329 Harrow Road, London, W9 3RB, United Kingdom
✆ (020) 7432 1100/ (020) 7286 8668
✉ info@sciencephoto.com
🖥 www.sciencephoto.com

REPORTAGE

Wonderfuel 118 Hatherley Gardens, London, E6 3HQ, United Kingdom
✆ 020 8548 1358
✉ info@wonderfuel.co.uk
🖥 www.wonderfuel.co.uk

SPORT

Kos Picture Source Ltd P O Box 52854, 7 Spice Court, London, SW11 3UU, United Kingdom
✆ (020) 7801 0044/ (020) 7801 0055
✉ images@kospictures.com
🖥 www.kospictures.com

Offside Sports Photography Ltd 271-273 City Road, London, EC1V 1LA, United Kingdom
✆ (020) 7253 3344/ (020) 7253 2923
✉ mail@welloffside.com
🖥 www.welloffside.com

Thoroughbred Photography Ltd The Hornbeams, 2 The Street, Worlington, Bury St. Edmunds, Suffolk, IP28 8RU, United Kingdom
✆ (01638) 713944/ (01638) 713945
✉ mail@thoroughbredphoto.com
🖥 www.thoroughbredphoto.com

TRANSPORT AND TRAVEL

Absolutely Wild Visuals PO Box 48694, London, NW8 1BG,
✆ 2076044998
✉ kate@wildvisuals.com.au
🖥 www.absolutelywildvisuals.com

Artseens Images The Hub, 123 Star Lane, London, E16 4PZ, United Kingdom
✆ (020) 7055 0005/ (020) 7055 0005
✉ info@artseens.com
🖥 www.artseens.com

BAA Aviation Photo Library Green Dragon Vaults, Parliament Square, Hertford, SG14 1PT, United Kingdom
✆ (01992) 501134/ (01992) 501174
✉ sales@in-press.co.uk
🖥 www.baa.com/photolibrary

Car Photo Library 28 Fernside Road, Talbot Park, Bournemouth, BH9 2LB, United Kingdom
✆ (01202) 528849/(07785) 537928
✉ davidkimber@carphoto.co.uk
🖥 www.carphoto.co.uk

Lonely Planet Images 72-82 Rosebery Avenue, London, EC1R 4RW, United Kingdom
✆ (020) 7841 9062/ (020) 7841 9001
✉ lpi@lonelyplanet.co.uk
🖥 www.lonelyplanetimages.com

Palestine Exploration Fund Photographic Archive 2 Hinde Mews, Marylebone Lane, London, W1U 2AA, United Kingdom
✆ (020) 7935 5379/ (020) 7486 7438
✉ curator@pef.org.uk
🖥 www.pef.org.uk

Pictures Colour Library Ltd 10 James Whatman Court, Turkey Mill, Maidstone, Kent, ME14 5SS, United Kingdom
✆ (01622) 609809/ (01622) 609806
✉ enquiries@picturescolourlibrary.co.uk
🖥 www.picturescolourlibrary.com

Robert Harding World Imagery 58-59 Great Marlborough Street, London, W1F 7JY, United Kingdom
✆ (020) 7478 4000/ (020) 7478 4161
✉ info@robertharding.com
🖥 www.robertharding.com

Royal Geographical Society 1 Kensington Gore, London, SW7 2AR, United Kingdom
✆ (020) 7591 3060/ (020) 7591 3001
✉ images@rgs.org
🖥 www.rgs.org/images

The Image Barn Ltd The Barn Studio, Hatches, Sandlecopse, Sandle Heath, Fordingbridge, Hampshire, SP6 1DX, United Kingdom
✆ (01425) 656657
✉ mike@theimagebarn.co.uk
🖥 www.theimagebarn.co.uk

every day we
break the news

every week
we piece
it together

Subscribe and sign up for news alerts at

MarketingWeek

MarketingWeek.co.uk

PEEPSHOW.ORG.UK

Models &
Casting

 ADÂGE MODELS

Tel: +44121 6934040
Fax: +441216934041
Email: info@adagemodels.net
Web: www.adagemodels.net

Models: Kim Rowley & Craig Jackson
Photography: Matt Cannon

Advertising showcase:
Models and casting
05.

Animal hire

A-Z Animals

A1 Animals

Amazing Animal

Models and casting

Hobsons

Models Plus

Spotlight

Sandra Reynolds

A★1
Animals

At home or abroad,
we specialise in supplying
all sorts of animals for
all sorts of advertising and
film work

Tel 01608 677348

Mobile 07860 416545

www.a1animals.co.uk
Email a1animals@btinternet.com

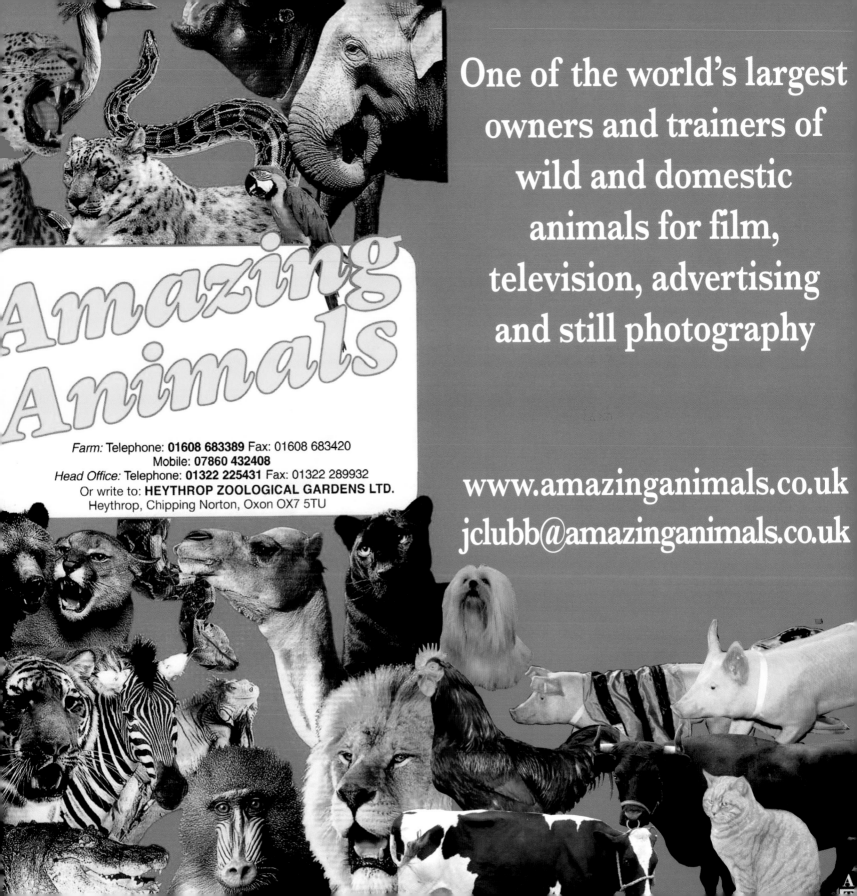

Amazing Animals

One of the world's largest owners and trainers of wild and domestic animals for film, television, advertising and still photography

Farm: Telephone: **01608 683389** Fax: 01608 683420
Mobile: **07860 432408**
Head Office: Telephone: **01322 225431** Fax: 01322 289932
Or write to: **HEYTHROP ZOOLOGICAL GARDENS LTD.**
Heythrop, Chipping Norton, Oxon OX7 5TU

www.amazinganimals.co.uk
jclubb@amazinganimals.co.uk

ACTORS, PRESENTERS,

KIDS, SINGERS,

VOICES, STUDIO

2008 21 YEARS OF VOICES FOR THE INDUSTRY

HOBSON'S

HOBSON'S 62 Chiswick High Road London W4 1SY
Tel 020 8995 3628 **Fax** 020 8996 5350
email info@hobsons-international.com **website** www.hobsons-international.com

The Model Agency
on everyone's lips

MODELSPLUS
LONDON LTD

0208 959 0008
www.modelsplus.com

Design **Karen Strutt** 07973 372556 **www.brandstrutt.com**   Photography **Fresh Academy** www.freshacademy.com

CASTING
from start to finish

Spotlight Database

Whether online or through our books, browse over 30,000 actors, actresses, presenters, stunt artists, children and dancers

View CVs, photos, showreels, portfolios and contact details for every performer

Be confident that every performer featured either trained professionally or has relevant experience

Spotlight Website

Email casting briefs to hundreds of UK agents and performers, and receive responses in minutes

Find exactly the right performer for the part, with our award-winning search engine

Search our database of behind-camera specialists

Spotlight Spaces

Audition in the heart of central London

Record onto any format, and post clips online free of charge

Cast live between the UK and any other country

---

www.spotlight.com   020-7437 7631   casting@spotlight.com

www.sandrareynolds.co.uk

sandrareynolds
commercial models
established 1975

Shakespeare House
168 Lavender Hill
London SW11 5TF
Tel: 020 7387 5858

Bacon House
35 St Georges Street
Norwich NR3 1DA
Telephone 01603 623842

photographer: nic donovan
models: sky, tamsyn, jaden & lola-rose
styling, make-up & hair: alex broome

ANIMAL HIRE

1st Choice Animals 147 Coppermill Road, Wraysbury, Middlesex, TW19 5NX, United Kingdom
(01753) 683773/(07860) 432385 (01753) 683773
firstchoiceanimals@blueyonder.co.uk
www.1stchoiceanimals.co.uk

A-Z Animals Ltd Bell House, 23 Bell Lane, Fetcham, Leatherhead, Surrey, KT22 9ND, United Kingdom
(01372) 377111/ (01372) 377666
info@a-zanimals.com
www.a-zanimals.com
See ad in showcase

A-Z Dogs Ltd Bell House, 23 Bell Lane, Fetcham, Leatherhead, Surrey, KT22 9ND, United Kingdom
(01372) 377111/(07836) 721288 (01372) 377666
info@a-zanimals.com
www.a-zanimals.com

A1 Animals 9 The Drive, Enstone, Chipping Norton, Oxfordshire, OX7 4NQ, United Kingdom
(01608) 677348/(07860) 416545 (01608) 677348
info@a1animals.freeserve.co.uk
www.a1animals.co.uk
See ad in showcase

Actadog Potterbyers, Pelton Farm, Chester le Street, County Durham, DH2 1LX, United Kingdom
0191 370 3684/07762 374 643 0191 370 3684
actadog@aol.com

Acting Animals 15 Wolstenvale Close, Middleton, Manchester, M24 2HP, United Kingdom
(0800) 387755/(07831) 800567 0161-655 3700
information@animalacting.com
www.animalacting.com

Action Stunt Dogs (ACTA) 3 The Chestnuts, Clifton Deddington, Oxford, OX15 0PE, United Kingdom
(01869) 338546/(07836) 717822 (01869) 338546
gill@stuntdogs.net
www.stuntdogs.net

Actor Dogs & Cats International Gamegards Cottage, Warwick Road, Dunmow, Essex, CM6 1SZ, United Kingdom
(01279) 871493
gameguardrotts@tiscali.co.uk

Amazing Animals Heythrop Zoological Gardens, East Lodge, Chipping Norton, Oxfordshire, OX7 5TU, United Kingdom
(01608) 683389/(07860) 432408 (01608) 683420
jclubb@amazinganimals.co.uk
www.amazinganimals.co.uk
See ad in showcase

Animal Actors 95 Ditchling Road, Brighton, BN1 4ST, United Kingdom
(020) 8654 0450/(07801) 338869 (0870) 2 418463
firstanimal@animalactors.co.uk
www.animalactors.co.uk

Animal Ambassadors Old Forest, Hampstead Norreys Road, Hermitage, Thatcham, Berkshire, RG18 9SA, United Kingdom
(01635) 200900/(07831) 558594 (01635) 200900
kayweston@tiscali.co.uk
www.animalambassadors.co.uk

Animal Consultants & Trainers Association (ACTA) 147 Coppermill Road, Wraysbury, Staines, Middlesex, TW19 5NX, United Kingdom
(0845) 257 2986/ (01753) 683773
members@acta4animals.co.uk
www.acta4animals.com

Animal Dramatics Porkers Cottage & Stables, Baughurst Road, Aldermaston, Berkshire, RG7 4PJ, United Kingdom
0118-981 5934/(07831) 409457 0118-981 5934
jackie@animaldramatics.co.uk
www.animaldramatics.co.uk

Animal House 8 Burcott Close, Bierton, Aylesbury, Buckinghamshire, HP22 5DH, United Kingdom
(07973) 155671

Animal Man (ACTA) 51 Halse Water, Didcot, Oxfordshire, OX11 7TX, United Kingdom
(01235) 512501/ (01235) 818175
animalman@animalhandling.freeserve.co.uk

Animal World Ltd 19 Greaves Road, High Wycombe, Buckinghamshire, HP13 7JU, United Kingdom
(01494) 442750/ (01494) 441385
animalworld@bushinternet.com
www.animalworld.org.uk

Animalation (ACTA) Sheen Cottage, 16 Wiltshire Avenue, Crowthorne, Berkshire, RG45 6NG, United Kingdom
(01344) 775244/(07860) 383560 (01344) 779437
ann@animalation.freeserve.co.uk

Animals Galore (ACTA) 208 Smallfield Road, Horley, Surrey, RH6 9LS, United Kingdom
(01342) 842400/(07850) 870884 (01342) 841546
info@animals-galore.co.uk
www.animals-galore.co.uk

Animals Work With Animals World 19 Greaves Road, High Wycombe, Buckinghamshire, HP13 7JU, United Kingdom
(01494) 442750/ (01494) 441385
animalworld@bushinternet.com
www.animalworld.org.uk

Animals-O-Kay (ACTA) 16 Queens Street, Chipperfield, Kings Langley, Hertfordshire, WD4 9BT, United Kingdom
(01923) 291277/(07831) 305793 (01923) 269076
kay@animalsokay.com
www.animalsokay.com

Animmed Production Radimovicka 1423/31, Prague, 4, Czech Republic
00 420 2 774
animmed@seznam.cz
www.animed.com

Aqua-Rep Heythrop Zoological Gardens Ltd, Chipping Norton, Oxfordshire, OX7 5TU, United Kingdom
(01608) 683389/(07860) 432408 (01608) 683420
jclubb@amazinganimals.co.uk
www.amazinganimals.co.uk

C N O C Animal Agency Cnoc Lodge, Creagan, Appin, Argyll, PA38 4BQ, United Kingdom
(01631) 730212/ (020) 7409 2557
info@animaldirector.com
www.animaldirector.com

Cop & Dog Services 25 Gunners Park, Bishops Waltham, Southampton, SO32 1PD, United Kingdom
(01489) 893028/(07802) 588438 (01489) 893028
peter@copanddog.co.uk
www.copanddog.co.uk

Creature Feature (ACTA) Gubhill Farm, Forest of Ae, Dumfries, DG1 1RL, United Kingdom
(01387) 860648/(07770) 774866 (01387) 860648
david@creaturefeature.co.uk
www.creaturefeature.co.uk

Cumberland Bird of Prey Centre Sand Hill, Thurstonfield, Carlisle, CA5 6HB, United Kingdom
(01228) 576889/(07900) 531032 (01228) 576615
cumberland@birdofprey.fsnet.co.uk
www.birdofpreycentre.co.uk

David McKinley Bournes House, 41 Church Street, Wiveliscombe, Taunton, Somerset, TA4 2LT, United Kingdom
(01984) 623097/ 01984 624445
mac@taxidermyuk.com
www.taxidermyuk.com

Dogs-on-Camera.com 22 Thornton Road, London, SW12 0LF, United Kingdom
(020) 8678 9604/020 8678 9604
sandra_hydrovet@yahoo.co.uk
www.dogs-on-camera.com

Film & TV Horses (ACTA) Oakley Green Road, Fitfield, Oakley Green, Windsor, Berkshire, SL4 4GW, United Kingdom
(01628) 675105/(07831) 629662 (01628) 675105
janet_rogers@whsmithnet.co.uk
www.filmhorses.com

Geoff Morton (MBE) Hasholme Carr Farm, Skiff Lane, Holme-on-Spalding-Moor, York, YO43 4BD, United Kingdom
(01430) 860393/(07768) 346905 (01430) 860057
m.morton306@btinternet.com

James Mackie Cownham Farm, Broadwell, Moreton-in-Marsh, Gloucestershire, GL56 0TT, United Kingdom
(01451) 830294
james@mackie.biz

Janimals 147 Coppermill Road, Wraysbury, Staines, Middlesex, TW19 5NX, United Kingdom
(01753) 683773/(07860) 432385 (01753) 683773
janimals2@blueyonder.co.uk
www.janimals2.co.uk

London Taxidermy Hire 144a Bridge Road, East Molesey, Surrey, KT8 9HW, United Kingdom
(020) 3274 4014/(07770) 880 960
info@londontaxidermy.com
www.londontaxidermy.com

Movie Animals 9 King Lane Cottages, Over Wallop, Stockbridge, Hampshire, SO20 8JF, United Kingdom
(01264) 781804/(07850) 820086 (01264) 782471
ronabrown@movie-animals.com
www.movie-animals.co.uk

Pooch Palace The Lee, Great Missenden, Buckinghamshire, HP16 9NQ, United Kingdom
(01494) 837420

Prop Farm Ltd Grange Farm, Elmton, Worksop, Nottinghamshire, S80 4LX, United Kingdom
(01909) 723100/(07836) 273322 (01909) 721465
pat-les@propfarm.co.uk

Rural Locations & Location Services Benefold Farm, Petworth, West Sussex, GU28 9NX, United Kingdom
(01798) 344066/(07836) 250882 (01798) 344077
heritage_oak@btconnect.com

Severnwye Llamas & Camels 10 Orchard Farm Close, Sedbury, Chepstow, Gwent, NP16 7BG, United Kingdom
(01291) 621593
info@severnwyeallamatrekking.co.uk
www.severnwyeallamatrekking.co.uk

Simon Wilson Taxidermy Hire 14 Canterbury Way, Croxley Green, Rickmansworth, Hertfordshire, WD3 3SS, United Kingdom
(01923) 212498/ (01923) 212498
animatronic@btconnect.com
www.animatronicanimals.com

Snowdonia Taxidermy Studios School Bank Road, Llanrwst, Gwynedd, LL26 0HU, United Kingdom
(01492) 640664/ (01492) 641643
sales@taxidermy-uk.com
www.taxidermy-uk.com

Tony Smart Special Action Horses Park View Stables, Maidenhead Road, Billingbear, Wokingham, Berkshire, RG40 5RR, United Kingdom
(01344) 424531/(07710) 604482 (01344) 360548
tony@tonysmart.com
www.tonysmart.com

Tyler Moore Big Top & Marquee Hire 103 Wheatcroft, Cheshunt, Hertfordshire, EN7 6JT, United Kingdom
(01992) 625138/(07989) 685972 (01992) 630390
atylermoore@aol.com
www.tylermoore.co.uk

Wolf & Hound Specialists Butlers Farm, Beenham, Reading, RG7 5NT, United Kingdom
0118-971 3330/ 0118-971 3330
ukwct@ukwolf.org
www.ukwolf.org

MODEL AGENCIES

A Q Models & Dancers 8 Westwood Park, London, SE23 3QB, United Kingdom
(020) 8291 5214/ (020) 8291 5214
info@aqmodels-dancers.com
www.aqmodels-dancers.com

Ace Model Agency 5 St. John's Lane, London, EC1M 4BH, United Kingdom
(020) 7250 4701/ (01279) 655111
office@acemod.co.uk
www.acemod.co.uk

ActNatural , St. Agnes, Cornwall, TR5 0RP, United Kingdom
(01872) 552552
info@actnatural.co.uk
www.actnatural.co.uk

Adage Models & Promotions Agency 314 The Greenhouse, The Custard Factory, Birmingham, B9 4AA, United Kingdom
0121-693 4040/ 0121-693 4041
info@adagemodels.net
www.adagemodels.net
See ad in showcase

All Directions of London Personal Management 7 Rupert Court, London, W1D 6EB, United Kingdom
(020) 7437 5879

Allsorts Freemeals Film Studios, Unit 1 Sugar House Business Centre, 24 Sugar House Lane, London, E15 2QS, United Kingdom
(020) 8555 0099/(07958) 511647 (020) 8555 0909
bookings@allsortsagency.com
www.allsortsagency.com

close

www.closemodels.com

MODEL AGENCY FOR WOMEN OF ALL AGES

2b Seagrave Road . London SW6 1RR
T: +44 (0)20 7385 2234 . F: +44 (0)20 7385 1888
M: +44 (0)7712 870 150 E: info@closemodels.com
www.closemodels.com

Alphabet Kidz Children's Talent & Modeling Agency, 189 Southampton Way, London, SE5 7EJ, United Kingdom
(020) 7252 4343
contact@alphabetkidz.co.uk
www.alphabetkidz.co.uk

Angelic-Promotions 7 Colquhoun Road, Milton, Dumbarton, G82 2TH, United Kingdom
(01389) 600758
hire@angelic-promotions.co.uk
www.angelic-promotions.co.uk

Angels Model & Promotion Agency Albany House, 14 Shute End, Wokingham, Berkshire, RG40 1BJ, United Kingdom
0118-977 4970/ 0118-989 3115
info@angelsagency.com
www.angelsagency.com

Artimis Models & Promotions , Shirley, Solihull, West Midlands, B90 4WH, United Kingdom
0121-703 3168/(07977) 252308
info@artimis.co.uk
www.artimis.co.uk

Artseens Images The Hub, 123 Star Lane, London, E16 4PZ, United Kingdom
(020) 7055 0005/ (020) 7055 0005
info@artseens.com
www.artseens.com

Avisford Models Avisford Cottage, Shellbridge Road, Slindon Common, Arundel, West Sussex, BN18 0LT, United Kingdom
(01243) 814788
abreezemodels@fsmail.net
www.abreezemodels.co.uk

Aztecmodels 13 Churchfields, Hethersett, Norwich, NR9 3AF, United Kingdom
(01603) 810912
aztecphotos@btinternet.com
www.aztecphotos.co.uk

Aztecphotos 13 Churchfields, Hethersett, Norwich, NR9 3AF, United Kingdom
(01603) 810912/(07775) 517691
aztecphotos@btinternet.com
www.aztecphotos.co.uk

B M A Model Agency East Passage, Marlowe House, 346 High Street, Berkhamsted, Hertfordshire, HP4 1HT, United Kingdom
(01442) 878878/ (01442) 879879
info@bmamodels.com
www.bmamodels.com

B M A Models Ltd 5 Blackwells, Northchurch, Berkhamsted, Hertfordshire, HP4 1RB, United Kingdom
(01442) 878878/ (01442) 879879
inf@bmamodels.com
www.bmamodels.com

Bellizzimo 44 Sharon Park Close, Grappenhall, Warrington, WA4 2YN, United Kingdom
(07900) 811856
isabellelouise@talk21.com
www.bellizzimo.co.uk

Bizzykidz Child Model Agency Bizzy House, 73a Mayplace Road West, Bexleyheath, Kent, DA7 4JL, United Kingdom
(020) 8303 2627/ (020) 8303 2730
bookings@bizzykidz.com
www.bizzykidz.com

Bookings Studio 6, 27A Pembridge Villas, London, W11 3EP, United Kingdom
(020) 7221 2603/ (020) 7229 4567
mail@bookingsmodels.co.uk
www.bookingsmodels.co.uk

Bruce & Brown London Kids Unit 203 Canalot Studios, 222 Kensal Road, London, W10 5BN, United Kingdom
(020) 8968 5585/ (020) 8964 0457
info@bruceandbrown.com
www.bruceandbrown.com

CAPE Glasgow Models 36 North Hanover Street, Glasgow, G1 2AD, United Kingdom
0141-416 1882
info@capelondon.com
www.capelondon.com

Cape London Model Management Unit 5, Zeus House, 16-30 Provost Street, London, Greater London, N1 7NG, United Kingdom
(020) 73360222/ (020) 73360225
info@capelondon.com
www.capelondon.com

Century Models Well House, Unit D, 23a Benwell Road, London, N7 7BL, United Kingdom
(020) 7619 8235/(07737) 124883/ (020) 7404 6778
models@cmtmodels.com
www.cmtmodels.com

Childrens Talent & Modelling Agency 189 Southampton Way, London, SE5 7EJ, United Kingdom
(020) 7252 4343/ (020) 7252 4341
contact@alphabetkidz.co.uk
www.alphabetkidz.co.uk

Childsplay Models 114 Avenue Road, Beckenham, Kent, BR3 4SA, United Kingdom
(020) 8659 9860/ (020) 8778 2672
info@childsplaymodels.co.uk
www.childsplaymodels.co.uk

Claire Barker Associates Ltd Barker Brooks Hpuse, 4 Green Gate, Cardale Park, Harrogate, North Yorkshire, HG2 1GY, United Kingdom
(01423) 873313/ (01423) 8511 61
info@clairebarker.co.uk
www.clairebarker.co.uk

Clive Corner Associates 73 Gloucester Road, Hampton, Middlesex, TW12 2UQ, United Kingdom
(020) 8287 2726/(07946) 894870/ (020) 8979 4983
cornerassociates@aol.com
www.cornerassociates.cwc.net

Close 2B Seagrave Road, London, SW6 1RR, United Kingdom
(020) 7385 2234/(07712) 870150/ (020) 7385 1888
harriet@closemodels.com
www.closemodels.com

Close Models 2B Seagrave Road, London, SW6 1RR, United Kingdom
(020) 7385 2234/07712 870150/ (020) 7385 1888
info@closemodels.com
www.closemodels.com
See ad

Coast 2 Coast , London, SW6 4UT, United Kingdom
(0870) 251 9550/ (0870) 251 9560
info@c2cp.com
www.coast2coastpersonalities.co.uk

Crawfords , London, SW20 0YP, United Kingdom
(020) 8947 9999/(07836) 249607/ (020) 3258 5037
cr@wfords.com
www.crawfords.tv

Dereks Hands 26-28 Hammersmith Grove, London, W6 7BA, United Kingdom
(020) 8834 1609/(07747) 535897
casting@derekshands.com
www.derekshands.com

Elisabeth Smith 81 Headstone Road, Harrow, Middlesex, HA1 1PQ, United Kingdom
(020) 8863 2331/ (020) 8861 1880
models@elisabethsmith.com
www.elisabethsmith.com

EyeCandy Model & Promotional Agency 54 Poland Street, London, W1F 7NJ, United Kingdom
(020) 7432 0760
vicki@eyecandy-promo.co.uk
www.eyecandy-promo.co.uk

F M Agency 11-29 Fashion Street, London, E1 6PX, United Kingdom
(020) 7225 1355/ (020) 7422 0680
info@fmmodelagency.com
www.fmmodelagency.com

Fashion Executives Via Monte, Di Pieta, Milan, Italy, 20121,
7717366567/ 8700625674
riz@fashionexecutives.com
www.fashionexecutives.com

Flair Talent 46 Barry Road, London, SW17 7BB, United Kingdom
(020) 8693 8649/ (0871) 2514778
aaron@flairtalent.com
www.flairtalent.com

Fresh Agents Ltd Suite 5, Saks House, 19 Ship Street, Hove, East Sussex, BN1 1AD, United Kingdom
(01273) 711777/ (01273) 711778
info@freshagents.com
www.freshagents.com

Gingersnap Long Barn, Stockwood Road, Bristol, BS4 5LU, United Kingdom
0117-300 5777
clare.w@virgin.net
www.gingersnap.co.uk

Glenbeigh Model & Promotion Agency 1-2 Elizabeth Court, Whimple Street, Plymouth, PL1 2DH, United Kingdom
(01752) 201331/ (01752) 204140
gmpa@glenbeigh.co.uk
www.glenbeigh.co.uk

Gridmodels 8 Kerry Path, Arklow Road, London, SE14 6DY, United Kingdom
(020) 8694 9126
enquiries@gridmodels.com
www.gridmodels.com

Hand Model Bull House, 41 Cheapside West, Rayleigh, Essex, SS6 9DE, United Kingdom
(01268) 783043/(07860) 188313
undrell@tinyworld.co.uk
www.hand-model.com

Hired Hands 12 Cressy Road, London, NW3 2LY, United Kingdom
(020) 7267 9212/(07870) 984510/ (020) 7267 1030
hiredhandsagency@aol.com
www.hiredhandsmodels.com

Hughes Models 74 Telford Avenue, London, SW2 4XF, United Kingdom
☎ (020) 8672 8494/✆ (020) 8623 9117
✉ info@hughesmodels12plus.co.uk
🖥 www.hughesmodels12plus.co.uk

I F M Unit 3, St. Vincent House, 99a Station Road, London, E4 7BU, United Kingdom
☎ (020) 8524 7111/✆ (020) 8524 7222
✉ jane@ifmevents.co.uk
🖥 www.ifmevents.co.uk

Ideal Modelling PO Box 12944, Birmingham, B31 9AU, United Kingdom
☎ (07966) 191906
✉ rjukes@idealmodelling.co.uk
🖥 www.idealmodelling.co.uk

Images Model Agency Flat 10, Brockwell Court, Effra Road, London, SW2 1NA, United Kingdom
☎ (020) 7326 1628
✉ darren@imagesmodelagency.uk.com
🖥 www.imagesmodelagency.uk.com

IMM/ International Model Management Ltd Elysium Gate, Unit 15, 126-128 New Kings Road, London, SW6 4LZ, United Kingdom
☎ (020) 7610 9111/✆ (020) 7736 2221
✉ karstenimm@aol.com
🖥 www.immmodels.com

Juliet Adams Model & Talent Agency 19 Gwyn House, Challice Way, London, SW2 3RB, United Kingdom
☎ (020) 8671 7673/✆ (020) 8671 9314
✉ models@julietadams.co.uk
🖥 www.julietadams.co.uk

K K Model Agency KK House, 48 Oakmead Road, London, SW12 9SJ, United Kingdom
☎ (020) 8675 4000/✆ (020) 8675 8888
✉ info@kamerakids.com
🖥 www.kamerakids.com

Kids London 67 Dulwich Road, London, SE24 0NJ, United Kingdom
☎ ((020) 7924 9595/✆ (020) 7924 9766
✉ kidslondon@btconnect.com
🖥 www.kidslondonltd.com

Kids Plus 2 Foresters Cottages, Barnet Wood Road, Bromley, BR2 8HJ, United Kingdom
☎ (020) 8462 4666/(07704) 583352 ✆ (020) 8462 4666
✉ office@kidsplus.wanadoo.co.uk
🖥 www.kidsplusuk.com

Kolours Children's Modelling Agency 11 Jacob Court, Spencer Road, Bromley, BR1 3SU, United Kingdom
☎ (0800) 0836436/(07958) 602347
✉ kolours.models1@ntlworld.com
🖥 www.kolours.co.uk

Lee's People Ltd 90 Longacre, London, WC2E 9RX, United Kingdom
☎ (020) 7734 5775/(07970) 527252 ✆ (020) 7734 3033
✉ lee@lees-people.co.uk
🖥 www.lees-people.co.uk

Manchester Model Agency 14 Albert Square, Manchester, M2 5PF, United Kingdom
☎ 0161-236 1335/(07840) 171796
✉ mma@btinternet.com
🖥 www.manchestermodelagency.com

Maverick , London, United Kingdom
☎ (020) 7351 3557/✆ (020) 7352 1410
✉ info@maverickmodels.net
🖥 www.maverickmodels.net

Model Team Ltd 180 Hope Street, Glasgow, G2 2UE, United Kingdom
☎ 0141-332 3951/✆ 0141-332 1915
✉ models@modelteam.co.uk
🖥 www.modelteam.co.uk

Modelplan 4th Floor, 4 Golden Square, London, W1F 9HT, United Kingdom
☎ (020) 7287 8444/✆ (0161) 819 1180
✉ michelle@modelplan.co.uk
🖥 www.modelplan.co.uk

Models One 12 Macklin Street, Covent Garden, London, WC2B 5SZ, United Kingdom
☎ (020) 7025 4900/✆ (020) 7025 4901
✉ info@models1.co.uk
🖥 www.models1.co.uk

Models Plus 82A Belsize Road, Swiss Cottage, London, NW6 4TG, United Kingdom
☎ **(020) 7624 5045**/✆ **(020) 7328 0177**
✉ **info@modelsplus.com**
🖥 **www.modelsplus.com**
See ad in showcase

Models Plus Model Agency 307 Holdenhurst Road, Bournemouth, BH8 8BX, United Kingdom
☎ (01202) 522102/(07970) 264331 ✆ (01202) 301156
✉ info@mpagency.co.uk
🖥 www.mpagency.co.uk

Models Required 142 Mildmay Road, London, Greater London, N1 4NE, United Kingdom
☎ 020 7275 7039
✉ mr@modelsrequired.com
🖥 www.modelsrequired.com

Models-Empire 25 Forest Drive West, London, E11 1JZ, United Kingdom
☎ (07796) 393346
✉ tarmo@models-empire.com
🖥 www.models-empire.com

MOT Models The Stables, Ashlyns Hall, Berkhamsted, Hertfordshire, HP4 2ST, United Kingdom
☎ (01442) 863918/✆ (01442) 873333
✉ agency@motmodel.com
🖥 www.motmodel.com

Mustard Models The Media Centre, 1 Riverside, St Annes Road, Bristol, BS4 4ED, United Kingdom
☎ 0117-903 0327/✆ 0117-903 0328
✉ agency@bigmustard.co.uk
🖥 www.bigmustard.co.uk

Nemesis Nemesis House, 1 Oxford Court, Bishopsgate, Manchester, M2 3WQ, United Kingdom
☎ 0161-228 6646/✆ 0161-228 6727
✉ sam@nmfmanagement.co.uk
🖥 www.nemesisagency.co.uk

Nevs Agency Regal House, 198 Kings Road, London, SW3 5XP, United Kingdom
☎ (020) 7352 4886/✆ (020) 7352 6068
✉ info@nevs.co.uk
🖥 www.nevs.co.uk

Next Management London Ltd 175-179 St Johns Street, London, EC1V 4LW, United Kingdom
☎ (020) 7251 9850/✆ (020) 7251 9851
✉ london@nextmodels.com
🖥 www.nextmodels.com

Norrie Carr Agency Ltd Holborn Studios, 49 Eagle Wharf Road, London, N1 7ED, United Kingdom
☎ (020) 7253 1771/✆ (020) 7253 1772
✉ info@norriecarr.com
🖥 www.norriecarr.com

Number One Model Agency Unit 408f, The Big Peg, 120 Vyse Street, Hockley, Birmingham, B18 6NF, United Kingdom
☎ 0121 233 2433/✆ 0121 233 2454
✉ info@numberonemodelagency.co.uk
🖥 www.numberonemodelagency.co.uk

Ordinary People Ltd 16 Camden Road, Camden, London, NW1 9DP, United Kingdom
☎ (020) 7267 7007/✆ (020) 7267 5677
✉ info@ordinarypeople.co.uk
🖥 www.ordinarypeople.co.uk

Oriental Afro Asian Artists care of FBI 4th Floor, 20-24 Kirby Street, London, EC1N 8TS, United Kingdom
☎ (020) 7242 5542/✆ (020) 7242 8125
✉ fbi@dircon.co.uk
🖥 www.fullybooked-inc.com

Origin Models 12 Cressy Road, London, NW3 2LY, United Kingdom
☎ (020) 7284 4337/✆ (020) 7267 1030
🖥 www.originmodels.com

P H A Icon Ltd Tanzaro House, Ardwick Green North, Manchester, M12 6FZ, United Kingdom
☎ 0161-273 4444/✆ 0161-273 4567
✉ info@pha-agency.co.uk
🖥 www.pha-agency.co.uk

Pat Keeling Model Agency 38 Northgate Street, Leicester, LE3 5BY, United Kingdom
☎ 0116-262 2540/✆ 0116-253 7712
✉ pat@patkeelingagency.freeserve.co.uk
🖥 www.patkeelingagency.freeserve.co.uk

Peggy Sirr Oriental Casting Agency Ltd 1 Wyatt Park Road, Streatham Hill, London, SW2 3TN, United Kingdom
☎ (020) 8671 8538/✆ (020) 8674 9303
✉ peggy.sirr@btconnect.com
🖥 www.orientalcasting.com

Perfect Look Model Agency Ltd Empire House, 175 Picadilly, Mayfair, London, W1J 9TB, United Kingdom
☎ (020) 7290 9004/(07709) 760411 ✆ (020) 7499 7517
✉ vicky@perfectlookmodels.co.uk
🖥 www.perfectlookmodels.co.uk

Physicality Ltd (IVCA) 8 Hatherley Mews, Walthamstow, London, E17 4QP, United Kingdom
☎ (020) 8521 5522/✆ (020) 8521 3744
✉ info@physicality.co.uk
🖥 www.physicality.co.uk

Plain Jane PO Box 2730, Romford, RM7 1AB, United Kingdom
☎ (07813) 667319
✉ info@plain-jane.co.uk
🖥 www.plain-jane.co.uk

Pregnant Pause Agency 11 Matham Road, East Molesey, Surrey, KT8 0SX, United Kingdom
☎ (020) 8979 8874/(07970) 698868 ✆ (020) 8783 0337
✉ sandy@pregnantpause.co.uk
🖥 www.pregnantpause.co.uk

Premier Elite House, 40-42 Parker Street, London, WC2B 5PQ, United Kingdom
☎ (020) 7333 0888/✆ (020) 7323 1221
✉ info@premiermodelmanagement.com
🖥 www.premiermodelmanagement.com

Profile 1-4 Langley Court, London, WC2E 9JY, United Kingdom
☎ (020) 7836 5282/✆ (020) 7497 2255
✉ info@profile-models.com
🖥 www.profile-models.com

Rage Tigris House, 256 Edgware Road, London, W2 1DS, United Kingdom
☎ (020) 7262 0515/✆ (020) 7402 0507
✉ ragemodels@ugly.org
🖥 www.ragemodels.org

Rascals Child Model Agency 13 Jubilee Parade, Snakes Lane East, Woodford Green, Essex, IG8 7QG, United Kingdom
☎ (020) 8504 1111/✆ (020) 8559 1035
✉ kids@rascals.co.uk
🖥 www.rascals.co.uk

Real People Scotland Ltd 4 Devonshire Gardens, Glasgow, G12 0UX, United Kingdom
☎ 0141-563 2792/✆ 0141-586 2639
✉ info@realpeople.co.uk
🖥 www.realpeople.co.uk

Risque Model Management 68a Friern Mount Drive, Whelstone, London, N20 9DL, United Kingdom
☎ (07802) 283890
✉ info@risquemodel.co.uk
🖥 www.risquemodel.co.uk

Role Models 12 Cressy Road, London, NW3 2LY, United Kingdom
☎ (020) 7284 4337/✆ (020) 7267 1030
✉ hiredhandsagency@aol.com

Samantha Bond Management Worlds End Studio, 134 Lots Road, London, SW10 0RJ, United Kingdom
☎ (020) 73497223
✉ nicky@samanthabond.net
🖥 www.samanthabond.net

Sapphires Model Management Studio 11, The Makers Dozen, 8 Wulfruna Street, Wolverhampton, WV1 1LW, United Kingdom
☎ (01902) 427740
✉ info@sapphiresmodelmanagement.co.uk
🖥 www.sapphiresmodelmanagement.co.uk

Sarah Daw Cameo House, 11 Bear Street, London, WC2H 7AS, United Kingdom
☎ (020) 7930 6996/✆ (020) 7930 5002
✉ hello@sarahdaw.com
🖥 www.sarahdawproduction.com

Scallywags Ltd 90-92 Ley Street, Ilford, Essex, IG1 4BX, United Kingdom
☎ (020) 8553 9999/✆ (020) 8533 4849
✉ info@scallywags.co.uk
🖥 www.scallywags.co.uk

So Dam Tuff & Family The Coach House, 136 Westbridge Road, Battersea, London, SW11 3PF, United Kingdom
☎ (020) 7223 7377/✆ (020) 7223 7387
✉ tiger@sodamtuff.com
🖥 www.sodamtuff.com

Source Models Sovereign House, 35 Laidlaw Close, Talbot Village, Poole, Dorset, BH12 5EW, United Kingdom
☎ (0845) 2263214/✆ (0845) 2263129
✉ dave@sourcemodels.co.uk
🖥 www.sourcemodels.co.uk

Split Image Unit 6, Kelvin Business Centre, Crawley, West Sussex, RH10 9SF, United Kingdom
☎ (01293) 403513/✆ (01293) 407764
✉ models@splitimage.co.uk
🖥 www.splitimage.co.uk

MODEL AGENCIES

Sports Workshop Promotions Ltd Jubilee Stand, Crystal Palace Sports Centre, London, SE19 2BH, United Kingdom
- (020) 8659 4561/(07770) 994043 / (020) 8776 7772
- info@sportspromotions.co.uk
- www.sportspromotions.co.uk

Stand Out Model Management 111 Ross Walk, Leicester, LE4 5HH, United Kingdom
- (0845) 1087870
- info@modelsstandout.co.uk
- www.modelsstandout.co.uk

Steve121 23 Uxbridge Avenue, Coventry, CV3 1HH, United Kingdom
- (024) 7626 5539
- keith.ashbourne@ntlworld.com

Storm Model Management 1st Floor, 5 Jubilee Place, London, SW3 3TD, United Kingdom
- (020) 7368 9900/ (020) 7376 5145
- info@stormmodels.co.uk
- www.stormmodels.com

Streetmodel.net 37 Foley Street, London, W1W 7TN, United Kingdom
- info@streetmodel.net
- www.streetmodel.net

Susan Scott Lookalikes 106 Tollington Park, Stroud Grn, London, N4 3RB, United Kingdom
- (020) 7387 9245/ (020) 7722 8261
- susan@lookalikes.info
- www.lookalikes.info

Thai Model Sutton Farm House, Sutton, Witney, Oxfordshire, OX29 5RD, United Kingdom
- (01865) 731309/ (01865) 883789
- thaimodel@btconnect.co.uk
- www.thaimodel.co.uk

The Model Academy 1 Atworth Grove, Littleover, Derby, DE23 3WZ, United Kingdom
- (01332) 540446
- ra@themodelacademy.co.uk
- www.themodelacademy.co.uk

The Model Bank 6 Hockley Hill, Birmingham, B18 5AA, United Kingdom
- (0845) 1662824/ (0870) 4225290
- info@themodelbank.co.uk
- www.themodelbank.co.uk

Tots 2 Teens Ltd 6 Fulham Park Studios, Fulham Park Road, London, SW6 4LW, United Kingdom
- (0870) 2519530/ (0870) 2519560
- info@tots2teens.ltd.uk
- www.tots2teens.ltd.uk

Tramp 2 Kendrey Gardens, Twickenham, TW2 7PA, United Kingdom
- (07968) 958825
- sophie_blackman@hotmail.com
- www.tramped.co.uk

Truly Scrumptious Ltd 66 Bidwell Gardens, London, N11 2AU, United Kingdom
- (020) 8888 4204/ (020) 8888 4584
- bookings@trulyscrumptious.co.uk
- www.trulyscrumptious.co.uk

Tuesdays Child Oakfield House, Springwood Way, Macclesfield, Cheshire, SK10 2XA, United Kingdom
- (01625) 501765/ (01625) 501765
- info.tuesdayschildagency.co.uk
- www.tuesdayschildagency.co.uk

Ugly Tigris House, 256 Edgware Road, London, W2 1DS, United Kingdom
- (020) 7402 5564/ (020) 7402 0507
- info@ugly.org
- www.ugly.org

Ultimate Models 11 Worster Court, Ranson Road, Norwich, NR1 4AW, United Kingdom
- (01603) 432166
- info@ultimatemodels.net
- www.ultimatemodels.net

Universal Model Management Ltd 26 Colwyn Road, Northampton, NN1 3PZ, United Kingdom
- (0844) 890 1111
- enquiries@universalmodels.tv
- www.universalmodels.tv

Urban Angels Agency Po Box 45453, London, SE26 6UZ, United Kingdom
- (08708) 710045/ (08708) 710046
- info@urbanangelsagency.com
- www.urbanangelsagency.com

Urban Angels Modelling Agency PO Box 45453, London, SE26 6UZ, United Kingdom
- (0870) 8710045/ (0870) 8710046
- info@urbanangelsagency.com
- www.urbanangelsagency.com

VisABLE People - Disabled Models & Actors , Droitwich, Worcestershire, WR9 0ZE, United Kingdom
- (01905) 776631/(07930) 345152 / (01905) 779942
- louise@visablepeople.com
- www.visablepeople.com

Yvonne Paul Management Unit 15, Elysium Gate, 126 New Kings Road, London, SW6 4LZ, United Kingdom
- (020)7610 9111/ (020) 7736 2221
- karstenimm@aol.com
- www.immmodels.com

HAIR AND MAKE UP

4photo Fernleigh, Sherburn Road, Durham, DH1 2JW, United Kingdom
- (07890) 022356
- shaun@4photo.co.uk
- www.shaunmcmanus.com

A & A Studios Ltd 8-10 Tanfield, Inverleith, Edinburgh, EH3 5HF, United Kingdom
- 0131-556 7057/ 0131-556 3223
- sales@aastudios.co.uk
- www.aastudios.co.uk

A H D Make-up 31 Talbot Road, London, W2 5JG, United Kingdom
- (020) 7229 9434/ (020) 7229 9434
- ahdmakeup@aol.com
- www.ahdmakeup.com

A1 Mobile Hair Extensions 14 Main Street, Middleton, Market Harborough, Leicestershire, LE16 8YU, United Kingdom
- (07743) 601285
- pandorapenn@yahoo.com

Adam Bryant/Bill Charles London Ltd. Unit 3E1, Zetland House, 5-25 Scrutton Street, London, EC2A 4HJ, United Kingdom
- 020 7033 9284/020 2033 9285/
- london@billcharles.com
- www.billcharles.com

Alexis Slaybaugh-Willard 99A Colney Thatch Lane, Muswell Hill, London, N10 1LR, United Kingdom
- (07981) 154413
- alexisfilmtvstage@yahoo.com

Angela Hamilton Daley 31 Talbot Road, London, W2 5JG, United Kingdom
- (020) 7229 9434
- ahdmakepu@aol.com
- www.pennyrich.co.uk

Angels Hair and Beauty 2 Moncktons Drive, Maidstone, Kent, ME14 2QD, United Kingdom
- (01622) 690459
- angelshairandbeauty@hotmail.com
- www.angelshairandbeauty.com

Anita 4 Percy Gardens, Isleworth, Middlesex, TW7 6BX, United Kingdom
- (07949) 029170
- aludhra@aol.com

Anita Keeling/Blunt Management The Courtyard Studio 2, Old Grammarphone Works, London, W10 5BZ, United Kingdom
- (020) 8960 2041/(07979) 900068 / (020) 8960 2039
- info@bluntlondon.com
- www.bluntlondon.com

Ann-Marie Simak/HERS Agency Ltd Cleaveside, Bickleigh, Tiverton, Devon, EX16 8RB, United Kingdom
- (0870) 429 6499/ (01884) 855855
- hers@hersagency.co.uk
- www.hersagency.co.uk

Anne Edwards (NASMAH) 33 Westbury Road, New Malden, Surrey, KT3 5AX, United Kingdom
- (020) 8942 2131/(07801) 884914 / (020) 8942 7621
- annepedwards@yahoo.co.uk

Annie Karlsson 43c Rhyl Street, London, NW5 3HB, United Kingdom
- (07903) 495834
- annie.karlsson@upmake.com
- www.upmake.com/

Artistic Licence 5A Hillgate Place, 18-20 Balham Hill, London, SW12 9ER, United Kingdom
- (020) 8675 7555/ (020) 8675 6090
- info@artisticlicenceagency.com
- www.artisticlicenceagency.com

Asashi/Blunt Management The Courtyard Studio 2, Old Grammarphone Works, London, W10 5BZ, United Kingdom
- (020) 8960 2041/(07979) 900068 / (020) 8960 2039
- info@bluntlondon.com
- www.bluntlondon.com

Ashley Ward/Terrie Tanaka Management 101 Talbot Rd, London, W11 2AT, United Kingdom
- (020) 7792 3500/ (020) 7792 2600
- danni@terrietanaka.com
- www.terrietanaka.com

Avril Russell (NASMAH) Meadow Cottage, Sibleys Grn, Thaxted, Dunmow, Essex, CM6 2NU, United Kingdom
- (01371) 830803/(07746) 421437

Barry Bish/HERS Agency Ltd Cleaveside, Bickleigh, Tiverton, Devon, EX16 8RB, United Kingdom
- (0870) 429 6499/ (01884) 855855
- hers@hersagency.co.uk
- www.hersagency.co.uk

Becca Harrison 50B Tubbs Road, London, NW10 4RE, United Kingdom
- (07779) 130392
- becca_harrison@hotmail.com
- www.beccaharrison.com

Belinda Green-Smith 480b Kingston Road, Wimbledon, London, SW20 8DX, United Kingdom
- (07967) 587235/ (020) 8540 3515
- belinda-greensmith@tiscali.co.uk
- www.belindagreensmith.com

Bellizzimo 44 Sharon Park Close, Grappenhall, Warrington, WA4 2YN, United Kingdom
- (07900) 811856
- isabellelouise@talk21.com
- www.bellizzimo.co.uk

Ben Skervin/Blunt Management The Courtyard Studio 2, Old Grammarphone Works, London, W10 5BZ, United Kingdom
- (020) 8960 2041/(07979) 900068 / (020) 8960 2039
- info@bluntlondon.com
- www.bluntlondon.com

Bernadine Long/Mandy Coakley Represents 18 Mandeville Courtyard, Warriner Gardens, London, SW11 4NB, United Kingdom
- (020) 7720 6234/ (020) 7720 0199
- mandy@mandycoakley.co.uk
- www.mandycoakley.co.uk

Beverly Toby Flat 8, 40-41 Whiskin Street, London, EC1 0BP, United Kingdom
- (07774) 834619
- btoby@btinternet.com

Bocek Production Cubuklu cad.agaclik mesire yeri, d+e burunbahce, beykoz, Istanbul, 34805,
- 00 9 02166801058
- selma@bocekyapim.com.tr
- www.bocekyapim.com.tr

Brendan Robertson/Shoot Production Ltd 23 Glebe Road, London, N8 7DA, United Kingdom
- (020) 8442 9171/ (020) 8348 7404
- adele@shootgroup.com
- www.shootgroup.com

C L M Hair & Make-up 19 All Saints Road, London, W11 1HE, United Kingdom
- (020) 7750 2990/ (020) 7792 8507
- nikki@clmuk.com
- www.clmuk.com

Candice Konig Flat 20, McNair Court, 292-302 Portland Road, Hove, East Sussex, BN3 5UD, United Kingdom
- (07824) 325716
- candice.konig@ntlworld.com
- www.makeupartistlondon.co.uk

CAPE Glasgow Models 36 North Hanover Street, Glasgow, G1 2AD, United Kingdom
- 0141-416 1882
- info@capelondon.com
- www.capelondon.com

Cape London Model Management Unit 5, Zeus House, 16-30 Provost Street, London, Greater London, N1 7NG, United Kingdom
- (020) 73360222/ (020) 73360225
- info@capelondon.com
- www.capelondon.com

Charlotte Lowes/Mandy Coakley Represents 18 Mandeville Courtyard, Warriner Gardens, London, SW11 4NB, United Kingdom
✆ (020) 7720 6234/✆ (020) 7720 0199
✉ mandy@mandycoakley.co.uk
🖳 www.mandycoakley.co.uk

Claire Savona 41 Canewdon Road, Westcliff-on-Sea, Essex, SS0 7NE, United Kingdom
✆ (07867) 897128
✉ clairesavona@waldonet.net.mt
🖳 www.clairesavona.com

Cor Kwakernaak/HERS Agency Ltd Cleaveside, Bickleigh, Tiverton, Devon, EX16 8RB, United Kingdom
✆ (0870) 429 6499/✆ (01884) 855855
✉ hers@hersagency.co.uk
🖳 www.hersagency.co.uk

Craig Taylor 3 Thornton Road, East Sheen, London, SW14 8NS, United Kingdom
✆ (020) 8487 8442/(07801) 161841 ✆ (020) 8487 8442
✉ carigtaylor153@aol.com
🖳 www.craigtaylor.net

Darren Evans/Mandy Coakley Represents 18 Mandeville Courtyard, Warriner Gardens, London, SW11 4NB, United Kingdom
✆ (020) 7720 6234/✆ (020) 7720 0199
✉ mandy@mandycoakley.co.uk
🖳 www.mandycoakley.co.uk

Dean Kennedy/Mandy Coakley Represents 18 Mandeville Courtyard, Warriner Gardens, London, SW11 4NB, United Kingdom
✆ (020) 7720 6234/✆ (020) 7720 0199
✉ mandy@mandycoakley.co.uk
🖳 www.mandycoakley.co.uk

Deborah Brider P.O. Box 11578, Amsterdam, 1001GN, Netherlands
✆ 00 31 62 492 26 22
✉ info@deborahbrider.com
🖳 www.deborahbrider.com

E N Y Makeup 3 Riverview Mews, Weybridge, Surrey, KT15 2RX, United Kingdom
✆ (07835) 068729
✉ info@eny-makeup.com
🖳 www.eny-whitehead.com

Emma Leon/Shoot Production Ltd 23 Glebe Road, London, N8 7DA, United Kingdom
✆ (020) 8442 9171/✆ (020) 8348 7404
✉ adele@shootgroup.com
🖳 www.shootgroup.com

Emma Motivala , , West Sussex, RH19 3EQ, United Kingdom
✆ (07702) 839051
✉ theatricalmakeup@aol.co.uk

Emma Osborne 69 Recreation Road, Bromley, BR2 0DY, United Kingdom
✆ (020) 7607 4628/(07930) 533849 ✆ (020) 8402 9922
✉ emma.oz@ntlworld.com
🖳 www.isphamous.com

Fiona Moore/Terrie Tanaka Management 101 Talbot Road, London, W11 2AT, United Kingdom
✆ (020) 7792 3500/✆ (020) 7792 2600
✉ danni@terrietanaka.com
🖳 www.terrietanaka.com

Fit4 the Part Ltd Covent Garden, London, WC2H 9HB, United Kingdom
✆ (0845) 0066348/✆ (0845) 4664477
✉ info@fit4thepart.com
🖳 www.fit4thepart.com

Frank Agency 12 Mandiville Courtyard, 142 Bettersy Park Road, London, SW11 4NB, United Kingdom
✆ (020) 7498 9700
✉ sarah@frankagency.co.uk
🖳 www.frankagency.co.uk

Gaunt Faces Windsor Court, East Grinstead House, East Grinstead, West Sussex, RH19 1XA, United Kingdom
✆ / ✆ (01342) 336113
✉ phewson@reedinfo.co.uk

Gianni Scumaci/Bill Charles London Ltd. Unit 3E1, Zetland House, 5-25 Scrutton Street, London, EC2A 4HJ, United Kingdom
✆ 020 7033 9284/020 2033 9285/
✉ london@billcharles.com
🖳 www.billcharles.com

Gina Kane/Blunt Management The Courtyard Studio 2, Old Grammarphone Works, London, W10 5BZ, United Kingdom
✆ (020) 8960 2041/(07979) 900068 ✆ (020) 8960 2039
✉ info@bluntlondon.com
🖳 www.bluntlondon.com

Gow Tanaka , London, United Kingdom
✆ (0207) 1216381/(07956) 503718
✉ gow@macunlimited.net
🖳 www.balconyjump.co.uk

Hair Make-Up Artist 21 Mannock Road, London, N22 6AB, United Kingdom
✆ (07881) 987876
✉ taro@ryutaro.co.uk
🖳 www.ryutaro.co.uk

Helen Archer 10 Ravenscar Terrace, Leeds, LS8 4AU, United Kingdom
✆ (07901) 601481
✉ helen.archer4@btinternet.com
🖳 www.nemesis.co.uk

Helen Bannon/Mandy Coakley Represents 18 Mandeville Courtyard, Warriner Gardens, London, SW11 4NB, United Kingdom
✆ (020) 7720 6234/✆ (020) 7720 0199
✉ mandy@mandycoakley.co.uk
🖳 www.mandycoakley.co.uk

Helen Pham/Mandy Coakley Represents 18 Mandeville Courtyard, Warriner Gardens, London, SW11 4NB, United Kingdom
✆ (020) 7720 6234/✆ (020) 7720 0199
✉ mandy@mandycoakley.co.uk
🖳 www.mandycoakley.co.uk

Helen Walsh/S Management 15 Rocks Lane, London, SW13 0BD, United Kingdom
✆ (020) 8487 9655/✆ (020) 8487 9541
✉ fiona@smanagement.co.uk
🖳 www.smanagement.co.uk

HERS Agency Ltd Cleaveside, Bickleigh, Tiverton, Devon, EX16 8RB, United Kingdom
✆ (0870) 429 6499/✆ (01884) 855855
✉ hers@hersagency.co.uk
🖳 www.hersagency.co.uk

Hirearchy Classic & Contemporary Costume 45-47 Palmerston Road, Boscombe, Bournemouth, BH1 4HW, United Kingdom
✆ (01202) 394465
✉ hirearchy1@aol.com
🖳 www.hirearchy.co.uk

In the Wings LLC 5 Rue Des Grands Augustins, St Michel, Paris, 75006, France
✆ 00 33 1 31 09 20 72 85
✉ junis11@aol.com

Jacqui Lupton/S Management 15 Rocks Lane, London, SW13 0BD, United Kingdom
✆ (020) 8487 9655/✆ (020) 8487 9541
✉ fiona@smanagement.co.uk
🖳 www.smanagement.co.uk

Jane Bradley/Mandy Coakley Represents 18 Mandeville Courtyard, Warriner Gardens, London, SW11 4NB, United Kingdom
✆ (020) 7720 6234/✆ (020) 7720 0199
✉ mandy@mandycoakley.co.uk
🖳 www.mandycoakley.co.uk

Jennifer Manon Eardley Crescent, London, SW5 9JZ, United Kingdom
✆ (020) 7259 2462
✉ jennifermanon@excite.com

Jo Gillingwater/S Management 15 Rocks Lane, London, SW13 0BD, United Kingdom
✆ (020) 8487 9655/✆ (020) 8487 9541
✉ fiona@smanagement.co.uk
🖳 www.smanagement.co.uk

Karen Mason/Mandy Coakley Represents 18 Mandeville Courtyard, Warriner Gardens, London, SW11 4NB, United Kingdom
✆ (020) 7720 6234/✆ (020) 7720 0199
✉ mandy@mandycoakley.co.uk
🖳 www.mandycoakley.co.uk

Kasal Make-Up & Hair 5d Third Avenue, Lancing, West Sussex, BN15 9PU, United Kingdom
✆ (07814) 687562
✉ lalaine@kasal.co.uk
🖳 www.kasal.co.uk

Kasal Make-Up & Hair Design & Photography Third Avenue, Lancing, West Sussex, BN15 9PU, United Kingdom
✆ (07973) 622629
✉ info@kasal.co.uk
🖳 www.kasal.co.uk

Keely M 34 Morrish Road, London, SW2 4EH, United Kingdom
✆ (07855) 403172
✉ keelym@gmail.com

Kerry September 385A Brockley Road, Brockley, London, SE4 2PH, United Kingdom
✆ (07748) 594442
✉ kerryseptember@hotmail.com
🖳 www.kerryseptember.com

Kit Hall 217 Upland Road, London, SE22 0DJ, United Kingdom
✆ (07813) 797192
✉ spenandkit@tiscali.co.uk
🖳 www.kithall.co.uk

Klara Capouskova 11 Hertslet Road, London, N7 6PJ, United Kingdom
✆ (07961) 012705/✆ (020) 7281 4068
✉ klarunka@hotmail.com
🖳 www.klara-c.co.uk

Kym Menzies-Foster/Areia London Studio1, 42 Theobalds Road, London, WC1X 8NW, United Kingdom
✆ (020) 7404 8600/✆ (020) 7404 8601
✉ info@areia.com
🖳 www.areia.com

Laura Jane Sessions 128 Galleria Court, Pennack Road, London, SE15 6PY, United Kingdom
✆ (07740) 777 910
✉ laurajsessions@yahoo.co.uk
🖳 www.laurajanesessions.co.uk

Lesly McMenamin/Terrie Tanaka Management 101 Talbot Road, London, W11 2AT, United Kingdom
✆ (020) 7792 3500/✆ (020) 7792 2600
✉ danni@terrietanaka.com
🖳 www.terrietanaka.com

Liberty Shaw/Milc Studio 7, Zeus Hse, 16-30 Provost St, London, N1 7NG, United Kingdom
✆ (020) 7278 8838/✆ (0870) 0941564
✉ gemma@milc.co.uk
🖳 www.milc.co.uk

Lisa Laudat/Mandy Coakley Represents 18 Mandeville Courtyard, Warriner Gardens, London, SW11 4NB, United Kingdom
✆ (020) 7720 6234/✆ (020) 7720 0199
✉ mandy@mandycoakley.co.uk
🖳 www.mandycoakley.co.uk

Liz Daxauer /Bill Charles London Ltd. Unit 3E1, Zetland House, 5-25 Scrutton Street, London, EC2A 4HJ, United Kingdom
✆ 020 7033 9284/020 2033 9285/
✉ london@billcharles.com
🖳 www.billcharles.com

Louise Constad/Mandy Coakley Represents 18 Mandeville Courtyard, Warriner Gardens, London, SW11 4NB, United Kingdom
✆ (020) 7720 6234/✆ (020) 7720 0199
✉ mandy@mandycoakley.co.uk
🖳 www.mandycoakley.co.uk

Luke Anthony/S Management 15 Rocks Lane, London, SW13 0BD, United Kingdom
✆ (020) 8487 9655/✆ (020) 8487 9541
✉ fiona@smanagement.co.uk
🖳 www.smanagement.co.uk

Magdalen Gaffney (NASMAH) 20 Powis Terrace, London, W11 1JH, United Kingdom
✆ (020) 7221 8289/✆ (020) 7792 9357
✉ info@screenface.co.uk
🖳 www.screenface.com

Make-Up by Carla 6 Carna Court, 145A Kew Road, Richmond, Surrey, TW9 2PN, United Kingdom
✆ (07734) 348 053
✉ carla@makeupbycarla.co.uk
🖳 www.makeupbycarla.co.uk

MakeupbyDonna , Church Street, Garstang, Preston, PR3 1PA, United Kingdom
✆ (07739) 808683
✉ donnamakeup@aol.com
🖳 www.makeupbydonna.com

Mandy Coakley Represents 18 Mandeville Courtyard, Warriner Gardens, London, SW11 4NB, United Kingdom
✆ (020) 7720 6234/✆ (020) 7720 0199
✉ mandy@mandycoakley.co.uk
🖳 www.mandycoakley.co.uk

Mariana Fabricante , London, United Kingdom
✆ (020) 8509 0832/(07957) 989315
✉ marianafx@hotmail.com

HAIR AND MAKE UP

Martin Carter/Victoria Lees Management (VLM) 2 Fairview Gardens, Woodford Green, Essex, IG8 7DJ, United Kingdom
☎ (07710) 287220/ 📠 (020) 8504 8125
✉ victoria@victorialeesmanagement.co.uk
🖥 www.victorialeesmanagement.co.uk

Mary Jane Frost/Blunt Management The Courtyard Studio 2, Old Grammarphone Works, London, W10 5BZ, United Kingdom
☎ (020) 8960 2041/(07979) 900068 📠 (020) 8960 2039
✉ info@bluntlondon.com
🖥 www.bluntlondon.com

Mary Vango/Mandy Coakley Represents 18 Mandeville Courtyard, Warriner Gardens, London, SW11 4NB, United Kingdom
☎ (020) 7720 6234/ 📠 (020) 7720 0199
✉ mandy@mandycoakley.co.uk
🖥 www.mandycoakley.co.uk

Matt Mulhall/Blunt Management The Courtyard Studio 2, Old Grammarphone Works, London, W10 5BZ, United Kingdom
☎ (020) 8960 2041/(07979) 900068 📠 (020) 8960 2039
✉ info@bluntlondon.com
🖥 www.bluntlondon.com

Maureen Hannaford-Naisbitt (NASMAH) 13 Oxford Road, Teddington, Middlesex, TWII 0QA, United Kingdom
☎ (020) 8977 6538/(07802) 323633 📠 (020) 8977 6538

Mayumari 13 Raynham Road, London, W6 0HY, United Kingdom
☎ (0870) 2418243
✉ louise@mayumari.com

Mellissa Brown/Mandy Coakley Represents 18 Mandeville Courtyard, Warriner Gardens, London, SW11 4NB, United Kingdom
☎ (020) 7720 6234/ 📠 (020) 7720 0199
✉ mandy@mandycoakley.co.uk
🖥 www.mandycoakley.co.uk

Merryn Watts 2 Princes Way, London, SW19 6QE, United Kingdom
☎ (07716) 957379
✉ makeup@merrynwatts.com
🖥 www.merrynwatts.com

Michaeljohn 25 Albemarle Street, London, W1S 4HU, United Kingdom
☎ (020) 7491 4401/ 📠 (020) 7495 0152
✉ info@michaeljohn.co.uk
🖥 www.michaeljohn.co.uk

Milla Smith 17 Lombard Street, Abingdon, Oxfordshire, OX14 5BJ, United Kingdom
☎ (07734) 714543
✉ milla@milla-smith.co.uk

Natasha Wiggins 2 Sandfiled Terrance, Guildford, Surrey, GU1 4LN, United Kingdom
☎ 01483 577306

Neusa Neves/S Management 15 Rocks Lane, London, SW13 0BD, United Kingdom
☎ (020) 8487 9655/ 📠 (020) 8487 9541
✉ fiona@smanagement.co.uk
🖥 www.smanagement.co.uk

Nicky Tavilla/Terrie Tanaka Management 101 Talbot Road, London, W11 2AT, United Kingdom
☎ (020) 7792 3500/ 📠 (020) 7792 2600
✉ danni@terrietanaka.com
🖥 www.terrietanaka.com

Nicole Hardie Make-up Artisit 41 Rutland Gardens, Hove, East Sussex, BN3 5PN, United Kingdom
☎ (01273) 725397
✉ info@nicolehardie.co.uk
🖥 www.nicolehardie.co.uk

Nikki Palmer/Mandy Coakley Represents 18 Mandeville Courtyard, Warriner Gardens, London, SW11 4NB, United Kingdom
☎ (020) 7720 6234/ 📠 (020) 7720 0199
✉ mandy@mandycoakley.co.uk
🖥 www.mandycoakley.co.uk

Oliver De Almeida/Blunt Management The Courtyard Studio 2, Old Grammarphone Works, London, W10 5BZ, United Kingdom
☎ (020) 8960 2041/(07979) 900068 📠 (020) 8960 2039
✉ info@bluntlondon.com
🖥 www.bluntlondon.com

Penny Bell (NASMAH) 12 Oast House Close, Wraysbury, Staines, Middlesex, TW19 5BX, United Kingdom
☎ (01784) 483168/(07850) 902384 📠 (01784) 483168

Penny Rich 27 Hoxton Street, London, N1 6NH, United Kingdom
☎ (020) 7613 3886/ 📠 (020) 7729 8500
✉ ahdmakeup@aol.com
🖥 www.pennyrich.co.uk

Phavulous Creations 819 Great West Road, Isleworth, Middlesex, TW7 5PB, United Kingdom
☎ (020) 8560 1347
✉ ghettophavhulous@hotmail.com

Pride of USA International 187 Shepherd's Bush Mkt, London, W12 8DF, United Kingdom
☎ (020) 8743 1772/ 📠 (020) 8459 0320
✉ doublegeelondon@aol.com
🖥 www.prideofusa.com

Ronit Meier Make-up 13 Regatta Point, 38 Kew Bridge Road, Brentford, TW8 0EB,
☎ 07729 056413
✉ contact@ronitmeier.com
🖥 www.ronitmeier.com

Russell Hudson/Mandy Coakley Represents 18 Mandeville Courtyard, Warriner Gardens, London, SW11 4NB, United Kingdom
☎ (020) 7720 6234/ 📠 (020) 7720 0199
✉ mandy@mandycoakley.co.uk
🖥 www.mandycoakley.co.uk

S B FX 4 Rush House, Three Mills Film Studios, Three Mills Lane, Stratford, London, E3 3DU, United Kingdom
☎ (07967) 192955/ 📠 (020) 8555 9588
✉ info@steviefx.com
🖥 www.steviefx.com

Sam Norman , London, United Kingdom
☎ (07932) 397465
✉ sam@samnorman.co.uk
🖥 www.samnorman.co.uk

Sandra Exelby (NASMAH) 68 Sarsfield Road, Perivale, Greenford, Middlesex, UB6 7AG, United Kingdom
☎ (020) 8998 7494/(07721) 623728 📠 (020) 8998 7494
✉ sandraxlb@nasmah.org.uk

Sapphires Model Management Studio 11, The Makers Dozen, 8 Wulfruna Street, Wolverhampton, WV1 1LW, United Kingdom
☎ (01902) 427740
✉ info@sapphiresmodelmanagement.co.uk
🖥 www.sapphiresmodelmanagement.co.uk

Sarah Gregory/Mandy Coakley Represents 18 Mandeville Courtyard, Warriner Gardens, London, SW11 4NB, United Kingdom
☎ (020) 7720 6234/ 📠 (020) 7720 0199
✉ mandy@mandycoakley.co.uk
🖥 www.mandycoakley.co.uk

Screenface 20 Powis Terrace, Notting Hill, London, W11 1JH, United Kingdom
☎ (020) 7221 8289/ 📠 (020) 7792 9357
✉ info@screenface.co.uk
🖥 www.screenface.com

Sheelagh Wells (NASMAH) 20A New Road, Brentford, Middlesex, TW8 0NX, United Kingdom
☎ (020) 8847 6270/(07979) 504393 📠 (020) 8847 6270
✉ sheelagh@makeupartist.fsbusiness.co.uk

Sherman Labs (NASMAH) 17 Tomswood Road, Chigwell, Essex, IG7 5QP, United Kingdom
☎ (020) 8559 1942/7710562830
✉ shermanmakeupfx@btinternet.com
🖥 www.shermanlabs.com

Shoot People 3rd Floor, 202 City Road, London, EC1V 2PH, United Kingdom
☎ (020) 7253 0009/(07767) 313007 📠 (020) 7253 0009
✉ victoria@shootpeople.com
🖥 www.shootpeople.com

Shoot Production Ltd 23 Glebe Road, London, N8 7DA, United Kingdom
☎ (020) 8442 9171/ 📠 (020) 8348 7404
✉ adele@shootgroup.com
🖥 www.shootgroup.com

Sian Pierce Make-Up Artist Cottage Studios, Unit 2 Hilltop Works, Earl Shilton, LE9 7DT, United Kingdom
☎ (01455) 850058/(07845) 720253
✉ sian@make-up-artists.co.uk
🖥 www.make-up-artists.co.uk

Siobhan Harper-Ryan , London, United Kingdom
☎ (07715) 695919/ 📠 (020) 8908 1156
✉ siobhanharperryan@hotmail.com
🖥 www.sionhanharperryan.com

Soho Management Ltd 17 St. Annes Court, London, W1F 0BQ, United Kingdom
☎ (020) 7479 7199/ 📠 (020) 7479 7198
✉ fiona@sohomanagement.co.uk
🖥 www.sohomanagement.co.uk

Stephanie Kaye (NASMAH) 1 Westbrook Avenue, Hampton, Middlesex, TW12 2RE, United Kingdom
☎ (020) 8941 4938/ 📠 (020) 8941 4938

Stevie FX 81 Oxford Street, London, W1D 2EU, United Kingdom
☎ (020) 7851 3575
✉ info@steviefx.com
🖥 www.steviefx.com

Stilorama , , United Kingdom
☎ (020) 8728 2299/(07904) 504945 📠 (020) 8728 2299
✉ editor@stilorama.com
🖥 www.stilorama.com

Terri Manduca The Basement, 11 Elvaston Place, London, SW7 5QG, United Kingdom
☎ (020) 7581 5844/ 📠 (020) 7581 5822
✉ terri@terrimanduca.co.uk
🖥 www.terrimanduca.co.uk

Terrie Tanaka Management 101 Talbot Road, London, W11 2AT, United Kingdom
☎ (020) 7792 3500/ 📠 (020) 7792 2600
✉ danni@terrietanaka.com
🖥 www.terrietanaka.com

Toko/HERS Agency Ltd Cleaveside, Bickleigh, Tiverton, Devon, EX16 8RB, United Kingdom
☎ (0870) 429 6499/ 📠 (01884) 855855
✉ hers@hersagency.co.uk
🖥 www.hersagency.co.uk

Trudi Branch Arch Cottage, Hampton Court Way, Esher, Surrey, KT10 9AN, United Kingdom
☎ (020) 8398 3119/(07890) 310152
✉ allmadeup@hotmail.com

Unconventional Productions 3 Heber Road, London, NW2 6AB, United Kingdom
☎ (020) 8450 6148/ 📠 (020) 8450 1574
✉ lou@unconventionalproductions.com
🖥 www.unconventionalproductions.com

Vanessa B 17 Torrington Place, Wapping, London, E1W 2UY, United Kingdom
☎ (07810) 348597
✉ vbevin@hotmail.com

Victoria Lees Management (VLM) 2 Fairview Gardens, Woodford Green, Essex, IG8 7DJ, United Kingdom
☎ (07710) 287220/ 📠 (020) 8504 8125
✉ victoria@victorialeesmanagement.co.uk
🖥 www.victorialeesmanagement.co.uk

Vigi Sawdon 299 Lillie Road, London, SW6 7LL, United Kingdom
☎ (020) 7610 3233/(07859) 896383
✉ vigisawdon@yahoo.co.uk
🖥 www.vigisawdon.co.uk

Wai Kan/Adrenalin Management Temple Works, Brett Passage, London, E8 1JR, United Kingdom
☎ (020) 8986 3939/ 📠 (020) 8986 3665
✉ info@adrenalinmanagement.com
🖥 www.adrenalinmanagement.com

Wendy Rowe/Blunt Management The Courtyard Studio 2, Old Grammarphone Works, London, W10 5BZ, United Kingdom
☎ (020) 8960 2041/(07979) 900068 📠 (020) 8960 2039
✉ info@bluntlondon.com
🖥 www.bluntlondon.com

Wig Specialities Ltd 173 Seymour Place, London, W1H 4PW, United Kingdom
☎ (020) 7262 6565/ 📠 (020) 7723 1566
✉ wigspecialities@btconnect.com
🖥 www.wigspecialities.co.uk

Wood Associates 62 Bell Street, London, NW1 6SP, United Kingdom
☎ (020) 7723 6600
✉ info@wood-associates.co.uk
🖥 www.wood-associates.co.uk

VOICE OVERS

1st Transnational 211-212 Piccadilly, London, W1J 9HF, United Kingdom
☎ (020) 7629 2787/ 📠 (020) 7629 2797
✉ voices@1sttransnational.com
🖥 www.1sttransnational.com

A S T Language Services Ltd Unit 8, Ayr Street Workshops, Ayr Street, Nottingham, NG7 4FX, United Kingdom
0115-970 5633/ 0115-978 0130
office@astls.co.uk
www.astls.co.uk

Actors World Production Ltd , 13 Briarbank Rd, London, W13 0HH, United Kingdom
(020) 8997 0744/ (020) 8997 0960

Adam Sinclair/Talking Heads 2-4 Noel Street, London, W1F 8GB, United Kingdom
(020) 7292 7575/ (020) 7292 7576
voices@talkingheadsvoices.com
www.talkingheadsvoices.com

Adelphi Translations 402 The Workstation, 15 Paternoster Row, Sheffield, South Yorkshire, S1 2BX,
0114 221 0250
james@adelphitranslations.com
www.adelphitranslation.com

Adrian Finighan/Speak Easy Ltd Harrington, Northampton, NN6 9XT, United Kingdom
(0870) 0135126/(07850) 018069 (01536) 418740
enquiries@speak-easy.co.uk
www.speak-easy.co.uk

Agent: VoiceShop Bakerloo Chambers, 304 Edgware Road, London, W2 1DY, United Kingdom
(020) 7402 3966
exbru@yahoo.co.uk

Alan Wogan/Speak Easy Ltd Harrington, Northampton, NN6 9XT, United Kingdom
(0870) 0135126/(07850) 018069 (01536) 418740
enquiries@speak-easy.co.uk
www.speak-easy.co.uk

Alec Westwood/Talking Heads 2-4 Noel Street, London, W1F 8GB, United Kingdom
(020) 7292 7575/ (020) 7292 7576
voices@talkingheadsvoices.com
www.talkingheadsvoices.com

Alex Derbyshire/Talking Heads 2-4 Noel Street, London, W1F 8GB, United Kingdom
(020) 7292 7575/ (020) 7292 7576
voices@talkingheadsvoices.com
www.talkingheadsvoices.com

Alex Lovell/Speak Easy Ltd Harrington, Northampton, NN6 9XT, United Kingdom
(0870) 0135126/(07850) 018069 (01536) 418740
enquiries@speak-easy.co.uk
www.speak-easy.co.uk

Alex Reid/Speak Easy Ltd Harrington, Northampton, NN6 9XT, United Kingdom
(0870) 0135126/(07850) 018069 (01536) 418740
enquiries@speak-easy.co.uk
www.speak-easy.co.uk

Ali Campbell/Star Management Ltd 16a Winton Drive, Kelvinside, Glasgow, G12 0QA, United Kingdom
(0870) 2422276
star@starmanagement.co.uk
www.starmanagement.co.uk

Alison Colvile/Speak Easy Ltd Harrington, Northampton, NN6 9XT, United Kingdom
(0870) 0135126/(07850) 018069 (01536) 418740
enquiries@speak-easy.co.uk
www.speak-easy.co.uk

Alison Douglas/Star Management Ltd 16a Winton Drive, Kelvinside, Glasgow, G12 0QA, United Kingdom
(0870) 2422276
star@starmanagement.co.uk
www.starmanagement.co.uk

Allan Stewart/Talking Heads 2-4 Noel Street, London, W1F 8GB, United Kingdom
(020) 7292 7575/ (020) 7292 7576
voices@talkingheadsvoices.com
www.talkingheadsvoices.com

Amanda Hussain/Shining Management Ltd 12 D'Arblay Street, London, W1F 8DU, United Kingdom
(020) 7734 1981/ (020) 7734 2528
info@shiningvoices.com
www.shiningvoices.com

Amanda Phillips/Talking Heads 2-4 Noel Street, London, W1F 8GB, United Kingdom
(020) 7292 7575/ (020) 7292 7576
voices@talkingheadsvoices.com
www.talkingheadsvoices.com

Amani Zain/Speak Easy Ltd Harrington, Northampton, NN6 9XT, United Kingdom
(0870) 0135126/(07850) 018069 (01536) 418740
enquiries@speak-easy.co.uk
www.speak-easy.co.uk

Andrew Brittain/Talking Heads 2-4 Noel Street, London, W1F 8GB, United Kingdom
(020) 7292 7575/ (020) 7292 7576
voices@talkingheadsvoices.com
www.talkingheadsvoices.com

Andrew Conlon/Speak Easy Ltd Harrington, Northampton, NN6 9XT, United Kingdom
(0870) 0135126/(07850) 018069 (01536) 418740
enquiries@speak-easy.co.uk
www.speak-easy.co.uk

Andy Grainger/Shining Management Ltd 12 D'Arblay Street, London, W1F 8DU, United Kingdom
(020) 7734 1981/ (020) 7734 2528
info@shiningvoices.com
www.shiningvoices.com

Andy Kershaw/Speak Easy Ltd Harrington, Northampton, NN6 9XT, United Kingdom
(0870) 0135126/(07850) 018069 (01536) 418740
enquiries@speak-easy.co.uk
www.speak-easy.co.uk

Andy Styles/Shining Management Ltd 12 D'Arblay Street, London, W1F 8DU, United Kingdom
(020) 7734 1981/ (020) 7734 2528
info@shiningvoices.com
www.shiningvoices.com

Angels Model & Promotion Agency Albany House, 14 Shute End, Wokingham, Berkshire, RG40 1BJ, United Kingdom
0118-977 4970/ 0118-989 3115
info@angelsagency.com
www.angelsagency.com

Angie Greaves/Shining Management Ltd 12 D'Arblay Street, London, W1F 8DU, United Kingdom
(020) 7734 1981/ (020) 7734 2528
info@shiningvoices.com
www.shiningvoices.com

Anna Bentinck/Speak Easy Ltd Harrington, Northampton, NN6 9XT, United Kingdom
(0870) 0135126/(07850) 018069 (01536) 418740
enquiries@speak-easy.co.uk
www.speak-easy.co.uk

Anna Godsiff/Speak Easy Ltd Harrington, Northampton, NN6 9XT, United Kingdom
(0870) 0135126/(07850) 018069 (01536) 418740
enquiries@speak-easy.co.uk
www.speak-easy.co.uk

Another Tongue 10-11 D'Arblay Street, London, W1F 8DS, United Kingdom
(020) 7494 0300/ (020) 7494 7080
marcus@anothertongue.com

Anthony Etherton/Speak Easy Ltd Harrington, Northampton, NN6 9XT, United Kingdom
(0870) 0135126/(07850) 018069 (01536) 418740
enquiries@speak-easy.co.uk
www.speak-easy.co.uk

Arlene Fleming/Speak Easy Ltd Harrington, Northampton, NN6 9XT, United Kingdom
(0870) 0135126/(07850) 018069 (01536) 418740
enquiries@speak-easy.co.uk
www.speak-easy.co.uk

Ashley Blake/Noel Gay Artists 19 Denmark Street, London, WC2H 8NA, United Kingdom
(020) 7836 3941/ (020) 7287 1816
mail@noelgay.com
www.noelgay.com

Astley Jones/Speak Easy Ltd Harrington, Northampton, NN6 9XT, United Kingdom
(0870) 0135126/(07850) 018069 (01536) 418740
enquiries@speak-easy.co.uk
www.speak-easy.co.uk

Atlas Translations Ltd 14a Goodwins Court, Covent Garden, London, WC2N 4LL, United Kingdom
(020) 7240 6666/ (020) 7240 6996
london@atlas-translations.co.uk
www.atlas-translations.co.uk

Barbara Houseman/Speak Easy Ltd Harrington, Northampton, NN6 9XT, United Kingdom
(0870) 0135126/(07850) 018069 (01536) 418740
enquiries@speak-easy.co.uk
www.speak-easy.co.uk

Barbara Young/Noel Gay Artists 19 Denmark Street, London, WC2H 8NA, United Kingdom
(020) 7836 3941/ (020) 7287 1816
mail@noelgay.com
www.noelgay.com

Barnes Media International Residence Hermes A, 751 av Pierre Sauvaigo, St. Laurent Du Var, 6700, France
00 33 49 314 0614/00 33 66 179 5283
rbarnes@monaco.mc
www.barnesvoice.com

Barry Clayton/Talking Heads 2-4 Noel Street, London, W1F 8GB, United Kingdom
(020) 7292 7575/ (020) 7292 7576
voices@talkingheadsvoices.com
www.talkingheadsvoices.com

Barunka O'Shaughnessy/Noel Gay Artists 19 Denmark Street, London, WC2H 8NA, United Kingdom
(020) 7836 3941/ (020) 7287 1816
mail@noelgay.com
www.noelgay.com

BB Music House 158 Trewhitt Road, Newcastle, Tyne & Wear, NE6 5DY,
0191 224 2457
info@bbmusichouse.co.uk
www.bbmusichouse.co.uk

Becky Chippindale/Talking Heads 2-4 Noel Street, London, W1F 8GB, United Kingdom
(020) 7292 7575/ (020) 7292 7576
voices@talkingheadsvoices.com
www.talkingheadsvoices.com

Ben Jackson/Speak Easy Ltd Harrington, Northampton, NN6 9XT, United Kingdom
(0870) 0135126/(07850) 018069 (01536) 418740
enquiries@speak-easy.co.uk
www.speak-easy.co.uk

Ben Jones/Speak Easy Ltd Harrington, Northampton, NN6 9XT, United Kingdom
(0870) 0135126/(07850) 018069 (01536) 418740
enquiries@speak-easy.co.uk
www.speak-easy.co.uk

Ben Small/Shining Management Ltd 12 D'Arblay Street, London, W1F 8DU, United Kingdom
(020) 7734 1981/ (020) 7734 2528
info@shiningvoices.com
www.shiningvoices.com

Beverley Fullen/Talking Heads 2-4 Noel Street, London, W1F 8GB, United Kingdom
(020) 7292 7575/ (020) 7292 7576
voices@talkingheadsvoices.com
www.talkingheadsvoices.com

Big Box Productions Ltd 31 Penrose Street, London, SE17 3DW, United Kingdom
(07974) 561579
jeremy@bigboxstudios.com
www.bigboxstudios.com

Bob Lampon/Talking Heads 2-4 Noel Street, London, W1F 8GB, United Kingdom
(020) 7292 7575/ (020) 7292 7576
voices@talkingheadsvoices.com
www.talkingheadsvoices.com

Brian Bennett Music 333 Washington Boulevard Suite 243, Marina Del Rey, 90292, United States of America
00 1 310 895 5635
brian.scott.bennett@lycos.co.uk

Brian Ford/Talking Heads 2-4 Noel Street, London, W1F 8GB, United Kingdom
(020) 7292 7575/ (020) 7292 7576
voices@talkingheadsvoices.com
www.talkingheadsvoices.com

Brian Greene/Talking Heads 2-4 Noel Street, London, W1F 8GB, United Kingdom
(020) 7292 7575/ (020) 7292 7576
voices@talkingheadsvoices.com
www.talkingheadsvoices.com

Bridge Creative Ltd The Coach House Studio, 40 Higher Lane, Upholland, Lancashire, WN8 0NL,
01695 624966
bridget@bridgecreative.co.uk
www.bridgecreative.co.uk

Brigid Calderhead/Speak Easy Ltd Harrington, Northampton, NN6 9XT, United Kingdom
(0870) 0135126/(07850) 018069 (01536) 418740
enquiries@speak-easy.co.uk
www.speak-easy.co.uk

Bryan Drew Ltd Quadrant House, 80-82 Regent Street, London, W1B 5AU, United Kingdom
(020) 7437 2293/ (020) 7437 0561
bryan@bryandrewltd.com

Calypso 25-26 Poland Street, London, W1F 8QN, UK
(020) 7734 6415/ (020) 7437 0410
calypso@calypsovoices.com
www.calypsovoices.com

Carol Holt/Talking Heads 2-4 Noel Street, London, W1F 8GB, United Kingdom
(020) 7292 7575/ (020) 7292 7576
voices@talkingheadsvoices.com
www.talkingheadsvoices.com

Carol Vorderman/John Miles Organisation Cadbury Camp Lane, Clapton in Gordano, Bristol, BS20 7SB, United Kingdom
(01275) 854675/ (01275) 810186
john@johnmiles.org.uk
www.johnmiles.org.uk

Carolanne Lyme/Speak Easy Ltd Harrington, Northampton, NN6 9XT, United Kingdom
(0870) 0135126/(07850) 018069 (01536) 418740
enquiries@speak-easy.co.uk
www.speak-easy.co.uk

Cassandra French/Talking Heads 2-4 Noel Street, London, W1F 8GB, United Kingdom
(020) 7292 7575/ (020) 7292 7576
voices@talkingheadsvoices.com
www.talkingheadsvoices.com

Castaway Suite 3, 15 Broad Court, London, WC2B 5QN, United Kingdom
(020) 7240 2345/ (020) 7240 2772
sheila@castaway.org.uk
www.castaway.org.uk

Cathy MacDonald/Star Management Ltd 16a Winton Drive, Kelvinside, Glasgow, G12 0QA, United Kingdom
(0870) 2422276
star@starmanagement.co.uk
www.starmanagement.co.uk

Catrin Darnell/Speak Easy Ltd Harrington, Northampton, NN6 9XT, United Kingdom
(0870) 0135126/(07850) 018069 (01536) 418740
enquiries@speak-easy.co.uk
www.speak-easy.co.uk

Charlotte Edmonds/John Miles Organisation Cadbury Camp Lane, Clapton in Gordano, Bristol, BS20 7SB, United Kingdom
(01275) 854675/ (01275) 810186
john@johnmiles.org.uk
www.johnmiles.org.uk

Chris Beardshaw/Speak Easy Ltd Harrington, Northampton, NN6 9XT, United Kingdom
(0870) 0135126/(07850) 018069 (01536) 418740
enquiries@speak-easy.co.uk
www.speak-easy.co.uk

Chris Cowdrey/Talking Heads 2-4 Noel Street, London, W1F 8GB, United Kingdom
(020) 7292 7575/ (020) 7292 7576
voices@talkingheadsvoices.com
www.talkingheadsvoices.com

Chris Jarvis/Talking Heads 2-4 Noel Street, London, W1F 8GB, United Kingdom
(020) 7292 7575/ (020) 7292 7576
voices@talkingheadsvoices.com
www.talkingheadsvoices.com

Chris McQuarry/Shining Management Ltd 12 D'Arblay Street, London, W1F 8DU, United Kingdom
(020) 7734 1981/ (020) 7734 2528
info@shiningvoices.com
www.shiningvoices.com

Chris Saul/Speak Easy Ltd Harrington, Northampton, NN6 9XT, United Kingdom
(0870) 0135126/(07850) 018069 (01536) 418740
enquiries@speak-easy.co.uk
www.speak-easy.co.uk

Claire Bloom/Talking Heads 2-4 Noel Street, London, W1F 8GB, United Kingdom
(020) 7292 7575/ (020) 7292 7576
voices@talkingheadsvoices.com
www.talkingheadsvoices.com

Claire Harman/Speak Easy Ltd Harrington, Northampton, NN6 9XT, United Kingdom
(0870) 0135126/(07850) 018069 (01536) 418740
enquiries@speak-easy.co.uk
www.speak-easy.co.uk

Clare Balding/Talking Heads 2-4 Noel Street, London, W1F 8GB, United Kingdom
(020) 7292 7575/ (020) 7292 7576
voices@talkingheadsvoices.com
www.talkingheadsvoices.com

Clarke Peters/Talking Heads 2-4 Noel Street, London, W1F 8GB, United Kingdom
(020) 7292 7575/ (020) 7292 7576
voices@talkingheadsvoices.com
www.talkingheadsvoices.com

Clive Tyldesley/Talking Heads 2-4 Noel Street, London, W1F 8GB, United Kingdom
(020) 7292 7575/ (020) 7292 7576
voices@talkingheadsvoices.com
www.talkingheadsvoices.com

Colin Griffiths-Brown/Shining Management Ltd 12 D'Arblay Street, London, W1F 8DU, United Kingdom
(020) 7734 1981/ (020) 7734 2528
info@shiningvoices.com
www.shiningvoices.com

Corie Brown/Speak Easy Ltd Harrington, Northampton, NN6 9XT, United Kingdom
(0870) 0135126/(07850) 018069 (01536) 418740
enquiries@speak-easy.co.uk
www.speak-easy.co.uk

Cormack Creative Management Ltd Suite 208, 95 Morrison Street, Glasgow, G5 8BE, United Kingdom
0141-429 6810/(07778) 323169 0141-429 2603
susie@cormackcreativemanagement.co.uk
www.cormackcreativemanagement.co.uk

Craig Barrett/Shining Management Ltd 12 D'Arblay Street, London, W1F 8DU, United Kingdom
(020) 7734 1981/ (020) 7734 2528
info@shiningvoices.com
www.shiningvoices.com

Craig Parker/Talking Heads 2-4 Noel Street, London, W1F 8GB, United Kingdom
(020) 7292 7575/ (020) 7292 7576
voices@talkingheadsvoices.com
www.talkingheadsvoices.com

Cut Glass Productions 7 Crouch Hall Rd, Crouch End, London, N8 8HT, United Kingdom
(020) 8374 4701
kerry@cutglassproductions.com
www.cutglassproductions.com

Damien Lyne/Talking Heads 2-4 Noel Street, London, W1F 8GB, United Kingdom
(020) 7292 7575/ (020) 7292 7576
voices@talkingheadsvoices.com
www.talkingheadsvoices.com

Dan Mersh/Noel Gay Artists 19 Denmark Street, London, WC2H 8NA, United Kingdom
(020) 7836 3941/ (020) 7287 1816
mail@noelgay.com
www.noelgay.com

Danny Baker/Noel Gay Artists 19 Denmark Street, London, WC2H 8NA, United Kingdom
(020) 7836 3941/ (020) 7287 1816
mail@noelgay.com
www.noelgay.com

Darren Tighe/Talking Heads 2-4 Noel Street, London, W1F 8GB, United Kingdom
(020) 7292 7575/ (020) 7292 7576
voices@talkingheadsvoices.com
www.talkingheadsvoices.com

Dave Roberts/Talking Heads 2-4 Noel Street, London, W1F 8GB, United Kingdom
(020) 7292 7575/ (020) 7292 7576
voices@talkingheadsvoices.com
www.talkingheadsvoices.com

Dave Vitty/Noel Gay Artists 19 Denmark Street, London, WC2H 8NA, United Kingdom
(020) 7836 3941/ (020) 7287 1816
mail@noelgay.com
www.noelgay.com

David Graham/Talking Heads 2-4 Noel Street, London, W1F 8GB, United Kingdom
(020) 7292 7575/ (020) 7292 7576
voices@talkingheadsvoices.com
www.talkingheadsvoices.com

David Jensen/Talking Heads 2-4 Noel Street, London, W1F 8GB, United Kingdom
(020) 7292 7575/ (020) 7292 7576
voices@talkingheadsvoices.com
www.talkingheadsvoices.com

David Menkin/Noel Gay Artists 19 Denmark Street, London, WC2H 8NA, United Kingdom
(020) 7836 3941/ (020) 7287 1816
mail@noelgay.com
www.noelgay.com

David Mercer/Talking Heads 2-4 Noel Street, London, W1F 8GB, United Kingdom
(020) 7292 7575/ (020) 7292 7576
voices@talkingheadsvoices.com
www.talkingheadsvoices.com

David Mounfield/Noel Gay Artists 19 Denmark Street, London, WC2H 8NA, United Kingdom
(020) 7836 3941/ (020) 7287 1816
mail@noelgay.com
www.noelgay.com

David Prever/Talking Heads 2-4 Noel Street, London, W1F 8GB, United Kingdom
(020) 7292 7575/ (020) 7292 7576
voices@talkingheadsvoices.com
www.talkingheadsvoices.com

David Pullan/Shining Management Ltd 12 D'Arblay Street, London, W1F 8DU, United Kingdom
(020) 7734 1981/ (020) 7734 2528
info@shiningvoices.com
www.shiningvoices.com

David Rolston/Talking Heads 2-4 Noel Street, London, W1F 8GB, United Kingdom
(020) 7292 7575/ (020) 7292 7576
voices@talkingheadsvoices.com
www.talkingheadsvoices.com

David Strong 41 Denton Crescent, Black Notley, Braintree, Essex, CM77 8ZZ, United Kingdom
(07941) 107263
voiceofds@msn.com

Dean Martin/Talking Heads 2-4 Noel Street, London, W1F 8GB, United Kingdom
(020) 7292 7575/ (020) 7292 7576
voices@talkingheadsvoices.com
www.talkingheadsvoices.com

Deborah Maclaren/Speak Easy Ltd Harrington, Northampton, NN6 9XT, United Kingdom
(0870) 0135126/(07850) 018069 (01536) 418740
enquiries@speak-easy.co.uk
www.speak-easy.co.uk

Deborah McAndrew/Speak Easy Ltd Harrington, Northampton, NN6 9XT, United Kingdom
(0870) 0135126/(07850) 018069 (01536) 418740
enquiries@speak-easy.co.uk
www.speak-easy.co.uk

Dermot Crowley/Talking Heads 2-4 Noel Street, London, W1F 8GB, United Kingdom
(020) 7292 7575/ (020) 7292 7576
voices@talkingheadsvoices.com
www.talkingheadsvoices.com

Dominic King Production , , United Kingdom
(07967) 375952/(07967) 375952
dominicking@aol.com
www.dominicking.com

Dominica Warburton/Talking Heads 2-4 Noel Street, London, W1F 8GB, United Kingdom
(020) 7292 7575/ (020) 7292 7576
voices@talkingheadsvoices.com
www.talkingheadsvoices.com

Donna Donovan/Shining Management Ltd 12 D'Arblay Street, London, W1F 8DU, United Kingdom
(020) 7734 1981/ (020) 7734 2528
info@shiningvoices.com
www.shiningvoices.com

Donna Pickup/Shining Management Ltd 12 D'Arblay Street, London, W1F 8DU, United Kingdom
(020) 7734 1981/ (020) 7734 2528
info@shiningvoices.com
www.shiningvoices.com

Dougie Donnelly/Star Management Ltd 16a Winton Drive, Kelvinside, Glasgow, G12 0QA, United Kingdom
(0870) 2422276
star@starmanagement.co.uk
www.starmanagement.co.uk

Dr Gareth Smith/Cormack Creative Management Ltd Suite 208, 95 Morrison Street, Glasgow, G5 8BE, United Kingdom
0141-429 6810/(07778) 323169 0141-429 2603
susie@cormackcreativemanagement.co.uk
www.cormackcreativemanagement.co.uk

Dubmaster Studios 62 Ashdell Road, Alton, Hampshire, GU34 2TA, United Kingdom
(01420) 82822
info@dubmaster.com
www.dubmaster.com

Duncan Wells 3 St. Marys Way, Chalfont St. Peter, Gerrards Cross, Buckinghamshire, SL9 9BL, United Kingdom
(01753) 890555/(07831) 300370 (01753) 892839
duncan@duncanwells.com
www.duncanwells.com

Eamonn Holmes/Talking Heads 2-4 Noel Street, London, W1F 8GB, United Kingdom
(020) 7292 7575/ (020) 7292 7576
voices@talkingheadsvoices.com
www.talkingheadsvoices.com

Eddie Matthews/Speak Easy Ltd Harrington, Northampton, NN6 9XT, United Kingdom
(0870) 0135126/(07850) 018069 (01536) 418740
enquiries@speak-easy.co.uk
www.speak-easy.co.uk

Edmund Dehn/Shining Management Ltd 12 D'Arblay Street, London, W1F 8DU, United Kingdom
(020) 7734 1981/ (020) 7734 2528
info@shiningvoices.com
www.shiningvoices.com

Edward Adoo/Talking Heads 2-4 Noel Street, London, W1F 8GB, United Kingdom
(020) 7292 7575/ (020) 7292 7576
voices@talkingheadsvoices.com
www.talkingheadsvoices.com

Eiry Hughes/Talking Heads 2-4 Noel Street, London, W1F 8GB, United Kingdom
(020) 7292 7575/ (020) 7292 7576
voices@talkingheadsvoices.com
www.talkingheadsvoices.com

Eleanor Oldroyd/Speak Easy Ltd Harrington, Northampton, NN6 9XT, United Kingdom
(0870) 0135126/(07850) 018069 (01536) 418740
enquiries@speak-easy.co.uk
www.speak-easy.co.uk

Elizabeth Dermot Walsh/Talking Heads 2-4 Noel Street, London, W1F 8GB, United Kingdom
(020) 7292 7575/ (020) 7292 7576
voices@talkingheadsvoices.com
www.talkingheadsvoices.com

Elizabeth Moynihan/Speak Easy Ltd Harrington, Northampton, NN6 9XT, United Kingdom
(0870) 0135126/(07850) 018069 (01536) 418740
enquiries@speak-easy.co.uk
www.speak-easy.co.uk

Ellen Collier/Shining Management Ltd 12 D'Arblay Street, London, W1F 8DU, United Kingdom
(020) 7734 1981/ (020) 7734 2528
info@shiningvoices.com
www.shiningvoices.com

Elodie Kendall/Talking Heads 2-4 Noel Street, London, W1F 8GB, United Kingdom
(020) 7292 7575/ (020) 7292 7576
voices@talkingheadsvoices.com
www.talkingheadsvoices.com

Emma Rydal/Shining Management Ltd 12 D'Arblay Street, London, W1F 8DU, United Kingdom
(020) 7734 1981/ (020) 7734 2528
info@shiningvoices.com
www.shiningvoices.com

Emma Weaver/Shining Management Ltd 12 D'Arblay Street, London, W1F 8DU, United Kingdom
(020) 7734 1981/ (020) 7734 2528
info@shiningvoices.com
www.shiningvoices.com

Eric Barton/Speak Easy Ltd Harrington, Northampton, NN6 9XT, United Kingdom
(0870) 0135126/(07850) 018069 (01536) 418740
enquiries@speak-easy.co.uk
www.speak-easy.co.uk

Eric Meyers/Shining Management Ltd 12 D'Arblay Street, London, W1F 8DU, United Kingdom
(020) 7734 1981/ (020) 7734 2528
info@shiningvoices.com
www.shiningvoices.com

Eva Birthistle/Talking Heads 2-4 Noel Street, London, W1F 8GB, United Kingdom
(020) 7292 7575/ (020) 7292 7576
voices@talkingheadsvoices.com
www.talkingheadsvoices.com

Evans O'Brien The Halstow Garage, 115 Humber Road, London, SE3 7LW, United Kingdom
(020) 8293 7077/ (020) 8293 7066
info@evansobrien.co.uk
www.evansobrien.co.uk

Faye Barker/Speak Easy Ltd Harrington, Northampton, NN6 9XT, United Kingdom
(0870) 0135126/(07850) 018069 (01536) 418740
enquiries@speak-easy.co.uk
www.speak-easy.co.uk

Federico Martone/Star Management Ltd 16a Winton Drive, Kelvinside, Glasgow, G12 0QA, United Kingdom
(0870) 2422276
star@starmanagement.co.uk
www.starmanagement.co.uk

Felicity Duncan/Shining Management Ltd 12 D'Arblay Street, London, W1F 8DU, United Kingdom
(020) 7734 1981/ (020) 7734 2528
info@shiningvoices.com
www.shiningvoices.com

Fenella Fielding/Talking Heads 2-4 Noel Street, London, W1F 8GB, United Kingdom
(020) 7292 7575/ (020) 7292 7576
voices@talkingheadsvoices.com
www.talkingheadsvoices.com

Fenella George/Speak Easy Ltd Harrington, Northampton, NN6 9XT, United Kingdom
(0870) 0135126/(07850) 018069 (01536) 418740
enquiries@speak-easy.co.uk
www.speak-easy.co.uk

Fit2Fill Ltd 172 Ferme Park Road, London, N8 9SE, United Kingdom
(020) 8340 9419
mail@pepperstock.co.uk
www.pepperstock.co.uk/voiceovers.html

Fleur Taylor/Noel Gay Artists 19 Denmark Street, London, WC2H 8NA, United Kingdom
(020) 7836 3941/ (020) 7287 1816
mail@noelgay.com
www.noelgay.com

Foreign Legion 1 Kendal Road, London, NW10 1JH, United Kingdom
(020) 8450 4451
voices@foreignlegion.co.uk
www.foreignlegion.co.uk

Foreign Versions Ltd 60 Blandford Street, London, W1U 7JD, United Kingdom
(020) 7935 0993/ (020) 7935 0507
info@foreignversions.co.uk
www.foreignversions.co.uk

Frank Bourke/Talking Heads 2-4 Noel Street, London, W1F 8GB, United Kingdom
(020) 7292 7575/ (020) 7292 7576
voices@talkingheadsvoices.com
www.talkingheadsvoices.com

Frank McAvennie/Cormack Creative Management Ltd Suite 208, 95 Morrison Street, Glasgow, G5 8BE, United Kingdom
0141-429 6810/(07778) 323169 0141-429 2603
susie@cormackcreativemanagement.co.uk
www.cormackcreativemanagement.co.uk

G L S Language Services 250 Crow Road, Glasgow, G11 7LA, United Kingdom
0141-357 6611/ 0141-357 6605
info@glslanguages.demon.co.uk
www.glslanguageservices.com

Gary Bloom/Talking Heads 2-4 Noel Street, London, W1F 8GB, United Kingdom
(020) 7292 7575/ (020) 7292 7576
voices@talkingheadsvoices.com
www.talkingheadsvoices.com

Gary King/Speak Easy Ltd Harrington, Northampton, NN6 9XT, United Kingdom
(0870) 0135126/(07850) 018069 (01536) 418740
enquiries@speak-easy.co.uk
www.speak-easy.co.uk

Gary Martin/Shining Management Ltd 12 D'Arblay St, London, W1F 8DU, United Kingdom
(020) 7734 1981/ (020) 7734 2528
info@shiningvoices.com
www.shiningvoices.com

Gary Terzza/Speak Easy Ltd Harrington, Northampton, NN6 9XT, United Kingdom
(0870) 0135126/(07850) 018069 (01536) 418740
enquiries@speak-easy.co.uk
www.speak-easy.co.uk

Gavin Abbott/Talking Heads 2-4 Noel Street, London, W1F 8GB, United Kingdom
(020) 7292 7575/ (020) 7292 7576
voices@talkingheadsvoices.com
www.talkingheadsvoices.com

Gavin Robertson/Speak Easy Ltd Harrington, Northampton, NN6 9XT, United Kingdom
(0870) 0135126/(07850) 018069 (01536) 418740
enquiries@speak-easy.co.uk
www.speak-easy.co.uk

Geoff Lloyd/Noel Gay Artists 19 Denmark Street, London, WC2H 8NA, United Kingdom
(020) 7836 3941/ (020) 7287 1816
mail@noelgay.com
www.noelgay.com

Gerry Wilson.com 35 Fitzwilliam Place, Dublin, Ireland, Republic of
00 353 87 250 9824/ 00 353 1 450 7670
studio@gerrywilson.com
www.gerrywilson.com

Get Real Productions 20 Bishop Road, Bournemouth, BH9 1HB, United Kingdom
(01202) 535182/(07973) 690257
info@getrealproduction.co.uk
www.getrealproduction.co.uk

Gloria Hunniford/Talking Heads 2-4 Noel Street, London, W1F 8GB, United Kingdom
(020) 7292 7575/ (020) 7292 7576
voices@talkingheadsvoices.com
www.talkingheadsvoices.com

Gordon Whistance/Speak Easy Ltd Harrington, Northampton, NN6 9XT, United Kingdom
(0870) 0135126/(07850) 018069 (01536) 418740
enquiries@speak-easy.co.uk

Graham Gold/Talking Heads 2-4 Noel Street, London, W1F 8GB, United Kingdom
(020) 7292 7575/ (020) 7292 7576
voices@talkingheadsvoices.com
www.talkingheadsvoices.com

Grand Central Sound Recording Studios 51-53 Gt Marlborough Street, London, W1F 7JT, United Kingdom
(020) 7306 5600/ (020) 7306 5616
info@gcrs.com
www.grand-central-studios.com

Greg Edwards/Talking Heads 2-4 Noel Street, London, W1F 8GB, United Kingdom
(020) 7292 7575/ (020) 7292 7576
voices@talkingheadsvoices.com
www.talkingheadsvoices.com

Hannah Emanuel/Talking Heads 2-4 Noel Street, London, W1F 8GB, United Kingdom
(020) 7292 7575/ (020) 7292 7576
voices@talkingheadsvoices.com
www.talkingheadsvoices.com

Harry Miller/Shining Management Ltd 12 D'Arblay Street, London, W1F 8DU, United Kingdom
(020) 7734 1981/ (020) 7734 2528
info@shiningvoices.com
www.shiningvoices.com

Harry Towb/Talking Heads 2-4 Noel Street, London, W1F 8GB, United Kingdom
(020) 7292 7575/ (020) 7292 7576
voices@talkingheadsvoices.com
www.talkingheadsvoices.com

Harvey Cook/Shining Management Ltd 12 D'Arblay Street, London, W1F 8DU, United Kingdom
(020) 7734 1981/ (020) 7734 2528
info@shiningvoices.com
www.shiningvoices.com

Harvey Voices 4th Floor, 54-55 Margaret Street, London, W1W 8SH, United Kingdom
(020) 7952 4361
info@harveyvoices.co.uk
www.harveyvoices.co.uk

Heather Suttie/Cormack Creative Management Ltd Suite 208, 95 Morrison Street, Glasgow, G5 8BE, United Kingdom
0141-429 6810/(07778) 323169 0141-429 2603
susie@cormackcreativemanagement.co.uk
www.cormackcreativemanagement.co.uk

Helen Mark/Speak Easy Ltd Harrington, Northampton, NN6 9XT, United Kingdom
(0870) 0135126/(07850) 018069 (01536) 418740
enquiries@speak-easy.co.uk
www.speak-easy.co.uk

Henry Blofeld/Shining Management Ltd 12 D'Arblay Street, London, W1F 8DU, United Kingdom
(020) 7734 1981/ (020) 7734 2528
info@shiningvoices.com
www.shiningvoices.com

Hobson's Actors 62 Chiswick High Road, London, W4 1SY, United Kingdom
(020) 8995 3628/ (020) 8996 5350
actors@hobsons-international.com
www.hobsons-international.com
See ad in showcase

Hobson's Voices 62 Chiswick High Road, London, W4 1SY, United Kingdom
☎ **(020) 8995 3628**/✆ **(020) 8996 5350**
✉ voices@hobsons-international.com
🖳 www.hobsons-international.com
See ad in showcase

Howard Fiddy/Shining Management Ltd 12 D'Arblay Street, London, W1F 8DU, United Kingdom
☎ (020) 7734 1981/✆ (020) 7734 2528
✉ info@shiningvoices.com
🖳 www.shiningvoices.com

Howard Ward/Shining Management Ltd 12 D'Arblay Street, London, W1F 8DU, United Kingdom
☎ (020) 7734 1981/✆ (020) 7734 2528
✉ info@shiningvoices.com
🖳 www.shiningvoices.com

Hugh Dallas/Cormack Creative Management Ltd Suite 208, 95 Morrison Street, Glasgow, G5 8BE, United Kingdom
☎ 0141-429 6810/(07778) 323169 ✆ 0141-429 2603
✉ susie@cormackcreativemanagement.co.uk
🖳 www.cormackcreativemanagement.co.uk

Hugh Dickson/Speak Easy Ltd Harrington, Northampton, NN6 9XT, United Kingdom
☎ (0870) 0135126/(07850) 018069 ✆ (01536) 418740
✉ enquiries@speak-easy.co.uk
🖳 www.speak-easy.co.uk

Ian Hughes/Shining Management Ltd 12 D'Arblay Street, London, W1F 8DU, United Kingdom
☎ (020) 7734 1981/✆ (020) 7734 2528
✉ info@shiningvoices.com
🖳 www.shiningvoices.com

Ian Mayhew/Speak Easy Ltd Harrington, Northampton, NN6 9XT, United Kingdom
☎ (0870) 0135126/(07850) 018069 ✆ (01536) 418740
✉ enquiries@speak-easy.co.uk
🖳 www.speak-easy.co.uk

Ian Michie/Speak Easy Ltd Harrington, Northampton, NN6 9XT, United Kingdom
☎ (0870) 0135126/(07850) 018069 ✆ (01536) 418740
✉ enquiries@speak-easy.co.uk
🖳 www.speak-easy.co.uk

Ian Payne/Noel Gay Artists 19 Denmark Street, London, WC2H 8NA, United Kingdom
☎ (020) 7836 3941/✆ (020) 7287 1816
✉ mail@noelgay.com
🖳 www.noelgay.com

Ignyter Studios Berry Hill, Mansfield, Nottinghamshire, NG18 4HZ, United Kingdom
☎ (01623) 474464/✆ (01623) 474464
✉ info@ignyterstudios.com
🖳 www.ignyterstudios.com

Inter-Com (Foreign Voices) Hurlingham Studios, Ranelagh Gardens, London, SW6 3PA, United Kingdom
☎ (020) 7731 8000/✆ (0870) 0941954
✉ mail@intercom-translations.co.uk
🖳 www.intercom-translations.co.uk

Irony Founders 33 Laburnum Avenue, Cranswick, Driffield, North Humberside, YO25 9QH, United Kingdom
☎ (01377) 271407/(07967) 002056
✉ veeblefeltzer@aol.com
🖳 www.bluesreal.co.uk

J T Electrons 42 Torridge Road, Thornton Heath, Surrey, CR7 7EY, United Kingdom
☎ (020) 8665 6595/✆ (020) 8665 6595
✉ jtelectrons@msn.com

Jack Roberts/Speak Easy Ltd Harrington, Northampton, NN6 9XT, United Kingdom
☎ (0870) 0135126/(07850) 018069 ✆ (01536) 418740
✉ enquiries@speak-easy.co.uk
🖳 www.speak-easy.co.uk

Jackie Bird/Star Management Ltd 16a Winton Drive, Kelvinside, Glasgow, G12 0QA, United Kingdom
☎ (0870) 2422276
✉ star@starmanagement.co.uk
🖳 www.starmanagement.co.uk

Jacqueline Duff/Speak Easy Ltd Harrington, Northampton, NN6 9XT, United Kingdom
☎ (0870) 0135126/(07850) 018069 ✆ (01536) 418740
✉ enquiries@speak-easy.co.uk
🖳 www.speak-easy.co.uk

James Bachman/Noel Gay Artists 19 Denmark Street, London, WC2H 8NA, United Kingdom
☎ (020) 7836 3941/✆ (020) 7287 1816
✉ mail@noelgay.com
🖳 www.noelgay.com

James Cannon/Shining Management Ltd 12 D'Arblay Street, London, W1F 8DU, United Kingdom
☎ (020) 7734 1981/✆ (020) 7734 2528
✉ info@shiningvoices.com
🖳 www.shiningvoices.com

James Hannaway 1 Waterside, Berkhamsted, Hertfordshire, HP4 2HD, United Kingdom
☎ (01442) 877759/(07799) 834529
✉ therex@hotmail.co.uk
🖳 www.therex.co.uk

James Hornsby/Speak Easy Ltd Harrington, Northampton, NN6 9XT, United Kingdom
☎ (0870) 0135126/(07850) 018069 ✆ (01536) 418740
✉ enquiries@speak-easy.co.uk
🖳 www.speak-easy.co.uk

James Hyman/Talking Heads 2-4 Noel Street, London, W1F 8GB, United Kingdom
☎ (020) 7292 7575/✆ (020) 7292 7576
✉ voices@talkingheadsvoices.com
🖳 www.talkingheadsvoices.com

Jan Haydn Rowles/Talking Heads 2-4 Noel Street, London, W1F 8GB, United Kingdom
☎ (020) 7292 7575/✆ (020) 7292 7576
✉ voices@talkingheadsvoices.com
🖳 www.talkingheadsvoices.com

Jan Shand/Speak Easy Ltd Harrington, Northampton, NN6 9XT, United Kingdom
☎ (0870) 0135126/(07850) 018069 ✆ (01536) 418740
✉ enquiries@speak-easy.co.uk
🖳 www.speak-easy.co.uk

Jane Copland/Speak Easy Ltd Harrington, Northampton, NN6 9XT, United Kingdom
☎ (0870) 0135126/(07850) 018069 ✆ (01536) 418740
✉ enquiries@speak-easy.co.uk
🖳 www.speak-easy.co.uk

Jane van Hool/Speak Easy Ltd Harrington, Northampton, NN6 9XT, United Kingdom
☎ (0870) 0135126/(07850) 018069 ✆ (01536) 418740
✉ enquiries@speak-easy.co.uk
🖳 www.speak-easy.co.uk

Janet Brown/Shining Management Ltd 12 D'Arblay Street, London, W1F 8DU, United Kingdom
☎ (020) 7734 1981/✆ (020) 7734 2528
✉ info@shiningvoices.com
🖳 www.shiningvoices.com

Janice Hunter/Talking Heads 2-4 Noel Street, London, W1F 8GB, United Kingdom
☎ (020) 7292 7575/✆ (020) 7292 7576
✉ voices@talkingheadsvoices.com
🖳 www.talkingheadsvoices.com

Jay Healy/Talking Heads 2-4 Noel Street, London, W1F 8GB, United Kingdom
☎ (020) 7292 7575/✆ (020) 7292 7576
✉ voices@talkingheadsvoices.com
🖳 www.talkingheadsvoices.com

Jenni Bale/Talking Heads 2-4 Noel Street, London, W1F 8GB, United Kingdom
☎ (020) 7292 7575/✆ (020) 7292 7576
✉ voices@talkingheadsvoices.com
🖳 www.talkingheadsvoices.com

Jenni Murray/Speak Easy Ltd Harrington, Northampton, NN6 9XT, United Kingdom
☎ (0870) 0135126/(07850) 018069 ✆ (01536) 418740
✉ enquiries@speak-easy.co.uk
🖳 www.speak-easy.co.uk

Jennifer Lawrence/Talking Heads 2-4 Noel Street, London, W1F 8GB, United Kingdom
☎ (020) 7292 7575/✆ (020) 7292 7576
✉ voices@talkingheadsvoices.com
🖳 www.talkingheadsvoices.com

Jenny Burrell/Talking Heads 2-4 Noel Street, London, W1F 8GB, United Kingdom
☎ (020) 7292 7575/✆ (020) 7292 7576
✉ voices@talkingheadsvoices.com
🖳 www.talkingheadsvoices.com

Jeremy Hardy/Noel Gay Artists 19 Denmark Street, London, WC2H 8NA, United Kingdom
☎ (020) 7836 3941/✆ (020) 7287 1816
✉ mail@noelgay.com
🖳 www.noelgay.com

Jeremy Limb/Noel Gay Artists 19 Denmark Street, London, WC2H 8NA, United Kingdom
☎ (020) 7836 3941/✆ (020) 7287 1816
✉ mail@noelgay.com
🖳 www.noelgay.com

Jeremy Vine/Noel Gay Artists 19 Denmark Street, London, WC2H 8NA, United Kingdom
☎ (020) 7836 3941/✆ (020) 7287 1816
✉ mail@noelgay.com
🖳 www.noelgay.com

Jo Parkerson/Talking Heads 2-4 Noel Street, London, W1F 8GB, United Kingdom
☎ (020) 7292 7575/✆ (020) 7292 7576
✉ voices@talkingheadsvoices.com
🖳 www.talkingheadsvoices.com

Joe Mills/Talking Heads 2-4 Noel Street, London, W1F 8GB, United Kingdom
☎ (020) 7292 7575/✆ (020) 7292 7576
✉ voices@talkingheadsvoices.com
🖳 www.talkingheadsvoices.com

John Beesley/Talking Heads 2-4 Noel Street, London, W1F 8GB, United Kingdom
☎ (020) 7292 7575/✆ (020) 7292 7576
✉ voices@talkingheadsvoices.com
🖳 www.talkingheadsvoices.com

John Brunning/Shining Management Ltd 12 D'Arblay St, London, W1F 8DU, United Kingdom
☎ (020) 7734 1981/✆ (020) 7734 2528
✉ info@shiningvoices.com
🖳 www.shiningvoices.com

John Craven/Talking Heads 2-4 Noel Street, London, W1F 8GB, United Kingdom
☎ (020) 7292 7575/✆ (020) 7292 7576
✉ voices@talkingheadsvoices.com
🖳 www.talkingheadsvoices.com

John Hammond/Talking Heads 2-4 Noel Street, London, W1F 8GB, United Kingdom
☎ (020) 7292 7575/✆ (020) 7292 7576
✉ voices@talkingheadsvoices.com
🖳 www.talkingheadsvoices.com

John Miles Organisation Cadbury Camp Lane, Clapton in Gordano, Bristol, BS20 7SB, United Kingdom
☎ (01275) 854675/✆ (01275) 810186
✉ john@johnmiles.org.uk
🖳 www.johnmiles.org.uk

John Pennington/Talking Heads 2-4 Noel Street, London, W1F 8GB, United Kingdom
☎ (020) 7292 7575/✆ (020) 7292 7576
✉ voices@talkingheadsvoices.com
🖳 www.talkingheadsvoices.com

John Pohlhammer/Talking Heads 2-4 Noel Street, London, W1F 8GB, United Kingdom
☎ (020) 7292 7575/✆ (020) 7292 7576
✉ voices@talkingheadsvoices.com
🖳 www.talkingheadsvoices.com

John Ratzenberger/Noel Gay Artists 19 Denmark St, London, WC2H 8NA, United Kingdom
☎ (020) 7836 3941/✆ (020) 7287 1816
✉ mail@noelgay.com
🖳 www.noelgay.com

John Sachs/Talking Heads 2-4 Noel Street, London, W1F 8GB, United Kingdom
☎ (020) 7292 7575/✆ (020) 7292 7576
✉ voices@talkingheadsvoices.com
🖳 www.talkingheadsvoices.com

John Sharian/Talking Heads 2-4 Noel Street, London, W1F 8GB, United Kingdom
☎ (020) 7292 7575/✆ (020) 7292 7576
✉ voices@talkingheadsvoices.com
🖳 www.talkingheadsvoices.com

Jon Monie/Noel Gay Artists 19 Denmark Street, London, WC2H 8NA, United Kingdom
☎ (020) 7836 3941/✆ (020) 7287 1816
✉ mail@noelgay.com
🖳 www.noelgay.com

Jonathan Pearce/Talking Heads 2-4 Noel Street, London, W1F 8GB, United Kingdom
☎ (020) 7292 7575/✆ (020) 7292 7576
✉ voices@talkingheadsvoices.com
🖳 www.talkingheadsvoices.com

Jonathan Wrather/Shining Management Ltd 12 D'Arblay Street, London, W1F 8DU, United Kingdom
☎ (020) 7734 1981/✆ (020) 7734 2528
✉ info@shiningvoices.com
🖳 www.shiningvoices.com

Julia Marshall/Talking Heads 2-4 Noel Street, London, W1F 8GB, United Kingdom
☎ (020) 7292 7575/✆ (020) 7292 7576
✉ voices@talkingheadsvoices.com
🖳 www.talkingheadsvoices.com

Julie MacDonald/Speak Easy Ltd Harrington, Northampton, NN6 9XT, United Kingdom
☎ (0870) 0135126/(07850) 018069 ✆ (01536) 418740
✉ enquiries@speak-easy.co.uk
🖳 www.speak-easy.co.uk

Karen Bowerman/Speak Easy Ltd Harrington, Northampton, NN6 9XT, United Kingdom
(0870) 0135126/(07850) 018069 (01536) 418740
enquiries@speak-easy.co.uk
www.speak-easy.co.uk

Karen Krizanovich/Talking Heads 2-4 Noel Street, London, W1F 8GB, United Kingdom
(020) 7292 7575/ (020) 7292 7576
voices@talkingheadsvoices.com
www.talkingheadsvoices.com

Katarina Olsson/Speak Easy Ltd Harrington, Northampton, NN6 9XT, United Kingdom
(0870) 0135126/(07850) 018069 (01536) 418740
enquiries@speak-easy.co.uk
www.speak-easy.co.uk

Kate Harper/Speak Easy Ltd Harrington, Northampton, NN6 9XT, United Kingdom
(0870) 0135126/(07850) 018069 (01536) 418740
enquiries@speak-easy.co.uk
www.speak-easy.co.uk

Kate Sachs/Talking Heads 2-4 Noel Street, London, W1F 8GB, United Kingdom
(020) 7292 7575/ (020) 7292 7576
voices@talkingheadsvoices.com
www.talkingheadsvoices.com

Katie Campbell/Shining Management Ltd 12 D'Arblay Street, London, W1F 8DU, United Kingdom
(020) 7734 1981/ (020) 7734 2528
info@shiningvoices.com
www.shiningvoices.com

Katy Carmichael/Shining Management Ltd 12 D'Arblay Street, London, W1F 8DU, United Kingdom
(020) 7734 1981/ (020) 7734 2528
info@shiningvoices.com
www.shiningvoices.com

Ken Richman Voiceovers 1d Mount Rd, Wimbledon Pk, London, SW19 8ES, United Kingdom
(07957) 487027/ (0870) 4583686
ken@kenrichman.co.uk
www.kenrichman.co.uk

Kevin Duala/Talking Heads 2-4 Noel Street, W1F 8GB, United Kingdom
(020) 7292 7575/ (020) 7292 7576
voices@talkingheadsvoices.com
www.talkingheadsvoices.com

Korenne Lofts/Talking Heads 2-4 Noel Street, London, W1F 8GB, United Kingdom
(020) 7292 7575/ (020) 7292 7576
voices@talkingheadsvoices.com
www.talkingheadsvoices.com

Krishna Kumari/Speak Easy Ltd Harrington, Northampton, NN6 9XT, United Kingdom
(0870) 0135126/(07850) 018069 (01536) 418740
enquiries@speak-easy.co.uk
www.speak-easy.co.uk

Lakeside Studios Wharf Road, Frimley Green, Camberley, Surrey, GU16 6JR, United Kingdom
(01252) 838588/ (01252) 838616
teresa@lakesidestudios.co.uk
www.lakesidestudios.co.uk

Lara Rostron/Speak Easy Ltd Harrington, Northampton, NN6 9XT, United Kingdom
(0870) 0135126/(07850) 018069 (01536) 418740
enquiries@speak-easy.co.uk
www.speak-easy.co.uk

Laura Wilson The Garden Flat, 66 Marmora Road, East Dulwich, London, SE22 0RY, United Kingdom
(07979) 916231/ (020) 8693 5862
laurajwilson_1@yahoo.com

Laurence Bouvard/Talking Heads 2-4 Noel Street, London, W1F 8GB, United Kingdom
(020) 7292 7575/ (020) 7292 7576
voices@talkingheadsvoices.com
www.talkingheadsvoices.com

Lela B/Talking Heads 2-4 Noel Street, London, W1F 8GB, United Kingdom
(020) 7292 7575/ (020) 7292 7576
voices@talkingheadsvoices.com
www.talkingheadsvoices.com

Lesley Riddoch/Star Management Ltd 16a Winton Drive, Kelvinside, Glasgow, G12 0QA, United Kingdom
(0870) 2422276
star@starmanagement.co.uk
www.starmanagement.co.uk

Lewis McKie/Shining Management Ltd 12 D'Arblay St, London, W1F 8DU, United Kingdom
(020) 7734 1981/ (020) 7734 2528
info@shiningvoices.com
www.shiningvoices.com

Lip Service Casting 60-66 Wardour Street, London, W1F 0TA, United Kingdom
(020) 7734 3393/(07841) 994170 (020) 7734 3373
bookings@lipservice.co.uk
www.lipservice.co.uk

Liz Whiting/Speak Easy Ltd Harrington, Northampton, NN6 9XT, United Kingdom
(0870) 0135126/(07850) 018069 (01536) 418740
enquiries@speak-easy.co.uk
www.speak-easy.co.uk

Louise Minchin/Noel Gay Artists 19 Denmark Street, London, WC2H 8NA, United Kingdom
(020) 7836 3941/ (020) 7287 1816
mail@noelgay.com
www.noelgay.com

Lowri Turner/Noel Gay Artists 19 Denmark Street, London, WC2H 8NA, United Kingdom
(020) 7836 3941/ (020) 7287 1816
mail@noelgay.com
www.noelgay.com

Lucy Longhurst/Shining Management Ltd 12 D'Arblay Street, London, W1F 8DU, United Kingdom
(020) 7734 1981/ (020) 7734 2528
info@shiningvoices.com
www.shiningvoices.com

M P C Entertainment MPC House, 15-16 Maple Mews, London, NW6 5UZ, United Kingdom
(020) 7624 1184/ (020) 7624 4220
mpc@mpce.com
www.mpce.com

Malcolm Ward/Speak Easy Ltd Harrington, Northampton, NN6 9XT, United Kingdom
(0870) 0135126/(07850) 018069 (01536) 418740
enquiries@speak-easy.co.uk
www.speak-easy.co.uk

Mali Harries/Talking Heads 2-4 Noel Street, London, W1F 8GB, United Kingdom
(020) 7292 7575/ (020) 7292 7576
voices@talkingheadsvoices.com
www.talkingheadsvoices.com

Mark Cameron/Shining Management Ltd 12 D'Arblay Street, London, W1F 8DU, United Kingdom
(020) 7734 1981/ (020) 7734 2528
info@shiningvoices.com
www.shiningvoices.com

Mark Dexter/Talking Heads 2-4 Noel Street, London, W1F 8GB, United Kingdom
(020) 7292 7575/ (020) 7292 7576
voices@talkingheadsvoices.com
www.talkingheadsvoices.com

Mark Evans/Noel Gay Artists 19 Denmark Street, London, WC2H 8NA, United Kingdom
(020) 7836 3941/ (020) 7287 1816
mail@noelgay.com
www.noelgay.com

Mark Levesley 6 Berestede Road, London, W6 9NP, United Kingdom
(020) 8563 0718/ (020) 8563 0718
mark@levesley.com
www.levesley.com

Mark Pougatch/Noel Gay Artists 19 Denmark Street, London, WC2H 8NA, United Kingdom
(020) 7836 3941/ (020) 7287 1816
mail@noelgay.com
www.noelgay.com

Mark Rawson/Speak Easy Ltd Harrington, Northampton, NN6 9XT, United Kingdom
(0870) 0135126/(07850) 018069 (01536) 418740
enquiries@speak-easy.co.uk
www.speak-easy.co.uk

Mark Roper/Noel Gay Artists 19 Denmark Street, London, WC2H 8NA, United Kingdom
(020) 7836 3941/ (020) 7287 1816
mail@noelgay.com
www.noelgay.com

Martin Bashir/John Miles Organisation Cadbury Camp Lane, Clapton in Gordano, Bristol, BS20 7SB, United Kingdom
(01275) 854675/ (01275) 810186
john@johnmiles.org.uk
www.johnmiles.org.uk

Martin Brundle/John Miles Organisation Cadbury Camp Lane, Clapton in Gordano, Bristol, BS20 7SB, United Kingdom
(01275) 854675/ (01275) 810186
john@johnmiles.org.uk
www.johnmiles.org.uk

Martin Ledwith/Talking Heads 2-4 Noel Street, London, W1F 8GB, United Kingdom
(020) 7292 7575/ (020) 7292 7576
voices@talkingheadsvoices.com
www.talkingheadsvoices.com

Martin T. Sherman/Talking Heads 2-4 Noel Street, London, W1F 8GB, United Kingdom
(020) 7292 7575/ (020) 7292 7576
voices@talkingheadsvoices.com
www.talkingheadsvoices.com

Mary Ann O'Donoghue/Shining Management Ltd 12 D'Arblay Street, London, W1F 8DU, United Kingdom
(020) 7734 1981/ (020) 7734 2528
info@shiningvoices.com
www.shiningvoices.com

Mary Nightingale/Noel Gay Artists 19 Denmark Street, London, WC2H 8NA, United Kingdom
(020) 7836 3941/ (020) 7287 1816
mail@noelgay.com
www.noelgay.com

Melanie Hill/Speak Easy Ltd Harrington, Northampton, NN6 9XT, United Kingdom
(0870) 0135126/(07850) 018069 (01536) 418740
enquiries@speak-easy.co.uk
www.speak-easy.co.uk

Melanie Nicholson/Talking Heads 2-4 Noel Street, London, W1F 8GB, United Kingdom
(020) 7292 7575/ (020) 7292 7576
voices@talkingheadsvoices.com
www.talkingheadsvoices.com

Melinda Walker/Speak Easy Ltd Harrington, Northampton, NN6 9XT, United Kingdom
(0870) 0135126/(07850) 018069 (01536) 418740
enquiries@speak-easy.co.uk
www.speak-easy.co.uk

Melissa Berry/Speak Easy Ltd Harrington, Northampton, NN6 9XT, United Kingdom
(0870) 0135126/(07850) 018069 (01536) 418740
enquiries@speak-easy.co.uk
www.speak-easy.co.uk

Melissa Chapin/Shining Management Ltd 12 D'Arblay Street, London, W1F 8DU, United Kingdom
(020) 7734 1981/ (020) 7734 2528
info@shiningvoices.com
www.shiningvoices.com

Melissa Pearce/Speak Easy Ltd Harrington, Northampton, NN6 9XT, United Kingdom
(0870) 0135126/(07850) 018069 (01536) 418740
enquiries@speak-easy.co.uk
www.speak-easy.co.uk

Michael Imerson/Talking Heads 2-4 Noel Street, London, W1F 8GB, United Kingdom
(020) 7292 7575/ (020) 7292 7576
voices@talkingheadsvoices.com
www.talkingheadsvoices.com

Michael Kilgarriff/Talking Heads 2-4 Noel Street, London, W1F 8GB, United Kingdom
(020) 7292 7575/ (020) 7292 7576
voices@talkingheadsvoices.com
www.talkingheadsvoices.com

Michael Poole/Speak Easy Ltd Harrington, Northampton, NN6 9XT, United Kingdom
(0870) 0135126/(07850) 018069 (01536) 418740
enquiries@speak-easy.co.uk
www.speak-easy.co.uk

Micheal Goldfarb/Speak Easy Ltd Harrington, Northampton, NN6 9XT, United Kingdom
(0870) 0135126/(07850) 018069 (01536) 418740
enquiries@speak-easy.co.uk
www.speak-easy.co.uk

Mike Burnside/Shining Management Ltd 12 D'Arblay St, London, W1F 8DU, United Kingdom
(020) 7734 1981/ (020) 7734 2528
info@shiningvoices.com
www.shiningvoices.com

Mike Mendoza 169 Old Fort Road, Shoreham-by-Sea, West Sussex, BN43 5HL, UK
(01273) 462213/(07808) 342322 (01273) 462214
Mdmhove@aol.com

VOICE OVERS

Mike O'Malley/Talking Heads 2-4 Noel Street, London, W1F 8GB, United Kingdom
(020) 7292 7575/ (020) 7292 7576
voices@talkingheadsvoices.com
www.talkingheadsvoices.com

Mike Sweeney/Shining Management Ltd 12 D'Arblay Street, London, W1F 8DU, United Kingdom
(020) 7734 1981/ (020) 7734 2528
info@shiningvoices.com
www.shiningvoices.com

Mike Turiansky/Speak Easy Ltd Harrington, Northampton, NN6 9XT, United Kingdom
(0870) 0135126/(07850) 018069 (01536) 418740
enquiries@speak-easy.co.uk
www.speak-easy.co.uk

Miranda Wilson/Noel Gay Artists 19 Denmark Street, London, WC2H 8NA, United Kingdom
(020) 7836 3941/ (020) 7287 1816
mail@noelgay.com
www.noelgay.com

Mishal Husain/Speak Easy Ltd Harrington, Northampton, NN6 9XT, United Kingdom
(0870) 0135126/(07850) 018069 (01536) 418740
enquiries@speak-easy.co.uk
www.speak-easy.co.uk

Mood Media Forest Lodge, Westerham Road, Keston, Kent, BR2 6HE, United Kingdom
(01689) 882200/ (01689) 882203
info.uk@moodmedia.com
www.moodmedia.com

Moray Firth Radio , Inverness, IV3 8UJ, United Kingdom
(01463) 224433/ (01463) 243224
news@mfr.co.uk
www.mfr.co.uk

Na Na/Noel Gay Artists 19 Denmark Street, London, WC2H 8NA, United Kingdom
(020) 7836 3941/ (020) 7287 1816
mail@noelgay.com
www.noelgay.com

Nadim Sawalha/Speak Easy Ltd Harrington, Northampton, NN6 9XT, United Kingdom
(0870) 0135126/(07850) 018069 (01536) 418740
enquiries@speak-easy.co.uk
www.speak-easy.co.uk

Nancy Baldwin/Speak Easy Ltd Harrington, Northampton, NN6 9XT, United Kingdom
(0870) 0135126/(07850) 018069 (01536) 418740
enquiries@speak-easy.co.uk
www.speak-easy.co.uk

Nancy Crane/Talking Heads 2-4 Noel Street, London, W1F 8GB, United Kingdom
(020) 7292 7575/ (020) 7292 7576
voices@talkingheadsvoices.com
www.talkingheadsvoices.com

Natasha Desborough/Speak Easy Ltd Harrington, Northampton, NN6 9XT, United Kingdom
(0870) 0135126/(07850) 018069 (01536) 418740
enquiries@speak-easy.co.uk
www.speak-easy.co.uk

Nathan Nolan/Talking Heads 2-4 Noel Street, London, W1F 8GB, United Kingdom
(020) 7292 7575/ (020) 7292 7576
voices@talkingheadsvoices.com
www.talkingheadsvoices.com

Nathan Osgood/Noel Gay Artists 19 Denmark Street, London, WC2H 8NA, United Kingdom
(020) 7836 3941/ (020) 7287 1816
mail@noelgay.com
www.noelgay.com

Neil Bentley/Talking Heads 2-4 Noel Street, London, W1F 8GB, United Kingdom
(020) 7292 7575/ (020) 7292 7576
voices@talkingheadsvoices.com
www.talkingheadsvoices.com

Nick Hancock/Noel Gay Artists 19 Denmark Street, London, WC2H 8NA, United Kingdom
(020) 7836 3941/ (020) 7287 1816
mail@noelgay.com
www.noelgay.com

Nick Harrison/Speak Easy Ltd Harrington, Northampton, NN6 9XT, United Kingdom
(0870) 0135126/(07850) 018069 (01536) 418740
enquiries@speak-easy.co.uk
www.speak-easy.co.uk

Nick Page/Talking Heads 2-4 Noel Street, London, W1F 8GB, United Kingdom
(020) 7292 7575/ (020) 7292 7576
voices@talkingheadsvoices.com
www.talkingheadsvoices.com

Nicky Adams/Talking Heads 2-4 Noel Street, London, W1F 8GB, United Kingdom
(020) 7292 7575/ (020) 7292 7576
voices@talkingheadsvoices.com
www.talkingheadsvoices.com

Nicola Jolly/Star Management Ltd 16a Winton Drive, Kelvinside, Glasgow, G12 0QA, United Kingdom
(0870) 2422276
star@starmanagement.co.uk
www.starmanagement.co.uk

Nigel Williams/Shining Management Ltd 12 D'Arblay Street, London, W1F 8DU, United Kingdom
(020) 7734 1981/ (020) 7734 2528
info@shiningvoices.com
www.shiningvoices.com

Noah Lee Margetts/Talking Heads 2-4 Noel Street, London, W1F 8GB, United Kingdom
(020) 7292 7575/ (020) 7292 7576
voices@talkingheadsvoices.com
www.talkingheadsvoices.com

Noel Edmonds/John Miles Organisation Cadbury Camp Lane, Clapton in Gordano, Bristol, BS20 7SB, United Kingdom
(01275) 854675/ (01275) 810186
john@johnmiles.org.uk
www.johnmiles.org.uk

Noel Gay Artists 19 Denmark Street, London, WC2H 8NA, United Kingdom
(020) 7836 3941/ (020) 7287 1816
mail@noelgay.com
www.noelgay.com

Paul Brennen/Shining Management Ltd 12 D'Arblay Street, London, W1F 8DU, United Kingdom
(020) 7734 1981/ (020) 7734 2528
info@shiningvoices.com
www.shiningvoices.com

Paul Burnett/John Miles Organisation Cadbury Camp Lane, Clapton in Gordano, Bristol, BS20 7SB, United Kingdom
(01275) 854675/ (01275) 810186
john@johnmiles.org.uk
www.johnmiles.org.uk

Paul Coyte/Talking Heads 2-4 Noel Street, London, W1F 8GB, United Kingdom
(020) 7292 7575/ (020) 7292 7576
voices@talkingheadsvoices.com
www.talkingheadsvoices.com

Paul Herzberg/Speak Easy Ltd Harrington, Northampton, NN6 9XT, United Kingdom
(0870) 0135126/(07850) 018069 (01536) 418740
enquiries@speak-easy.co.uk
www.speak-easy.co.uk

Paul Jamieson Flat 6, Wildcroft Manor, Wildcroft Road, London, SW15 3TS, United Kingdom
(07977) 125565
pauljamieson81@aol.com
www.pauljamieson.tv

Paul Popplewell/Speak Easy Ltd Harrington, Northampton, NN6 9XT, United Kingdom
(0870) 0135126/(07850) 018069 (01536) 418740
enquiries@speak-easy.co.uk
www.speak-easy.co.uk

Paul Seed/Speak Easy Ltd Harrington, Northampton, NN6 9XT, United Kingdom
(0870) 0135126/(07850) 018069 (01536) 418740
enquiries@speak-easy.co.uk
www.speak-easy.co.uk

PDQ Productions The Beeches, Goldsborough, Knaresborough, North Yorkshire, HG5 8NR, United Kingdom
(01423) 865339/(07717) 312281
pauldunstan717@hotmail.com

Penny Gore/Talking Heads 2-4 Noel Street, London, W1F 8GB, United Kingdom
(020) 7292 7575/ (020) 7292 7576
voices@talkingheadsvoices.com
www.talkingheadsvoices.com

Pete Mitchell/Noel Gay Artists 19 Denmark Street, London, WC2H 8NA, United Kingdom
(020) 7836 3941/ (020) 7287 1816
mail@noelgay.com
www.noelgay.com

Peter Bramhill/Talking Heads 2-4 Noel Street, London, W1F 8GB, United Kingdom
(020) 7292 7575/ (020) 7292 7576
voices@talkingheadsvoices.com
www.talkingheadsvoices.com

Peter Curran/Talking Heads 2-4 Noel Street, London, W1F 8GB, United Kingdom
(020) 7292 7575/ (020) 7292 7576
voices@talkingheadsvoices.com
www.talkingheadsvoices.com

Peter Harlowe/Speak Easy Ltd Harrington, Northampton, NN6 9XT, United Kingdom
(0870) 0135126/(07850) 018069 (01536) 418740
enquiries@speak-easy.co.uk
www.speak-easy.co.uk

Peter Jefferson/Speak Easy Ltd Harrington, Northampton, NN6 9XT, United Kingdom
(0870) 0135126/(07850) 018069 (01536) 418740
enquiries@speak-easy.co.uk
www.speak-easy.co.uk

Peter Mair/Talking Heads 2-4 Noel Street, London, W1F 8GB, United Kingdom
(020) 7292 7575/ (020) 7292 7576
voices@talkingheadsvoices.com
www.talkingheadsvoices.com

Peter Silverleaf/Speak Easy Ltd Harrington, Northampton, NN6 9XT, United Kingdom
(0870) 0135126/(07850) 018069 (01536) 418740
enquiries@speak-easy.co.uk
www.speak-easy.co.uk

Peter Skellern/Noel Gay Artists 19 Denmark Street, London, WC2H 8NA, United Kingdom
(020) 7836 3941/ (020) 7287 1816
mail@noelgay.com
www.noelgay.com

Pierre Maubouche , London, NW2 2NW, United Kingdom
(07973) 284 158
pierre@thefrenchvoice.com
www.thefrenchvoice.com

Piers Gibbon/Speak Easy Ltd Harrington, Northampton, NN6 9XT, United Kingdom
(0870) 0135126/(07850) 018069 (01536) 418740
enquiries@speak-easy.co.uk
www.speak-easy.co.uk

Presenter Promotions 123 Corporation Road, Gillingham, Kent, ME7 1RG, United Kingdom
(01634) 851077/(07782) 224207 (01634) 851077
info@presenterpromotions.com
www.presenterpromotions.com

Qarie Marshall/Talking Heads 2-4 Noel Street, London, W1F 8GB, United Kingdom
(020) 7292 7575/ (020) 7292 7576
voices@talkingheadsvoices.com
www.talkingheadsvoices.com

Rabbit Vocal Management 2nd Floor, 18 Broadwick Street, London, W1F 8HS, United Kingdom
(020) 7287 6466/ (020) 7287 6566
info@rabbit.uk.net
www.rabbit.uk.net

Rachel O'Shea/Speak Easy Ltd Harrington, Northampton, NN6 9XT, United Kingdom
(0870) 0135126/(07850) 018069 (01536) 418740
enquiries@speak-easy.co.uk
www.speak-easy.co.uk

Radio Ga Ga 74 Hastings Street, Luton, LU1 5BH, United Kingdom
(07749) 141330
leanne_pinkgirl@yahoo.co.uk

Raewyn Lippert/Speak Easy Ltd Harrington, Northampton, NN6 9XT, United Kingdom
(0870) 0135126/(07850) 018069 (01536) 418740
enquiries@speak-easy.co.uk
www.speak-easy.co.uk

Randall Lee Rose/Shining Management Ltd 12 D'Arblay Street, London, W1F 8DU, United Kingdom
(020) 7734 1981/ (020) 7734 2528
info@shiningvoices.com
www.shiningvoices.com

Rebecca Deren/Speak Easy Ltd Harrington, Northampton, NN6 9XT, United Kingdom
(0870) 0135126/(07850) 018069 (01536) 418740
enquiries@speak-easy.co.uk
www.speak-easy.co.uk

Rebecca Wright/Talking Heads 2-4 Noel Street, London, W1F 8GB, United Kingdom
- (020) 7292 7575/ (020) 7292 7576
- voices@talkingheadsvoices.com
- www.talkingheadsvoices.com

Reece Dinsdale/Talking Heads 2-4 Noel Street, London, W1F 8GB, United Kingdom
- (020) 7292 7575/ (020) 7292 7576
- voices@talkingheadsvoices.com
- www.talkingheadsvoices.com

Revolution Post 11 Utopia Village, 7 Chalcot Road, London, NW1 8LH, United Kingdom
- (020) 7586 1271/ (020) 7586 4488
- torin@revolutionpost.tv
- www.revolutionpost.tv

Rhubarb Voice-Overs 1st Floor, 1a Devonshire Road, Chiswick, London, W4 2EU, United Kingdom
- (020) 8742 8683/ (020) 8742 8693
- enquiries@rhubarbvoices.co.uk
- www.rhubarbvoices.co.uk

Richard Graham/Talking Heads 2-4 Noel Street, London, W1F 8GB, United Kingdom
- (020) 7292 7575/ (020) 7292 7576
- voices@talkingheadsvoices.com
- www.talkingheadsvoices.com

Richard Mitchley/Speak Easy Ltd Harrington, Northampton, NN6 9XT, United Kingdom
- (0870) 0135126/(07850) 018069 / (01536) 418740
- enquiries@speak-easy.co.uk
- www.speak-easy.co.uk

Richard Ryder/Talking Heads 2-4 Noel Street, London, W1F 8GB, United Kingdom
- (020) 7292 7575/ (020) 7292 7576
- voices@talkingheadsvoices.com
- www.talkingheadsvoices.com

Richard Stilgoe/Noel Gay Artists 19 Denmark Street, London, WC2H 8NA, United Kingdom
- (020) 7836 3941/ (020) 7287 1816
- mail@noelgay.com
- www.noelgay.com

Ritchie Zealand/Speak Easy Ltd Harrington, Northampton, NN6 9XT, United Kingdom
- (0870) 0135126/(07850) 018069 / (01536) 418740
- enquiries@speak-easy.co.uk
- www.speak-easy.co.uk

Rob Curling/Speak Easy Ltd Harrington, Northampton, NN6 9XT, United Kingdom
- (0870) 0135126/(07850) 018069 / (01536) 418740
- enquiries@speak-easy.co.uk
- www.speak-easy.co.uk

Rob Dorsett/Speak Easy Ltd Harrington, Northampton, NN6 9XT, United Kingdom
- (0870) 0135126/(07850) 018069 / (01536) 418740
- enquiries@speak-easy.co.uk
- www.speak-easy.co.uk

Robert Elms/Talking Heads 2-4 Noel Street, London, W1F 8GB, United Kingdom
- (020) 7292 7575/ (020) 7292 7576
- voices@talkingheadsvoices.com
- www.talkingheadsvoices.com

Roberta Kanal Agency 82 Constance Road, Twickenham, TW2 7JA, United Kingdom
- (020) 8894 2277/ (020) 8894 7952

Robin Browne/Speak Easy Ltd Harrington, Northampton, NN6 9XT, United Kingdom
- (0870) 0135126/(07850) 018069 / (01536) 418740
- enquiries@speak-easy.co.uk
- www.speak-easy.co.uk

Robin Hood Music 2 Grange Road, Alresford, Hampshire, SO24 9HB, United Kingdom
- (01962) 735588/ (01962) 738400
- robinhoodmusic@clara.net
- www.robinhoodmusic.com

Robin Houston/Speak Easy Ltd Harrington, Northampton, NN6 9XT, United Kingdom
- (0870) 0135126/(07850) 018069 / (01536) 418740
- enquiries@speak-easy.co.uk
- www.speak-easy.co.uk

Robin Ince/Noel Gay Artists 19 Denmark Street, London, WC2H 8NA, United Kingdom
- (020) 7836 3941/ (020) 7287 1816
- mail@noelgay.com
- www.noelgay.com

Robin Lustig/Speak Easy Ltd Harrington, Northampton, NN6 9XT, United Kingdom
- (0870) 0135126/(07850) 018069 / (01536) 418740
- enquiries@speak-easy.co.uk
- www.speak-easy.co.uk

Rod Arthur/Talking Heads 2-4 Noel Street, London, W1F 8GB, United Kingdom
- (020) 7292 7575/ (020) 7292 7576
- voices@talkingheadsvoices.com
- www.talkingheadsvoices.com

Rod Culbertson/Talking Heads 2-4 Noel Street, London, W1F 8GB, United Kingdom
- (020) 7292 7575/ (020) 7292 7576
- voices@talkingheadsvoices.com
- www.talkingheadsvoices.com

Rod Liddle/Noel Gay Artists 19 Denmark Street, London, WC2H 8NA, United Kingdom
- (020) 7836 3941/ (020) 7287 1816
- mail@noelgay.com
- www.noelgay.com

Rossiters Voice St. James House, 150 London Road, East Grinstead, West Sussex, RH19 1HB, United Kingdom
- / (01342) 332037
- kemps@reedinfo.co.uk

Roxane Vacca Voices 73 Beak Street, London, W1F 9SR, United Kingdom
- (020) 7734 8085/ (020) 7734 8086
- dane@roxanevacca.co.uk
- www.roxanevaccamanagement.com

Russia House 61a Queen Mary Road, Sheffield, S2 1HQ, United Kingdom
- (07814) 920071/ 0114-283 5973
- anna@russia-house.co.uk
- www.russia-house.co.uk

Ruth Langsford/Talking Heads 2-4 Noel Street, London, W1F 8GB, United Kingdom
- (020) 7292 7575/ (020) 7292 7576
- voices@talkingheadsvoices.com
- www.talkingheadsvoices.com

Ruth Wishart/Star Management Ltd 16a Winton Drive, Kelvinside, Glasgow, G12 0QA, United Kingdom
- (0870) 2422276
- star@starmanagement.co.uk
- www.starmanagement.co.uk

Saffron/Talking Heads 2-4 Noel Street, London, W1F 8GB, United Kingdom
- (020) 7292 7575/ (020) 7292 7576
- voices@talkingheadsvoices.com
- www.talkingheadsvoices.com

Sally Gray/Star Management Ltd 16a Winton Drive, Kelvinside, Glasgow, G12 0QA, United Kingdom
- (0870) 2422276
- star@starmanagement.co.uk
- www.starmanagement.co.uk

Sally Hope Associates 108 Leonard Street, London, EC2A 4XS, United Kingdom
- (020) 7613 5353/ (020) 7613 4848
- casting@sallyhope.biz
- www.sallyhope.biz

Sam Battersea/Noel Gay Artists 19 Denmark Street, London, WC2H 8NA, United Kingdom
- (020) 7836 3941/ (020) 7287 1816
- mail@noelgay.com
- www.noelgay.com

Sam Beckinsale/Talking Heads 2-4 Noel Street, London, W1F 8GB, United Kingdom
- (020) 7292 7575/ (020) 7292 7576
- voices@talkingheadsvoices.com
- www.talkingheadsvoices.com

Sam Pinkham/Speak Easy Ltd Harrington, Northampton, NN6 9XT, United Kingdom
- (0870) 0135126/(07850) 018069 / (01536) 418740
- enquiries@speak-easy.co.uk
- www.speak-easy.co.uk

Sandy Walsh/Shining Management Ltd 12 D'Arblay Street, London, W1F 8DU, United Kingdom
- (020) 7734 1981/ (020) 7734 2528
- info@shiningvoices.com
- www.shiningvoices.com

Sarah Cartwright/Shining Management Ltd 12 D'Arblay Street, London, W1F 8DU, United Kingdom
- (020) 7734 1981/ (020) 7734 2528
- info@shiningvoices.com
- www.shiningvoices.com

Sarah Coutts/Speak Easy Ltd Harrington, Northampton, NN6 9XT, United Kingdom
- (0870) 0135126/(07850) 018069 / (01536) 418740
- enquiries@speak-easy.co.uk
- www.speak-easy.co.uk

Sarah Montague/Noel Gay Artists 19 Denmark Street, London, WC2H 8NA, United Kingdom
- (020) 7836 3941/ (020) 7287 1816
- mail@noelgay.com
- www.noelgay.com

Sarah O'Flaherty/Star Management Ltd 16a Winton Drive, Kelvinside, Glasgow, G12 0QA, United Kingdom
- (0870) 2422276
- star@starmanagement.co.uk
- www.starmanagement.co.uk

Scott Ainslie/Noel Gay Artists 19 Denmark Street, London, WC2H 8NA, United Kingdom
- (020) 7836 3941/ (020) 7287 1816
- mail@noelgay.com
- www.noelgay.com

Sebastian Abineri/Speak Easy Ltd Harrington, Northampton, NN6 9XT, United Kingdom
- (0870) 0135126/(07850) 018069 / (01536) 418740
- enquiries@speak-easy.co.uk
- www.speak-easy.co.uk

Serreta Wilson/Talking Heads 2-4 Noel Street, London, W1F 8GB, United Kingdom
- (020) 7292 7575/ (020) 7292 7576
- voices@talkingheadsvoices.com
- www.talkingheadsvoices.com

Sevi Lawson/Speak Easy Ltd Harrington, Northampton, NN6 9XT, United Kingdom
- (0870) 0135126/(07850) 018069 / (01536) 418740
- enquiries@speak-easy.co.uk
- www.speak-easy.co.uk

Shereen Nanjiani/Star Management Ltd 16a Winton Drive, Kelvinside, Glasgow, G12 0QA, United Kingdom
- (0870) 2422276
- star@starmanagement.co.uk
- www.starmanagement.co.uk

Shining Management Ltd 12 D'Arblay Street, London, W1F 8DU, United Kingdom
- (020) 7734 1981/ (020) 7734 2528
- info@shiningvoices.com
- www.shiningvoices.com

Shirley King/Talking Heads 2-4 Noel Street, London, W1F 8GB, United Kingdom
- (020) 7292 7575/ (020) 7292 7576
- voices@talkingheadsvoices.com
- www.talkingheadsvoices.com

Sian Williams/Noel Gay Artists 19 Denmark Street, London, WC2H 8NA, United Kingdom
- (020) 7836 3941/ (020) 7287 1816
- mail@noelgay.com
- www.noelgay.com

Side UK Ltd 14-18 Great Titchfield Street, London, W1W 8BD, United Kingdom
- (020) 7631 4800/ (020) 7631 4801
- info@sideuk.com
- www.sideuk.com

Simon Clayton/Talking Heads 2-4 Noel Street, London, W1F 8GB, United Kingdom
- (020) 7292 7575/ (020) 7292 7576
- voices@talkingheadsvoices.com
- www.talkingheadsvoices.com

Simon Fanshawe/Noel Gay Artists 19 Denmark Street, London, WC2H 8NA, United Kingdom
- (020) 7836 3941/ (020) 7287 1816
- mail@noelgay.com
- www.noelgay.com

Simon Hickson/Talking Heads 2-4 Noel Street, London, W1F 8GB, United Kingdom
- (020) 7292 7575/ (020) 7292 7576
- voices@talkingheadsvoices.com
- www.talkingheadsvoices.com

Sir David Frost/Noel Gay Artists 19 Denmark Street, London, WC2H 8NA, United Kingdom
- (020) 7836 3941/ (020) 7287 1816
- mail@noelgay.com
- www.noelgay.com

Skye Loneragan/Talking Heads 2-4 Noel Street, London, W1F 8GB, United Kingdom
- (020) 7292 7575/ (020) 7292 7576
- voices@talkingheadsvoices.com
- www.talkingheadsvoices.com

Sophie Benzing/Talking Heads 2-4 Noel Street, London, W1F 8GB, United Kingdom
- (020) 7292 7575/ (020) 7292 7576
- voices@talkingheadsvoices.com
- www.talkingheadsvoices.com

Sophie Hein/Speak Easy Ltd Harrington, Northampton, NN6 9XT, United Kingdom
(0870) 0135126/(07850) 018069 / (01536) 418740
enquiries@speak-easy.co.uk
www.speak-easy.co.uk

Sound Conception 82-84 York Road, Bedminster, Bristol, BS3 4AL, United Kingdom
0117-966 2932/ 0117-963 5059
soundconception@btconnect.com
www.soundconception.co.uk

Spatial Audio Theatre 8, Pinewood Studios, Iver, Buckinghamshire, SL0 0NH, United Kingdom
(01753) 654288/(07802) 657258 (020) 8932 3465
gerry@spatial-audio.co.uk
www.spatial-audio.co.uk

Speak Easy Ltd Harrington, Northampton, NN6 9XT, United Kingdom
(0870) 0135126/(07850) 018069 / (01536) 418740
enquiries@speak-easy.co.uk
www.speak-easy.co.uk

Star Management Ltd 16a Winton Drive, Kelvinside, Glasgow, G12 0QA, United Kingdom
(0870) 2422276
star@starmanagement.co.uk
www.starmanagement.co.uk

Stephen Armstrong/Speak Easy Ltd Harrington, Northampton, NN6 9XT, United Kingdom
(0870) 0135126/(07850) 018069 / (01536) 418740
enquiries@speak-easy.co.uk
www.speak-easy.co.uk

Stephen Fry/Noel Gay Artists 19 Denmark Street, London, WC2H 8NA, United Kingdom
(020) 7836 3941/ (020) 7287 1816
mail@noelgay.com
www.noelgay.com

Stephen Jardine/Cormack Creative Management Ltd Suite 208, 95 Morrison Street, Glasgow, G5 8BE, United Kingdom
0141-429 6810/(07778) 323169 0141-429 2603
susie@cormackcreativemanagement.co.uk
www.cormackcreativemanagement.co.uk

Steve Punt/Noel Gay Artists 19 Denmark Street, London, WC2H 8NA, United Kingdom
(020) 7836 3941/ (020) 7287 1816
mail@noelgay.com
www.noelgay.com

Steve Rider/Talking Heads 2-4 Noel Street, London, W1F 8GB, United Kingdom
(020) 7292 7575/ (020) 7292 7576
voices@talkingheadsvoices.com
www.talkingheadsvoices.com

Stewart Alexander/Talking Heads 2-4 Noel Street, London, W1F 8GB, United Kingdom
(020) 7292 7575/ (020) 7292 7576
voices@talkingheadsvoices.com
www.talkingheadsvoices.com

Stuart Laing/Shining Management Ltd 12 D'Arblay Street, London, W1F 8DU, United Kingdom
(020) 7734 1981/ (020) 7734 2528
info@shiningvoices.com
www.shiningvoices.com

Su Pollard/Noel Gay Artists 19 Denmark Street, London, WC2H 8NA, United Kingdom
(020) 7836 3941/ (020) 7287 1816
mail@noelgay.com
www.noelgay.com

Sue Cook/John Miles Organisation Cadbury Camp Lane, Clapton in Gordano, Bristol, BS20 7SB, United Kingdom
(01275) 854675/ (01275) 810186
john@johnmiles.org.uk
www.johnmiles.org.uk

Sue Green/Talking Heads 2-4 Noel Street, London, W1F 8GB, United Kingdom
(020) 7292 7575/ (020) 7292 7576
voices@talkingheadsvoices.com
www.talkingheadsvoices.com

Susannah Hitching/Talking Heads 2-4 Noel Street, London, W1F 8GB, United Kingdom
(020) 7292 7575/ (020) 7292 7576
voices@talkingheadsvoices.com
www.talkingheadsvoices.com

Susie Webb/Talking Heads 2-4 Noel Street, London, W1F 8GB, United Kingdom
(020) 7292 7575/ (020) 7292 7576
voices@talkingheadsvoices.com
www.talkingheadsvoices.com

Suzanne Dawe/Talking Heads 2-4 Noel Street, London, W1F 8GB, United Kingdom
(020) 7292 7575/ (020) 7292 7576
voices@talkingheadsvoices.com
www.talkingheadsvoices.com

Talking Heads 2-4 Noel Street, London, W1F 8GB, United Kingdom
(020) 7292 7575/ (020) 7292 7576
voices@talkingheadsvoices.com
www.talkingheadsvoices.com

Tara Lester/Talking Heads 2-4 Noel Street, London, W1F 8GB, United Kingdom
(020) 7292 7575/ (020) 7292 7576
voices@talkingheadsvoices.com
www.talkingheadsvoices.com

Tara Newley/Shining Management Ltd 12 D'Arblay Street, London, W1F 8DU, United Kingdom
(020) 7734 1981/ (020) 7734 2528
info@shiningvoices.com
www.shiningvoices.com

Taylor Jones/Shining Management Ltd 12 D'Arblay Street, London, W1F 8DU, United Kingdom
(020) 7734 1981/ (020) 7734 2528
info@shiningvoices.com
www.shiningvoices.com

Terry Nutkins/John Miles Organisation Cadbury Camp Lane, Clapton in Gordano, Bristol, BS20 7SB, United Kingdom
(01275) 854675/ (01275) 810186
john@johnmiles.org.uk
www.johnmiles.org.uk

The Big Mouth Co. , Walmer, Deal, Kent, CT14 9YA, United Kingdom
(0871) 7500 075/(07739) 117007 (0871) 7500 075
info@thebigmouthcompany.com
www.thebigmouthcompany.com

The Conrad Voice Consultancy 20 Courtenay Street, London, SE11 5PQ, United Kingdom
(020) 7582 8213
conradvoiceconsultancy@yahoo.co.uk
www.geocities.com/conradvoiceconsultancy

The Creative Department The Grange Annexe, Mill Lane, Carlton, Goole, East Yorkshire, DN14 9NG, United Kingdom
(01405) 861131/(07836) 244477 (01405) 861807
mail@mikehurley.co.uk
www.mikehurley.co.uk

The Dialect Coach 37 Berwick Street, London, W1F 8RS, United Kingdom
(07970) 026621
jocameronbrown@hotmail.com

The Sound Co. Ltd 23 Gosfield Street, Fitzrovia, London, W1W 6HG, United Kingdom
(020) 7580 5880/ (020) 7580 6454
admin@sound.co.uk
www.sound.co.uk

The Spotlight Casting Directories 7 Leicester Place, London, WC2H 7RJ, United Kingdom
(020) 7437 7631/ (020) 7437 5881
info@spotlight.com
www.spotlight.com
See ad in showcase

The Voice Box Agency Ltd 1st Floor, 100 Talbot Road, Old Trafford, Manchester, M16 0PG, United Kingdom
0161-874 5741/ 0161-888 2242
elinors@thevoicebox.co.uk
www.thevoicebox.co.uk

The Voiceover Gallery PO Box 213, Manchester, M21 9ZA, United Kingdom
0161-881 8844/ 0161-718 1009
info@thevoiceovergallery.co.uk
www.thevoiceovergallery.co.uk

Tiff Needell/Talking Heads 2-4 Noel Street, London, W1F 8GB, United Kingdom
(020) 7292 7575/ (020) 7292 7576
voices@talkingheadsvoices.com
www.talkingheadsvoices.com

Tim Birkett/Speak Easy Ltd Harrington, Northampton, NN6 9XT, United Kingdom
(0870) 0135126/(07850) 018069 / (01536) 418740
enquiries@speak-easy.co.uk
www.speak-easy.co.uk

Tim Smith/Speak Easy Ltd Harrington, Northampton, NN6 9XT, United Kingdom
(0870) 0135126/(07850) 018069 / (01536) 418740
enquiries@speak-easy.co.uk
www.speak-easy.co.uk

Timmy Mallett/John Miles Organisation Cadbury Camp Lane, Clapton in Gordano, Bristol, BS20 7SB, United Kingdom
(01275) 854675/ (01275) 810186
john@johnmiles.org.uk
www.johnmiles.org.uk

Timothy Watson/Shining Management Ltd 12 D'Arblay Street, London, W1F 8DU, United Kingdom
(020) 7734 1981/ (020) 7734 2528
info@shiningvoices.com
www.shiningvoices.com

Toby Longworth/Noel Gay Artists 19 Denmark Street, London, WC2H 8NA, United Kingdom
(020) 7836 3941/ (020) 7287 1816
mail@noelgay.com
www.noelgay.com

Tom Hodgkins/Speak Easy Ltd Harrington, Northampton, NN6 9XT, United Kingdom
(0870) 0135126/(07850) 018069 / (01536) 418740
enquiries@speak-easy.co.uk
www.speak-easy.co.uk

Tongue Tied (East Anglia) Ltd 23 Impington Lane, Impington, Cambridge, CB4 9LT, United Kingdom
(01223) 479391/ (01223) 504985
sales@tonguetiedeastanglia.co.uk
www.tonguetiedeastanglia.co.uk

Tony Clarkin/Noel Gay Artists 19 Denmark Street, London, WC2H 8NA, United Kingdom
(020) 7836 3941/ (020) 7287 1816
mail@noelgay.com
www.noelgay.com

Tony Hirst/Shining Management Ltd 12 D'Arblay St, London, W1F 8DU, United Kingdom
(020) 7734 1981/ (020) 7734 2528
info@shiningvoices.com
www.shiningvoices.com

Tony Lockwood/Shining Management Ltd 12 D'Arblay Street, London, W1F 8DU, United Kingdom
(020) 7734 1981/ (020) 7734 2528
info@shiningvoices.com
www.shiningvoices.com

Townend Music 44 Eastwick Crescent, Rickmansworth, Hertfordshire, WD3 8YJ, United Kingdom
(01923) 720083/(07974) 480972 (01923) 710587
townendmus@aol.com

Tres Hanley/Speak Easy Ltd Harrington, Northampton, NN6 9XT, United Kingdom
(0870) 0135126/(07850) 018069 / (01536) 418740
enquiries@speak-easy.co.uk
www.speak-easy.co.uk

Trevor Neal/Talking Heads 2-4 Noel Street, London, W1F 8GB, United Kingdom
(020) 7292 7575/ (020) 7292 7576
voices@talkingheadsvoices.com
www.talkingheadsvoices.com

U P S Translations 111 Baker Street, London, W1U 6RR, United Kingdom
(020) 7224 1220/ (020) 7486 3272
info@upstranslations.com
www.upstranslations.com

Valerie Sanderson/Speak Easy Ltd Harrington, Northampton, NN6 9XT, United Kingdom
(0870) 0135126/(07850) 018069 / (01536) 418740
enquiries@speak-easy.co.uk
www.speak-easy.co.uk

Veronika Hyks/Speak Easy Ltd Harrington, Northampton, NN6 9XT, United Kingdom
(0870) 0135126/(07850) 018069 / (01536) 418740
enquiries@speak-easy.co.uk
www.speak-easy.co.uk

Vocal Coach Studio Berry Hill, Mansfield, Nottinghamshire, NG18 4HZ, United Kingdom
01623 474464
business@vocalcoachstudio.co.uk
www.vocalcoachstudio.co.uk

Voice Gallery 28 Lexington Street, London, W1F 0LF, United Kingdom
(020) 7439 3325/ (020) 7734 9417
info@voice-gallery.com
www.voice-gallery.com

Voice Overs UK Middle Highfield Barn, Aughton Halton, Lancaster, LA2 6PQ, United Kingdom
(0700) 0802280/ (0700) 0802280
lunchboxtheatre@btinternet.com
www.lunchboxtheatrecompany.co.uk

Voice Shop First Floor, 1a Devonshire Road, London, W4 2EU, United Kingdom
(020) 8742 7077/ (020) 8742 7011
info@voice-shop.co.uk
www.voice-shop.co.uk

Voice Squad Ltd 1 Kendal Road, London, NW10 1JH, United Kingdom
(020) 8450 4451
voices@voicesquad.com
www.voicesquad.com

Voicebookers.com 45 Gloucester Square, London, W2 2TQ, United Kingdom
(07050) 366311
office@voicebookers.com
www.voicebookers.com

Voiceovers-UK.com Shireshead Old Church, Stony Lane, Forton, Preston, PR3 1DE, United Kingdom
(01524) 792020/ (01524) 792305
martin@voiceovers-uk.com
www.voiceovers-uk.com

Voices 2 Kirkgate Lane, Wighton, Wells-next-the-Sea, Norfolk, NR23 1PL, United Kingdom
(01328) 820950/ (01328) 820951

Voicetape Ltd 1 Chestnut Lane, Kingsnorth, Ashford, Kent, TN23 3LR, United Kingdom

voicetape@voicetape.com
www.voicetape.com

VSI Aradco House, 132 Cleveland Street, London, W1T 6AB, United Kingdom
(020) 7692 7700/ (020) 7692 7711
info@vsi.tv
www.vsi.tv

Wessex Translations Unit A1, The Premier Centre, Abbey Park Industrial Estate, Romsey, Hampshire, SO51 9DG, United Kingdom
(0870) 166 9300/ (0870) 166 9299
sales@wt-lm.com
www.wt-lm.com

Yakety Yak 7A Bloomsbury Square, London, WC1A 2LP, United Kingdom
(020) 7430 2600/ (020) 7404 6109
info@yaketyyak.co.uk
www.yaketyyak.co.uk

Zhivila Roche/Speak Easy Ltd Harrington, Northampton, NN6 9XT, United Kingdom
(0870) 0135126/(07850) 018069 / (01536) 418740
enquiries@speak-easy.co.uk
www.speak-easy.co.uk

CASTING

All Directions of London Personal Management 7 Rupert Court, London, W1D 6EB, United Kingdom
(020) 7437 5879

AM:PM The Actors' Agency 25 Centre Park, 33 Alfred Street, Belfast, BT2 8ED, United Kingdom
(028) 9023 5568/ (028) 9023 5568
mark@ampm.actors.com
www.ampmactors.com

Bespoke Production 72 Belleville Road, London, SW11 6PP, United Kingdom
(020) 7585 2536/ (020) 7585 2536
info@bespokeproduction.com
www.bespokeproduction.com

Bocek Production Cubuklu cad.agaclik mesire yeri, d+e burunbahce, beykoz, Istanbul, 34805,
00 9 02166801058
selma@bocekyapim.com.tr
www.bocekyapim.com.tr

Casting at Sweet Sweet Entertainments, 42 Theobalds Road, London, WC1X 8NW, United Kingdom
(020) 7404 6411/ (020) 7404 6412
info@sweet-uk.com
www.sweet-uk.com

Casting Studios International Ltd Ramillies House, 1-2 Ramillies Street, London, W1F 7LN, United Kingdom
(020) 7437 2070/ (020) 7437 2080
info@castingstudios.com
www.castingstudios.com

CastNet Ltd 20 Sparrows Herne, Bushey, WD23 1FU, United Kingdom
(020) 8420 4259/ (020) 8421 9666
admin@castingnetwork.co.uk
www.castingnetwork.co.uk

Century Models Well House, Unit D, 23a Benwell Road, London, N7 7BL, United Kingdom
(020) 7619 8235/(07737) 124883 / (020) 7404 6778
models@cmtmodels.com
www.cmtmodels.com

Cops On The Box BM Box 7301, London, WC1N 3XX, United Kingdom
(07710) 065851
info@tvcops.co.uk
www.cotb.co.uk

David Hall Casting 9 Falconet Court, 123 Wapping High Street, London, E1W 3NX, United Kingdom
(020) 7488 9916
davidhall@casting.wanadoo.co.uk

Donna Gray Photographic & Casting Services 1 Bale Avenue, Southborough, Cambridgewells, Tonbridge, Kent, TN4 0QQ, United Kingdom
(07976) 244090/ (01892 522 545
donna@donnagray.co.uk
www.donnagray.co.uk

Dubmaster Studios 62 Ashdell Road, Alton, Hampshire, GU34 2TA, United Kingdom
(01420) 82822
info@dubmaster.com
www.dubmaster.com

Folm Peaks Nabrezi 8, Prague, 120 00, Czech Republic
602 790 375/ 224 912 675
tomasiso@volny.cz

Fresh Agents Ltd Suite 5, Saks House, 19 Ship Street, Hove, East Sussex, BN1 1AD, United Kingdom
(01273) 711777/ (01273) 711778
info@freshagents.com
www.freshagents.com

Gwyndows Photographic Services 1 Collyberry Road, Woodmancote, Cheltenham, Gloucestershire, GL52 9HH, United Kingdom
(0845) 057 3268
gwyn@gwyndowsphotographic.co.uk
www.gwyndowsphotographic.co.uk

Kent Public Relations 131-151 Great Titchfield Street, London, W1W 5BB,
020 7022 9825/ 020 7022 9824
info@kentpr.com
www.kentpr.com

Lee's People Ltd 90 Longacer, London, WC2E 9RX, United Kingdom
(020) 7734 5775/(07970) 527252 / (020) 7734 3033
lee@lees-people.co.uk
www.lees-people.co.uk

Lees Casting Ltd 2nd Floor, 16 Manette Street, London, W1D 4AR, United Kingdom
(020) 7734 2070/(07970) 527252 / (020) 7734 3033
lee@lees-casting.co.uk
www.lees-casting.com

Marmalade Photographics 104 Heathwood Gardens, London, SE7 8ER, United Kingdom
(020) 8854 1973
wendy@marmaladephotos.co.uk
www.marmaladephotos.co.uk

Outsource Media 13 North Park Road, Harrogate, North Yorkshire, HG1 5PD, United Kingdom
(0800) 1958653
info@omuk.com
www.omuk.com

P H A Casting Tanzaro House, Ardwick Green North, Manchester, M12 6FZ, United Kingdom
(0161) 2734444/ (0161) 2734567
info@pha-agency.co.uk
www.pha-agency.co.uk

P H A Icon Ltd Tanzaro House, Ardwick Green North, Manchester, M12 6FZ, United Kingdom
0161-273 4444/ 0161-273 4567
info@pha-agency.co.uk
www.pha-agency.co.uk

Perceptive Photography Deacons Cottage, Cross in Hand Road, Heathfield, East Sussex, TN21 0UR, UK
(01435) 865214
info@perceptivephotography.com
www.perceptivephotography.com

PLC 7 Edith Grove, London, SW10 0JZ, United Kingdom
(020) 7352 4008/(07774) 694140 / (020) 7351 9969
julia@plcinternational.com
www.plcinternational.com

Polepeople Ltd The bonmarshy Centre, 241-251 Ferndale Road, London, SW9 8BJ, United Kingdom
(020) 7737 0831/ (0870) 1353335
info@polepeople.co.uk
www.polepeople.co.uk

Pure Productions Unit 105, Canalot Studios, 222 Kensal Road, London, W10 5BN, United Kingdom
(020) 8964 4664/ (020) 8694 4774
info@pureproduction.net
www.pureproduction.net

SA19 The Uniformed Artiste Agency, 2020 Hopgood St, London, W12 7JU, United Kingdom
(020) 8746 2523/ (020) 8735 2727
info@sa19.co.uk
www.sa19.co.uk

Star Production Spring House, 10 Spring Place, London, NW5 3BH, United Kingdom
(020) 7428 1414/ (020) 7428 1415
neena@starproduction.co.uk
www.starproduction.co.uk

Streetmodel.net 37 Foley Street, London, W1W 7TN, United Kingdom
info@streetmodel.net
www.streetmodel.net

Studio 7 10 Jamestown Road, London, NW1 7BY, United Kingdom
(020) 7284 5700/ (020) 7284 5708
contact@studiosevenphotography.co.uk
www.studiosevenphotography.co.uk

The Casting Suite 8-10 Lower James Street, London, W1F 9EL, United Kingdom
(020) 7434 2331/ (020) 7534 5799
info@thecastingsuite.com
www.thecastingsuite.com

The Invisible Picture Company 56 Falconer Road, Bushey, WD23 3AW, United Kingdom
(020) 8950 2901
terry@invisiblepicture.com
www.invisiblepicturecompany.com

The Lemon Group Studio 13, Old Truman Brewery, 91 Brick Lane, London, E1 6QL, United Kingdom
(020) 7053 2091/ (020) 7987 1571
matt@thelemongroup.com
http;/www.lemonauditions.com

The Spotlight Casting Directories 7 Leicester Place, London, WC2H 7RJ, United Kingdom
(020) 7437 7631/ (020) 7437 5881
info@spotlight.com
www.spotlight.com

Theatre Clwyd Wales 1b Northumberland Street, Cardiff, CF5 1LZ, United Kingdom
(029) 2021 1332
ctcrhian@hotmail.com

Tomo London Production Ltd Unit 305, Kingswharf, London, E8 4DS, United Kingdom
(020) 7249 5707/(07958) 954901 / (020) 7249 6557
info@tomolondon.com
www.tomolondon.com

Unconventional Productions 3 Heber Road, London, NW2 6AB, United Kingdom
(020) 8450 6148/ (020) 8450 1574
lou@unconventionalproductions.com
www.unconventionalproductions.com

Vanessa Warren , London, United Kingdom
(07708) 111027
vanessa@vanessawarren.com
www.vanessawarren.com

World Locations 3 Rue de Turbigo, Paris, 75001, France
00 33 6 18 41 47 05/ 00 33 1 42 33 89 23
clare@worldlocations.com
www.worldlocations.com

"from one prop to the whole production"

ncouvemtional

www.unconventionalproductions.com
Louise de Ville Morel +44 (0)20 8450 6148   +44 (0)7966 173 913

CREATIVE REVIEW PRESENTS
CREATIVEHANDBOOK.CO.UK

Creative Review presents the launch of the brand new Creative Handbook website. Featuring regularly updated portfolios from leading image makers and unique editorial by the Creative Review team, it's an invaluable tool for finding creative suppliers and resources across the UK.

GET LISTED

If you're a photographer, illustrator, designer, agency, or if you work in any of the related creative service industries, then it's not too late to make sure your details are included in the website: For a FREE listing, which provides basic contact details, go to: creativehandbook.co.uk and click on Get Listed. From here you can provide details of your company and your work.

Alternatively, we are offering a limited number of suppliers the chance to post up a full portfolio of their work, (12 images or video clips which can be updated as many times as you like) full contact details including a link to your own website, details of your current work in progress and award nominations.

All for a special price of £300.

To take advantage of this offer call:
Emma Nicolle: 020 7970 6267
Dave Harvey: 020 7970 6455
Russell Jamieson: 020 7943 8020

PEEPSHOW.ORG.UK

Commercials

jelly

illustration
motion graphics
animation
creative solutions

9-10 charlotte mews, london w1t 4ef
t: 020 7323 3307   f: 020 7636 2455

www.jellylondon.com

   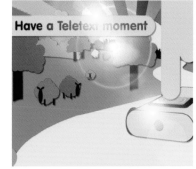

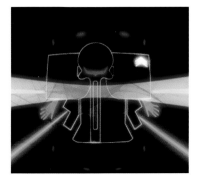   

PRIME
FOCUS
LONDON

Visual Effects • **Animation** • **Design** • **Telecine**

Prime Focus London • 37 Dean Street • London • W1D 4PT • UK

T • +44 (0)207 565 1000 W • www.primefocuslondon.com E • info@primefocusworld.com

from first thought...

TUSSAUD

YES

PHONES 4U

NU:U

MORTAL KOMBAT

GHD

RONSEAL

IMAX

SEVEN SEAS

RUSSELL HOBBS

PARK

SCHOLL

ICELAND

TV COMMERCIALS

ANIMATION

LIVE ACTION

TV COMMERCIALS

ANIMATION

LIVE ACTION

TV COMMERCIALS

ANIMATION

LIVE ACTION

to finished film...

Iceland sponsors I'm a Celebrity

kronfli · duliba
PRODUCTIONS
MANCHESTER OFFICE HAREFIELD SOUTH LODGE ALDERLEY ROAD WILMSLOW CHESHIRE SK9 1RA
t. 01625 536606 enquiries @kronfli-duliba .com www.kronfli-duliba.com

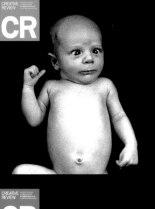

SUBSCRIBE TO CREATIVE REVIEW TODAY FOR JUST £64

BY PHONE
0207 292 3703
ONLINE
CREATIVEREVIEW.CO.UK/SUBSCRIBE.PHP

ANIMATICS

A3 Ltd 3rd Floor, Shropshire House, 2-10 Capper Street, London, WC1E 6JA, United Kingdom
☎ (020) 7631 5398/ (020) 7436 4195
✉ info@a3studios.com
🖥 www.a3studios.com

Daydream Linton House, 164-180 Union Street, London, SE1 0LH,
☎ +44 (0) 20 7096 1471/+44 (0) 20 7117 1636
✉ ralph@daydream.co.uk
🖥 www.daydream.co.uk

Storyboards Ltd 18 Greek Street, London, W1D 4JD, United Kingdom
☎ (020) 7734 1437/ (020) 7760 7713
✉ info@storyboards.co.uk
🖥 www.storyboards.co.uk

ANIMATION

04:02:02 St John's Court, Whiteladies Road, Bristol, BS8 2QY, United Kingdom
☎ 0117-946 7222/ 0117-946 7722
✉ mail@422.com
🖥 www.422south.com

422 South St. Johns Court, Whiteladies Road, Bristol, BS8 2QY, United Kingdom
☎ 0117-946 7222/ 0117-946 7722
✉ debbiet@422.com
🖥 www.422south.com

4th Wave Graphics Flat 1, 56 West Park, London, SE9 4RH, United Kingdom
☎ (020) 8851 6484
✉ chris@4thwave.freeserve.co.uk
🖥 www.4thwave.freeserve.co.uk

A Productions Ltd 52 Old Market Street, Bristol, BS2 0ER, United Kingdom
☎ 0117-929 9005/ 0117-929 9004
✉ katherine@aproductions.co.uk
🖥 www.aproductions.co.uk

A T Productions Ltd 6 Curley Hill Road, Lightwater, Surrey, GU18 5YG, United Kingdom
☎ (01276) 472179/ (01276) 451112
✉ atvideo@btopenworld.com
🖥 www.atproductions.co.uk

Aardman Animations Ltd (APA, PACT) Gas Ferry Road, Bristol, BS1 6UN, United Kingdom
☎ 0117-984 8485/ 0117-984 8486
✉ mail@aardman.com
🖥 www.aardman.com

Absolutely Production Ltd (PACT) 77 Beak Street, London, W1F 9DB, United Kingdom
☎ (020) 7930 3113/ (020) 7930 4114
✉ info@absolutely-uk.com
🖥 www.absolutely-uk.com

Alive Digital Media 83 Riversdale Road, London, N5 2ST, United Kingdom
☎
✉ info@areyoualive.com
🖥 www.areyoualive.com

All Handmade Unit 6-8, Stapley Manor Farm, Long Lane, Odiham, Hook, Hampshire, RG29 1JE, United Kingdom
☎ (01256) 862111

Andy Potts Illustration 15 Upper Bardsey Walk, London, N1 2RZ, United Kingdom
☎ (07817) 159049
✉ info@andy-potts.com
🖥 www.andy-potts.com

Animage Ltd 62 West Croft Close, London, NW2 2RR, United Kingdom
☎ (020) 7435 3883/ (020) 7435 3883
✉ mail@animageltd.com
🖥 www.animageltd.com

Animation People Ltd 22 Churchmead Close, East Barnet, Barnet, Hertfordshire, EN4 8UY, UK
☎ (020) 8449 1601/(07714) 203737 (020) 8449 1601
✉ brianlarks@aol.com
🖥 www.animationpeople.co.uk

Animation Source The Command Centre, Hunting Hill, Tain, Ross-shire, IV19 1PE, United Kingdom
☎ (01862) 894203/(07721) 331991
✉ claire@animationsource.net
🖥 www.animationsource.net

Animation Studio Ltd 119 Sutton Court, Chiswick, London, W4 3EE, United Kingdom
☎ (020) 8995 9386/ (020) 8995 8335
✉ bob@animationstudio.co.uk
🖥 www.animationstudio.co.uk

Anna Lubecka 77 Tyne Court, Hanway Road, Hanwell, London, W7 3RR, United Kingdom
☎ (07745) 639213
✉ alubecka@hotmail.com
🖥 www.annalubecka.com

Another-Fine-Mesh.com 33a Fossgate, York, YO1 9TA, United Kingdom
☎ (01904) 630721
✉ 3d@another-fine-mesh.com
🖥 www.another-fine-mesh.com

Antics Workshop 42 Champion Hill, Camberwell, London, SE5 8BS, United Kingdom
☎ (01283) 701441/ (020) 7274 0135
✉ info@antics1.demon.co.uk
🖥 www.antics1.demon.co.uk

Apple Agency Ltd Design House, Exmoor Avenue, Scunthorpe, North Lincolnshire, DN15 8NJ, United Kingdom
☎ (01724) 289081/ (01724) 289381
✉ simonb@appleagency.co.uk
🖥 www.apple.co.uk

Arcmedia Ltd 5 Hardhorn Road, Poulton-le-Fylde, Lancashire, FY6 7SR, United Kingdom
☎ (01253) 896616/ (01253) 896996
✉ info@arc-media.org
🖥 www.arc-media.org

Atomic Arts 3 Hanson Street, London, W1W 6TB, United Kingdom
☎ (020) 7419 4190/ (020) 7419 4194
✉ info@atomicarts.net
🖥 www.atomicarts.net

kronfli · duliba
P R O D U C T I O N S

Yorkshire Water

MANCHESTER OFFICE HAREFIELD SOUTH LODGE ALDERLEY ROAD WILMSLOW CHESHIRE SK9 1RA
t. 01625 536606 enquiries @kronfli-duliba.com www.kronfli-duliba.com

Aura Studios Ltd 30 Devizes Road, Swindon, SN1 4BG, United Kingdom
℡ (01793) 420002
✎ studio@aurastudios.co.uk
🖳 www.aurastudios.co.uk

Axis Animation Suite 225, Pentagon Business Centre, Washington Street, Glasgow, G3 8AZ, United Kingdom
℡ 0141-572 2802/✆ 0141-572 2809
✎ enquiries@axisanimation.com
🖳 www.axisanimation.com

B E N A Flat 1, Grove Mansions, High Street, Wanstead, London, E11 2AE, United Kingdom
℡ (07976) 512269
✎ benaustin@hotmail.co.uk

Banana Park Ltd 6 Cranleigh Mews, Battersea, London, SW11 2QL, United Kingdom
℡ (020) 7228 7136/✆ (020) 7738 1887
✎ studio@bananapark.co.uk
🖳 www.bananapark.co.uk

Be Animation 13 Risborough Street, London, SE1 0HF, United Kingdom
℡ (020) 7620 2595/✆ (020) 7620 2596
✎ studio@beanimation.com
🖳 www.beanimation.com

Bermuda Shorts Ltd Circus House, 5th Floor, 21 Great Titchfield Street, London, W1W 8BA, UK
℡ (020) 7437 7335/✆ (020) 7437 7334
✎ info@bermudashorts.com
🖳 www.bermudashorts.com

Bernard Heyes Design Ltd 7 Meard Street, London, W1F 0EW, United Kingdom
℡ (020) 7287 0202/✆ (020) 7434 9334
✎ info@bernardheyesdesign.co.uk
🖳 www.bernardheyesdesign.co.uk

Beryl Stevens Associates Ltd 1 Linersh Wood Close, Bramley, Surrey, GU5 0EG, United Kingdom
℡ (01483) 892138
✎ berylstevens@tiscali.co.uk

Bigfish Net Ltd 58 Friar Gate, Derby, DE1 1DF, United Kingdom
℡ (01332) 370088
✎ andy@bfcc.co.uk
🖳 www.bfcc.co.uk

BigMan Designs 3 Oaklands Park, Bishop's Stortford, Hertfordshire, CM23 2BY, United Kingdom
℡ (01279) 504263
✎ kevin@bigmandesigns.com
🖳 www.bigmandesigns.com

Blobina Animations 21 Ladysmith Road, Edinburgh, EH9 3EU, United Kingdom
℡ 0131-467 4446
✎ selina@blobina.com
🖳 www.blobina.com

Blue-Toe Productions Brickouse, Lambourne Hall Road, Canewdon, Essex, SS4 3PG, United Kingdom
℡ (01702) 258029/(07974) 763138 ✆ (01702) 258029
✎ blue-toe@freeuk.com

bluegfx Hyde House, 2 Guildford Park Road, Guildford, Surrey, GU2 7PB, United Kingdom
℡ (01483) 467200/✆ (01483) 467201
🖳 www.bluegfx.com

Bold Endeavours Ltd 7 Manor Park, Staines, Middlesex, TW18 4XE,
℡ 01784 460 064
✎ derek@boldendeavours.com
🖳 www.big-easy-footage-library-software.co.uk

Bolexbrothers Ltd 6 Brunel Lock Development, Smeaton Road, Cumberland Basin, Bristol, BS1 6SE, United Kingdom
℡ 0117-985 8000/✆ 0117-985 8899
✎ mail@bolexbrothers.co.uk
🖳 www.bolexbrothers.co.uk

Box 5th Floor, 121 Princess Street, Manchester, M1 7AD, United Kingdom
℡ 0161-228 2399/(07973) 344606 ✆ (08719) 002009
✎ mike@the-box.co.uk
🖳 www.the-box.co.uk

Box-head 45 Grove Road, Harrogate, North Yorkshire, HG1 5EP, United Kingdom
℡ (01423) 566318
✎ david@box-head.co.uk
🖳 www.box-head.co.uk

Brandt Animation 11 D'Arblay Street, London, W1F 8DT, United Kingdom
℡ (020) 7734 0196
✎ finn@brandtanim.co.uk
🖳 www.brandtanim.co.uk

Bright Idea Flat 31, Pavia Court, Graigwen Road, Pontypridd, Mid Glamorgan, CF37 2TW, United Kingdom
℡ (07952) 663680
✎ info@brightidea.org.uk
🖳 www.brightidea.org.uk

Brightworks Product Design Mendip House, Silver Street, Cheddar, Somerset, BS27 3LE, United Kingdom
℡ (01934) 744956/✆ (01934) 744986
✎ graeme@brightworks.co.uk
🖳 www.brightworks.co.uk

Built from scratch design New Plot, 1-2 Ivy cottages, Chapmans Lane, St Pauls Cray, Orpington, Kent, BR5 3JA, United Kingdom
℡ 01689 897740/✆ 01689 897740
✎ Info@builtfromscratch-design.co.uk
🖳 www.builtfromscratch-design.co.uk

Bunch 27 Phipp Street, London, EC2A 4NP, United Kingdom
℡ (020) 7168 2539
✎ info@bunchdesign.com
🖳 www.bunchdesign.com

Calon TV Ltd Phoenix Buildings, 3 Mount Stuart Square, Butetown, Cardiff, CF10 5EE, United Kingdom
℡ (029) 2048 8400/✆ (029) 2048 5962
✎ enquiries@calon.tv
🖳 www.calon.tv

Candy Lab Ltd 130 Shaftesbury Avenue, London, W1D 5EU, United Kingdom
℡ (020) 7166 5353/✆ (020) 7031 4302
✎ info@candylab.co.uk
🖳 www.candylab.co.uk

Canning Factory 11B Albert Place, London, W8 5PD, United Kingdom
℡ (020) 7937 1136/✆ (020) 7938 1896
✎ katec@canningfactory.com
🖳 www.canningfactory.com

Capricorn Digital 41b Montagu Road, London, Greater London, NW4 3ER, United Kingdom
℡ (020) 8202 9594/✆ (0870) 7623203
🖳 www.capricorn-digital.com

Carl Gover Animation 11 Henrietta Street, Covent Garden, London, WC2E 8PY, United Kingdom
℡ (020) 7636 3300
✎ carl@animationpartnership.co.uk
🖳 www.animationpartnership.co.uk

Carolan Productions The Coach House, adjacent Ealing Film Studios, Ealing Green, London, W5 5ER, United Kingdom
℡ (020) 8566 1900/(07833) 917178 ✆ (020) 8566 1900
✎ andrew@carolanproductions.com
🖳 www.carolanproductions.com

Cartoon Network Turner House, 16 Great Marlborough Street, London, W1F 7HS, United Kingdom
℡ (020) 7693 1000/✆ (020) 7693 1001
🖳 www.cartoonnetwork.co.uk

Cartoon World
London, NW11 6WS, United Kingdom
℡ (020) 8455 3906/✆ (020) 8455 3906
✎ info@cartoonworld.org
🖳 www.cartoonworld.org

Cartwn Cymru (TAC) 32 Wordsworth Avenue, Roath, Cardiff, CF24 3FR, United Kingdom
℡ (029) 2046 3556/07771 640 400 ✆
✎ production@cartwn-cymru.com

Catalyst Pictures Ltd 34 Chester Square, Ashton-under-Lyne, Lancashire, OL6 7TW, United Kingdom
℡ 0161-339 3353/✆ 0161-339 2914
✎ nik@catalystpics.co.uk
🖳 www.catalystpics.co.uk

Cinedrome Studios 240 St 54, I8/3, Islamabad, 44000, Pakistan
℡ 51 443 5217/✆ 51 443 5218
✎ info@cinedromestudios.com
🖳 www.cinedromestudios.com

Clear Post Production 37 Dean Street, London, W1D 4PT, United Kingdom
℡ (020) 7734 5557/✆ (020) 7494 0059
✎ clear@clearpost.co.uk
🖳 www.clear.ltd.uk

Clement Graphics 21 John Tofts House, Leicester Row, Coventry, CV1 4LY, United Kingdom
℡ (07958) 009133
✎ jeanette@clementgraphics.com
🖳 www.clementgraphics.com

Codsteaks Unit 18, Albion Dockside Est, Bristol, BS1 6UT, United Kingdom
℡ 0117 929 2729/✆ 0117 925 2729
✎ mail@codsteaks.com
🖳 www.codsteaks.com

Cog Ltd No 1 Mill Cottage, Tilstone Bank, Near Tarporley, Cheshire, CW6 9QH, United Kingdom
℡ (020) 7358 4751/✆ (020) 7358 4751
✎ mail@consortium-of-gentlemen.co.uk
🖳 www.consortium-of-gentlemen.co.uk

Commercials Unlimited Garden Studios, 11-15 Betterton Street, London, WC2H 9BP, United Kingdom
℡ (020) 7470 8791/(07836) 523604 ✆ (020) 7470 8792
✎ mail@commercialsunlimited.net
🖳 www.commercialsunlimited.net

Concept & Storyboard Artist Flat 3, Europa House, 11 Marsham Way, Gerrards Cross, Buckinghamshire, SL9 8BQ, United Kingdom
℡ (01753) 899352
✎ kimberly.pope@virgin.net
🖳 www.musecube.com/kimpope/84879

Creative Edge Design & Advertising 1st Floor Donald Hendry Building, Auchincruive, Ayr, KA6 5HW, United Kingdom
℡ (01292) 521404/✆ (01292) 521693
✎ paul@cedge.co.uk
🖳 www.cedge.co.uk

Creative Presentations Ltd 5 The Square, Bagshot, Surrey, GU19 5AX, United Kingdom
℡ (01276) 474182/✆ (01276) 472982
✎ info@creative-presentations.com
🖳 www.creative-presentations.com

Dano Battista 3D Ltd 9-10 Charlotte Mews, London, W1T 4EF, United Kingdom
℡ (07958) 735069/✆ (020) 7636 2455
✎ enquiries@danobattista.com
🖳 www.danobattista.com

Dave Cockburn's Squeaky Pictures 40 Onslow Gardens, Wallington, Surrey, SM6 9QN, United Kingdom
℡ (020) 8773 0024/✆ (020) 8773 9963
✎ dave@squeakypics.co.uk
🖳 www.squeakypics.co.uk

Daydream Linton House, 164-180 Union Street, London, SE1 0LH,
℡ +44 (0) 20 7096 1471/+44 (0) 20 7117 1636
✎ ralph@daydream.co.uk
🖳 www.daydream.co.uk

Daylight Moving Image Ltd 3rd Floor, 72 Tib Street, Manchester, M4 1LG, United Kingdom
℡ 0161-839 9088/✆ 0161-835 9292
✎ talk@day-light.co.uk
🖳 www.day-light.co.uk

Denis Russo Associates 161 Clapham Road, London, SW9 0PU, United Kingdom
℡ (020) 8892 7514/(07956) 276954 ✆ (020) 7582 2725

Denman Productions 60 Mallard Place, Strawberry Vale, Twickenham, TW1 4SR, United Kingdom
℡ (020) 8891 3461/✆ (020) 8891 6413
✎ info@denman.co.uk
🖳 www.denman.co.uk

Design is Central (PACT) 23 Argyll Court, 1103 Argyll Street, Glasgow, G3 8ND, United Kingdom
℡ 0141-847 0077
✎ work@designiscentral.com
🖳 www.designiscentral.com

Designated Designs 11 Balmoral Close, Wellingborough, Northamptonshire, NN8 2EG, United Kingdom
℡ (01933) 277207
✎ ltpdebs@talktalk.net
🖳 www.designateddesign.co.uk

Digital Animation Group The Lighthouse, 70 Mitchell Street, Glasgow, G1 3LX, United Kingdom
℡ 0141-582 0600/✆ 0141-582 0699
✎ angie.collins@dagroupplc.com
🖳 www.dagroupplc.com

Discochimp
Glasgow, G4 9ED, United Kingdom
℡ (07769) 811908
✎ louis@discochimp.com
🖳 www.discochimp.com

Dogfish Internet Ltd 26 Messenger Close, Bungay, Suffolk, NR35 1PW, United Kingdom
(01986) 892965/ (01986) 892965
pete@dogfish.co.uk
www.dogfish.co.uk

Dragonfly Media 3 Berkeley Crescent, Clifton, Bristol, Avon, BS8 1HA,
0845 6520 888/ 0845 6520 808
jon@dragonfly-media.co.uk
www.dragonfly-media.co.uk

Drawn Design Flat 34, Belgrave Court, Wellesley Road, London, W4 4LG, United Kingdom
(020) 8994 4373/ (020) 8994 4373
david@drawndesign.com
www.drawndesign.com

Duplexx Productions Ltd (APA) Penthouse B, 14 Riverview Court, Salford, Manchester, M7 3NX, United Kingdom
0161-792 4144/ 0161-792 5144
duplexx@zoom.co.uk

Electric Lemon Design The Manor House, 126 High Street, Solihull, West Midlands, B91 3SX, United Kingdom
0121-704 0820/ 0845 0099770
julien@electriclemon.net
www.electriclemon.co.uk

Entity Studios 9 Old School House, Brittania Road, Kingswood, Bristol, BS15 8DB, United Kingdom
(0845) 8904430
info@entitystudios.com
www.entitystudios.com

Exwyzee Communication House, Hillhouse Business Park, Thornton-Cleveleys, Lancashire, FY5 4QD, United Kingdom
(01253) 856000/ (01253) 682208
lee@exwyzee.com
www.exwyzee.com

Fictitious Egg 52 Oldmarket Street, Bristol, BS2 0ER, United Kingdom
(07899) 927724
admin@eggtoons.com
www.eggtoons.com

Fijit Ltd 5 Great James Street, London, WC1N 3DB, United Kingdom
(08702) 418053
admin@fijit-design.co.uk
www.fijit-design.co.uk

Flicks Films Ltd 101 Wardour Street, London, W1F 0UG, United Kingdom
(020) 7734 4892/ (020) 7287 2307
flicks@btconnect.com
www.flicksfilms.com

Framestore CFC 9 Noel Street, London, W1F 8GH, United Kingdom
(020) 7208 2600/ (020) 7208 2626
info@framestore-cfc.com
www.framestore-cfc.com

Gecko Studios Ltd 20 Norton Road, Roundhay, Leeds, LS8 2DE, United Kingdom
0113-393 0011/ (07092) 106705
info@gecko-studios.com
www.gecko-studios.com

Glowfrog Studios Unit 7G, Clapham North Arts Centre, 26 - 32 Voltaire Road, London, SW4 6DH, United Kingdom
(020) 7652 5749/ (020) 7627 4705
studio@glowfrog.com
www.glowfrog.com

Goatpix Ltd 105 High Street, Maldon, Essex, CM9 5EP, United Kingdom
(01621) 850528
alas@goatpix.com
www.goatpix.com

Gouty Foot 47 Culvers, South Harting, Petersfield, Hampshire, GU31 5LE, United Kingdom
(01730) 826850/(07901) 582677
gary@goutyfoot.com
www.goutyfoot.com

Grand Slamm Childrens Films Ltd 39 Grafton Way, London, London, W1T 5DE, United Kingdom
(020) 7388 0789/ (020) 7388 2789
studio@gscfilms.com
www.gscfilms.com

Graphi Services Lower Ground Floor, University House, 11-13 Lower Grosvenor Place, London, SW1W 0EX, United Kingdom
(020) 7630 2090/ (020) 7828 6837
sales@graphi.co.uk
www.graphi.co.uk

Happy Hour Productions Ltd The Picture House, 4 Lower Park Road, Bristol, BS1 5BJ, United Kingdom
0117-929 9797/ 0117-923 0862
info@hhour.co.uk
www.happyhourproductions.co.uk

Hibbert Ralph Animation Ltd 10 D'Arblay Street, London, W1F 8DS, United Kingdom
(020) 7494 3011/ (020) 7494 0383
info@hra-online.com
www.hra-online.com

Hit Entertainment Plc (PACT) 5th Floor, Maple House, 149 Tottenham Court Road, London, W1T 7NF, United Kingdom
(020) 7554 2500/ (020) 7388 9321
creative@hitentertainment.com
www.hitentertainment.com

Honeycomb Animation Enterprises Ltd 27 High St, Cullompton, Devon, EX15 1AB, United Kingdom
(01884) 839202
studio@honeycombanimation.co.uk
www.honeycombanimation.co.uk

Hothouse IWG 10 St Leonards Road, Park Royal, London, NW10 6SY, United Kingdom
(020) 8961 3666/(07801) 612061 (020) 8961 3777
info@hothousefx.co.uk
www.hothousefx.co.uk

Ian Rossenrode Silk Mill Road, Redbourn, St. Albans, Hertfordshire, AL3 7GE, United Kingdom
(01582) 792046
rossenrode@btinternet.com
www.rossenrode-art.co.uk

Ice Pics Ltd 111A Wardour Street, London, W1F 0UJ, United Kingdom
(020) 7437 3505/ (020) 7287 0393
mike@icepics.co.uk
www.icepics.co.uk

iChihuahua.net 160-162 Old South Lambeth Road, Vauxhall, London, SW8 1XX, United Kingdom
(07795) 332037
dave@iChihuahua.net
www.iChihuahua.net

Image Refinery 156 Royal George Road, Burgess Hill, West Sussex, RH15 9SL, United Kingdom
(020) 8133 8083/ (07050) 651800
creativehandbook@tir.co.uk
www.tir.co.uk

Industrial Art Studio Consols, St. Ives, Cornwall, TR26 2HW, United Kingdom
(01736) 797651/ (01736) 797651
roger@ind-art.co.uk
www.ind-art.co.uk

Ink & Colors Ltd 27 Old Gloucester Street, London, WC1N 3XX, United Kingdom
(020) 7558 8374
info@inkandcolors.com
www.inkandcolors.com

Jelly Fish Pictures 47 Poland Street, London, W1F 7NB, United Kingdom
(020) 7287 6024/ (020) 7287 0373
info@jellyfishpictures.co.uk
www.jellyfishpictures.co.uk

Jelly London 9-10 Charlotte mews, London, W11 4EF, United Kingdom
(020) 7323 3307/ (020) 7636 2455
info@jellylondon.com
www.jellylondon.com
See ad in showcase

JeremyGetsCash 505 Hackney Road, London, E2 9ED, United Kingdom
(020) 8299 1737/(07944) 450422
jeremy@jeremygetscash.com
www.jeremygetscash.com

John Adams c/o Illustration Ltd, Unit 2, Brooks Court, Cringle Street, London, SW8 5BX, United Kingdom
(020) 7720 5202
team@illustrationweb.com
www.illustrationgb.com/johnadams

John Ashton 29 Stalybridge Road, Mottram, Hyde, Cheshire, SK14 6NF, United Kingdom
/(07747) 088018
john@piersharayashton.freeserve.co.uk

John Dunne Illustration No. 1 The Lake, Ampney Crucis, Cirencester, Gloucestershire, GL7 5SE, United Kingdom
(01285) 851195/(07813) 813733
john@thepencils.com
www.thepencils.com

John Wright Studio 1, Centre Space, 6 Leonard Lane, Bristol, BS1 1EA, United Kingdom
0117-927 2854/ 0117-927 2606
www.jwmm.co.uk

JR7 21 Broadhaven, Cardiff, CF11 8DA, United Kingdom
(07050) 076050/ (029) 2030 2792
enquiries@jr7.co.uk
www.jr7.co.uk

Julian Tewkesbury 1 Britten Drive, Barnstaple, Devon, EX32 8AQ, United Kingdom
(01271) 343507
julian@juliantewkesbury.com
www.juliantewkesbury.com

King Rollo Films Ltd Dolphin Court, High Street, Honiton, Devon, EX14 1HT, United Kingdom
(01404) 45218/ (01404) 45328
leo@kingrollofilms.co.uk
www.kingrollofilms.co.uk

Kino Creative Holy Jesus Hospital, City Road, Newcastle Upon Tyne, Tyne & Wear, NE1 2AS,
0191 2333 880
seth@kinocreative.co.uk
www.kinocreative.co.uk

Knock Knock S L Calle Paris 175, entresuelo 2B, Barcelona, 8036, Spain
00 34 93 5321625

Kralinator 43 Belmont Street, Brighton, BN1 4HN, United Kingdom
(01273) 241554/ (01273) 241554
phil@kralinator.com
www.kralinator.com

Kronfli Duliba Productions Ltd Harefield South Lodge, Alderley Road, Wilmslow, Cheshire, SK9 1RA, United Kingdom
(01625) 536606/ (01625) 536603
enquiries@kronfli-duliba.com
www.kronfli-duliba.com
See ad in showcase

L W T Drama Department London Television Centre, Upper Ground, London, SE1 9LT, United Kingdom
(020) 7620 1620/ (020) 7261 3041
www.granadamedia.com

LairdSquared Wrenswood, Chope Road, Northam, Bideford, Devon, EX39 3QE, United Kingdom
(01237) 479397
tim@lairdsquared.co.uk
www.lairdsquared.co.uk

Lasso Design 42 Norham Street, Glasgow, G41 3XQ, United Kingdom
0141-632 5679
info@lassodesign.co.uk
www.lassodesign.co.uk

Leeds Animation Workshop 45 Bayswater Row, Leeds, LS8 5LF, United Kingdom
0113-248 4997/ 0113-248 4997
law@leedsanimation.co.uk
www.leedsanimation.org.uk

Liberty Bell Adamson House, 65 Westgate Road, Newcastle upon Tyne, NE1 1SG, United Kingdom
0191-222 1200/ 0191-222 1210
louise.mitchell@libertybell.tv
www.libertybell.tv

Liquid TV Ltd (AFVPA, IVCA) 1-2 Portland Mews, Soho, London, W1F 8JE, United Kingdom
(020) 7437 2623/ (020) 7437 2618
info@liquid.co.uk
www.liquid.co.uk

Littleloud 1 Sidney Street, Brighton, BN1 4EN, United Kingdom
(01273) 625066
david@littleloud.com
www.littleloud.com

Longneck Afgan Road 27, Battersea, London, SW11 2QD,
7506018062
vlad@longneck.ro
www.longneck.ro

3

M G B Facilities Ltd Sheepscar Court, Leeds, LS7 2BB, United Kingdom
0113-243 6868/ 0113-243 8886
contact@mgbtv.co.uk
www.mgbtv.co.uk

Mackinnon & Saunders 148 Seamons Road, Altrincham, Cheshire, WA14 4LJ, United Kingdom
0161-929 4441/ 0161-929 1441
info@mackinnonandsaunders.com
www.mackinnonandsaunders.com

Mark Woollard 79 Trevelyan, Tawfield Copse, Bracknell, Berkshire, RG12 8YD, United Kingdom
(01344) 429275/(07973) 256057 (01344) 429275
mark.woollard@ntlworld.com

Melendez Films Julia House, 44 Newman Street, London, W1T 1QD, United Kingdom
(020) 7323 5273/(07785) 224295 (020) 7323 5373
steven.melendez@dsl.pipex.com
www.billmelendez.tv

Milkhouse.co.uk Fernhill Farm, Kingswells, Aberdeen, AB15 8PR, United Kingdom
(07790) 729836
marie@milkhouse.co.uk
www.milkhouse.co.uk

Mindfizz Ltd 11 Barton Road, Eastleigh, Hampshire, SO50 6RN, United Kingdom
(023) 8061 4649
clare@mindfizz.com
www.mindfizz.com

Mokko Blue 21 Arncott Hall, 13 Poole Road, Bournemouth, BH2 5QR, United Kingdom
01202 269 257/ 01202 269 257
info@mokko-blue.com
www.mokko-blue.com

Monkey Business 5 Nelson Place West, Bath, BA1 2BA, United Kingdom
(01225) 428998
monkey@monk-ebusiness.co.uk
www.monk-ebusiness.co.uk

Moonoo Productions Ltd 2 Alexandra Gate, Ffordd Pengam, Cardiff, CF24 2SA, United Kingdom
(02920) 894845
info@moonoo.co.uk
www.moonoo.co.uk

Motion Blur Ltd Bryn Hyfryd, Bryncroes, Pwllheli, Gwynedd, LL53 8ET, United Kingdom
(01758) 730777
pix@motionblur.tv
www.motionblur.tv

Motion FX Units B4-B6, Askew Crescent Workshops, London, W12 9DP, United Kingdom
(020) 8740 4560/ (020) 8749 0309
info@motionfx.co.uk
www.motionfx.co.uk

N V Films Ltd 75-77 Margaret Street, London, W1W 8SY, United Kingdom
(020) 7323 0321
info@nvfilms.tv
www.nvfilms.tv

NBS Studio 12 Kempson Drive, Great Cornard, Sudbury, Suffolk, CO10 0ND, United Kingdom
(01787) 376763
info@nbs-studio.com
www.nbs-studio.com

Newangle Productions Ltd 102 Harmood Street, London, NW1 8DS, United Kingdom
(020) 7916 0106/ (020) 7916 0107
bev@newangle.co.uk
www.newangle.co.uk

Oxygen 12A Churchyard, Hitchin, Hertfordshire, SG5 1HR, United Kingdom
(01462) 636800/ (01462) 636900
geoff.ide@oxygenate.net
www.oxygenate.net

P S Creative Moorfield Farm, Waystone Lane, Belbroughton, Stourbridge, West Midlands, DY9 0BG, United Kingdom
(01562) 731724
martin@pscreative.co.uk
www.pscreative.co.uk

Paradox Production Nato Caddesi No: 2/5, Seyrantepe, Istanbul, 34418, Turkey
00 90 2155 704 074
meltem@paradox.ws
www.paradox.ws

Passion Pictures (AFVPA) 3rd Floor, 33-34 Rathbone Place, London, W1T 1JN, United Kingdom
(020) 7323 9933/ (020) 7323 9030
info@passion-pictures.com
www.passion-pictures.com

paulgillard.com Hatherleigh, Devon, United Kingdom
(01837) 811811
paul@paulgillard.com
www.paulgillard.com

Pearly Oyster Productions 204 Stockwell Road, London, SW9 9TB, United Kingdom
(020) 3177 3033
enquiries@pearlyoyster.com
www.pearlyoyster.com

Pencil & Pepper Design & Animation 54 Windsor Road, Cambridge, CB4 3JN, United Kingdom
(01223) 500235/7960958857
philip@pencilandpepper.com
www.pencilandpepper.com

Peter Dobbin Flat 23, Tudor House, Tudor Grove, London, E9 7QJ, United Kingdom
(07814) 855218
peter@peterdobbin.co.uk
www.peterdobbin.co.uk

Picasso Pictures Ltd 9-11 Broadwick Street, London, W1F 0DB, United Kingdom
(020) 7437 9888/ (020) 7437 9040
info@picassopictures.com
www.picassopictures.com

Pict 8 7 Lyndedoch Crescent, Glasgow, G3 6DZ, United Kingdom
0141-332 3815/ 0141-332 5295
al@pict8.com
www.pict8.com

Picturedisc Co. Ltd Capheaton Hall, Capheaton, Newcastle upon Tyne, NE19 2AB, United Kingdom
(01830) 530371/ (01830) 530380
www.picturedisc.co.uk

Pictures on the Wall Studio 14, 74-76 Firhill Road, Glasgow, G20 7BA, United Kingdom
0141-576 0117/ 0141-946 0001
animation@potw.co.uk
www.potw.co.uk

Pixel Perfect The White House, Copse Road, Haslemere, Surrey, GU27 3QQ, United Kingdom
(01428) 643500/ (0871) 7502375
jason@pixelperfect.co.uk
www.pixelperfect.co.uk

planetnewmedia Unit 226, Great Guildford Business Square, 30 Great Guildford Street, London, SE1 0HS, United Kingdom
(020) 7620 6060/ (020) 7620 6050
create@planetnewmedia.com
www.planetnewmedia.com

Pocket Laboratories J101, The Bakehouse, 100 Clements Road, London, SE16 4DG, United Kingdom
(020) 7237 7800/ (020) 7237 7800
adrian@pocketlaboratories.com
www.pocketlaboratories.com

radimus.co.uk Suite 4, Putney Bridge Road, London, SW15 2PX, United Kingdom
(07711) 049227/ (020) 8871 2261
mail@radimus.co.uk
www.radimus.co.uk

Realtime UK Willows Farm Studios, Ballam Road, Westby, Preston, PR4 3PN, United Kingdom
(01772) 682363/ (01772) 683592
info@realtimeuk.com
www.realtimeuk.com

Red Vision Cambos House, 3 Canal Street, Manchester, M1 3HE, United Kingdom
0161-907 3764/ 0161-907 3762
cl@redvision.co.uk
www.redvision.co.uk

reeldimension 60 Leominster Road, Portsmouth, PO6 4DD, United Kingdom
/(07919) 860903
info@reeldimension.co.uk
www.reeldimension.co.uk

Richard Klein 61 Cleveden Drive, Glasgow, G12 0NX, United Kingdom
0141-337 2203
rkderj@yahoo.com
www.rkderj.com

Richard Ollive Animation Ltd 22 Great Queen Street, London, WC2B 5BH, United Kingdom
(020) 7430 1862
olliveanimation@btconnect.com

Richard Purdum Productions (AFVPA) Unit 224, Aberdeen House, 22-24 Highbury Grove, London, N5 2EA, United Kingdom
(020) 7359 1777
jill@purdums.com

Ripe Design (UK) Ltd Clarence House, 48 Black Bull Street, Leeds, LS10 1HW, United Kingdom
0113-204 2800/ 0113-204 2801
info@ripe.co.uk
www.ripe.co.uk

Rocky Road Productions Ltd 9 Wellington Road, Wimbledon Park, London, SW19 8EQ, United Kingdom
(020) 8947 2404/ (020) 8947 2404
john@rockyroad.fsnet.co.uk

Rod Lord Old Lodge Farm, Coningsby Lane, Fifield, Maidenhead, Berkshire, SL6 2PF, United Kingdom
(01628) 627032
rod@rodlord.com
www.rodlord.com

Rogue Rocket Ltd 13 Upper Crescent, Belfast, BT7 1NT, United Kingdom
(02890) 331600
info@roguerocket.com
www.roguerocket.com

Roland Davies Animation 16 Rushmere Road, Ipswich, IP4 4LA, United Kingdom
(01473) 728081/ (01473) 728081
rd.animation@btinternet.com

Rosie Brooks Illustration London, United Kingdom
(07909) 924384
rosie@rosiebrooks.co.uk
www.rosiebrooks.co.uk

Ruffle Brothers Ltd Sycamore Cottage, Bussage, Stroud, Gloucestershire, GL6 8AX, United Kingdom
(01453) 885953/ (01453) 885953
mark@rufflebrothers.com
www.rufflebrothers.com

Russell Hall Films Ltd 26 Lady Somerset Road, London, NW5 1UP, United Kingdom
(020) 7267 8080/ (020) 7267 8080

Shaun Askew Illustrator Animator, Third Floor, 3-11 Westland Place, London, N1 7LP, United Kingdom
(020) 7490 3769/ (020) 7490 3769
shaun@holistic-hamster.com
www.holistic-hamster.com

Sherbet Ltd (AVFPA, PACT) 112-114 Great Portland Street, London, W1W 6PH, United Kingdom
(020) 7636 6435/ (020) 7436 3221
info@sherbet.co.uk
www.sherbet.co.uk

Shufti 142 Avonvale Road, Bristol, BS5 9RX, United Kingdom
0117-939 0337
nick@shufti.co.uk
www.shufti.co.uk

Shutterbug Productions 59 Lyndhurst Avenue, Twickenham, TW2 6BQ, United Kingdom
(020) 8894 0799
ian@shutterbug-studios.com
www.shutterbug-studios.com

Simon Knowles Illustration Studio 10, 21 Berry Close, London, N21 2RY, United Kingdom
(020) 8292 5126/ (020) 8292 5126
simon@skillustration.co.uk
www.skillustration.co.uk

Simonetti Productions 18 Leighton Crescent, London, NW5 2QY, United Kingdom
(020) 7284 1164/ (020) 7284 1392
ssimonetti@blueyonder.co.uk

Skyline Imaging Ltd The Forum, 277 London Road, Burgess Hill, West Sussex, RH15 9QU, United Kingdom
(01825) 721147
info@skylineimaging.co.uk
www.skylineimaging.co.uk

Sliced Bread Animation 15 King Street, Covent Garden, London, WC2E 8HN, United Kingdom
(020) 7379 7873/ (0870) 7620852
info@sbanimation.com
www.thebestthingsince.com

Slinky Pictures, Old Truman Brewery, 91 Brick Lane, London, E1 6QN, United Kingdom
☎ (020) 7247 6444/ (020) 7247 0164
✉ info@slinkypics.com
🖳 www.slinkypics.com

Slinky Pictures Ltd Old Truman Brewery, 91 Brick Lane, London, E1 6QL, United Kingdom
☎ (020) 7247 6444/ (020) 7247 0164
✉ info@slinkypics.com
🖳 www.slinkypics.com

Smoothe 1st Floor, 1 Portland Street, Manchester, M1 3BE, United Kingdom
☎ (0870) 890 9836
✉ samcrothers@smoothe.com
🖳 www.smoothe.com

Social Fabric UK Ltd William Blake Hse, 8 Marshall St, London, W1F 7EJ, United Kingdom
☎ (020) 7788 7876
✉ us@thesocialfabric.com
🖳 www.thesocialfabric.com

Sonica Studios SW4 17 Welmar Mews, 154 Clapham Park Road, London, SW4 7DD, United Kingdom
☎ (020) 7498 2990
✉ info@sonicamusic.co.uk
🖳 www.sonicamusic.co.uk

Soup (Studio Soup) St. James Mill, 12-20 Whitefriars, Norwich, NR3 1SH, United Kingdom
☎ (01603) 751 310/ (01603) 751 311
✉ info@soup.com
🖳 www.soup.com

Specs Art 93 London Road, Cheltenham, Gloucestershire, GL52 6HL, United Kingdom
☎ (01242) 515951
✉ roland@specsart.com
🖳 www.specsart.com

Spider Eye Ltd Penlee House, Market Street, St. Just, Penzance, Cornwall, TR19 7HU, United Kingdom
☎ (01736) 788000/ (01736) 788103
✉ post@spider-eye.com
🖳 www.spider-eye.com

SquareZero Suna House, 65 Rivington Street, London, EC2A 3QQ, United Kingdom
☎ (020) 7729 8998
✉ vicky@squarezero.co.uk
🖳 www.squarezero.co.uk

Start Creative 2 Sheraton Street, Soho, London, W1F 8BH, United Kingdom
☎ (020) 7269 0101/ (020) 7269 0102
✉ jen@startcreative.co.uk
🖳 www.startcreative.co.uk

Studio AKA 30 Berwick Street, London, W1F 8RH, United Kingdom
☎ (020) 7434 3581/ (020) 7437 2309
✉ pam@studioaka.co.uk
🖳 www.studioaka.co.uk

Surrender Films 22 Great Queen Street, London, WC2B 5BH, United Kingdom
☎ (01829) 720858/ (01829) 720858
✉ surrender.films@btinternet.com

Tag 3D & DS 57-59 Beak Street, London, W1F 9SJ, United Kingdom
☎ (020) 7468 1000/(07957) 422665 (020) 7468 1001
✉ amandad@smoke-mirrors.co.uk
🖳 www.smoke-mirrors.com

Telemagination Ltd (PACT) Royalty House, 72-74 Dean Street, London, London, W1D 3SG, United Kingdom
☎ (020) 7534 2060/ (020) 7534 2062
✉ mail@tmation.co.uk
🖳 www.telemagination.co.uk

Televirtual Ltd The Medialab, 9 Whitlingham Lane, Norwich, NR7 0QA, United Kingdom
☎ (01603) 431030
✉ tim@televirtual.com
🖳 www.televirtual.com

The Juice Group Ltd President Way, Sheffield, S4 7UR, United Kingdom
☎ 0114-275 5858/ 0114-275 5888
✉ designed@thejuice.co.uk
🖳 www.thejuice.com

The Mozzarella Legion 12 Doyle Gardens, London, NW10 3DA, United Kingdom
☎ (07787) 588219
✉ rosapopulos@yahoo.com

The Wax Mill Partenrship The Raylor Centre, James Street, York, YO24 4BP, United Kingdom
☎ (01904) 422114

Three Blind Mice 9-10 Charlotte Mews, London, W1T 4EF, United Kingdom
☎ (020) 7636 2502/ (020) 7636 2455
✉ andy@three-blind-mice.co.uk
🖳 www.three-blind-mice.co.uk

Tony Cuthbert 7 Dials Court, Flat 14, 3 Shorts Gardens, Covent Garden, London, WC2H 9AP, United Kingdom
☎ (020) 7836 3432
✉ info@tonycuthbert.com
🖳 www.tonycuthbert.com

Touchwood Animation Ltd Stanford House, 27A Floral Street, London, WC2E 9DP, United Kingdom
☎ (020) 7379 3331
✉ andy@touchwood-animation.com

Trilby Multimedia Ltd 47-49 Loveday Street, Birmingham, B4 6NR, United Kingdom
☎ 0121-333 6860/ 0121-359 8989
✉ team@trilby.co.uk
🖳 www.trilby.co.uk

TV Cartoons Ltd 39 Grafton Way, London, W1T 5PE, United Kingdom
☎ (020) 7388 2222/ (020) 7383 4192
✉ alex.tham@btconnect.com

Uli Meyer Animation 172A Arlington Road, London, NW1 7HL, United Kingdom
☎ (020) 7284 2828/ (020) 7284 2255
✉ matt@ulimeyer.com
🖳 www.ulimeyer.com

Uniform 200 Vanilla Factory, 39 Fleet Street, Liverpool, L1 4AR, United Kingdom
☎ 0151-709 9055/ 0151-709 9950
✉ info@uniform.net
🖳 www.uniform.net

Virtalis Chester House, 79 Dane Road, Sale, Cheshire, M33 7BP, United Kingdom
☎ 0161-969 1155/ 0161-969 1166
✉ info@virtalis.com
🖳 www.virtalis.com

Visible Ink Television Ltd (PACT) Nine Mile Burn, Penicuik, Midlothian, EH26 9LX, United Kingdom
☎ (01968) 661291/ (01968) 661291
✉ contact@visibleink.co.uk
🖳 www.visibleink.co.uk

Visual Eyes Media 117-121 Curtain Road, London, EC2A 3AD, United Kingdom
☎ (020) 7613 1777
✉ info@visual-eyes-media.co.uk
🖳 www.visual-eyes-media.co.uk

VooDooDog Ltd 4th Floor, Suffolk House, 1-8 Whitfield Place, London, W1T 5JU, United Kingdom
☎ (020) 7387 2049/ (020) 7387 2049
✉ info@voodoodog.com
🖳 www.voodoodog.com

Zacella Since 1982 87 Roberts Road, High Wycombe, Buckinghamshire, HP13 6XD, United Kingdom
☎ (07763) 842297
✉ zacella@hotmail.com

Zoo Films 74 Wells Street, London, W1T 3QQ, United Kingdom
☎ (020) 7580 1700/(07973) 221802
✉ neil@zoodf.co.uk

CAMERA EQUIPMENT RENTAL

2.35 Research P.L.C. Elstree Film Studios, Shenley Road, Borehamwood, Hertfordshire, WD6 1JG, United Kingdom
☎ (020) 8324 2351/ (020) 8324 2336
✉ info@joedunton.com
🖳 www.joedunton.com

400 Company Unit B3, The Workshops, 2A Askew Crescent, Shepherds Bush, London, W12 9DP, United Kingdom
☎ (020) 8746 1400/ (020) 8746 0847
✉ info@the400.co.uk
🖳 www.the400.co.uk

99 Cars Ltd Hyde Meadow Farm, Hyde Lane, Hemel Hempstead, Hertfordshire, HP3 8SA, United Kingdom
☎ (01923) 266373/(07785) 382448 (01923) 260852
✉ david@nineninecars.com
🖳 www.nineninecars.com

Acorn Film & Video Ltd 13 Fitzwilliam Street, Belfast, BT9 6AW, United Kingdom
☎ (028) 9024 0977/(07802) 238693 (028) 9022 2309
✉ info@acorntv.com
🖳 www.acorntv.com

Aerial Camera Systems Ltd Innovation House, Douglas Drive, Catteshall Lane, Godalming, Surrey, GU7 1JX, United Kingdom
☎ (01483) 426767/ (01483) 413900
✉ info@aerialcamerasystems.com
🖳 www.acsmedia.com

Aimimage Camera Co. Unit 5, St. Pancras Commercial Centre, 63 Pratt Street, London, NW1 0BY, United Kingdom
☎ (020) 7482 4340/ (020) 7267 3972
✉ hire@aimimage.com
🖳 www.aimimage.com

Ares Productions Bosque de Bugambilias 216, Col Bosques de las Lomas, Mexico City, 5120, Mexico
☎ 00 52 55 5251 6541/ 00 52 55 5596 4968
✉ a.fernandez@aresproducciones.com
🖳 www.aresproducciones.com

Arri Media 3 Highbridge, Oxford Road, Uxbridge, Middlesex, UB8 1LX, United Kingdom
☎ (01895) 457100/ (01895) 457101
✉ info@arrimedia.com
🖳 www.arrimedia.com

Awfully Nice Video Company Ltd 30 Long Lane, Ickenham, London, UB10 8TA, United Kingdom
☎ (07000) 345678/(07831) 515678 (07000) 345679
✉ nicevideo@aol.com
🖳 www.awfullynicevideo.com

Axis Glasgow 64-68 Brand Street, Glasgow, G51 1TG, United Kingdom
☎ 0141-427 9944/ 0141-427 1199
✉ glasgow@axisfilms.co.uk
🖳 www.axisfilms.co.uk

Axis London Ltd 93 Shepperton Studios, Studios Road, Shepperton, Middlesex, TW17 0QD, United Kingdom
☎ (01932) 592244/ (01932) 592246
✉ info@axisfilms.co.uk
🖳 www.axisfilms.co.uk

Blue Planet TV Ltd Unit 9, Regis Road, London, NW5 3EW, United Kingdom
☎ (020) 7267 4537/ (020) 7428 0252
✉ info@blueplanet-tv.com
🖳 www.blueplanet-tv.com

Bluefin TV 34 Fitzwilliam Road, London, SW4 0DN, United Kingdom
☎ (020) 7622 0870/(07973) 502349 (020) 7720 7875
✉ info@bluefintv.com
🖳 www.bluefintv.com

Bocek Production Cubuklu cad.agaclik mesire yeri, d+e burunbahce, beykoz, Istanbul, 34805,
☎ 00 9 02166801058
✉ selma@bocekyapim.com.tr
🖳 www.bocekyapim.com.tr

Broadcast Services The Coach House, Ruxbury Road, Chertsey, Surrey, KT16 9EP, United Kingdom
☎ (01932) 570001/ (01932) 570443
✉ hire@broadcast-services.co.uk
🖳 www.broadcast-services.co.uk

C V P Ltd Priory Mill, Castle Road, Studley, Warwickshire, B80 7AA, United Kingdom
☎ (01527) 854222/ (01527) 857666
✉ info@creativevideo.co.uk
🖳 www.creativevideo.co.uk

Calumet Bradbourne Drive, Tilbrook, Milton Keynes, MK7 8AJ, United Kingdom
☎ (01908) 366344/ (01908) 366857
🖳 www.calumetphoto.co.uk

Calumet - Belfast 3 Loughside Industrial Park, Dargan Crescent, Belfast, BT3 9JP, United Kingdom
☎ (028) 9077 7770/ (028) 9077 4230
✉ belfast@calumetphoto.co.uk
🖳 www.calumetphoto.com

Calumet - Birmingham 23 Aston Cross Business Centre, Wainwright Street, Aston, Birmingham, B6 5TH, United Kingdom
☎ 0121-326 7636/ 0121-328 1713
✉ tom.gately@calumetphoto.co.uk
🖳 www.calumetphoto.com

Calumet - Bristol 7 Montpelier Central Trading Estate, Station Road, Montpelier, Bristol, BS6 5EE, United Kingdom
☎ 0117-942 2000/ 0117-942 7722
✉ andy.adams@calumetphoto.co.uk
🖳 www.calumetphoto.com

Calumet - Edinburgh 3 Bonnington Business Centre, Tennant Street, Edinburgh, EH6 5HG, United Kingdom
☎ 0131-554 7648/ 0131-554 6105
✉ vanessa.cox@calumetphoto.co.uk
🖳 www.calumetphoto.com

Calumet - Glasgow Block 4, Unit 1, Oakbank Industrial Estate, off Garscube Road, Glasgow, G20 7LU, United Kingdom
0141-353 0875/ 0141-332 1275
tommy.rodgers@calumetphoto.co.uk
www.calumetphoto.co.uk

Calumet - Liverpool 7 Century Building, Summers Road, Brunswick Business Park, Liverpool, L3 4BL, United Kingdom
0151-709 1665/ 0151-709 6516
liverpool@calumetphoto.co.uk
www.calumetphoto.co.uk

Calumet - London 93-103 Drummond Street, London, NW1 2HJ, United Kingdom
(020) 7380 1144/ (020) 7387 3354
film@calumetphoto.com
www.calumetphoto.co.uk

Calumet - Manchester Unit 4, Downing Street Industrial Estate, Charlton Place, Manchester, M12 6HH, United Kingdom
0161-274 4455/ 0161-274 3406
michael.collins@calumetphoto.co.uk
www.calumetphoto.co.uk

Calumet - Nottingham 2 Nelson Street, Nottingham, NG1 1DR, United Kingdom
0115-958 6888/ 0115-959 9061
nottingham@calumetphoto.co.uk
www.calumetphoto.co.uk

Calumet Direct
Milton Keynes, United Kingdom
(0800) 0964396/ (0870) 6060061
www.calumetphoto.co.uk

Camera Dynamics Ltd Western Way, Bury St. Edmunds, Suffolk, IP33 3TB, United Kingdom
(01284) 752121/ (01284) 750560
sales@vinten.com
www.vinten.com

Cruet Co. Ltd 11 Ferrier Street, London, SW18 1SN, United Kingdom
(020) 8874 2121/ (020) 8874 9850
info@cruet.com
www.cruet.com

Cuebox Unit 5, Dares Farm, Farnham Road, Ewshot, Farnham, Surrey, GU10 5BB, United Kingdom
(0845) 8801270/ (0845) 8801280
info@cuebox.com
www.cuebox.com

Electra Film & Television Ltd Wharf House, Brentwaters Business Park, Brentford, Middlesex, TW8 8HQ, United Kingdom
(020) 8232 8899/ (020) 8232 8877
mail@electra-tv.com
www.electra-tv.com

Elite Television Production Facilities Ltd (IVCA)
Elite Television House, 248 Meanwood Road, Leeds, LS7 2HZ, United Kingdom
0113-262 3342/ 0113-262 3798
bookings@elitetv.co.uk
www.elitetv.co.uk

Extreme Facilities 15-17 Este Road, Battersea, London, SW11 2TL, United Kingdom
(020) 7801 9111
info@extremefacilities.com
www.extremefacilities.com

Eyewitness Hazardous Facilities Ltd The Drove, Sherfield English Road, Romsey, Hampshire, SO51 6EF, United Kingdom
(01794) 322500/ (01794) 323601
eyewitnessrental@aol.com
www.eyewitnessuk.co.uk

Feral Equipment 7 Wilsden Lane, Kilburn, London, NW6 7RB, United Kingdom
(07957) 370619
rob@feralequipment.com
www.feralequipment.com

Fine Point Broadcast Ltd Hill House, Furze Hill, Kingswood, Surrey, KT20 6EZ, United Kingdom
(0800) 9702020/ (0800) 9702030
hire@finepoint.co.uk
www.finepoint.co.uk

Gearhouse Broadcast Unit 12, Imperial Park, Imperial Way, Watford, WD24 4PP, United Kingdom
(0845) 820 0000/ (01923) 691499
marketing@gearhousebroadcast.com
www.gearhousebroadcast.com

Goldmoor Television Ltd 30 Granby Court, Milton Keynes, MK1 1NE, United Kingdom
(01908) 370516
crewhire@goldmoor.co.uk
www.goldmoor.co.uk

Green Door Films 38 Glenham Road, Thame, Oxfordshire, OX9 3WD, United Kingdom
(01844) 217148/(07831) 396266 (01844) 217148
info@greendoorfilms.co.uk
www.greendoorfilms.co.uk

Gripak 106 Noak Hill Road, Billericay, Essex, CM12 9UH, United Kingdom
(01277) 656759/(07973) 217184 (01277) 656777
stugrip@aol.com
www.members.aol.com/stugrip

Hammerhead Television Facilities Ltd Unit 19, 80 Liongate Enterprise Park, Morden Road, Mitcham, Surrey, CR4 4NY, United Kingdom
(020) 8646 5511/ (020) 8646 6163
london@hammerheadtv.com
www.hammerheadtv.com

Hire Co (UK) Ltd Unit 18, Priory Industrial Park, Highcliffe, Christchurch, Dorset, BH23 4HD, United Kingdom
(01425) 272002/ (01425) 270094
scott@thehireco.co.uk
www.thehireco.co.uk

Hyperactive Broadcast Ltd 5 The Royston Centre, Lynchford Lane, Ash Vale, Aldershot, Hampshire, GU12 5PQ, United Kingdom
(01252) 519191/(07887) 743145 (01252) 513939
lawrie@hyperactivebroadcast.com
www.hyperactivebroadcast.com

Ice Film Equipment Ltd Unit 2, Bridge Wharf, 156 Caledonian Road, London, N1 9UU, United Kingdom
(020) 7278 0908/ (020) 7278 4552
sales@icefilm.com
www.icefilm.com

Kinetic Units 3 & 4, Cremer Business Centre, 37 Cremer Street, London, E2 8HD, United Kingdom
(020) 7729 7442/ (020) 7749 4299
info@go-kinetic.com
www.go-kinetic.com

Kitroom Monkey Ltd Ealing Film Studios, Ealing Green, London, W5 5EP, United Kingdom
(0845) 166 2597/(07739) 806807
mail@kitroommonkey.co.uk
www.kitroommonkey.co.uk

Limelight Design Limited 27 Bolingbroke Grove, London, SW11 6EJ,
7946582074
tom@limelight-design.co.uk
www.limelight-design.co.uk

Media Control Ltd Unit C, Moorpark Central, Broomloan Road, Glasgow, G51 2BS, United Kingdom
0141-425 2016/ 0141-425 2017
info@mcl-scotland.com
www.mclav.com

Mercury Conference AV Ltd 4 Shakespeare Avenue, London, N11 1AY, United Kingdom
(0870) 2000805/ (0870) 2000815
www.mercury-av.com

Metro Broadcast 5-7 Great Chapel Street, London, W1F 8FF, United Kingdom
(020) 7434 7700/ (020) 7434 7701
info@metrobroadcast.com
www.metrobroadcast.com

Movietech Camera Rentals Ltd Pinewood Studios, Pinewood Road, Iver Heath, Iver, Buckinghamshire, SL0 0NH, United Kingdom
(01753) 650007/ (01753) 650006
info@movietech.co.uk
www.movietech.co.uk

Newland Corporate Communications Arrow Business Park, Arrow Close, Killingworth, Newcastle Upon Tyne, NE12 6QN, United Kingdom
0191-256 6000/ 0191-256 6056
hire@newlandcc.co.uk
www.newlandcc.co.uk

Newland Electronics Ltd The Exchange, Whitley Road, Newcastle upon Tyne, NE7 7XB, United Kingdom
0191-215 0088/ 0191-266 4298
newland@dial.pipex.com
www.newland.dial.pipex.com

On Sight Broadcast Hire 14-15 Berners Street, London, W1T 3LJ, United Kingdom
(020) 7637 0888/ (020) 7637 0444
hire@onsight.co.uk
www.onsight.co.uk

ONE8SIX Ltd Unit 1, Heron Trading Estate, Alliance Road, London, W3 0RA, United Kingdom
(020) 8896 8600/ (020) 8896 8616
info@one8six.com
www.one8six.com

P E C Video Ltd 65-66 Dean Street, London, W1D 4PL, United Kingdom
(020) 7437 4633/ (020) 7025 1320
sales@pec.co.uk
www.pec.co.uk

Panavision Belfast Unit 4, Hawthorn Business Centre, 6 Wildflower Way, Belfast, BT12 6TA, United Kingdom
(028) 9057 2525/(07860) 592476 (028) 9057 2526
roy.harrison@panavision.co.uk
www.panavision.com

Panavision London Bristol Road, Greenford, Middlesex, UB6 8GD, United Kingdom
(020) 8839 7333/ (020) 8839 7300
enquiries@panavision.co.uk
www.panavision.co.uk

Paul Marwaha Communications 34 Washington Drive, St Leonards Park, Windsor, Berkshire, SL4 4NS, United Kingdom
(01753) 859618/(07860) 664037
paulmarwaha@hotmail.com

Peartree Rental Ltd Lower Ground Floor, 53 Central Street, London, EC1V 8AD, United Kingdom
(020) 7251 2044/078 41260777 (020) 7251 2455
info@peartreerental.com
www.peartreerental.com

Photo Elevate 1 Rosemary Crescent, Tiptree, Colchester, Essex, CO5 0XA,
07757 417066
photo-elevate@hotmail.co.uk
www.photo-elevate.com

Picture Canning Co. 55 Bendon Valley, London, SW18 4LZ, United Kingdom
(020) 8874 9277/ (020) 8874 6623
info@picturecanning.co.uk
www.picturecanning.co.uk

Presteigne Broadcast Hire Unit 4, Manor Gate, Manor Royal, Crawley, West Sussex, RH10 9SX, United Kingdom
(01293) 651300/ (01293) 651301
hire@presteigne.co.uk
www.presteigne.co.uk

Prime Television Unit 7, Latimer Road Industrial Estate, Latimer Road, London, W10 6RQ, United Kingdom
(020) 8969 6122/ (020) 8969 6144
moreinfo@primetv.com
www.primetv.com

Pro Centre 5/6 Mallow Street, London, EC1Y 8RS, United Kingdom
(020) 7490 3122/ (020) 7490 1292
procentre@hasselblad.co.uk
www.procentre.co.uk

ProVision 96 Kirkstall Road, Leeds, LS3 1HD, United Kingdom
0113-222 8222/ 0113-222 8110
adrian.bleasdale@itv.com
www.provisionequipment.tv

Rolling Stock Ltd Telscombe Lodge, Cromwell Road, Marlow, Buckinghamshire, SL7 1BQ, United Kingdom
(01628) 487272/ (01628) 487272
rsl@btinternet.com
www.rollingstocklimited.com

S L V 70-74 Stewarts Road, London, London, SW8 4DE, United Kingdom
(020) 7720 6464/ (020) 7622 3666
shoot@slvision.co.uk
www.slvision.co.uk

Scorpion Group Security Solutions (UK) 7 Shergar Close, Abbeydale, Gloucester, GL4 4FD, United Kingdom
(01452) 525397/ (01452) 525397
sales@scorpion-group.co.uk
www.scorpion-goup.co.uk

Shift 4 Ltd Unit 3, Crusader Industrial Estate, 167 Hermitage Road, London, N4 1LZ, United Kingdom
(020) 8809 8680/ (020) 8809 8690
info@shift-4.com
www.shift-4.com

South London Filter Ltd 3 Richborne Terrace, London, SW8 1AS, United Kingdom
(020) 7735 1900/ (020) 7820 1718
info@camerafilters.co.uk
www.camerafilters.co.uk

Spring Lighting Spring House, 10 Spring Place, London, NW5 3BH, United Kingdom
☎ (020) 7267 8735/📠 (020) 7267 8481
✉ lighting@springstudios.com
🖳 www.springstudios.com

Spring Lighting - Palma Calle Sagasta 53, Palma De Mallorca, 7011, Spain
☎ 6622 49162/📠 207 267 8481
✉ palma@springstudios.com
🖳 www.springstudios.com

Star Street Video 92 Star Street, London, W2 1QF, United Kingdom
☎ (020) 7402 1330/(07836) 234740 📠 (020) 7706 1084
✉ info@star-street-video.com
🖳 www.star-street-video.com

Studio-D 86 Greenfield Road, London, E1 1EJ, United Kingdom
☎ (020) 7247 9842/📠 (020) 7247 9843
✉ info@studio-d.co.uk
🖳 www.studio-d.co.uk

Super 8 Film Camera Co. 10A Granville Gardens, Ealing Common, London, W5 3PA, United Kingdom
☎ (020) 8992 6451/(07973) 225506 📠 (020) 8992 6451
✉ antiochus66@yahoo..co.uk

Switch Digital 21 Lanercost Road, Brixton, London, SW2 3DP, United Kingdom
☎ (020) 8674 2255/📠 (020) 8674 1973
✉ bookings@switch-digital.co.uk
🖳 www.switch-digital.co.uk

Technovision London Ltd Metropolitan Ctre, Bristol Rd, Greenford, Middlesex, UB6 8GD, United Kingdom
☎ (020) 8839 7314/(07970) 654618 📠 (020) 8813 2113
✉ info@technovision-uk.com
🖳 www.technovision-uk.com

Teletronics 24 Upper Tooting Road, London, SW17 7PG, United Kingdom
☎ (020) 8672 2171/📠 (020) 8672 7955
✉ teletronics@btconnect.com
🖳 www.teletronics.tv

The Hire Co. (UK) Ltd The Picture House, 4 Lower Park Row, Bristol, BS1 5BJ, United Kingdom
☎ 0117-927 7473/(07860) 341141 📠 0117-923 0862
✉ mail@thehireco.co.uk
🖳 www.thehireco.co.uk

The Street Studios 2 Dunston Street, London, E8 4EB, United Kingdom
☎ (020) 7923 9430/📠 (020) 7923 9429
✉ mail@streetstudios.co.uk
🖳 www.streetstudios.co.uk

Transmission (TX) Ltd Units 1A-2A, Shepperton Studios, Studios Road, Shepperton, Middlesex, TW17 0QD, United Kingdom
☎ (020) 8547 0208/📠 (01932) 592571
✉ info@ttx.co.uk
🖳 www.ttx.co.uk

Two Four Studios 3 Bush Park, Pestover, Plymouth, PL6 7RG, United Kingdom
☎ (01752) 727400/📠 (01752) 727450
✉ enq@twofour.co.uk
🖳 www.twofour.co.uk

V F G Higher Ltd Glen Mill Studio, Glen Road, Laxey, Isle of Man, IM4 7AJ, United Kingdom
☎ (01624) 862559/07624 497982 📠 (01624) 862560
✉ richard.miles@vfg.co.uk
🖳 www.vfg.co.uk

V M I Ltd 19 D'Arblay Street, London, W1F 8ED, United Kingdom
☎ (0870) 8501444/📠 (0870) 8501445
✉ vmi@vmi.tv
🖳 www.vmi.tv

Video Europe Ltd 4-5 Union Court, 20-22 Union Road, London, SW4 6JP, United Kingdom
☎ (020) 7627 9000/📠 (020) 7627 9001
✉ hire@videoeurope.co.uk
🖳 www.videoeurope.co.uk

Visionworks Television Ltd Vision House, 56 Donegall Pass, Belfast, BT7 1BU, United Kingdom
☎ (028) 9024 1241/📠 (028) 9024 1777
✉ production@visionworks.co.uk
🖳 www.visionworks.co.uk

CORPORATE VIDEO

Bridge Creative Ltd The Coach House Studio, 40 Higher Lane, Upholland, Lancashire, WN8 0NL, 01695 624966
✉ bridget@bridgecreative.co.uk
🖳 www.bridgecreative.co.uk

Daydream Linton House, 164-180 Union Street, London, SE1 0LH,
☎ +44 (0) 20 7096 1471/+44 (0) 20 7117 1636
✉ ralph@daydream.co.uk
🖳 www.daydream.co.uk

FILM LIBRARIES

4 Clip Sales c/o ITN Source, 200 Gray's Inn Road, London, WC1X 8XZ, United Kingdom
☎ (020) 7430 4480/📠 (020) 7430 4453
✉ uksales@itnsource.com
🖳 www.itnsource.com

Adventure Archive Fudge Cottage, Dalditch Lane, Budleigh Salterton, Devon, EX9 7AH, United Kingdom
☎ (01395) 446242/(07711) 787737 📠
✉ leo@adventurearchive.com
🖳 www.adventurearchive.com

Aerial Archives Hangar 23, Box 470455, San Francisco, 94147, United States of America
☎ 00 1 415 771 2555/📠 00 1 707 769 7277
✉ herb@aerialarchives.com
🖳 www.aerialarchives.com

Associated Press Television News The Interchange, Oval Road, Camden Lock, London, NW1 7DZ, United Kingdom
☎ (020) 7413 8301/📠 (020) 7413 8327
✉ info@aptnlibrary.com
🖳 www.aptn.com

Barnardos Film & Photographic Archive Tanners Lane, Barkingside, Ilford, Essex, IG6 1QG, United Kingdom
☎ (020) 8498 7345/📠 (020) 8498 7090
✉ stephen.pover@barnardos.org.uk
🖳 www.barnardos.org.uk

BBC Motion Gallery Room E251, 80 Wood Lane, White City, London, W12 0TT, United Kingdom
☎ (020) 8433 2861/📠 (020) 8433 2939
✉ motiongallery.uk@bbc.co.uk
🖳 www.bbcmotiongallery.com

BDFL British Defence Film Library (FOCAL) Chalfont Grove, Narcot Lane, Chalfont St Peter, Gerrards Cross, Buckinghamshire, SL9 8TN, United Kingdom
☎ (01494) 878278/📠 (01494) 878007
✉ footage@bdfl.co.uk
🖳 www.bdfl.co.uk

Black Diamond Films Ltd Bedford Chambers, The Piazza, London, WC2E 8HA, United Kingdom
☎ (020) 7240 4071/(07801) 438737 📠 (020) 7836 6339
✉ jim@blackdiamond.co.uk
🖳 www.blackdiamond.co.uk

British Movietonews Ltd (FOCAL) Denham Media Park, North Orbital Road, Uxbridge, Middlesex, UB9 5HQ, United Kingdom
☎ (01895) 833071/📠 (01895) 834893
✉ library@mtone.co.uk
🖳 www.movietone.com

Bulletin International UK (FOCAL) 4th Floor, 121-141 Westbourne Terrace, London, W2 6JR, United Kingdom
☎ (020) 7479 0450/📠 (020) 7479 0490
✉ rabia.bapu@uk.bulletin.com
🖳 www.bulletin.com

Canal + Image UK Ltd (FOCAL) Pinewood Studios, Pinewood Road, Iver, Buckinghamshire, SL0 0NH, United Kingdom
☎ (01753) 631111/📠 (01753) 655813
✉ jherron@canalplus.freeserve.co.uk
🖳 www.studiocanal.com

Chain Production Ltd 2 Clanricarde Gardens, London, W2 4NA, United Kingdom
☎ (020) 7229 4277/📠 (020) 7229 0861
✉ garwin.davison@chainproduction.com
🖳 www.chainproduction.com

Clips & Footage Studio 112, Spitfire Studios, 63-71 Collier Street, London, N1 9BE, United Kingdom
☎ (020) 7278 1007/📠 (020) 7278 1009
✉ info@clipsandfootage.com
🖳 www.clipsandfootage.com

CNN Imagesource Turner House, 16 Great Marlborough Street, London, W1F 7HS, United Kingdom
☎ (020) 7693 1540/📠 (020) 7693 1541
✉ cnn.imagesourceUK@turner.com
🖳 www.cnnimagesource.com

Colstar International Television Ltd 78 York Street, London, W1H 1DP, United Kingdom
☎ (020) 7625 6200
🖳 www.colstar.tv

Concord Media 22 Hines Road, Ipswich, IP3 9BG, United Kingdom
☎ (01473) 726012/📠 (01473) 274531
✉ sales@concordmedia.org.uk
🖳 www.concordmedia.org.uk

D T Productions Maygrove House, 67 Maygrove Road, London, NW6 2EG, United Kingdom
☎ (020) 7644 8888/📠 (020) 7644 8889
✉ toby@dtproductions.co.uk
🖳 www.dtproductions.co.uk

Domaine Productions Ltd 8 Whitepost Hill, Redhill, RH1 6AL, United Kingdom
☎ (01737) 766100/📠 (01737) 766588
✉ dpltv@btinternet.com

Education Distribution Services Education House, Castle Road, Sittingbourne, Kent, ME10 3RL, United Kingdom
☎ (01795) 427614/📠 1795437988
✉ info@edist.co.uk
🖳 www.edist.co.uk

Environmental Investigation Agency 62-63 Upper Street, London, N1 0NY, United Kingdom
☎ (020) 7354 7960/📠 (020) 7354 7961
✉ communications@eia-international.org
🖳 www.eia-international.org

Film Images (London) Ltd (AMIA, BKSTS, BUFVC, FOCAL) 2 The Quadrant, 135 Salusbury Road, London, NW6 6RJ, United Kingdom
☎ (020) 7624 3388/📠 (020) 7624 3377
✉ research@film-images.com
🖳 www.film-images.com

Film Research London, SE27 9WZ, United Kingdom
☎ (020) 8670 2959/📠 (020) 8670 1793
✉ frps@aol.com
🖳 www.filmresearch.co.uk

Focal International Pentax House, South Hill Avenue, South Harrow, Harrow, Middlesex, HA2 0DU, United Kingdom
☎ (020) 8423 5853/📠 (020) 8933 4826
✉ info@focalint.org
🖳 www.focalint.org

G M T V Library Sales The London Television Centre, Upper Ground, London, SE1 9TT, United Kingdom
☎ (020) 7827 7363/📠 (020) 7827 7043
✉ librarysales@gm.tv
🖳 www.gm.tv

Granada ITN Archive c/o ITN Source, 200 Gray's Inn Road, London, WC1X 8XZ, United Kingdom
☎ (020) 7430 4480/📠 (020) 7430 4453
✉ uksales@itnsource.com
🖳 www.itnsource.com

Granada Visual c/o ITN Source, 200 Gray's Inn Road, London, WC1X 8XZ, United Kingdom
☎ (020) 7430 4480/📠 (020) 7430 4453
✉ uksales@itnsource.com
🖳 www.itnsource.com

Greenpark Productions Ltd (FOCAL) Illand, Launceston, Cornwall, PL15 7LS, United Kingdom
☎ (01566) 782107/📠 (01566) 782127
✉ info@greenparkimages.co.uk
🖳 www.greenparkimages.co.uk

Huntley Film Archives 22 Islington Green, London, N1 8DU, United Kingdom
☎ (020) 7226 9260/📠 (020) 7359 9337
✉ films@huntleyarchives.com
🖳 www.huntleyarchives.com

Images of War 3/A Regents Park Road, London, NW1 7TL, United Kingdom
☎ (020) 7267 9198/07748 906 609 📠 (020) 7267 8852
✉ Derek@dircon.co.uk
🖳 www.warfootage.com

Imperial War Museum Film & Video Archive All Saints Annexe, Austral Street, London, SE11 4SJ, United Kingdom
☎ (020) 7416 5291/📠 (020) 7416 5299
✉ filmcommercial@iwm.org.uk
🖳 www.iwmcollections.org.uk

FILM LIBRARIES

Index Stock Shots Technicolour Estate, Bath Road, West Drayton, Middlesex, UB7 0DB, United Kingdom
- (020) 8754 9858
- info@indexstockshots.com
- www.indexstockshots.com

Journeyman Pictures 75A Walton Road, East Molesey, Surrey, KT8 0DP, United Kingdom
- (020) 8941 9994/ (020) 8941 9899
- info@journeyman.tv
- www.journeyman.tv

London Film Archives Ltd 78 Mildmay Park, Islington, London, N1 4PR, United Kingdom
- (020) 7437 5855/ (020) 7287 8001
- info@londonfilmarchive.org
- www.londonfilmarchive.org

Maverick Enterprises 31 Dobree Avenue, London, NW10 2AD, United Kingdom
- (020) 8459 3858
- ghizela@copyrightgroup.info
- www.copyrightgroup.info

Moving Image Communications Ltd Maidstone Studios, Vinters Park, Maidstone, Kent, ME14 5NZ, United Kingdom
- (01622) 684569/ (01622) 687444
- mail@milibrary.com
- www.milibrary.com

National Motor Museum Trading Ltd John Montague Building, Beaulieu, Brockenhurst, Hampshire, SO42 7ZN, United Kingdom
- (01590) 614664/(07818) 454522 (01590) 612655
- stephen.vokins@beaulieu.co.uk
- www.beaulieu.co.uk

NIFTC - Digital Film Archive Alfred House, 21 Alfred Street, Belfast, BT2 8ED, United Kingdom
- (028) 9023 2444/ (028) 9023 9918
- archive@niftc.co.uk
- www.niftc.co.uk

Nigel G. Heath c/o Hackenbacker Audio Post Production, 10 Bateman Street, London, W1D 4AQ, United Kingdom
- (020) 7734 1324/ (020) 7439 1236
- hackenbacker@btconnect.com
- www.hackenbacker.com

North West Film Archive Minshull House, 47-49 Chorlton Street, Manchester, M1 3EU, United Kingdom
- 0161-247 3097/ 0161-247 3098
- n.w.filmarchive@mmu.ac.uk
- www.nwfa.mmu.ac.uk

Olympic Television Archive Bureau (OTAB) McCormack House, Burlington Lane, London, W4 2TH, United Kingdom
- (020) 8233 5353/ (020) 8233 5354
- webmaster@otab.com
- www.otab.com

Open University Library Learning Resources Centre, Walton Hall, Milton Keynes, MK7 6AA, United Kingdom
- (01908) 858785/ (01908) 858787
- ouweng@open.ac.uk
- www.open.ac.uk/library

Reid & Casement Research 3rd Floor, Bedford Chambers, The Piazza, Covent Garden, London, WC2E 8HA, United Kingdom
- (020) 7240 4550/ (020) 7379 0061
- research@reidandcasement.co.uk
- www.reidandcasement.co.uk

Riley Research 190 Ladbroke Grove, London, W10 5LZ, United Kingdom
- (020) 8968 7236/(07793) 818819 (020) 8960 1678
- rileyresearch.uk@virgin.net

Viewtech Educational Media (FOCAL) 7-8 Falcons Gate, Northavon Business Centre, Bristol, BS37 5NH, United Kingdom
- (01454) 858055/ (01454) 858056
- footage@viewtech.co.uk
- www.viewtech.co.uk

W W F Video Library World Images, 8 Fitzroy Square, London, W1T 5HN, United Kingdom
- (020) 7388 8555/ (020) 7387 8444
- info@world-images.org
- www.world-images.org

World Backgrounds Millennium Studios, Elstree Way, Borehamwood, Hertfordshire, WD6 1SF, United Kingdom
- (020) 8236 0011/(07918) 083340 (020) 8953 6633
- paul@worldbackgrounds.com
- www.worldbackgrounds.com

Xtreme Information 45 Fouberts Place, London, W1F 7QH, United Kingdom
- (020) 7575 1800/ (020) 7575 1888
- information@ads.xtremeinformation.com
- www.xtremeinformation.com

LIGHTING EQUIPMENT RENTAL

1 Off Neon Creations 797 Lea Bridge Road, Walthamstow, London, E17 9DS, United Kingdom
- (020) 8503 7300/ (020) 8521 1150
- robfromsoak@aol.com

10 out of 10 Productions Unit 14, Forest Hill Business Centre, Clyde Vale, London, SE23 3JF, United Kingdom
- (0845) 1235664/ (020) 8699 8968
- info@10outof10.co.uk
- www.10outof10.co.uk

24Kare Film Ltd Tomtom Mah. Bogazkesen Cad., No. 183/1 Beyoglu, Istanbul, 34433, Turkey
- 00 90 212 252 2751/ 00 90 212 251 9089
- uarmadort.kare@yahoo.com

2Can Productions PO Box 668, Cardiff, CF11 1EZ,
- 0845 0545096/ 0845 0545097
- info@2canproductions.com
- www.2canproductions.com

Adrian Thurston Gordon Productions Flat B, 44 Eardley Crescent, London, SW5 9JZ, United Kingdom
- (020) 7373 3668/(07985) 861616 (020) 7373 3668
- adrian@syncfilms.com
- www.adrianthurston.co.uk

Almik Signs Ltd 10a Wendell Road, London, W12 9RT, United Kingdom
- (020) 8743 1090/ (020) 8749 5774
- 3d@almik-signs.co.uk
- www.eclipse.co.uk/almik-signs

Arri Lighting Rental Manchester Unit 6, Orchard Street Industrial Estate, Salford, M6 6FL, United Kingdom
- 0161-736 8034/ 0161-745 8023
- sales@arrirental.com
- www.arri.com

AV Matrix Ltd
Harrogate, North Yorkshire, HG3 2GR, United Kingdom
- (01423) 521011/(07790) 496655 (01423) 521011
- info@av-matrix.com
- www.av-matrix.com

Black Light 18 West Harbour Road, Granton, Edinburgh, EH5 1PN, United Kingdom
- 0131-551 2337/ 0131-551 6827
- enquiries@black-light.com
- www.black-light.com

Blacklight Ltd 18 West Harbour Road, Granton, Edinburgh, EH5 1PN, United Kingdom
- 0131-551 2337/ 0131-551 6827
- edinburgh@black-light.com
- www.black-light.com

Bluefin TV 34 Fitzwilliam Road, London, SW4 0DN, United Kingdom
- (020) 7622 0870/(07973) 502349 (020) 7720 7875
- info@bluefintv.com
- www.bluefintv.com

Bocek Production Cubuklu cad.agaclik mesire yeri, d+e burunbahce, beykoz, Istanbul, 34805,
- 00 9 02166801058
- selma@bocekyapim.com.tr
- www.bocekyapim.com.tr

Calumet - London The Werx Studios, 10 Heathmans Rd, Fulham, London, SW6 4TJ, United Kingdom
- (020) 7384 3270/ (020) 7384 3270
- fulham@calumetphoto.com
- www.calumetphoto.com

Cirro Lite (Europe) Ltd 3 Barretts Green Road, London, NW10 7AE, United Kingdom
- (020) 8955 6700/ (020) 8961 9343
- info@cirrolite.com
- www.cirrolite.com

Electro Signs Ltd 97 Vallentin Road, London, E17 3JJ, United Kingdom
- (020) 8521 8066/ (020) 8520 8127
- info@electrosigns.co.uk
- www.electrosigns.co.uk

ELP (National Distribution Centre) Hanger 15, Alconbury Airfield, Huntingdon, Cambridgeshire, PE28 4WX, United Kingdom
- (01480) 443800/ (01480) 443888
- info@elp.tv
- www.elp.tv

Entec Sound & Light 517 Yeading Lane, Northolt, Middlesex, UB5 6LN, United Kingdom
- (020) 8842 4004/ (020) 8842 3310
- sales@entec-soundandlight.com
- www.entec-soundandlight.com

Eyelights Ltd Vision Studios, Old Mill Road, Portishead, Bristol, BS20 7BX, United Kingdom
- (01275) 847257/(07836) 349342 (01275) 814187
- colin_eylights@yahoo.com
- www.eyelights.co.uk

Film & TV Services (EF) Ltd Unit 3, Matrix Park, Coronation Road, London, NW10 7PH, United Kingdom
- (020) 8961 0090/ (020) 8961 8635
- operations@ftvs.co.uk
- www.ftvs.co.uk

Hawthorn Theatrical Ltd Crown Business Park, Old Dalby, Melton Mowbray, Leicestershire, LE14 3NQ, United Kingdom
- (01664) 821111/ (01664) 821119
- info@hawthorns.uk.com
- www.hawthorns.uk.com

Kinetic Units 3 & 4, Cremer Business Centre, 37 Cremer Street, London, E2 8HD, United Kingdom
- (020) 7729 7442/ (020) 7749 4299
- info@go-kinetic.com
- www.go-kinetic.com

Kitroom Monkey Ltd Ealing Film Studios, Ealing Green, London, W5 5EP, United Kingdom
- (0845) 166 2597/(07739) 806807
- mail@kitroommonkey.co.uk
- www.kitroommonkey.co.uk

L H S Ltd The Business Village, 3-9 Broomhill Road, Wandsworth, London, London, SW18 4JQ, United Kingdom
- (020) 8870 4855/ (020) 8871 9811
- hire@lhsltd.com
- www.lhsltd.com

Lancelyn Theatre Supplies Poulton Road, Bebbington, Wirral, Merseyside, CH63 9LN, United Kingdom
- 0151-334 3000/ 0151-334 4047
- northwest@lancelyn.co.uk
- www.lancelyn.co.uk

Laser Animation 22 Leicester Street, Melton Mowbray, Leicestershire, LE13 0PP, United Kingdom
- (01664) 561600/ (01664) 561568
- laseranim@aol.com
- www.laseranimation.co.uk

Laser Grafix Sales Ltd Unit 4a, Stratton Park, Biggleswade, Bedfordshire, SG18 8QS, United Kingdom
- (01767) 315948
- mail@lgfx.co.uk
- www.lgfx.co.uk

Laser Hire Ltd Fole Spring Farm, Fole, Uttoxeter, Staffordshire, ST14 5EF, United Kingdom
- (01889) 507067/(07836) 526834 (01889) 507068
- info@laserhire.co.uk
- www.laserhire.co.uk

LCA - Lights, Camera, Action Unit 30, The Metropolitan Centre, Taunton Road, Greenford, Middlesex, UB6 8UQ, United Kingdom
- (020) 8833 7600/ (020) 8575 8219
- sales@lcauk.com
- www.lcauk.com

Lee Lighting Ltd Wycombe Road, Off Beresford Avenue, Wembley, Middlesex, HA0 1QD, United Kingdom
- (020) 8900 2900/ (020) 8902 5500
- info@lee.co.uk
- www.lee.co.uk

Light Works Ltd 2A Greenwood Road, London, E8 1AB, United Kingdom
- (020) 7249 3627/ (020) 7254 0306

Limelight Design Limited 27 Bolingbroke Grove, London, SW11 6EJ,
- 7946582074
- tom@limelight-design.co.uk
- www.limelight-design.co.uk

N S L X 21 Warren Road, Woodley, Reading, RG5 3AR, United Kingdom
- 0118-376 9683/(07981) 266163
- neilscrivener@hotmail.com
- www.pulselighting.net/nslx/

Newland Corporate Communications Arrow Business Park, Arrow Close, Killingworth, Newcastle Upon Tyne, NE12 6QN, United Kingdom
☎ 0191-256 6000/✆ 0191-256 6056
✉ hire@newlandcc.co.uk
🖥 www.newlandcc.co.uk

Newman Hire Co. 16 The Vale, Acton, London, W3 7SB, United Kingdom
☎ (020) 8743 0741/✆ (020) 8749 3513
✉ sales@newmanhireco.uk

P F L Pro Audio & Lighting Tweedside Trading Estate, Tweedmouth, Berwick-upon-Tweed, TD15 2XF, United Kingdom
☎ (01289) 308030/✆ (01289) 308030
✉ info@pflaudio.co.uk
🖥 www.pflaudio.co.uk

P R G Europe Unit 3, Beddington Cross, Beddington Farm Road, Croydon, CR0 4XH, United Kingdom
☎ (020) 8665 8500/✆ (020) 8664 8819
✉ croydoninfo@prgeurope.com
🖥 www.prgeurope.com

Panavision Belfast Unit 4, Hawthorn Business Centre, 6 Wildflower Way, Belfast, BT12 6TA, United Kingdom
☎ (028) 9057 2525/(07860) 592476 ✆ (028) 9057 2526
✉ roy.harrison@panavision.co.uk
🖥 www.panavision.co.uk

PRG Europe 20-22 Fairway Drive, Greenford, Middlesex, UB6 8PW, United Kingdom
☎ (020) 8575 6666/✆ (020) 8575 0424
✉ greenfordinfo@prgeurope.com
🖥 www.prgeurope.com

Rainbow Powerhouse 415 Oakleigh Road North, London, N20 0RU, United Kingdom
☎ (020) 8368 9852/✆ (020) 8361 1143
✉ sales@discoequipmenthire.co.uk
🖥 www.discoequipmenthire.co.uk

S P S Lighting Film & Video Manor Mead, Risborough Road, Terrick, Aylesbury, Buckinghamshire, HP17 0UB, United Kingdom
☎ (01296) 614799/(07831) 428015 ✆
✉ steve@spslighting.co.uk
🖥 www.spslighting.co.uk

S2 Events Ltd 3-5 Valentine Place, London, SE1 8QH, United Kingdom
☎ (020) 7928 5474/✆ (020) 7928 6082
✉ info@s2events.co.uk
🖥 www.s2events.co.uk

Snap Productions 151-155 New North Road, London, N1 6TA, United Kingdom
☎ (020) 7684 7555/✆ (020) 7684 7556
✉ rich@snap-pro.com
🖥 www.snap-pro.com

Spring Studios Ltd 10 Spring Place, Kentish Town, London, NW5 3BH, United Kingdom
☎ (020) 7267 8383/(07764) 331234 ✆ (020) 7267 8481
✉ info@springstudios.com
🖥 www.springstudios.com

Stage Control Ltd 20 Station Parade, Whitchurch Lane, Edgware, Middlesex, HA8 6RW, United Kingdom
☎ (020) 8952 8982/✆ (020) 8951 4178
✉ info@stagecontrol.com
🖥 www.stagecontrol.com

Stage Electrics Third Way, Avonmouth, Bristol, BS11 9YL, United Kingdom
☎ 0117-938 4000/✆ 0117-916 2828
✉ sales@stage-electrics.co.uk
🖥 www.stage-electrics.co.uk

Stage Two Hire Services Unit J, Penfold Estate, Imperial Way, Watford, WD24 4YY, United Kingdom
☎ (01923) 230789/✆ (01923) 255048
✉ info@stage-two.co.uk
🖥 www.stage-two.co.uk

Tech Hire & Sales Unit 4, Frontier Works, 33 Queen Street, London, N17 8JA, United Kingdom
☎ (020) 8493 0526/✆ (020) 8493 0528
✉ office@techequip.co.uk
🖥 www.techequip.co.uk

Tower Productions Ltd Unit 8, Forth Industrial Estate, Sealcarr Street, Edinburgh, EH5 1RF, United Kingdom
☎ 0131-552 0100/✆ 0131-552 0200
✉ info@tower-productions.com
🖥 www.tower-productions.com

Trafalgar Lighting 9 &10 Northway Claverings Industrial Estate, Montague Road, London, N9 0AD, United Kingdom
☎ (020) 8887 0082/✆ (020) 8887 0072
✉ hire@trafalgarlighting.co.uk
🖥 www.trafalgarlighting.co.uk

UK Rigging Undershore Business Park, Brookside Road, Bolton, BL2 2SE, United Kingdom
☎ (01204) 391343/✆ (01204) 363238
✉ mail@ukrigging.net
🖥 www.ukrigging.net

White Light Ltd Unit 20, 20 Merton Industrial Park, Jubilee Way, London, SW19 3WL, United Kingdom
☎ (020) 8254 4600/✆ (020) 8254 4801
✉ info@whitelight.ltd.uk
🖥 www.whitelight.ltd.uk

Zig Zag Lighting 68 Morton Gardens, Wallington, Surrey, SM6 8EX, United Kingdom
☎ (020) 8647 1968/✆ (020) 8401 2216
✉ info@zigzag-lighting.co.uk
🖥 www.zigzag-lighting.co.uk

MODEL MAKERS

Daydream Linton House, 164-180 Union Street, London, SE1 0LH,
☎ +44 (0) 20 7096 1471/+44 (0) 7117 1636
✉ ralph@daydream.co.uk
🖥 www.daydream.co.uk

POST PRODUCTION/SPECIAL EFFECTS

124 Facilities 124 Horseferry Road, London, SW1P 2TX, United Kingdom
☎ (020) 7306 8040/✆ (020) 7306 8041
✉ dbrowne@channel4.co.uk
🖥 www.124.co.uk

1410 Degrees 5A Noel Street, London, W1F 8GE, United Kingdom
☎ (020) 7287 1410/✆ (020) 7287 1496
✉ robin@1410degrees.co.uk
🖥 www.1410degrees.co.uk

3di Unit C, Dragon House, Back off Dragon Road, Harrogate, North Yorkshire, HG1 5DB, United Kingdom
☎ (0845) 4582898/✆ (0871) 2220189
✉ paul@threedi.net
🖥 www.threedi.net

3sixtymedia The Manchester Studio, Quay Street, Manchester, M60 9EA, United Kingdom
☎ 0161-839 0360/✆ 0161-827 2360
✉ enquiry@3sixtymedia.com
🖥 www.the-manchester-studios.tv

4 Reel Design 9 Ixworth Close, Northampton, NN3 8TW, United Kingdom
☎ (07940) 125004
✉ johnl@4reel.biz
🖥 www.4reel.biz

422 Manchester Ltd 4th Floor, South Central, 11 Peter Street, Manchester, M2 5QR, United Kingdom
☎ 0161-839 6080/✆ 0161-839 6081
✉ richard@422.tv
🖥 www.422.tv

Abbey Road Studios Ltd 3 Abbey Road, London, NW8 9AY, United Kingdom
☎ (020) 7286 1161
✉ bookings@abbeyroad.com
🖥 www.abbeyroad.com

Actaeon Films 50 Gracefield Gardens, London, SW16 2ST, United Kingdom
☎ (020) 87693339/✆ (0870) 1347980
✉ info@actaeonfilms.com
🖥 www.actaeonfilms.com

Altered TV 166a Lancaster Road, London, W11 1QU, United Kingdom
☎ (07974) 070990
✉ leer@edgy.co.uk
🖥 www.altered.tv

Andrew Sumners Associates Ltd Suite 401, Barclay House, 35 Whitworth Street West, Manchester, M1 5NG, United Kingdom
☎ 0161-228 0330/✆ 0161-228 0770
✉ janet@sumners.co.uk
🖥 www.sumners.co.uk

Andy Godwin 44 Carminia Road, London, SW17 8AH, United Kingdom
☎ (020) 8675 2626/(07973) 520646 ✆
✉ andrew@andygodwin.co.uk
🖥 www.andygodwin.co.uk

Anvil Post Production Technicolor Perivale Park, Horsenden Lane South, Perivale, Greenford, Middlesex, UB6 7RL, United Kingdom
☎ (020) 8799 0555/✆ (020) 8799 0799
✉ mike.anscombe@thomson.net
🖥 www.anvilpost.com

Arc Facilities 40 Dalintober Street, Glasgow, G5 8NW, United Kingdom
☎ 0141-333 5560/✆ 0141-332 6002
✉ info@arcfacilities.com
🖥 www.arcfacilities.com

Arena P3 74 Newman Street, London, W1T 3EL, United Kingdom
☎ (020) 7436 4360/✆ (020) 7436 3989
✉ edit@arenap3.tv
🖥 www.arenap3.tv

ArenaP3 (IVCA) 74 Newman Street, London, W1T 3EL, United Kingdom
☎ (020) 7436 4360/✆ (020) 7436 3989
✉ edit@arenap3.tv
🖥 www.arenap3.tv

Arqiva Satellite Media Solutions Chalfont Grove, Narcot Lane, Chalfont St. Peter, Gerrards Cross, Buckinghamshire, SL9 8TW, United Kingdom
☎ (0870) 879 8787
🖥 www.arqiva.com

ArtemDigital Unit 4 Perivale Park, Horsenden Lane South, Perivale, Greenford, Middlesex, UB6 7RL, United Kingdom
☎ (020) 8991 6060/✆ (020) 8997 1557
✉ info@artemdigital.com
🖥 www.artemdigital.com

Ascent Media - Wardour Street (IVCA) Film House, 142 Wardour Street, London, W1F 8DD, United Kingdom
☎ (020) 7878 0000/✆ (020) 7878 7800
✉ info@ascent-media.co.uk
🖥 www.ascent-media.co.uk

Ascent Media Todd-AO 13 Hawley Crescent, Camden, London, NW1 8NP, United Kingdom
☎ (020) 7284 7900/✆ (020) 7284 1018
🖥 www.ascent-media.co.uk

Ashdown Imaging Ltd Pippingford Manor, Pippingford Park, Nutley, Uckfield, East Sussex, TN22 3HW, United Kingdom
☎ (0800) 58747400
✉ info@ashdownimaging.co.uk
🖥 www.ashdownimaging.co.uk

Aura Studios Ltd 30 Devizes Road, Swindon, SN1 4BG, United Kingdom
☎ (01793) 420002
✉ studio@aurastudios.co.uk
🖥 www.aurastudios.co.uk

Baraka 11 Greek Street, London, W1D 4DJ, United Kingdom
☎ (020) 7734 2227/✆ (020) 7479 7810
✉ mikemorley@baraka.co.uk
🖥 www.baraka.co.uk

Barcud Derwen Cyf Cibyn Industrial Estate, Caernarfon, Gwynedd, LL55 2BD, United Kingdom
☎ (01286) 671671/✆ (01286) 684379
✉ barcud@barcudderwen.co.uk
🖥 www.barcudderwen.com

Barcud Derwen Ltd 74-78 Park Road, Whitchurch, Cardiff, CF14 7BR, United Kingdom
☎ (029) 2061 1515/✆ (029) 2052 1226
✉ enq@barcudderwen.com
🖥 www.barcudderwen.com

BBC Scotland (Glasgow) 40 Pacific Quay, Glasgow, G51 1BA, United Kingdom
☎ 0141-339 8844
✉ enquiries.scot@bbc.co.uk
🖥 www.bbc.co.uk/scotland

Black Diamond Films Ltd Bedford Chambers, The Piazza, London, WC2E 8HA, United Kingdom
☎ (020) 7240 4071/(07801) 438737 ✆ (020) 7836 6339
✉ jim@blackdiamond.co.uk
🖥 www.blackdiamond.co.uk

Blitz Interactive 100 Centennial Avenue, Elstree, Hertfordshire, WD6 3SA, United Kingdom
☎ (0870) 1621234/✆ (020) 8327 1111
✉ enquiries@blitzinteractive.co.uk
🖥 www.blitzinteractive.co.uk

Blitz Vision 7-8 Piccadilly Trading Estate, Giddings Road, Manchester, M1 2NP, United Kingdom
(0870) 1623300/ (0870) 1623333
man@blitzvision.com
www.blitzvision.com

Blue Post Production 58 Old Compton Street, London, W1D 4US, United Kingdom
(020) 7437 2626/ (020) 7439 2477
info@bluepp.co.uk
www.bluepp.co.uk

Bocek Production Cubuklu cad.agaclik mesire yeri, d+e burunbahce, beykoz, Istanbul, 34805,
00 9 02166801058
selma@bocekyapim.com.tr
www.bocekyapim.com.tr

Box 5th Floor, 121 Princess Street, Manchester, M1 7AD, United Kingdom
0161-228 2399/(07973) 344606 (08719) 002009
mike@the-box.co.uk
www.the-box.co.uk

Brandt Animation 11 D'Arblay Street, London, W1F 8DT, United Kingdom
(020) 7734 0196
finn@brandtanim.co.uk
www.brandtanim.co.uk

Broadcast Television Facilities Aucuba House, Lymm Road, Little Bollington, Altrincham, Cheshire, WA14 4SY, United Kingdom
0161-926 9808/ 0161-929 9000
info@broadcast-tv.co.uk
www.broadcast-tv.co.uk

Bucks Laboratories 714-715 Banbury Avenue, Slough, SL1 4LR, United Kingdom
(01753) 501501/ (01753) 691762
mail@bucks.co.uk
www.bucks.co.uk

Canongate Studios 9 Waters Close, Leith, Edinburgh, EH6 6RB, United Kingdom
0131-555 4455/ 0131-555 2021
al@canongate.com
www.canongate.com

Capital FX Ltd 20 Dering Street, London, W1S 1AJ, United Kingdom
(020) 7493 9998/ (020) 7493 9997
liz.clarke@capital-fx.co.uk
www.capital-fx.co.uk

Capital Studios Wandsworth Plain, London, SW18 1ET, United Kingdom
(020) 8877 1234/ (020) 8877 0234
info@capitalstudios.co.uk
www.capitalstudios.com

Carolan Productions The Coach House, adjacent Ealing Film Studios, Ealing Green, London, W5 5ER, United Kingdom
(020) 8566 1900/(07833) 917178 (020) 8566 1900
andrew@carolanproductions.com
www.carolanproductions.com

Catwalk Creations 63, March Court, Warwick Drive, London, SW15 6LE, United Kingdom
(07834) 470117
nicola@catwalkcreations.com
www.catwalkcreations.com

Centre for Media Arts & Performance Priory Street, Coventry, CV1 5FB, United Kingdom
(024) 7688 7462

Channel Television Ltd La Pouquelaye, St Helier, Jersey, JE1 3ZD, United Kingdom
(01534) 816816/ (01534) 816817
broadcast@channeltv.co.uk
www.channelonline.tv

Cheerful Scout P.L.C. 25-27 Riding House Street, London, W1W 7DU, United Kingdom
(020) 7291 0444/ (020) 7291 0445
info@cheerfulscout.com
www.cheerfulscout.com

Cine Wessex Ltd Unit 13, Winnall Valley Road, Winchester, Hampshire, SO23 0LD, United Kingdom
(01962) 865454/ (01962) 840004
info@cinewessex.co.uk
www.cinewessex.co.uk

Cineimage 7A Langley Street, Covent Garden, London, WC2H 9JA, United Kingdom
(020) 7240 6222/ (020) 7240 6242
info@cineimage.co.uk
www.cineimage.co.uk

Cinesite (Europe) Ltd Medius House, 2 Sheraton Street, London, W1F 8BH, United Kingdom
(020) 7973 4000/ (020) 7973 4040
filmfx@cinesite.co.uk
www.cinesite.com

Clear Cut Pictures 1 Springvale Terrace, London, W14 0AE, United Kingdom
(020) 7605 1700/ (020) 7603 6883
info@clearcutpictures.com
www.clearcutpictures.com

Clear Post Production 37 Dean Street, London, W1D 4PT, United Kingdom
(020) 7734 5557/ (020) 7494 0059
clear@clearpost.com
www.clear.ltd.uk

Clearcut Sound Studios Ltd 8-12 Broadwick Street, London, W1F 8HW, United Kingdom
(020) 7437 5225/ (020) 7734 1149
office@clearcutsound.com
www.clearcutsound.com

Component Broadcasting Facilities Ltd 6 Springwell Court, Holbeck Lane, Leeds, LS12 1AL, United Kingdom
0113-242 5460/ 0113-244 9094
info@cbfmedia.tv
www.cbfmedia.tv

Component Graphics (IVCA) 2nd Flo, 5 Berners Mews, London, W1T 3AJ, United Kingdom
(020) 7631 4477/ (020) 7436 9883
mike@component.co.uk
www.component.co.uk

Concrete 34-35 Dean Street, London, W1D 4PR, United Kingdom
(020) 7439 9080/ (020) 7434 0714
info@concretepost.co.uk
www.concretepost.co.uk

Connections The Meadlands, 11 Oakleigh Road, Hatch End, Pinner, Middlesex, HA5 4HB, United Kingdom
(020) 8420 1444/(07831) 305518 (020) 8428 5836
mail@connectionsuk.com
www.connectionsuk.com

Constantin von Seld Rue de l'Olivier, Marseille, Bouches du Rhone, 13005,
4.91511E+12
mail@here2rock.com
www.here2rock.com

Continuum St. Edmunds House, Margaret Street, York, YO10 4UX, United Kingdom
(01904) 527700/ (01904) 527701
rbriggs@continuum-group.com
www.continuum-group.com

Creative Edge Design & Advertising 1st Floor Donald Hendry Building, Auchincruive, Ayr, KA6 5HW, United Kingdom
(01292) 521404/ (01292) 521693
paul@cedge.co.uk
www.cedge.co.uk

Creative FX 10 Bocking End, Braintree, Essex, CM7 9AA, United Kingdom
(01376) 323461/(07815) 430439
creative.fx@ntlworld.com

Creative Staging Ltd The Creative Studio, Church Path, Chiswick, London, W4 5BJ, United Kingdom
(020) 8994 3636/ (020) 8994 3748
info@creativestaging.co.uk
www.creativestaging.co.uk

Crow TV Ltd (IVCA) Shepherds Building East, Richmond Way, Shepherds Bush, London, W14 0DQ, United Kingdom
(0870) 8501008/ (0207) 603 5846
info@crowtv.com
www.crowtv.com

CTS Studios Ltd Suite 1A, Lansdowne House, Lansdowne Road, London, W11 3LP, United Kingdom
(020) 8846 9444/ (020) 7792 8904
info@cts-lansdowne.co.uk
www.cts-lansdowne.co.uk

Cut & Run Ltd (APPC) Cinema House, 93 Wardour Street, London, W1F 0UD, United Kingdom
(020) 7432 9696/ (020) 7432 9697
simon@cutandrun.tv
www.cutandrun.tv

Cutting Edge (APPC) 44 Berwick Street, London, W1F 8SE, United Kingdom
(020) 7287 0080/ (020) 7287 0090
cuttingedge@clara.co.uk

D G P Portland House, 12-13 Greek Street, London, W1D 4DL, United Kingdom
(020) 7734 4501/ (020) 7734 7034
mail@dgpsoho.co.uk
www.dgpsoho.co.uk

D V A Ltd (IVCA) 7 Campbell Court, Bramley, Tadley, Hampshire, RG26 5EG, United Kingdom
(01256) 882032/ (01256) 882024
barrieg@dva.com
www.dvafacilities.co.uk

Dave Edwards GFX
London, United Kingdom
(07855) 495135
info@daveedwards.co.uk
www.daveedwards.co.uk

Daydream Linton House, 164-180 Union Street, London, SE1 0LH,
+44 (0) 20 7096 1471/+44 (0) 20 7117 1636
ralph@daydream.co.uk
www.daydream.co.uk

De Lane Lea Ltd 75 Dean Street, London, W1D 3PU, United Kingdom
(020) 7432 3800/ (020) 7432 3838
solutions@delanelea.com
www.delanelea.com

Definitely Red 204-205 Scott House, Gibb Street, Birmingham, B9 4AA, United Kingdom
(0870) 9777997
talk@definitelyred.com
www.definitelyred.com

Definitive Special Projects Ltd
Stevenage, Hertfordshire, SG2 7SG, United Kingdom
(01438) 869005/ (01438) 869006
steve@laserlightshows.co.uk
www.laserlightshows.co.uk

Deluxe Laboratories Ltd North Orbital Road, Denham, Uxbridge, Middlesex, UB9 5HQ, United Kingdom
(01895) 832323/ (01895) 832446
www.bydeluxe.com

Digiffects 2nd Floor, 127 Charing Cross Road, London, WC2H 0QY, United Kingdom
(020) 7412 9111/ (020) 7413 0061
enquiries@musichouse.co.uk
www.kpmmusichouse.com

Digital Film Lab London Ltd 52 St. John Street, London, EC1M 4HF, United Kingdom
(020) 7907 0928/ (020) 7251 8430
lon@digitalfilmlab.com
www.digitalfilmlab.com

Dragonfly Media 3 Berkeley Crescent, Clifton, Bristol, Avon, BS8 1HA,
0845 6520 888/ 0845 6520 808
jon@dragonfly-media.co.uk
www.dragonfly-media.co.uk

Dubmaster Studios 62 Ashdell Road, Alton, Hampshire, GU34 2TA, United Kingdom
(01420) 82822
info@dubmaster.com
www.dubmaster.com

E V T Magnetic Industries Havenhurst, 2 Pashley Road, Wadhurst, East Sussex, TN5 7HE, United Kingdom
(01580) 200528
magevt@amserve.com

E-kit.co.uk Field Cottage, Main Street, Goadby Marwood, Melton Mowbray, Leicestershire, LE14 4LN, United Kingdom
(01664) 464713
edward@e-kit.co.uk
www.e-kit.co.uk

Eddy French Associates 90 Dean Street, London, W1D 3SX, United Kingdom
(020) 7734 3313/ (020) 7494 1357
efrench@dircon.co.uk

Edit 123 123 Blythswood Street, Glasgow, G2 4EN, United Kingdom
0141-248 3123/ 0141-248 3423
www.edit123.co.uk

Edit Video Ltd Odley House, 9 Margret Street, London, W1W 8RH, United Kingdom
(020) 7637 2288/ (020) 7637 2299
mail@editvideo.co.uk
www.editvideo.co.uk

Editworks 77-79 Charlotte Street, London, W1T 4PW, United Kingdom
(020) 7079 2900/ (020) 7079 2901
edit@editworks.co.uk
www.editworks.co.uk

Editz Ltd 2nd Floor, Astley House, Quay Street, Manchester, M3 4AE, United Kingdom
0161-906 4900/ 0161-906 4901
sales@editz.co.uk
www.editz.co.uk

Elements Special Effects Ltd Unit P04, Acton Business Centre, London, NW10 6TD, United Kingdom
(020) 8961 4244/(07968) 613030 (020) 8961 4255
info@elementsfx.co.uk
www.elementsfx.co.uk

Estelle Baylis
London, United Kingdom
(07958) 562239
estellebaylis@homechoice.co.uk
www.estellebaylis.homechoice.co.uk

Evolutions (NATS) 10 Soho Square, London, W1D 3NT, United Kingdom
(020) 7287 9900/ (020) 7637 1942
info@evolutions.tv
www.evolutions.tv

Factory Group 54-55 Margaret Street, London, W1W 8SH, United Kingdom
(020) 7580 5810/ (020) 7582 5810
info@factory.uk.com
www.factory.uk.com

Film Editors (APPC) 6-10 Lexington Street, London, W1F 3HS, United Kingdom
(020) 7439 8655/ (020) 7437 0409
postroom@thefilmeditors.com
www.thefilmeditors.com

Films@59 Ltd 59 Cotham Hill, Bristol, BS6 6JR, United Kingdom
0117-906 4300/ 0117-923 7003
info@filmsat59.com
www.filmsat59.com

Fine Point Broadcast Ltd Hill House, Furze Hill, Kingswood, Surrey, KT20 6EZ, United Kingdom
(0800) 9702020/ (0800) 9702030
hire@finepoint.co.uk
www.finepoint.co.uk

Finishing Post Creative Ltd 10, Giltway, Giltbrook, Nottingham, NG16 2GN, United Kingdom
0115-945 8800/ 0115-945 8801
info@finishing-post.co.uk
www.finishing-post.co.uk

Finishing Post Productions Ltd Denham Media Park, North Orbital Road, Denham, Middlesex, UB9 5HQ, United Kingdom
(01895) 834490/ (01895) 832332
info@finishing-post.com

Fliptop Films 22 Cheal Close, Brighton, BN43 5RQ, United Kingdom
(07973) 428510
charlie@fliptopfilms.com
www.fliptopfilms.com

Flix Facilities 8 Albany Road, Chorlton-cum-Hardy, Manchester, M21 0AW, United Kingdom
0161-882 2525/ 0161-882 2534
mail@flixfacilities.com
www.flixfacilities.com

Frameline County House, 33-34 Rathbone Place, London, W1T 1JN, United Kingdom
(020) 7636 1303/ (020) 7436 8878
email@frameline.plus.com
www.framelineproductions.com

Framestore CFC 9 Noel Street, London, W1F 8GH, United Kingdom
(020) 7208 2600/ (020) 7208 2626
info@framestore-cfc.com
www.framestore-cfc.com

Frontier Post 67 Wells Street, London, W1T 3PZ, United Kingdom
(020) 7291 9191/ (020) 7291 9199
info@frontierpost.co.uk
www.frontierpost.co.uk

Gary Scott Avid Editor 5/1 Blackfriars Street, Edinburgh, EH1 1NB, United Kingdom
0131-557 4570/(07976) 640994
grassy@f2s.com
www.castleapartment.com

Gemini Audio Hammer House, 117 Wardour Street, London, W1F 0UN, United Kingdom
(020) 7734 8962/ (020) 7439 3122
nigel@geminiaudio.co.uk
www.geminiaudio.co.uk

Gizmo Animation Ltd 56 St. Johns Road, Slough, SL2 5EZ, United Kingdom
(01753) 536578
lee@gizmoanimation.co.uk
www.gizmoanimation.co.uk

Glassworks 33-34 Great Pulteney Street, London, W1F 9NP, United Kingdom
(020) 7434 1182/ (020) 7434 1183
reception@glassworks.co.uk
www.glassworks.co.uk

Goldcrest Post Production Facilities Ltd 1 Lexington Street, Soho, London, W1F 9AF, United Kingdom
(020) 7437 7972/ (020) 7437 5402
bookings@goldcrestpost.co.uk
www.goldcrest.co.uk

Golden Square Post Production 11 Golden Square, London, W1F 9JB, United Kingdom
(020) 7300 3555/ (020) 7494 3288
info@goldensq.com
www.goldensq.com

Graham Young Longmeadow Thatch, Spring Lane, Cold Ash, Thatcham, Berkshire, RG18 9PL, United Kingdom
(01635) 861732/(07990) 516205
gygraphics@aol.com

Grassy Knoll 5/1 Blackfriars Street, Edinburgh, EH1 1NB, United Kingdom
0131-557 4570
grassy@f2s.com

Griffin Video Communications 53 Regent Place, Birmingham, B1 3NJ, United Kingdom
0121-212 0044/ 0121-212 2114
info@askgriffin.co.uk
www.askgriffin.co.uk

Happy Hour Productions Ltd The Picture House, 4 Lower Park Road, Bristol, BS1 5BJ, United Kingdom
0117-929 9797/ 0117-923 0862
info@hhour.co.uk
www.happyhourproductions.co.uk

Helicopter Grafix Ltd Evelyn House, 142 -144 New Cavendish Street, London, W1W 6YF, United Kingdom
(020) 7612 2757/(07814) 362714 (020) 7612 2789
info@missioncontrol-fx.co.uk
www.helicoptergrafix.com

Hobson's Actors 62 Chiswick High Road, London, W4 1SY, United Kingdom
(020) 8995 3628/ (020) 8996 5350
actors@hobsons-international.com
www.hobsons-international.com

Hobson's Studio 62 Chiswick High Road, London, W4 1SY, United Kingdom
(020) 8995 3628/ (020) 8996 5350
studio@hobsons-international.com
www.hobsons-international.com

Hothouse IWG 10 St Leonards Road, Park Royal, London, NW10 6SY, United Kingdom
(020) 8961 3666/(07801) 612061 (020) 8961 3777
info@hothousefx.co.uk
www.hothousefx.co.uk

Hullabaloo Studios Ltd 8 Albany Road, Chorlton-cum-Hardy, Manchester, M21 0AW, United Kingdom
0161-882 0007/ 0161-882 0774
admin@hullabaloo-studios.com
www.hullabaloo-studios.com

Ian J. Richards
Staines, United Kingdom
(07710) 743716
ianjrichards@mac.com
www.ianjrichards.com

IBF (International Broadcast Facilities) 13-15 Monmouth Street, London, WC2H 9DA, United Kingdom
(020) 7497 1515/ (020) 7379 8562
admin@ibf.co.uk
www.ibf.co.uk

Imagine 4th Floor, Adamson House, 65 Westgate Road, Newcastle upon Tyne, NE1 1SG, United Kingdom
0191-230 0488/ 0191-230 0485
info@imagine-nonlinear.co.uk
www.imagine-nonlinear.co.uk

Inhouse Post Production Building 14, Shepperton Studios, Studios Road, Shepperton, Middlesex, TW17 0QD, United Kingdom
(01932) 592455/(07879) 426869
martin@ihpp.co.uk
www.ihpp.co.uk

Jelly Fish Pictures 47 Poland Street, London, W1F 7NB, United Kingdom
(020) 7287 6024/ (020) 7287 0373
info@jellyfishpictures.co.uk
www.jellyfishpictures.co.uk

JR7 21 Broadhaven, Cardiff, CF11 8DA, United Kingdom
(07050) 076050/ (029) 2030 2792
enquiries@jr7.co.uk
www.jr7.co.uk

justaperfectday 25a Swains Lane, Highgate, London, N6 6QX, United Kingdom
(07903) 666104
marieta@justaperfectday.com
www.justaperfectday.com

KamPra Productions 2-10 Calypso Crescent, London, SE15 6GE, United Kingdom
(020) 7708 1354
kamal@kampra.com
www.kampra.com

Lansdowne Recording Studios
London, W6 6QA, United Kingdom
(020) 8846 9444/ (056) 0115 5009
info@cts-lansdowne.co.uk
www.cts-lansdowne.co.uk

Lip Sync Post Screen House, 123 Wardour Street, London, W1F 0UW, United Kingdom
(020) 7534 9123/ (020) 7534 9124
lisa@lipsyncpost.co.uk
www.lipsyncpost.co.uk

Locomotion 1-8 Bateman's Buildings, South Soho Square, London, W1D 3EN, United Kingdom
(020) 7304 4403/ (020) 7304 4400
knowledge@locomotion.co.uk
www.locomotion.co.uk

Lola 14-16 Great Portland Street, London, W1W 8QW, United Kingdom
(020) 7907 7878/ (020) 7907 7879
reception@lola-post.com
www.lola-post.com

Longneck Afgan Road 27, Battersea, London, SW11 2QD,
7506018062
vlad@longneck.ro
www.longneck.ro

M 2 Television Soho Ingestre Court, Ingestre Place, London, W1F 0JL, United Kingdom
(020) 7343 6543/ (020) 7343 6555
info@m2tv.com
www.m2tv.com

M G B Facilities Ltd Sheepscar Court, Leeds, LS7 2BB, United Kingdom
0113-243 6868/ 0113-243 8886
contact@mgbtv.co.uk
www.mgbtv.co.uk

M W N C I 20 Cathedral Road, Cardiff, CF11 9LJ, United Kingdom
(029) 2039 9800/ (029) 2039 9700
mail@mwnci.tv
www.mwnci.tv

Mac 7 Ltd 105 Great Portland Street, London, W1W 6QF, United Kingdom
(020) 7636 7575/ (020) 7291 4099
neil@mac7.tv
www.mac7.tv

Maidstone Studios Vinters Park, Maidstone, Kent, ME14 5NZ, United Kingdom
(01622) 691111/ (01622) 684411
info@maidstonestudios.com
www.maidstonestudios.com

Marc Cass Primrose House, Herne Poplar Farm, Toddington, Dunstable, Bedfordshire, LU5 6HG, United Kingdom
(07860) 776978
info@marccass.com
www.marccass.com

Mariana FX 114 Erskine Road, London, E17 6SA, United Kingdom
(020) 8509 0832/(07957) 989315
marianafx@hotmail.com

Masterpiece Mastering Unit 14, The Talina Centre, Bagleys Lane, London, SW6 2BW, United Kingdom
(020) 7731 5758/ (020) 7384 1750
leena.bahtti@masterpiecelondon.com
www.masterpiecelondon.com

Maxim Young Editing
London, United Kingdom
(07710) 418546
post@maximyoung.co.uk
www.maximyoung.co.uk

Merlin Television Ltd The Wharf, Schooner Way, Cardiff, CF10 4EU, United Kingdom
(029) 2030 4050/ (029) 2030 4051
general@merlin-digital.co.uk
www.merlin-digital.co.uk

Metro Broadcast 5-7 Great Chapel Street, London, W1F 8FF, United Kingdom
(020) 7434 7700/ (020) 7434 7701
info@metrobroadcast.com
www.metrobroadcast.com

Metropolis Video 34-35 Dean Street, London, W1D 4PR, United Kingdom
(020) 7432 4810/ (020) 7255 2529
mail@metropolispost.co.uk
www.metropolispost.co.uk

Michael Johns (GBFE) 2 Grove Road, Amersham, Buckinghamshire, HP6 6ND, United Kingdom
(01494) 728892/(07801) 657062 (01494) 728892
michaeleditor@btinternet.com

Mighty Media Unit M, Bourne End Business Park, Bourne End, Buckinghamshire, SL8 5AS, United Kingdom
(01628) 522002/ (01628) 526530
info@mightymedia.co.uk
www.mightymedia.co.uk

Mike Liddall West London Film Office, 5th Floor Percival House, 14-16 Uxbridge Road, London, W5 2HL, United Kingdom
(020) 8825 7575/ (020) 8825 7667
liddallm@ealing.gov.uk
www.westlondonfilmoffice.co.uk

Mindorchard Ltd 11 Jew Street, Brighton, BN1 1UT, United Kingdom
(08700) 847441/ (08702) 862605
info@mindorchard.com
www.mindorchard.com

Mokko Blue 21 Arncott Hall, 13 Poole Road, Bournemouth, BH2 5QR, United Kingdom
01202 269 257/ 01202 269 257
info@mokko-blue.com
www.mokko-blue.com

Molinare Ltd 34 Fouberts Place, London, W1F 7PX, United Kingdom
(020) 7478 7200/ (020) 7734 6813
kateg@molinare.co.uk
www.molinare.co.uk

movingarts.tv Ltd 13-14 Barley Shots Business Park, London, W10 5YG, United Kingdom
(07973) 381283
craig@movingarts.tv
www.movingarts.tv

Murricane & Murricane Kensington House, 227 Sauchiehall Street, Glasgow, G2 3EX, United Kingdom
0141-332 7282/ 0141-332 6517
dawn@murricanes.co.uk
www.murricanes.co.uk

Music 4 Ltd 41/42 Berners Street, London, W1T 3NB, United Kingdom
(020) 7016 2000/ (020) 7016 2001
studios@music4.com
www.music4.com

N V Films Ltd 75-77 Margaret Street, London, W1W 8SY, United Kingdom
(020) 7323 0321
info@nvfilms.tv
www.nvfilms.tv

Nasdesigns Romford, Essex, United Kingdom
(07900) 612864
nasibamoola@gmail.com

New Forest Post Production Powells Fm, Salisbury Rd, Plaitford, Romsey, Hampshire, SO51 6EE, United Kingdom
(01794) 324147/(07747) 611026
info@nfpp.com
www.nfpp.com

Nice Biscuits 177 Wardour Street, London, W1F 8WX, United Kingdom
(020) 7855 3619/ (020) 7855 3693
lisa@nicebiscuits.co.uk
www.nicebiscuits.co.uk

Nigel G. Heath c/o Hackenbacker Audio Post Production, 10 Bateman Street, London, W1D 4AQ, United Kingdom
(020) 7734 1324/ (020) 7439 1236
hackenbacker@btconnect.com
www.hackenbacker.com

NWH Editing Ltd (APPC) 81 Berwick Street, London, W1F 8TW, United Kingdom
(020) 7734 2744/ (020) 7287 5285
mail@nwhediting.com
www.nwhediting.com

Oakslade Studios Oakslade Studios, Station Road, Hatton, Warwick, CV35 7LH, United Kingdom
(01926) 844000/ (01926) 844045
sales@oakslade.com
www.oakslade.com

Oasis Television Ltd (IVCA) 6-7 Great Pulteney Street, London, W1F 9NA, United Kingdom
(020) 7434 4133/ (020) 7494 2843
sales@oasistv.co.uk
www.oasistv.co.uk

oddpixel.com Unit 13, 58 Dalston Lane, London, E8 2NG, United Kingdom
(07891) 777374
info@oddpixel.com
www.oddpixel.com

Off The Planet Productions Okehampton, Devon, EX20 4ZQ, United Kingdom
(01837) 658805/ (0870) 4322040
info@offtheplanet.tv
www.offtheplanet.tv

Opus Productions Ltd 9A Coverdale Road, Sheperds Bush, London, W12 8JJ, United Kingdom
(020) 8743 3910/ (020) 8749 4537
info@opusproductions.com
www.opusproductions.com

Original Image Digital Media 21-25 St Annes Court, London, W1F 0BJ, United Kingdom
(020) 7494 0777/ (020) 7494 0309
info@originalimage.co.uk
www.originalimage.co.uk

Outpost Facilities Pinewood Studios, Pinewood Road, Iver Heath, Iver, Buckinghamshire, SL0 0NH, United Kingdom
(01753) 630770/ (01753) 630771
jo@outpostfacilities.co.uk
www.outpostfacilities.co.uk

Outsource Media 13 North Park Road, Harrogate, North Yorkshire, HG1 5PD, United Kingdom
(0800) 1958653
info@omuk.com
www.omuk.com

P R G Europe Unit 3, Beddington Cross, Beddington Farm Road, Croydon, CR0 4XH, United Kingdom
(020) 8665 8500/ (020) 8664 8819
croydoninfo@prgeurope.com
www.prgeurope.com

Pepper 3 Slingsby Place, Long Acre, London, WC2E 9AB, United Kingdom
(020) 7836 1188/ (020) 7490 4238
mailus@pepperpost.tv
www.pepperpost.tv

Periscope 11 St. James Avenue West, Stanford-le-Hope, Essex, SS17 7BB, United Kingdom
(0845) 6446681
info@periscope.co.uk
www.periscope.co.uk

Phil Turner Productions 39 Nero Court, Justin Close, Brentford, Middlesex, TW8 8QB, United Kingdom
(07956) 203559
phil@philturnerproductions.com
www.philturnerproductions.com

Phoenix Video Ltd Global House, Denham Media Park, Denham, Uxbridge, Middlesex, UB9 5HL, United Kingdom
(01895) 837000
terry@phoenix-video.co.uk
www.phoenix-video.co.uk

Pinewood Studios (Part of the Pinewood Group), Pinewood Road, Iver Heath, Buckinghamshire, SL0 0NH, United Kingdom
(01753) 651700/ (01753) 656844
info@pinewoodgroup.com
www.pinewoodgroup.com

Pinkhouse 33 West Park, Clifton, Bristol, BS8 2LX, United Kingdom
0117-923 7087/ 0117-923 7090
bridget@pinkhousepp.com
www.pinkhousepp.com

Piranha Graphics Ltd Studio 310, Mill Studio Business Centre, Ware, Hertfordshire, SG12 9PY, United Kingdom
(01920) 444240/(07836) 202329
davidc@piranhasys.co.uk
www.piranhasys.co.uk

Pixel Perfect The White House, Copse Road, Haslemere, Surrey, GU27 3QQ, United Kingdom
(01428) 643500/ (0871) 7502375
jason@pixelperfect.co.uk
www.pixelperfect.co.uk

Prime Focus London 37 Dean Street London W1D 4PT, United Kingdom
(020) 7565 1000
info@primefocusworld.com
www.primefocusworld.com

Pyramid TV Ltd 36 Cardiff Road, Llandaff, Cardiff, CF5 2DR, United Kingdom
(029) 2057 6888/ (029) 2057 5777
info@pyramidtv.co.uk
www.pyramidtv.co.uk

Quantel Ltd Turnpike Road, Newbury, Berkshire, RG14 2NX, United Kingdom
(01635) 48222/ (01635) 815815
quantel@quantel.com
www.quantel.com

Rainbow Post Production 16 Ingestre Place, London, W1F 0JJ, United Kingdom
(020) 7434 4566/ (020) 7439 4565
client@rainbowpost.com
www.rainbowpost.com

Reality 3D 17 St Clements Road, Parkstone, Poole, Dorset, BH15 3PB, United Kingdom
(07973) 534171
Steve@reality3d.co.uk
www.reality3d.co.uk

Red @ Smoke and Mirrors 57-59 Beak Street, London, W1F 9SJ, United Kingdom
(020) 7468 1000/ (020) 7468 1001
production-lon@smoke-mirrors.co.uk
www.smoke-mirrors.co.uk

Red Bug Productions The Old School House, Worldham Hill, East Worldham, Alton, Hampshire, GU34 3AT, United Kingdom
(01420) 590420/ (01420) 590426
nicky@redbug.co.uk
www.redbug.tv

Red Square Editing (APPC) 4th Floor, Circus House, 21 Great Titchfield Street, London, W1W 8BA, United Kingdom
(020) 7580 1880/ (020) 7580 1890
info@redsquare.tv
www.redsquare.tv

Redwood Studios Ltd 20 Great Chapel Street, London, W1F 8FW, United Kingdom
(020) 7287 3799
andrestudios@yahoo.co.uk
www.sound-design.net

Reelsound Shepperton Studios, Studios Road, Shepperton, Middlesex, TW17 0QD, United Kingdom
(01932) 592209/ (01932) 592290
max@reelsound.com
www.reelsound.com

Resolution 26 D'Arblay Street, London, W1F 8EL, United Kingdom
(020) 7437 1336/ (020) 7734 5186
info@resolution.tv
www.resolution.tv

Revolution Post 11 Utopia Village, 7 Chalcot Road, London, NW1 8LH, United Kingdom
(020) 7586 1271/ (020) 7586 4488
torin@revolutionpost.tv
www.revolutionpost.com

Richard Klein 61 Cleveden Drive, Glasgow, G12 0NX, United Kingdom
0141-337 2203
rkderj@yahoo.com
www.rkderj.com

Ripe Design (UK) Ltd Clarence House, 48 Black Bull Street, Leeds, LS10 1HW, United Kingdom
0113-204 2800/ 0113-204 2801
info@ripe.co.uk
www.ripe.co.uk

Rob Harris Productions The Studio, 310 King Street, Hammersmith, London, W6 0RR, United Kingdom
(020) 8748 2430/(07860) 798450
rob@robharrisproductions.com
www.robharrisproductions.com

Rushes Post Production Ltd (APPC) 66 Old Compton Street, London, W1D 4UH, United Kingdom
(020) 7437 8676/ (020) 7734 2519
info@rushes.co.uk
www.rushes.co.uk

Sanctuary Post 53 Frith Street, London, W1D 4SN, United Kingdom
℡ (020) 7734 4480/ (020) 7439 7394
✉ info@thesanctuary.tv
🖳 www.thesanctuary.tv

Sandstorm 12 Oxford Road, Newbury, Berkshire, RG14 1PA, United Kingdom
℡ (020) 7379 5432
✉ tom@sandstormmedia.co.uk
🖳 www.sandstormmedia.co.uk

Saville Group Ltd Millfield Lane, Nether Poppleton, York, YO26 6PQ, United Kingdom
℡ (01904) 782782/ (01904) 782700
✉ headoffice@saville.co.uk
🖳 www.saville.co.uk

Scootman Music & Sound Design 2021 21st Avenue South, Suite C-100, Nashville, 37212, United States of America
℡ 615 319 9556/615 319 9556 615 777 2122
✉ scott@scootmanmusic.com
🖳 www.scootmanmusic.com

Scopitone Ltd Tower Bridge Business Complex, Block J Suite 212, 100 Clements Road, London, SE16 4DG, United Kingdom
℡ (020) 7193 6528
✉ info@scopitone.co.uk
🖳 www.scopitone.co.uk

Scramble 8 Portland Mews, London, W1F 8JH, United Kingdom
℡ (020) 7479 4400/ (020) 7479 4404
✉ post@scramble.co.uk
🖳 www.scramble.co.uk

Screen Ventures (PACT) 49 Goodge Street, London, W1T 1TE, United Kingdom
℡ (020) 7580 7448/ (020) 7631 1265
✉ info@screenventures.com
🖳 www.screenventures.com

Shepperton Post Production Building 14, Shepperton Studios, Shepperton, Middlesex, TW17 0QD, United Kingdom
℡ (01932) 592124/ (01932) 592134
✉ mail@sheppertonpostproduction.com
🖳 www.sheppertonpostproduction.com

Shepperton Studios (Part of the Pinewood Group), Pinewood Road, Iver Heath, Iver, Buckinghamshire, SL0 0NH, United Kingdom
℡ (01932) 562611/ (01932) 568989
✉ info@pinewoodgroup.com
🖳 www.pinewoodshepperton.com

Silk Sound Ltd 13 Berwick Street, London, W1F 0PW, United Kingdom
℡ (020) 7434 3461/ (020) 7494 1748
✉ bookings@silk.co.uk
🖳 www.silk.co.uk

Silverglade Associates Ltd 11A Enterprise House, 1-2 Hatfields, London, SE1 9PG, United Kingdom
℡ (020) 7827 9510/ (020) 7827 9511
✉ info@silverglade.com
🖳 www.silverglade.com

Smart Pixels Ltd 38 Given Wilson Walk, Plaistow, London, E13 0EB, United Kingdom
℡ (07956) 804611
✉ rekha@smartpixels.co.uk
🖳 www.smartpixels.co.uk

Smoke & Mirrors Production 57-59 Beak Street, London, W1F 9SJ, United Kingdom
℡ (020) 7468 1000/ (020) 7468 1001
✉ producers@smoke-mirrors.co.uk
🖳 www.smoke-mirrors.com

Soho Images, 8-14 Meard Street, London, W1F 0EQ, United Kingdom
℡ (020) 7437 0831/ (020) 7734 9471
✉ info@sohoimages.com
🖳 www.sohoimages.com

Sound Discs CD & DVD Ltd Sunnydale (Opp. Rookery Farm), North Bersted Street, North Bersted, Bognor Regis, West Sussex, PO22 9AH, United Kingdom
℡ (0845) 37070080/(07721) 624868
✉ info@sound-discs.co.uk
🖳 www.sound-discs.co.uk

Sparkle Media Ltd 85-89 Duke Street, Liverpool, L1 5AP, United Kingdom
℡ (0845) 8381849/ (0870) 1390768
✉ alison@sparklemedia.co.uk
🖳 www.sparklemedia.co.uk

Sparx 34 rue du Sentier, Paris, 75002, France
℡ 00 33 1 44 34 29 29/ 00 33 1 55 73 17 07
✉ contact@sparx.com
🖳 www.sparx.com

Station Ltd 46 Bloomsbury Street, London, WC1B 3QJ, United Kingdom
℡ (020) 7292 9595/ (020) 7292 9596
✉ info@the-station.com
🖳 www.the-station.com

Stealth Creative 29 Holden Park Road, Tunbridge Wells, Kent, TN4 0ER, United Kingdom
℡ (01892) 529443/ (01892) 618787
✉ stealthcreative@mac.com

Stevie FX 81 Oxford Street, London, W1D 2EU, United Kingdom
℡ (020) 7851 3575
✉ info@steviefx.com
🖳 www.steviefx.com

Storm Creation Ltd Suite 1, 20 Old Steine, Brighton, BN1 1EL, United Kingdom
℡ (01273) 605880/ (01273) 605881
✉ info@storm-creation.co.uk
🖳 www.storm-creation.co.uk

Stream UK Media Services Ltd Studio 522, 53-79 Highgate Road, London, NW5 1TL, United Kingdom
℡ (020) 7387 6090/ (020) 7419 1819
✉ jessica@streamuk.com
🖳 www.streamuk.com

STV (North) Ltd Craigshaw Business Park, Craigshaw Road, West Tullos Industrial Estate, Aberdeen, AB12 3QH, United Kingdom
℡ (01224) 848848/ (01224) 848800
✉ northtonight@stv.tv
🖳 www.stv.tv

Sue Moles Editing Ltd 1 Marlborough Court, London, W1F 7EE, United Kingdom
℡ (020) 7494 3383/ (020) 7287 1952
✉ info@suemoles.com
🖳 www.suemoles.com

T M C Ltd Hillam Road, Bradford, West Yorkshire, BD2 1QN, United Kingdom
℡ (01274) 370966/ (01274) 308706
✉ sales@tmc.ltd.uk
🖳 www.tmc.ltd.uk

T S I Broadcast Ltd 7 Grape Street, London, WC2H 8DW, United Kingdom
℡ (020) 7419 1400
✉ info@tsibroadcast.com
🖳 www.tsibroadcast.com

T V M S Scotland Ltd 3rd Floor, 420 Sauchiehall Street, Glasgow, G2 3JD, United Kingdom
℡ 0141-331 1993/(07710) 121153 0141-332 9040
✉ mail@tvms.wanadoo.co.uk
🖳 www.tvms.tv

Tag 3D & DS 57-59 Beak Street, London, W1F 9SJ, United Kingdom
℡ (020) 7468 1000/(07957) 422665 (020) 7468 1001
✉ amandad@smoke-mirrors.co.uk
🖳 www.smoke-mirrors.com

Tele-An Productions Ltd 1st Floor, 12-14 Denman St, London, W1D 7HJ, United Kingdom
℡ (020) 7440 3720/ (020) 7440 3721
✉ dean@tele-an.co.uk

Television Set Group (FOCAL, IVCA) 22 Newman St, London, W1T 1PH, United Kingdom
℡ (020) 7637 3322/ (020) 7637 1011
✉ info@tvsetgroup.co.uk
🖳 www.tvset.biz

Thameside UK Terminal House, Station Approach, Shepperton, Middlesex, TW17 8AS, United Kingdom
℡ (01932) 240204/ (01932) 240206
✉ sales@thameside.tv
🖳 www.thameside.tv

The Allottment Downfields Villa, 1D Downfields Road, Bristol, BS8 2TG, United Kingdom
℡ (07900) 690906/ 0117-937 3003
✉ laurie@the-allottment.com
🖳 www.the-allottment.com

The Bridge Ltd 55 Great Marlborough Street, London, W1F 7JX, United Kingdom
℡ (020) 7434 9861/ (020) 7494 4658
✉ bookings@thebridge.co.uk
🖳 www.thebridge.co.uk

The Byte Sized Image Flat 7, Carlton Court, 277-279 Nether Street, London, N3 1PD, United Kingdom
℡ (07766) 750275/ (020) 8349 9388
✉ bvallins@alteredimages.demon.co.uk
🖳 www.thebytesizedimage

The Club 35 Bedfordbury, Covent Garden, London, WC2N 4DU, United Kingdom
℡ (020) 7759 7100/ (020) 7379 5210
✉ info@frontline-tv.com

The Facility Ltd 62 Dean Street, London, W1D 4QF, United Kingdom
℡ (020) 7734 9193/ (020) 7434 2786
✉ info@thefacility.tv
🖳 www.thefacility.tv

The Farm 13 Soho Square, London, W1D 3QF, United Kingdom
℡ (020) 7437 6677/ (020) 7437 4466
✉ info@farmgroup.tv
🖳 www.farmgroup.tv

The London Studios Upper Ground, London, SE1 9LT, United Kingdom
℡ (020) 7737 8888/ (020) 7928 8405
✉ sales@londonstudios.co.uk
🖳 www.londonstudios.co.uk

The Machine Room Ltd (FOCAL) 54-58 Wardour Street, London, W1D 4JQ, United Kingdom
℡ (020) 7734 3433/ (020) 7287 3773
✉ info@themachineroom.co.uk
🖳 www.themachineroom.co.uk

The Mill 40-41 Great Marlborough Street, London, W1F 7JQ, United Kingdom
℡ (020) 7287 4041/ (020) 7287 8393
✉ mproducers@the-mill.com
🖳 www.the-mill.com

The Moving Picture Company (MPC) 127 Wardour Street, London, W1F 0NL, United Kingdom
℡ (020) 7434 3100/ (020) 7287 5187
✉ bookings@moving-picture.com
🖳 www.moving-picture.com

The Post Factory 7th Floor, Newcombe House, 43-45 Notting Hill Gate, London, W11 3LQ, United Kingdom
℡ (020) 7183 1600/ 2077278509
✉ info@postfactory.co.uk
🖳 www.postfactory.co.uk

The Quarry 26-28 Brewer Street, London, W1F 0SP, United Kingdom
℡ (020) 7437 4961/ (020) 7437 1491
✉ info@the-quarry.co.uk
🖳 www.the-quarry.co.uk

The Sound Co. Ltd 23 Gosfield Street, Fitzrovia, London, W1W 6HG, United Kingdom
℡ (020) 7580 5880/ (020) 7580 6454
✉ admin@sound.co.uk
🖳 www.sound.co.uk

The Sound House Post Production 10th Floor, Astley House, Quay Street, Manchester, M3 4AE, United Kingdom
℡ 0161-832 7299/ 0161-832 7266
✉ mail@thesoundhouse.tv
🖳 www.thesoundhouse.tv

The Sound House Post Production Ltd 10th Astley House, 23 Quay Street, Manchester, M3 4AE, United Kingdom
℡ 0161-832 7299/ 0161-832 7266
✉ suekeane@thesoundhouse.tv
🖳 www.thesoundhouse.tv

The Soundhouse Ltd Unit 11, Goldhawk Industrial Estate, Vinery Way, off Brackenbury Road, London, W6 0BA, United Kingdom
℡ (020) 8743 2677/ (020) 8740 9122
✉ thesoundhouse@btconnect.com
🖳 www.thesoundhousestudios.co.uk

The Tape Gallery 28 Lexington Street, London, W1F 0LF, United Kingdom
℡ (020) 7439 3325/ (020) 7734 9417
✉ info@tape-gallery.co.uk
🖳 www.tape-gallery.co.uk

The Visual Effects Co. Ltd c/o Dukes Island Studios, Dukes Road, Western Avenue, London, W3 0SL, United Kingdom
℡ (020) 8956 5674/ (020) 8956 5604
✉ Mick@thevfxco.co.uk
🖳 www.thevfxco.co.uk

The Whitehouse 12-13 Kingly Street, London, W1B 5PP, United Kingdom
℡ (020) 7287 3404/ (020) 7287 9670
✉ kate.o'mulloy@whitehousepost.com
🖳 www.whitehousepost.com

POST-PRODUCTION/SPECIAL EFFECTS

The Yard W1 Ltd 38 Great Pulteney Street, London, W1F 9NT, United Kingdom
(020) 7287 7279/ (020) 7287 7229
info@theyard.tv
www.theyard.tv

Three S Films Ltd 12 Regent Square, Penzance, Cornwall, TR18 4BG, United Kingdom
(01736) 367 912/07718 793 766 (01736) 367 912
john@threesfilms.com
www.threesfilms.com

Toast Ltd 10 Frith Street, London, W1D 3JF, United Kingdom
(020) 7437 0506/ (020) 7439 8852
anna@toasttv.co.uk
www.toasttv.co.uk

Tony Swinney 44 Hogshill Lane, Cobham, Surrey, KT11 2AQ, United Kingdom
(07768) 993022
tony@mustardpost.co.uk
www.mustardpost.co.uk

Top Banana Broome, Hagley, Stourbridge, West Midlands, DY9 0HA, United Kingdom
(01562) 700404/ (01562) 700930
talk@top-b.com
www.top-b.com

Toucan Pictures 200 Elsenham Street, London, SW18 5NR, United Kingdom
(020) 8870 6049/(07976) 177119
johnwilsoneditor@homecall.co.uk
www.johnwilsoneditor.com

Transdigital 5R North Mill, Bridge Foot, Belper, Derbyshire, DE56 1YD, United Kingdom
(01773) 829320
info@transdigital.co.uk
www.transdigital.co.uk

Twickenham Film Studios Ltd The Barons, St Margaret's, Twickenham, TW1 2AW, United Kingdom
(020) 8607 8888/ (020) 8607 8889
caroline@twickenhamstudios.com
www.twickenhamstudios.com

Two Four Studios 3 Bush Park, Pestover, Plymouth, PL6 7RG, United Kingdom
(01752) 727400/ (01752) 727450
enq@twofour.co.uk
www.twofour.co.uk

Uptown Studios 22 Denmark Street, London, WC2H 8NG, United Kingdom
(020) 7379 0003/(07951) 712480
info@uptownstudios.co.uk
www.uptownstudios.co.uk

V C L Video 43-44 Hoxton Square, London, N1 6PB, United Kingdom
(020) 7729 6967/ (020) 7613 0544
info@vclvideo.com
www.vclvideo.com

V P TV Oddfellows Hall, London Road, Chipping Norton, Oxfordshire, OX7 5AR, United Kingdom
(01608) 641592/ (01608) 641969
info@vptv.com
www.vptv.com

Video Lab Ltd 4 St. David's Road South, Lytham St. Annes, Lancashire, FY8 1TB, United Kingdom
(01253) 725499/ (01253) 725499
blakeydonald@aol.co.uk
www.video-lab.co.uk

Video Playback Company Pinewood Studios, Pinewood Road, Iver, Buckinghamshire, SL0 0NH, United Kingdom
(01753) 652452/ (01753) 652090
ian.dobbs@videoplayback.co.uk
www.videoplayback.co.uk

Videosonics Ltd 13 Hawley Crescent, London, NW1 8NP, United Kingdom
(020) 7209 0209/ (020) 7419 4460
info@videosonics.com
www.videosonics.com

Vineyard C G 17 Lyndhurst Road, Exeter, EX2 4PA, United Kingdom
(01392) 430316
james@vineyardcg.com
www.vineyardcg.com

West Digital Ltd 65 Goldhawk Road, London, W12 8EG, United Kingdom
(020) 8743 5100/ (020) 8743 2345
darren@westdigital.co.uk
www.westdigital.co.uk

Weston Point Studios Ltd Mersey Road, Western Point, Runcorn, Cheshire, WA7 1DA, United Kingdom
(01928) 700404/ (01928) 572482
lizhelsby@wpsltd.co.uk
www.wpsltd.co.uk

White Noise Productions Ltd Suite 308, India Mill Centre, Darwen, Lancashire, BB3 1AE, United Kingdom
(01254) 777444/(07976) 515105 (01254) 777373
info@whitenoiseonline.com
www.whitenoiseonline.com

WIDEi Films Ealing Studios, Ealing Green, Ealing, London, W5 5EP,
08718 552790/ 07092 218009
info@widei-films.co.uk
www.widei-films.com

Wild Tracks Audio Studios Ltd 2nd Floor, 55 Greek Street, London, W1D 3DT, United Kingdom
(020) 7734 6331/ (020) 7734 6195
bookings@wildtracks.co.uk
www.wildtracks.co.uk

Xpression (APPC) Warwick House, Chapone Place, Dean Street, London, W1D 3BF, United Kingdom
(020) 7437 8182/ (020) 7437 8183
dave@xpression.tv
www.xpression.tv

Xube Ltd Unit 4, 51 Derbyshire Street, London, E2 6JQ, United Kingdom
(020) 7739 5811/ 020 7900 6867
info@xube.co.uk
www.xube.co.uk

PRODUCTION COMPANIES

2 AM Films Ltd (AFVPA) 1 Lawfords Wharf, Lyme Street, London, NW1 0SF, United Kingdom
(020) 7428 8800/ (020) 7428 8801
production@2amfilms.co.uk
www.2amfilms.co.uk

24Kare Film Ltd Tomtom Mah. Bogazkesen Cad., No. 183/1 Beyoglu, Istanbul, 34433, Turkey
00 90 212 252 2751/ 00 90 212 251 9089
uarmadort.kare@yahoo.com

2Can Productions PO Box 668, Cardiff, CF11 1EZ,
0845 0545096/ 0845 0545097
info@2canproductions.com
www.2canproductions.com

2CS Communications (IVCA) 5 St. Johns Lane, London, EC1M 4BH, United Kingdom
(020) 7250 4724/ (020) 7336 8589
mail@2cs.co.uk
www.2cs.com

3BM Television (PACT) 32 Woodstock Grove, London, W12 8LE, United Kingdom
(020) 8740 4780/ (020) 8740 4470
3bmtv@3bmtv.co.uk
www.3bmtv.co.uk

3D Pixel Perfect Visualisation Services The White House, Copse Road, Haslemere, Surrey, GU27 3QQ, United Kingdom
(01428) 643500
info@pixelperfect.co.uk
www.pixelperfect.co.uk

4FILMS Beyaz Karanfil Sok.No.17, Levent, Istanbul, 34330, Turkey
00 90 212 270 8001/ 00 90 212 278 4486
selma@dortfilm.com
www.dortfilm.com

A S D Lionheart G06 Clerkenwell Workshops, 31 Clerkenwell Close, London, EC1R 0AT, United Kingdom
(020) 7437 3898/ (027) 014 3811
firstname@asdlionheart.com
www.asdlionheart.com

A S F Productions Ltd 38 Clunbury Court, Manor Street, Berkhamsted, Hertfordshire, HP4 2FF, United Kingdom
(01442) 872999/(07770) 277637 (01442) 872536
info@asfproductions.co.uk
www.asfproductions.co.uk

Abacus Film Productions Ltd Lomond, Horsehill, Horley, Surrey, RH6 0HN, United Kingdom
(01293) 862318/(07710) 335186 (01293) 863790
lomondabs@aol.com

Absolutely Production Ltd (PACT) 77 Beak Street, London, W1F 9DB, United Kingdom
(020) 7930 3113/ (020) 7930 4114
info@absolutely-uk.com
www.absolutely-uk.com

Academy Productions Ltd 16 West Central Street, London, WC1A 1JJ, United Kingdom
(020) 7395 4155/ (020) 7240 0355
post@academyfilms.com
www.academyfilms.com

Accidental Productions Ltd 36 Barratt Avenue, London, N22 7EZ, United Kingdom
(020) 8881 8000/ (020) 8881 8008
info@accidental.co.uk
www.accidental.co.uk

Actaeon Films 50 Gracefield Gardens, London, SW16 2ST, United Kingdom
(020) 87693339/ (0870) 1347980
info@actaeonfilms.com
www.actaeonfilms.com

Adam Media Ltd (IVCA) 21 Dungarvan Avenue, Roehampton, London, SW15 5QU, United Kingdom
(020) 8876 3333/(07785) 357077 (020) 8876 3333
adamprods@aol.com

Adrian Rowbotham Films Bohemia, Eridge Park, Eridge Green, Tunbridge Wells, Kent, TN3 9HA, United Kingdom
(01892) 750201/(07860) 459664 (01892) 750978
avr@avrofilms.com

Adrian Thurston Gordon Productions Flat B, 44 Eardley Crescent, London, SW5 9JZ, United Kingdom
(020) 7373 3668/(07985) 861616 (020) 7373 3668
adrian@syncfilms.com
www.adrianthurston.co.uk

Alex Myers and Associates 63 Endell Street, London, WC2H 9TP, United Kingdom
(020) 7379 5124/ (020) 7379 0269
info@alexmyersassociates.co.uk
www.alexmyersassociates.co.uk

Amber Films 5-9 Side, Newcastle upon Tyne, NE1 3JE, United Kingdom
0191-232 2000
amberside@btinternet.com
www.amber-online.com

AMCO Industrial Valves 6 Thandava Murthy Street, Royapuram, Chennai, Tamil Nadu, 600 013,
044 42052172/ 044 25901646
amcovalves@hotmail.com
www.amcovalves.com

Amicus Enterprises Amicus Street, PO Box 1745, Sialkot, 51310, Pakistan
00 92 52 459 3854/ 00 92 52 458 8777
amicus@skt.comstats.net.pk

Animage Ltd 62 West Croft Close, London, NW2 2RR, United Kingdom
(020) 7435 3883/ (020) 7435 3883
mail@animageltd.com
www.animageltd.com

Animation People Ltd 22 Churchmead Close, East Barnet, Barnet, Hertfordshire, EN4 8UY, United Kingdom
(020) 8449 1601/(07714) 203737 (020) 8449 1601
brianlarks@aol.com
www.animationpeople.co.uk

Animation Studio Ltd 119 Sutton Court, Chiswick, London, W4 3EE, United Kingdom
(020) 8995 9386/ (020) 8995 8335
bob@animationstudio.co.uk
www.animationstudio.co.uk

Annex Films (AFVPA) 101 Dean Street, London, W1D 3TG, United Kingdom
(020) 7440 1400/ (020) 7437 7507
info@annexfilms.co.uk
www.annexfilms.co.uk

Antena (TAC) Unit 2, Cibyn Industrial Estate, Caernarfon, Gwynedd, LL55 2BD, United Kingdom
(01286) 678592/ (01286) 678594
swyddfa@antena.co.uk
www.antena.co.uk

Antidote Produxions The Green House, Studio 406, The Custard Factory, Birmingham, B9 4AA, United Kingdom
0121-224 7710
info@antidoteproduxions.com
www.antidoteproduxions.com

Arc Facilities 40 Dalintober Street, Glasgow, G5 8NW, United Kingdom
0141-333 5560/ 0141-332 6002
info@arcfacilties.com
www.arcfacilities.com

Arqiva Ltd Chalfont Grove, Chalfont St. Peter, Narcot Lane, Gerrards Cross, Buckinghamshire, SL9 8TW, United Kingdom
📞 (01494) 878787/📠 (01494) 878478
🖥 www.arqiva.com

Associated Press Television News The Interchange, Oval Road, Camden Lock, London, NW1 7DZ, United Kingdom
📞 (020) 7413 8301/📠 (020) 7413 8327
✉ info@aptnlibrary.com
🖥 www.aptn.com

At It Productions (PACT) 68 Salusbry Road, Queenspark, London, NW6 6NU, United Kingdom
📞 (020) 8964 2122
✉ enquiries@atitproductions.com
🖥 www.atitproductions.com

Autonomy Multimedia Ltd 1 Spring Lane, Olney, Buckinghamshire, MK46 5BN, United Kingdom
📞 (01234) 240552/📠 (01234) 240530
✉ production@autonomy-multimedia.com
🖥 www.autonomy-multimedia.com

Avalon Television (PACT) 4A Exmoor Street, London, London, W10 6BD, United Kingdom
📞 (020) 7598 8000/📠 (020) 7598 7388
✉ press@avalonuk.com
🖥 www.avalonuk.com

Axis Animation Suite 225, Pentagon Business Centre, Washington Street, Glasgow, G3 8AZ, United Kingdom
📞 0141-572 2802/📠 0141-572 2809
✉ enquiries@axisanimation.com
🖥 www.axisanimation.com

B D P Media Ltd Unit 12, The Leathermarket, Weston Street, London, SE1 3ER, United Kingdom
📞 (020) 7407 7060/📠 (020) 7407 7090
✉ info@bdpmediagroup.com
🖥 www.bdpmediagroup.com

B H R Communications The White Cottage, The Street, Long Stratton, Norwich, NR15 2XJ, United Kingdom
📞 (0845) 4026527/(07803) 086462 📱 (0845) 4026528
✉ bhr@bhrcommunications.co.uk
🖥 www.bhrcommunications.co.uk

B-Line Productions 135 Sydney Road, London, N10 2ND, United Kingdom
📞 (020) 8444 9574/(07831) 289283 📱 (020) 8365 3664
✉ info@b-lineproductions.co.uk
🖥 www.b-lineproductions.co.uk

Banana Park Ltd 6 Cranleigh Mews, Battersea, London, SW11 2QL, United Kingdom
📞 (020) 7228 7136/📠 (020) 7738 1887
✉ studio@bananapark.co.uk
🖥 www.bananapark.co.uk

Barford Productions 35 Bedfordbury, Covent Garden, London, WC2N 4DU, United Kingdom
📞 (020) 7240 4188/📠 (020) 7379 5210
✉ info@barford.co.uk
🖥 www.barford.co.uk

Barrie Joll Associates (AFVPA) 58 Frith Street, London, W1D 3JQ, United Kingdom
📞 (020) 7437 9965/📠 2074349444
✉ barrie@barriejoll.com

Bermuda Shorts Ltd Circus House, 5th Floor, 21 Great Titchfield Street, London, W1W 8BA, United Kingdom
📞 (020) 7437 7335/📠 (020) 7437 7334
✉ info@bermudashorts.com
🖥 www.bermudashorts.com

Berwick Universal Pictures (PACT) 45 Brookfield, London, N6 6AT, United Kingdom
📞 (020) 7272 4500
✉ info@berwickuniversal.com
🖥 www.berwickuniversal.com

Beryl Stevens Associates Ltd 1 Linersh Wood Close, Bramley, Surrey, GU5 0EG, United Kingdom
📞 (01483) 892138
✉ berylstevens@tiscali.co.uk

Big Heart Media Flat 4, 6 Pear Tree Court, London, EC1R 0DW, United Kingdom
📞 (020) 7608 0352/📠 (020) 7250 1138
✉ mail@bigheartmedia.com
🖥 www.bigheartmedia.com

Big Wave Productions (PACT) 156 St. Pancras, Chichester, West Sussex, PO19 7SH, United Kingdom
📞 (01243) 532531/📠 (01243) 532153
✉ info@bigwavetv.com
🖥 www.bigwavetv.com

Blackbird Productions (IVCA, PACT) 6 Molasses Row, Plantation Wharf, London, SW11 3UX, United Kingdom
📞 (020) 7924 6440
✉ enquiries@blackbirdproductions.co.uk
🖥 www.blackbirdproductions.co.uk

Blackwatch Productions Ltd (PACT) 3 Royal Exchange Court, 17 Royal Exchange Square, Glasgow, G1 3DB, United Kingdom
📞 (07891) 511664/📠 0141-222 2646
✉ info@blackwatchtv.com
🖥 www.blackwatchtv.com

Blakeway 3BM (PACT) 32 Woodstock Grove, London, W12 8LE, United Kingdom
📞 (020) 8743 2040/📠 (020) 8743 2141
✉ kate.macky@blakeway3bm.com
🖥 www.blakeway.co.uk

Blast Films (PACT) Unit C, 2 Imperial Works, Perren Street, London, NW5 3ED, United Kingdom
📞 (020) 7267 4260/📠 (020) 7485 2340
✉ blast@blastfilms.co.uk
🖥 www.blastfilms.co.uk

Blink Productions Ltd (AFVPA) 181 Wardour Street, London, W1F 8WZ, United Kingdom
📞 (020) 7494 0747/📠 (020) 7494 3771
✉ info@blinkprods.com
🖥 www.blinkprods.com

Blue Dolphin Film & Video Ltd 40 Langham Street, London, W1W 7AS, United Kingdom
📞 (020) 7255 2494/📠 (020) 7580 7670
✉ info@bluedolphinfilms.com
🖥 www.bluedolphinfilms.com

Bob Ginger Partnership 19-21 High Street, Acton, London, W3 6NG, United Kingdom
📞 (020) 8993 6773/📠 (020) 8993 9982
✉ info@bobginger.co.uk
🖥 www.bobginger.co.uk

Bocek Production Cubuklu cad.agaclik mesire yeri, d+e burunbahce, beykoz, Istanbul, 34805,
📞 00 9 02166801058
✉ selma@bocekyapim.com.tr
🖥 www.bocekyapim.com.tr

Bolexbrothers Ltd 6 Brunel Lock Development, Smeaton Road, Cumberland Basin, Bristol, BS1 6SE, United Kingdom
📞 0117-985 8000/📠 0117-985 8899
✉ mail@bolexbrothers.co.uk
🖥 www.bolexbrothers.co.uk

Brian Jackson Films Ltd 39-41 Hanover Steps, St Georges Fields, London, W2 2YG, United Kingdom
📞 (020) 7402 7543/📠 (020) 7262 5736
✉ brianjfilm@aol.com

Brighter Pictures Ltd Shepherds Building Central, Sharecroft Way, Shepherds Bush, London, W14 0EE, United Kingdom
📞 (020) 8222 4100/📠 (0870) 333 1800
✉ info@brighter.co.uk
🖥 www.brighter.co.uk

Bro2media 180 Walton Road, East Molesey, Surrey, KT8 0HR, United Kingdom
📞 (020) 8941 0740
✉ info@bro2media.co.uk
🖥 www.bro2media.co.uk

Broadcast Television Facilities Aucuba House, Lymm Road, Little Bollington, Altrincham, Cheshire, WA14 4SY, United Kingdom
📞 0161-926 9808/📠 0161-929 9000
✉ info@broadcast-tv.co.uk
🖥 www.broadcast-tv.co.uk

Brunswick Films Ltd 26 Macroom Road, London, W9 3HY, United Kingdom
📞 (020) 8960 0066/📠 (020) 8960 4997
✉ info@brunswickfilms.com
🖥 www.brunswickfilms.com

Buccaneer Films 5 Rainbow Court, Watford, WD19 4RP, United Kingdom
📞 (01923) 254000

Bullet Movies
Brighton, United Kingdom
📞 (01273) 301608/(07717) 400968 📱
✉ info@bulletmovies.com
🖥 www.bulletmovies.com

Burrell Durrant Hifle 71 South Parade, Oakfield Road, Bristol, BS8 2BB, United Kingdom
📞 0117-973 7575/📠 0117-923 7823
✉ pic@bdh.net
🖥 www.bdh.net

Bye Jones Productions The Brewhouse, Salisbury Road, Sherfield English, Romsey, Hampshire, SO51 6FL, United Kingdom
📞 (01794) 324461
✉ byejones@btinternet.com
🖥 www.byejones.co.uk

C T V C (PACT) 1st Floor, 9-10 Copper Row, Tower Bridge Piazza, London, SE1 2LH, United Kingdom
📞 (020) 7940 8480/📠 (020) 7940 8490
✉ production@ctvc.co.uk
🖥 www.ctvc.co.uk

Caboose 1-8 Bateman's Buildings, South Soho Square, London, W1D 3EN, United Kingdom
📞 (020) 7851 1352/📠 (020) 7304 4400
✉ info@caboose.tv
🖥 www.caboose.tv

Caledonia TV (PACT) 1st Floor, 147 Bath Street, Glasgow, G2 4SQ, United Kingdom
📞 0141-564 9100/📠 0141-564 9200
✉ info@caledonia.tv
🖥 www.caledonia.tv

Calon TV Ltd Phoenix Buildings, 3 Mount Stuart Square, Butetown, Cardiff, CF10 5EE, United Kingdom
📞 (029) 2048 8400/📠 (029) 2048 5962
✉ enquiries@calon.tv
🖥 www.calon.tv

Cantab Films Ltd St Johns Innovation Centre, Cowley Road, Cambridge, CB4 0WS, United Kingdom
📞 (01223) 212014/📠 (01223) 212015
✉ info@cantabfilms.com
🖥 www.cantabfilms.com

Capitol House Productions Capitol House, 662 London Road, Cheam, Surrey, SM3 9BY, United Kingdom
📞 (020) 8644 6194/📠 (020) 8641 5539
✉ mail@capitol.co.uk
🖥 www.capitol.co.uk

Capricorn Productions 3rd Floor, 23-29 Albion Place, Maidstone, Kent, ME14 5DY, United Kingdom
📞 (01622) 766998/(07979) 412224 📱 (01622) 673787
✉ info@capricornproductions.co.uk
🖥 www.capricornproductions.co.uk

Caramel Pictures 6 Seascape, Gough Road, Sandgate, Folkestone, Kent, CT20 3BF, United Kingdom
📞 (01303) 220 230/📠 (01303) 220 230
✉ mark@caramelpictures.com
🖥 www.caramelpictures.com

Carl Gover Animation 11 Henrietta Street, Covent Garden, London, WC2E 8PY, United Kingdom
📞 (020) 7636 3300
✉ carl@animationpartnership.co.uk
🖥 www.animationpartnership.co.uk

Carnival Ltd (PACT) 47 Marylebone Lane, London, London, W1U 2NT, United Kingdom
📞 (020) 7317 1370/📠 (020) 7317 1380
✉ info@carnival-films.co.uk
🖥 www.carnival-films.co.uk

Carolan Media The Coach House, Adjacent Ealing Film Studios, Ealing, London, W5 5ER, United Kingdom
📞 (020) 8566 1900/📠 (020) 8566 1900
✉ info@carolanmedia.com
🖥 www.carolanmedia.com

Cartwn Cymru (TAC) 32 Wordsworth Avenue, Roath, Cardiff, CF24 3FR, United Kingdom
📞 (029) 2046 3556/07771 640 400 📱
✉ production@cartwn-cymru.com

Catalyst Television (PACT) 220 Shepherds Bush Road, London, W6 7NL, United Kingdom
📞 (020) 7603 7030/📠 (020) 7603 9519
✉ info@catalystfilm.co.uk

Celador Productions Ltd 39 Long Acre, London, WC2E 9LG, United Kingdom
📞 (020) 7240 8101
✉ tvhits@celador.co.uk
🖥 www.celador.co.uk

Centre Screen Productions Ltd (IVCA) Eastgate, Castle Street, Manchester, M3 4LZ, United Kingdom
📞 0161-832 7151/📠 0161-832 8934
✉ info@centrescreen.co.uk
🖥 www.centrescreen.co.uk

Centreline Video 138 Westwood Road, Tilehurst, Reading, RG31 6LL, United Kingdom
📞 0118-941 0033
🖥 www.centrelinevideo.com

Century Films (PACT) Studio 32, Clink Street Studios, 1 Clink Street, London, London, SE1 9DG, United Kingdom
📞 (020) 7378 6106/📠 (020) 7407 6711
✉ info@centuryfilmsltd.com
🖥 www.centuryfilmsltd.com

Chameleon Television Ltd (PACT) Greatminster House, Listerhill, Leeds, LS18 5DL, United Kingdom
0113-205 0040/ 0113-281 9454
firstname@chameleontv.com
www.chameleontv.com

Channel 20/20 Ltd 20/20 House, 26-28 Talbot Lane, Leicester, LE1 4LR, United Kingdom
0116-233 2220/ 0116-222 1113
info@channel2020.co.uk
www.channel2020.co.uk

Channel X Ltd 17 Dufferin Street, London, EC1Y 8PE, United Kingdom
(020) 7428 3999/ (020) 7428 3998
info@channelx.co.uk

Charles Stewart Hill View, Henders Lane, Huntly, Gloucester, GL19 3EZ, United Kingdom
(01452) 830500/(07802) 967369
charlescstewart@aol.com

Chase Production Management Unit 31, Waylett House, London, SE11 5PZ, United Kingdom
(020) 8265 4701
mail@chasingit.com
www.chasingit.com

Check The Gate Rua Rodrigo Albuquerque e Melo 4, 4D, L.A. Velha, Lisboa, Portugal
00 351 91 819 6577
jose@checkthegate.com
www.checkthegate.com

Chrysallis Entertainment (PACT) Chrysalis Building, 13 Bramley Road, London, W10 6SP, United Kingdom
(020) 7221 2213/ (020) 7221 6455
sarahc@chrysalis.co.uk

Cicada Films (PACT) 1 Marylands Road, Maida Vale, London, London, W9 2DU, United Kingdom
(020) 7266 4646/ (020) 7289 2599
cicada@cicadafilms.com
www.cicadafilms.com

Cineimage 7A Langley Street, Covent Garden, London, WC2H 9JA, United Kingdom
(020) 7240 6222/ (020) 7240 6242
info@cineimage.co.uk
www.cineimage.co.uk

Circa Group Imperial House, 15-19 Kingsway, London, WC2B 6UN, United Kingdom
(020) 7836 1600/ (020) 7420 1777
info@circagroup.co.uk
www.circagroup.co.uk

Cleveland Film Productions 5 Rainbow Court, Watford, WD19 4RP, United Kingdom
(01923) 254000

Cog Ltd No 1 Mill Cottage, Tilstone Bank, Near Tarporley, Cheshire, CW6 9QH, United Kingdom
(020) 7358 4751/ (020) 7358 4751
mail@consortium-of-gentlemen.co.uk
www.consortium-of-gentlemen.co.uk

Collingwood O'Hare Entertainment Ltd 10-14 Crown Street, London, W3 8SB, United Kingdom
(020) 8993 3666/ (020) 8993 9595
info@crownstreet.co.uk
www.collingwoodohare.com

Colstar International Television Ltd 78 York Street, London, W1H 1DP, United Kingdom
(020) 7625 6200
www.colstar.tv

Comedy Unit (PACT) Glasgow TV & Film Studio, Glasgow Media Park, 24 Craigmont Street, Glasgow, G20 9BT, United Kingdom
0141-305 6666/ 0141-305 6600
info@comedyunit.co.uk
www.comedyunit.co.uk

Commercials Unlimited Garden Studios, 11-15 Betterton Street, London, WC2H 9BP, United Kingdom
(020) 7470 8791/(07836) 523604/ (020) 7470 8792
mail@commercialsunlimited.net
www.commercialsunlimited.net

Communicator Ltd (IVCA) 199 Upper Street, London, N1 1RQ, United Kingdom
(020) 7704 8333/(07798) 525872/ (020) 7704 8444
info@communicator.ltd.uk
www.communicator.ltd.uk

Company Pictures (PACT) 2nd Floor, Suffolk House, 1-8 Whitfield Place, London, W1T 5JU, United Kingdom
(020) 7380 3900/ (020) 7380 1166
enquiries@companypictures.co.uk
www.companypictures.co.uk

Composure Number 15, London, W7 3PX, United Kingdom
(07836) 325586/ (020) 8840 6810
composure@s4kmedia.tv

Comtec Ltd Unit 19, Tait Road, Croydon, CR0 2DP, United Kingdom
(020) 8684 6615/ (020) 8684 6947
info@comtecav.co.uk
www.comtecav.co.uk

Concise Ltd 5 The Quadrant Centre, 135 Salisbury Road, London, NW6 6RJ, United Kingdom
(020) 7644 6444/ (020) 7644 6445
mail@concisegroup.com
www.concisegroup.com

Conference Dynamics Ltd 2 Hart House, The Hart, Farnham, Surrey, GU9 7HJ, United Kingdom
(01252) 711772/ (01252) 719971
team@conferencedynamics.com
www.conferencedynamics.com

Cosgrove Hall Films (PACT) 8 Albany Road, Chorlton-cum-Hardy, Manchester, M21 0AW, United Kingdom
0161-882 2500/ 0161-882 2555
lisa.hall@cosgrovehall.com
www.cosgrovehall.com

Create Media Partners 39 Telegraph Lane, Four Marks, Alton, Hampshire, GU34 5AX, United Kingdom
(01420) 561144/(07939) 040720/ (01420) 560020
info@create-media.co.uk
www.create-media.co.uk

Creative Channel (IVCA) La Pouquelaye, The Television Centre, St. Helier, Jersey, JE1 3ZD, United Kingdom
(01534) 816816/ (01534) 816889
david.evans@channeltv.co.uk
www.channelonline.tv

Creative Partnership 13 Bateman Street, London, London, W1D 3AF, United Kingdom
(020) 7439 7762/ (020) 7437 1467
info@thecreativepartnership.co.uk
www.thecreativepartnership.co.uk

Crossroads Films UK 2nd Floor, 87 Notting Hill Gate, London, W11 3JZ, United Kingdom
(020) 7792 5400/ (020) 7792 0592
info@crossroadsfilms.co.uk
www.crossroadsfilms.com

Crystal Media (PACT) 28 Castle Street, Edinburgh, EH2 3HT, United Kingdom
0131-240 0988/ 0131-240 0989
hello@crystal-media.co.uk
www.crystal-media.co.uk

Cwmni Da (TAC) Cae Llenor, LÙn Park, Caernarfon, Gwynedd, LL55 2HH, United Kingdom
(01286) 685300/ (01286) 685301
post@cwmnida.co.uk
www.cwmnida.co.uk

D L T Entertainment UK Ltd (PACT) 10 Bedford Square, London, WC1B 3RA, United Kingdom
(020) 7631 1184/ (020) 7636 4571
jbartlett@dltentertainment.co.uk

Dareks Production House 58 Wickham Road, Beckenham, Kent, BR3 6RQ, United Kingdom
(020) 8658 2012/(07973) 664189/ (020) 8325 0629
dareks@btconnect.com
www.dareks.fsnet.co.uk

Darlow Smithson Productions Ltd (PACT) Highgate Studios, 53 - 79 Highgate Road, London, NW5 1TL, United Kingdom
(020) 7482 7027/ (020) 7482 7039
mail@darlowsmithson.com
www.darlowsmithson.com

David Wickes Productions 10 Abbey Orchard Street, London, SW1P 2LD, United Kingdom
(020) 7222 0820/ (020) 7222 0822
wickesco@aol.com
www.davidwickesproductions.com

Daydream Linton House, 164-180 Union Street, London, SE1 0LH,
+44 (0) 20 7096 1471/+44 (0) 20 7117 1636
ralph@daydream.co.uk
www.daydream.co.uk

Denham Productions Ltd (PACT) Boydell House, Quay West Studios, Old Newnham, Plymouth, PL7 5BH, United Kingdom
(01752) 345444/ (01752) 345448
mike.foreign@denhams.tv
www.denhams.tv

Denis Russo Associates 161 Clapham Road, London, SW9 0PU, United Kingdom
(020) 8892 7514/(07956) 276954/ (020) 7582 2725

Denman Productions 60 Mallard Place, Strawberry Vale, Twickenham, TW1 4SR, United Kingdom
(020) 8891 3461/ (020) 8891 6413
info@denman.co.uk
www.denman.co.uk

Design is Central (PACT) 23 Argyll Court, 1103 Argyll Street, Glasgow, G3 8ND, United Kingdom
0141-847 0077
work@designiscentral.com
www.designiscentral.com

Digital Classics DVD 151 Wardour Street, London, W1F 8WE, United Kingdom
(020) 7297 8035/ (020) 7297 8022
rb@nbdtv.com
www.nbdtv.com

Directions Walden, Beech Hill, Colchester, CO3 4DU, United Kingdom
(01206) 574120/(07989) 462687
duncan@directionsfilms.co.uk

Diverse Production Ltd (PACT) 6 Gorleston Street, London, W14 8XS, United Kingdom
(020) 7603 4567/ (020) 7603 2148
info@diverse.tv
www.diverse.tv

Dominic King Production
United Kingdom
(07967) 375952/(07967) 375952
dominicking@aol.com
www.dominicking.com

Dragonfly Media 3 Berkeley Crescent, Clifton, Bristol, Avon, BS8 1HA,
0845 6520 888/ 0845 6520 808
jon@dragonfly-media.co.uk
www.dragonfly-media.co.uk

Drake Audio Visual 89 St Fagans Road, Fairwater, Cardiff, CF5 3AE, United Kingdom
(029) 2056 0333/ (029) 2055 4909
sales@drakeav.com
www.drakeav.com

Duplexx Productions Ltd (APA) Penthouse B, 14 Riverview Court, Salford, Manchester, M7 3NX, United Kingdom
0161-792 4144/ 0161-792 5144
duplexx@zoom.co.uk

Dusk Films 2/2 Maddock Street, Windsor, 3181 VIC, Australia
00 61 3 9521 1080/ 00 61 3 9521 1080
luke@duskfilms.com.au
www.duskfilms.com.au

Ecosse Films (PACT) Brigade House, 8 Parsons Green, London, SW6 4TN, United Kingdom
(020) 7371 0290/ (020) 7736 3436
info@ecossefilms.com
www.ecossefilms.com

Edinburgh Film Productions (PACT) Traquair House, Innerleithen, Peeblesshire, EH44 6PP, United Kingdom
(01896) 831188/ (01896) 831199
crichton.efp@virgin.nert

Edric Audio Visual Ltd (IVCA) 34-36 Oak End Way, Gerrards Cross, Buckinghamshire, SL9 8BR, United Kingdom
(01753) 481400/ (01753) 887163
info@edric-av.co.uk
www.edric-av.co.uk

Electronic Camera Co. Ltd 31 Thirty Street, London, E1W 2QR, United Kingdom
(020) 7734 5021/(07860) 327866
info@electronic-camera.co.uk
www.electronic-camera.co.uk

Element Productions (PACT, TAC) 5th Floor, Crichton House, 11-12 Mount Stuart Square, Cardiff Bay, Cardiff, CF10 5EE, United Kingdom
(029) 2047 2122/ (029) 2047 2230
office@elementproductions.co.uk
www.elementproductions.co.uk

Endemol UK P.L.C. (PACT) Shepherds Building Central, Charecroft Way, Shepherds Bush, London, W14 0EE, United Kingdom
(0870) 333 1700/ (0870) 333 1800
info@endemoluk.com
www.endemoluk.com

endorfin.tv Tower House, 9 Lower Green Road, Rusthall, Tunbridge Wells, Kent, TN4 8TE, United Kingdom
(01892) 533577
mark@endorfin.tv
www.endorfin.tv

English & Pockett Ltd 13-19 Vine Hill, London, EC1R 5DW, United Kingdom
(020) 7278 4272/ (020) 7278 8632
info@english-pockett.com
www.english-pockett.com

Epcot Images 5 Charles Street, Epping, Essex, CM16 7AU, United Kingdom
(01992) 574291/(07710) 783271
jprice@epcotimages.com
www.epcotimages.com

Europa Interactive Ltd Flat 5, Holly House, Avenue Road, Ilfracombe, Devon, EX34 9AT, United Kingdom
(01271) 863061/ (01271) 863061
info@europa-i.com
www.europa-i.com

Evolution Event Management Ltd Printer's Yard, 90a The Broadway, Wimbledon, London, SW19 1RD, United Kingdom
(020) 8543 3033/ (020) 8543 3040
info@evolutionevent.com
www.evolutionevent.com

ExtraGoodLuck Ltd Pinewood Studios, Pinewood Road, Iver, Buckinghamshire, SL0 0NH, United Kingdom
(01753) 785533/ (01753) 783857
extragoodluck@aol.com
www.extragoodluck.co.uk

Eyewitness Underwater Facilities Ltd The Drove, Sherfield English Road, Plaitford, Romsey, Hampshire, SO51 6EF, United Kingdom
(01794) 322500/ (01794) 323601
eyewitnessrental@aol.com
www.eyewitnessuk.co.uk

Face Films International Ltd 16 Dean Road, Hounslow, TW3 2EZ, United Kingdom
(020) 8898 6328
yavar21@hotmail.com

Farnham Film Co. Ltd 34 Burnt Hill Road, Lower Bourne, Farnham, Surrey, GU10 3LZ, United Kingdom
(01252) 710313/ (01252) 725855
info@farnfilm.com
www.farnfilm.com

Fat Fish Films (AFVPA) 25 Kyrle Road, London, SW11 6BD, United Kingdom
(07770) 890608/ (020) 7924 1403
jacci@fatfish.co.uk

Festival Film & TV (PACT) Festival House, Tranquil Passage, Blackheath, London, SE3 0BJ, United Kingdom
(020) 8297 9999/ (020) 8297 1155
info@festivalfilm.com
www.festivalfilm.com

Film & Edit 52 Moss Road, Bridge of Weir, Renfrewshire, PA11 3LS, United Kingdom
(01505) 615008
info@erroch.com
www.erroch.com

Film & General Productions Ltd 4 Bradbrook House, Studio Place, London, SW1X 8EL, United Kingdom
(020) 7235 4495/ (020) 7245 9853
cparsons@filmgen.co.uk

Film Editors (APPC) 6-10 Lexington Street, London, W1F 3HS, United Kingdom
(020) 7439 8655/ (020) 7437 0409
postroom@thefilmeditors.com
www.thefilmeditors.com

Film Work Group Studios Top Floor Chelsea Reach, 79-89 Lots Road, London, SW10 0RN, United Kingdom
(020) 7352 0538/ (020) 7351 6479

Films of Record Ltd 2 Elgin Avenue, London, W9 3QP, United Kingdom
(020) 7286 0333/ (020) 7286 0444
janeb@filmsofrecord.com
www.filmsofrecord.com

Firehouse Productions (IVCA) 42 Glasshouse Street, London, W1B 5DW, United Kingdom
(020) 7439 2220/ (020) 7439 2210
postie@firehouse.biz
www.firehouse.biz

Flashback Television Ltd (FOCAL, PACT) 11 Bowling Green Lane, London, EC1R 0BG, United Kingdom
(020) 7490 8996/ (020) 7490 5610
mailbox@flashbacktv.co.uk
www.flashbacktelevision.com

Flaxman Wilkie Reed Hall, Ipswich Road, Holbrook, Ipswich, IP9 2QR, United Kingdom
(01473) 326999/ (01473) 328422
mike@flaxmanwilkie.com
www.flaxmanwilkie.com

Flicks Films Ltd 101 Wardour Street, London, W1F 0UG, United Kingdom
(020) 7734 4892/ (020) 7287 2307
flicks@btconnect.com
www.flicksfilms.com

Focalpoint Television 1 Capital Park, Combe Lane, Wormley, Godalming, Surrey, GU8 5TJ, United Kingdom
(01428) 684468/ (01428) 684089
office@focal-point.co.uk
www.focal-point.co.uk

Folm Peaks Nabrezi 8, Prague, 120 00, Czech Republic
602 790 375/ 224 912 675
tomasiso@volny.cz

Footloose Films Ltd Film House, 17 Langland Gardens, Hampstead, London, NW3 6QE, United Kingdom
(020) 7435 1330
charlesharris@footloosefilms.com
www.footloosefilms.com

Four23 Ltd The Apex, 6 Southern Street, Manchester, M3 4WP, United Kingdom
0161-835 9466/ 0161-835 9468
mailman@four23.net
www.four23.net

Freeform Productions 15th Floor, 111 Piccadilly, Manchester, M1 2HY, United Kingdom
0161-236 5983/ 0161-236 2920
sarahl@fftv.co.uk

Fremantle Media Ltd 1 Stephen Street, London, W1T 1AL, United Kingdom
(020) 7691 6000
firstname.surname@fremantlemedia.com
www.fremantlemedia.com

Fulcrum TV (PACT) 3rd Floor, Bramah House, 65-71 Bermondsey Street, London, London, SE1 3XF, United Kingdom
(020) 7939 3160/ (020) 7403 2260
info@fulcrumtv.com
www.fulcrumtv.com

Fusion Design Associates Ltd The Studio, Little Cutts Farm, Kimpton Bottom, Harpenden, Hertfordshire, AL5 5ED, United Kingdom
(01582) 768783
info@fusiondesignltd.com
www.fusiondesignltd.com

G H A Group 1 Great Chapel Street, London, W1F 8FA, United Kingdom
(020) 7439 8705/ (020) 7437 5880
sales@ghagroup.co.uk
www.ghagroup.co.uk

Garton Media 26 Easenby Avenue, Kirk Ella, Hull, HU10 7JP, United Kingdom
(01482) 651317/(07721) 007100 / (01482) 651317
info@gartonmedia.com
www.gartonmedia.com

Gasworks Productions
London, E8 2WT, United Kingdom
(07837) 348838
info@gasworksproductions.com
www.gasworksproductions.com

George Downes Decorative Artist 21A Farleigh Road, London, N16 7TB, United Kingdom
(020) 7249 8747/(07929) 025104

Gerard De Thame Films Ltd (AFVPA) 25A Old Compton Street, London, W1D 5LB, United Kingdom
(020) 7437 3339/ (020) 7437 3338
post@gdtfilms.co.uk
www.gdtfilms.co.uk

Get Real Productions 20 Bishop Road, Bournemouth, BH9 1HB, United Kingdom
(01202) 535182/(07973) 690257
info@getrealproduction.co.uk
www.getrealproduction.co.uk

Ginger Television (PACT) 3 Waterhouse Square, 138-142 Holborn, London, EC1N 2NY, United Kingdom
(020) 7882 1020/ (020) 7882 1005
office@ginger.com
www.ginger.com

Godman Ltd (AFVPA) 10a Belmont Street, London, NW1 8HH, United Kingdom
(020) 7428 2288/ (020) 7428 2299
info@godman.co.uk
www.godman.co.uk

Golem Productions Ltd 31 Queens Walk, Ruislip, Middlesex, HA4 0LX, United Kingdom
(07733) 003873/ (020) 8845 8289
richard@golemproductions.co.uk
www.golemproductions.co.uk

Good Film Co. Ltd (APA) The Studio, 5-6 Eton Garages, Lambolle Place, London, NW3 4PE, United Kingdom
(020) 7794 6222/ (020) 7794 4651
info@goodfilms.co.uk
www.goodfilms.co.uk

Gorgeous Enterprises (AFVPA) Gorgeous House, 11 Portland Mews, London, W1F 8JL, United Kingdom
(020) 7287 4060/ (020) 7287 4994
gorgeous@gorgeous.co.uk
www.gorgeous.co.uk

Graham Whistler Productions 9 Cherrygarth Road, Catisfield, Fareham, Hampshire, PO15 5NA, United Kingdom
(01329) 847944/(07836) 217176
graham@gwpmultimedia.com
www.gwpmultimedia.com

Granada International The London Television Centre, Upper Ground, London, SE1 9TT, United Kingdom
(020) 7491 1441
gi-marketing@granadamedia.com
www.granadamedia.com/international

Green Inc Film & Television Ltd 47A Botanic Avenue, Belfast, BT7 1JL, United Kingdom
(028) 9057 3000/ (028) 9057 0057
tv@greeninc.tv
www.greeninc.tv

Green Olive Films 27 Kyprou Street, Halandri, 152 33, Greece
210 6897 241 2/ 210 6897 245
simos@greenolivefilms.gr
www.greenolivefilms.com

Green Umbrella Ltd (PACT) The Production House, 147A St Michaels Hill, Bristol, BS2 8DB, United Kingdom
0117-973 1729/ 0117-946 7432
postmaster@umbrella.co.uk
www.umbrella.co.uk

Gremlin UK Ltd 70 Dalnabay, Silverglades, Aviemore, Inverness-Shire, PH22 1RG, United Kingdom
(0845) 1661432/ (07092) 197823
enquiries@gremlinuk.com
www.gremlinuk.com

H C A Entertainment Ltd 18 Soho Square, London, W1D 3QL, United Kingdom
(020) 7287 7622/ (020) 7287 3494
info@hcaentertainment.com

H C V F Television Wells Street Studios, 33 Wells Street, Inverness, IV3 5JU, United Kingdom
(01463) 224788/(07860) 285872 / (01463) 711460
info@hcvf.co.uk
www.hcvf.co.uk

H L A 3rd Floor, 19-21 Great Portland Street, London, W1W 8QB, United Kingdom
(020) 7299 1000/ (020) 7299 1001
post@hla.net
www.hla.net

Hammonds A V S Ltd 34 -36 Oak End Way, Gerrards Cross, Buckinghamshire, SL9 8BR, UK
(01923) 239733/ (01753) 887163
info@hammonds-avs.co.uk
www.hammonds-avs.co.uk

Happy Hour Productions Ltd The Picture House, 4 Lower Park Road, Bristol, BS1 5BJ, United Kingdom
0117-929 9797/ 0117-923 0862
info@hhour.co.uk
www.happyhourproductions.co.uk

Harcourt Films Ltd (PACT) 58 Camden Square, London, NW1 9XE, United Kingdom
(020) 7267 0882/ (020) 7267 1064
marre@blueyonder.co.uk
www.harcourtfilms.com

Harry Nash (AFVPA) 27-29 Beak Street, London, W1F 9RU, United Kingdom
(020) 7025 7500/ (020) 7025 7501
www.harrynash.co.uk

17

Hart Davies Television 6 Anglers Lane, London, NW5 3DG, United Kingdom
✆ (020) 7428 4700/ ✆ (020) 7428 4776
✉ guydavies@hartdavies.tv

Hartswood Films Ltd (PACT) Twickenham Studios, The Barons, Twickenham, TW1 2AW, United Kingdom
✆ (020) 8607 8736/ ✆ (020) 8607 8744
✉ films.tv@hartswoodfilms.co.uk
🖥 www.hartswoodfilms.co.uk

Hat Trick Productions Ltd (PACT) 10 Livonia Street, London, W1F 8AF, United Kingdom
✆ (020) 7434 2451/ ✆ (020) 7287 9791
✉ info@hattrick.com
🖥 www.hattrick.com

Hibbert Ralph Animation Ltd 10 D'Arblay Street, London, W1F 8DS, United Kingdom
✆ (020) 7494 3011/ ✆ (020) 7494 0383
✉ info@hra-online.com
🖥 www.hra-online.com

Hiss & Boo Co Nyes Hill, Wineham Lane, Bolney, Haywards Heath, West Sussex, RH17 5SD, United Kingdom
✆ (01444) 881707/ ✆ (01444) 882057
✉ hissboo@msn.com
🖥 www.hissboo.co.uk

Hit Entertainment Plc (PACT) 5th Floor, Maple House, 149 Tottenham Court Road, London, W1T 7NF, United Kingdom
✆ (020) 7554 2500/ ✆ (020) 7388 9321
✉ creative@hitentertainment.com
🖥 www.hitentertainment.com

Hive Associates Bewlay House, 2 Swallow Place, London, W1B 2AE, United Kingdom
✆ (020) 7664 0480/ ✆ (020) 7664 0481
✉ consult@hiveassociates.co.uk
🖥 www.hiveassociates.co.uk

Home Corp 5th Floor, Fenton House, 55-57 Great Marlborough Street, London, W1F 7JX, United Kingdom
✆ (020) 7439 3093/ ✆ (020) 7439 3192
✉ home@homecorp.tv
🖥 www.homecorp.tv

Honeycomb Animation Enterprises Ltd 27 High St, Cullompton, Devon, EX15 1AB, United Kingdom
✆ (01884) 839202
✉ studio@honeycombanimation.co.uk
🖥 www.honeycombanimation.co.uk

Hot Bed Media Ltd (PACT) 16 Regents Place, Birmingham, B1 3NJ, United Kingdom
✆ 0121-248 3900/ ✆ 0121-248 4900
✉ mail@hotbedmedia.co.uk
🖥 www.hotbedmedia.co.uk

Hourglass Productions 27 Princes Road, Wimbledon, London, London, SW19 8RA, United Kingdom
✆ (020) 8540 8786/ ✆ (020) 8543 8396
✉ productions@hourglass.co.uk
🖥 www.hourglass.co.uk

I B C Video 5 Barns Place, Hale Barns, Altrincham, Cheshire, WA15 0HP, United Kingdom
✆ (07976) 566701
✉ ibcvideo@aol.com
🖥 www.ibcvideo.com

I W C Media St. Georges Studio, 93-97 St Georges Road, Glasgow, G3 6JA, United Kingdom
✆ 0141-353 3222/ ✆ 0141-353 3221
✉ mailglasgow@iwcmedia.co.uk
🖥 www.iwcmedia.co.uk

I W C Media Ltd 3-6 Kenrick Place, London, W1U 6HD, United Kingdom
✆ (020) 7317 2230/ ✆ (020) 7317 2231
🖥 www.iwcmedia.co.uk

Iambic Productions Ltd (PACT) 89 Whiteladies Road, Bristol, BS8 2NT, United Kingdom
✆ 0117-923 7222/ ✆ 0117-923 8343
✉ admin@iambic.tv
🖥 www.digitalclassics.co.uk

Ian White General Moulders 28 Stirling Close, Washington, Tyne and Wear, NE38 8QD, United Kingdom
✆ 0191- 417 1040
✉ iangrp@hotmail.co.uk
🖥 www.iwgeneralmoulders.co.uk

Ice Film Equipment Ltd Unit 2, Bridge Wharf, 156 Caledonian Road, London, N1 9UU, United Kingdom
✆ (020) 7278 0908/ ✆ (020) 7278 4552
✉ sales@icefilm.com
🖥 www.icefilm.com

Ice Pics Ltd 111A Wardour Street, London, W1F 0UJ, United Kingdom
✆ (020) 7437 3505/ ✆ (020) 7287 0393
✉ mike@icepics.co.uk
🖥 www.icepics.co.uk

iceni Productions Ltd The Studio, Long Lane, Fradley, Lichfield, Staffordshire, WS13 8NX, United Kingdom
✆ (01283) 792990/ ✆ (01283) 792993
✉ studio@iceni-tv.co.uk
🖥 www.iceni-tv.co.uk

Icon Films (PACT) 10 Redland Terrace, Bristol, BS6 6TD, United Kingdom
✆ 0117-970 6882
✉ info@iconfilms.co.uk
🖥 www.iconfilms.co.uk

Igloo Films The Filmvaults, Halliford Studios, Manygate Lane, Shepperton, Middlesex, TW17 9EG, United Kingdom
✆ (01932) 223843/ ✆ (01932) 246336
✉ info@iglooprod.com
🖥 www.iglooprod.com

Illuminations Television (PACT) 19-20 Rheidol Mews, Rheidol Terrace, London, N1 8NU, United Kingdom
✆ (020) 7288 8400/ ✆ (020) 7359 1151
✉ info@illumin.co.uk
🖥 www.illumin.co.uk

Imagicians TV Ltd (PACT) 34 Fouberts Place, London, W1F 7PX, United Kingdom
✆ (020) 8374 4429/(07973) 736502 ✆ (020) 8374 4436
✉ imagicians@blueyonder.co.uk
🖥 www.imagicians.tv

Imagination 25 Store Street, South Crescent, London, WC1E 7BL, United Kingdom
✆ (020) 7323 3300/ ✆ (020) 7462 2840
✉ firstname.lastname@imagination.com
🖥 www.imagination.com

In Motion Productions 69 Lancaster Road, Southampton, SO16 5DN, United Kingdom
✆ (023) 8070 1340/ ✆ (023) 8078 3911
✉ filminfo@inmoprog.org
🖥 www.inmoprog.org

Independent Films 7/8 Bourlet Close, London, W1W 7BW, United Kingdom
✆ (020) 7927 9400/ ✆ (020) 7927 9401
✉ mail@independ.net
🖥 www.independ.net

Interesting Television Ltd Oakslade Studios, Station Road, Hatton, Warwick, CV35 7LH, United Kingdom
✆ (01926) 844044/ ✆ (01926) 844045
✉ sales@oakslade.com
🖥 www.interestingtv.co.uk

Intro (AFVPA) 42 St John's Street, London, EC1M 4DL, United Kingdom
✆ (020) 7324 3244/ ✆ (020) 7324 3245
✉ intro@intro-uk.com
🖥 www.introwebsite.com

IQ Media The Coach House, Sundial House, Altringham Road, Styal, Near Wilmslow, Cheshire, SK9 4JE, United Kingdom
✆ (01625) 418666/ ✆ (01625) 522253
✉ info@iqmedia-uk.com
🖥 www.iqmedia-uk.com

ITV Border TV Centre, Carlisle, CA1 3NT, United Kingdom
✆ (01228) 525101/ ✆ (01228) 541384
🖥 www.itv.com/border

IWC Media Ltd St George's Studio, 93 - 97 St George's Road, Glasgow, G3 6JA, United Kingdom
✆ 0141-353 3222/ ✆ 0141-353 3221
✉ mailglasgow@iwcmedia.co.uk
🖥 www.iwcmedia.co.uk

J B Communications Ltd 15 Brackenbury Road, London, W6 0BE, United Kingdom
✆ (020) 8749 6036/ ✆ (020) 8749 9676
✉ inspire@jbcommunications.co.uk
🖥 www.jbcommunications.co.uk

J D Associates Ltd The Courtyard, 60 Station Road, Marlow, Buckinghamshire, SL7 1NX, United Kingdom
✆ (01628) 890015/ ✆ (01628) 890361
✉ enquiries@jda-multimedia.co.uk
🖥 www.jda-mulitmedia.co.uk

J K Advertising Ltd 730 Pershore Road, Selly Oak, Birmingham, B29 7NJ, United Kingdom
✆ 0121-472 1000/ ✆ 0121-414 1290
✉ info@jkadvertising.co.uk
🖥 www.jkadvertising.co.uk

Jacaranda Productions Ltd (IVCA) 6 Studland Street, London, W6 0JS, United Kingdom
✆ (020) 8741 9088/ ✆ (020) 8748 5670
✉ creative@jacaranda.co.uk
🖥 www.jacaranda.co.uk

Jaidcreative 5/12/27, Shirokane, Minato-Ku, Tokyo, 108-0072, Japan
✆ 00 81 3 5423 6855/ ✆ 00 81 3 5423 0071
✉ justin@jaidcreative.com
🖥 www.jaidcreative.com

JiB Productions Royal Docks Business Centre Ltd, University of East London, 4-6 University Way, London, E16 2RD, United Kingdom
✆ (07811) 988 108
✉ info@jibproductions.co.uk
🖥 www.jibproductions.co.uk

Joe & Co Music Ltd 59 Dean Street, London, W1D 6AN, United Kingdom
✆ (020) 7439 1272/ ✆ (020) 7437 5504
✉ justine@joeandco.com
🖥 www.joeandco.com

John Burder Films
Bournemouth, United Kingdom
✆ (01202) 295395
✉ burderfilms@aol.com
🖥 www.johnburder.co.uk

John Mills Film & Television 4 Effingham Road, Surbiton, Surrey, KT6 5JY, United Kingdom
✆ (020) 8398 8084/(07973) 699804 ✆
✉ mills.film@btclick.com

Joy@RSA Films Ltd 42-44 Beak Street, London, W1F 9RH, United Kingdom
✆ (020) 7432 3155/ ✆ (020) 7734 4978
✉ firstname-joy@rsafilms.co.uk
🖥 www.rsafilms.com

K D C Films Ltd The Old Bridge, Taggs Island, Hampton, Middlesex, TW12 2HA, United Kingdom
✆ (020) 8941 7776/ ✆ (020) 7736 5594
✉ kdcfilms@globalnet.co.uk

Keo Films (PACT) 101 St John's Street, London, EC1M 4AF, United Kingdom
✆ (020) 7490 3580/ ✆ (020) 7490 8419
✉ keo@keofilms.com
🖥 www.keofilms.com

King Rollo Films Ltd Dolphin Court, High Street, Honiton, Devon, EX14 1HT, United Kingdom
✆ (01404) 45218/ ✆ (01404) 45328
✉ leo@kingrollofilms.co.uk
🖥 www.kingrollofilms.co.uk

Kinsman & Co. Ltd (AFVPA) 17 Chepstow Crescent, London, W11 3EA, United Kingdom
✆ (020) 7727 2455/ ✆ (020) 7727 6944
✉ kinsmanco@hotmail.com

Kronfli Duliba Productions Ltd Harefield South Lodge, Alderley Road, Wilmslow, Cheshire, SK9 1RA, United Kingdom
✆ (01625) 536606/ ✆ (01625) 536603
✉ enquiries@kronfli-duliba.com
🖥 www.kronfli-duliba.com
See ad in showcase

Kudos Film & TV Ltd (PACT) 12-14 Amwell Street, London, EC1R 1UQ, United Kingdom
✆ (020) 7812 3270/ ✆ (020) 7812 3271
✉ info@kudosfilmandtv.com
🖥 www.kudosfilmandtv.com

LAM Communications 52 Elmwood Road, Chiswick, London, W4 3DZ,
✆ 020 8995 9652/ ✆ 020 8994 3164
✉ larry@lamcomms.com
🖥 www.lamcomms.com

LC1 Ltd 55 Merthyr Terrace, Barnes, London, SW13 8DL, United Kingdom
✆ (020) 8741 5747/ ✆ (020) 8748 9879
✉ contact@lci-uk.com
🖥 www.lci-uk.com

Leeds Animation Workshop 45 Bayswater Row, Leeds, LS8 5LF, United Kingdom
✆ 0113-248 4997/ ✆ 0113-248 4997
✉ law@leedsanimation.org.uk
🖥 www.leedsanimation.org.uk

Legs Productions Throstle Farm, Glossop Road, Little Hayfield, High Peak, Derbyshire, SK22 2NG, United Kingdom
✆ (01663) 742255/ ✆ (01663) 742255
✉ lyndone@onetel.com

Liberty Bell Adamson House, 65 Westgate Road, Newcastle upon Tyne, NE1 1SG, United Kingdom
✆ 0191-222 1200/ ✆ 0191-222 1210
✉ louise.mitchell@libertybell.tv
🖥 www.libertybell.tv

Light Division Ltd 11 Christchurch Gardens, Reading, RG2 7AH, United Kingdom
☎ 0118-931 3859

Lime Pictures Ltd Campus Manor, Childwall Abbey Road, Liverpool, L16 0JP, United Kingdom
☎ 0151-722 9122/☏ 0151-722 1969
🖳 www.limepictures.com

Line Communications Group Ltd (IVCA) 6th Floor, 14-16 Westbourne Grove, London, W2 5RH, United Kingdom
☎ (020) 7243 7181/☏ (020) 7243 9080
✉ info@line.co.uk
🖳 www.line.co.uk

Lion Television Ltd (PACT) 26 Paddenswick Road, London, W6 0UB, United Kingdom
☎ (020) 8846 2000/☏ (020) 8846 2001
✉ firstname.surname@liontv.co.uk
🖳 www.liontv.co.uk

Lion Television Scotland (PACT) 14 Royal Crescent, Glasgow, G3 7SL, United Kingdom
☎ 0141-331 0450/☏ 0141-331 0451
✉ mail@liontv.co.uk
🖳 www.liontv.co.uk

Little King Communications The Studio, 2 Newport Road, London, SW13 9PE, United Kingdom
☎ (020) 8741 7658/☏ (020) 8563 2742
✉ littleking@squaremail.co.uk

Little Piece of Jamaica 55 Finsbury Park Road, Highbury, London, N4 2JY, United Kingdom
☎ (020) 7359 0788/(07973) 630729 ☏
✉ paulhuelpoj@yahoo.co.uk
🖳 www.lpoj.co.uk

Logistik Live Carlton Mills, Pickering Street, Leeds, LS12 2QG, United Kingdom
☎ 0113-224 4800/☏ 0113-224 4801
✉ lindsay.kemp@logistik.co.uk
🖳 www.logistik.co.uk

London Fields Film & Video Ltd 10 Martello Street, London, E8 3PE, United Kingdom
☎ (020) 7241 2997/☏ (020) 7241 2997

London Media Link 20 Harvard Mans, St John's Hill, London, SW11 1TB, United Kingdom
☎ (020) 7228 5805/☏ (020) 7738 9168

Lonestar Ltd The Old Dance Hall, 338 London Road, Portsmouth, PO2 9JY, United Kingdom
☎ (023) 9265 1657/☏ (023) 9265 1658
✉ info@lonestar.co.uk
🖳 www.lonestar.co.uk

Look-Hear.com Westland Studios, PO Box 111, Watford, WD17 1PQ, United Kingdom
☎ (01923) 233030/(07831) 802223 ☏ (0870) 7053006
✉ jon@look-hear.com
🖳 www.look-hear.com

LOOK: Photographers & Production Room 8, 94 Oxford Street, Sydney, 2010, Australia
☎ 00 61 29 380 8822/☏ 00 61 29 380 8988
✉ shoot@lookproduction.com
🖳 www.lookproduction.com

Loose Moose Ltd (AFVPA, PACT) 74 Berwick Street, London, W1F 8TF, United Kingdom
☎ (020) 7287 3821/☏ (020) 7734 4220
✉ info@loosemoose.net
🖳 www.loosemoose.net

M C L Birmingham 69 Dartmouth Middleway, Birmingham, B7 4UA, United Kingdom
☎ 0121-333 3333/☏ 0121-333 3347
✉ hire@mcl-birmingham.com
🖳 www.mclav.com

M O D Films 9 Wyndham Street, London, W1H 1DB, United Kingdom
☎ (020) 7723 4674/☏ (020) 7723 4764
✉ reception@modfilms.com
🖳 www.modfilms.com

Malachite Ltd (PACT) East Kirkby House, Spilsby, Lincolnshire, PE23 4BX, United Kingdom
☎ (01790) 763538/☏ (01790) 763409
✉ info@malachite.co.uk
🖳 www.malachite.co.uk

Mandarin Kite Productions 94 Broxash Road, Battersea, London, SW11 6AB, United Kingdom
☎ (020) 7924 1210
✉ hello@mandarin-kite.com
🖳 www.mandarin-kite.com

Mandrill Television 1 Holly Tree House, Northminster Business Park, Northfield Lane, Upper Poppleton, York, YO26 6QU, United Kingdom
☎ (01904) 788700
✉ chris.wise@mandrill-television.com

Mantaplan Ltd Douglas Drive, Godalming, Surrey, GU7 1HJ, United Kingdom
☎ (01483) 420088/☏ (01483) 424566
✉ production@mantaplan.com
🖳 www.mantaplan.com

Map Films (AFVPA) 21 Little Portland Street, London, W1W 8BT, United Kingdom
☎ (020) 7612 0190/☏ (020) 7612 0199
✉ mail@mapfilms.com
🖳 www.mapfilms.com

Maritz Communications Ltd (IVCA) Alexander House, 3rd Avenue, Marlow, Buckinghamshire, SL7 1YW, United Kingdom
☎ (01628) 486011/☏ (01628) 475737
✉ info@maritz.co.uk
🖳 www.maritz.co.uk

Mark Wesley Productions 15 Fitz Piers, Saffron Walden, Essex, CB10 2BD, United Kingdom
☎ (01799) 521299/☏ (01799) 502202
✉ enquiries@markwesleyproductions.co.uk
🖳 www.markwesleyproductions.co.uk

Maverick Media Moray House, 23-31 Great Titchfield Street, London, W1W 7PA, United Kingdom
☎ (020) 7291 3450/☏ (020) 7323 4143
✉ info@maverickmedia.co.uk
🖳 www.maverickmedia.co.uk

Maverick Television (PACT) Progress Works, Heathmill Lane, Birmingham, B9 4AL, United Kingdom
☎ 0121-771 1812/☏ 0121-771 1550
✉ mail@mavericktv.co.uk
🖳 www.mavericktv.co.uk

Maya Vision International (PACT) 6 Kinghorn Street, London, EC1A 7HW, United Kingdom
☎ (020) 7796 4842/☏ (020) 7796 4580
✉ info@mayavisionint.com
🖳 www.mayavisionint.com

Medialink International 52-58 Shorts Gardens, London, WC2H 9AN, United Kingdom
☎ (020) 7845 7300/☏ (020) 7845 7310
✉ office@europe.medialink.com
🖳 www.europe.medialink.com

Mendoza Productions (APA) 3-5 Barrett Street, London, W1U 1AY, United Kingdom
☎ (020) 7935 4674/☏ (020) 7935 4417
✉ office@mendozafilms.com
🖳 www.mendozafilms.com

Michael Fogarty Associates 91 Sterndale Road, London, W14 0HX, United Kingdom
☎ (020) 7602 0814/☏ (020) 7603 6692
✉ mike@corporatemovies.co.uk
🖳 www.corporatemovies.co.uk

Mighty Media Unit M, Bourne End Business Park, Bourne End, Buckinghamshire, SL8 5AS, United Kingdom
☎ (01628) 522002/☏ (01628) 526530
✉ info@mightymedia.co.uk
🖳 www.mightymedia.co.uk

Mirtos Productions Flat 3, 307 Norwood Road, London, SE24 9AQ, United Kingdom
☎ (07973) 302908
✉ info@mirtosproductions.co.uk
🖳 www.mirtosproductions.co.uk

Mob Film Co. 10-11 Great Russell Street, London, WC1B 3NH, United Kingdom
☎ (020) 7580 8142/☏ (020) 7255 1721
✉ mail@mobfilm.com
🖳 www.mobfilm.com

Morrison Co. 302 Clive Court, Maida Vale, London, W9 1SF, United Kingdom
☎ (020) 7289 9807/(07831) 256959 ☏
✉ don@morrisonco.com
🖳 www.morrisonco.com

Mosaic Films Ltd 1a Flaxman Court, London, W1F 0AU, United Kingdom
☎ (020) 7734 7224
✉ info@mosaicfilms.com

Multi Media Arts (PACT) 4th Floor, Mauldeth House, Nell Lane, Manchester, M21 7RL, United Kingdom
☎ 0161-374 5566/☏ 0161-374 5535
✉ info@mmarts.com
🖳 www.mmarts.com

Multicord Audio Visual Services Hilltop Cottage, Coatham Mundeville, Darlington, County Durham, DL1 3NJ, United Kingdom
☎ (0845) 6060545/(07736) 808411 ☏
✉ info@multicord.co.uk
🖳 www.multicord.co.uk

N S L X 21 Warren Road, Woodley, Reading, RG5 3AR, United Kingdom
☎ 0118-376 9683/(07981) 266163 ☏
✉ neilscrivener@hotmail.com
🖳 www.pulselighting.net/nslx/

NBS Studio 12 Kempson Drive, Great Cornard, Sudbury, Suffolk, CO10 0ND, United Kingdom
☎ (01787) 376763
✉ info@nbs-studio.com
🖳 www.nbs-studio.com

Nebraska Productions 12 Grove Avenue, London, N10 2AR, United Kingdom
☎ (0)8444 5317/07710 850 373 ☏
✉ nebraskaprods@aol.com

Nick Veasey Radar Studios, Coldblow Lane, Thurnham, Maidstone, Kent, ME14 3LR, United Kingdom
☎ (01622) 737722/☏ (01622) 738644
✉ nick@nickveasey.com
🖳 www.nickveasey.com

Nicolas Kullmann Big Bird Film Company, 54 Ladbroke Grove, London, W11 2PB, United Kingdom
☎ (07785) 323952/☏ (020) 7792 0874
✉ kimex@lineone.net

North One Television Ltd (PACT) Mayward House, 46-52 Pentonville Road, London, N1 9HF, United Kingdom
☎ (020) 7502 6000/☏ (020) 7502 5600
✉ firstname.surname@northonetv.com
🖳 www.northonetv.com

North West Video Productions 9A New Street, Carnforth, Lancashire, LA5 9BX, United Kingdom
☎ (01524) 735774/☏ (01524) 736386
✉ steve@telerail.co.uk
🖳 www.telerail.co.uk

Nowadays Saarbrücker Str. 37a, Berlin, 10405, Germany
☎ 30 4435 1900/☏ 30 4435 1909 9
✉ contact@nowadays.de
🖳 www.nowadays.de

Ocean Magic Entertainment
Maidstone, Kent, ME14 5XU, United Kingdom
☎ (01622) 729593
✉ oceanmagicent@yahoo.co.uk
🖳 www.crescentmoon.org.uk/om

October Films (PACT) 4th & 5th Floors, Spring House, 10 Spring Place, London, London, NW5 3BH, United Kingdom
☎ (020) 7284 6868/☏ (020) 7284 6869
✉ info@octoberfilms.co.uk
🖳 www.octoberfilms.co.uk

Off The Planet Productions
Okehampton, Devon, EX20 4ZQ, United Kingdom
☎ (01837) 658805/☏ (0870) 4322040
✉ info@offtheplanet.tv
🖳 www.offtheplanet.tv

ON Communication The Media Lab, 5 East Saint Helen Street, Abingdon, Oxford, Oxfordshire, OX14 5EG, United Kingdom
☎ (01235) 537400/☏ (01235) 530581
✉ info@oncommunication.com
🖳 www.oncommunication.com

One World Productions Ltd 1 Sycamore Street, London, EC1Y 0SF, United Kingdom
☎ (020) 7336 8996/☏ (020) 7336 8626
✉ lindsay@oneworldproduction.co.uk
🖳 www.oneworldproduction.co.uk

Ooops Creative agency 37 Rue Capitaine Marchal, Paris, 75020, France
☎ 00 33 1 43 79 22 10/☏ 00 33 1 43 79 22 10
✉ andreaturek@wanadoo.fr
🖳 www.ooops-agency.com

Opus Television (PACT, TAC) 60 Severn Grove, Canton, Cardiff, CF11 9EP, United Kingdom
☎ (029) 2022 3456/☏ (029) 2037 7746
✉ opus@opustf.com
🖳 www.opustf.com

Or TV Ltd 22 The Green, Richmond, Surrey, TW9 1PX, United Kingdom
☎ (020) 8614 7200/☏ (020) 8614 7220
✉ reception@ortv.co.uk
🖳 www.ortv.co.uk

Oriel Communications (IVCA) 4 Baron's Gate, Rothschild Road, London, W4 5HT, United Kingdom
☎ (020) 8995 3445/☏ (020) 8742 7578
✉ oriel@cix.co.uk
🖳 www.orielcommunications.com

Original Film & Video Productions Ltd (IVCA) 84 St Dionis Road, London, SW6 4TU, United Kingdom
- (020) 7731 0012/(07850) 780370
- original.films@btinternet.com
- www.originalproductions.co.uk

Outsider Ltd (AFVPA) 2nd Floor, 41-42 Foley Street, London, W1W 7TS, United Kingdom
- (020) 7636 6666/ (020) 7323 0242
- anyone@outsider.tv
- www.outsider.tv

Oxford Film & Television Co. Ltd (PACT) Leeder House, 6 Erskine Road, London, NW3 3AJ, United Kingdom
- (020) 7483 3637/ (020) 7483 3567
- email@oftv.co.uk
- www.oftv.co.uk

Ozono Filmes Rua Pero Covilh, 38, Lisboa, 1400-297, Portugal
- 21 300 5000/ 21 300 5008
- geral@ozonofilmes.com
- www.ozonofilmes.com

P S Creative Moorfield Farm, Waystone Lane, Belbroughton, Stourbridge, West Midlands, DY9 0BG, United Kingdom
- (01562) 731724
- martin@pscreative.co.uk
- www.pscreative.co.uk

P V A Management Ltd Hallow Park, Hallow, Worcester, WR2 6PG, United Kingdom
- (01905) 640663/ (01905) 641842
- pvamanltd@aol.com
- www.pva.co.uk

Pace Productions Ltd (IVCA) 7 Barnsway, Kings Langley, Hertfordshire, WD4 9PW, United Kingdom
- (01923) 269590
- info@paceproductions.com
- www.paceproductions.com

Paladin Invision Ltd (PACT) 8 Barb Mews, London, London, W6 7PA, United Kingdom
- (020) 7371 2123/ (020) 7371 2160
- clive@pitv.com
- www.pitv.com

Panama Productions Sovereign House, 12 Trewartha Road, Praa Sands, Penzance, Cornwall, TR20 9ST, United Kingdom
- (01736) 762826/(07721) 449477/ (01736) 763328
- panamus@aol.com
- www.panamamusic.co.uk

Parallax East Ltd (PACT) Victoria Chambers, St. Runwalds Street, Colchester, CO1 1HF, United Kingdom
- (01206) 574909
- assistant@parallaxindependent.co.uk
- www.parallaxindependent.co.uk

Paramount Home Entertainment UK Ltd 45 Beadon Road, Hammersmith, London, W6 0EG, United Kingdom
- (020) 8741 9333/ (020) 8741 5690
- www.paramount.com

Park Village Ltd 1 Park Village East, Regents Park, London, London, NW1 7PX, United Kingdom
- (020) 7387 8077/ (020) 7388 3051
- reception@parkvillage.co.uk
- www.parkvillage.co.uk

Partizan Ltd (AFVPA) 40-42 Lexington Street, London, W1F 0LM, United Kingdom
- (020) 7851 0200/ (020) 7851 0249
- kate.redvers@partizan.com
- www.partizan.com

Passion Pictures (AFVPA) 3rd Floor, 33-34 Rathbone Place, London, W1T 1JN, United Kingdom
- (020) 7323 9933/ (020) 7323 9030
- info@passion-pictures.com
- www.passion-pictures.com

Pat Shirreff-Thomas (IVCA) 5 Morris Street, Hook, Hampshire, RG27 9NT, United Kingdom
- (01256) 767090/(07831) 519217/ (01256) 767612
- www.greenshoots.co.uk

Patricia Murphy Films 14 Lawfords Wharf, Lyme Street, London, NW1 0SF, United Kingdom
- (020) 7267 0007
- office@patriciamurphy.co.uk
- www.patriciamurphy.co.uk

Paul Knight Film & TV Production 2nd Floor, 26 St Annes Court, London, W1F 0BL, United Kingdom
- (020) 7734 7042/ (020) 7734 9270
- pknight@dircon.co.uk

Paul Weiland Film Co. (AFVPA) 14 Newburgh Street, London, W1F 7RT, United Kingdom
- (020) 7287 6900/ (020) 7434 0146
- action@paulweiland.com
- www.paulweiland.com

PCI Fitch G4 Harbour Yard, Chelsea Harbour, London, SW10 0XD, United Kingdom
- (020) 7544 7500/ (020) 7352 7906
- www.pcifitch.com

Peppers Ghost Productions (PACT) Clarendon House, 147 London Road, Kingston upon Thames, Surrey, KT2 6NH, United Kingdom
- (020) 8546 4900/ (020) 8546 4284
- enquiries@peppersghost.com
- www.peppersghost.com

Peter Batty Productions Ltd Claremont House, Renfrew Road, Kingston upon Thames, Surrey, KT2 7NT, United Kingdom
- (020) 8942 6304
- peter@wbatty.freeserve.co.uk

Phil Turner Productions 39 Nero Court, Justin Close, Brentford, Middlesex, TW8 8QB, United Kingdom
- (07956) 203559
- phil@philturnerproductions.com
- www.philturnerproductions.com

Photoflex Studios 36 Spindus Road, Liverpool, L24 1YA, United Kingdom
- (07860) 836145
- mail@photoflex.co.uk
- www.photoflex.co.uk

Picardy Media & Communication 1 Park Circus, Glasgow, G3 6AX, United Kingdom
- 0141-333 5555/ 0141-332 6002
- info@picardy.co.uk
- www.picardy.co.uk

Picasso Pictures Ltd 9-11 Broadwick Street, London, W1F 0DB, United Kingdom
- (020) 7437 9888/ (020) 7437 9040
- info@picassopictures.com
- www.picassopictures.com

Picture Palace Productions (PACT) 13 Egbert Street, London, NW1 8LJ, United Kingdom
- (020) 7586 8763/ (020) 7586 9048
- info@picturepalace.com
- www.picturepalace.com

Pilot Film & Television Productions (PACT) The Old Studio, 18 Middle Row, London, W10 5AT, United Kingdom
- (020) 8960 2771/ (020) 8960 2721
- info@pilot.co.uk
- www.pilotguides.com

Pioneer Productions (PACT) Voyager House, 32 Gallena Road, London, W6 0LT, United Kingdom
- (020) 8748 0888/ (020) 8748 7888
- pioneer@pioneertv.com
- www.pioneertv.com

Planet 24 Productions (PACT) 35-38 Portman Square, London, W1H 0NU, United Kingdom
- (020) 7486 6268/ (020) 7612 0679
- aliceb@planet24.co.uk
- www.planet24.com

Polecam TV Studio 2, 77 Beak Street, London, W1F 9DB, United Kingdom
- (020) 7734 3571/(07770) 747443
- keith@tx-2.com
- www.polecam.tv

Popsushi 82 Merchants Quay, East Street, Leeds, LS9 8BB, United Kingdom
- (0870) 4029947/ (0870) 4029948
- getmore@popsushi.co.uk
- www.popsushi.com

Presentable Ltd (PACT) 46 Cardiff Road, Llandaff, Cardiff, CF5 2DT, United Kingdom
- (029) 2057 5729/ (029) 2057 5605
- all@presentable.co.uk
- www.presentable.co.uk

Princess Productions Princess Studios, 3rd Floor, Whiteleys Centre, 151 Queensway, London, W2 4YN, United Kingdom
- (020) 7985 1985/ (020) 7985 1986
- reception@princesstv.com
- www.princesstv.com

Principal Films Picture House, 65 Hopton Street, London, SE1 9LR, United Kingdom
- (020) 7928 9287/ (020) 7928 9886
- films@principalmedia.com
- www.principalmedia.com

Production 726 Wilmslow Road, Manchester, M20 2DW, United Kingdom
- 0161-438 0383/ (0870) 1338119
- guyferrington@aol.com

Production International Ltd (AFVPA) 114 New Cavendish Street, London, W1W 6XT, United Kingdom
- (020) 7631 2400/ (020) 7631 2401
- info@prodint.co.uk
- www.productioninternational.co.uk

Prospect Pictures Ltd (PACT) Capitol Studios, Wandsworth Plain, London, SW18 1ET, United Kingdom
- (020) 7636 1234/ (020) 7636 1236
- pp@prospect-uk.com
- www.prospect-uk.com

Push4 Ltd 12 York Place, Barry, South Glamorgan, CF62 7ED, United Kingdom
- (01446) 722200/ (0871) 4332398
- info@push4.com
- www.push4.com

Quickfire Media Ltd 33 West Park, Bristol, BS8 2LX, United Kingdom
- 0117-946 6838/ 0117-946 6840
- info@quickfiremedia.com
- www.quickfiremedia.com

R D F Media Ltd (PACT) The Gloucester Building, Kensington Village, Avonmore Road, London, W14 8RF, United Kingdom
- (020) 7013 4000/ (020) 7013 4001
- contactus@rdfmedia.com
- www.rdfmedia.com

R S A Films Ltd (AFVPA) 42-44 Beak Street, London, W1F 9RH, United Kingdom
- (020) 7437 7426/ (020) 7734 4978
- info@rsafilms.com
- www.rsafilms.com

R S P B Film Collection (FOCAL) The Lodge, Sandy, Bedfordshire, SG19 2DL, United Kingdom
- (01767) 680551/ (01767) 683262
- lynda.whytock@rspb.org.uk
- www.rspb.org.uk/films

Radical Films 21 Birchval Drive, Romiley, Stockport, Cheshire, SK6 4LD, United Kingdom
- 0161-494 9400/(07710) 443318
- radical@woollams.co.uk

Radical Media Ltd (AFVPA) 140 Wardour Street, London, W1F 8ZT, United Kingdom
- (020) 7432 6800/ (020) 7432 6899
- info@radicalmedia.com
- www.radicalmedia.com

Ragdoll Ltd Timothy's Bridge Road, Stratford-upon-Avon, Warwickshire, CV37 9NQ, United Kingdom
- (01789) 404100/ (01789) 404178
- reception@ragdoll.co.uk
- www.ragdoll.co.uk

Ragdoll Ltd (PACT) Heathfarm, Pinewood Studios, Iver Heath, Iver, Buckinghamshire, SL0 0NH, United Kingdom
- (01753) 631800/ (01753) 631831
- pinewood@ragdoll.co.uk
- www.ragdoll.co.uk

Reach Marketing Ltd Trinity Hall, Trinity Lane, Leicester, LE1 6WP, United Kingdom
- 0116-233 5592/ 0116-233 5595
- info@reachmarketing.co.uk
- www.reachmarketing.co.uk

Real To Reel Productions Ltd (IVCA) 61-63 Churchfield Road, London, W3 6AY, United Kingdom
- (020) 8993 6000/ (020) 8993 6006
- office@realtoreel.co.uk
- www.realtoreel.co.uk

Reality Fades Ltd 1341 High Road, Whetstone, London, N20 9HR, United Kingdom
- (020) 8441 7252/(07831) 201534/ (020) 8441 7252
- info@realityfades.com
- www.realityfades.com

Red Door Television (PACT) Ltd 13 Ingram Road, London, N2 9QA, United Kingdom
- (020) 8829 4949/ (020) 8829 4969
- anita@rdoor.co.uk
- www.rdoor.co.uk

Renard TV Westbere Cottage, Westbere, Canterbury, Kent, CT2 0HH, United Kingdom
- (01227) 710505/ (01227) 710505
- adrian.moore@renard-tv.com

Richmond Films & Television Ltd (PACT)
London, NW3 4AZ, United Kingdom
(020) 7722 6464/ (020) 7722 6232
mail@richmondfilms.com

Rodney Read 45 Richmond Road, Twickenham, TW1
3AW, United Kingdom
(020) 8891 2875/(07956) 321550/ (020) 8744 9603
rodney_read@blueyonder.co.uk
www.rodney-read.com

Roger Bolton Productions (The Flame TV) (PACT) 6-
9 Cynthia Street, London, N1 9JF, United Kingdom
(020) 7713 6868/ (020) 7713 6999
info@flametv.co.uk
www.theflamegroup.co.uk

Rogue Films (AFVPA) 2-3 Bourlet Close, London, W1W
7BQ, United Kingdom
(020) 7907 1000/ (020) 7907 1001
www.roguefilms.com

Ronin Entertainment (PACT) 17 Newburgh Street,
London, W1F 7RZ, United Kingdom
(020) 7734 3844/ (020) 7434 1949
mail@ronintv.com
www.ronintv.com

Rooster Film & TV Productions 40 Weston Park,
Thames Ditton, Surrey, KT7 0HL, United Kingdom
(020) 8398 6839/ (020) 8398 6848
stuartorme@yahoo.co.uk

Rose Hackney Barber 5-6 Kingly Street, London, W1B
5PF, United Kingdom
(020) 7380 3435/ (020) 7434 4102
info@rosehackneybarber.com
www.rosehackneybarber.com

RoSPA Head Office 353 Bristol Road, Edgbaston,
Birmingham, B5 7ST, United Kingdom
0121-248 2000/ 0121-248 2001
help@rospa.com
www.rospa.com

Russell Hall Films Ltd 26 Lady Somerset Road, London,
NW5 1UP, United Kingdom
(020) 7267 8080/ (020) 7267 8080

Rutherford & Lennox Ltd 12a London Road, Tunbridge
Wells, Kent, TN1 1DE, United Kingdom
(01892) 538000
andrew@rutherford-lennox.co.uk
www.rutherford-lennox.co.uk

Sally Head Productions (PACT) Twickenham Film
Studios, St Margarets, Twickenham, TW1 2AW, United
Kingdom
(020) 8607 8730/ (020) 8607 8964
sally@shpl.demon.co.uk

Sands Film Studio (PACT) Grices Wharf, 119
Rotherhithe Street, London, SE16 4NF, United Kingdom
(020) 7231 2209/ (020) 7231 2119
ostockman@sandsfilms.co.uk
www.sandsfilms.co.uk

Scopitone Ltd Tower Bridge Business Complex, Block J
Suite 212, 100 Clements Road, London, SE16 4DG,
United Kingdom
(020) 7193 6528
info@scopitone.co.uk
www.scopitone.co.uk

Screen Ventures (PACT) 49 Goodge Street, London,
W1T 1TE, United Kingdom
(020) 7580 7448/ (020) 7631 1265
info@screenventures.com
www.screenventures.com

September Films (PACT) Glen House, 22 Glenthorne
Road, Hammersmith, London, W6 0NG, United Kingdom
(020) 8563 9393/ (020) 8741 7214
september@septemberfilms.com
www.septemberfilms.com

Serious Pictures (AFVPA) 1A Rede Place, London, W2
4TU, United Kingdom
(020) 7792 4477/ (020) 7792 4488
info@seriouspictures.com
www.seriouspictures.com

Seton Production 12 The Arundel Wing, Tortington
Manor, Ford Road, Arundel, West Sussex, BN18 0FG,
United Kingdom
(01903) 883720/(07770) 236938/
pgawith@btinternet.com

Seven Stones Media Ltd The Old Butchers Shop, High
Street, St. Briavels, Lydney, Gloucestershire, GL15 6TA,
United Kingdom
(01594) 530708/ (01594) 530094
info@sevenstonesmedia.com
www.sevenstonesmedia.com

Seventh Art Productions Ltd (PACT) 63 Ship Street,
Brighton, BN1 1AE, United Kingdom
(01273) 777678/ (01273) 323777
info@seventh-art.com
www.seventh-art.com

Shenanigans Berthelot 55, Pache Protopopescu 1,
Bucharest, 10165, Romania
00 40 72 224 6385/00 40 21 310 3737/ 00 40 21 310
3737
info@shenanigans.ro
www.shenanigans.ro

Shine Ltd 140-142 Kensington Church Street, London,
W8 4BN, United Kingdom
(020) 7985 7000/ (020) 7985 7001
info@shinelimited.com
www.shinelimited.com

Shooting Pictures Studio 18, Blue Lion Place, 237 Long
Lane, London, SE1 4PU, United Kingdom
(020) 7378 7988
info@shootingpictures.co.uk
www.shootingpictures.co.uk

Shop Film Production Co. Mallard Cottage, Newtown
Road, Ramsbury, Wiltshire, SN8 2PP, United Kingdom
(01672) 521272/(07836) 576093/
cof@appleinter.net

Silver Fox Films 2nd Floor, 118 Baker Street, London,
W1U 6TT, United Kingdom
(020) 7486 6546/ (020) 7486 6561
info@silverfoxfilms.com
www.silverfoxfilms.com

Six Digital 130 Mount Street, London, W1K 3NY, United
Kingdom
(020) 7409 0711
jeremy@six-digital.com
www.six-digital.com

Skyline Productions Ltd 10 Scotland Street, Edinburgh,
EH3 6PS, United Kingdom
0131-557 4580/ 0131-556 4377
admin@skyline.uk.com
www.skyline.uk.com

Sledge The Millhouse, Millers Way, London, W6 7NH,
United Kingdom
(020) 8743 3232/ (020) 8743 5062
ian.irving@sledge.co.uk
www.sledge.co.uk

Slyde Media 134 Windy House Lane, Sheffield, S2 1BY,
United Kingdom
(07719) 280804
slydeproductions@hotmail.com
www.slydemedia.plus.uk

Smoking Dogs Films (PACT) 26 Shacklewell Lane,
London, E8 2EZ, United Kingdom
(020) 7249 6644/ (020) 7249 6655
david@smokingdogsfilms.com
www.smokingdogsfilms.com

So Television 18 Hatfields, London, SE1 8GN, United
Kingdom
(020) 7960 2000/ (020) 7960 2095
info@sotelevision.co.uk
www.sotelevision.co.uk

Sound & Picture House The Coach House, 29
Woodburn Road, Edgbaston, Birmingham, B17 8BY,
United Kingdom
0121-429 5462/ 0121-429 6952
sph@sph.uk.com
www.soundandpicturehouse.com

Sounds Amusing Ltd
Leek, Staffordshire, ST13 7RF, United Kingdom
(01538) 304330/078 50 780802/ (01538) 304330
sales@soundsamusing.co.uk

Space City Productions 77 Blythe Road, London, W14
0HP, United Kingdom
(020) 7371 4000/ (020) 7371 4001
info@spacecity.co.uk
www.spacecity.co.uk

Spoken Image Ltd 8 Hewitt Street, Knottmill,
Manchester, M15 4GB, United Kingdom
0161-236 7522/ 0161-236 0020
multimedia@spoken-image.com
www.spoken-image.com

Spoton Film & TV Services Ltd Ormeau Business Park,
8 Cromac Avenue, Belfast, BT7 2JA, United Kingdom
(028) 9023 6111/(07860) 620743/ (028) 9023 6068
micky@spotontv.net
www.spotontv.net

Square Eyes Ltd 7 St. James's Avenue, Hampton Hill,
Middlesex, TW12 1HH, United Kingdom
(020) 8941 7520

SquareZero Suna House, 65 Rivington Street, London,
EC2A 3QQ, United Kingdom
(020) 7729 8998
vicky@squarezero.co.uk
www.squarezero.co.uk

Star Production Spring House, 10 Spring Place, London,
NW5 3BH, United Kingdom
(020) 7428 1414/ (020) 7428 1415
neena@starproduction.co.uk
www.starproduction.co.uk

Stewart Film Distributors The Dial House, Westmill,
Buntingford, Hertfordshire, SG9 9LG, United Kingdom
(01763) 271260/ (01763) 271473

Stink Ltd (AFVPA) 1 Alfred Mews, London, W1T 7AA,
United Kingdom
(020) 7462 4000/ (020) 7462 4001
info@stink.tv
www.stink.tv

Straker Films 3 St Marks Place, London, SW19 7ND,
United Kingdom
(020) 8605 2012/ (020) 8605 2121
nick@strakerfilms.com
www.strakerfilms.com

Studio AKA 30 Berwick Street, London, W1F 8RH,
United Kingdom
(020) 7434 3581/ (020) 7437 2309
pam@studioaka.co.uk
www.studioaka.co.uk

Sunset & Vine Production Ltd 30 Sackville Street,
London, W1S 3DY, United Kingdom
(020) 7478 7300/ (020) 7478 7407
nickv@sunsetvine.co.uk
www.sunsetvine.co.uk

Swerve Ltd 22 Denmark Street, London, WC2H 8NJ,
United Kingdom
(020) 7379 8444/ (020) 7379 8333
info@swerve.co.uk
www.swerve.co.uk

T V M S Scotland Ltd 3rd Floor, 420 Sauchiehall Street,
Glasgow, G2 3JD, United Kingdom
0141-331 1993/(07710) 121153/ 0141-332 9040
mail@tvms.wanadoo.co.uk
www.tvms.com

Take 3 Video & Film Production Ltd (IVCA) 72-73
Margaret Street, London, W1W 8ST, United Kingdom
(020) 7637 2694/ (020) 7637 4678
mail@take3.co.uk
www.take3.co.uk

TalkbackThames Ltd (AFVPA, IVCA, PACT) 20-21
Newman Street, London, W1T 1PG, United Kingdom
(020) 7861 8000/ (020) 7861 8001
reception.talkback@talkbackthames.tv
www.talkbackthames.tv

Talote Films 13 Shelley Road, Horsham, West Sussex,
RH12 2JH, United Kingdom
07792 056546
jonners99@hotmail.com
www.talote.co.uk

Tangerina Azul Filmes Praça De Goa 2, Lisbon, 1400-
184, Portugal
21 303 16 00/939 430 048/ 21 303 16 09
info@tangerinaazul.com
www.tangerinaazul.com

Taylor Made Broadcast Unit 3B, Marston House,
Cromwell Park, Chipping Norton, Oxfordshire, OX7 5SR,
United Kingdom
(01608) 646444/ (01608) 646461
post@tmtv.co.uk

TECTV 5 Woodfall Avenue, Barnet, Hertfordshire, EN5
2EZ, United Kingdom
(020) 8447 0001/(07754) 680999/

Tele-An Productions Ltd 1st Floor, 12-14 Denman
Street, London, W1D 7HJ, United Kingdom
(020) 7440 3720/ (020) 7440 3721
dean@tele-an.co.uk

PRODUCTION COMPANIES

Telegenic Ltd 4 Merlin Centre, Lancaster Road, High Wycombe, Buckinghamshire, HP12 3QL, United Kingdom
✆ (01494) 557400/ ✆ (01494) 557410
✉ telegenic@telegenic.co.uk
▨ www.telegenic.co.uk

Telemagination Ltd (PACT) Royalty House, 72-74 Dean Street, London, London, W1D 3SG, United Kingdom
✆ (020) 7534 2060/ ✆ (020) 7534 2062
✉ mail@tmation.co.uk
▨ www.telemagination.co.uk

Televirtual Ltd The Medialab, 9 Whitlingham Lane, Norwich, NR7 0QA, United Kingdom
✆ (01603) 431030
✉ tim@televirtual.com
▨ www.televirtual.com

Television Junction (PACT) Waterside House, 46 Gas Street, Birmingham, B1 2JT, United Kingdom
✆ 0121-248 4466/ ✆ 0121-248 4477
✉ info@televisionjunction.co.uk
▨ www.televisionjunction.co.uk

Ten Alps Brook Lapping Productions Ltd (PACT) 6 Anglers Lane, Kentish Town, London, NW5 3DG, United Kingdom
✆ (020) 7428 3100/ ✆ (020) 7284 0626
✉ info@brooklapping.com
▨ www.brooklapping.com

Tern Television Productions (PACT) 73 Crown Street, Aberdeen, AB11 6EX, United Kingdom
✆ (01224) 211123/ ✆ (01224) 211199
✉ aberdeen@terntv.com
▨ www.terntv.com

Tetra Films Ltd 24 Stormont Road, London, N6 4NP, United Kingdom
✆ (020) 8341 4032/ ✆ (020) 8341 4033
✉ alan.horrox@tetrafilms.demon.co.uk
▨ www.tetrafilms.demon.co.uk

Th1ng 53 Beak Street, London, W1F 9SH, United Kingdom
✆ (020) 7439 7966/ ✆ (020) 7437 8211
✉ dominic@th1ng.com
▨ www.th1ng.com

The 5YLAC Group 26 York Street, London, W1U 6PZ, United Kingdom
✆ (0845) 3104314/ ✆ (0870) 7623212
✉ info56@5ylac.biz
▨ www.5ylac.biz

The Bank (IPA) 16-18 Berners Street, London, W1T 3LN, United Kingdom
✆ (020) 7612 8000/ ✆ (020) 7612 8001
✉ reception@thebank.co.uk
▨ www.thebank.co.uk

The Direct Response TV Centre 20 Orange Street, London, WC2H 7EF, United Kingdom
✆ (020) 7389 0828/ ✆ (020) 7839 6993
✉ david@drtvcentre.com
▨ www.drtvcentre.com

The Loop Communication Agency 5th Flr, Hanover Hse, Queen Charlotte Street, Bristol, BS1 4EX, UK
✆ 0117-311 2040/ ✆ 0117-311 2041
✉ info@theloopagency.com
▨ www.theloopagency.com

The Media Merchants Television Centre, Vinters Park, Maidstone, Kent, ME14 5NZ, United Kingdom
✆ (01622) 684622/ ✆ (01622) 684627
✉ lallen@hitentertainment.com
▨ www.hitentertainment.com

The Producers (AFVPA, PACT) 8 Berners Mews, London, W1T 3AW, United Kingdom
✆ (020) 7636 4226/ ✆ (020) 7636 4099
✉ info@theproducersfilms.co.uk
▨ www.theproducersfilms.co.uk

The Refinery (Films) Ltd B101 Jam Factory, London, SE1 4TX, United Kingdom
✆ (020) 7234 0774/ ✆ (0870) 128 2588
✉ info@refineryfilms.com
▨ www.refineryfilms.com

The Whitehouse 12-13 Kingly Street, London, W1B 5PP, United Kingdom
✆ (020) 7287 3404/ ✆ (020) 7287 9670
✉ kate.o'mulloy@whitehousepost.com
▨ www.whitehousepost.com

Therapy Films Ltd 2nd Floor, 26 Market Place, London, W1W 8AN, United Kingdom
✆ (020) 7436 5191/ ✆ (020) 7637 1707
✉ info@therapyfilms.com
▨ www.therapyfilms.com

Tiger Aspect Productions Ltd (PACT) 7 Soho Street, London, W1D 3QJ, United Kingdom
✆ (020) 7434 6700/ ✆ (020) 7434 1798
✉ general@tigeraspect.co.uk
▨ www.tigeraspect.co.uk

Tiger Vision 27 Maiden Lane, Covent Garden, London, WC2E 7JS, United Kingdom
✆ (020) 7438 9960/ ✆ (020) 7438 9980
✉ production@tigervision.com
▨ www.tigervision.com

Tigress Productions (PACT) 7 Soho Street, London, W1D 3DQ, United Kingdom
✆ (020) 7434 4411/ ✆ (020) 7434 6821
✉ general@tigressproductions.co.uk
▨ www.tigressproductions.co.uk

Toast Ltd 10 Frith Street, London, W1D 3JF, United Kingdom
✆ (020) 7437 0506/ ✆ (020) 7439 8852
✉ anna@toasttv.co.uk
▨ www.toasttv.co.uk

Tom Dick & Debbie Productions Unit 2, The Gallery, 54 Marston Street, Oxford, OX4 1LF, United Kingdom
✆ (01865) 201564/ ✆ (01865) 201935
✉ info@tomdickanddebbie.com
▨ www.tomdickanddebbie.com

Tomboy Films Ltd 13A Hewer Street, London, W10 6DU, United Kingdom
✆ (020) 8962 3456/ ✆ (020) 8962 3457
✉ tomboy@tomboyfilms.co.uk
▨ www.tomboyfilms.co.uk

Tomboy Films Ltd (AFVPA) The Old Dairy, 13A Hewer Street, London, W10 6DU, United Kingdom
✆ (020) 8962 3456/ ✆ (020) 8962 3457
✉ info@tomboyfilms.co.uk
▨ www.tomboyfilms.co.uk

Tony Kaye Films (AFVPA) 27-29 Beak Street, London, W1F 9RU, United Kingdom
✆ (020) 7025 7542/ ✆ (020) 7025 7522
✉ mail@tonyk.ltd.uk

Topical Television (PACT) Devonshire House, 61 Devonshire Road, Southampton, SO15 2GR, United Kingdom
✆ (023) 8071 2233/ ✆ (023) 8033 9835
✉ topical.tv@topical.co.uk

Touch Productions Ltd (PACT) 18 Queens Square, Bath, BA1 2HN, United Kingdom
✆ (01225) 484666/ ✆ (01225) 483620
✉ enquiries@touchproductions.co.uk
▨ www.touchproductions.co.uk

Trans World International (PACT) McCormack House, 3 Burlington Lane, London, W4 2TH, United Kingdom
✆ (020) 8233 5400/ ✆ (020) 8233 5301
✉ jackie.myberg@imgworld.com
▨ www.imgworld.com

Transatlantic Films (PACT) Studio 1, 3 Brackenbury Road, London, W6 0BE, United Kingdom
✆ (020) 8735 0505/ ✆ (020) 8735 0605
✉ mail@transatlanticfilms.com
▨ www.transatlanticfilms.com

Travelshots.com Longfield Cottage, 3B Uplands Close, London, SW14 7AS, United Kingdom
✆ (020) 8878 2226/ ✆ (020) 8392 2920
✉ sales@travelshots.com
▨ www.travelshots.com

Turn on Television (PACT) Warehouse 4, 121 Princess Street, Manchester, M1 7AG, United Kingdom
✆ 0161-247 7700/ ✆ 0161-247 7711
✉ mail@turnontv.co.uk
▨ www.turnontv.co.uk

TV 6 (PACT) Unit 29, The Quadrangle, 49 Atalanta Street, London, SW6 6TU, United Kingdom
✆ (020) 7610 0266/ ✆ (020) 8392 1313
✉ mail@tv6.co.uk
▨ www.tv6.co.uk

TV Choice Ltd PO Box 597, Bromley, BR2 0YB, United Kingdom
✆ (020) 8464 7402/ ✆ (020) 8464 7845
✉ tvchoiceuk@aol.com
▨ www.tvchoice.co.uk

Twenty Twenty Television 20 Kentish Town Road, London, NW1 9NX, United Kingdom
✆ (020) 7284 2020/ ✆ (020) 7284 1810
✉ mail@twentytwenty.tv
▨ www.twentytwenty.tv

Two Four Productions (IVCA, PACT) 20-24 Kirby Street, London, EC1N 8TS, United Kingdom
✆ (020) 7438 1800/ ✆ (020) 7438 1850
✉ enq@twofour.co.uk
▨ www.twofour.co.uk

Two Four Studios 3 Bush Park, Pestover, Plymouth, PL6 7RG, United Kingdom
✆ (01752) 727400/ ✆ (01752) 727450
✉ enq@twofour.co.uk
▨ www.twofour.co.uk

Two Sides TV Ltd (PACT) 53A Brewer Street, London, W1F 9UH, United Kingdom
✆ (020) 7439 9882/ ✆ (020) 7287 2289
✉ info@2sidestv.co.uk
▨ www.2sidestv.co.uk

TX-2 Broadcast Ltd Studio 2, 77 Beak Street, Soho, London, W1F 9DB, United Kingdom
✆ (07770) 747443
✉ keith@tx-2.tv
▨ www.specialtycameras.tv

Tye Phillips Associates The Barn, Almners Farm House, Chertsey, Surrey, KT16 0BH, United Kingdom
✆ (01932) 560101/ ✆ (01932) 562647
✉ info@tyephillips.com

Uden Associates Ltd (IVCA, PACT) Unit 37, Chelsea Wharf, 15 Lots Road, Chelsea, London, SW10 0QJ, United Kingdom
✆ (020) 7351 1255/ ✆ (020) 7376 3937
▨ www.simonharries.com/miscproductions/udenassociates.htm

Union Commercials (AFVPA) 25 Beak Street, London, W1F 9RT, United Kingdom
✆ (020) 7734 5555/ ✆ (020) 7494 0604
✉ jonathon@union-commercials.com
▨ www.union-commercials.com

Update 70 Park Street, St. Albans, Hertfordshire, AL2 2PW, United Kingdom
✆ (01727) 875893/ ✆ (01727) 875730
✉ update@update-uk.com
▨ www.update-uk.com

Upstart Films 23 Denmark Street, London, WC2 8NH, United Kingdom
✆ (020) 7240 7411/ ✆ (020) 7240 9311
✉ anita@upstartfilms.co.uk
▨ www.upstartfilms.co.uk

UVL Film Production International PO Box 1358, Laise koppel 010, Biedenkopf, 35216, Germany
✆ 06461 924600/172 6403325 ✆ 06461 924655
✉ contact@uvl-filmproduction.de
▨ uvl-filmproduction.de

V C L Video 43-44 Hoxton Square, London, N1 6PB, United Kingdom
✆ (020) 7729 6967/ ✆ (020) 7613 0544
✉ info@vclvideo.com
▨ www.vclvideo.com

V M A International White House Studios, 40 New Street, Wigton, Cumbria, CA7 9AL, United Kingdom
✆ (01697) 343886/ ✆ (01697) 344958
✉ info@vma-international.com
▨ www.vma-international.com

Vanbrugh Films 10 Martello Street, London, E8 3PE, United Kingdom
✆ (020) 7241 2997/ ✆ (020) 7241 2997

Venner Television Ltd 30 Sackville Street, London, W1S 3DY, United Kingdom
✆ (020) 7478 7300/ ✆ (020) 7478 7415
✉ vtv@venner.tv
▨ www.venner.tv

Vera Productions (PACT) 3rd Floor, 66-68 Margaret Street, London, W1W 8SR, United Kingdom
✆ (020) 7436 6116/ ✆ (020) 7436 6117
✉ phoebe@vera.co.uk

Victoria Real (PACT) The Shepherds Building, Charecroft Way, London, W14 0EE, United Kingdom
✆ (0870) 3331700/ ✆ (020) 8222 4415
✉ sarah.hienmarsh@victoriareal.com
▨ www.victoriareal.com

Video & Film Production Robin Hill, The Ridge, Lower Basildon, Reading, RG8 9NX, United Kingdom
✆ 0118-984 2488/(07836) 544955 ✆ 0118-984 4316
✉ david.fisher@videoandfilm.co.uk
▨ www.videoandfilm.co.uk

Viewpress Television Woods Way, Goring-by-Sea, West Sussex, BN12 4QY, United Kingdom
✆ (01903) 534141/ ✆ (01903) 534142
✉ info@viewpress.co.uk
▨ www.viewpress.tv

Visible Ink Television Ltd (PACT) Nine Mile Burn, Penicuik, Midlothian, EH26 9LX, United Kingdom
✆ (01968) 661291/ (01968) 661291
✉ contact@visibleink.co.uk
🖥 www.visibleink.co.uk

Visual Link (IVCA) Kingstown Broadway, Carlisle, CA3 0HA, United Kingdom
✆ (01228) 403900/ (01228) 511267
✉ info@tvl.co.uk
🖥 www.tvl.co.uk

Vivum Intelligent Media Ltd 17 Scawfell Street, London, E2 8NG, United Kingdom
✆ (020) 7729 2749/(07971) 543703 (020) 7684 8128
✉ livewire@vivum.net
🖥 www.vivum.net

Waddell Media Ltd Strand Studios, 5-7 Shore Road, Holywood, County Down, BT18 9HX, United Kingdom
✆ (028) 9042 7646/ (028) 9042 7922
✉ info@waddellmedia.com
🖥 www.waddellmedia.com

Wall To Wall (PACT) 8-9 Spring Place, Kentish Town, London, NW5 3ER, United Kingdom
✆ (020) 7485 7424/ (020) 7267 5292
✉ mail@walltowall.co.uk
🖥 www.walltowall.co.uk

Walnut Media Communications Ltd 4 Sadler Close, Leeds, LS16 8NN, United Kingdom
✆ 0113-285 7906/(07850) 935541
✉ gary@walnutmedia.com
🖥 www.walnutmedia.com

Waterfall Multimedia Ltd 2 Silver Road, Wood Lane, London, W12 7SG, United Kingdom
✆ (020) 8746 2000/ (020) 8746 0180
✉ info@waterfall-studios.com
🖥 www.waterfall-studios.com

Weatherby Harvey Productions 6 Windmill Street, London, W1T 2JB, United Kingdom
✆ (020) 7637 9302/ (020) 7637 9303
✉ whprods@aol.com

Weston Point Studios Ltd Mersey Road, Western Point, Runcorn, Cheshire, WA7 1DA, United Kingdom
✆ (01928) 516050/ (01928) 572482
✉ lizhelsby@wpsltd.co.uk
🖥 www.wpsltd.co.uk

Westside Video Productions Blossom Lodge, 20 High Beeches, Gerrards Cross, Buckinghamshire, SL9 7HX, United Kingdom
✆ (01753) 890400
✉ stu@westsidevideo.co.uk
🖥 www.westsidevideo.co.uk

White Noise Productions Ltd Suite 308, India Mill Centre, Darwen, Lancashire, BB3 1AE, United Kingdom
✆ (01254) 777444/(07976) 515105 (01254) 777373
✉ info@whitenoiseonline.com
🖥 www.whitenoiseonline.com

Why Not Associates 22C Shepherdess Walk, London, N1 7LB, United Kingdom
✆ (020) 7253 2244/ (020) 7253 2299
✉ info@whynotassociates.com
🖥 www.whynotassociates.com

Wide Angle 10-Nov, 254-256 Belfize Road, London, Greater London, NW6 4BT, United Kingdom
✆ (020) 7916 3790/ (020) 7916 3799
✉ info@wideangle.co.uk
🖥 www.wideangle.co.uk

Wienerworld Ltd Unit 7, Free Trade House, Lowther Road, Stanmore, Stanmore, Middlesex, HA7 1EP, United Kingdom
✆ (020) 8206 1177/ (020) 8206 3757
✉ ordersplease@wienerworld.com
🖥 www.wienerworld.com

Wild Dream Films (PACT) Brighton, BN1 1WB, United Kingdom
✆ (01273) 236168/ (01273) 236165
✉ mail@wild-dream.com
🖥 www.wild-dream.com

Wilder 21 Montrose Avenue, London, NW6 6LE, United Kingdom
✆ (020) 7461 0713
✉ paulgowers@wilderfilms.co.uk
🖥 www.wilderfilms.co.uk

William Martin Productions (IVAC) The Studio, Tubney Warren Barns, Tubney, Abingdon, Oxfordshire, OX13 5QJ, United Kingdom
✆ (01865) 390258/ (01865) 390148
✉ info@wmproductions.co.uk
🖥 www.wmproductions.co.uk

Windfall Films Ltd (PACT) 1 Underwood Row, London, N1 7LZ, United Kingdom
✆ (020) 7251 7676/ (020) 7253 8468
✉ enquiries@windfallfilms.com
🖥 www.windfallfilms.com

WiseGuy Pictures Ltd Studio 54, Soho Wharf, Clink Street, London, SE1 9DG, United Kingdom
✆ (020) 7407 2007
✉ mail@wiseguy.co.uk
🖥 www.wiseguy.co.uk

Wish Films Elstree Film Studios, Shenley Road, Borehamwood, Hertfordshire, WD6 1JG, United Kingdom
✆ (020) 8324 2308/ (020) 8324 2696
✉ info@wishfilms.com
🖥 www.wishfilms.com

World of Wonder (PACT) Studio 700, Highgate Studios, 53-79 Highgate Road, London, NW5 1TL, United Kingdom
✆ (020) 7428 3444/ (020) 7428 3440
✉ wow@worldofwonder.co.uk
🖥 www.worldofwonder.net

World Productions Ltd (IVCA) 16 Dufours Place, London, W1F 7SP, United Kingdom
✆ (020) 7734 3536/ (020) 7758 7000
✉ info@world-productions.com
🖥 www.world-productions.com

World Wide Pictures (IVCA, PACT) 21-25 St Annes Court, London, W1F 0BJ, United Kingdom
✆ (020) 7434 1121/ (020) 7734 0619
✉ reception@worldwidegroup.ltd.uk
🖥 www.worldwidegroup.ltd.uk

Xube Ltd Unit 4, 51 Derbyshire Street, London, E2 6JQ, United Kingdom
✆ (020) 7739 5811/ 020 7900 6867
✉ info@xube.co.uk
🖥 www.xube.co.uk

Zenith Entertainment P.L.C. (PACT) 43-45 Dorset Street, London, W1U 7NA, United Kingdom
✆ (020) 7224 2440/ (020) 7224 1027
✉ general@zenith-entertainment.co.uk
🖥 www.zenith-entertainment.co.uk

SPOTLIGHT SPACES

- Record, edit & share your casting sessions
- Post audition clips online **for free**
- Hold live video-casting sessions to/from other locations

7 Leicester Place London WC2H 7RJ   www.spotlight.com/studios   020 7440 5041

Zig Zag Productions (PACT) 13-14 Great Sutton Street, Clerkenwell, London, EC1V 0BX, United Kingdom
✆ (020) 7017 8755/ (020) 7017 8750
✉ production@zigzag.uk.com
🖥 www.zigzag.uk.com

Zoo Gang Ltd 9 Wellington Road, Wimbledon Park, London, SW19 8EQ, United Kingdom
✆ (020) 8947 2404/ (020) 8947 2404

STORYBOARDS

Daydream Linton House, 164-180 Union Street, London, SE1 0LH,
✆ +44 (0) 20 7096 1471/+44 (0) 20 7117 1636
✉ ralph@daydream.co.uk
🖥 www.daydream.co.uk

Nicola L Robinson Mynachdy, Cardiff, Glamorgan, CF14 3AG,
✆
✉ nlrobinson@thesurrealdemon.co.uk
🖥 www.thesurrealdemon.co.uk

STUDIO HIRE

124 Facilities 124 Horseferry Road, London, SW1P 2TX, United Kingdom
✆ (020) 7306 8040/ (020) 7306 8041
✉ dbrowne@channel4.co.uk
🖥 www.124.co.uk

3 Mills Studios Three Mill Lane, Bromley By Bow, London, E3 3DU, United Kingdom
✆ **(020) 7363 3336/ (020) 8215 3499**
✉ **info@3mills.com**
🖥 **www.3mills.com**
See ad in showcase

3sixtymedia The Manchester Studio, Quay Street, Manchester, M60 9EA, United Kingdom
✆ 0161-839 0360/ 0161-827 2360
✉ enquiry@3sixtymedia.com
🖥 www.the-manchester-studios.tv

68 Dean Street 68 Dean Street, London, W1D 4QJ, United Kingdom
✆ (020) 7437 5512/(07855) 256860 (020) 7437 6612
✉ db@sixty8.com
🖥 www.sixty8.com

A Village Underground 52-54 Holywell Lane, Shoreditch, London, EC2A 3PQ, United Kingdom
✆ (07886) 751205
✉ info@villageunderground.co.uk
🖥 www.villageunderground.co.uk

Aimimage Camera Co. Unit 5, St. Pancras Commercial Centre, 63 Pratt Street, London, NW1 0BY, United Kingdom
✆ (020) 7482 4340/ (020) 7267 3972
✉ hire@aimimage.com
🖥 www.aimimage.com

Albada Studios Unit 83, Portmanmoor Road Industrial Estate, Ocean Way, Cardiff, CF24 5HB,
✆ 02920 495123
✉ adrian@albada.co.uk
🖥 www.albada.co.uk

Angelspace 27-28 St. Albans Place, London, N1 0NX, United Kingdom
 (020) 7704 8803
 greg@angelstudio.freeserve.co.uk
 www.angelspace.co.uk

Arqiva Ltd Chalfont Grove, Chalfont St. Peter, Narcot Lane, Gerrards Cross, Buckinghamshire, SL9 8TW, United Kingdom
 (01494) 878787/ (01494) 878478
 www.arqiva.com

Barcud Derwen Cyf Cibyn Industrial Estate, Caernarfon, Gwynedd, LL55 2BD, United Kingdom
 (01286) 671671/ (01286) 684379
 barcud@barcudderwen.co.uk
 www.barcudderwen.com

Big Sky London 29-31 Brewery Road, London, N7 9QH, United Kingdom
 (0870) 1996699/ (0870) 1992299
 them@bigskylondon.com
 www.bigskylondon.com

Birmingham Sound Hire Robannas Studios, Robanna House, Cliveland Street, Birmingham, B19 3SN, United Kingdom
 0121-333 3201/ 0121-359 3647
 info@birminghamsoundhire.co.uk
 www.birminghamsoundhire.co.uk

Bladon Studios Ltd Studio 2, Lower Road, Long Hanborough, Oxfordshire, OX29 8LW, United Kingdom
 (0845) 1082237
 steve@rsimail.co.uk
 www.bladonstudios.com

Bocek Production Cubuklu cad.agaclik mesire yeri, d+e burunbahce, beykoz, Istanbul, 34805,
 00 9 02166801058
 selma@bocekyapim.com.tr
 www.bocekyapim.com.tr

Bray Management Ltd Bray Film Studios, Down Place, Water Oakley, Windsor, Berkshire, SL4 5UG, United Kingdom
 (01628) 622111
 bray.studios@btinternet.com

C T V C (PACT) 1st Floor, 9-10 Copper Row, Tower Bridge Piazza, London, SE1 2LH, United Kingdom
 (020) 7940 8480/ (020) 7940 8490
 production@ctvc.co.uk
 www.ctvc.co.uk

Capital Studios Wandsworth Plain, London, SW18 1ET, United Kingdom
 (020) 8877 1234/ (020) 8877 0234
 info@capitalstudios.co.uk
 www.capitalstudios.com

Casting Studios International Ltd Ramillies House, 1-2 Ramillies Street, London, W1F 7LN, United Kingdom
 (020) 7437 2070/ (020) 7437 2080
 info@castingstudios.co.uk
 www.castingstudios.com

Casting Suite 8-10 Lower James Street, London, W1F 9EL, United Kingdom
 (020) 7434 2331/ (020) 7494 0803
 info@thecastingsuite.com
 www.thecastingsuite.com

Cinebuild Ltd Studio House, 34 Rita Road, London, SW8 1JU, United Kingdom
 (020) 7582 8750/(07836) 220441 / (020) 7793 0467
 cinebuild@btclick.com
 www.cinebuild.com

Duthy Hall Studios Duthy Hall, Great Guildford Street, London, SE1 0ES, United Kingdom
 (020) 7652 3322
 www.duthyhall.com

Edinburgh Film Studios West Marfield, Nine Mile Burn, Penicuik, Midlothian, EH26 9LT, United Kingdom
 (01968) 672131/(07956) 307381 /
 info@edinburghfilmstudios.co.uk
 www.edinburghfilmstudios.co.uk

Expressions Studios Linton House, 39-51 Highgate Road, London, NW5 1RS, United Kingdom
 (020) 7813 1580/ (020) 78131582
 info@expressionsstudios.com
 www.ExpressionsStudios.com

Eyewitness Hazardous Facilities Ltd The Drove, Sherfield English Road, Romsey, Hampshire, SO51 6EF, United Kingdom
 (01794) 322500/ (01794) 323601
 eyewitnessrental@aol.com
 www.eyewitnessuk.co.uk

Eyewitness Underwater Facilities Ltd The Drove, Sherfield English Road, Plaitford, Romsey, Hampshire, SO51 6EF, United Kingdom
 (01794) 322500/ (01794) 323601
 eyewitnessrental@aol.com
 www.eyewitnessuk.co.uk

First Option Studio 11 Perseverance Works, 38 Kingsland Road, London, E2 8DD, United Kingdom
 (020) 7739 0132/ (020) 7729 7066
 studio@christinehanscomb.co.uk
 www.christinehanscomb.co.uk

Halliford Studios Manygate Lane, Shepperton, Middlesex, TW17 9EG, United Kingdom
 (01932) 226341/ (01932) 246336
 sales@hallifordstudios.com
 www.hallifordfilmstudios.co.uk

Holborn Studios 49-50 Eagle Wharf Road, London, N1 7ED, United Kingdom
 (020) 7490 4099/ (020) 7253 8120
 reception@holborn-studios.co.uk
 www.holbornstudios.com

Home Studios 215-217 Coldharbour Lane, London, SW9 8RU,
 020 7099 9441
 info@homestudios.eu
 www.homestudios.eu

L H 2 142 Mildmay Road, London, N1 4NE, United Kingdom
 (020) 7275 7039/ (020) 7249 5376
 info@lh2.co.uk
 www.lh2.co.uk

Maidstone Studios Vinters Park, Maidstone, Kent, ME14 5NZ, United Kingdom
 (01622) 691111/ (01622) 684411
 info@maidstonestudios.com
 www.maidstonestudios.com

Moving Arts Base Syracusae, 134 Liverpool Road, London, N1 1LA, United Kingdom
 (020) 7609 6969
 info@movingartsbase.co.uk
 www.movingartsbase.co.uk

Perch 283 Camberwell New Road, London, SE5 0TF, United Kingdom
 (07767) 836221
 les@theperch.co.uk
 www.theperch.co.uk

Picture It Studios Units 47-49, Brunell Road, London, W3 7XR, United Kingdom
 (020) 8749 6767/ (020) 8743 9680
 abbie@picit.net
 www.picit.net

Pinewood Studios (Part of the Pinewood Group), Pinewood Road, Iver Heath, Buckinghamshire, SL0 0NH, United Kingdom
 (01753) 651700/ (01753) 656844
 info@pinewoodgroup.com
 www.pinewoodgroup.com

Pixeleye Studio 73 St. John Street, London, EC1M 4AN, United Kingdom
 (020) 7253 3202
 studio@pixeleye.co.uk
 www.pixeleye.co.uk

Quince Studios 62a Balcombe Street, London, NW1 6NE, United Kingdom
 (07810) 752765/ (020) 7723 1010
 info@quincestudios.co.uk
 www.quincestudios.co.uk

Shepperton Studios (Part of the Pinewood Group), Pinewood Road, Iver Heath, Iver, Buckinghamshire, SL0 0NH, United Kingdom
 (01932) 562611/ (01932) 568989
 info@pinewoodgroup.com
 www.pinewoodshepperton.com

South Manchester Studios Ltd Studio House, Battersea Road, Stockport, Cheshire, SK4 3EA, United Kingdom
 0161-432 9000/ 0161-443 1325
 enquiries@southmanchesterstudios.co.uk
 www.southmanchesterstudios.co.uk

Space-2 Battersea Studios, 80 Silverthorne Road, London, SW8 3HE, United Kingdom
 (07922) 224216
 mark@space2online.com
 www.space2online.com

Spring Studios Ltd 10 Spring Place, Kentish Town, London, NW5 3BH, United Kingdom
 (020) 7267 8383/(07764) 331234 / (020) 7267 8481
 info@springstudios.com
 www.springstudios.com

Stratford Studios Unit 122, Stratford Workshops, Burford Road, London, E15 2SP, United Kingdom
 (020) 8503 0304/ (020) 8503 0709
 info@stratfordstudios.co.uk
 www.stratfordstudios.co.uk

Studio 19 19 London Lane, London, E8 3PR, United Kingdom
 (020) 8525 7976/ (020) 8525 7976

Terry Payne Packshot & Food Photographer First Floor, Building D, The Chocolate Factory, Clarendon Road, London, N22 6XJ,
 020 8889 6609
 terry.payne1@ntlworld.com
 www.terrypaynephotog.co.uk

The Other Studio The Old School, 1 Thirsk Street, Ardwick Green, Manchester, M12 6FW, United Kingdom
 (0161) 273 7489/ (0161) 274 3449
 hire@theotherstudio.co.uk
 www.theotherstudio.co.uk

The ROOST 142 Sandringham Road, London, E8 2HJ, United Kingdom
 /07767 836221 / (020) 7703 7419
 les@theroost.co.uk
 www.theroost.co.uk

The Spotlight Casting Studios 7 Leicester Place, London, WC2H 7RJ, United Kingdom
 (020) 7437 5041/ (020) 7287 1201
 studios@spotlight.com
 www.spotlight.com/studios
 See ad in showcase

The Street Studios 2 Dunston Street, London, E8 4EB, United Kingdom
 (020) 7923 9430/ (020) 7923 9429
 mail@streetstudios.co.uk
 www.streetstudios.co.uk

The Studio 21 Cabul Road, London, SW11 2PR, United Kingdom
 (020) 7228 5228/07740 417278 / (020) 7228 9975
 thestudio@filmed.com
 the-studio.co.uk

The Village Studio Unit 5, The Village, 101 Amies Street, London, SW11 2JW, United Kingdom
 (020) 7738 2233/ (020) 7738 2244
 helen@thevillagestudio.net
 www.thevillagestudio.net

Thornton Howdle Photographic 4 Carter Terrace, Whitkirk, Leeds, LS15 7AH, United Kingdom
 0113-257 9041/07932 372216 /
 thorntonhowdle@mac.com
 www.thorntonhowdle.com

Touch Studios Unit 10, Waterside, 44-48 Wharf Road, London, N1 7UX, United Kingdom
 (020) 7608 2345/(07702) 290931 / (020) 7608 0017
 viv@touchstudios.co.uk
 www.touchstudios.co.uk

Twickenham Film Studios Ltd The Barons, St Margaret's, Twickenham, TW1 2AW, United Kingdom
 (020) 8607 8888/ (020) 8607 8889
 caroline@twickenhamstudios.com
 www.twickenhamstudios.com

Zownir Locations Ltd Studio 9, The Village, 101 Amies Street, London, SW11 2JW, United Kingdom
 (020) 7738 2002/ (020) 7652 1946
 hq@zownirlocations.com
 www.zownirlocations.com

Print

printers . monitors . light booths . finishing . workflow . colour management

bringing colour to life...

XEROX *efi* EIZO

1st Byte
Leading Digital Print

FOR ALL YOUR DIGITAL PRINT NEEDS
24 HOUR SERVICE

Fastest Turnrounds
All but the largest jobs are completed in 24 hours.

Litho Quality
Our latest digital presses, HP Indigo 5000's and Xeikon 5000 will now match offset Litho.

24 Hour Service
We run all production departments 24 hours so we can help you day or night.

In-House Finishing
Encompassing all aspects of finishing to give us the best control of quality and deadlines.

Personalisation
All our presses can print with variable data to give the best impressions.

Format Versatility
Unlike the majority of digital presses our Xeikon 5000 offers printing at A2 and more.

Poster Service
Our ink-jet service prints in 6 colours up to 60" wide.

Folder Service
Our downloadable templates means reduced costs and faster short run folders.

Special Offers
A1 posters from £25
A0 posters from £40

10 Years Experience
Means you benefit from our having dealt with every eventuality...

Tel 020 7841 4300
estimate@1stbyte.co.uk

www.1stbyte.co.uk
For all your digital print needs – Contact us 24 hrs
Baker's Yard, Clerkenwell, London EC1R 3DD

PH
MEDIA

WORKING WITH THE
CREATIVE COMMUNITY.

HIGH-QUALITY SOLUTIONS
TAILOR-MADE TO FIT YOUR NEEDS

VISIT WWW.PHMEDIA.COM

REPRO-
GRAPHICS

CONTACT

INFORMATION :

DVD AUTHORING

A & C Audio Visual Ltd 98 Goremire Road, Carluke, Lanarkshire, ML8 4PF, United Kingdom
📞 (01555) 772648/📠 (01555) 752060
✉ alistair@aandcaudio.co.uk
🖥 www.aandcaudio.co.uk

AFA Creations Ltd 4 Glastonbury Road, Sully, Penarth, South Glamorgan, CF64 5PZ, United Kingdom
📞 (029) 2053 0438
✉ john@afa-creations.com
🖥 www.afa-creations.com

Amstore CD+DVD Production Block J, Tower Bridge Business Complex, 100 Clements Road, London, SE16 4DG, United Kingdom
📞 (020) 7232 2779/📠 (020) 7237 6097
✉ james@amstore.co.uk
🖥 www.amstore.co.uk

Atreum Cotswold Innovation Centre, Rissington Business Park, Upper Rissington, Cheltenham, Gloucestershire, GL54 2QB, United Kingdom
📞 (01451) 812955/📠 (01451) 812216
✉ becky@atreum.co.uk
🖥 www.atreum.co.uk

Blank Canvass Media 20 Fearnley Street, Watford, WD18 0RD, United Kingdom
📞 (01923) 223034
✉ bendibble@aol.com
🖥 www.blankcanvassmedia.co.uk

Brever Web Design Edinburgh 60a Craigour Drive, Edinburgh, EH17 7NT, United Kingdom
📞 (0845) 129 8534
✉ info@breverwebdesign.com
🖥 www.breverwebdesign.com

Catwalk Creations 63, March Court, Warwick Drive, London, SW15 6LE, United Kingdom
📞 (07834) 470117
✉ nicola@catwalkcreations.com
🖥 www.catwalkcreations.com

Creative Design in Marketing India Mill Business Centre, Darwen, Lancashire, BB3 1AE, United Kingdom
📞 (01254) 777752/📠 (01254) 777759
✉ claire@cd-marketing.co.uk
🖥 www.cd-marketing.co.uk

Creative Edge Design & Advertising 1st Floor Donald Hendry Building, Auchincruive, Ayr, KA6 5HW, United Kingdom
📞 (01292) 521404/📠 (01292) 521693
✉ paul@cedge.co.uk
🖥 www.cedge.co.uk

D G P Portland House, 12-13 Greek Street, London, W1D 4DL, United Kingdom
📞 (020) 7734 4501/📠 (020) 7734 7034
✉ mail@dgpsoho.co.uk
🖥 www.dgpsoho.co.uk

Digital Disc Duplication Ltd 25 Huntingfield Road, Bury St. Edmunds, Suffolk, IP33 2JA, United Kingdom
📞 (01284) 700773
✉ info@digitaldiscduplication.com
🖥 www.digitaldiscduplication.com

Digiverse Ltd 28 Whitehorse Street, Baldock, Hertfordshire, SG7 6QQ, United Kingdom
📞 (01462) 639816/📠 (01462) 895777
✉ sales@digiverse.co.uk
🖥 www.digiverse.co.uk

Dischromtics Ltd Unit 20, Prince of Wales Industrial Estate, Abercarn, Newport, Gwent, NP11 5AR, United Kingdom
📞 (01495) 243222/📠 (01495) 243777
✉ stewart@dischro.co.uk
🖥 www.dischromatics.co.uk

Dragonfly Media 3 Berkeley Crescent, Clifton, Bristol, Avon, BS8 1HA,
📞 0845 6520 888/📠 0845 6520 808
✉ jon@dragonfly-media.co.uk
🖥 www.dragonfly-media.co.uk

Eek Films Ltd Liverpool Science Park, 131 Mount Pleasant, Liverpool, L3 5TF, United Kingdom
📞 0151-705 3501/(07980) 214890 📱
✉ info@eekfilms.com
🖥 www.eekfilms.com

Figment Media 34 Fouberts Place, London, W1F 7PX, United Kingdom
📞 (020) 7478 7656
✉ mail@figment-media.com
🖥 www.figment-media.com

Freehand Graphics (IVCA) Dunsfold Park, Cranleigh, Surrey, GU6 8TB, United Kingdom
📞 (01483) 200111/📠 (01483) 200101
✉ matt.wright@freehand.co.uk
🖥 www.freehand.co.uk

Glasseye Ltd 20A Iliffe Yard, London, SE17 3QA, United Kingdom
📞 (020) 7701 4300/📠 (020) 7701 4300
✉ info@glasseyeltd.com
🖥 www.glasseyeltd.com

Green Earth Production Inc Redondo Beach, Los Angeles, 90278, United States of America
📞 00 1 310 318 9675/📠 00 1 310 318 9995
✉ info@greenearthproductions.com
🖥 www.greenearthproductions.com

HDC Associates Ltd Bracken House, 53 Broad Lane, Bradford, West Yorkshire, BD4 8PA, United Kingdom
📞 (01274) 656565/📠 (01274) 656575
✉ info@hdc.uk.com
🖥 www.discpack.co.uk

HiViz Ltd 14 Oakley Drive, Bromley, BR2 8PP, United Kingdom
📞 (01689) 862096/(07900) 915134 📱 (01689) 862096
✉ sabine@hiviz-ltd.co.uk
🖥 www.hiviz-ltd.co.uk

Hot Knife Digital Media Ltd 1 First Avenue, Nottingham, NG7 6JL, United Kingdom
📞 0115-969 3600/📠 0151-969 1800
✉ hot@hotknife.co.uk
🖥 www.hotknife.co.uk

Mediaplant Limited 3a lancaster House, edison park, Hindle Way, Swindon, SN3 3RT, United Kingdom
📞 01793 498040/📠 01793 498041
✉ sales@mediaplant.co.uk
🖥 www.mediaplant.co.uk

Paggraphicsandmedia 73C Ballards Lane, London, N3 1XT, United Kingdom
📞 (020) 8371 9969
✉ info@paggraphicsandmedia.com
🖥 www.paggraphicsandmedia.com

Peninsula Films 9 Saxon Road, Cambridge, CB5 8HS, United Kingdom
📞 (01223) 460459
✉ taplin@peninsulafilms.com
🖥 www.peninsulafilms.com

reeldimension 60 Leominster Road, Portsmouth, PO6 4DD, United Kingdom
📞 /(07919) 860903 📱
✉ info@reeldimension.co.uk
🖥 www.reeldimension.co.uk

Richard Klein 61 Cleveden Drive, Glasgow, G12 0NX, United Kingdom
📞 0141-337 2203
✉ rkderj@yahoo.com
🖥 www.rkderj.com

Ripe Design (UK) Ltd Clarence House, 48 Black Bull Street, Leeds, LS10 1HW, United Kingdom
📞 0113-204 2800/📠 0113-204 2801
✉ info@ripe.co.uk
🖥 www.ripe.co.uk

Sanctuary Post 53 Frith Street, London, W1D 4SN, United Kingdom
📞 (020) 7734 4480/📠 (020) 7439 7394
✉ info@thesanctuary.tv
🖥 www.thesanctuary.tv

Scopitone Ltd Tower Bridge Business Complex, Block J Suite 212, 100 Clements Road, London, SE16 4DG, United Kingdom
📞 (020) 7193 6528
✉ info@scopitone.co.uk
🖥 www.scopitone.co.uk

Sound Recording Technology Audio House, Edison Road, St. Ives, Cambridgeshire, PE27 3LF, United Kingdom
📞 (01480) 461880/📠 (01480) 496100
✉ sales@soundrecordingtechnology.co.uk
🖥 www.soundrecordingtechnology.com

Storm Music 14 Neville Avenue, Anchorsholme, Blackpool, FY5 3BG, United Kingdom
📞 (01253) 864598/📠 (01253) 864598
✉ enquiries@photo-stock.co.uk
🖥 www.photo-stock.co.uk

Take2Media 3 Woodside Road, Sutton, Surrey, SM1 3SU, United Kingdom
📞 (020) 8644 6712/📠 (020) 8644 6712
✉ take2@btclick.com

Tamborine Productions Ltd 14 Livonia Street, London, W1F 8AG, United Kingdom
📞 (020) 7434 1812/📠 (020) 7434 1813
✉ tim@tamborine.co.uk
🖥 www.tamborine.co.uk

The Post Factory 7th Floor, Newcombe House, 43-45 Notting Hill Gate, London, W11 3LQ, United Kingdom
📞 (020) 7183 1600/📠 2077278509
✉ info@postfactory.co.uk
🖥 www.postfactory.co.uk

Thinking Fish Trafalgar House, Grenville Place, London, NW7 3SA, United Kingdom
📞 (0845) 4588211/📠 (0845) 588688
✉ jonathan.kirsten@thinkingfish.com
🖥 www.thinkingfish.com

Those Media Guys Ltd 3rd Floor, 13 James Court, Edinburgh, EH1 2PB, United Kingdom
📞 0131-466 2639
✉ info@thosemediaguys.com
🖥 www.thosemediaguys.com

Three S Films Ltd 12 Regent Square, Penzance, Cornwall, TR18 4BG, United Kingdom
📞 (01736) 367 912/07718 793 766 📱 (01736) 367 912
✉ john@threesfilms.com
🖥 www.threesfilms.com

Tidal Creative 62 Frith Street, London, W1D 3JN, United Kingdom
📞 (020) 7287 6422/📠 (020) 7437 7764
✉ info@printout.co.uk
🖥 www.printout.co.uk

Transdigital 5R North Mill, Bridge Foot, Belper, Derbyshire, DE56 1YD, United Kingdom
📞 (01773) 829320
✉ info@transdigital.co.uk
🖥 www.transdigital.co.uk

Truespirit 49 High Street, Kingston upon Thames, Surrey, KT1 1LQ, United Kingdom
📞 (020) 8547 3112
✉ info@truespirit.co.uk
🖥 www.truespirit.co.uk

Vega TV Minerva Mill Innovation Centre, Station Road, Alcester, Warwickshire, B49 5ET, United Kingdom
📞 (0870) 0801979
✉ web@avi.co.uk
🖥 www.avi.co.uk

VSI Aradco House, 132 Cleveland Street, London, W1T 6AB, United Kingdom
📞 (020) 7692 7700/📠 (020) 7692 7711
✉ info@vsi.tv
🖥 www.vsi.tv

VT Group P.L.C. Portland Gate, Portland Square, Bristol, BS2 8SJ, United Kingdom
📞 0117-987 7711/📠 0117-987 7721
✉ sales@vt.tv
🖥 www.vt.tv

Woodcote Marketing The Atrium, Curtis Road, Dorking, Surrey, RH4 1XA, United Kingdom
📞 (01306) 646515/📠 (01306) 646517
✉ graham@britisheventsonline.co.uk
🖥 www.britisheventsonline.co.uk

Xube Ltd Unit 4, 51 Derbyshire Street, London, E2 6JQ, United Kingdom
📞 (020) 7739 5811/📠 020 7900 6867
✉ info@xube.co.uk
🖥 www.xube.co.uk

DIGITAL FILE TRANSFER

Acrom Photographic Lab Ltd 19 Heathmans Road, London, SW6 4TJ, United Kingdom
📞 (020) 7751 9922/📠 (020) 7751 9955
✉ mail@acrom.co.uk
🖥 www.acrom.co.uk

AlphaWave Technology Ltd 7 Queens Road, Thame, Oxfordshire, OX9 3NF, United Kingdom
📞 (01844) 216912/📠 (07092) 171894
✉ info@awtltd.co.uk
🖥 www.awtltd.co.uk

Ballinger Media Solutions Limited 6 Alstonefield, Emerson Valley, Milton Keynes, MK4 2HA, United Kingdom
📞 (0870) 765 4840/📠 (0870) 754 841
✉ matthew@ballinger.co.uk
🖥 www.ballinger.co.uk

Blaze Creative Ltd 77 East Road, London, N1 6AH, United Kingdom
📞 (020) 7253 0099/📠 (020) 7253 4358
✉ mail@blaze-creative.co.uk
🖥 www.blaze-creative.co.uk

DIGITAL FILE TRANSFER

Bold Endeavours Ltd 7 Manor Park, Staines, Middlesex, TW18 4XE,
☎ 01784 460 064
✉ derek@boldendeavours.com
🖥 www.big-easy-footage-library-software.co.uk

Catwalk Creations 63, March Court, Warwick Drive, London, SW15 6LE, United Kingdom
☎ (07834) 470117
✉ nicola@catwalkcreations.com
🖥 www.catwalkcreations.com

design@djhunter 133 Ravensbourne Avenue, Bromley, BR2 0AZ, United Kingdom
☎ (020) 8466 7196/✆ (020) 8466 7196
✉ design@djhunter.co.uk

Enhanced Images Ltd The Stables, 21A St. James Road, East Grinstead, West Sussex, RH19 1DL, United Kingdom
☎ (01342) 327574/✆ (01342) 326540
✉ info@enhancedimages.co.uk
🖥 www.enhancedimages.co.uk

Inoya Photography Flat 23, Key House, Bowling Green Street, London, SE11 5TT, United Kingdom
☎ (07888) 723 197
✉ admin@inoya.co.uk
🖥 www.inoya.co.uk

Pro2col Ltd Arena Business Centre, Nimrod Way, Wimborne, Dorset, BH21 7SH, United Kingdom
☎ (0870) 2502220/07899 982745 ✆ (0870) 2502225
✉ jl@pro2colgroup.com
🖥 www.pro2colgroup.com

Stream UK Media Services Ltd Studio 522, 53-79 Highgate Road, London, NW5 1TL, United Kingdom
☎ (020) 7387 6090/✆ (020) 7419 1819
✉ jessica@streamuk.com
🖥 www.streamuk.com

TECTV 5 Woodfall Avenue, Barnet, Hertfordshire, EN5 2EZ, United Kingdom
☎ (020) 8447 0001/(07754) 680999 ✆
✉

Thinking Fish Trafalgar House, Grenville Place, London, NW7 3SA, United Kingdom
☎ (0845) 4588211/✆ (0845) 588688
✉ jonathan.kirsten@thinkingfish.com
🖥 www.thinkingfish.com

DIGITAL PRINTING AND LARGE SCREEN GRAPHICS

1st BYTE 1st House, Bakers Yard, Bakers Row, London, EC1R 3DD, United Kingdom
☎ **(020) 7841 4300**/✆ **(020) 7841 4302**
✉ **info@1stbyte.co.uk**
🖥 **www.1stbyte.co.uk**
See ad in showcase

A D S Visual Group 246-250 Seaward Street, Kinning Park, Glasgow, G41 1NG, United Kingdom
☎ 0141-420 1266/✆ 0141-420 1345
✉ info@ads-visual.com
🖥 www.ads-visual.com

A. Miah 98 Heath Road, Twickenham, TW1 4BW, United Kingdom
☎ (020) 8892 1100/✆ (07090) 740501
✉ amiah@mac.com

Accura Imaging Ltd Harvest House, Cranborne Road, Potters Bar, Hertfordshire, EN6 3JF, United Kingdom
☎ (01707) 660055/✆ (01707) 660052
✉ sales@accuraimaging.co.uk
🖥 www.accuraimaging.co.uk

Acre Jean Ltd Unit 7 The Kimber Centre, 54 Kimber Road, London, SW18 4PP,
☎ 020 8877 3211/✆ 020 8877 3213
✉ dan.hill@acrejean.com
🖥 www.acrejean.com

Acrom Photographic Lab Ltd 19 Heathmans Road, London, SW6 4TJ, United Kingdom
☎ (020) 7751 9922/✆ (020) 7751 9955
✉ mail@acrom.co.uk
🖥 www.acrom.co.uk

Adam B. Studios Duchess House, 18-19 Warren Street, London, W1T 5LR, United Kingdom
☎ (020) 7388 8050/✆ (020) 7387 5215
✉ info@adamb.co.uk
🖥 www.adamb.co.uk

Adbell Sign Systems Unit 5, 2 Freemans Way, Harrogate, North Yorkshire, HG3 1DH, United Kingdom
☎ (01423) 885045/✆ (01423) 885046
✉ info@adbellsigns.co.uk
🖥 www.adbellsigns.co.uk

Adelphi Graphic 52-54 Rosebury Avenue, London, EC1R 4RP, United Kingdom
☎ (020) 7278 6926/✆ (020) 7833 2605
✉ adelphigraphics@btclick.com
🖥 www.adelphigraphics.com

Alien Display Ltd 61 Frith Street, London, W1D 3JL, United Kingdom
☎ (020) 7494 3777/✆ (020) 7494 3778
✉ aliendisplay@btconnect.com
🖥 www.aliendisplay.co.uk

Allied Photolabs Ltd Allied House, Bay Tree Avenue, Leatherhead, Surrey, KT22 7UE, United Kingdom
☎ (01372) 379933/✆ (01372) 372867
✉ sales@alliedphotolabs.co.uk
🖥 www.alliedphotolabs.com

Approved Creative Services Ltd 2 Grafton Mews, London, W1T 5JD, United Kingdom
☎ (020) 7383 3811/✆ (020) 7916 3774
✉ sales@approved.co.uk
🖥 www.approved.co.uk

Artisan 4 Riley Road, Telford Way Industrial Estate, Kettering, Northamptonshire, NN16 8NN, United Kingdom
☎ (01536) 522777/✆ (01536) 522666
✉ sales@artisansigns.co.uk
🖥 www.artisansigns.co.uk

Azographics Ltd Unit 1, 22 Pakenham Street, London, WC1X 0LB, United Kingdom
☎ (020) 7833 0667/✆ (020) 7833 3036
✉ printing@azographics.com
🖥 www.azographics.com

B & S Graphics City Link Central, 145 Helen Street, Glasgow, G51 3HD, United Kingdom
☎ 0141-425 2300/✆ 0141-445 4619
✉ enq@b-s.co.uk
🖥 www.b-s.co.uk

BAF Graphics Ltd 25-27 Lydden Road, London, SW18 4LT, United Kingdom
☎ (020) 8875 8100/✆ (020) 8871 1693
✉ gavin@baf.co.uk
🖥 www.baf.co.uk

Bartlett Printing Swan Yard, St. Thomas, Exeter, EX4 1HU, United Kingdom
☎ (01392) 254086/✆ (01392) 256224
✉ sales@bartlett-printing.co.uk
🖥 www.bartlett-printing.co.uk

BIG Display Ltd Unit 11, Chillingham Industrial Estate, Back Chapman Street, Newcastle upon Tyne, NE6 2XX, United Kingdom
☎ 0191-265 4032/✆ 0191-275 9123
✉ keith@bigdisplay.co.uk
🖥 www.bigdisplay.co.uk

BigStuff Ltd, Southampton, United Kingdom
☎ (023) 8033 4332/✆ (023) 8033 4330
✉ info@bigstuff.org.uk
🖥 www.bigstuff.org.uk

C 3 Imaging London City Ltd Lector Court, 153 Farringdon Road, London, EC1 3AF, United Kingdom
☎ (020) 7833 9100/✆ (020) 7833 9119
✉ work@c3londoncity.com
🖥 www.c3imaging.com

C A D A Design Group Suite 4, 155 Bermondsey Street, London, SE1 3UY, United Kingdom
☎ (020) 7234 9700/✆ (020) 7403 5692
✉ design@cada.co.uk
🖥 www.cada.co.uk

Calumet Photographic Ltd Unit 4, Charlton Place, Downing Street Industrial Estate, Manchester, M12 6HH, United Kingdom
☎ 0161-274 4455/✆ 0161-274 3406
✉ michael.collins@calumetphoto.co.uk
🖥 www.calumetphoto.com

Chromatics 79-80 Western Road, Hove, East Sussex, BN3 2JQ, United Kingdom
☎ (01273) 722242/✆ (01273) 739588
✉ sales@chromatics.ltd.co.uk
🖥 www.chromatics.ltd.co.uk

Colab Ltd Unit 7 Lambourne Crescent, Cardiff Business Park, Llanishen, Cardiff, CF14 5GF, United Kingdom
☎ (029) 2074 7457/✆ (029) 2074 7864
✉ cardiff@colab.com
🖥 www.colab.com

Collective Colour Unit 11, Dolphin Point, Dolphin Way, Purfleet, Essex, RM19 1NR, United Kingdom
☎ (01708) 804706/07768) 528072 ✆ (0870 0510 468
✉ repro@collectivecolour.co.uk
🖥 www.collectivecolour.co.uk

Color Co. 24 Mortimer Street, London, W1T 3JP, United Kingdom
☎ (020) 7631 1232/✆ (020) 7436 1131
✉ mortimer@color.co.uk
🖥 www.color.co.uk

Colorscope Printers Ltd Charlwoods Road, East Grinstead, West Sussex, RH19 2HF, United Kingdom
☎ (01342) 311821/✆ (01342) 315358
✉ sales@colorscope.co.uk
🖥 www.colorscope.co.uk

Colossal Solutions Little Brittin House, Alna Road, Chesham, Buckinghamshire, HP5 3HB, United Kingdom
☎ (01494) 793700/✆ (01494) 773594
✉ graham@colossal.co.uk
🖥 www.colossal.co.uk

Colour Network Studio B9, 3A Queensly Court, Glasgow, G33 4DB, United Kingdom
☎ 0141-774 8388/✆ 0141-774 9797
✉ rgray@colour-network.co.uk
🖥 www.colour-network.co.uk

Colourshack High Street, Lane End, High Wycombe, Buckinghamshire, HP14 3JG, United Kingdom
☎ (01494) 882823/✆ (01494) 881826
✉ colourshack@supanet.com

Creative Colour Bureau Unit 4, 230-260 Garscube Road, Glasgow, G4 9RR, United Kingdom
☎ 0141-353 3206/✆ 0141-353 2267
✉ info@ccb.co.uk
🖥 www.ccb.co.uk

Creative Edge Design & Advertising 1st Floor Donald Hendry Building, Auchincruive, Ayr, KA6 5HW, United Kingdom
☎ (01292) 521404/✆ (01292) 521693
✉ paul@cedge.co.uk
🖥 www.cedge.co.uk

Customimages.co.uk 12 Mill Brow, Armathwaite, Carlisle, CA4 9PJ, United Kingdom
☎ (01697) 472522/✆ (01697) 472522
✉ info@customimages.co.uk
🖥 www.customimages.co.uk

Cyber 42 Ltd MTL Centre, Tranmere Avenue, Middlesbrough, Cleveland, TS3 8PB, United Kingdom
☎ (01642) 247345/✆ (01642) 249345
✉ enquiries@cyber42.co.uk
🖥 www.cyber42.co.uk

D A R Colourskill Ltd Unit 1, Cornwall Road, Hatch End, Middlesex, HA5 4JR, United Kingdom
☎ (020) 8428 1055/✆ (020) 8428 3268
✉ info@darimages.co.uk
🖥 www.darimages.co.uk

Digital Imaging Services Ltd Unit A1, Hilton Trading Estate, Hilton Road, Lanesfield, Wolverhampton, WV4 6DW, United Kingdom
☎ (01902) 406000/✆ (01902) 406001
✉ sales@digital-is.co.uk
🖥 www.digital-is.co.uk

Digital Print Factory Ltd 12-12A Rosebery Avenue, London, EC1R 4TD, United Kingdom
☎ (020) 7837 8666/✆ (020) 7404 4762
✉ t.harding@colyer.co.uk
🖥 www.colyer.co.uk

Disc to Print (UK) Ltd 25 Liddell Road, West Hampstead, London, NW6 2EW, United Kingdom
☎ (020) 7625 5225/✆ (020) 7624 1647
✉ info@dtp.co.uk
🖥 www.dtp.co.uk

Dragonfly Media 3 Berkeley Crescent, Clifton, Bristol, Avon, BS8 1HA,
☎ 0845 6520 888/✆ 0845 6520 808
✉ jon@dragonfly-media.co.uk
🖥 www.dragonfly-media.co.uk

Easibind Adams Close, Heanor Gate Industrial Estate, Heanor, Derbyshire, DE75 7SW, United Kingdom
☎ (01773) 761341/✆ (01773) 765065
✉ ian.bertie@easibind.com
🖥 www.easibind.com

Electro-Tech Colour Ltd Image House, 1 Blenheim Court, 62 Brewery Road, London, N7 9NY, United Kingdom
☎ (020) 7636 6677/✆ (020) 7636 5566
✉ info@etcltd.co.uk
🖥 www.etcltd.co.uk

Exacta Print Glasgow 90-92 West Regent Street, Glasgow, G2 2QD, United Kingdom
📞 0141-352 6800/ 📠 0141-352 6811
✉ info@exactaprint.co.uk
🖥 www.exactaprint.co.uk

Exe Valley Dataset Ltd 43 Marsh Green Road West, Marsh Barton Trading Estate, Exeter, EX2 8PN, United Kingdom
📞 (01392) 426464/ 📠 (01392) 491066
✉ sales@evdataset.co.uk
🖥 www.evdataset.co.uk

Expocentric 31 Broadwick Street, London, W1F 0DG, United Kingdom
📞 (020) 7432 0000/ 📠 (020) 7287 3090
✉ graphics.studio@expocentric.co.uk
🖥 www.expocentric.co.uk

Face Creative Services Ltd 2-10 Baron Street, London, N1 9LL, United Kingdom
📞 (020) 7713 9777/ 📠 (020) 7713 9788
✉ colin.harding@facecreative.co.uk

Faraway Islands GiclÈe Digital Printing Higher Tor Farm, Whitchurch, Tavistock, Devon, PL19 9EQ, United Kingdom
📞 (01822) 617337
✉ info@farawayislands.co.uk
🖥 www.farawayislands.co.uk

Firstline Interactive Systems Ltd Albert House, Rothbury, Morpeth, Northumberland, NE65 7SR, United Kingdom
📞 (01669) 621800
✉ gary@firstlineinteractive.co.uk
🖥 www.firstlineinteractive.co.uk

Folex Ltd 18 & 19 Monkspath Business Park, Shirley, Solihull, West Midlands, B90 4NY, United Kingdom
📞 0121-733 3833/ 📠 0121-733 3222
✉ sales@folex.co.uk
🖥 www.folex.co.uk

FreelanceImages The Core Business Centre, Milton Hill, Steventon, Abingdon, Oxfordshire, OX13 6AB, United Kingdom
📞 (01235) 828 286/(07919) 181830
✉ garethlewis@freelanceimages.co.uk
🖥 www.freelanceimages.co.uk

Fusioncom Via della Magliana, 63, Rome, 146, Italy
📞 00 39 06 553 4061/ 📠 00 39 06 5538 1440
✉ frankstahlberg@fusioncom.it
🖥 www.fusioncom.it

Genesis Imaging (Chelsea) Unit D2, The Depot, 2 Michael Road, London, SW6 2AD, United Kingdom
📞 (020) 7731 2227/ 📠 (020) 7731 8778
✉ chelsea@genesisimaging.co.uk
🖥 www.genesisimaging.co.uk

Genesis Imaging (City) The Depo, 2 Michael Road, Fulham, London, SW6 2AD, United Kingdom
📞 (020) 7731 2227/ 📠 (020) 7731 8778
✉ city@genesisimaging.co.uk
🖥 www.genesisimaging.co.uk

Genix Imaging Ltd 32 Broadwick Street, London, W1F 8JB, United Kingdom
📞 (020) 7734 0742/ 📠 (020) 7434 1528
✉ sales@genix.co.uk
🖥 www.genix.co.uk

Glorious Productions 6 Hoxton Square, Top Floor, London, N1 6NU, United Kingdom
📞 (020) 7729 9510/(07718) 878454
✉ keith@gloriousproductions.co.uk
🖥 www.gloriousproductions.co.uk

Go Cre8 Queens Dock Commercial Centre, 67-83 Norfolk Street, Liverpool, L1 0BG, United Kingdom
📞 (0845) 2263086/ 📠 0151 709 0560
✉ info@gocre8.co.uk
🖥 www.gocre8.co.uk

Harry's Studio B5R, Metropolitan Wharf, London, E1W 3SS, United Kingdom
📞 (020) 7488 1154/ 📠 (020) 7488 1176
✉ harrymatthews68@hotmail.com

Harvest Studios Chapel Place, Abington Square, Northampton, NN1 4AQ, United Kingdom
📞 (01604) 624422/ 📠 (01604) 233032
✉ mail@harveststudios.co.uk
🖥 www.harveststudios.co.uk

Hierographics Ltd Designer House, Sandford Lane Industrial Estate, Sandford Lane, Wareham, Dorset, BH20 4DY, United Kingdom
📞 (01929) 554454/ 📠 (01929) 554460
✉ info@hierographics.co.uk
🖥 www.hierographics.co.uk

Howitt Digital Unit 5, Block 8, Enterprise Way, Edenbridge, Kent, TN8 6HF, United Kingdom
📞 (01732) 864669/ 📠 (01732) 864912
✉ enquiries@howitt.co.uk
🖥 www.howitt.co.uk

Image 1 Ltd The Old Forge, 38a North Road, Preston, Brighton, BN1 6SP, United Kingdom
📞 (01273) 543888/ 📠 (01273) 236365
✉ info@image1.co.uk
🖥 www.image1.co.uk

Image Group Barton Hall, Hardy Street, Eccles, Manchester, M30 7NB, United Kingdom
📞 0161-707 8886/ 📠 0161-707 8898
✉ sales@imagegroupuk.com
🖥 www.imagegroupuk.com

Imaginators 51 Hill Grove Business Park, Nazeing Road, Nazeing, Essex, EN9 2HB, United Kingdom
📞 (01992) 890700/ 📠 (01992) 890900
✉ sales@imaginators.co.uk
🖥 www.imaginators.co.uk

Indusfoto 39-41 Margravine Road, London, W6 8LL, United Kingdom
📞 (020) 7385 7618/ 📠 (020) 7381 0047
✉ mark@indusfoto.co.uk
🖥 www.indusfoto.com

Infinite Eye 2 Claremont Gardens, Glasgow, G3 7LW, United Kingdom
📞 0141 - 5507 509
✉ hello@infinite-eye.com
🖥 www.infinite-eye.com

John E. Wright & Co. Ltd Blue Print House, 115 Huntingdon Street, Nottingham, NG1 3NF, United Kingdom
📞 0115-950 6633/ 📠 0115-958 5067
✉ nottingham@johnewright.com
🖥 www.johnewright.com

Jupiter Display Ltd City Pavlion, 33 Britain Street, London, EC1M 5UG, United Kingdom
📞 (0870) 7509200/ 📠 (0870) 7509250
✉ robert.ward@jupiterdisplay.com
🖥 www.jupiterdisplay.com

1st Byte
Leading Digital Print

FOR ALL YOUR DIGITAL PRINT NEEDS 24 HOUR SERVICE

Fastest Turnrounds
All but the largest jobs are completed in 24 hours.

Format Versatility
Unlike the majority of digital presses our Xeikon 5000 offers printing at A2 and more.

Litho Quality
Our latest digital presses, HP Indigo 5000's and Xeikon 5000 will now match offset Litho.

Poster Service
Our ink-jet service prints in 6 colours up to 60" wide.

24 Hour Service
We run all production departments 24 hours so we can help you day or night.

Folder Service
Our downloadable templates means reduced costs and faster short run folders.

In-House Finishing
Encompassing all aspects of finishing to give us the best control of quality and deadlines.

Special Offers
A1 posters from £25
A0 posters from £40

Personalisation
All our presses can print with variable data to give the best impressions.

10 Years Experience
Means you benefit from our having dealt with every eventuality...

Tel 020 7841 4300
estimate@1stbyte.co.uk

www.1stbyte.co.uk
For all your digital print needs – Contact us 24 hrs
Baker's Yard, Clerkenwell, London EC1R 3DD

K & S Digital Imaging Ltd Freemens Common, 90 Commercial Square, Leicester, LE2 7SR, United Kingdom
📞 0116-247 0270/ 📠 0116-247 1026
✉ sales@kands.co.uk
🖥 www.kands.co.uk

Kall Kwik Printing 26-28 Carters Green, West Bromwich, West Midlands, B70 9LW, United Kingdom
📞 0121-553 1291/ 📠 0121-500 5245
✉ enquiries@kallkwikprinting.co.uk
🖥 www.kallkwikprinting.co.uk

Kelleway Media Unit 8, Thesiger Close, Worthing, West Sussex, BN11 2RN, United Kingdom
📞 (01903) 218111/ 📠 (019030 288659
✉ sales@kellewaymedia.com
🖥 www.kellewaymedia.com

Keyframe Computer Graphics Ltd 431 Meanwood Road, Unity Court, Leeds, LS7 2LL, United Kingdom
📞 0113-246 5913/ 📠 0113-234 0038
✉ info@keyframe.co.uk
🖥 www.keyframe.co.uk

Koi Reprographics Ltd 7 Warren Way, Digswell, Welwyn, Hertfordshire, AL6 0DQ, United Kingdom
📞 07767 437298/07767 437298/ 📠 01438 717189
✉ peter.howard@koi-epro.co.uk
🖥 www.koirepro.co.uk

Lea-Valley Colour Unit 4B, Charlton Mead Lane South, Hoddesdon, Hertfordshire, EN11 0DJ, United Kingdom
📞 (01992) 443461/ 📠 (01992) 467131
✉ info@lea-valley.co.uk
🖥 www.lea-valley.co.uk/graphix

Leach Colour Ltd Bradley Business Park, Dyson Wood Way, Bradley, Huddersfield, HD2 1GN, United Kingdom
📞 (01484) 551200/ 📠 (01484) 551211
✉ info@leachcolour.com
🖥 www.leachcolour.com

Leeds PhotoVisual Ltd 20-22 Brunswick Centre, Bernard Street, London, WC1N 1AE, United Kingdom
📞 (020) 7833 1661/ 📠 (020) 7833 1570
🖥 www.leedsphoto.co.uk

Linney Print Adams Way, Mansfield, Nottinghamshire, NG18 4FW, United Kingdom
📞 (01623) 450450/ 📠 (01623) 450451
✉ sales@linney.com
🖥 www.linney.com

London Digital Printing Group Ltd Kirkman House, 12-14 Whitfield Street, London, W1T 2RF, United Kingdom
📞 (020) 7637 4440/ 📠 (020) 7637 4441
✉ lesbexfield@ldpg.com
🖥 www.ldpg.com

M P C Professional Digital & Photographic Imaging Ltd MPC House, Francis Road, Manchester, M20 4XP, United Kingdom
📞 0161-445 3145/ 📠 0161-445 5563
✉ info@mpclabs.co.uk
🖥 www.mpclabs.co.uk

MacroVision 1 Beech Copse, Sheldons Lane, Hook, Hampshire, RG27 9LH, United Kingdom
📞 (01256) 763372/ 📠 (01256) 766370
✉ peterfpowell@aol.com
🖥 macro-art.co.uk

Maxim 11-13 Macklin Street, London, WC2B 5NH, United Kingdom
(020) 7427 7690/ (020) 7427 7691
nigel@maximservices.co.uk
www.maximservices.co.uk

McKenzie Clark Ltd 14-22 Ossory Road, London, SE1 5AN, United Kingdom
(020) 7231 6070/ (020) 7232 1843
sales@mckenzieclark.co.uk
www.mckenzieclark.co.uk

Multigraphics Ltd 21 Commondale Way, Euroway Trading Estate, Bradford, West Yorkshire, BD4 6SF, United Kingdom
(01274) 683434/ (01274) 686464
enquiries@multigraphics.co.uk
www.multigraphics.co.uk

Norwyn Ltd 1 Hardy Close, Nelson Business Center, Preston, PR2 2XP, United Kingdom
(01772) 739985/ (01772) 739984
info@norwyn.co.uk
www.norwyn.co.uk

Outdoor Partners Ltd Unit 6, 129 Coldharbour Lane, London, SE5 9NU, United Kingdom
(020) 7733 7995
info@outdoorpartners.co.uk
www.outdoorpartners.co.uk

P S Print Studio 315 Entwisle Road, Rochdale, Lancashire, OL16 2LH, United Kingdom
(01706) 654692/ (01706) 643007

Pacer Graphics 28 Berechurch Road, Colchester, CO2 7QH, United Kingdom
(01206) 760760/ (01206) 762626
adam@wordtech.co.uk

Panther Professionals 87 Clerkenwell Road, London, EC1R 5BX, United Kingdom
(020) 7405 0055/ (020) 7405 8877
panther@globalnet.co.uk
www.panther-imaging.com

Phil Kashdan Design, Print & Display Ltd The Studio, 47 Povey Cross Road, Horley, Surrey, RH6 0AG,
(01293) 773129/ (01293) 773129
phil@pk-design.co.uk

Photo Tile Co. Ltd 2 Podmore Road, London, SW18 1AJ, United Kingdom
(020) 8877 3733/ (020) 8877 3400
sales@phototile.co.uk
www.phototile.co.uk

PictureSelect, Staines, Middlesex, TW18 1XX, United Kingdom
(08701) 995070
info@pictureselect.com
www.pictureselect.com

Poliprints 57 Lancaster Road, Barnet, Hertfordshire, EN4 8AS, United Kingdom
(020) 8441 4364/(07976) 900695 (020) 8449 0317
steve@leopold.co.uk
www.poliprints.com

Powerprint Partnership 254-258 Goswell Road, London, EC1V 7EB, United Kingdom
(020) 7250 1700/ (020) 7250 4114
mail@powerprint.co.uk
www.powerprint.co.uk

Prom Print Digital 6 Imperial Square, Cheltenham, Gloucestershire, GL50 1QB, United Kingdom
(01242) 235926/ (01242) 582330
promprint@btconnect.com

Pure Colour Solutions Rushmere House, 99 Hockliffe Road, Leighton Buzzard, Bedfordshire, LU7 3FL
0845 009 8455 07772 510616 0845 009 8456
richard@purecoloursolutions.com
www.purecoloursolutions.com
See ad in showcase

Quantum 7 Ltd 293 New Hall Lane, Preston, PR1 5XE, United Kingdom
01254 53830/ (01772) 701070
sabbir@quantum7.biz
www.quantum7.biz

Realistic Photo Graphics (Ariel Photo) Ltd Stafford Studios, 129A Stafford Road, Wallington, Surrey, SM6 9BN, United Kingdom
(020) 8669 4900/ (020) 8773 0129
info@realistic-digital.com
www.realistic-digital.com

Redwood Photographic Laboratories Ltd 7 Brunel Court, Brunel Way, Colchester, CO4 9XW, United Kingdom
(01206) 751241/(07887) 796635 (01206) 855134
info@redwoodphoto.com
www.redwoodphoto.com

Repro Arts Monument Road, Great Yarmouth, Norfolk, NR30 3PS, United Kingdom
(01493) 855515/ (01493) 851557
sales@reproarts.co.uk
www.repro-arts.co.uk

Reproscan 20 Elliot Place, Glasgow, G3 8EP, United Kingdom
0141-248 7480/ 0141-221 1366
mail@reproscan-scotland.co.uk

Resolution Creative 204 Latimer Road, London, W10 6QY, United Kingdom
(020) 8969 7333/ (020) 8969 7444
info@resolveandcreate.co.uk
www.resolveandcreate.co.uk

Roy Snell (Silver Gelatine / Giclee) 54 Summerly Street, London, SW18 4EX, United Kingdom
(020) 8946 7536/(07764) 354700
print@roysnell.demon.co.uk

S D C Reprographics Ltd 2 Oldfields Parade, Sutton, Surrey, SM1 2NA, United Kingdom
(020) 8644 3788/ (020) 8641 6541
sales@sdcprint.co.uk
www.sdcprint.co.uk

Saint Albans Photoprint Photoprint House, Stonecross, St. Albans, Hertfordshire, AL1 4AA, United Kingdom
(01727) 850777/ (01727) 866068

Scantech Unit 22/23, Ghyll Industrial Estate, Heathfield, East Sussex, TN21 8AW, United Kingdom
(01435) 867500/ (01435) 866177
neil@scan-tech.co.uk
www.scan-tech.co.uk

Screaming Colour Ltd 2 Pear Tree Street, London, EC1V 3SB, United Kingdom
(020) 7549 3400/(07814) 010014
info@screamingcolour.com
www.screamingcolour.com

Service Graphics Ltd, 3 Osiers Road, London, SW18 1NL, United Kingdom
(020) 8874 4152/ (020) 8871 3521
newenquiries@servicegraphics.co.uk
www.servicegraphics.co.uk

Service Point 161-165 Farringdon Road, London, EC1R 3AL, United Kingdom
(020) 7520 0212/ (020) 7837 7806
marketing@servicepointuk.com
www.servicepointuk.com

Simon Isaacs 7 Lymore Terrace, Oldfield Park, Bath, BA2 2JL, United Kingdom
(01225) 335228/(07976) 758430
design@simonisaacs.co.uk
www.simonisaacs.co.uk

Sonoco Trident Unit 4, Connaught Road, Kingswood Business Park, Hull, HU7 3AP, United Kingdom
(01482) 828 100/ (01482) 710 600
david.keel@sonoco-trident.com
www.sonoco-trident.com

Streetcards The Old Clinc, 59 North Warple Way, Mortlake, London, SW14 8PS, United Kingdom
(020) 8876 5466
info@streetcards.com
www.streetcards.com

Studio Studio House, Invar Business Park, Invar Road, Manchester, M27 9HF, United Kingdom
0161-793 7377/ 0161-793 7376
info@thestudio.co.uk
www.thestudio.co.uk

T P S Visual Communications Ltd Warner House, Jubilee Business Park, Letchworth Garden City, Hertfordshire, SG6 1SP, United Kingdom
(01462) 650700/ (01462) 650707
sales@tpsdisplay.com
www.tpsvisual.com

Tara Signs Ltd St. Peters Place, Western Road, Lancing, West Sussex, BN15 8SB, United Kingdom
(01903) 750710/ (01903) 754008
admin@tarasigns.com
www.tarasigns.com

Techniques Group Ltd 29-31 Greville Street, London, EC1N 8SU, United Kingdom
(020) 7404 3175/ (020) 7831 8173
techniques@btconnect.com
www.techniquesgroup.co.uk

The 3D Centre London House, 100 New Kings Road, Fulham, London, SW6 4LX, United Kingdom
(0870) 242 0638/ (0870) 242 0639
trb@3dcentre.com
www.3dcentre.com

The D P C Ltd Linear House, Peyton Place, London, London, SE10 8RS, United Kingdom
(020) 8858 8351/ (020) 8305 0268
richard@thedpc.com
www.thedpc.com

The London Display Co Ltd 74 Pulteney Road, London, E18 1PS, United Kingdom
(020) 8530 4728/ (020) 8530 4500
sales@thelondondisplay.co.uk
www.londondisplay.co.uk

The Tinsley Lockhart Group 44 West Preston Street, Edinburgh, EH8 9PY, United Kingdom
0131-466 7767
creative@tinsleylockhart.com
www.tinsleylockhart.com

The Transfer Function 11 Northburgh Street, London, EC1V 0AN, United Kingdom
(020) 7490 0002/ (020) 7490 0007
wes@transfunction.co.uk
www.transfunction.co.uk

Urban Ink Ltd Units 22-23, The Bic Centre, Innova Science Park, Enfield, Middlesex, EN3 7XU, United Kingdom
(020) 8373 5000/ (020) 8373 5001
vanessa@urban-ink.co.uk
www.urban-ink.co.uk

V G L Ltd 268 Elgar Road South, Reading, RG2 0BT, United Kingdom
0118-922 1300/ 0118-922 1325
sales@vgl.co.uk
www.vgl.co.uk

W B P Visual Solutions Ltd 6 Progess Works, Heathmill Lane, Birmingham, B9 4DY, United Kingdom
0121-224 8333
birmingham@wbp.co.uk
www.wbp.co.uk

W P Digital 13 Leyton Business Centre, Etloe Road, London, E10 7BT, United Kingdom
(020) 8558 9290/ (020) 8558 3722
info@wpdigital.co.uk
www.wellingtonpress.co.uk

Wall Candi High Street, Lane End, High Wycombe, Buckinghamshire, HP14 3JG, United Kingdom
(01494) 883250/ (01494) 881826
info@wallcandi.com
www.wallcandi.com

Web Media Works 72/78 Morfa Road, Swansea, SA1 2EP, United Kingdom
(01792) 470394/ (01792) 455176
info@webmediaworks.co.uk
www.webmediaworks.co.uk

Wessex Books 2 Station Cottages, Newton Toney, Salisbury, Wiltshire, SP4 0HD,
01980 629349
info@wessexbooks.co.uk
www.wessexbooks.co.uk

William Smith & Sons Grove Works, Barnard Castle, County Durham, DL12 8JG, United Kingdom
01833 690305

Wingnut Designs Waterfront Farm, Biddisham Lane, Biddisham, Axbridge, Somerset, BS26 2RS, United Kingdom
(01934) 750827
chris@wingnutdesigns.co.uk
www.wingnutdesigns.co.uk

Wonderfuel 118 Hatherley Gardens, London, E6 3HQ, United Kingdom
020 8548 1358
info@wonderfuel.co.uk
www.wonderfuel.co.uk

XXLpix Waldemarstrasse 33, Berlin, 10999, Germany
00 49 30 44008380/ 00 49 30 74073244
markus.haaga@xxlpix.net
www.xxlpix.co.uk

Zeta Image To Print Ltd 54 Ayres Street, London, SE1 1EU, United Kingdom
(020) 7787 3993/ (020) 7403 5768
sales@hiero-design.co.uk
www.zeta-print.co.uk

FONTS AND TYPEFACES

Assembly 3rd Floor, 38 Turner Street, London, E1 2AS, United Kingdom
(020) 7265 8856
www.assemblylondon.com

Byboth Ltd 145 Marlborough Road, London, N19 4AN, United Kingdom
(020) 7281 1109
us@byboth.com
www.byboth.com

Carol Kemp Little Mephams, Little London Road, Heathfield, East Sussex, TN21 0BD, United Kingdom
(01435) 812235/ (01435) 813305
www.carolkemp.com

Faces 349 Yorktown Road, College Town, Sandhurst, Berkshire, GU47 0PX, United Kingdom
(01276) 38888/ (01276) 38111
info@faces.co.uk
www.faces.co.uk

Fontworks UK Ltd New North House, 202-208 New North Road, London, N1 7BJ, United Kingdom
(020) 7226 4411/ (020) 7226 4422
sales@type.co.uk
www.type.co.uk

Gaffa Ltd 60 Downham Road, London, N1 5AY, United Kingdom
(07932) 008917
info@dreibholz.com
www.dreibholz.com

Hope Services Typesetting The Ridges, Abingdon Road, Clifton Hampden, Abingdon, Oxfordshire, OX14 3EG, United Kingdom
(01235) 530439/ (01235) 530439
mark.harvey@hopeservices.co.uk
www.hopeservices.co.uk

Naked Alphabet Studio 4 The Workshops, 43 Carol Street, London, NW1 0HT, United Kingdom
info@makedalphabet.com
www.nakedalphabet.com

Paul Antonio Scribe Studio 6c, Clapham North Art Centre, 26-32 Voltaire Road, London, SW4 6DH,
020 7720 8883
paulantonioscribe@yahoo.co.uk
www.paulantonioscribe.com

Sushi-Boi 15 Doran Close, Halesowen, West Midlands, B63 1JZ, United Kingdom
(07762) 966051
sushiboi@fsmail.net

The Gate Marketing & Design Ltd Murlain Business Centre, Union Street, Chester, CH1 1QP, United Kingdom
(01244) 357242/ (01244) 357215
info@thegatemarketing.com
www.thegatemarketing.com

Wingnut Designs Waterfront Farm, Biddisham Lane, Biddisham, Axbridge, Somerset, BS26 2RS, United Kingdom
(01934) 750827
chris@wingnutdesigns.co.uk
www.wingnutdesigns.co.uk

LENTICULARS

BIG Display Ltd Unit 11, Chillingham Industrial Estate, Back Chapman Street, Newcastle upon Tyne, NE6 2XX, United Kingdom
0191-265 4032/ 0191-275 9123
keith@bigdisplay.co.uk
www.bigdisplay.co.uk

Dragonfly Media 3 Berkeley Crescent, Clifton, Bristol, Avon, BS8 1HA,
0845 6520 888/ 0845 6520 808
jon@dragonfly-media.co.uk
www.dragonfly-media.co.uk

Easibind Adams Close, Heanor Gate Industrial Estate, Heanor, Derbyshire, DE75 7SW, United Kingdom
(01773) 761341/ (01773) 765065
ian.bertie@easibind.com
www.easibind.com

Hive Associates Bewlay House, 2 Swallow Place, London, W1B 2AE, United Kingdom
(020) 7664 0480/ (020) 7664 0481
consult@hiveassociates.co.uk
www.hiveassociates.co.uk

PAPER

Antalis Ltd Abbeydale Road, Watford, WD24 4PP, United Kingdom
(0870) 6073114/ (0870) 6073168
contact@antalis.co.uk
www.antalis.com

Bergamot 72 Lightermans Walk, London, SW18 1PS, United Kingdom
(020) 8877 8810/ (020) 8877 8818
info@bergamot.co.uk
www.bergamot.co.uk

Beswick Paper Ltd 1 Gateway, Crewe Gates Farm Industrial Estate, Crewe, CW1 6YB, United Kingdom
(01270) 587721/ (01270) 588405
salescrewe@beswick.co.uk

Cell Paper & Board Ltd Hallsteads, Dove Halls, Buxton, Derbyshire, SK17 8BJ, United Kingdom
(01298) 816692/ (01298) 816277
enquire@cell-limited.co.uk
www.cell-limited.co.uk

Connect@McNaughton Jaymac House, Church Manorway, Erith, Kent, DA8 1DF, United Kingdom
(0870) 600 4400/ (0870) 600 4401
connect@mcnaughton-paper.com
www.jmcpaper.com/connect

County Paper Co. Ltd 32 Nobel Square, Burnt Mill Industrial Estate, Basildon, Essex, SS13 1LT, United Kingdom
(01268) 729629/ (01268) 590569
basildon@countypaper.com
www.jmcpaper.com

Curtis Fine Papers Ltd Main Street, Guardbridge, St. Andrews, Fife, KY16 0UU, United Kingdom
(01334) 839551/ (01334) 839322
curtis@curtisfinepapers.com
www.curtisfinepapers.com

Davies Harvey & Murrell Ltd Mostyn House, Record Street, London, SE15 1TL, United Kingdom
(020) 7732 9988/ (020) 7732 5415
mail@dhmpaper.com
www.dhmpaper.com

Direct Communications Design Solutions Edison Road, St. Ives, Cambridgeshire, PE27 3LH, United Kingdom
(01480) 466300/ (01480) 495618
dave.sheppard@directcoms.co.uk
www.dcds.co.uk

Dixon & Roe Units 1 & 2, Bricklayers Arms, London, SE1 5SP, United Kingdom
(020) 7231 0044/ (020) 7252 0583
sales@dixonandroe.co.uk
www.paperco.co.uk

Donald Murray Paper 211 MacLellan Street, Kinning Park, Glasgow, G41 1RR, United Kingdom
0141-427 1271/ 0141-427 6999
sales@donald-murray-paper.co.uk
www.paperco.co.uk

Elliott Baxter Co Ltd Solent Industrial Estate, Hedge Road, Southampton, SO30 2FY, United Kingdom
(01489) 788411/ (01489) 788572
southamptonsales@ebbpaper.co.uk
www.ebbpaper.co.uk

Elliott Baxter Co. Ltd Unit D, Ventura Park, Old Parkbury Lane, Colney Street, St. Albans, Hertfordshire, AL2 2DB, United Kingdom
(01923) 859944/ (01923) 859009
watfordsales@ebbpaper.co.uk
www.ebbpaper.co.uk

Europoint Display Units 1 & 2, Bricklayers Arms, London, SE1 5SP, United Kingdom
(020) 7231 8711/ (020) 7231 0042
sales.london@europointdisplay.com
www.paperco.co.uk

Falkiner Fine Papers 76 Southampton Row, London, WC1B 4AR, United Kingdom
(020) 7831 1151/ (020) 7430 1248
info@Falkiner
www.Falkiner.com

Fedrigoni UK Ltd Brampton Grange, Sandy Lane, Chapel Brampton, Northampton, NN6 8AD, United Kingdom
(01604) 820820/ (01604) 842665
info@fedrigoni.co.uk
www.fedrigoni.co.uk

Fibermark Red Bridge International Ltd, Ainsworth, Bolton, BL2 5PD, United Kingdom
(01204) 556900/ (01204) 384754
sales@redbridge.co.uk
www.redbridge.co.uk

Folex Ltd 18 & 19 Monkspath Business Park, Shirley, Solihull, West Midlands, B90 4NY, United Kingdom
0121-733 3833/ 0121-733 3222
sales@folex.co.uk
www.folex.co.uk

G.F. Smith & Son London Ltd Lockwood Street, Hull, HU2 0HL, United Kingdom
(01482) 323503/ (01482) 223174
info@gfsmith.com
www.gfsmith.com

H.V. Beever Ltd Unit 2, Marshgate Trading Estate, Marshgate Lane, London, E15 2NG, United Kingdom
(020) 8519 1777/ (020) 8534 5420
sales@hvbeeverltd.com

H.V. Sier Ltd Unit 5, Meridian Trading Estate, Bugsby's Way, London, SE7 7SJ, United Kingdom
(020) 8331 2070/ (020) 8331 2001
info@sierpaper.com
www.paperflowgroup.com

Howard Smith Paper Ltd Rhosili Road, Brackmills Industrial Estate, Northampton, NN4 7JE, United Kingdom
(0870) 6082385/ (01604) 443549
creativepapers@hsp.hspg.com
www.hspg.com/hsp

Iscal The Coaster Factory Unit 20, Calderdale Business Park, Club Lane, Halifax, West Yorkshire, HX2 8DB, United Kingdom
(01422) 352054/ (01422) 380297
iscal@btconnect.com
www.iscal.co.uk

James McNaughton Paper Birchlands Business Centre, Benhall Mill Road, Tunbridge Wells, Kent, TN2 5JH, United Kingdom
(01892) 549180/ (01892) 614469
south@mcnaughton-paper.com
www.jmcpaper.com

James McNaughton Paper (NI) Ltd 7 Duncrue Road, Belfast, BT3 9BP, United Kingdom
(028) 9077 4004/ (028) 9077 1105
www.jmcpaper.com

James McNaughton Paper Merchants Ltd Burton Road, Norwich, NR6 6AX, United Kingdom
(01603) 410248/ (01603) 424688
norwich@mcnaughton-paper.com
www.jmcpaper.co.uk

John Heyer Paper Ltd Unit 14, Langwood House, Rickmansworth, Hertfordshire, WD3 1EQ, United Kingdom
(0870) 2423355/ (0870) 2421114
sales@johnheyerpaper.co.uk
www.johnheyerpaper.co.uk

John McCormick & Co. Ltd McCormick House, 46 Darnley Street, Glasgow, G41 2TY, United Kingdom
0141-429 4222/ 0141-429 6777
enquire@jmccormick.co.uk
www.jmccormick.co.uk

Kentmere Photographic Ltd Staveley, Kendal, Cumbria, LA8 9PB, United Kingdom
(01539) 821365/ (01539) 821399
sales@kentmere.co.uk
www.kentmere.co.uk

Logistix Ltd 62-68 Oak End Way, Gerrards Cross, Buckinghamshire, SL9 8BR, United Kingdom
(01753) 890666/ (01753) 890698
info@logistix.co.uk
www.logistix.co.uk

M 6 Paper Group Ltd Unit 2, Barshaw Park, Leicester, LE4 1ET, United Kingdom
0116-235 2670/ 0116-235 2712
leicester@m6papers.co.uk
www.m6papers.co.uk

M-Real UK Ltd Setinel House, 16 Harcrourt Street, London, W1H 4AD, United Kingdom
☎ (01628) 411611/ 🖷 (01628) 411793
✉ info.uk@mreal.com
🖥 www.mreal.com

M6 Paper Group Ltd Hawley Manor, Hawley Road, Dartford, DA1 1PX, United Kingdom
☎ (01322) 226221/ 🖷 (01322) 227553
🖥 www.m6papers.co.uk

Mass Technology (UK) Ltd 36b Evington Road, Leicester, Leicestershire, LE2 1HG,
☎ 0116 25 44 171
✉ masstechnology@hotmail.com
🖥 www.masstechnologyonline.com

North West Paper Group 182 Bradkirk Place, Walton Summit Centre, Bamber Bridge, Preston, PR5 8AJ, United Kingdom
☎ (01772) 311593/ 🖷 (01772) 627032
✉ sales@northwestpaper.co.uk
🖥 www.paperco.co.uk

Optima Office Supplies Limited Unit 12 Woodmoor Court, Wharncliffe Business Park, Carlton, Barnsley, South Yorkshire, S71 3HT,
☎ 01226 321177/01226 321188
✉ elliot@optimaoffcesupplies.co.uk
🖥 www.optimaoffcesupplies.co.uk

P. Gray Ltd 13 Lower Addiscombe Road, Croydon, CR9 6EQ, United Kingdom
☎ (020) 8681 6637/ 🖷 (020) 8681 6630
✉ pgraylimited@aol.com
🖥 www.pgraypaper.com

Paper Co. Units 1 & 2, Bricklayers Arms, Mandela Way, London, SE1 5SP, United Kingdom
☎ (020) 7740 2234/ 🖷 (020) 7231 0910
✉ samples@paperco.co.uk
🖥 www.paperco.co.uk

Paperback Ltd Unit 2, Bow Triangle Business Centre, Eleanor Street, London, E3 4NP, United Kingdom
☎ (020) 8980 2233/ 🖷 (020) 8980 2399
✉ sales@paperback.coop
🖥 www.paperback.coop

Premier Hale Paper Premier House, Faringdon Avenue, Romford, RM3 8SP, United Kingdom
☎ (01708) 330380/ 🖷 (01708) 330390
✉ information@paper.co.uk
🖥 www.premierpapergroup.co.uk

Premier Paper Ltd Mercury Way, Mercury Park, Manchester, M41 7PA, United Kingdom
☎ 0161-865 8585/ 🖷 0161-864 5354
🖥 www.paper.co.uk

Printall Display Ltd Cyan House, 1 Canada Road, Byfleet, West Byfleet, Surrey, KT14 7JL, United Kingdom
☎ (01932) 337910/ 🖷 (01932) 347598
✉ printallsouth@mcnaughton-paper.com
🖥 www.printall.co.uk

Red Box 2 Western Avenue Business Park, Mansfield Road, London, W3 0BZ, United Kingdom
☎ (020) 8753 7000/ 🖷 (020) 8753 7001
🖥 www.redboxoffce.co.uk

Robert Horne (Birmingham) Paper Co. Ltd 40 Hayward Industrial Park, Tameside Drive, Castle Bromwich, B35 7BD, United Kingdom
☎ 0121-776 7777/ 🖷 0121-749 2670
✉ rh.birmingham@robertthorne.co.uk
🖥 www.robertthorne.co.uk

Robert Horne (Bracknell) Paper Group Huntsman House, Eastern Road, Bracknell, Berkshire, RG12 2UP, United Kingdom
☎ (01344) 786300/ 🖷 (01344) 306584
✉ rh.bracknell@robertthorne.co.uk
🖥 www.robertthorne.co.uk

Robert Horne (Bristol) Paper Group Ltd Bonville Road, Brislington, Bristol, BS4 5QF, United Kingdom
☎ 0117-977 0799/ 🖷 0117-971 7958
✉ rh.bristol@robertthorne.co.uk
🖥 www.robertthorne.co.uk

Robert Horne (Chelmsford) Paper Co. Ltd Huntsman House, Unit B, London, SE8 5DL, United Kingdom
☎ (01245) 325344
🖥 www.robertthorne.co.uk

Robert Horne (Eastleigh) Paper Co. Ltd Huntsman House, Woodside Road, Eastleigh, Hampshire, SO50 4ET, United Kingdom
☎ (023) 8061 8811/ 🖷 (023) 8061 0005
✉ rh.eastleigh@robertthorne.co.uk
🖥 www.robertthorne.co.uk

Robert Horne (Leeds) Paper Co. Ltd Huntsman House, Pontefract Road, Leeds, LS10 1DD, United Kingdom
☎ 0113-387 2468/ 🖷 0113-271 9408
✉ rh.leeds@robertthorne.co.uk
🖥 www.robertthorne.co.uk

Robert Horne (Liverpool) Paper Co. Ltd 5th Floor, Orleans House, Edmund Street, Liverpool, L3 9NG, United Kingdom
☎ 0151-236 4411/ 🖷 0151-255 0359
✉ rh.liverpool@robertthorne.co.uk
🖥 www.robertthorne.co.uk

Robert Horne (London) Paper Co. Ltd Huntsman House, Unit B, 2 Evelyn Street, London, SE8 5DL, United Kingdom
☎ (020) 7231 9634/ 🖷 (020) 7231 5641
✉ rh.london@robertthorne.co.uk
🖥 www.robertthorne.co.uk

Robert Horne (Manchester) Paper Co. Ltd Huntsman House, Tenax Road, Manchester, M17 1JT, United Kingdom
☎ 0161-886 7575/ 🖷 0161-886 7599
✉ rh.manchester@robertthorne.co.uk
🖥 www.robertthorne.co.uk

Robert Horne (Newcastle) Paper Co. Ltd Unit 1, Brooklands Way, Boldon Colliery, Tyne & Wear, NE35 9LZ, United Kingdom
☎ 0191-537 7177/ 🖷 0191-537 7178
✉ rh.newcastle@robertthorne.co.uk
🖥 www.robertthorne.co.uk

Robert Horne (Scotland) Paper Co. Ltd Huntsman House, Deer Dykes Court South, Cumbernauld, G68 9HW, United Kingdom
☎ (01236) 617777/ 🖷 (01236) 735463
✉ rh.scotland@robertthorne.co.uk
🖥 www.robertthorne.co.uk

Robert Horne Group (Design Support Team) Ltd Huntsman House, Unit B, Evelyn Street, London, SE8 5DL, United Kingdom
☎ (0845) 7443322/ 🖷 (020) 7231 5516
🖥 www.robertthorne.co.uk

Robert Horne Group (N.I.) Ltd Nicholson Drive, Mallusk, Newtownabbey, County Antrim, BT36 4FB, United Kingdom
☎ (028) 9034 2742/ 🖷 (028) 9034 2413
✉ rh.northern.ireland@robertthorne.co.uk
🖥 www.robertthorne.co.uk

Robert Horne Group Ltd Huntsman House, Mansion Close, Morton Park, Northampton, NN3 6LA, United Kingdom
☎ (01604) 495333/ 🖷 (01604) 491909
✉ total.support@robertthorne.co.uk
🖥 www.robertthorne.co.uk

Robert Horne Group P.L.C. Horse Fair House, St. Faith's Lane, Norwich, NR1 1NE, United Kingdom
☎ (01603) 610386/ 🖷 (01603) 633381
✉ rh.norwich@robertthorne.co.uk
🖥 www.robertthorne.co.uk

Robert Horne Paper Co. Ltd Kingston House, Brooks Road, Lewes, East Sussex, BN7 2BY, United Kingdom
☎ (01273) 476141/ 🖷 (01273) 480526
✉ rh.southernhq@robertthorne.co.uk
🖥 www.robertthorne.co.uk

Rothera & Brereton Fairfield House, Armley Road, Leeds, LS12 2QH, United Kingdom
☎ 0113-263 2541/ 🖷 0113-387 4820
✉ sales@rotheraandbrereton.co.uk
🖥 www.paperco.co.uk

Ryman Ltd 19-20 High Holborn, London, WC1V 6BS, United Kingdom
☎ (020) 7440 8750/ 🖷 (020) 7404 4859
✉ personnel@lasenza.co.uk
🖥 www.ryman.co.uk

Scheufelen Premium Papers 83 Bell Street, Reigate, Surrey, RH2 7YT, United Kingdom
☎ (01737) 234530/ 🖷 (01737) 234539
✉ marketing@spp.scheufelen.de
🖥 www.scheufelen.de

South Wales Paper Co. Ltd Priority Enterprise Park, Ty Verlon, Barry, South Glamorgan, CF63 2BG, United Kingdom
☎ (01446) 735522/ 🖷 (01446) 732322
✉ geoffclode@southwalespaper.co.uk

Southern Paper Group Ltd Unit 3, Nelson Industrial Park, Hedge End, Southampton, SO30 2JH, United Kingdom
☎ (01489) 789222/ 🖷 (01489) 789214
🖥 www.paperco.co.uk

St. Regis Paper Co. Ltd Wansbrough Paper Mill, Watchet, Somerset, TA23 0AY, United Kingdom
☎ (01984) 631456/ 🖷 (01984) 634123
✉ info@stregis.co.uk
🖥 www.stregis.co.uk

Stora Enso UK Ltd Stora Enso House, New Mill Road, Orpington, Kent, BR5 3TW, United Kingdom
☎ (01689) 892700/ 🖷 (01689) 876693
✉ patrick.carty@storaenso.com
🖥 www.storaenso.com

Sun Paper & Board Ltd 2 Churchill Court, Hortons Way, Westerham, Kent, TN16 1BT, United Kingdom
☎ (01959) 568040/ 🖷 (01959) 569480
✉ sales@sunpaper.co.uk
🖥 www.sunpaper.org

Thom & Cook Ltd Units 1-2, Bricklayers Arms, Mandela Way, London, SE1 5SP, United Kingdom
☎ (020) 7231 1114/ 🖷 (020) 7252 0583
✉ sales@thomandcook.co.uk
🖥 www.paperco.co.uk

Tullis Russell Papermakers Markinch, Glenrothes, Fife, KY7 6PB, United Kingdom
☎ (0800) 747477/ 🖷 (01592) 610672
✉ designline@trg.co.uk
🖥 www.trg.co.uk

U P M-Kymmene Ltd 2 Victoria Street, Altrincham, Cheshire, WA14 1ET, United Kingdom
☎ (0870) 6000876/ 🖷 (0870) 6060876
🖥 www.upm-kymmene.com

Wiles Group Centre Ltd Walmgate Road, Perivale, Greenford, Middlesex, UB6 7LN, United Kingdom
☎ (020) 8758 7700/ 🖷 (020) 8758 7722
✉ sales@wiles.co.uk
🖥 www.wiles.co.uk

Winter & Co. UK Ltd Stonehill, Stukeley Meadows Industrial Estate, Huntingdon, Cambridgeshire, PE29 6ED, United Kingdom
☎ (01480) 377177/ 🖷 (01480) 377166
✉ sales@winteruk.com
🖥 www.winter-company.com

PREPRESS

Abacus Printing Co. Ltd Gloucester House, 34-38 Gloucester Way, London, EC1R 0BN, United Kingdom
☎ (020) 7278 9392/ 🖷 (020) 7278 8535
✉ sales@abacusprinting.com
🖥 www.abacusprinting.com

Aradco VSI Aradco House, 132 Cleveland Street, London, W1T 6AB, United Kingdom
☎ **(020) 7692 7700**/ 🖷 (020) 7692 7711
✉ **info@aradco.com**
🖥 **www.aradco.com**
See ad in showcase

Arnold Cook (Graphic Arts) Ltd Riverside, Stanstead Abbots, Ware, Hertfordshire, SG12 8AP, United Kingdom
☎ (01920) 870991/ 🖷 (01920) 871904
✉ info@arnold-cook.co.uk
🖥 www.arnold-cook.co.uk

Azographics Ltd Unit 1, 22 Pakenham Street, London, WC1X 0LB, United Kingdom
☎ (020) 7833 0667/ 🖷 (020) 7833 3036
✉ printing@azographics.com
🖥 www.azographics.com

B B C Worldwide Ltd Woodlands, 80 Wood Lane, London, W12 0TT, United Kingdom
☎ (020) 8433 2000/ 🖷 (020) 8749 0538
🖥 www.bbcworldwide.co.uk

Blaze Creative Ltd 77 East Road, London, N1 6AH, United Kingdom
☎ (020) 7253 0099/ 🖷 (020) 7253 4358
✉ mail@blaze-creative.co.uk
🖥 www.blaze-creative.co.uk

Boldface Typesetters 17A Clerkenwell Road, London, EC1M 5RD, United Kingdom
☎ (020) 7253 2014/ 🖷 (020) 7251 3443
✉ boldface@easynet.co.uk

Brady Corporation, Wildmere Industrial Estate, Banbury, Oxon, OX16 3JU, United Kingdom
☎ (01295) 228288/ 🖷 (01295) 228219
✉ elaine_hathaway@bradycorp.com
🖥 www.bradyeurope.com

Buccleuch Printers Ltd Tweed Horizon, Newtown St. Boswells, Melrose, Roxburghshire, TD6 0SG, United Kingdom
☎ (01835) 825970/ 🖷 (01835) 824859
✉ sales@buccleuchprinters.co.uk
🖥 www.buccleuchprinters.co.uk

Butler & Tanner Ltd Caxton Road, Frome, Somerset, BA11 1NF, United Kingdom
(01373) 451500/ (01373) 451333
manufacturing@butlerandtanner.com
www.butlerandtanner.com

Byron Advertising Byron House, Wallingford Road, Uxbridge, Middlesex, UB8 2RW, United Kingdom
(01895) 252131/ (01895) 252137
www.byron.co.uk

C D S Yorks Ltd Reprographic House, Canal Road, Armley, Leeds, LS12 2ND, United Kingdom
0113-263 0601/ 0113-231 0305
sales@cds-yorks.com
www.cds-yorks.com

C K Press 231 Brompton Road, London, SW3 2EP, United Kingdom
(020) 7584 2928/ (020) 7589 8125
br@ckpress.com
www.ckpress.com

C3 Colchester Telford Way, Severalls Park, Colchester, CO4 9QP, United Kingdom
(01206) 845544/ (01206) 845856
brian@c3colchester.co.uk
www.c3imaging.co.uk

Cantate Battley Cantate Centre, Parkfield, London, SW11 5DZ, United Kingdom
(020) 7622 3401/ (020) 7498 1497
info@cantate.biz
www.cantate.biz

Cavendish Press Ltd Richmond House, Cambridge Road, Whetstone, Leicester, LE8 6BB, United Kingdom
0116-284 4600/ 0116-284 4646
enquiries@cavendish-print.co.uk
www.cavendish-print.co.uk

Charles Thurnam & Sons Ltd Kingstown, Broadway, Kingstown Industrial Estate, Carlisle, CA3 0HA, United Kingdom
(01228) 520222/ (01228) 511185
mail@thurnams.co.uk
www.thurnams.co.uk

Charterhouse Litho 87 Great North Road, Hatfield, Hertfordshire, AL9 5DA, United Kingdom
(01707) 262222/ (01707) 268888
sales@charterhouseuk.com
www.charterhouse.tv

Collective Colour Unit 11, Dolphin Point, Dolphin Way, Purfleet, Essex, RM19 1NR, United Kingdom
(01708) 804706/(07768) 528072 / (0870 0510 468
repro@collectivecolour.co.uk
www.collectivecolour.co.uk

Color Co. Unit 41 Elizabeth House, 39 York Road, London, SE1 7NJ, United Kingdom
(020) 7928 3082/ (020) 7261 1602
waterloo@color.co.uk
www.color.co.uk

Composing Operations Ltd Sheffield Hall, Sheffield Road, Southborough, Tunbridge Wells, Kent, TN4 0PG, United Kingdom
(01892) 511725/ (01892) 511726
compops@btconnect.com
www.composingoperations.co.uk

Corniche Fine Arts Ltd Lancaster Road, Carnaby Industrial Estate, Bridlington, East Yorkshire, YO15 3QY, United Kingdom
(0845) 230 6565/ (01262) 606724
info@corniche.co.uk
www.corniche.co.uk

Creative Print & Design Group Unit 2 Saxon Way, West Drayton, Middlesex, UB7 0LW, United Kingdom
(020) 8759 9111/ (020) 8897 6977
cpd@cpd-group.co.uk
www.cpd-group.co.uk

D L Interactive UK 46-47 Britton Street, London, EC1M 5UJ, United Kingdom
(020) 7253 0854/ (020) 7490 0235
imad@dlrepro.com
www.dlrepro.com

Dainippon Screen (UK) Ltd Michigan Drive, Tongewell, Milton Keynes, MK15 8HT, United Kingdom
(01908) 848500/ (01908) 848501
sales@screeneurope.com
www.screen.co.uk

Digicol Link 49 Leesons Hill, Orpington, Kent, BR5 2LF, United Kingdom
(0845) 2322311/ (0845) 2322333
info@digicol.co.uk
www.digicol.co.uk

Digital Printed Word 19 Briset Street, London, EC1M 5NR, United Kingdom
(020) 7250 1404/ (020) 7253 4675
printedword@btconnect.com
www.printed-word.co.uk

E A E Creative Colour Ltd 3 Morgan Way, Bowthorpe, Norwich, NR5 9JJ, United Kingdom
(01603) 741278/ (01603) 749227
reception@castlecolour.co.uk
www.eaecreative.com

Elanders Hindson Ltd Merlin Way, New York Business Park, Newcastle Upon Tyne, NE27 0YT, United Kingdom
0191-280 0400/ 0191-280 0401
info@elandershindson.com
www.elanders.se

Evergreen Graphics 11 The Drive, Craigweil On Sea, Bognor Regis, West Sussex, PO21 4DU, United Kingdom
(01243) 262887/ (01243) 262887
www.evergreengraphics.co.uk

F.E. Burman Ltd 20 Crimscott Street, London, SE1 5TF, United Kingdom
(020) 7206 1000/ (020) 7206 1040
info@feburman.co.uk
www.feburman.co.uk

Fericon Press Ltd Unit 12, Stadium Way, Tilehurst, Reading, RG30 6BX, United Kingdom
0118-945 6100/ 0118-945 4146
fericon@dircon.co.uk

Florence Production Ltd Stoodleigh Court, Stoodleigh, Tiverton, Devon, EX16 9PN, United Kingdom
(01398) 351556

Forward Ltd 84-86 Regent Street, London, W1B 5DD, United Kingdom
(020) 7734 2303/ (020) 7494 2570
www.theforwardgroup.com

Garnett Dickinson Print Ltd Brookfields Way, Manvers, Wath upon Dearne, Rotherham, South Yorkshire, S63 5DL, United Kingdom
(01709) 768000/ (01709) 768010
info@garnett-dickinson.co.uk
www.garnett-dickinson.co.uk

Gask & Hawley Ltd 3 Commerce Way, Avocado Court, Trafford Park, Manchester, M17 1HW, United Kingdom
0161-869 5880/ 0161-873 7501
dave.hatton@gaskandhawley.com
www.gaskandhawley.com

Gemini Press Ltd Unit A1, Dolphin Way, Shoreham-by-Sea, West Sussex, BN43 6NZ, United Kingdom
(01273) 464884/ (01273) 464744
info@gemini-group.co.uk
www.gemini-group.co.uk

Geo-Graphics 1190 Argyle Street, Glasgow, G3 8TE, United Kingdom
0141-337 3333/ 0141-337 3335
info@geo-graphics.com
www.geo-graphics.com

Greenshires Group Ltd 160-164 Barkby Road, Leicester, LE4 9LF, United Kingdom
0116-202 2600/ 0116-202 2601
marketing@greenshires.com
www.greenshires.com

Greenwich Press Ltd Standard House, 107-115 Eastmoor Street, London, SE7 8LX, United Kingdom
(020) 8858 3202/ (020) 8853 2103
info@greenwichpress.co.uk
www.greenwichpress.co.uk

Halstan Music Setting & Printing 2-10 Plantation Road, Amersham, Buckinghamshire, HP6 6HJ, United Kingdom
(01494) 725525/ (01494) 432305
sales@halstan.co.uk
www.halstan.co.uk

Hartley Reproductions Ltd 217 London Road, Stone, Greenhithe, Kent, DA9 9DQ, United Kingdom
(01322) 287676/ (01322) 289597
support@hartleyrepro.co.uk
www.hartleyrepro.co.uk

Hi-Speed Photos 60 Broadway, West Ealing, London, W13 0SU, United Kingdom
(020) 8840 4850/ (020) 8840 1800
sales@hi-speed.co.uk
www.hi-speed.co.uk

Higgs & Co. (Printers) Ltd Caxton House, 1 Station Road, Henley-on-Thames, Oxfordshire, RG9 1AD, United Kingdom
(01491) 419400/ (01491) 419401
mail@higgsgroup.co.uk
www.henley-on-thames.com

Hobs Ltd 21-27 Marylebone Lane, London, W1U 2NG, United Kingdom
(020) 7935 9539/ (020) 7486 3958
marylebone@hobsrepro.com
www.hobsreprographics.co.uk

Howitt Digital Unit 5, Block 8, Enterprise Way, Edenbridge, Kent, TN8 6HF, United Kingdom
(01732) 864669/ (01732) 864912
enquiries@howitt.co.uk
www.howitt.co.uk

I B A Graphics Ltd 12 Allied Way, Off Warple Way, London, W3 0RQ, United Kingdom
(020) 8743 2414/(07803) 022368 / (020) 8749 9448
hamilton@ibagraphics.co.uk
www.ibagraphics.co.uk

Impress Print Services Ltd 10 Thornsett Road, London, SW18 4EN, United Kingdom
(020) 8871 9950/ (020) 8871 9908
sales@impressprint.net
www.impressprint.com

J.W. Northend Ltd Clyde Road, Sheffield, S8 0TZ, United Kingdom
0114-250 0331/ 0114-250 0676
info@northend.co.uk
www.northend.co.uk

Jaggerprint Victoria House, 86-90 Richmond Road, Kingston upon Thames, Surrey, KT2 5EW, United Kingdom
(020) 8546 0593/ (020) 8541 5708
sales@jaggerprint.co.uk
www.jaggerprint.co.uk

Kall Kwik Centre 186 Fleet Street, London, EC4A 2HR, United Kingdom
(020) 7405 5686/ (020) 7404 4814
natalie@kkfleetst.co.uk
www.fleetstreet.kallkwik.co.uk

Kall Kwik Centre 367 21 Kingly Street, London, W1B 5QA, United Kingdom
(020) 7434 2471/ (020) 7494 0260
kallkwik@regentstreet.kallkwik.co.uk
www.regentstreet.kallkwik.co.uk

Kall Kwik Centre 787 17 Silvermills Court, Henderson Place, Edinburgh, EH3 5DG, United Kingdom
0131-523 0400/ 0131-523 0430
info@edinburgh.kallkwik.co.uk
www.edinburgh.kallkwik.co.uk

Karran Group Karran House, Woodbridge Meadows, Guildford, Surrey, GU1 1BA, United Kingdom
(01483) 576777/ (01483) 458558
sales@karran.co.uk
www.karran.co.uk

Keene Repro Ltd 33-41 Dallington Street, London, EC1V 0BB, United Kingdom
(020) 7251 2722/ (020) 7490 8736
contact@keenes.co.uk
www.keenes.co.uk

Kingswood Steele 89 Worship Street, London, EC2A 2BF, United Kingdom
(020) 7655 3000/ (020) 7426 0569
info@kingswood-steele.co.uk
www.kingswood-steele.co.uk

Koi Reprographics Ltd 7 Warren Way, Digswell, Welwyn, Hertfordshire, AL6 0DQ, United Kingdom
07767 437298/07767 437298 / 01438 717189
peter.howard@koi-epro.co.uk
www.koirepro.co.uk

Leyprint Leyland Lane, Leyland, PR25 1UT, United Kingdom
(01772) 422234/ (01772) 425001
info@leyprint.co.uk
www.leyprint.co.uk

Litho Supplies Unit 1, Thamebridge Industrial Estate, Birmingham, B42 2TX, United Kingdom
0121-344 4222/ 0121-344 4494
midland@litho.co.uk
www.litho.co.uk

Lithograve 50 Cardigan Street, Birmingham, B4 7SA, United Kingdom
0121-359 3350/ 0121-359 3119
dave@lithograve.com

Lonsdale Press 43-47 Lonsdale Road, Queens Park, London, NW6 6RA, United Kingdom
(020) 7328 3355/ (020) 7328 1840
info@lonsdalepress.com

Mass Technology (UK) Ltd 36b Evington Road, Leicester, Leicestershire, LE2 1HG,
0116 25 44 171
masstechnology@hotmail.com
www.masstechnologyonline.com

Matrix Graphics Ltd 31 Lee Bank Business Centre, 55 Holloway Head, Birmingham, B1 1HP, United Kingdom
0121-643 2227/ 0121-643 1345
carl.prosser@matrixgraphics.co.uk
www.matrixgraphics.co.uk

Modern Graphic Arts Ltd 52-54 Milton Road, Westcliff-on-Sea, Essex, SS0 7JX, United Kingdom
(01702) 349541/ (01702) 335487
sales@mgaprinting.co.uk
www.mgaprinting.co.uk

Multiplex Medway Ltd Gleaming Wood Drive, Walderslade, Kent, ME5 8XT, United Kingdom
(01634) 684371/ (01634) 683840
enquiries@multiplex-medway.co.uk
www.multiplex-medway.co.uk

N T A Printers Ltd Andrew House, Market Street, Hyde, Cheshire, SK14 1HE, United Kingdom
0161-368 0000/ 0161-367 8710
print@ntaprinters.com
www.ntaprinters.com

N W Printers Dukesway, Team Valley Trading Estate, Gateshead, Tyne & Wear, NE11 0PZ, United Kingdom
0191-487 6041/ 0191-491 5554
sales@nwprinters.co.uk
www.nwprinters.co.uk

Newnorth-Print Ltd Newnorth House, College Street, Kempston, MK42 8NA, United Kingdom
(01234) 341111/ (01234) 271112
newnorth@newnorth.co.uk
www.newnorth.co.uk

Offsite Ltd Unit 5, Bolding Hatch Business Centre, Bishops Stortford Road, Chelmsford, CM1 4LF, UK
(01245) 231900/ (01245) 231911
sales@offsitegroup.net
www.offsitegroup.net

Optichrome 98 Maybury Road, Woking, Surrey, GU21 5HX, United Kingdom
(01483) 740290/ (01483) 732609
optisales@optichrome.com
www.optichrome.com

Original Business Print Unit 8, Menin Works, Bond Road, Mitcham, Surrey, CR4 3HG, United Kingdom
(020) 8640 6061/ (020) 8640 6614
pat@originalbusinessprint.com

Oxbow Data Services 5 & 6 Donington Park, Birdham Road, Chichester, West Sussex, PO20 7DU, United Kingdom
(01243) 788878/ (01243) 789246
info@oxbowmedia.co.uk
www.oxbowmedia.co.uk

P W Reproprint Ltd (Hendi Systems) 10 East Road, London, N1 6AJ, United Kingdom
(020) 7324 2632/ (020) 7608 1501
ian.downie@hendi.net
www.hendigroup.co.uk

Paragraphics Ltd 65 Leonard Street, London, EC2A 4QS, United Kingdom
(020) 7613 5161/ (020) 7395 805
info@paragraphics.co.uk
www.paragraphics.co.uk

Peak Press Ltd Eccles Road, Chapel-en-le-Frith, High Peak, Derbyshire, SK23 9RQ, United Kingdom
(01298) 812738/ (01298) 815220
sales@peakpress.co.uk
www.peakcreative.co.uk

Phillips Print & Stationery Ltd 115 High Street, Crediton, Devon, EX17 3LG, United Kingdom
(01363) 772060/ (01363) 774030
info@phillipsprint.co.uk
www.phillipsprint.co.uk

Pillans & Waddies Ormolu House, 455 Chester Road, Manchester, M16 9HA, United Kingdom
0161-855 3760/ 0161-877 5273
mail@pillanswaddies.com
www.pillanswaddies.com

Polestar Whitefriars Ltd 3rd Floor, Northgate Place, Tunbridge Wells, Kent, TN1 2AX, United Kingdom
(01892) 544366/ (01892) 543464
paul.seaborn@polestar-group.com
www.polestar-group.com

Pure Print Group Ltd Bellbrook Park, Uckfield, East Sussex, TN22 1PL, United Kingdom
(01825) 768611/ (01825) 768042
print@beaconpress.co.uk
www.beaconpress.co.uk

Reach Marketing Ltd Trinity Hall, Trinity Lane, Leicester, LE1 6WP, United Kingdom
0116-233 5592/ 0116-233 5595
info@reachmarketing.co.uk
www.reachmarketing.co.uk

Regal Engravers Hamlin Lane, Polsloe Bridge Works, Exeter, EX1 2RY, United Kingdom
(01392) 278790/ (01392) 278790
regalengravers@yahoo.com

Saint Albans Photoprint Photoprint House, Stonecross, St. Albans, Hertfordshire, AL1 4AA, United Kingdom
(01727) 850777/ (01727) 866068

Santype Netherhampton Road, Salisbury, SP2 8PS, United Kingdom
(01722) 334261/ (01722) 333171
info@santype.co.uk
www.santype.com

Schwak St Marks House, Shepherdess Walk, London, N1 7LH, United Kingdom
(020) 7861 7777/ (020) 7871 7777
www.schawk.com

Scottish Studios & Engravers 80 Kilbirnie Street, Glasgow, G5 8JD, United Kingdom
0141-418 0444/ 0141-420 1720
admin@scottishstudios.co.uk

Screaming Colour Ltd 2 Pear Tree Street, London, EC1V 3SB, United Kingdom
(020) 7549 3400/(07814) 010014
info@screamingcolour.com
www.screamingcolour.com

Seacourt Press Pony Road, Horspath Road Industrial Estate, Cowley, Oxford, OX4 2SE, United Kingdom
(01865) 770140/ (01865) 747347
jimdinnage@seacourt.net
www.seacourt.net

Select Typesetters Ltd Barber & Surgeons Hall, 1st Floor, Monkwell Square, London, EC2Y 5BL, United Kingdom
(020) 7606 4397/ (020) 7606 3961
business@select-typesetters.com
www.select-typesetters.com

Service Point 27 Prince of Wales Road, Norwich, NR1 1BG, United Kingdom
(01603) 660061/ (01603) 630838
norwich@servicepointuk.com
www.servicepointuk.com

Servicepoint UK 192-198 Vauxhall Bridge Road, London, SW1V 1DX, United Kingdom
(020) 7931 0222
mark.dobson@servicepointuk.com
www.servicepointuk.com

Smudge Ltd Unit 21/22, Bermondsey Trading Estate, Rotherhithe New Road, London, SE16 3LL, United Kingdom
(020) 7232 1234/ (020) 7237 5700
info@smudgegroup.com
www.smudgegroup.com

Sol Communications Ltd 46 Great Eastern Street, London, EC2A 3EP, United Kingdom
(020) 7613 3600/ (020) 7613 2203
info@sol.uk.com
www.sol.uk.com

Square Group Ltd 18 Rushworth Street, London, SE1 0RB, United Kingdom
(020) 7803 1500

St. Ives Burrups Ltd St Ives House, Lavington Street, London, SE1 0NX, United Kingdom
(020) 7928 8844/ (020) 7902 6572
www.st-ives.com

Stanley L. Hunt Printers Ltd Midland Road, Rushden, Northamptonshire, NN10 9UA, United Kingdom
(01933) 356226/ (01933) 356613
admin@stanleyhunt.co.uk

Stephen Green Print & Design 12 Hargreaves Way, Fords Farm, Reading, RG31 7QA, United Kingdom
0118-941 0294/(07831) 098 811
stephen.green17@virgin.net
www.sgpdgraphics.co.uk

Stones the Printers Ltd Unit 10, Wates Way, Wildmere Industrial Estate, Banbury, Oxfordshire, OX16 3ES, United Kingdom
(01295) 252211/ (01295) 819390
receptionban@stonestheprinters.co.uk
www.stonestheprinters.co.uk

Stream 8th Floor, Astley House, Quay Street, Manchester, M3 4AS, United Kingdom
0161-832 9552/ 0161-832 2885
dave.buckley@jwt.com
www.cheethambelljwt.com

Swift Print 186 Campden Hill Road, London, W8 7TH, United Kingdom
(020) 7229 5012/ (020) 7229 3068
mail@swiftprint.co.uk
www.swiftprint.co.uk

T A G Adplates Group 29 Clerkenwell Road, London, EC1M 5TA, United Kingdom
(020) 7251 4571/ (020) 7253 5355
info@tagworldwide.com
www.tagmedia.co.uk

T D Graphics Graphic House, 26-34 Southwell Road, London, SE5 9PQ, United Kingdom
(020) 7274 8722/ (020) 7733 5496
sales@tdgraphics.co.uk
www.tdgraphics.co.uk

Technik Unit 4, River Park Industrial Estate, Billet Lane, Berkhamsted, Hertfordshire, HP4 1HL, United Kingdom
(01442) 871117/ (01442) 869619
sales@technik.com
www.technik.com

The Kent Art Printers Ltd Caxton House, Hopewell Drive, Chatham, Kent, ME5 7NP, United Kingdom
(01634) 844644/ (01634) 842114
paul@kap.co.uk
www.kap.co.uk

Transcript Ltd 31-35 Kirby Street, London, EC1N 8TE, United Kingdom
(020) 7242 4334/ (020) 7242 3629
sales@transcript.co.uk
www.transcript.co.uk

Unigraph Design 64 Old Street, London, EC1V 9AN, United Kingdom
(020) 7253 0950/ (020) 7253 1835
john.mcneil@unigraph-design.com
www.unigraph-design.com

VeriVide Ltd Quartz Close, Warrens Business Park, Leicester, LE19 4SG, United Kingdom
0116-284 7790/ 0116-284 7799
enquiries@verivide.com
www.verivide.com

Visual Aspects Ltd 18 Leather Lane, London, EC1N 7SU, United Kingdom
(020) 7404 1290/ (020) 7404 1291
info@visualaspects.co.uk
www.visualaspects.co.uk

White Knight 360 Degrees Ltd Latimer Road, Luton, LU1 3XG, United Kingdom
(01582) 456082/ (01582) 402682
www.whiteknight360.com

Wiles Group Centre Ltd Walmgate Road, Perivale, Greenford, Middlesex, UB6 7LN, United Kingdom
(020) 8758 7700/ (020) 8758 7722
sales@wiles.co.uk
www.wiles.co.uk

William Clowes Ltd Copland Way, Ellough, Beccles, Suffolk, NR34 7TL, United Kingdom
(01502) 712884/(01768) 658820 / (01502) 717003
user@clowes.co.uk
www.clowes.co.uk

Winstanley & Watkins 104 Duke Street, Liverpool, L1 5AG, United Kingdom
0151-709 0808/ 0151-709 3060
info@wwprint.co.uk
www.wwprint.co.uk

Witney Press 11 Linkwood Road, Windrush Industrial Park, Witney, Oxfordshire, OX29 7HA, United Kingdom
(01993) 703981/ (01993) 776096
print@witneypress.co.uk
www.witneypress.co.uk

WorldAccent 30-31 Great Sutton Street, London, London, EC1V 0NA, United Kingdom
(020) 7865 8300/ (020) 7865 8400
sales@worldaccent.com
www.worldaccent.com

X1 Herschel Industrial Centre, 24 Church Street, Slough, SL1 1PT, United Kingdom
(01753) 215300/ (01753) 215301
info@x1.ltd.uk
www.x1.ltd.uk

Xyron UK Ltd Waterside House, Cowley Business Park, Cowley, Uxbridge, Middlesex, UB8 2HP, United Kingdom
(01895) 878700/ (01895) 878874
studio@xyron.com
www.xyron.com

Y R G Manchester Ltd Trafford Plaza, Seymour Grove, Manchester, M16 0LD, United Kingdom
0161-872 3735/ 0161-877 7531
yrgmanchester@aol.com

PRINT MANAGEMENT

1st Creative Services 4th Floor, Lafore House, The Leathermarket, Weston Street, London, SE1 3ER, United Kingdom
(0870) 7461381/ (0870) 120 9560
phil@1stcreative.co.uk
www.1stcreative.co.uk

Blaze Creative Ltd 77 East Road, London, N1 6AH, United Kingdom
(020) 7253 0099/ (020) 7253 4358
mail@blaze-creative.co.uk
www.blaze-creative.co.uk

C & P Media.com 17 Canonsleigh Crescent, Leigh-on-Sea, Essex, SS9 1RJ, United Kingdom
(01702) 714220/ (01702) 714220
info@candpmedia.com
www.candpmedia.com

Charterhouse Printing 87 Great North Road, Hatfield, Hertfordshire, AL7 5DA, United Kingdom
(01707) 262222/ (01707) 268888
sales@charterhouseuk.com
www.charterhouse.tv

Chris Price Designs 121 Engleheart Road, Catford, London, SE6 2EU,
2081230016
info@chrispricedesigns.com
www.chrispricedesigns.com

Creative Edge Design & Advertising 1st Floor Donald Hendry Building, Auchincruive, Ayr, KA6 5HW, United Kingdom
(01292) 521404/ (01292) 521693
paul@cedge.co.uk
www.cedge.co.uk

Design Matters Ltd 33 Cambridge Gardens, Hastings, East Sussex, TN34 1EN,
01424 722311/ 01424 722310
paul@design-matters.co.uk
www.design-matters.co.uk

DL Design Associates Limited 38a Duke Street, Chelmsford, CM1 1HY,
01245 299047/ 01245 299047
darren@dl-design.co.uk
www.dl-design.co.uk

Giraffe Print, Epsom, Surrey, KT18 7WJ, United Kingdom
0800 328 4712
info@giraffeprint.com
www.giraffeprint.com

HiViz Ltd 14 Oakley Drive, Bromley, BR2 8PP, United Kingdom
(01689) 862096/(07900) 915134 / (01689) 862096
sabine@hiviz-ltd.co.uk
www.hiviz-ltd.co.uk

Insight Design Concepts Ltd 1st Floor, 9 Benbow Road, London, W6 0AT, United Kingdom
(020) 8834 7001/ (020) 8834 7002
info@insightdc.co.uk
www.insightdc.co.uk

Jolanta Damski Freelance Design Flat 1, 40 Ewelme Road, London, SE23 3BH, United Kingdom
(020) 8291 6023
jolantadamski@btinternet.com
www.jolantadamski.co.uk

London Calling Arts Ltd 14a Ardleigh Road, London, N1 4HP, United Kingdom
(020) 7275 7225/ (020) 7241 4856
colin@londoncalling.com
www.londoncalling.com

Mass Technology (UK) Ltd 36b Evington Road, Leicester, Leicestershire, LE2 1HG,
0116 25 44 171
masstechnology@hotmail.com
www.masstechnologyonline.com

Northstar Marketing & Design Northstar House, 5 Ferns Mead, Farnham, Surrey, GU9 7XP, United Kingdom
(01252) 734070/ (01252) 734071
info@northstarmarketng.co.uk
www.northstarmarketing.co.uk

Olympic Print & Design Olympic Hse, 66 Vulcan Way, New Addington, Croydon, CR0 9UG, United Kingdom
(020) 8405 0065/ (020) 8405 0070
marketing@olympicprint.com
www.olympicprint.com

Print Assessment & Solutions, Coventry, CV5 7BB, United Kingdom
(024) 7646 0734/ (024) 7669 4016
printassltd@macunlimited.net

Raucous Creative Services 5 Oak Lane, Wilmslow, Cheshire, SK9 6AA, United Kingdom
(01625) 530697
paul@raucous.co.uk

Redrova Ltd The Big Barn, Red House Farm, Woodwalton, Huntingdon, Cambridgeshire, PE28 5YL, United Kingdom
(01487) 773679/ (01487) 773659
zoe@redrova.co.uk
www.redrova.co.uk

Scantech Unit 22/23, Ghyll Industrial Estate, Heathfield, East Sussex, TN21 8AW, United Kingdom
(01435) 867500/ (01435) 866177
neil@scan-tech.co.uk
www.scan-tech.co.uk

Scarlet Creative Solutions Ltd 3 Yew Walk, Hoddesdon, Hertfordshire, EN11 8BB, United Kingdom
(0845) 4085402
solutions@scarletcreative.co.uk
www.scarletcreative.co.uk

Servicepoint UK 192-198 Vauxhall Bridge Road, London, SW1V 1DX, United Kingdom
(020) 7931 0222
mark.dobson@servicepointuk.com
www.servicepointuk.com

Signs 73 Upper Marehay, Ripley, Derbyshire, DE5 8JF, United Kingdom
(01773) 741500/ (01773) 741555
lindensign@aol.com
www.lindensigns.org

Supserchrome Ltd 69 Enid Street, London, SE16 3RA, United Kingdom
(0870) 2421761/ (020) 7237 9444
sales@superchrome.co.uk
www.superchrome.co.uk

The Gate Marketing & Design Ltd Murlain Business Centre, Union Street, Chester, CH1 1QP, United Kingdom
(01244) 357242/ (01244) 357215
info@thegatemarketing.com
www.thegatemarketing.com

The Hub London 4-5 Warner Yard, London, EC1R 5EY, United Kingdom
(020) 7837 4423/ (020) 7837 9576
michael@hublimited.com
www.thehublondon.co.uk

The Kent Art Printers Ltd Caxton House, Hopewell Drive, Chatham, Kent, ME5 7NP, United Kingdom
(01634) 844644/ (01634) 842114
paul@kap.co.uk
www.kap.co.uk

Urban Ink Ltd Units 22-23, The Bic Centre, Innova Science Park, Enfield, Middlesex, EN3 7XU, United Kingdom
(020) 8373 5000/ (020) 8373 5001
vanessa@urban-ink.co.uk
www.urban-ink.co.uk

PRINTERS

1st BYTE 1st House, Bakers Yard, Bakers Row, London, EC1R 3DD, United Kingdom
(020) 7841 4300/ (020) 7841 4302
info@1stbyte.co.uk
www.1stbyte.co.uk
See ad in showcase

1st Stop Direct.Com Middleton Hall, Brinkwood Road, Brentwood, Essex, CM13 3LX, United Kingdom
(01277) 811670/ (01277) 811185
sales@1ststopdirect.com
www.1ststopdirect.com

A B P Web P.L.C. Britannia House, 26-28 Central Avenue, West Molesey, Surrey, KT8 2QT, United Kingdom
(07768) 903140/ (020) 8224 1111
phil.watts@aldersonbrothers.co.uk
www.aldersonbrothers.co.uk

A G I Media Packaging, Birmingham, United Kingdom
0121-607 7300/ 0121-607 7400
birmingham@agimedia.com
www.agimedia.com

A M Print Ltd 104 Duke Street, Liverpool, L1 5AG, United Kingdom
0151-709 8452/ 0151-709 3060
enquiries@amprint.co.uk
www.amprint.co.uk

Abacus Printing Co. Ltd Gloucester House, 34-38 Gloucester Way, London, EC1R 0BN, United Kingdom
(020) 7278 9392/ (020) 7278 8535
sales@abacusprinting.com
www.abacusprinting.com

Accappella Nightingale Farm, Whiteacre Lane, Waltham, Canterbury, Kent, CT4 5SR, United Kingdom
(01227) 700725/ (01227) 700725
emma@accappellastudio.co.uk
www.accappellastudio.co.uk

Act Two 3rd Floor, 16 Bishops Bridge Road, London, W2 6AA
0207 863 9570/0207 863 9571 **info@acttwo.biz**
www.acttwo.biz
See ad in showcase

Advision Advertising Vision House, Main Cross Road, Great Yarmouth, Norfolk, NR30 3NZ, United Kingdom
(01493) 854000/ (01493) 330016
advision@btconnect.com
www.advision-advertising.net

Alden Group Ltd Osney Mead, Oxford, OX2 0EF, United Kingdom
(01865) 253200/ (01865) 249070
info@alden.co.uk
www.alden.co.uk

Aldridge Print Group Unit 9, Mitcham Industrial Estate, Streatham Road, Mitcham, Surrey, CR4 2AP, United Kingdom
(020) 8239 4100/ (020) 8239 4120
darbya@apgprint.com
www.apgprint.com

Ancient House Printing Group 8 Whittle Road, Hadleigh Road Industrial Estate, Ipswich, IP2 0HA, United Kingdom
(01473) 232777/ (01473) 231648
sales@ancienthouse.co.uk
www.ancienthouse.co.uk

Andus Print Ltd 47 Highcroft Villas, Brighton, BN1 5PT, United Kingdom
(01273) 558880/ (01273) 554445
andus@mistral.co.uk

Antony Rowe Ltd Bumper's Farm, Chippenham, Wiltshire, SN14 6LH, United Kingdom
(01249) 659705/ (01249) 443103
sales@antonyrowe.co.uk
www.antonyrowe.co.uk

Arbrose Press Unit 25, Water House Business Centre, Cromar Way, Chelmsford, CM1 2QE, United Kingdom
(020) 8518 6638/ (020) 8518 0350
enquiries@arbrosepress.co.uk

Archant Print Centre St Andrews Business Park, Northside, Norwich, NR7 0HT, United Kingdom
(01603) 628311/ (01603) 772359
www.archant.co.uk

Augustus Martin Ltd 8-20 St. Andrews Way, Bromley-By-Bow, London, E3 3PB, United Kingdom
(020) 7537 4200/ (020) 7537 2182
sales@amartin.co.uk
www.augustusmartin.com

Barnard & Westwood 9 Railway Street, London, N1 9EE, United Kingdom
(020) 7837 0252/ (020) 7837 0386
barnwest1@aol.com

PRINTERS

Bartlett Printing Swan Yard, St. Thomas, Exeter, EX4 1HU, United Kingdom
☎ (01392) 254086/✆ (01392) 256224
✎ sales@bartlett-printing.co.uk
🖥 www.bartlett-printing.co.uk

Benwell Sebard Ltd 24 Crimscott Street, London, SE1 5TE, United Kingdom
☎ (020) 7237 5111/✆ (020) 7252 0683
✎ info@benwellsebard.co.uk
🖥 www.benwellsebard.co.uk

Bergamot 72 Lightermans Walk, London, SW18 1PS, United Kingdom
☎ (020) 8877 8810/✆ (020) 8877 8818
✎ info@bergamot.co.uk
🖥 www.bergamot.co.uk

Berrico Ltd 57-63 Churchfield Road, London, W3 6AU, United Kingdom
☎ (020) 8992 6454/✆ (020) 8752 0670
✎ berrico@berrico.co.uk

Bezier Corporate Print 87-89 Cleveland Street, Room 121C, London, W1T 6PJ, United Kingdom
☎ (020) 7436 1875/(07816) 962101 /✆ (020) 7436 1867
✎ firstinitiallastname@london.bezier.co.uk
🖥 www.bezier.co.uk

Blockfoil Ltd Foxtail Road, Ransomes Europark, Ipswich, IP3 9RT, United Kingdom
☎ (01473) 721701/✆ (01473) 718220
✎ ipswich@blockfoil.com
🖥 www.blockfoil.com

Blocking Services Ltd 1 Hill House Road, Ipswich, IP3 8AP, United Kingdom
☎ (01473) 281083/✆ (01473) 225456
✎ clementsm@btconnect.com

Bprint Units 11-13 Petre Road, Clayton Business Park, Clayton-Le-Moors Accrington, Lancashire, BB5 5JB, United Kingdom
☎ 01254 396097/✆ 01254 872352
✎ tony@bprint.co.uk
🖥 www.bprint.co.uk

Bridge & Co. 25 Holliwell Row, London, EC2A 4XE, United Kingdom
☎ (020) 7539 3486/(07775) 560270 ✆
✎ sales@bridgeandco.com
🖥 www.bridgeandco.com

Broglia Press Enterprise House, 52 Holton Road, Poole, Dorset, BH16 6LQ, United Kingdom
☎ (01202) 621621/✆ (01202) 632634
✎ firstname.surname@broglia.co.uk
🖥 www.broglia.co.uk

Brook Office Supplies 12-18 Summer Lane, Barnsley, South Yorkshire, S70 6BN, United Kingdom
☎ (01226) 288916/✆ (01226) 730365
✎ sales@bos-office-supplies.co.uk
🖥 www.bos-office-supplies.co.uk

Brown Knight & Truscott Ltd North Farm Road, Tunbridge Wells, Kent, TN2 3BW, United Kingdom
☎ (01892) 511678/✆ (01892) 511343
🖥 www.bkt.co.uk

Buccleuch Printers Ltd Tweed Horizon, Newtown St. Boswells, Melrose, Roxburghshire, TD6 0SG, United Kingdom
☎ (01835) 825970/✆ (01835) 824859
✎ sales@buccleuchprinters.co.uk
🖥 www.buccleuchprinters.co.uk

Buckland Press Group Barwick Road, Dover, Kent, CT17 0LG, United Kingdom
☎ (01304) 205900/✆ (01304) 205619
✎ info@buckland.co.uk
🖥 www.buckland.co.uk

Buckleys The Welkin, Welkin Lane, Lower Bredbury, Stockport, Cheshire, SK6 2BL, United Kingdom
☎ 0161-430 4211/✆ 0161-494 2837
✎ tony.stevens@buckleys-print.co.uk
🖥 www.buckleys-print.co.uk

Burford Printing Co. Ltd 9 Eccleston Street, London, SW1W 9LX, United Kingdom
☎ (020) 7730 8765/✆ (020) 7730 8065
✎ burfordprinting@btinternet.com
🖥 www.burford-printing.com

Burleigh Press Ltd One Harbourmead, Harbour Road, Portishead, Bristol, BS20 7AY, United Kingdom
☎ (01275) 841280/✆ (01275) 814354
✎ info@burleighpress.co.uk
🖥 www.burleighpress.co.uk

Butler & Tanner Ltd 35 Headfort Place, Belgravia, London, SW1X 7DE, United Kingdom
☎ (020) 7235 8236/✆ (020) 7245 6741
✎ sales@butlerandtanner.com
🖥 www.butlerandtanner.com

Buyright Print Ltd 34 Acomb Wood Drive, York, YO24 2XN, United Kingdom
☎ (01904) 345854/✆ (01904) 345465
✎ info@buyrightprint.com
🖥 www.buyrightprint.com

C & P Media.com 17 Canonsleigh Crescent, Leigh-on-Sea, Essex, SS9 1RJ, United Kingdom
☎ (01702) 714220/✆ (01702) 714220
✎ info@candpmedia.com
🖥 www.candpmedia.com

C D M S Whiston Enterprise Park, Fallows Way, Whiston, Prescot, Merseyside, L35 1RZ, United Kingdom
☎ 0151-290 5500/✆ 0151-290 5599
✎ solutions@cdms.co.uk
🖥 www.cdms.co.uk

C D S Yorks Ltd Reprographic House, Canal Road, Armley, Leeds, LS12 2ND, United Kingdom
☎ 0113-263 0601/✆ 0113-231 0305
✎ sales@cds-yorks.com
🖥 www.cds-yorks.com

C I T Creative Print Press Buildings, Old Hakin Road, Haverfordwest, Pembrokeshire, SA61 1XF, United Kingdom
☎ (01437) 772200/✆ (01437) 772215
✎ info@citcreativeprint.co.uk
🖥 www.citcreativeprint.co.uk

C K Press 231 Brompton Road, London, SW3 2EP, United Kingdom
☎ (020) 7584 2928/✆ (020) 7589 8125
✎ br@ckpress.com
🖥 www.ckpress.com

C P G Complete Print Group 9/10 Orchard Business Centre, Sanderson Way, Tonbridge, Kent, TN9 1QJ, United Kingdom
☎ (01732) 366666/✆ (01732) 368999
✎ enquires@cpg-net.co.uk
🖥 www.cpg-net.co.uk

C T D Printers C T D House, Summit Business Park, Hanworth Road, Sunbury-on-Thames, Middlesex, TW16 5BH, United Kingdom
☎ (01932) 771300/✆ 1932789229
✎ ctd@ctdprinters.co.uk
🖥 www.ctdprinters.co.uk

C3 Colchester Telford Way, Severalls Park, Colchester, CO4 9QP, United Kingdom
☎ (01206) 845544/✆ (01206) 845856
✎ brian@c3colchester.co.uk
🖥 www.c3imaging.co.uk

Calverts 9-10 The Oval, London, E2 9DT, United Kingdom
☎ (020) 7739 1474/✆ (020) 7739 0881
✎ info@calverts.coop
🖥 www.calverts.coop

Cantate Battley Cantate Centre, Parkfield, London, SW11 5DZ, United Kingdom
☎ (020) 7622 3401/✆ (020) 7498 1497
✎ info@cantate.biz
🖥 www.cantate.biz

Cantate Ltd Building B, Parkfield Industrial Estate, Culvert Place, London, SW11 5DZ, United Kingdom
☎ (020) 7622 3401/✆ (020) 7498 1497
🖥 www.cantate.biz

Cavendish Press Ltd Richmond House, Cambridge Road, Whetstone, Leicester, LE8 6BB, United Kingdom
☎ 0116-284 4600/✆ 0116-284 4646
✎ enquiries@cavendish-print.co.uk
🖥 www.cavendish-print.co.uk

Chandlers Printers Ltd 8a Bretts Drive, Bexhill-on-Sea, East Sussex, TN40 2JP, United Kingdom
☎ (01424) 212684/✆ (01424) 225878
✎ chandlers@chandlers.co.uk
🖥 www.chandlers.co.uk

Charles Lett & Co. Ltd Thornybank Industrial Estate, Dalkeith, Midlothian, EH22 2NE, United Kingdom
☎ 0131-663 1971/✆ 0131-660 3225
🖥 www.letts.co.uk

Chris Price Designs 121 Engleheart Road, Catford, London, SE6 2EU,
☎ 2081230016
✎ info@chrispricedesigns.com
🖥 www.chrispricedesigns.com

Claremont Press Ltd 23 Star Road, Partridge Green, Horsham, West Sussex, RH13 8RA, United Kingdom
☎ (01403) 711474/✆ (01403) 711575
✎ mikesturt@claremont-press.co.uk
🖥 www.claremont-press.co.uk

Clement & Foster Ltd JED House, 177-184 Grange Road, London, SE1 3AA, United Kingdom
☎ (020) 7231 8171/✆ (020) 7237 7664
✎ clementfoster@btinternet.com
🖥 www.clementfoster.com

Color Co. 24 Mortimer Street, London, W1T 3JP, United Kingdom
☎ (020) 7631 1232/✆ (020) 7436 1131
✎ mortimer@color.co.uk
🖥 www.color.co.uk

Colorscope Printers Ltd Charlwoods Road, East Grinstead, West Sussex, RH19 2HF, United Kingdom
☎ (01342) 311821/✆ (01342) 315358
✎ sales@colorscope.co.uk
🖥 www.colorscope.co.uk

Colourhouse Unit A, Arklow Road Trading Estate, London, SE14 6EB, United Kingdom
☎ (020) 8305 8305/✆ (020) 8305 8306
✎ sales@thecolourhouse.com
🖥 www.thecolourhouse.com

ColourSeen Design & Print Ltd Lea Industrial Estate, 151 Lower Luton Road, Harpenden, Hertfordshire, AL5 5EQ, United Kingdom
☎ (01582) 461188/✆ (01582) 469500

Communisis Chorley's Ltd Manston Lane, Leeds, LS15 8AH, United Kingdom
☎ 0113-225 5000/✆ 0113-225 5400
✎ enquiries@communisis.com
🖥 www.communisis.com

Compact Group Ltd Unit 4, Deacon Industrial Estate, Maidstone, Kent, ME20 7SP, United Kingdom
☎ (01622) 719365/✆ (01622) 790659
✎ directmail@compactgroup.co.uk
🖥 www.compactgroup.co.uk

Concept Marketing Lion House, 56 Kingsbridge Crescent, Southall, Middlesex, UB1 2DL, United Kingdom
☎ (0845) 2706565/✆ (020) 8574 8666
✎ cms@conceptmarketing.co.uk
🖥 www.conceptmarketing.co.uk

Connekt Colour North Bridge Road, Berkhamsted, Hertfordshire, HP4 1EH, United Kingdom
☎ (01442) 879701/✆ (01442) 879702
✎ simon@connektcolour.com
🖥 www.connektcolour.com

Creative Colour Bureau Unit 4, 230-260 Garscube Rd, Glasgow, G4 9RR, United Kingdom
☎ 0141-353 3206/✆ 0141-353 2267
✎ info@ccb.co.uk
🖥 www.ccb.co.uk

Creative Edge Design & Advertising 1st Floor Donald Hendry Building, Auchincruive, Ayr, KA6 5HW, United Kingdom
☎ (01292) 521404/✆ (01292) 521693
✎ paul@cedge.co.uk
🖥 www.cedge.co.uk

Crown Press 121 Barfillan Drive, Glasgow, G52 1BD, United Kingdom
☎ 0141-810 4000

Curtis Screenprint 26 Fairfax Road, Colchester, CO2 7EW, United Kingdom
☎ (01206) 760666/✆ (01206) 571505
✎ sales@curtisscreenprint.co.uk
🖥 www.curtisscreenprint.co.uk

D P 21 136 Elliot Street, Glasgow, G3 8EX, United Kingdom
☎ 0141-204 5600/✆ 0141-204 5601
✎ info@dp21.co.uk
🖥 www.dp21.co.uk

Darwin Print Solutions 26-28 Willow Street, London, EC2A 4BH, United Kingdom
☎ (020) 7729 6537/✆ (020) 7729 1433
✎ b.darwin@darwinprint.com
🖥 www.darwinprint.com

Denny Brothers Ltd Kempson Way, Bury St. Edmunds, Suffolk, IP32 7AR, United Kingdom
☎ (01284) 701381/✆ (01284) 705575
✎ denny.bros@dennybros.com
🖥 www.dennybros.com

Design Associates The Oast, Farleigh Green Yard, Maidstone, Kent, ME15 0PF, United Kingdom
☎ (01622) 812818/(07850) 684135 📠 (01622) 816765
✉ info@goldoak.co.uk
🖥 www.goldoak.co.uk

Diamond Printed Products Ltd Maidstone Road, Nettlestead, Maidstone, Kent, ME18 5HP, United Kingdom
☎ (01622) 871 088/📠 (01622) 872628
✉ info@diamondprinted.com
🖥 www.diamondprinted.com

Digital Fabric Innovations Olympic Court, Third Avenue, Trafford Park Village, Lancs, M17 1AP,
☎ 0161 8775000
✉ ann.marie@digitalfabrics.co.uk
🖥 www.digitalfabrics.co.uk

Digital Print Studio 40 Bowling Green Lane, London, EC1R 0NE, United Kingdom
☎ (07790) 368554
✉ info@dprints.co.uk
🖥 www.dprints.co.uk

Digital Printed Word 19 Briset Street, London, EC1M 5NR, United Kingdom
☎ (020) 7250 1404/📠 (020) 7253 4675
✉ printedword@btconnect.com
🖥 www.printed-word.co.uk

Direct Works Ltd Unit 1, Union Park, Bircholt Road, Maidstone, Kent, ME15 9XT, United Kingdom
☎ (01622) 757111/📠 (01622) 757222
✉ matt@direct-works.com
🖥 www.direct-works.com

Disc to Print (UK) Ltd 25 Liddell Rd, West Hampstead, London, NW6 2EW, United Kingdom
☎ (020) 7625 5225/📠 (020) 7624 1647
✉ info@dtp.co.uk
🖥 www.dtp.co.uk

Dixon Target 21-25 Main Street, Cross Hills, Keighley, West Yorkshire, BD20 8TX, United Kingdom
☎ (01535) 632138/📠 (01535) 635983
✉ sales@dixontarget.com
🖥 www.dixontarget.com

Duncan Print & Packaging Broadwater House, Mundells, Welwyn Garden City, Hertfordshire, AL7 1EU, United Kingdom
☎ (01707) 336271/📠 (01707) 338731
✉ sales@duncanprint.co.uk
🖥 www.duncanprint.co.uk

E K A Services Ltd 11-12 Hampton Court Parade, East Molesey, Surrey, KT8 9HB, United Kingdom
☎ (020) 8979 3466/📠 (020) 8941 4332
✉ sales@ekaservices.co.uk
🖥 www.ekaservices.co.uk

Eaveswood Colour 1 Keyfield, St. Albans, Hertfordshire, AL1 1QL, United Kingdom
☎ (01727) 893770/(07880) 748778 📠 (01727) 893391
✉ sales@eaveswoodcolour.co.uk
🖥 www.eaveswoodcolour.co.uk

Elanders Hindson Ltd Merlin Way, New York Business Park, Newcastle Upon Tyne, NE27 0YT, United Kingdom
☎ 0191-280 0400/📠 0191-280 0401
✉ info@elandershindson.co.uk
🖥 www.elanders.se

Elanders UK Ltd Elanders House, 32 Kings Road, Harrogate, North Yorkshire, HG1 5JW, United Kingdom
☎ (01423) 530362/📠 (01423) 530610
✉ sales@elanders.co.uk
🖥 www.elanders.co,

Ellis Printers Ltd Orchard Printing Works, Kent Road, Dartford, DA1 2AJ, United Kingdom
☎ (01322) 223159/📠 (01322) 288014
✉ admin@ellisprinters.com
🖥 www.ellisprinters.com

Fericon Press Ltd Unit 12, Stadium Way, Tilehurst, Reading, RG30 6BX, United Kingdom
☎ 0118-945 6100/📠 0118-945 4146
✉ fericon@dircon.co.uk

Fernedge Printers 18 Colville Road, London, W3 8BL, United Kingdom
☎ (020) 8992 4895/📠 (020) 8992 8313
✉ info@fernedge.co.uk
🖥 www.fernedge.co.uk

Fingerprint Communications Ltd 61-79 Field Lane, Litherland, Liverpool, L21 9LY, United Kingdom
☎ 0151-928 1602/📠 0151-928 7262
✉ info@fingerprint-comms.co.uk
🖥 www.fingerprint-comms.co.uk

First Impression Units 10 & 12, Camberwell Trading Estate, London, SE5 9LB, United Kingdom
☎ (020) 7733 1182/📠 (020) 7326 5332
✉ sales@firstimpression.co.uk
🖥 www.firstimpression.co.uk

Fisk Printers Ltd Gemini House, Lee Smith Street, Hull, HU9 1SD, United Kingdom
☎ (01482) 328677/📠 (01482) 212767
✉ daveg@fiskprinters.co.uk
🖥 www.fiskprinters.co.uk

Fox Transfers / Cranberry Graphics 4 Hill Lane Close, Markfield Industrial Estate, Markfield, Leicestershire, LE67 9PN, United Kingdom
☎ (01530) 245618
✉ info@fox-transfers.co.uk
🖥 www.fox-transfers.co.uk

Fulmar Colour Printing Co. Ltd Orion Centre, 108 Deddington Lane, Croydon, CR0 4YY, United Kingdom
☎ (020) 8688 7500/📠 (020) 8688 9500
✉ sales@fulmar.com
🖥 www.fulmar.com

Futura Printing Ltd Unit 21, Perseverance Works, Kingsland Road, London, E2 8DD, United Kingdom
☎ (020) 7739 4995/📠 (020) 7739 9673
✉ mail@futuraprinting.com
🖥 www.futuraprinting.com

G & B Printers 4 Mount Road, Feltham, Middlesex, TW13 6AR, United Kingdom
☎ (020) 8755 1822/📠 (020) 8893 3854
✉ info@gbprinters.co.uk
🖥 www.gbprinters.co.uk

G S M Graphic Arts Ltd Castlegarth Works, Thirsk, North Yorkshire, YO7 1PS, United Kingdom
☎ (01845) 522184/📠 (01845) 522206
✉ gsmgraphicarts@gsmgroup.co.uk
🖥 www.gsmgraphicarts.co.uk

Garnett Dickinson Print Ltd Brookfields Way, Manvers, Wath upon Dearne, Rotherham, South Yorkshire, S63 5DL, United Kingdom
☎ (01709) 768000/📠 (01709) 768010
✉ info@garnett-dickinson.co.uk
🖥 www.garnett-dickinson.co.uk

GC Print Solutions 5 Gurnon Walk, Letchworth Garden City, Hertfordshire, SG6 3HW, United Kingdom
☎ (0800) 0268618/📠 (01462) 670070
✉ martyn@gardencityprint.com
🖥 www.gardencityprint.com

Gee Brothers Printers 221 Saint Johns Hill, London, SW11 1TH, United Kingdom
☎ (020) 7228 4081/📠 (020) 7228 2075
✉ sales@geebrothers.co.uk
🖥 www.geebrothers.co.uk

Geerings of Ashford Ltd Cobbs Wood House, Chart Rd, Ashford, Kent, TN23 1EP, United Kingdom
☎ (01233) 633366/📠 (01233) 646994
✉ hotelproduct@geerings.co.uk
🖥 www.geerings.co.uk

Gemini Press Ltd Unit A1, Dolphin Way, Shoreham-by-Sea, West Sussex, BN43 6NZ, United Kingdom
☎ (01273) 464884/📠 (01273) 464744
✉ info@gemini-group.co.uk
🖥 www.gemini-group.co.uk

Goodhead Group P.L.C. Chaucer Business Park, Launton Road, Bicester, Oxfordshire, OX26 4QZ, United Kingdom
☎ (01869) 363333/📠 (01869) 363306
✉ sales@bgprint.co.uk
🖥 www.bgp-print.co.uk

Gordon Bishop Associates 23A Paddington Street, London, W1U 5QT, United Kingdom
☎ (020) 7486 1464/📠 (020) 7487 2984
✉ g@blackandwhiteprocessing.com
🖥 www.blackandwhiteprocessing.com

Graphic Impressions Graphic House, 8 Northburgh St, London, EC1V 0AY, United Kingdom
☎ (020) 7253 5444/📠 (020) 7608 0720
✉ gi@graphicimpressions.co.uk
🖥 www.graphicimpressions.co.uk

Greenwich Press Ltd Standard House, 107-115 Eastmoor Street, London, SE7 8LX, United Kingdom
☎ (020) 8858 3202/📠 (020) 8853 2103
✉ info@greenwichpress.co.uk
🖥 www.greenwichpress.co.uk

H M Printers Ltd The Cromwell Centre, Minerva Road, London, NW10 6HJ, United Kingdom
☎ (020) 8965 4621/📠 (020) 8965 4181
✉ print@hmprinters.com
🖥 www.hmprinters.com

H S Impressions 69 Gregories Road, Beaconsfield, Buckinghamshire, HP9 1HL, United Kingdom
☎ (01494) 680566/📠 (0870) 0511522
✉ sales@hstrading.demon.co.uk
🖥 www.printanddesign.com

Halstan Music Setting & Printing 2-10 Plantation Road, Amersham, Buckinghamshire, HP6 6HJ, United Kingdom
☎ (01494) 725525/📠 (01494) 432305
✉ sales@halstan.co.uk
🖥 www.halstan.co.uk

Hammer Lab Ltd Unit 2, Building 5, Long Street Workshops, Long Street, London, E2 8HJ, United Kingdom
☎ (020) 7033 2702
✉ hammerlabs@mac.com
🖥 www.hammerlab.co.uk

Hardings Design to Print Aintree Avenue, White Horse Business Park, Trowbridge, Wiltshire, BA14 0XB, United Kingdom
☎ (01225) 752888/📠 (01225) 752666
✉ alan@hardingsprinters.co.uk
🖥 www.hardingsprinters.co.uk

Harry's Studio B5R, Metropolitan Wharf, London, E1W 3SS, United Kingdom
☎ (020) 7488 1154/📠 (020) 7488 1176
✉ harrymatthews68@hotmail.com

Hartley Reproductions Ltd 217 London Road, Stone, Greenhithe, Kent, DA9 9DQ, United Kingdom
☎ (01322) 287676/📠 (01322) 289597
✉ support@hartleyrepro.co.uk
🖥 www.hartleyrepro.co.uk

Harwood Press (Advertising) Ltd 47-49 West Street, Harrow, Middlesex, HA1 3EQ, United Kingdom
☎ (020) 8422 5656

Haynes Publishing Group Sparkford, Yeovil, Somerset, BA22 7JJ, United Kingdom
☎ (01963) 440635/📠 (01963) 440001
✉ sales@haynes.co.uk
🖥 www.haynes.co.uk

Herbert Walker & Son Ltd Dockfield Road, Shipley, West Yorkshire, BD17 7AS, United Kingdom
☎ (01274) 531828/📠 (01274) 592563
🖥 www.herbertwalker.co.uk

Highland Printers 13 Henderson Road, Longman Industrial Estate, Inverness, IV1 1SP, United Kingdom
☎ (01463) 224444/📠 (01463) 235601
✉ spp@postmaster.co.uk

Highlight 12 Chesford Grange, Wolfton, Warrington, WA1 4RE, United Kingdom
☎ (01925) 831678/📠 (01925) 820472
✉ info@highlightprint.co.uk
🖥 www.highlightprint.co.uk

Hill Print Ltd Unit 6, Park 2000, Millennium Way, Heighington Lane Business Park, Newton Aycliffe, County Durham, DL5 6AR, United Kingdom
☎ (01325) 245555/📠 (01325) 245560
✉ studio@hillprintmedia.com
🖥 www.hillprintmedia.com

Holbrooks Printers Ltd Norway Road, Hilsea, Portsmouth, PO3 5HX, United Kingdom
☎ (023) 9266 1485/📠 (023) 9267 1119
✉ mail@holbrooks.com
🖥 www.holbrooks.com

Hudson & Pearson Ltd Bradwood Works, Manchester Road, Dunnockshaw, Burnley, Lancashire, BB11 5PW, United Kingdom
☎ (01706) 210582/📠 (01706) 215692
✉ info@handp.co.uk

Hunts Lithoprint Ltd 12A Station Fields Industrial Estate, Kidlington, Oxford, OX5 1JD, United Kingdom
☎ (01865) 853633/📠 (01865) 853622
✉ print@hunts.co.uk
🖥 www.hunts.co.uk

ICW 2000 Ltd Unit 26, Rake Industries, Rogate, Petersfield, Hampshire, GU31 5DU, United Kingdom
☎ (0845) 226 0813/📠 (0845) 226 0814
✉ matt@icw2000.com
🖥 www.icw2000.com

Impress Print Services Ltd 10 Thornsett Road, London, SW18 4EN, United Kingdom
☎ (020) 8871 9950/📠 (020) 8871 9908
✉ sales@impressprint.net
🖥 www.impressprint.co.uk

Invigorate Creative Print Solutions Ltd 1st Floor, 25 Watery Road, Wrexham, Clwyd, LL13 7NW, United Kingdom
📞 (01978) 290091/ (01978) 290091
✎ mail@invigorate-creative.com
🖳 www.invigorate-creative.com

Iscal The Coaster Factory Unit 20, Calderdale Business Park, Club Lane, Halifax, West Yorkshire, HX2 8DB, United Kingdom
📞 (01422) 352054/ (01422) 380297
✎ iscal@btconnect.com
🖳 www.iscal.co.uk

J. Thomson Colour Printers 14 Carnoustie Place, Glasgow, G5 8PB, United Kingdom
📞 0141-429 1094/ 0141-429 5638
✎ production@jtcp.co.uk
🖳 www.jtcp.co.uk / www.sales@jtcp.co.uk

J.W. Northend Ltd Clyde Road, Sheffield, S8 0TZ, United Kingdom
📞 0114-250 0331/ 0114-250 0676
✎ info@northend.co.uk
🖳 www.northend.co.uk

J.W. Ruddock & Sons Ltd 56 Great Northern Terrace, Lincoln, LN5 8HL, United Kingdom
📞 (01522) 529591/ (01522) 535108
✎ info@ruddocks.co.uk
🖳 www.ruddocks.co.uk

Jackson Screenprint Ltd 986-1008 Pollokshaws Road, Glasgow, G41 2HE, United Kingdom
📞 0141-649 1783/ 0141-649 6087
✎ sales@jacksonscreenprint.co.uk
🖳 www.jacksonscreenprint.co.uk

Jaggerprint Victoria House, 86-90 Richmond Road, Kingston upon Thames, Surrey, KT2 5EW, United Kingdom
📞 (020) 8546 0593/ (020) 8541 5708
✎ sales@jaggerprint.co.uk
🖳 www.jaggerprint.co.uk

Jamaica Press 37 Fore Street, Hartland, Bideford, Devon, EX39 6BE, United Kingdom
📞 (01237) 441411/ (01237) 441419
🖳 www.jamaicapress.co.uk

Jarrold Printing Whitefriars, Norwich, NR3 1SH, United Kingdom
📞 (01603) 660211/ (01603) 630162
✎ e.thorpe@njp.co.uk
🖳 www.jarrold.com

Jigsaw Print Unit 1 Moorfield Business Park, Moorfield Close, Yeadon, Leeds, LS19 7YA, United Kingdom
📞 0113-250 0855/ 0113-238 6505
✎ peter@jigsaw-print.co.uk
🖳 www.jigsaw-print.co.uk

John McCormick & Co. Ltd McCormick House, 46 Darnley Street, Glasgow, G41 2TY, United Kingdom
📞 0141-429 4222/ 0141-429 6777
✎ enquire@jmccormick.co.uk
🖳 www.jmccormick.co.uk

John McGavigan Ltd 111 Westerhill Road, Westerhill Business Park, Bishopbriggs, Glasgow, G64 2QR, United Kingdom
📞 0141-302 0000/ 0141-302 0290
✎ enquiries@mcgavigan.co.uk
🖳 www.advanceddecorative.com

John Watson & Co. Ltd 35-47 Kyle Street, Glasgow, G4 0JQ, United Kingdom
📞 0141-332 8672/ 0141-332 6752
✎ info@johnwatsonprinters.com
🖳 www.johnwatsonprinters.com

Jupiter Associates Ltd 21 The Waldrons, Croydon, CR0 4HB, United Kingdom
📞 (020) 8688 6133/ (020) 8688 0316
✎ studio@jupiterassociates.co.uk
🖳 www.jupiterassociates.co.uk

K M D Co. Ltd 140 Queens Road, Leicester, LE2 3FX, United Kingdom
📞 0116-270 9221/ 0116-270 2334
✎ steve@kmd-company.co.uk
🖳 www.kmdcompany.net

Kall Kwik 76 Old Brompton Road, South Kensington, London, SW7 3LQ, United Kingdom
📞 (020) 7581 2604/ (020) 7589 5530
✎ kz@kksw7.co.uk
🖳 www.southkensington.kallkwik.co.uk

Kall Kwik Centre 186 Fleet Street, London, EC4A 2HR, United Kingdom
📞 (020) 7405 5686/ (020) 7404 4814
✎ natalie@kkfleetst.co.uk
🖳 www.fleetstreet.kallkwik.co.uk

Kall Kwik Centre 787 17 Silvermills Court, Henderson Place, Edinburgh, EH3 5DG, United Kingdom
📞 0131-523 0400/ 0131-523 0430
✎ info@edinburgh.kallkwik.co.uk
🖳 www.edinburgh.kallkwik.co.uk

Kall Kwik Printing 26-28 Carters Green, West Bromwich, West Midlands, B70 9LW, United Kingdom
📞 0121-553 1291/ 0121-500 5245
✎ enquiries@kallkwikprinting.co.uk
🖳 www.kallkwikprinting.co.uk

Keeley & Lowe Ltd 38-40 The Oval, Cambridge Heath, London, E2 9DT, United Kingdom
📞 (020) 7729 3350/ (020) 7739 5654
✎ keeleylowe@btconnect.com

Laserlife New London Bridge House, 25 London Bridge Street, London, SE1 9SG, United Kingdom
📞 (020) 8960 1233/ (020) 8964 4445
✎ servicedesk@laserlife.co.uk
🖳 www.laserlife.co.uk

Leyprint Leyland Lane, Leyland, PR25 1UT, United Kingdom
📞 (01772) 422234/ (01772) 425001
✎ info@leyprint.co.uk
🖳 www.leyprint.co.uk

Linkway C C P Ltd 5-8 Helmet Row, London, EC1V 3QJ, United Kingdom
📞 (020) 7566 1200/ (020) 7566 1201
✎ team@linkwayccp.com

Linney Print Adams Way, Mansfield, Nottinghamshire, NG18 4FW, United Kingdom
📞 (01623) 450450/ (01623) 450451
✎ sales@linney.com
🖳 www.linney.com

Litho Supplies Unit 1, Thamebridge Industrial Estate, Birmingham, B42 2TX, United Kingdom
📞 0121-344 4222/ 0121-344 4494
✎ midland@litho.co.uk
🖳 www.litho.co.uk

Lithograve 50 Cardigan Street, Birmingham, B4 7SA, United Kingdom
📞 0121-359 3350/ 0121-359 3119
✎ dave@lithograve.com

Lonsdale Press 43-47 Lonsdale Road, Queens Park, London, NW6 6RA, United Kingdom
📞 (020) 7328 3355/ (020) 7328 1840
✎ info@lonsdalepress.com

Loudmouth Studios Ltd 23 Hall Road, Handsworth, Sheffield, S13 9AG, United Kingdom
📞 (0845) 230 9805/ 0114-288 0044
✎ paul@loudworld.co.uk
🖳 www.loudworld.co.uk

Mailing & Printing Group 5 Myson Way, Raynham Close, Bishop's Stortford, Hertfordshire, CM23 5JZ, United Kingdom
📞 (01279) 656800/ (01279) 655777
✎ sales@map-int.com
🖳 www.map-int.com

Manson Group Reynolds House, 8 Porters Wood, St. Albans, Hertfordshire, AL3 6PZ, United Kingdom
📞 (01727) 848440/ (01727) 848460
✎ sales@manson-grp.co.uk
🖳 www.manson-grp.co.uk

Martell Press Ltd Hopes Lane, Ramsgate, Kent, CT12 6UW, United Kingdom
📞 (01843) 582567/(07970) 371410 (01843) 583641
✎ sales@martellpress.co.uk
🖳 www.martellpress.co.uk

Martin Edwards Printers Ltd 17-18 Haywards Place, London, EC1R 0EQ, United Kingdom
📞 (020) 7253 8444/ (020) 7608 0546
✎ sales@martinedwards.co.uk
🖳 www.martinedwardsprint.co.uk

Mass Technology (UK) Ltd 36b Evington Road, Leicester, Leicestershire, LE2 1HG,
📞 0116 25 44 171
✎ masstechnology@hotmail.com
🖳 www.masstechnologyonline.com

Mastrom Ltd Park Road, Alrewas, Burton-on-Trent, Staffordshire, DE13 7AG, UK
📞 (01283) 790030/ (01283) 791068
✎ sales@mastrom.co.uk
🖳 www.mastrom.co.uk

Matchless Prints Ltd 36 Lambs Conduit Street, London, WC1N 3LJ, United Kingdom
📞 (020) 7405 8899
🖳 www.dannypope.com

Menzies & Young Atlantic House, 38 Gardens Crescent, Edinburgh, EH3 8DR, United Kingdom
📞 0131-228 4500/ 0131-228 4680
✎ info@menzies-young.com
🖳 www.menzies-young.com

Mercer Print UK Ltd Star Works, Newark Street, Accrington, Lancashire, BB5 0BP, United Kingdom
📞 (01254) 395512/ (01254) 395262
✎ info@mercer-print.co.uk
🖳 www.mercer-print.co.uk

Midas Press Unit C3, Columbus Drive, South Wood, Farnborough, Hampshire, GU14 0NZ, United Kingdom
📞 (01252) 517221/ (01252) 516455
✎ sales@midaspress.co.uk
🖳 www.midaspress.co.uk

Midway Colour Print P.L.C. 16-20 The Midlands Industrial Estate, Holt, Wiltshire, BA14 6RU, United Kingdom
📞 (01225) 782305/ (01225) 783211
✎ salesforce@midwaycolourprint.co.uk
🖳 www.midwaycolourprint.co.uk

Millet Colour Printers Pym Street, Hunslet Road, Leeds, LS10 1PG, United Kingdom
📞 0113-243 4734/ 0113-246 5551
✎ production@milletprinters.co.uk
🖳 www.milletprinters.co.uk

Modern Graphic Arts Ltd 52-54 Milton Road, Westcliff-on-Sea, Essex, SS0 7JX, United Kingdom
📞 (01702) 349541/ (01702) 335487
✎ sales@mgaprinting.co.uk
🖳 www.mgaprinting.co.uk

Moore Old Jamaica Business Estate, Old Jamaica Road, London, SE16 4FS, United Kingdom
📞 (020) 7232 4700/ (020) 7232 4750
✎ mail@mooreprint.co.uk
🖳 www.mooreprint.co.uk

Mouldtype Leyland Lane, Leyland, Preston, PR25 1UT, United Kingdom
📞 (01772) 425026/ (01772) 425001
✎ nts@leyprint.co.uk

N T A Printers Ltd Andrew House, Market Street, Hyde, Cheshire, SK14 1HE, United Kingdom
📞 0161-368 0000/ 0161-367 8710
✎ print@ntaprinters.com
🖳 www.ntaprinters.com

N W Printers Dukesway, Team Valley Trading Estate, Gateshead, Tyne & Wear, NE11 0PZ, United Kingdom
📞 0191-487 6041/ 0191-491 5554
✎ sales@nwprinters.co.uk
🖳 www.nwprinters.co.uk

Nampak Cartons Cockburn Fields Factory, Middleton Grove, Leeds, LS11 5LX, United Kingdom
📞 0113-276 0730/ 0113-276 0165

Newnorth-Print Ltd Newnorth House, College Street, Kempston, MK42 8NA, United Kingdom
📞 (01234) 341111/ (01234) 271112
✎ newnorth@newnorth.co.uk
🖳 www.newnorth.co.uk

Nimmos Colour Printers Tennant House, 21 Tennant Street, Edinburgh, EH6 5NA, United Kingdom
📞 0131-554 2431/ 0131-553 6292
🖳 www.nimmos.co.uk

Norwich Screen Art 15 St. Augustines, Norwich, NR3 3BY, United Kingdom
📞 (01603) 630530/ (01603) 630530
✎ sales@norwichscreenart.co.uk
🖳 www.norwichscreenart.co.uk

Nuffield Press 21 Nuffield Way, Ashville Trading Estate, Abingdon, Oxfordshire, OX14 1RL, United Kingdom
📞 (01235) 554422/ (01235) 535445
✎ sales@nuffield.co.uk
🖳 www.nuffield.co.uk

O'Sullivan Printing Corporation Unit 10, Trident Way, International Trading Estate, Southall, Middlesex, UB2 5LF, United Kingdom
📞 (020) 8606 9839/ (020) 8606 9860
✎ opcuk@airlinemenus.com
🖳 www.airlinemenus.com

Oberthur Card Systems Ltd Alexandre Way, Ashchurch Business Centre, Tewkesbury, Gloucestershire, GL20 8GA, United Kingdom
☎ (01684) 290290/✆ (01684) 290111
✉ s.west@oberthurcs.com
🖥 www.oberthurcs.com

Octograph Unit B3, Manor Way Business Park, Manor Way, Swanscombe, Kent, DA10 0PP, United Kingdom
☎ (01322) 518 479
✉ sales@octograph.uk.com
🖥 www.octograph.uk.com

Optichrome 98 Maybury Road, Woking, Surrey, GU21 5HX, United Kingdom
☎ (01483) 740290/✆ (01483) 732609
✉ optisales@optichrome.com
🖥 www.optichrome.com

Oriel Printing Co. Ltd Bontoft Avenue, Hull, HU5 4HF, United Kingdom
☎ (01482) 342352/✆ (01482) 342332
✉ inver@orielprinting.com
🖥 www.orielprinting.co.uk

Original Business Print Unit 8, Menin Works, Bond Road, Mitcham, Surrey, CR4 3HG, United Kingdom
☎ (020) 8640 6061/✆ (020) 8640 6614
✉ pat@originalbusinessprint.com

Outdoor Partners Ltd Unit 6, 129 Coldharbour Lane, London, SE5 9NU, United Kingdom
☎ (020) 7733 7995
✉ info@outdoorpartners.co.uk
🖥 www.outdoorpartners.co.uk

P B Group 3 Gateway, Castle Road, Eurolink, Sittingbourne, Kent, ME10 3AG, United Kingdom
☎ (01795) 413880/✆ (01795) 413881
✉ pb@pbgroup.co.uk
🖥 www.pbgroup.co.uk

P K M Studio Ltd Unit 2, Wash Road, Hutton Industrila Estate, Brentwood, Essex, CM13 1TA, United Kingdom
☎ (01277) 234544/✆ (01277) 231093
✉ mail@pkmstudio.com
🖥 www.pkmstudio.com

P W Reproprint Ltd (Hendi Systems) 10 East Road, London, N1 6AJ, United Kingdom
☎ (020) 7324 2632/✆ (020) 7608 1501
✉ ian.downie@hendi.net
🖥 www.hendigroup.co.uk

Paramount Printers Ltd 199 Causewayside, Edinburgh, EH9 1PH, United Kingdom
☎ 0131-667 4441/✆ 0131-662 0659
✉ sales@ourprinters.com

Park Communications Ltd Lea Mill, Eastway, London, E9 5NU, United Kingdom
☎ (020) 8525 6200/✆ (020) 8525 6201
✉ e.deboer@parkcom.co.uk
🖥 www.parkcom.co.uk

Peak Press Ltd Eccles Road, Chapel-en-le-Frith, High Peak, Derbyshire, SK23 9RQ, United Kingdom
☎ (01298) 812738/✆ (01298) 815220
✉ sales@peakpress.co.uk
🖥 www.peakcreative.co.uk

Pegasus Colourprint Ltd 10 Osier Way, Willow Lane, Mitcham, Surrey, CR4 4NF, United Kingdom
☎ (020) 8640 1201/✆ (020) 8640 2781
✉ pegasussales@pegasuscolour.co.uk

Phil Kashdan Design, Print & Display Ltd The Studio, 47 Povey Cross Road, Horley, Surrey, RH6 0AG,
☎ 01293 773129/✆ 01293 773129
✉ phil@pk-design.com

Phillips Print & Stationery Ltd 115 High Street, Crediton, Devon, EX17 3LG, United Kingdom
☎ (01363) 772060/✆ (01363) 774030
✉ info@phillipsprint.co.uk
🖥 www.phillipsprint.co.uk

Pica Press, 2 Sovereign Way, Tonbridge, Kent, TN9 1RH, United Kingdom
☎ (01732) 362186/✆ (01732) 770471
✉ nicola@windsor-print.co.uk

Piggott Black Bear Ltd The Paddocks, Cherry Hinton Road, Cambridge, CB1 8DH, United Kingdom
☎ (01223) 404800/✆ (01223) 404801
✉ sales@piggottblackbear.co.uk
🖥 www.piggottblackbear.co.uk

Pillans & Waddies Ormolu House, 455 Chester Road, Manchester, M16 9HA, United Kingdom
☎ 0161-855 3760/✆ 0161-877 5273
✉ mail@pillanswaddies.com
🖥 www.pillanswaddies.com

Pinnacle Images Ltd 50-52 Great Sutton Street, London, EC1V 0DF, United Kingdom
☎ (020) 7253 0383/✆ (020) 7253 2159
✉ studio@pinnacleimages.co.uk

Polite Print Canalside 3, Clarence Mill, Bollington, Cheshire, SK10 5JZ, United Kingdom
☎ (01625) 560055/✆ (01625) 560749
✉ mail@reallygoodprint.com
🖥 www.reallygoodprint.com

Post & Time Series Ltd 21-24 Smithfield Centre, Haywood Street, Leek, Staffordshire, ST13 5JL, United Kingdom
☎ (01538) 399599/✆ (01538) 392248
🖥 www.leekpostandtimes.co.uk

Post Haste Print & Design 2 Roslin Square, Roslin Road, London, W3 8BW, United Kingdom
☎ (020) 8992 1222/✆ (020) 8993 2758
✉ sales@post-haste-print.co.uk
🖥 www.post-haste-print.co.uk

Precision Printing 47 Thames Road, Barking, Essex, IG11 0HQ, United Kingdom
☎ (0845) 6064001/✆ (0845) 6064002
🖥 www.precisionprinting.co.uk

Pressing Matters UK Ltd 44A Curlew Street, London, SE1 2ND, United Kingdom
☎ (020) 7089 0364/✆ (020) 7407 5880
✉ sales@pressingmatters.co.uk
🖥 www.pressingmatters.co.uk

Print Art & Design Services Ltd Mortfield Mill, Mortfield Lane, Bolton, BL1 3AF, United Kingdom
☎ (01204) 397137/✆ (01204) 363693
✉ info@pads.uk.com
🖥 www.printartdesign.co.uk

Print Forum Ltd 132 St. Albans Road, Watford, WD24 4AE, United Kingdom
☎ (01923) 222119/✆ (01923) 228110
✉ pf@pforum.co.uk

Print It Ltd Camilla Court, Nacton, Ipswich, Suffolk, IP10 0EU,
☎ 01473 655141/✆ 01473 655148
✉ neil@print-it.tv
🖥 www.print-it.tv

Printing.com @ Fluidmedia 56-58 Bolton Street, Bury, Lancashire, BL9 0LL, United Kingdom
☎ 0161-764 6464/✆ 0161-761 0408
✉ bury@printing.com
🖥 www.buryprinting.com

Pulsar Print Management Suite 176, Airport House, Purley Way, Croydon, CR0 0XZ, United Kingdom
☎ (020) 8288 3510/✆ (020) 8288 3642
✉ steve@pulsarpm.co.uk
🖥 www.pulsarpm.co.uk

Pure Colour Solutions Rushmere House, 99 Hockliffe Road, Leighton Buzzard, Bedfordshire, LU7 3FL
☎ 0845 009 8455/07772 510616/0845 009 8456 ✆
✉ richard@purecoloursolutions.com
🖥 www.purecoloursolutions.com
See ad in showcase

Pure Print Group Ltd Bellbrook Park, Uckfield, East Sussex, TN22 1PL, United Kingdom
☎ (01825) 768611/✆ (01825) 768042
✉ print@beaconpress.co.uk
🖥 www.beaconpress.co.uk

Quadracolour Ltd Units 2-3, Kangley Bridge Road, London, London, SE26 5AR, United Kingdom
☎ (020) 8676 6700/✆ (020) 8659 1869
✉ quad@quadracolour.co.uk
🖥 www.quadracolour.co.uk

Quentin Press Ltd Victoria Road, Burgess Hill, West Sussex, RH15 9LR, United Kingdom
☎ (01444) 258833/✆ (01444) 258255
✉ info@quentinpress.co.uk
🖥 www.quentinpress.co.uk

Quill Colour Printers Trenant Industrial Estate, Wadebridge, Cornwall, PL27 6HB, United Kingdom
☎ (01208) 816120
✉ quillprinters1@btconnect.com

Qwerty Ltd 20-21 The Markham Centre, Station Road, Theale, RG7 4PE, United Kingdom
☎ 0118-930 2222/✆ 0118-930 3016
✉ sales@qwertyltd.com
🖥 www.qwertyltd.com

Ralph Allen Press Ltd 1 Locksbrook Court, Locksbrook Road, Bath, BA1 3EN, United Kingdom
☎ (01225) 461888/✆ (01225) 446239
✉ jason@ralphallenpress.com
🖥 www.ralphallenpress.co.uk

Ricoh Print Scotland 197 Pollokshaws Road, Glasgow, G41 1TS, United Kingdom
☎ 0141-287 9626/✆ 0141-287 9618
✉ sales@ricohprintscotland.co.uk
🖥 www.ricohprintscotland.co.uk

Ripping Image 131 Great Suffolk Street, London, SE1 1PP, United Kingdom
☎ (020) 7357 7774/✆ (020) 7357 7710
✉ sales@ripping.co.uk
🖥 www.ripping.co.uk

Robert Pearce & Co. 49 Leesons Hill, Orpington, Kent, BR5 2LF, United Kingdom
☎ (01689) 839433/✆ (01689) 870523
✉ sales@robertpearceprinting.co.uk
🖥 www.leaprinters.co.uk

Robin Bell 3 Epirus Mews, London, SW6 7UP, United Kingdom
☎ (020) 7610 1020
✉ robin@robinbell.com
🖥 www.robinbell.com

Royal Printers & Stationers Ltd 111A Sheen Lane, London, SW14 8AE, United Kingdom
☎ (020) 8408 2000

Royle Print & Royle Financial Print Gatehouse, 1 St John's Square, London, EC1N 4DH, United Kingdom
☎ (020) 7553 3535/✆ (020) 7553 3536
✉ sales@roylecorporate.com
🖥 www.royle-print.co.uk

Rustin Clark Waterloo Road, Cricklewood, London, NW2 7TX, United Kingdom
☎ (020) 8452 1091/✆ (020) 8452 2008
✉ rustinclark@rustinclark.co.uk
🖥 www.rustinclark.co.uk

S B Marketing Ltd Hallam Way, Old Mill Lane Industrial Estat, Mansfield Woodhouse, Mansfield, Nottinghamshire, NG19 9BG, United Kingdom
☎ (01623) 662423
🖥 www.sbmarketingandprint.co.uk

S P D Advertising Design Ltd 21 Bateman Street, London, W1D 3AL, United Kingdom
☎ (020) 7734 4955/✆ (020) 7439 0599
✉ info@spd-art.com

S P Group Ltd Hedera Road, Ravensbank Business Park, Redditch, Worcestershire, B98 9EY, United Kingdom
☎ (01527) 508000/✆ (01527) 508001
✉ enquiries@spgroup.co.uk
🖥 www.spgroup.co.uk

S R Comms Ltd SR House, 64-65 Childers Street, London, SE8 5JT, United Kingdom
☎ (020) 8516 7000/✆ (020) 8692 8057
✉ sr@sr-comms.co.uk
🖥 www.sr-comms.co.uk

Safair Print Services Ltd Units 16-18 Orion Business Centre, Surrey Canal Road, London, SE14 5RT, United Kingdom
☎ (020) 7232 0553/✆ (020) 7231 9491
✉ a.fairbairn@safair.co.uk
🖥 www.safair.co.uk

Saint Ives P.L.C. St. Ives House, Lavington Street, London, SE1 0NX, United Kingdom
☎ (020) 7928 8844/✆ (020) 7902 6436
🖥 www.st-ives.co.uk

Sanders & Co. (UK) Ltd 181 Wellingborough Road, Northampton, NN1 4DX, United Kingdom
☎ (01604) 630195/✆ (01604) 633972
✉ sandersltd@aol.com

Seacourt Press Pony Road, Horspath Road Industrial Estate, Cowley, Oxford, OX4 2SE, United Kingdom
☎ (01865) 770140/✆ (01865) 747347
✉ jimdinnage@seacourt.net
🖥 www.seacourt.net

Service Graphics 49 Glebe Road, Skelmersdale, Lancashire, WN8 9JP, United Kingdom
☎ (01695) 725486/✆ (01695) 722695
✉ sales@scanachrome.co.uk
🖥 www.servicegraphics.co.uk

Service Point Landore Court, 49 Charles Street, Cardiff, CF1 4ED, United Kingdom
☎ (029) 2066 4420/✆ (029) 2034 2712
✉ info@servicepointuk.com
🖥 www.servicepointuk.com

Silk & Terry Ltd Warstock Road, Birmingham, B14 4RS, United Kingdom
☎ 0121-474 2295/✆ 0121-474 2407
✉ sales@silkandterry.co.uk
🖥 www.silkandterry.co.uk

Slik Screeners Ltd Units 6 & 7, Eagle Road, Ilkeston, Derbyshire, DE7 4RB, United Kingdom
☎ 0115-932 7223/✆ 0115-930 4955
✉ steve@slik-screeners.co.uk
🖥 www.slik-screeners.co.uk

Smudge Ltd Unit 21/22, Bermondsey Trading Estate, Rotherhithe New Road, London, SE16 3LL, United Kingdom
☎ (020) 7232 1234/✆ (020) 7237 5700
✉ info@smudgegroup.com
🖥 www.smudgegroup.com

Solways, 5 Vine Yard, London, SE1 1QL, United Kingdom
☎ (020) 7407 2875/✆ (020) 7357 7333
✉ sales@solways.co.uk
🖥 www.solways.co.uk

Speedprint 432 Cranbrook Road, Gants Hill, Ilford, Essex, IG2 6LL, United Kingdom
☎ (020) 8518 6131/✆ (020) 8554 1736
✉ info@speedprintessex.co.uk
🖥 www.speedprintessex.co.uk

Square Group Ltd 18 Rushworth Street, London, SE1 0RB, United Kingdom
☎ (020) 7803 1500

SSDM Ltd Freemantle Road, Lowestoft, Suffolk, NR33 0EA, United Kingdom
☎ (01502) 501234/✆ (01502) 583544
✉ sales@ssdm.co.uk
🖥 www.ssdm.co.uk

St. Ives Burrups Ltd St Ives House, Lavington Street, London, SE1 0NX, United Kingdom
☎ (020) 7928 8844/✆ (020) 7902 6572
🖥 www.st-ives.com

St. Ives Westerham Press Westerham House, Faircroft Way, Edenbridge, Kent, TN8 6EL, United Kingdom
☎ (01732) 867234/✆ (01732) 867277
✉ sales@stiveswesterham.com
🖥 www.stiveswesterham.com

Stanley L. Hunt Printers Ltd Midland Road, Rushden, Northamptonshire, NN10 9UA, United Kingdom
☎ (01933) 356226/✆ (01933) 356613
✉ admin@stanleylhunt.co.uk

Stones the Printers Ltd Unit 10, Wates Way, Wildmere Industrial Estate, Banbury, Oxfordshire, OX16 3ES, United Kingdom
☎ (01295) 252211/✆ (01295) 819390
✉ receptionban@stonestheprinters.co.uk
🖥 www.stonestheprinters.co.uk

Summerhall Press 5 St. Clair Street, Edinburgh, EH6 8LB, United Kingdom
☎ 0131-661 2156/✆ 0131-652 2931
✉ info@summerhall.biz
🖥 www.summerhall.biz

Swift Print 186 Campden Hill Road, London, W8 7TH, United Kingdom
☎ (020) 7229 5012/✆ (020) 7229 3068
✉ mail@swiftprint.co.uk
🖥 www.swiftprint.co.uk

T A G Printers, Adplates Group Unit 2C, 16 Baldwins Gardens, London, EC1N 7RJ, United Kingdom
☎ (020) 7831 8800
🖥 www.tagworldwide.com

T D Graphics Graphic House, 26-34 Southwell Road, London, SE5 9PQ, United Kingdom
☎ (020) 7274 8722/✆ (020) 7733 5496
✉ sales@tdgraphics.co.uk
🖥 www.tdgraphics.co.uk

Tag Print 3-4 Bakers Yard, Bakers Row, London, EC1R 3DD, United Kingdom
☎ (020) 7837 0123/✆ (020) 7278 3364
🖥 www.tagworldwide.com

The Copy Centre 70 Park Lane, London, N17 0JR, United Kingdom
☎ (020) 8808 7275/✆ (020) 8365 1430
✉ irwin@thecopycentre.com
🖥 www.thecopycentre.com

The Curwen Studio Chilford Hall, Balsham Road, Linton, Cambridge, CB1 6LE, United Kingdom
☎ (01223) 893544/✆ (01223) 893638
✉ jenny@thecurwenstudio.co.uk
🖥 www.thecurwenstudio.co.uk

The Letter Press House Ltd Frogmore Mill, Mill Street, Hemel Hempstead, Hertfordshire, HP3 9RY, United Kingdom
☎ (01442) 241244/✆ (01442) 230701
✉ info@theletterpresshouse.co.uk
🖥 www.theletterpresshouse.co.uk

The Max Design & Print Company Kettlestring Lane, Clifton Moor, York, YO30 4XF, United Kingdom
☎ (01904) 692000/✆ (01904) 692059
✉ info@themaxdp.com
🖥 www.themaxdesignandprint.co.uk

The Plastic Card Shop Unit 26 Rake Industries, Rogate, Petersfield, Hampshire, GU31 5DU, United Kingdom
☎ (0845) 2260813/✆ (0845) 2260814
✉ sales@theplasticcardshop.com
🖥 www.theplasticcardshop.com

The Print Factory South Portway Close, Round Spinney, Northampton, NN3 8RH, United Kingdom
☎ (01604) 790079/✆ (01604) 790880
🖥 www.tpfgroup.co.uk

The Printroom Unit 103, Cramer Business Centre, 37 Cramer Street, London, E2 8HD, United Kingdom
☎ (020) 7739 9923/✆ (020) 7739 9881
✉ ian@theprintrooms.co.uk
🖥 www.theprintrooms.co.uk

The Quoin Print Co Ltd 2 Pillings Road, Oakham, Leicestershire, LE15 6QF, United Kingdom
☎ (01572) 770044/✆ (01572) 770123
✉ sales@quoinprint.net

The Transfer Function 11 Northburgh Street, London, EC1V 0AN, United Kingdom
☎ (020) 7490 0002/✆ (020) 7490 0007
✉ wes@transfunction.co.uk
🖥 www.transfunction.co.uk

Thomson Print Services (Glasgow) Ltd 52 Kelvingrove Street, Glasgow, G3 7RZ, United Kingdom
☎ 0141-332 8686/✆ 0141-331 1028
✉ sales@tpsmarketing.co.uk
🖥 www.tpsmarketing.co.uk

Tollit & Harvey Ltd Oldmeadow Road, King's Lynn, Norfolk, PE30 4LW, United Kingdom
☎ (01553) 696600/✆ (01553) 767235
✉ sales@tollitandharvey.co.uk
🖥 www.tollitandharvey.co.uk

Tom Hill Hoo Lodge, Dagnall Road, Hemel Hempstead, Hertfordshire, HP1 3BP, United Kingdom
☎ (01442) 256208
🖥 www.tomhill-designer.co.uk

Trichrom (IVCA) 2 Orchard Business Centre, Salfords, Redhill, RH1 5EL, United Kingdom
☎ (01293) 823623/✆ (01293) 820615
✉ steve@trichrom.co.uk

Unwin Brothers The Gresham Press, Old Woking, Woking, Surrey, GU22 9LH, United Kingdom
☎ (01483) 757588/✆ (01483) 755168
✉ print@unwinbros.co.uk
🖥 www.mpgltd.co.uk

Victoria Printing Works Ltd t/a Jaggerprint 86-90 Richmond Road, Kingston upon Thames, Surrey, KT2 5EW, United Kingdom
☎ (020) 8546 0593/✆ (020) 8541 5708
✉ graham@jaggerprint.co.uk
🖥 www.jaggerprint.co.uk

W.E. Baxter Ltd 10 Osier Way, Mitcham, Surrey, CR4 4NF, United Kingdom
☎ (020) 8685 1234/✆ (020) 8640 2781
✉ baxter_sales@we-baxter.co.uk
🖥 www.fulmar.co.uk

Walkers M C R Crabtree Lane, Clayton, Manchester, M11 4GU, United Kingdom
☎ 0161-223 7814/✆ 0161-231 7212
✉ info@walkersmcr.com
🖥 www.walkersmcr.com

Ward Philipson Group Ltd Halifax Road, Dunston Industrial Estate, Gateshead, Tyne & Wear, NE11 9HW, United Kingdom
☎ 0191-460 5915/(07768) 061347 ☎ 0191-460 8540
✉ hitcham@wardphilipson.co.uk
🖥 www.wardphilipson.co.uk

Watson & Presley Ltd Unit 2, 214 Purley Way, Croydon, CR0 4XG, United Kingdom
☎ (020) 8649 7058/✆ (020) 8649 7118
✉ studio@watsonpresley.com
🖥 www.watsonpresley.com

William Clowes Ltd Copland Way, Ellough, Beccles, Suffolk, NR34 7TL, United Kingdom
☎ (01502) 712884/(07768) 658820 ✆ (01502) 717003
✉ user@clowes.co.uk
🖥 www.clowes.co.uk

Wiltshire (Bristol) Ltd First Avenue, Portbury West, Bristol, BS20 7WP, United Kingdom
☎ (01275) 375555/✆ (01275) 375590
✉ enquiries@wiltshireprint.co.uk

Winstanley & Watkins 104 Duke Street, Liverpool, L1 5AG, United Kingdom
☎ 0151-709 0808/✆ 0151-709 3060
✉ info@wwprint.co.uk
🖥 www.wwprint.co.uk

Witney Press 11 Linkwood Road, Windrush Industrial Park, Witney, Oxfordshire, OX29 7HA, United Kingdom
☎ (01993) 703981/✆ (01993) 776096
✉ print@witneypress.co.uk
🖥 www.witneypress.co.uk

Wren Press 1 Chelsea Wharf, 15 Lots Road, London, SW10 0QJ, United Kingdom
☎ (020) 7351 5887/✆ (020) 7352 7063
✉ nicky.granville@wrenpress.com
🖥 www.wrenpress.com

X Card Technology Unit 8, Cowley Mill Trading Estate, Longbridge Way, Uxbridge, Middlesex, UB8 2YG, United Kingdom
☎ (01895) 256332/✆ (01895) 230902
✉ info@xcardtechnology.com
🖥 www.xcardtechnology.com

Zeta Image To Print Ltd 54 Ayres Street, London, SE1 1EU, United Kingdom
☎ (020) 7787 3993/✆ (020) 7403 5768
✉ sales@hiero-design.co.uk
🖥 www.zeta-print.co.uk

TRANSLATION SERVICES

Adelphi Translations 402 The Workstation, 15 Paternoster Row, Sheffield, South Yorkshire, S1 2BX,
☎ 0114 221 0250
✉ james@adelphitranslations.com
🖥 www.adelphitranslation.com

Language Link PO Box 8599, Swanshurst Lane, Birmingham, West Midlands, B13 0DQ,
☎ 0121 777 7374/✆ 0121 777 8883
✉ info@lang-link.co.uk
🖥 www.lang-link.co.uk

TRANSLATION

1-2 Translate 30 Counting House Lane, Dunmow, Essex, CM6 1BX, United Kingdom
☎ (01371) 876588
✉ jonathan.spooner@academy-life.com
🖥 www.12translate.co.uk

1st Applied Translations Ltd 107-111 Fleet Street, London, EC4A 2AB, United Kingdom
☎ (020) 7248 7711/✆ (020) 7248 7722
✉ translate@1stapplied.co.uk
🖥 www.1stapplied.co.uk

1st Temple Translations Ltd 197 Temple Chambers, Temple Avenue, London, EC4Y 0DT, United Kingdom
☎ (020) 7842 0171/✆ (020) 7842 0172
✉ enquiry@templetranslations.com
🖥 www.templetranslations.com

1st Transnational 211-212 Piccadilly, London, W1J 9HF, United Kingdom
☎ (020) 7629 2787/✆ (020) 7629 2797
✉ voices@1sttransnational.com
🖥 www.1sttransnational.com

A G E T Ltd 195 Kenton Road, Kenton, Harrow, Middlesex, HA3 0HD, United Kingdom
☎ (020) 8907 0104/✆ (020) 8907 8785
✉ info@aget.co.uk
🖥 www.aget.net

A S T Language Services Ltd Unit 8, Ayr Street Workshops, Ayr Street, Nottingham, NG7 4FX, United Kingdom
☎ 0115-970 5633/✆ 0115-978 0130
✉ office@astls.co.uk
🖥 www.astls.co.uk

Accent Multilingual Services 9-11 Mansell Street, St. Peter Port, Guernsey, GY1 1HP, United Kingdom
☎ (01481) 714909/ (01481) 715880
✉ accent@guernsey.net
🖥 www.accent.guernsey.net

Accurate Translations Ltd Scotland Lane, Haslemere, Surrey, GU27 3AW, United Kingdom
☎ (01428) 654013/ (01428) 651401
✉ ceedassociation@aol.com
🖥

Akerbeltz Translations 1/2 47 Wilton Street, Glasgow, G20 6RT, United Kingdom
☎ 0141-946 4437/ 0141-945 2701
✉ fios@akerbeltz.org
🖥 www.akerbeltz.org

Alchemy Translations 17 Sunnybank Road, Oldbury, West Midlands, B68 0DB, United Kingdom
☎ 01214 221414/ 01214 218117
✉ info@alchemy-translations.co.uk
🖥 www.alchemy-translations.co.uk

Alden Group Ltd Osney Mead, Oxford, OX2 0EF, United Kingdom
☎ (01865) 253200/ (01865) 249070
✉ info@alden.co.uk
🖥 www.alden.co.uk

All Languages Ltd Nelson House, 362-364 Old Street, London, EC1V 9LT, United Kingdom
☎ (020) 7739 6641/ (020) 7739 6542
✉ info@alllanguages.co.uk
🖥 www.alllanguages.co.uk

Andiamo! Language Services Ltd Swan Yard, West Market Place, Cirencester, Gloucestershire, GL7 2NH, United Kingdom
☎ (01285) 659100/ (01285) 659369
✉ info@andiamo.co.uk
🖥 www.andiamo.co.uk

Anglia Translations Ltd Montagu House, 81 High Street, Huntingdon, Cambridgeshire, PE29 3NY, United Kingdom
☎ (01480) 411514/ (01480) 434665
✉ sales@anglia-translations.co.uk
🖥 www.anglia-translations.co.uk

APT Transtelex Ltd Unit F. The Mews, 6 Putney Common, London, SW15 1HL, United Kingdom
☎ (020) 8246 4050/ (020) 8246 4059
✉ marketing@aptplc.net
🖥 www.aptplc.net

Aquent Multilingual Communications 60 Parker Street, London, WC2B 5PZ, United Kingdom
☎ (020) 7404 0077/ (020) 7404 0055
✉ translation@aquent.com
🖥 www.mlc.aquent.com

Assoc of Translation Companies 5th Floor, Greener House, 66-68 Haymarket, London, SW1Y 4RF, United Kingdom
☎ (020) 7930 2200/ (020) 7451 7051
✉ info@atc.org.uk
🖥 www.atc.org.uk

Atlas Translations Ltd 14a Goodwins Court, Covent Garden, London, WC2N 4LL, United Kingdom
☎ (020) 7240 6666/ (020) 7240 6996
✉ london@atlas-translations.co.uk
🖥 www.atlas-translations.co.uk

Baytu Enterprises 29c Keyes Road, London, NW2 3XB, United Kingdom
☎ (07717) 830809
✉ bbaytu@baytu.com
🖥 www.baytu.com

BBC Languages Ltd Balfour House, 39 Brooklands Road, Weybridge, Surrey, KT13 0RU, United Kingdom
☎ (01932) 348800/ (01932) 351400
✉ jeyne@bbclanguages.prestel.co.uk
🖥 www.bbclang.co.uk

Bigmouth Translations 24-26 Broad Street, Staple Hill, Bristol, BS16 5NU, United Kingdom
☎ (0845) 1304547/ (0870) 0114547
✉ sales@bigmts.com
🖥 www.bigmts.com

Bilinguagroup 4th Floor East, 79-80 Margaret Street, London, W1W 8TA, United Kingdom
☎ (020) 7580 4441/ (020) 7580 1909
✉ info@bilinguagroup.com
🖥 www.bilinguagroup.com

Bond Street Translators Ltd 1 Hay Hill, Berkeley Square, London, W1J 6DH, United Kingdom
☎ (020) 7493 2418/ (020) 7491 7971
✉ info@bond-st-translators.co.uk
🖥 www.bond-st-translators.co.uk

Bridge Translation & Publishing 3 Albert Chambers, Canal Street, Congleton, Cheshire, CW12 4AA, United Kingdom
☎ (01260) 299148/ (01260) 299352
✉ martin@bridgetrans.co.uk
🖥 www.bridgetrans.co.uk

Brightlines Translation Ltd Freestone House, Box Hill, Corsham, Wiltshire, SN13 8HN, United Kingdom
☎ (01225) 740011/ (01225) 744099
✉ info@brightlines.co.uk
🖥 www.brightlines.co.uk

Business Language Services Ltd Westgate House, 2 Union Road East, Abergavenny, Monmouthshire, NP7 5UW, United Kingdom
☎ (01873) 856762/ (01873) 855006
✉ info@businesslanguageservices.co.uk
🖥 www.businesslanguageservices.co.uk

Central Translations Ltd 21 Woodstock Street, Mayfair, London, W1C 2AP, United Kingdom
☎ (020) 7493 5511/ (020) 7409 2774
✉ info@centraltranslations.co.uk
🖥 www.centraltranslations.co.uk

Chinese Marketing & Communications 4th Floor, 16 Nicholas Street, Manchester, M1 4EJ, United Kingdom
☎ /7971888080 / 0161-228 3739
✉ simon.jones@sino-be.com
🖥 www.china-britain.org

Cicero Translations 5 Clanricarde Gardens, Tunbridge Wells, Kent, TN1 1PE, United Kingdom
☎ (01892) 676655/ (01892) 515514
✉ enquiries@cicerotranslations.co.uk
🖥 www.cicerotranslations.co.uk

Comtec Translations 168 The Parade, Leamington Spa, Warwickshire, CV32 4AF, United Kingdom
☎ (01926) 335681/ (01926) 833619
✉ info@comtectranslations.co.uk
🖥 www.comtectranslations.com

D Q A Ltd Suite 300, 18-20 Barter Street, London, WC1A 2AH, United Kingdom
☎ (07041) 450220
✉ pottinger@datafileportugal.com
🖥 www.worthywords-translations.com

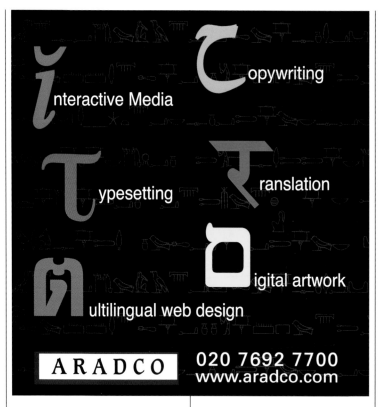

ARADCO — interactive Media, Copywriting, Typesetting, Translation, multilingual web design, Digital artwork
020 7692 7700
www.aradco.com

Dixon Associates The Creative Industry Centre, Wolverhampton Science Park, Wolverhampton, WV10 9TG, United Kingdom
☎ (0845) 6124888/ (01902) 312188
✉ info@dixon-associates.co.uk
🖥 www.dixon-associates.co.uk

E L S International 16 Church Road, Webheath, Redditch, Worcestershire, B97 5PG, United Kingdom
☎ (01527) 541725/ (08707) 059654
✉ mail@els-int.co.uk
🖥 www.els-int.co.uk

Eclipse Translations Ltd European Translation Centre, Lionheart Enterprise Park, Alnwick, Northumberland, NE66 2HT, United Kingdom
☎ (01665) 511000/ (01665) 511058
✉ info@eclipse-translation.co.uk
🖥 www.eclipse-translation.co.uk

Engineering Languages Ltd 6 West Cromwell Road, London, SW5 9QJ, United Kingdom
☎ (020) 7370 2728/ (020) 7373 3012
✉
🖥

English into Polish Translation Flat 906, Cascades Tower, 4 Westferry Road, London, E14 8JN, United Kingdom
☎ (020) 7515 6381/ (0870) 0516763
✉ monika@wheelerfamily.ws
🖥 monika.wheelerfamily.ws

Etymax Ltd 6 Bickels Yard, 151-153 Bermondsey Street, London, SE1 3HA, United Kingdom
☎ (020) 7089 9098/ (020) 7089 9099
✉ info@etymax.com
🖥 www.etymax.com

Europa Technical Translators Dunlewey House, 134 Greenfield Road, Birmingham, B17 0EG, United Kingdom
☎ 0121-427 2555/ 0121-427 1055
✉ info@europatrans.co.uk
🖥 www.europatechtrans.co.uk

Eurotransnet Ltd Chesham House, 150 Regents Street, London, W1R 5FA, United Kingdom
☎ (020) 7636 1881/ (020) 7636 1396
✉ translation@eurotransnet.co.uk
🖥 www.eurotransnet.co.uk

Foreign Legion 1 Kendal Road, London, NW10 1JH, United Kingdom
☎ (020) 8450 4451
✉ voices@foreignlegion.co.uk
🖥 www.foreignlegion.co.uk

Foreign Versions Ltd 60 Blandford Street, London, W1U 7JD, United Kingdom
☎ (020) 7935 0993/ (020) 7935 0507
✉ info@foreignversions.co.uk
🖥 www.foreignversions.co.uk

G L S Language Services 250 Crow Road, Glasgow, G11 7LA, United Kingdom
☎ 0141-357 6611/ 0141-357 6605
✉ info@glslanguages.co.uk
🖥 www.glslanguageservices.co.uk

Gala Publishing and Copestone Copy Writers The Write House, 6 Park Meadow, Hatfield, Hertfordshire, AL9 5HA, United Kingdom
☎ (01707) 890118/ (01707) 895587
✉ mail@galapublishing.com
🖥 www.galapublishing.com

GoUK.com Translations, Petersfield, Hampshire, GU32 2FA, United Kingdom
☎ (01730) 263006
✉ translations@gouk.com
🖥 www.gouk.com/translations

Inter-Com (Foreign Voices) Hurlingham Studios, Ranelagh Gardens, London, SW6 3PA, United Kingdom
☎ (020) 7731 8000/☏ (0870) 0941954
✉ mail@intercom-translations.com
🖥 www.intercom-translations.co.uk

International Translations Ltd 9 Queensway, Heswall, Wirral, Merseyside, CH60 3SL, United Kingdom
☎ 0151-342 7044/☏ 0151-342 9407
✉ admin@itltranslations.com
🖥 www.itltranslations.com

Italian Translations - Words You Can Rely On
Billingsley Farm, Holme Lacy, Hereford, HR2 6PH, United Kingdom
☎ (01432) 870661
✉ lorenz@claranet.co.uk
🖥 www.martinelli.co.uk

J R Translations 2 Delft Close, Locks Heath, Southampton, SO31 7TQ, United Kingdom
☎ (01489) 576415/☏ (01489) 576541
✉ jrtranslation@ntlworld.com
🖥

K International Carina Building East, Sunrise Parkway, Linford Wood, Milton Keynes, MK14 6PW, United Kingdom
☎ (01908) 670399/☏ (01908) 670170
✉ info@k-international.com
🖥 www.k-international.com

Key Language Services Linford Forum, 32 Rockingham Drive, Milton Keynes, MK14 6LY, United Kingdom
☎ (01908) 232101/☏ (01908) 232815
✉ sales@keylanguageservices.co.uk
🖥 www.keylanguageservices.co.uk

Kunze London 12 Byron Road, Mill Hill, London, NW7 4AD, United Kingdom
☎ (020) 8959 2513/☏ (020) 8959 7626
✉ info@kunzelondon.com
🖥 www.kunzelondon.com

Language Bureau Ltd 77-79 Lee Lane, Horwich, Bolton, BL6 7AU, United Kingdom
☎ (01204) 669622/☏ (01204) 698192
✉ enquiries@languagebureau.co.uk
🖥 www.languagebureau.co.uk

Leagal & Technical Translations Ltd 16 Old Market Place, Altrincham, Cheshire, WA14 4DF, United Kingdom
☎ 0161-941 2024/☏ 0161-927 7024
✉ enquiries@itsgroup.co.uk
🖥 www.itsgroup.co.uk

Legal & Technical Translation Services 13 Earl Street, Maidstone, Kent, ME14 1PL, United Kingdom
☎ (01622) 751537/☏ (01622) 754431
✉ translations.ltts@virgin.net
🖥 www.ltts.co.uk

Lifeline Language Services Premier House, Church Street, Preston, PR1 3BQ, United Kingdom
☎ (01772) 558858/☏ (01772) 558878
✉ info@lifelinelanguageservices.co.uk
🖥 www.lifelinelanguageservices.co.uk

Linguaset Sunderland House, Sunderland Street, Macclesfield, Cheshire, SK11 6JF, United Kingdom
☎ (01625) 617174/☏ (0871) 2510455
✉ info@linguaset.co.uk
🖥 www.linguaset.co.uk

Linguatext (Scotland) 8 Randolph Place, Edinburgh, EH3 7TE, United Kingdom
☎ 0131-624 2091/☏ 0131-624 1220
✉ sylvia@linguatext.com
🖥 www.linguatext.com

Liquid Translations 1 Devonshire Terrace, Glasgow, G12 0XE, United Kingdom
☎ 0141-334 9031/☏ 0141-334 9031
✉ info@liquid-translations.com
🖥 www.liquid-translations.com

Lloyd International Translation Ltd Birch Heath Road, Tarporley, Cheshire, CW6 9UR, United Kingdom
☎ (01829) 730050/☏ (01829) 730060
✉ mail@lloyd.co.uk
🖥 www.lloyd.co.uk

Monde Media 4 Ransomes Dock, Park Gate Road, London, SW11 4NP, United Kingdom
☎ (020) 7924 6299/☏ (020) 7924 6301
✉ info@monde.net
🖥 www.monde.net

Newcom Language Services Ltd Newcom House, 125 Poplar High Street, London, E14 0AE, United Kingdom
☎ (020) 7517 1270/☏ (020) 7517 1271
✉ newcom@newcomgroup.com
🖥 www.newcomgroup.com

P B S S Translations PO Box 371, Pembury, Tunbridge Wells, Kent, TN2 4XE, United Kingdom
☎ (01892) 824833/☏ (01892) 825134
✉ partners@pbss-uk.com
🖥 www.pbss-uk.com

PASSWORD Ltd 118 Chevening Road, London, NW6 6TP, United Kingdom
☎ (020) 8723 8841
✉ info@password-eu.net
🖥 www.password-eu.net

Peak Translations Shepherd's Bank, Kettleshume, High Peak, Derbyshire, SK23 7QU, United Kingdom
☎ (01663) 732074/☏ (01663) 735499
✉ info@peak-translations.co.uk
🖥 www.peak-translations.co.uk

Planet Languages Ltd 1 St. George's Yard, Castle Street, Farnham, Surrey, GU9 7LW, United Kingdom
☎ (01252) 713444/☏ (01252) 713445
✉ post@planetlanguages.com
🖥 www.planetlanguages.com

R F Translations Office 410, 98 Woodlands Road, Glasgow, G3 6HB, United Kingdom
☎ (07005) 900919/☏ (07092) 810417
✉ info@rf-translations.com
🖥 www.rf-translatins.com

Reach Marketing & Communications 3 Harrow Drive, Sale, Cheshire, M33 3TB, United Kingdom
☎ 0161-969 4515
✉ leoaspden@reach-mc.co.uk
🖥 ww.reach-mc.co.uk

Roevin Translations Concorde House, Trinity Park, Birmingham, B37 7UQ, United Kingdom
☎ 0121-635 5060/☏ 0121-635 5061
✉ birmingham.translation@roevin.co.uk
🖥 www.roevin.co.uk/translations

Rovin Computype Ltd Park Road Estate, Park Road, Timperley, Altrincham, Cheshire, WA14 5QH, United Kingdom
☎ 0161-935 2000/☏ 0161-973 5682
✉ manchester.translation@rovin.co.uk
🖥 www.rovin.co.uk/translation

Russia House 61a Queen Mary Road, Sheffield, S2 1HQ, United Kingdom
☎ (07814) 920071/☏ 0114-283 5973
✉ anna@russia-house.co.uk
🖥 www.russia-house.co.uk

Salford Translations Ltd 66 Lower Hillgate, Stockport, Cheshire, SK1 3AL, United Kingdom
☎ 0161-968 7100/☏ 0161-968 7109
✉ info@salftrans.co.uk
🖥 www.salftrans.co.uk

Star UK 15-17 Bridge Street, Leatherhead, Surrey, KT22 8BL, United Kingdom
☎ (01372) 377300/☏ (01372) 373355
✉ info@star-uk.co.uk
🖥 www.star-group.net

Thames Translations International Old Batsord Mill, Lower Luton Road, Harpenden, Hertfordshire, AL5 5BZ, United Kingdom
☎ (0870) 0111130/☏ (0870) 0111140
✉ info@thames.net
🖥 www.thames-translations.com

The Ask Group Ltd Ask House, 2 Northgate Avenue, Bury St. Edmunds, Suffolk, IP32 6BB, United Kingdom
☎ (01284) 768278/☏ (01284) 764025
✉ help@translate.co.uk
🖥 www.translate.co.uk

The Big Word 59 Charlotte Street, London, W1T 4PE, United Kingdom
☎ (0870) 748 8000/☏ (0870) 748 8001
✉ email@thebigword.com
🖥 www.thebigword.com

Tongue Tied (East Anglia) Ltd 23 Impington Lane, Impington, Cambridge, CB4 9LT, United Kingdom
☎ (01223) 479391/☏ (01223) 504985
✉ sales@tonguetiedeastanglia.co.uk
🖥 www.tonguetiedeastanglia.co.uk

Total Translation Co. Ltd 75 Railway Street, Hertford, SG14 1RP, United Kingdom
☎ (01284) 768278/☏ (01992) 532799
✉ vacancies@totaltranslations.com
🖥 www.totaltranslations.com

Tramont Translation Management 57 Upper Park Road, London, NW3 2UL, United Kingdom
☎ (0845) 6448254/☏ (0845) 6448259
✉ tramont@globalnet.co.uk
🖥 www.tramont.co.uk

Transaction Translators Ltd Redlands, Tapton House Road, Sheffield, S10 5BY, United Kingdom
☎ 0114-266 1103/☏ 0114-263 1959
✉ transaction@transaction.co.uk
🖥 www.transaction.co.uk

Transworld Linguist Services 38-40 Broad Green Avenue, Croydon, CR0 2ST, United Kingdom
☎ (020) 8683 4031/☏ (020) 8689 6015
✉ mail@transworld.co.uk
🖥 www.transworld.co.uk

TTC Creative Ltd Creative House, 20 St. Marys Road, London, W5 5ES, United Kingdom
☎ (020) 8567 5902/☏ (020) 8840 7349
✉ info@ttcweb.com
🖥 www.ttcweb.com

U P S Translations 111 Baker Street, London, W1U 6RR, United Kingdom
☎ (020) 7224 1220/☏ (020) 7486 3272
✉ info@upstranslations.com
🖥 www.upstranslations.com

Voice Squad Ltd 1 Kendal Road, London, NW10 1JH, United Kingdom
☎ (020) 8450 4451
✉ voices@voicesquad.com
🖥 www.voicesquad.com

VSI Aradco House, 132 Cleveland Street, London, W1T 6AB, United Kingdom
☎ (020) 7692 7700/☏ (020) 7692 7711
✉ info@vsi.tv
🖥 www.vsi.tv

Wessex Translations Unit A1, The Premier Centre, Abbey Park Industrial Estate, Romsey, Hampshire, SO51 9DG, United Kingdom
☎ (0870) 166 9300/☏ (0870) 166 9299
✉ sales@wt-lm.com
🖥 www.wt-lm.com

World Writers 29 Clerkenwell Road, London, EC1M 5TA, United Kingdom
☎ (020) 7287 4877/☏ (020) 7287 6159
✉ info@worldwriters.com
🖥 www.worldwriters.com

WorldAccent 30-31 Great Sutton Street, London, EC1V 0NA, United Kingdom
☎ (020) 7865 8300/☏ (020) 7865 8400
✉ sales@worldaccent.com
🖥 www.worldaccent.com

PEEPSHOW.ORG.UK

Sound

EMPOWERING THE BEST IN
AUDIO POST PRODUCTION AND SOUND DESIGN

Scrub recommends these Pro Tools/ICON equipped facilities.

Blue Post Production
Tel: 0207 437 2626
www.bluepp.co.uk

Envy
Tel: 0207 908 4600
www.envypost.co.uk

Films@59
Tel: 0117 9064300
www.filmsat59.com

Goldcrest Post
Tel: 0207 437 7972
www.goldcrestpost.co.uk

Hullabaloo Studios
Tel: 0161 882 0007
www.hullabaloo-studios.com

M2 Television
Tel: 0207 343 6543
www.m2tv.com

Platform Post Production
Tel: 0207 287 6766
www.platformpp.tv

Sanctuary@Oasis
Tel: 0207 434 4133
www.thesanctuary.tv

Scramble Sound
Tel: 0207 479 4400
www.scramble.co.uk

Soundworks
Tel: 029 2033 1010
www.soundworks.co.uk

Splice TV
Tel: 0207 033 9944
www.splicetv.com

St Anne's Post
Tel: 0207 155 1500
www.saintannespost.co.uk

TwoFour TV
Tel: 01752 727 400
www.twofour.co.uk

Supplied and supported by Scrub, Digidesign Pro Tools / ICON technology is revolutionising the world of audio post production and sound design, presenting exciting new opportunities for facilities houses to realise their clients' creative visions.

DIGIDESIGN | ICON
INTEGRATED CONSOLE

PRO TOOLS **HD**ACCEL

Scrub - A division of HHB
2nd Floor, 80 Berwick Street, London W1F 8TU
Tel: 020 7025 6020 Email: scrub@hhb.co.uk

www.hhb.co.uk/scrub

scrub
A DIVISION OF HHB

MUSIC - ORIGINAL & LIBRARY

2002 Studios 123a Kenton Road, Harrow, Middlesex, HA3 0AZ, United Kingdom
(020) 8907 8634/ (020) 8907 8632
info@2002studios.com
www.2002studios.com

5M Communication 11 Grove Crescent South, Boston Spa, Leeds, LS23 6AY, United Kingdom
(01937) 844637/ (01937) 844637
enquiries@5mc.co.uk

Air-Edel Associates 18 Rodmarton Street, London, W1U 8BJ, United Kingdom
(020) 7486 6466/ (020) 7224 0344
air-edel@air-edel.co.uk
www.air-edel.co.uk

Alan Parker 80-88 Wardour Street, London, W1V 3LF, United Kingdom
(020) 7439 8481/

Amber Music 1st Floor, 12 Oval Road, London, NW1 7DH, United Kingdom
(020) 7428 6366/ (020) 7428 6377
briony@ambermusic.co.uk
www.ambermusic.co.uk

Amphonic Music Ltd 20 The Green, Warlingham, Surrey, CR6 9HN, United Kingdom
(01737) 832837/ (01737) 833812
info@amphonic.co.uk
www.amphonic.co.uk

Angela Allen/Mcasso Music Production Ltd 32-34 Great Marlborough Street, London, W1F 7JB, United Kingdom
(020) 7734 3664/ (020) 7439 2375
music@mcasso.com
www.mcasso.com

Apple Corps Ltd 27 Ovington Square, London, SW3 1LJ, United Kingdom
(020) 7761 9600/ (020) 7225 0661
post@applecorpsltd.com
www.applecorpsltd.com

Arcadia Production Music (UK) Greenlands, Payhembury, Honiton, Devon, EX14 3HY, United Kingdom
(01404) 841601/ (01404) 841687
admin@arcadiamusic.tv
www.arcadiamusic.tv

Artists Known As PO Box 3124, Ripponlea, VIC 3185, Australia
00 61 42 131 3049/ 00 61 42 368 3173
contact@akaltd.com
www.akaltd.com

Asitis Music PO Box 2029, Watford, WD25 7XN, United Kingdom
(01923) 663051/
producerguy@boltblue.com

Audio Visual Media Music Library Sovereign House, 12 Trewartha Road, Praa Sands, Penzance, Cornwall, TR20 9ST, United Kingdom
(01736) 762826/(07721) 449477 (01736) 763328
panamus@aol.com
www.panamamusic.co.uk

Barrie Bignold 15 Barlby Road, North Kensington, London, W10 6AN, United Kingdom
(020) 8964 9212/ (020) 8964 9212
barriebignold@hotmail.com

Bazza Productions 1 Chemin De La Sini, Ille-Sur-Tît, 66130, France
46 88 41 72 6/(07973) 383219
bsguard@aol.com
www.villacanigov.com

BB Music House 158 Trewhitt Road, Newcastle, Tyne & Wear, NE6 5DY,
0191 224 2457/
info@bbmusichouse.co.uk
www.bbmusichouse.co.uk

Bella Russell 7 The Paragon, Clifton, Bristol, BS8 4LA, United Kingdom
0117-973 1619/ 0117-973 0377
nigel@ddmp.demon.co.uk
www.ddmp.demon.co.uk

Benjamin Wallfisch/Air-Edel Associates 18 Rodmarton Street, London, W1U 8BJ, United Kingdom
(020) 7486 6466/ (020) 7224 0344
air-edel@air-edel.co.uk
www.air-edel.co.uk

Big Box Productions Ltd 31 Penrose Street, London, SE17 3DW, United Kingdom
(07974) 561579/
jeremy@bigboxstudios.com
www.bigboxstudios.com

Birdland Productions 4 The Straight, Southall, Middlesex, UB1 1QX, United Kingdom
(020) 8571 6794/ (020) 8813 8398
crummel@msn.com

Blackangel Ltd Flat 32, 9 Laxton Place, London, NW1 3PT, United Kingdom
(07885) 657373/
rat-fink@lineone.net

Blaze Music Ltd 16 Steele Road, London, W4 5AF, United Kingdom
(020) 8987 6111/(07802) 844388 (020) 8747 9194
claire@blazemusic.co.uk
www.blazemusic.co.uk

Bling/Air-Edel Associates 18 Rodmarton Street, London, W1U 8BJ, United Kingdom
(020) 7486 6466/ (020) 7224 0344
air-edel@air-edel.co.uk
www.air-edel.co.uk

Boiler Room New York 149 Fifth Avenue, New York City, 10010, United States of America
00 1 212 388 1212/
kevin@boiler-music.com

Boosey and Hawkes Production Music Aldwych House, 71-91 Aldwych, London, WC2B 4HN, United Kingdom
(020) 7054 7275/ (020) 7054 7293
pm@boosey.com
www.booseypm.com

Brian Bennett Music 333 Washington Boulevard Suite 243, Marina Del Rey, 90292, United States of America
00 1 310 895 5635/
brian.scott.bennett@lycos.co.uk

Brian Gascoigne/Air-Edel Associates 18 Rodmarton Street, London, W1U 8BJ, United Kingdom
(020) 7486 6466/ (020) 7224 0344
air-edel@air-edel.co.uk
www.air-edel.co.uk

Bridge Creative Ltd The Coach House Studio, 40 Higher Lane, Upholland, Lancashire, WN8 0NL,
01695 624966/
bridget@bridgecreative.co.uk
www.bridgecreative.co.uk

Bright Blue Studios 36 The Ellers, Pennington, Ulverston, Cumbria, LA12 7NT, United Kingdom
(01229) 585242/
info@brightbluestudios.co.uk
www.brightbluestudios.co.uk

British Music Information Centre Lincoln House, 75 Westminster Bridge Road, London, SE1 7HS, United Kingdom
(020) 7928 1902/ (020) 7928 2957
info@bmic.co.uk
www.bmic.co.uk

Caribbean Music Library Sovereign House, 12 Trewartha Road, Praa Sands, Penzance, Cornwall, TR20 9ST, United Kingdom
(01736) 762826/(07721) 449477 (01736) 763328
panamus@aol.com
www.panamamusic.co.uk

Carlin Production Music Iron Bridge House, 3 Bridge Approach, Chalk Farm, London, NW1 8BD, United Kingdom
(020) 7734 3251/ (020) 7439 2391
cpm@carlinmusic.co.uk
www.carlinmusic.co.uk

Cavendish Music Aldwych House, 71-91 Aldwych, London, WC2B 4HN, United Kingdom
(020) 7054 7275/ (020) 7054 7293
cavendish@boosey.com
www.cavendishmusic.com

Chandos Records Ltd Chandos House, 1 Commerce Park, Commerce Way, Colchester, CO2 8HX, United Kingdom
(01206) 225200/ (01206) 225201
enquiries@chandos.net
www.chandos.net

Chantelle Music 3A Ashfield Parade, London, N14 5EH, United Kingdom
(020) 8886 6236/
www.chantellemusic.co.uk

Christian Henson/Air-Edel Associates 18 Rodmarton Street, London, W1U 8BJ, United Kingdom
(020) 7486 6466/ (020) 7224 0344
air-edel@air-edel.co.uk
www.air-edel.co.uk

Classical Series (KPM) KPM Music Ltd, 127 Charing Cross Road, London, WC2H 0QY, United Kingdom
(020) 7412 9111/ (020) 7413 0061
kpm@kpm.co.uk
www.playkpm.com

Click 31 Colburn Avenue, Hatch End, Pinner, Middlesex, HA5 4PQ, United Kingdom
(020) 8428 2876/(07973) 286718 (020) 8428 2876
clickmusic@onetel.com

Cliff Adams Management Studio 5A, Fairbank Studios, 75-81 Burnaby Street, London, SW10 0NS, United Kingdom
(020) 7751 4244/ (020) 7751 4255
camltd@btconnect.com

Cliff Haywood 161 Clapham Road, London, SW9 0PU, United Kingdom
(020) 7642 1951/(07976) 687975
cliff@cliffhaywood.com
www.cliffhaywood.com

Cousin Cluny Unit 7H, Clapham North Arts Centre, 26-32 Voltaire Road, London, SW4 6DH,
01571 833325/
cluny@clunystrachan.com
www.clunystrachan.com

Crocodile Music 431 Linenhall, 162/168 Regent Street, London, W1B 5TE, United Kingdom
(020) 7039 0165/ (020) 7580 0080
info@crocodilemusic.com
www.crocodilemusic.com

Dankworth Management The Old Rectory, Stockwell Lane, Wavendon, Milton Keynes, MK17 8LU, United Kingdom
(01908) 583151/ (01908) 584414
dankworth@btconnect.com
www.quarternotes.com

Dario Marianelli/Air-Edel Associates 18 Rodmarton Street, London, W1U 8BJ, United Kingdom
(020) 7486 6466/ (020) 7224 0344
air-edel@air-edel.co.uk
www.air-edel.co.uk

David A. Hughes/Air-Edel Associates 18 Rodmarton Street, London, W1U 8BJ, United Kingdom
(020) 7486 6466/ (020) 7224 0344
air-edel@air-edel.co.uk
www.air-edel.co.uk

davidbunce.co.uk 130 Brownspring Drive, London, SE9 3LD, United Kingdom
(020) 8851 5911/
mail@davidbunce.co.uk
www.davidbunce.co.uk

De Wolfe Ltd Shropshire House, 2nd Floor East, 11-20 Capper Street, London, WC1E 6JA, United Kingdom
(020) 7631 3600/ (020) 7631 3700
info@dewolfemusic.co.uk
www.dewolfemusic.co.uk

Dead Clever Sound Studios Ltd 1 Bolton Road, Southbourne, Bournemouth, BH6 3DZ, United Kingdom
(01202) 423372/
heather@deadcleversounds.co.uk
www.deadcleversounds.co.uk

Derek C. Griffiths 19 Staunton Road, Kingston upon Thames, Surrey, KT2 5TJ, United Kingdom
(020) 8549 2499/(07815) 803973
delboy_savona@blueyonder.co.uk

Derek Wadsworth 11 Blacksmiths Hill, Aynho, Banbury, Oxfordshire, OX17 3AH, United Kingdom
(01869) 819920/(07808) 988002
derek.wadsworth@btclick.com
www.derekwadsworth.com

Digiffects 2nd Floor, 127 Charing Cross Road, London, WC2H 0QY, United Kingdom
(020) 7412 9111/ (020) 7413 0061
enquiries@musichouse.co.uk
www.kpmmusichouse.com

Dirk Brossè/Air-Edel Associates 18 Rodmarton Street, London, W1U 8BJ, United Kingdom
(020) 7486 6466/ (020) 7224 0344
air-edel@air-edel.co.uk
www.air-edel.co.uk

DitherNoise 26 Arlington Gardens, London, W4 4EY, United Kingdom
✆ (020) 8747 3055/✆ (020) 8747 3055
✉ simonlongo@btinternet.com

Duguid 53 Braeside Street, Glasgow, G20 6QT, United Kingdom
✆ (07802) 615031/✆
✉ id@irvinduguid.com
🖥 www.irvinduguid.com

E M I Records EMI House, 43 Brook Green, London, W6 7EF, United Kingdom
✆ (020) 7605 5000/✆ (020) 7605 5050
🖥 www.emirecords.co.uk

EMI Music Publishing Ltd 127 Charing Cross Road, London, WC2H 0QY, United Kingdom
✆ (020) 7434 2131/✆ (020) 7434 3531
🖥 www.emimusicpub.co.uk

Eschenbach Editions Achmore, Moss Road, Ullapool, Ross-Shire, IV26 2TF, United Kingdom
✆ 01854 612 938/✆ 01854 612 938
✉ eschenbach@caritas-music.co.uk
🖥 www.caritas-music.co.uk

Eventide Music Library Sovereign House, 12 Trewartha Road, Praa Sands, Penzance, Cornwall, TR20 9ST, United Kingdom
✆ (01736) 762826/(07721) 449477 ✆ (01736) 763328
✉ panamus@aol.com
🖥 www.panamamusic.co.uk

Extreme Music Greenland Place, 115-123 Bayham St, London, NW1 0AG, United Kingdom
✆ (020) 7485 0111/✆ (020) 7482 4871
✉ info@extrememusic.com
🖥 www.extrememusic.com

Faber Music Ltd 3 Queen Square, London, WC1N 3AU, United Kingdom
✆ (020) 7833 7922/✆ (020) 7833 7939
✉ media@fabermusic.com
🖥 www.fabermusicmedia.com

Fat Lady Music Productions 13 Bowstead Court, Parkham Street, London, SW11 3JP, United Kingdom
✆ (020) 7350 1666/(07812) 046355 ✆
✉ enquiry@fatladymusic.com
🖥 www.fatladymusic.com

Felt Music 75 Berwick Street, London, W1F 8TG, United Kingdom
✆ (020) 7287 1233/07939 234853 ✆ (020) 7287 1236
✉ natalie@feltmusic.com
🖥 www.feltmusic.com

Fiachra Trench/Air-Edel Associates 18 Rodmarton Street, London, W1U 8BJ, United Kingdom
✆ (020) 7486 6466/✆ (020) 7224 0344
✉ air-edel@air-edel.co.uk
🖥 www.air-edel.co.uk

Figment Group Ltd Figment House, Church Street, Ware, Hertfordshire, SG12 9EN, United Kingdom
✆ (01920) 484040/✆ (01920) 463883
✉ music@figmentgroup.co.uk
🖥 www.figmentgroup.co.uk

Final Touch Productions Ltd 4 The Oaks, Uxbridge Road, Hanworth, Feltham, Middlesex, TW13 5EF, United Kingdom
✆ (0870) 8444422/(07879) 400121 ✆ (0870) 8444433
✉ mail@finaltouch.co.uk
🖥 www.finaltouch.co.uk

Focus Music Library Studio 3, 166 Haverstock Hill, London, NW3 2AT, United Kingdom
✆ (020) 7722 3399/✆
✉ info@focusmusic.com
🖥 www.focusmusic.com

Frank Van Laecke/Air-Edel Associates 18 Rodmarton Street, London, W1U 8BJ, United Kingdom
✆ (020) 7486 6466/✆ (020) 7224 0344
✉ air-edel@air-edel.co.uk
🖥 www.air-edel.co.uk

Frederik Du Chau/Air-Edel Associates 18 Rodmarton Street, London, W1U 8BJ, United Kingdom
✆ (020) 7486 6466/✆ (020) 7224 0344
✉ air-edel@air-edel.co.uk
🖥 www.air-edel.co.uk

G. Ricordi & Co (London) Ltd 20 Fulham Broadway, London, SW6 1AH, United Kingdom
✆ (020) 7835 5381/✆
✉ sarah.bruce@bmg.com
🖥 www.ricordi.co.uk

Generika.com 3 Norfolk Street, Northampton, NN2 6HR, United Kingdom
✆ (01604) 474944/✆
✉ info@generika.com
🖥 www.generika.com

Gigi D'Amico 29 Ridley Road, London, NW10 5UB, United Kingdom
✆ (020) 8961 0290/✆
✉ gigidamico@hotmail.com

Greentrax Recordings Ltd Unit 2, Cockenzie Business Centre, 23 Edinburgh Road, Cockenzie, Prestonpans, East Lothian, EH32 0XL, United Kingdom
✆ (01875) 814155/✆ (01875) 813545
✉ greentrax@aol.com
🖥 www.greentrax.com

Greg Patmore.com The Coach House Studio, 40 Higher Lane, Upholland, Lancashire, WN8 0NL,
✆ 01695 624966/✆
✉ becky@gregpatmore.com
🖥 www.gregpatmore.com

Grosvenor Studios 16 Grosvenor Rd, Handsworth Wood, Birmingham, B20 3NP, United Kingdom
✆ 0121-356 9636/✆ 0121-356 9636

Happy Vibes Corporation, Worthing, West Sussex, BN14 7FB, United Kingdom
✆ (01903) 202426/✆ (01903) 202426
✉ music@happyvibes.co.uk
🖥 www.happyvibes.co.uk

Headjog 5b Church Street, Carleton, Skipton, North Yorkshire, BD23 3HA, United Kingdom
✆ (07985) 433090/✆ (01756) 795966
✉ j.richard@headjog.co.uk
🖥 www.headjog.net

Heraldic Production Music Library 5-7 Victoria Road, Plymouth, PL5 1RN, United Kingdom
✆ (01752) 350785/(07944) 933787 ✆
✉ firsttimerecords@btconnect.com
🖥 www.firsttimerecords.co.uk

Hudson Music Co. Ltd 2nd Floor, 11-20 Capper Street, London, WC1E 6JA, United Kingdom
✆ (020) 7631 3600/✆ (020) 7631 3700
✉ info@hudsonmusic.com
🖥 www.dewolfemusic.co.uk

Hum 31 Oval Road, London, NW1 7EA, United Kingdom
✆ (020) 7482 2345/✆ (020) 7482 6242
✉ info@hum.co.uk
🖥 www.hum.co.uk

Hyde Park Music Co. Ltd 8 Garden, Flat 15 Westbourne Terrace, London, W2 3UN, United Kingdom
✆ (020) 7402 8419/✆
✉ tony@tonyhiller.com
🖥 www.tonyhiller.com

Ian MacTavish 143 Wardour Street, London, W1S 8WA, United Kingdom
✆ (020) 7734 2705/✆ (020) 7434 1468
✉ shaun@macand.co.uk
🖥 www.macand.co.uk

Ian Ritchie 16 Gay Close, Willesden Green, London, NW2 4PR, United Kingdom
✆ (020) 8452 1684/✆
✉ ian@hyperlink.com
🖥 www.ian-ritchie.com

Image and Music Little Orchard, Trenewan, Looe, Cornwall, PL13 2QD, United Kingdom
✆ (01503) 272633/(07779) 703281 ✆
✉ admin@imageandmusic.com
🖥 www.imageandmusic.com

Infinite Potential, United Kingdom
✆ (07870) 676870/✆
✉ info@infinite-potential.info
🖥 www.infinite-potential.info

J W Media Music Ltd Dolphyn Court, 10-11 Great Turnstile, London, WC1V 7JU, United Kingdom
✆ (020) 7681 8900/✆ (020) 7681 8911
✉ info@jwmediamusic.com
🖥 www.jwmediamusic.com

James Harpham Tog Hill, Calstone, Calne, Wiltshire, SN11 8PZ, United Kingdom
✆ (01249) 812300/(07976) 945055 ✆ (01249) 812300
✉ harphammusic@hotmail.com
🖥 www.jamesharpham.co.uk

James Shearman/Air-Edel Associates 18 Rodmarton Street, London, W1U 8BJ, United Kingdom
✆ (020) 7486 6466/✆ (020) 7224 0344
✉ air-edel@air-edel.co.uk
🖥 www.air-edel.co.uk

Jamie Robertson 32 Havelock Road, Great Yarmouth, Norfolk, NR30 3HJ, United Kingdom
✆ (01493) 330536/(07706) 142257 ✆
✉ jamie@jamierobertson.me.uk
🖥 www.jamierobertson.me.uk

Jeff Wayne Music Group Ltd 97 Mortimer Street, London, W1W 7SU, United Kingdom
✆ (020) 7724 2471/✆ (020) 7927 8364
✉ info@jeffwaynemusic.com
🖥 www.jeffwaynemusic.com

Jelly Studios Vinehall Road, Mountfield, Robertsbridge, East Sussex, TN32 5JN, United Kingdom
✆ (07957) 478318/✆ (01580) 881310
✉ ray@jellorecords.com
🖥 www.jellorecords.com

Jody K. Jenkins/Air-Edel Associates 18 Rodmarton Street, London, W1U 8BJ, United Kingdom
✆ (020) 7486 6466/✆ (020) 7224 0344
✉ air-edel@air-edel.co.uk
🖥 www.air-edel.co.uk

Joe & Co Music Ltd 59 Dean Street, London, W1D 6AN, United Kingdom
✆ (020) 7439 1272/✆ (020) 7437 5504
✉ justine@joeandco.com
🖥 www.joeandco.com

Joe Williams Music 4 Darnley Road, Leeds, LS16 5JF, United Kingdom
✆ 0113-295 6111/(07760) 375712 ✆
✉ joe@joewilliams.co.uk
🖥 www.joewilliams.co.uk

John Bell 132 Brondesbury Villas, London, NW6 6AE, United Kingdom
✆ (020) 7328 0060/(07968) 339003 ✆
✉ orchestrations@mac.com

John Fiddy Music Unit 3, Moorgate Business Centre, Dereham, Norfolk, NR19 1PT, United Kingdom
✆ (01362) 697922/(07860) 562558 ✆ (01362) 697923
✉ info@johnfiddymusic.co.uk
🖥 www.johnfiddymusic.co.uk

K P M Music House 127 Charing Cross Road, London, WC2H 0QY, United Kingdom
✆ (020) 7412 9111/✆ (020) 7413 0061
✉ info@kpmmusichouse.com
🖥 www.kpmmusichouse.com

Kaleidophon Electronic Music 1 Chalcot Gardens, London, NW3 4YB, United Kingdom
✆ (020) 7483 4714/✆
✉ dv@kaleidophon.freeserve.co.uk
🖥 www.whitenoise.org.uk

Karl Jenkins/Air-Edel Associates 18 Rodmarton Street, London, W1U 8BJ, United Kingdom
✆ (020) 7486 6466/✆ (020) 7224 0344
✉ air-edel@air-edel.co.uk
🖥 www.air-edel.co.uk

Kassner Associated Publishers Ltd Unit 6-7, 11 Wyfold Road, London, SW6 6SE, United Kingdom
✆ (020) 7385 7700/✆ (020) 7385 3402
✉ songs@kassner-music.co.uk
🖥 www.president-records.co.uk

Katherine Howard Public Relations Eastwick, Clay Lane, Stoke Ash, Eye, Suffolk, IP23 7DZ, United Kingdom
✆ (01379) 678811/✆
✉ info@katherinehoward.co.uk
🖥 www.katherinehoward.co.uk

Keith Atack/Air-Edel Associates 18 Rodmarton Street, London, W1U 8BJ, United Kingdom
✆ (020) 7486 6466/✆ (020) 7224 0344
✉ air-edel@air-edel.co.uk
🖥 www.air-edel.co.uk

Kosinus 127 Charing Cross Road, London, WC2H 0QY, United Kingdom
✆ (020) 7412 9111/✆ (020) 7413 0061
✉ kpm@kpm.co.uk
🖥 www.playkpm.com

KPM Music House 127 Charing Cross Road, London, WC2H 0QY, United Kingdom
✆ (020) 7412 9111/✆ (020) 7413 0061
✉ kpm@kpm.co.uk
🖥 www.playkpm.com

L B S Manchester Ltd 11-13 Bamford Street, Stockport, Cheshire, SK1 3NZ, United Kingdom
✆ 0161-477 2710/✆ 0161-480 9497
✉ info@lbs.co.uk
🖥 www.lbs.co.uk

Laurie Templar Knight Ltd 10 Swanston Steading, 109 Swanston Road, Edinburgh, EH10 7DS, United Kingdom
✆ 0131-445 7895/✆ 0141-445 7871
✉ ross@laurietemplarknight.com
🖥 www.laurietemplarknight.com

Lebrecht Music & Arts Photo Library 58B Carlton Hill, London, NW8 0ES, United Kingdom
✆ (020) 7625 5341/✆ (020) 7625 5341
✉ pictures@lebrecht.co.uk
🖥 www.lebrecht.co.uk

Little Piece of Jamaica 55 Finsbury Park Road, Highbury, London, N4 2JY, United Kingdom
✆ (020) 7359 0788/(07973) 630729 ✆
✉ paulhuelpoj@yahoo.co.uk
🖥 www.lpoj.co.uk

Lorraine Feather/Air-Edel Associates 18 Rodmarton Street, London, W1U 8BJ, United Kingdom
✆ (020) 7486 6466/✆ (020) 7224 0344
✉ air-edel@air-edel.co.uk
🖥 www.air-edel.co.uk

M.T. Music 25 Ollands Road, Reepham, Norwich, NR10 4EL, United Kingdom
✆ (01603) 870255/✆
✉ music@mtmusic.co.uk
🖥 www.mtmusic.co.uk

Making Tracks 9A Church Row, London, NW3 6UT, United Kingdom
✆ (020) 7794 5956/✆
✉ makingtracks@netmatters.co.uk

Marcos D'Cruze/Air-Edel Associates 18 Rodmarton St, London, W1U 8BJ, United Kingdom
✆ (020) 7486 6466/✆ (020) 7224 0344
✉ air-edel@air-edel.co.uk
🖥 www.air-edel.co.uk

Martin A Smith 40 Lancaster Road, London, W11 1QR, United Kingdom
✆ (07956) 451894/✆
✉ martinsmith165@hotmail.com
🖥 www.martinasmith.co.uk

Martin Vishnick 78 Summer Street, Slip End, Luton, LU1 4BN, United Kingdom
✆ (01582) 414701/(07899) 908609 ✆
✉ mvish@waitrose.com
🖥 www.mvish.com

Maximum Production The Dove Wing Studio, Sutton, Shepton Mallet, Somerset, BA4 6QF, United Kingdom
✆ (01749) 860718/✆ (01749) 860766
✉ info@maximumproduction.co.uk
🖥 www.maximumproduction.co.uk

Mcasso Music Production Ltd 32-34 Great Marlborough Street, London, W1F 7JB, United Kingdom
✆ (020) 7734 3664/✆ (020) 7439 2375
✉ music@mcasso.com
🖥 www.mcasso.com

Mechanical Copyright Protection Society Ltd (IVCA) Copyright House, 29-33 Berners Street, London, W1T 3AB, United Kingdom
✆ (020) 7306 4535/✆ (020) 7306 4380
✉ featurefilms@mcps.co.uk
🖥 www.mcps.co.uk

Megatrax 127 Charing Cross Road, London, WC2H 0QY, United Kingdom
✆ (020) 7412 9111/✆ (020) 7413 0061
✉ kpm@kpm.co.uk
🖥 www.playkpm.com

Melody First Music Library Sovereign House, 12 Trewartha Road, Praa Sands, Penzance, Cornwall, TR20 9ST, United Kingdom
✆ (01736) 762826/(07721) 449477 ✆ (01736) 763328
✉ panamus@aol.com
🖥 www.panamamusic.co.uk

Michael Csanyi-Wills/Air-Edel Associates 18 Rodmarton Street, London, W1U 8BJ, United Kingdom
✆ (020) 7486 6466/✆ (020) 7224 0344
✉ air-edel@air-edel.co.uk
🖥 www.air-edel.co.uk

Michael Walton Music Unit 26, Townmead Business Centre, William Morris Way, London, SW6 2SZ, United Kingdom
✆ (020) 7736 9332/(07941) 791601 ✆
✉ mwgm@btinternet.com

Mike Connaris/Mcasso Music Production Ltd 32-34 Great Marlborough Street, London, W1F 7JB, United Kingdom
✆ (020) 7734 3664/✆ (020) 7439 2375
✉ music@mcasso.com
🖥 www.mcasso.com

Mollusc Music 83 Great Titchfield Street, London, W1W 6RU, United Kingdom
✆ (020) 7580 8928/✆
✉ ant.smith@btconnect.com
🖥 www.molluscmusic.co.uk

Mood Media Forest Lodge, Westerham Road, Keston, Kent, BR2 6HE, United Kingdom
✆ (01689) 882200/✆ (01689) 882203
✉ info.uk@moodmedia.com
🖥 www.moodmedia.com

Murfin Music International Ltd The Old Smithy, 1 Post Office Lane, Kempsey, Worcester, WR5 3NS, United Kingdom
✆ (01905) 820659/✆ (01905) 820015
✉ muffmurfin@btconnect.com
🖥 www.oldsmithy.com

Music by Design Ltd Top Floor, 142 Wardour Street, London, W1F 8ZU, United Kingdom
✆ (020) 7434 3244/✆ (020) 7434 1064
✉ enquiries@musicbydesign.co.uk
🖥 www.musicbydesign.co.uk

Music Factory Entertainment Group Ltd Hawthorne House, Fitzwilliam Street, Rotherham, South Yorkshire, S62 6EP, United Kingdom
✆ (01709) 710022/✆ (01709) 523141
✉ info@musicfactory.co.uk
🖥 www.musicfactory.co.uk

Music Gallery 28 Lexington Street, London, W1F 0LF, United Kingdom
✆ (020) 7439 3325/✆ (020) 7734 9417
✉ info@music-gallery.co.uk
🖥 www.music-gallery.co.uk

Music Mall (FOCAL, PACT) 1 Upper James Street, London, W1F 9DE, United Kingdom
✆ (020) 7534 1444/✆ (020) 7534 1440
✉ info@musicmall.co.uk
🖥 www.musicmall.co.uk

MusicWing 69 Riley Road, Brighton, BN2 4AG, United Kingdom
✆ (01273) 699768/✆
✉ andy@musicwing.co.uk
🖥 www.musicwing.co.uk

Musik' Image Music Library Sovereign House, 12 Trewartha Road, Praa sands, Penzance, Cornwall, TR20 9ST, United Kingdom
✆ (01736) 762826/(07721) 449477 ✆ (01736) 763328
✉ panamus@aol.com
🖥 www.panamamusic.co.uk

Nicky Heinen Jazz Flute Music 4th Floor, 2-4 Whitfield Street, London, W1T 2RB, United Kingdom
✆ (020) 7636 3915/✆

Nicky Heinen Music 4th Floor, 2-4 Whitfield Street, London, W1T 2RB, United Kingdom
✆ (020) 7636 3915/✆

Nigel Beaham-Powell 7 The Paragon, Clifton, Bristol, BS8 4LA, United Kingdom
✆ 0117-973 1619/(07753) 573995 ✆
✉ nigel@ddmp.demon.co.uk

Nigel Clarke/Air-Edel Associates 18 Rodmarton Street, London, W1U 8BJ, United Kingdom
✆ (020) 7486 6466/✆ (020) 7224 0344
✉ air-edel@air-edel.co.uk
🖥 www.air-edel.co.uk

O2/Air-Edel Associates 18 Rodmarton Street, London, W1U 8BJ, United Kingdom
✆ (020) 7486 6466/✆ (020) 7224 0344
✉ air-edel@air-edel.co.uk
🖥 www.air-edel.co.uk

Onespaceman 24a York Road, North Berwick, East Lothian, EH39 4LX, United Kingdom
✆ (01620) 892024/(07976) 909506 ✆
✉ info@onespaceman.co.uk
🖥 www.onespacaceman.co.uk

Panama Music Library Sovereign House, 12 Trewartha Road, Praa Sands, Penzance, Cornwall, TR20 9ST, United Kingdom
✆ (01736) 762826/(07721) 449477 ✆ (01736) 763328
✉ panamus@aol.com
🖥 www.panamamusic.co.uk

Panyotis Kalantzopoulos/Air-Edel Associates 18 Rodmarton Street, London, W1U 8BJ, United Kingdom
✆ (020) 7486 6466/✆ (020) 7224 0344
✉ air-edel@air-edel.co.uk
🖥 www.air-edel.co.uk

Patrick Doyle/Air-Edel Associates 18 Rodmarton Street, London, W1U 8BJ, United Kingdom
✆ (020) 7486 6466/✆ (020) 7224 0344
✉ air-edel@air-edel.co.uk
🖥 www.air-edel.co.uk

Paul Boyd Music Comiston Road, Edinburgh, EH10 6AB, United Kingdom
✆ (0131) 4772756/✆
✉ info@paulboydmusic.com
🖥 www.paulboydmusic.com

Paul Grabowsky/Air-Edel Associates 18 Rodmarton Street, London, W1U 8BJ, United Kingdom
✆ (020) 7486 6466/✆ (020) 7224 0344
✉ air-edel@air-edel.co.uk
🖥 www.air-edel.co.uk

Paul Lewis 9 Westbourne Street, Hove, East Sussex, BN3 5PE, United Kingdom
✆ (01273) 204064/✆ (01273) 204064
✉ info@paullewiscomposer.co.uk
🖥 www.paullewiscomposer.co.uk

Pearly Oyster Productions 204 Stockwell Road, London, SW9 9TB, United Kingdom
✆ (020) 3177 3033/✆
✉ enquiries@pearlyoyster.com
🖥 www.pearlyoyster.com

Pete Moore Services 34 King Edwards Gardens, London, W3 9RQ, United Kingdom
✆ (020) 8992 6287/✆

Peter Michaels Bridge House, Adelaide Road, London, NW3 3QD, United Kingdom
✆ (020) 7722 1480/✆
✉ podm@yahoo.com
🖥 www.petermichaels.net

Peter Spencer Beech House, Watermill Lane, Icklesham, Winchelsea, East Sussex, TN36 4AP, United Kingdom
✆ (01424) 813974/(07767) 896807 ✆
✉ peter@peterspencer.net
🖥 www.peterspencer.net

Phelps Music 34 Cae'r Gerddi, Church Village, Pontypridd, Mid Glamorgan, CF38 1UQ, United Kingdom
✆ (01443) 203256/✆
✉ dan_phelps81@yahoo.co.uk
🖥 www.cnmc.moonfruit.co.uk

Phil Sawyer/Air-Edel Associates 18 Rodmarton Street, London, W1U 8BJ, United Kingdom
✆ (020) 7486 6466/✆ (020) 7224 0344
✉ air-edel@air-edel.co.uk
🖥 www.air-edel.co.uk

Philip Pope/Air-Edel Associates 18 Rodmarton Street, London, W1U 8BJ, United Kingdom
✆ (020) 7486 6466/✆ (020) 7224 0344
✉ air-edel@air-edel.co.uk
🖥 www.air-edel.co.uk

Picture Sound The Old Chapel, Hardwick, Aylesbury, Buckinghamshire, HP22 4DZ, United Kingdom
✆ (01296) 640839/✆
✉ librarymusicpics@aol.com
🖥 www.moondogs.co.uk

Pierre Tubbs 14 Montpellier Villas, Brighton, BN1 3DG, United Kingdom
✆ (01273) 771488/✆ (01273) 775147
✉ pierretubbs@aol.com
🖥 www.kiss-it.net/pierretubbs

PkBoo Music, London, United Kingdom
✆ (07901) 955204/✆ (07075) 009851
✉ info@pkboomusic.com
🖥 www.pkboomusic.com

Post Production Music Aldwych House, 71-91 Aldwych, London, WC2B 4HN, United Kingdom
✆ (020) 7054 7275/✆ (020) 7054 7293
✉ info@postproductionmusic.com
🖥 www.postproductionmusic.com

President Records Ltd Units 6-7, 11 Wyfold Road, London, SW6 6SE, United Kingdom
✆ (020) 7385 7700/✆ (020) 7385 3402
✉ hits@president-records.co.uk
🖥 www.president-records.co.uk

Primrose Music 1 Leitrim House, 36 Worple Road, London, SW19 4EQ, United Kingdom
✆ (020) 8946 7808/✆ (020) 8946 3392
✉ primrose-uk@primrosemusic.com
🖥 www.primrosemusicworld.com

Promo Sonor International Music Library Sovereign House, 12 Trewartha Road, Praa Sands, Penzance, Cornwall, TR20 9ST, United Kingdom
(01736) 762826/(07721) 449477 (01736) 763328
panamus@aol.com
www.panamamusic.co.uk

Radio Clyde Ltd Clydebank Business Park, Glasgow, G81 2RX, United Kingdom
0141-565 2200/ 0141-565 2266
clyde.creative@radioclyde.com
www.clydeone.com

Ray Davies 10 Princess Mews, Hampstead, London, NW3 5AP, United Kingdom
(020) 7431 1771/ (020) 7431 8422
ray@buttondown.co.uk

Redwood Studios Ltd 20 Great Chapel Street, London, W1F 8FW, United Kingdom
(020) 7287 3799/
andrestudios@yahoo.co.uk
www.sound-design.net

Ricall Ltd 14 Buckingham Palace Road, London, SW1W 0QP, United Kingdom
(020) 7592 1710/ (020) 7592 1713
claire.kelly@ricall.com www.ricall.com

Richard Atkinson/Mcasso Music Production Ltd 32-34 Great Marlborough Street, London, W1F 7JB, United Kingdom
(020) 7734 3664/ (020) 7439 2375
music@mcasso.com
www.mcasso.com

Richard Stilgoe/Noel Gay Artists 19 Denmark Street, London, WC2H 8NA, United Kingdom
(020) 7836 3941/ (020) 7287 1816
mail@noelgay.com www.noelgay.com

Rob Gold Music for Films 34 Batchelor Street, Islington, London, N1 0EG, United Kingdom
(07899) 993 670/

Robin Hood Music 2 Grange Road, Alresford, Hampshire, SO24 9HB, United Kingdom
(01962) 735588/ (01962) 738400
robinhoodmusic@clara.net
www.robinhoodmusic.com

Rod Thompson Music Ltd 73 Bromfelde Road, London, SW4 6PP, United Kingdom
(020) 7720 0866/(07768) 288023 (020) 7720 0866
rodthompson@f2s.com

Roger Harmar 89 Poplar Avenue, Hove, East Sussex, BN3 8PT, United Kingdom
(01273) 885379/ (01273) 277614
info@rogerharmar.net
www.rogerharmar.net

Ron Geesin Headrest, Street End Lane, Broadoak, Heathfield, East Sussex, TN21 8TU, United Kingdom
(01435) 863994/
ron@geesin.demon.co.uk
www.rongeesin.com

Ronnie Bond Music Churchwood Studio, 1 Woodchurch Road, London, NW6 3PL, United Kingdom
(020) 7372 2229/(07963) 694117 (020) 7372 3339
rbm@easynet.co.uk

Sam Babenia/Air-Edel Associates 18 Rodmarton Street, London, W1U 8BJ, United Kingdom
(020) 7486 6466/ (020) 7224 0344
air-edel@air-edel.co.uk
www.air-edel.co.uk

Schott Music 48 Great Marlborough Street, London, W1F 7BB, United Kingdom
(020) 7534 0710/ (020) 7534 0719
eric.forder@schott-music.com
www.schott-music.com

Scootman Music & Sound Design 2021 21st Avenue South, Suite C-100, Nashville, 37212, United States of America
615 319 9556/615 319 9556 615 777 2122
scott@scootmanmusic.com
www.scootmanmusic.com

Selected Sound 127 Charing Cross Road, London, WC2H 0QY, United Kingdom
(020) 7412 9111/ (020) 7413 0061
kpm@kpm.co.uk
www.playkpm.com

Shady Zane 94 Hammersmith Grove, London, W6 7HB, United Kingdom
(020) 8741 9635/
chris@chriswhite.info
www.chriswhite.info

Shriek, London, United Kingdom
(020) 7499 7778/(0779) 3083581 (020) 7499 7654
info@shriek-music.com
www.shriek-music.com

Simon Russell/Air-Edel Associates 18 Rodmarton Street, London, W1U 8BJ, United Kingdom
(020) 7486 6466/ (020) 7224 0344
air-edel@air-edel.co.uk
www.air-edel.co.uk

Sonoton Recorded Music Libraries Suite 4, Pottersfield, 1A Lincoln Road, Enfield, Middlesex, EN1 2DF, United Kingdom
(01362) 697922/ (01362) 697923
pb015H1295@blueyonder.co.uk
www.sonoton.com

Sony BMG Bedford House, 69-79 Fulham High Street, London, SW6 3JW, United Kingdom
(020) 7384 7500/
www.sonybmg.co.uk

Sound Lounge Broadley House, 48 Broadley Terrace, London, NW1 6LG, United Kingdom
(020) 7724 2420/(07968) 872905 (020) 7706 1025
marion@soundlounge.co.uk
www.soundlounge.co.uk

Spectrum Sound & Light 12 North Bridge Street, Hawick, Roxburghshire, TD9 9QW, United Kingdom
(01450) 371371/
ray.spectrum@talk21.com
www.spectrumsoundlight.co.uk

Splash Sound Productions 1 Mossley Hill Drive, Liverpool, L17 1AJ, United Kingdom
0151-724 2100/(07973) 816708 0151-724 5813
rick@splashsoundproductions.co.uk
www.splashsoundproductions.co.uk

Stainer & Bell Ltd Victoria House, 23 Gruneisen Road, London, N3 1DZ, United Kingdom
(020) 8343 3303/ (020) 8343 3024
post@stainer.co.uk
www.stainer.co.uk

Standard Music Library Onward House, 11 Uxbridge Street, London, W8 7TQ, United Kingdom
(020) 7221 4275/ (020) 7229 6893
standard@bucksmusicgroup.co.uk
www.bucksmusicgroup.com

Storm Music 14 Neville Avenue, Anchorsholme, Blackpool, FY5 3BG, United Kingdom
(01253) 864598/ (01253) 864598
enquiries@photo-stock.co.uk
www.photo-stock.co.uk

Streets Ahead Music Productions 7 The Paragon, Clifton, Bristol, BS8 4LA, United Kingdom
0117-973 1619/(07753) 573995
nigel@ddmp.demon.co.uk
www.ddmp.demon.co.uk

Synesthesia Ltd 29 Admiral Way, Berkhamsted, Hertfordshire, HP4 1TE, United Kingdom
(020) 7242 4362/(07801) 547631 (020) 7242 4336
paul@synesthesia.net
www.synesthesia.net

syntrax.tv. 29 Admiral Way, Berkhamsted, Hertfordshire, HP4 1TE, United Kingdom
(01442) 872597/
music@syntrax.tv
www.syntrax.tv

T K O Publishing Ltd, Hove, East Sussex, BN3 6QU, United Kingdom
(01273) 550088/ (01273) 540969
publishing@tkogroup.com
www.tkogroup.com

T P L Media The Studio, 3 Beeching Close, Didcot, Oxfordshire, OX11 9JR, United Kingdom
(01235) 851500/ (01235) 851600
graham@tplmedia.co.uk
www.tplmedia.co.uk

Tate Music Ltd 77 Beak Street, Soho, London, W1F 9DB, United Kingdom
(07969) 372044/
vanesa@tatemusic.co.uk
www.tatemusic.co.uk

Terry Davies/Air-Edel Associates 18 Rodmarton Street, London, W1U 8BJ, United Kingdom
(020) 7486 6466/ (020) 7224 0344
air-edel@air-edel.co.uk
www.air-edel.co.uk

The 5YLAC Group 26 York Street, London, W1U 6PZ, United Kingdom
(0845) 3104314/ (0870) 7623212
info56@5ylac.biz
www.5ylac.biz

The Neil Williams Classical Collection 22 Avon, Hockley, Tamworth, Staffordshire, B77 5QA, United Kingdom
(01827) 286086/07963 194921 (01827) 286086
neil@classicalcollection.co.uk

The Tinsley Lockhart Group 44 West Preston Street, Edinburgh, EH8 9PY, United Kingdom
0131-466 7767/
creative@tinsleylockhart.com
www.tinsleylockhart.com

The Voice and Music Company 8A Shelton Street, Covent Garden, London, WC2H 9JP, United Kingdom
(020) 7240 7755/ (020) 7240 7752
info@thevoiceandmusiccompany.com
www.thevoiceandmusiccompany.com

Tim Cross Smythotts, 25 Fair Lane, Robertsbridge, East Sussex, TN32 5AT, United Kingdom
(01580) 881047/
timxmusic@btinternet.com

Tim Stone 13 Clapton Common, Hackney, London, E5 9AA, United Kingdom
(020) 8806 6037/(07855) 370471
stone.music@virgin.net
www.audiostone.co.uk

Toby Jarvis/Mcasso Music Production Ltd 32-34 Great Marlborough Street, London, W1F 7JB, United Kingdom
(020) 7734 3664/ (020) 7439 2375
music@mcasso.com
www.mcasso.com

Tom Dick & Debbie Productions Unit 2, The Gallery, 54 Marston Street, Oxford, OX4 1LF, United Kingdom
(01865) 201564/ (01865) 201935
info@tomdickanddebbie.com
www.tomdickanddebbie.com

Tony Kinsey 5 The Pennards, Sunbury-on-Thames, Middlesex, TW16 5JZ, United Kingdom
(01932) 783160/ (01932) 78345
tony.kinsey@btinternet.com

Townend Music 44 Eastwick Crescent, Rickmansworth, Hertfordshire, WD3 8YJ, United Kingdom
(01923) 720083/(07974) 480972 (01923) 710587
townendmus@aol.com

Trackline Music Services 68 Alton Street, Crewe, CW2 7QB, United Kingdom
(01270) 665750/
enquiries@trackline.com
www.trackline.com

Tsunami Sounds Ltd Muscott House, Meadrow, Godalming, Surrey, GU7 3HN, United Kingdom
(01483) 410100/ (01483) 410100
ken.easter@tsunami.co.uk
www.tsunami.co.uk

Vibey Library 98 Elgin Avenue, London, W9 2HD, United Kingdom
(020) 7289 9045/
info@vibeylibrary.com
www.vibeylibrary.com

VideoHelper 127 Charing Cross Road, London, WC2H 0QY, United Kingdom
(020) 7412 9111/ (020) 7413 0061
kpm@kpm.co.uk
www.playkpm.com

VirusAudio Ltd 8-10 Stanley Street, Liverpool, L1 6AF, United Kingdom
0151-227 2345/ 0151-227 3456
mail@virusaudio.com
www.virusaudio.com

Walls Have Ears, Leeds, LS25 7RW, United Kingdom
(07977) 733862/
stewart@wallshaveears.co.uk
www.wallshaveears.co.uk

West One Music Ltd 28 Percy Street, London, W1T 2BZ, United Kingdom
(020) 7907 1500/
info@westonemusic.com
www.westonemusic.com

Wienerworld Ltd Unit 7, Free Trade House, Lowther Road, Stanmore, Stanmore, Middlesex, HA7 1EP, United Kingdom
(020) 8206 1177/ (020) 8206 3757
ordersplease@wienerworld.com
www.wienerworld.com

World Circuit 138 Kingsland Road, London, E2 8DY, United Kingdom
✆ (020) 7749 3222/✆ (020) 7749 3232
✉ post@worldcircuit.co.uk
🖥 www.worldcircuit.co.uk

World of Woosh Music 94 Hammersmith Grove, London, W6 7HB, United Kingdom
✆ (020) 8741 9635/(07946) 530734 ✆
✉ info@worldofwooshmusic.com
🖥 www.worldofwooshmusic.com

www.ctrlav.com 3 Farnell Mews, London, SW5 9DL, United Kingdom
✆ (07956) 173793/✆
✉ kyan@ctrlav.biz
🖥 www.myspace/creativeviolence

X-Ray Dog 127 Charing Cross Road, London, WC2H 0QY, United Kingdom
✆ (020) 7412 9111/✆ (020) 7413 0061
✉ kpm@kpm.co.uk
🖥 www.playkpm.com

Zig Zag Music Productions Croeso Church Lane, Hilton, Huntingdon, Cambridgeshire, PE28 9NH, United Kingdom
✆ (01480) 830073/✆ (01480) 830073
✉ info@zigzagmusic.com
🖥 www.zigzagmusic.com

RADIO PRODUCTION

Angell Sound Studios Top Floor, Film House, 142 Wardour Street, London, W1F 8ZU, United Kingdom
✆ (020) 7478 7777/✆ (020) 7478 7700
✉ info@angellsound.co.uk
🖥 www.angellsound.co.uk

B H R Communications The White Cottage, The Street, Long Stratton, Norwich, NR15 2XJ, United Kingdom
✆ (0845) 4026527/(07803) 086462 ✆ (0845) 4026528
✉ bhr@bhrcommunications.co.uk
🖥 www.bhrcommunications.co.uk

Bazza Productions 1 Chemin De La Sini, Ille-Sur-TÍt, 66130, France
✆ 46 88 41 72 6/(07973) 383219 ✆
✉ bsguard@aol.com
🖥 www.villacanigov.com

BBC East Midlands London Road, Nottingham, NG2 4UU, United Kingdom
✆ 0115-955 0500/✆ 0115-902 1984
✉ emt@bbc.co.uk
🖥 www.bbc.co.uk/nottingham

BBC North (Manchester) New Broadcasting House, Manchester, M60 1SJ, United Kingdom
✆ 0161-200 2020/✆ 0161-244 3122
✉ nwt@bbc.co.uk
🖥 www.bbc.co.uk/manchester

BBC Northern Ireland Broadcasting House, Ormeau Avenue, Belfast, BT2 8HQ, United Kingdom
✆ (028) 9033 8000/✆ (028) 9033 8800
🖥 www.bbc.co.uk/ni

BBC Scotland (Aberdeen) Broadcasting House, Beechgrove Terrace, Aberdeen, AB15 5ZT, United Kingdom
✆ (01224) 625233/✆ (01224) 384810
✉ news.aberdeen@bbc.co.uk
🖥 www.bbc.co.uk/scotland

BBC South (Southampton) Broadcasting House, Havelock Road, Southampton, SO14 7PU, United Kingdom
✆ (023) 8022 6201/✆ (023) 8033 9931
✉ south.today@bbc.co.uk
🖥 www.bbc.co.uk/southampton

BBC Wales (Bangor) Bryn Meirion, Bangor, Gwynedd, LL57 2BY, United Kingdom
✆ (01248) 370880/✆ (01248) 351443
🖥 www.bbc.co.uk

BBC Wales (Cardiff) Broadcasting House, Llantrisant Road, Llandarf, Cardiff, CF5 2YQ, United Kingdom
✆ (029) 2032 2000/✆ (029) 2032 2666
✉ feedback.wales@bbc.co.uk
🖥 www.bbc.co.uk/wales

Canongate Studios 9 Waters Close, Leith, Edinburgh, EH6 6RB, United Kingdom
✆ 0131-555 4455/✆ 0131-555 2021
✉ al@canongate.com
🖥 www.canongate.com

Dave Dixon 5 Gilpin Avenue, London, SW14 8QX, United Kingdom
✆ (020) 8876 8391/✆ (020) 8876 8391
✉ ddixn@supanet.com

Eardrum 177 Wardour Street, London, W1F 8WX, United Kingdom
✆ (020) 7287 2211/✆ (020) 7287 2288
✉ info@eardrum.com
🖥 www.eardrum.com

GCap Ideas London 30 Leicester Square, London, WC2H 7LE, United Kingdom
✆ (020) 7766 6018/✆ (020) 7766 6088
🖥 www.gcapmedia.com

Hobo Partnership 5 Warwick Road, London, W5 3XH, United Kingdom
✆ (020) 7434 2907/✆ (020) 7437 9984
✉ deb@hobopartnership.com
🖥 www.hobopartnership.com

Ian MacTavish 143 Wardour Street, London, W1S 8WA, United Kingdom
✆ (020) 7734 2705/✆ (020) 7434 1468
✉ shaun@macand.co.uk
🖥 www.macand.co.uk

J K Advertising Ltd 730 Pershore Road, Selly Oak, Birmingham, B29 7NJ, United Kingdom
✆ 0121-472 1000/✆ 0121-414 1290
✉ info@jkadvertising.co.uk
🖥 www.jkadvertising.co.uk

Joa Productions 27 Ainger Road, London, NW3 3AS, United Kingdom
✆ (020) 7722 1755/✆ (020) 7722 1755
✉ joaprod@tiscali.co.uk

Jungle Studios Royalty Mews, Off Dean Street, London, W1D 3AR, United Kingdom
✆ (020) 7851 1234/✆ (020) 7851 1212
✉ mail@junglestudios.co.uk
🖥 www.jungle.co.uk

L B S Manchester Ltd 11-13 Bamford Street, Stockport, Cheshire, SK1 3NZ, United Kingdom
✆ 0161-477 2710/✆ 0161-480 9497
✉ info@lbs.co.uk
🖥 www.lbs.co.uk

Laurel Business Services 33 Valley View, Biggin Hill, Kent, TN16 3QN, United Kingdom
✆ (01959) 573940/(07932) 580782 ✆ (01959) 573940

Mac & Co. 143 Wardour Street, London, W1 8WA, United Kingdom
✆ (020) 7734 2705/✆ (020) 7434 1468
✉ info@macand.co.uk
🖥 www.macand.co.uk

Metro Radio 55 Degrees North, Newcastle upon Tyne, NE1 6BF, United Kingdom
✆ 0191-230 6100/✆ 0191-279 0288
✉ enquiries@metroandmagic.com
🖥 www.metroradio.co.uk

PLRS PA System Hire 20 The Chase, Holland on Sea, Clacton, Essex, CO15 5PZ,
✆ 7931300117/✆
✉ peter@plrs.co.uk
🖥 www.parig.co.uk

Popsushi 82 Merchants Quay, East Street, Leeds, LS9 8BB, United Kingdom
✆ (0870) 4029947/✆ (0870) 4029948
✉ getmore@popsushi.co.uk
🖥 www.popsushi.com

Pulse Production Forster Square, Bradford, West Yorkshire, BD1 5NE, United Kingdom
✆ (01274) 203040/✆ (01274) 203140
✉ ivan.renhard@pulse.co.uk
🖥 www.pulse.co.uk

Radio City (Sound of Merseyside) Ltd St. Johns Beacon, 1 Houghton Street, Liverpool, L1 1RL, United Kingdom
✆ 0151-472 6800/✆ 0151-472 6821
✉ david.brown@radiocity.co.uk
🖥 www.radiocity.co.uk

Radio Clyde Ltd Clydebank Business Park, Glasgow, G81 2RX, United Kingdom
✆ 0141-565 2200/✆ 0141-565 2266
✉ clyde.creative@radioclyde.com
🖥 www.clydeone.com

Radio Ga Ga 74 Hastings Street, Luton, LU1 5BH, United Kingdom
✆ (07749) 141330/✆
✉ leanne_pinkgirl@yahoo.co.uk

Radio Trent Ltd chapel, Maid Marian way, Nottingham, NG1 7JR, United Kingdom
✆ 0115-873 1500/✆ 0115-873 1569
🖥 www.gcapmedia.com

Riverfront Media 28 Plum Lane, London, SE18 3AE, United Kingdom
✆ (020) 8854 7563/✆
✉ info@riverfrontmedia.co.uk
🖥 www.riverfrontmedia.co.uk

Rod Thompson Music Ltd 73 Bromfelde Road, London, SW4 6PP, United Kingdom
✆ (020) 7720 0866/(07768) 288023 ✆ (020) 7720 0866
✉ rodthompson@f2s.com

Rorschach 62 Chiswick High Road, London, W4 1SY, United Kingdom
✆ (020) 8749 6123/✆ (020) 8996 9088
✉ office@rorschachradio.com
🖥 www.rorschachradio.com

Savin Productions 19 Woodlea Drive, Shirley, Solihull, West Midlands, B91 1PG, United Kingdom
✆ 0121-240 1100/✆ 0121-240 4042
🖥 www.savinproductions.com

Silk Sound Ltd 13 Berwick Street, London, W1F 0PW, United Kingdom
✆ (020) 7434 3461/✆ (020) 7494 1748
✉ bookings@silk.co.uk
🖥 www.silk.co.uk

Splash Sound Productions 1 Mossley Hill Drive, Liverpool, L17 1AJ, United Kingdom
✆ 0151-724 2100/(07973) 816708 ✆ 0151-724 5813
✉ rick@splashsoundproductions.co.uk
🖥 www.splashsoundproductions.co.uk

Swansea Sound & The Wave Victoria Road, Gowerton, Swansea, SA4 3AB, United Kingdom
✆ (01792) 511964/✆ (01792) 511171
✉ admin@swanseasound.co.uk
🖥 www.swanseasound.co.uk

T F M Radio Radio House, Yale Crescent, Stockton-on-Tees, Cleveland, TS17 6AA, United Kingdom
✆ (01642) 888222/✆ 0870 4299104
✉ tfm.reception@tfmradio.co.uk
🖥 www.tfmradio.co.uk

Tamborine Productions Ltd 14 Livonia Street, London, W1F 8AG, United Kingdom
✆ (020) 7434 1812/✆ (020) 7434 1813
✉ tim@tamborine.co.uk
🖥 www.tamborine.co.uk

The Bridge Ltd 55 Great Marlborough Street, London, W1F 7JX, United Kingdom
✆ (020) 7434 9861/✆ (020) 7494 4658
✉ bookings@thebridge.co.uk
🖥 www.thebridge.co.uk

The Creative Department The Grange Annexe, Mill Lane, Carlton, Goole, East Yorkshire, DN14 9NG, United Kingdom
✆ (01405) 861131/(07836) 244477 ✆ (01405) 861807
✉ mail@mikehurley.co.uk
🖥 www.mikehurley.co.uk

Unique Facilities 50 Lisson Street, London, NW1 5DF, United Kingdom
✆ (020) 7723 0322/✆ (020) 7453 1666
✉ info@uniquefacilities.co.uk
🖥 www.uniquefacilities.com

Unique the Production Co. 50 Lisson Street, London, NW1 5DF, United Kingdom
✆ (020) 7453 1600/✆ (020) 7723 6132
✉ info@upcmedia.com
🖥 www.upcmedia.com

Wise Buddah Ltd 74 Great Titchfield Street, London, W1W 7QP, United Kingdom
✆ (020) 7307 1600/✆ (020) 7307 1601
✉ becky.maxted@wisebuddah.com
🖥 www.wisebuddah.com

Zoo Studios 145 Wardour Street, London, W1F 8WB, United Kingdom
✆ (020) 7734 2000/✆ (020) 7734 2200
✉ mail@zoostudios.co.uk
🖥 www.soho-studios.co.uk

RECORDING STUDIOS

2002 Studios 123a Kenton Road, Harrow, Middlesex, HA3 0AZ, United Kingdom
✆ (020) 8907 8634/✆ (020) 8907 8632
✉ info@2002studios.com
🖥 www.2002studios.com

A G P Studio 58 King Street, Broseley, Shropshire, TF12 5NA, United Kingdom
(01952) 882909/
alistair@agpstudio.co.uk
www.agpstudio.co.uk

Abbey Road Studios Ltd 3 Abbey Road, London, NW8 9AY, United Kingdom
(020) 7286 1161/
bookings@abbeyroad.com
www.abbeyroad.com

Amphonic Music Ltd 20 The Green, Warlingham, Surrey, CR6 9HN, United Kingdom
(01737) 832837/ (01737) 833812
info@amphonic.co.uk
www.amphonic.com

Amstore CD+DVD Production Block J, Tower Bridge Business Complex, 100 Clements Road, London, SE16 4DG, United Kingdom
(020) 7232 2779/ (020) 7237 6097
james@amstore.co.uk
www.amstore.co.uk

Angell Sound Studios Top Floor, Film House, 142 Wardour Street, London, W1F 8ZU, United Kingdom
(020) 7478 7777/ (020) 7478 7700
info@angellsound.co.uk
www.angellsound.co.uk

Arcsound 443 New Cross Road, London, SE14 6TA, United Kingdom
(020) 8691 8161/ (020) 8691 8161
info@arcsound.co.uk
www.arcsound.co.uk

Audio Workshop 217 Askew Road, London, W12 9AZ, United Kingdom
(020) 8742 9242/ (020) 8743 4231
info@theaudioworkshop.co.uk
www.theaudioworkshop.co.uk

B L Z Productions Ltd 58 Martello Street, London, E8 3QP, United Kingdom
(07939) 543160/
enquiries@blzproductions.com
www.blzproductions.com

BB Music House 158 Trewhitt Road, Newcastle, Tyne & Wear, NE6 5DY,
0191 224 2457/
info@bbmusichouse.co.uk
www.bbmusichouse.co.uk

Birdland Productions 4 The Straight, Southall, Middlesex, UB1 1QX, United Kingdom
(020) 8571 6794/ (020) 8813 8398
crummel@msn.com

Blossom Studio The Old Surgery, Station Road, Blaina, Abertillery, Gwent, NP13 3BW, United Kingdom
(01495) 290960/
info@blossomstudio.co.uk
www.myspace.com/BlossomStudio

Blue Post Production 58 Old Compton Street, London, W1D 4US, United Kingdom
(020) 7437 2626/ (020) 7439 2477
info@bluepp.co.uk
www.bluepp.co.uk

Cafe Music 18 Ordell Road, London, E3 2DS, United Kingdom
(020) 8981 2588/
info@cafestudio.co.uk
www.cafestudio.co.uk

Classical Communications Worton, Witney, Oxfordshire, OX29 4SZ, United Kingdom
(01865) 882920/ (01865) 882947
mail@classicalmusicshop.com
www.classicalmusicshop.com

Clearcut Sound Studios Ltd 8-12 Broadwick Street, London, W1F 8HW, United Kingdom
(020) 7437 5225/ (020) 7734 1149
office@clearcutsound.com
www.clearcutsound.com

Cryonica Music 19 Ford Square, London, E1 2HS, United Kingdom
(020) 7780 9846/ (020) 7068 0086
info@cryonica.com
www.cryonica.com

CTS Studios Ltd Suite 1A, Lansdowne House, Lansdowne Road, London, W11 3LP, United Kingdom
(020) 8846 9444/ (020) 7792 8904
info@cts-lansdowne.co.uk
www.cts-lansdowne.co.uk

Cut Glass Productions 7 Crouch Hall Rd, Crouch End, London, N8 8HT, United Kingdom
(020) 8374 4701/
kerry@cutglassrproductions.com
www.cutglassproductions.com

De Lane Lea Ltd 75 Dean Street, London, W1D 3PU, United Kingdom
(020) 7432 3800/ (020) 7432 3838
solutions@delanelea.com
www.delanelea.com

De Wolfe Ltd Shropshire House, 2nd Floor East, 11-20 Capper Street, London, WC1E 6JA, United Kingdom
(020) 7631 3600/ (020) 7631 3700
info@dewolfemusic.co.uk
www.dewolfemusic.co.uk

Dentedaudio Therfield Road, Odsey, Baldock, Hertfordshire, SG7 6SE, United Kingdom
(01462) 742881/
dentedaudio@aol.com
www.dented-audio.co.uk

Department of Media & Communications Goldsmiths College, University of London, London, SE14 6NW, United Kingdom
(020) 7919 7601/ (020) 7717 2991
j.rowland@gold.ac.uk
www.gold.ac.uk

Digitallunarsea, Birmingham, United Kingdom
(07765) 708899/
matt@digitallunarsea.co.uk
www.digitallunarsea.co.uk

DitherNoise 26 Arlington Gardens, London, W4 4EY, United Kingdom
(020) 8747 3055/ (020) 8747 3055
simonlongo@btinternet.com

Drake Audio Visual 89 St Fagans Road, Fairwater, Cardiff, CF5 3AE, United Kingdom
(029) 2056 0333/ (029) 2055 4909
sales@drakeav.com
www.drakeav.com

E V T Magnetic Industries Havenhurst, 2 Pashley Road, Wadhurst, East Sussex, TN5 7HE, United Kingdom
(01580) 200528/
magevt@amserve.co.uk

Eden Studios Ltd 20-24 Beaumont Road, Chiswick, London, W4 5AP, United Kingdom
(020) 8995 5432/ (020) 8747 1931
eden@edenstudios.com
www.edenstudios.com

Elleven Studios, Main Road, Rettendon Common, Chelmsford, CM3 8DY, United Kingdom
(01245) 400359/ (01245) 400359
info@elleven.co.uk
elleven.co.uk

Emerald Music 120A Coach Road, Templepatrick, Ballyclare, County Antrim, BT39 0HA, United Kingdom
(028) 9443 2619/ (028) 9443 2162
info@emeraldmusic.co.uk
www.emeraldmusiconline.com

Ers Studios 9 Neilston Street, Leamington Spa, Warwickshire, CV31 2AZ, United Kingdom
(01296) 889153/
andy@ersstudios.co.uk
www.ersstudios.co.uk

Face Studios 7 The Engineering Offices, 2 Michael Road, Fulham, London, SW6 2AD, United Kingdom
(020) 7731 7808/
info@facestudios.co.uk
www.facestudios.co.uk

Fairview Music Cavewood Grange Farm, Common Lane, Brough, East Yorkshire, HU15 2PE, United Kingdom
(01430) 425546/ (01430) 425547
andy@fairviewstudios.co.uk
www.fairviewrecording.co.uk

Farm Factory Studios The Farm Factory, Unit 5 Woodfield Road, Welwyn Garden City, Hertfordshire, AL7 1JQ, United Kingdom
(01707) 392030/
info@farmfactorystudios.co.uk
www.farmfactorystudios.com

Farmyard Studios Blue Close Bungalow, Great Rissington, Cheltenham, Gloucestershire, GL54 2LL, United Kingdom
(01451) 821256/
simon@farmyardstudios.co.uk
www.farmyardstudios.co.uk

Felt Music 75 Berwick Street, London, W1F 8TG, United Kingdom
(020) 7287 1233/07939 234853 / (020) 7287 1236
natalie@feltmusic.com
www.feltmusic.com

Fleetwood Mobiles Ltd Denham Media Park, Denham, Middlesex, UB9 5HQ, United Kingdom
(0870) 0771071/ (0870) 0771068
ian.davidson@fleetwoodmobiles.com
www.fleetwoodmobiles.com

Gemini Audio Hammer House, 117 Wardour Street, London, W1F 0UN, United Kingdom
(020) 7734 8962/ (020) 7439 3122
nigel@geminiaudio.co.uk
www.geminiaudio.co.uk

Gigi D'Amico 29 Ridley Road, London, NW10 5UB, United Kingdom
(020) 8961 0290/
gigidamico@hotmail.com

Glass House Music Ltd Unit 3A, Riverside Business Park, Bath, BA2 3DW, United Kingdom
(07973) 730161/
info@glasshousemusic.co.uk
www.glasshousemusic.co.uk

Glass Tone Productions Ltd Unit 3a, Riverside Business Park, Bath, BA2 3DW, United Kingdom
(07973) 730161/
info@glasstone.co.uk
www.glasstone.co.uk

Goldcrest Post Production Facilities Ltd 1 Lexington Street, Soho, London, W1F 9AF, United Kingdom
(020) 7437 7972/ (020) 7437 5402
bookings@goldcrestpost.co.uk
www.goldcrest.com

Grand Central Sound Recording Studios 51-53 Gt Marlborough Street, London, W1F 7JT, United Kingdom
(020) 7306 5600/ (020) 7306 5616
info@gcrs.com
www.grand-central-studios.com

Grosvenor Studios 16 Grosvenor Rd, Handsworth Wood, Birmingham, B20 3NP, United Kingdom
0121-356 9636/ 0121-356 9636

Happy Vibes Corporation, Worthing, West Sussex, BN14 7FB, United Kingdom
(01903) 202426/ (01903) 202426
music@happyvibes.co.uk
www.happyvibes.co.uk

Hollick & Taylor Recording Co. Ltd 16 Grosvenor Road, Handsworth Wood, Birmingham, B20 3NP, United Kingdom
0121-356 9636/ 0121-356 9636

Hubert Grove Studios 157a Hubert Grove, Clapham, London, SW9 9NZ, United Kingdom
(07956) 945417/
dadastudios@mac.com
www.dadastudios.co.uk

Ian Ritchie 16 Gay Close, Willesden Green, London, NW2 4PR, United Kingdom
(020) 8452 1684/
ian@hyperlink.com
www.ian-ritchie.com

Ignyter Studios Berry Hill, Mansfield, Nottinghamshire, NG18 4HZ, United Kingdom
(01623) 474464/ (01623) 474464
info@ignyterstudios.com
www.ignyterstudios.com

Jungle Studios Royalty Mews, Off Dean Street, London, W1D 3AR, United Kingdom
(020) 7851 1234/ (020) 7851 1212
mail@junglestudios.co.uk
www.jungle.co.uk

Keynote Audio Services Ltd Smoke Tree House, Tilford Road, Farnham, Surrey, GU10 2EN, United Kingdom
(01252) 794253/ (01252) 792642
admin@keynoteaudio.co.uk
www.keynoteaudio.co.uk

Konk Studios 84-86 Tottenham Lane, Hornsey, London, N8 7EE, United Kingdom
(020) 8340 7873/ (020) 8348 3952
linda@konkstudios.com

Lansdowne Recording Studios, London, W6 60A, United Kingdom
(020) 8846 9444/ (056) 0115 5009
info@cts-lansdowne.co.uk
www.cts-lansdowne.co.uk

Linden Studio Music Composition & Production & Recording Studio, High Bankhill Farmhouse, Kirkoswald, Penrith, Cumbria, CA10 1EZ, United Kingdom
(01768) 870353/
guy@lindenstudio.co.uk
www.lindenstudio.co.uk

Livewire Duplication Tamarind, Copthorne Common, Copthorne, Crawley, West Sussex, RH10 3LF, United Kingdom
(01342) 714183/
sales@livewire-cds.com
www.livewire-cds.com

Loungecore 63 Albert Street, Camden, London, NW1 7LX, United Kingdom
(020) 7388 2605/
olly@loungecore.co.uk
www.loungecore.co.uk

M V D Unit 4, Rampart Business Park, Greenbank Industrial Estate, Newry, County Down, BT34 2QU, United Kingdom
(028) 3026 2926/ (028) 3026 2671
mail@wrenrecords.ie
www.wren.ie

Matinee Sound & Vision 132-134 Oxford Road, Reading, RG1 7NL, United Kingdom
0118-958 4934/ 0118-959 4936
info@matinee.co.uk
www.matinee.co.uk

Matrix Wessex Ltd 91 Peterborough Road, Parsons Green, London, SW6 3BU, United Kingdom
(020) 7384 6400/ (020) 7384 6401
nigel@matrix-studios.co.uk

Mayfair Recording Studios 11A Sharpleshall Street, London, NW1 8YN, United Kingdom
(020) 7586 7746/ (020) 7586 9721
bookings@mayfair-studios.co.uk
www.mayfair-studios.co.uk

Mike Moran Photography 33 Warner Road, Ware, Hertfordshire, SG12 9JL, United Kingdom
(01920) 466003/(07801) 615952
mikemoran/moran01.wannado.co.uk
www.photography-london.com

Miloco Studios 36 Leroy Street, London, SE1 4SP, United Kingdom
(020) 7232 0008/ (020) 7237 6109
nick@miloco.co.uk
www.miloco.co.uk

Motivation Sound Studios Ltd 35A Broadhurst Gardens, London, NW6 3QT, United Kingdom
(020) 7328 8305/ (020) 7624 4879
info@motivationsound.co.uk
www.motivationsound.co.uk

Murfin Music International Ltd The Old Smithy, 1 Post Office Lane, Kempsey, Worcester, WR5 3NS, United Kingdom
(01905) 820659/ (01905) 820015
muffmurfin@btconnect.com
www.oldsmithy.com

Olympic Studios 117 Church Road, Barnes, London, SW13 9HL, United Kingdom
(020) 8286 8600/ (020) 8286 8625
www.olympicstudios.co.uk

Orchard Cottage Recording Studio 60 High Street, Willingham, Cambridge, CB4 5ES, United Kingdom
(01954) 202350/
info@orchardcottagestudio.co.uk
www.orchardcottagestudio.co.uk

Pepper 3 Slingsby Place, Long Acre, London, WC2E 9AB, United Kingdom
(020) 7836 1188/ (020) 7490 4238
mailus@pepperpost.tv
www.pepperpost.tv

Picture Sound The Old Chapel, Hardwick, Aylesbury, Buckinghamshire, HP22 4DZ, United Kingdom
(01296) 640839/
librarymusicpics@aol.com
www.moondogs.co.uk

Q Sound Ltd 117-121 Salusbury Road, London, NW6 6RG, United Kingdom
(020) 7625 5359/ (020) 7625 5355
queries@qsound.uk.com
www.qsound.uk.com

Quince Studios 62a Balcombe Street, London, NW1 6NE, United Kingdom
(07810) 752765/ (020) 7723 1010
info@quincestudios.co.uk
www.quincestudios.co.uk

R A K Recording Studios 42-48 Charlbert Street, London, NW8 7BU, United Kingdom
(020) 7586 2012/ (020) 7722 5823
trisha@rakstudios.co.uk
www.rakstudios.co.uk

Radium Audio Ltd 7 Leicester Road, Sale, Manchester, M33 7DU,
0161 282 0768/
andrew@radium-audio.com
www.radium-audio.com

Real Deal Productions New Barnes Cottage, Conington, Cambridge, CB3 8LU, United Kingdom
(07909) 542121/
tom@realdealproductions.co.uk
www.realdealproductions.co.uk

redroom Productions Flat 14, Hazelwood Lodge, Red Lodge Road, West Wickham, Kent, BR4 0EN, United Kingdom
(020) 8776 0193/
redroom@redroomproductions.co.uk
www.redroomproductions.co.uk

Resident Studios Ltd 57a Windsor Road, Willesden Green, London, NW2 5DT, United Kingdom
(020) 8830 4321/
info@residentstudios.com
www.residentstudios.com

Rockfield Recording Studio Amberley Court, Monmouth, Gwent, NP25 5ST, United Kingdom
(01600) 712449/ (01600) 714421
lisaward@rockfieldstudios.com
www.rockfieldstudios.com

Rubyfruits Park House Production Village, 17 Sugar House Lane, Stratford, London, E15 2QS, United Kingdom
(020) 8534 7247/(07941) 808715/ (020) 8534 7247
georgette@rubyfruits.com
www.rubyfruits.co.uk

Sanctuary Town House 150 Goldhawk Road, London, W12 8HH, United Kingdom
(020) 8932 3200/ (020) 8932 3207
recording@sanctuarystudios.co.uk
www.sanctuarystudios.co.uk

Sanctuary Town House Mastering 150 Goldhawk Road, London, W12 8HH, United Kingdom
(020) 8932 3200/ (020) 8932 3209
mastering@sanctuarystudios.co.uk
www.sanctuarystudios.co.uk

Sarner Ltd 5 Princess Mews, Horace Road, Kingston Upon Thames, Surrey, KT1 2SZ, United Kingdom
(020) 8481 0600/ (020) 8481 0601
info@sarner.com
www.sarner.com

SCL Studio Sir Charles Lucas Art College Sir Charles Lucas Art College, Hawthorn Avenue, Colchester, CO4 3JL, United Kingdom
(01206) 878881/ (01206) 865940
studio@sclucas.essex.sch.uk
www.sclucas.essex.sch.uk

Scootman Music & Sound Design 2021 21st Avenue South, Suite C-100, Nashville, 37212, United States of America
615 319 9556/615 319 9556 615 777 2122
scott@scootmanmusic.com
www.scootmanmusic.com

Scramble 8 Portland Mews, London, W1F 8JH, United Kingdom
(020) 7479 4400/ (020) 7479 4404
post@scramble.co.uk
www.scramble.co.uk

Seahorse Recording Studio Unit 2, Middleton Hall, Brentwood Road, West Horndon, Brentwood, Essex, CM13 3LX, United Kingdom
(07803) 055646/
davish@blueyonder.co.uk
www.seahorserecording.com

Sensible Music Ltd Rebond Ho, 98-124 Brewery Rd, London, N7 9PG, United Kingdom
(020) 7700 6655/
gemma@sensible-music.co.uk
www.sensible-music.co.uk

Side UK Ltd 14-18 Great Titchfield Street, London, W1W 8BD, United Kingdom
(020) 7631 4800/ (020) 7631 4801
info@sideuk.com
www.sideuk.com

Skywave Studio 1 Trinity Hall, The Gill, Ulverston, Cumbria, LA12 7BJ,
01229 580066/
studio@skywave.plus.com
www.skywavestudio.com

Sound Conception 82-84 York Road, Bedminster, Bristol, BS3 4AL, United Kingdom
0117-966 2932/ 0117-963 5059
soundconception@btconnect.com
www.soundconception.co.uk

Sound Design Ltd 20 Heathfield Gardens, London, W4 4JY, United Kingdom
(020) 8994 0603/(07973) 303679
conrad@soundesign.co.uk
www.soundesign.co.uk

Sound-Board Studios 7 Kenmore Avenue, Harrow, Middlesex, HA8 8PG, United Kingdom
(07939) 418819/
studio@sound-board.com
www.sound-board.com

Soundscape Studios The Barn, Little Oxon Lane, Shrewsbury, Shropshire, SY3 5AQ,
01743 363660/
soundscapestudios@btinternet.com
www.soundscape-studios.co.uk

Spatial Audio Theatre 8, Pinewood Studios, Iver, Buckinghamshire, SL0 0NH, United Kingdom
(01753) 654288/(07802) 657258 (020) 8932 3465
gerry@spatial-audio.co.uk
www.spatial-audio.co.uk

Speech Recording Studio The Beeches, Effingham Road, London, SE12 8NY, United Kingdom
(020) 8318 7752/(07763) 799866
graham@speechrecordings.co.uk
www.speechrecordings.co.uk

Storm Recording Studio Unit 10, Globe Works, Bromley Street, Lye, Stourbridge, West Midlands, DY9 8HU, United Kingdom
(07811) 291913/
stormrecordingstudio@hotmail.com
www.stormrecordingstudio.co.uk

Studio A V P 82 Clifton Hill, Abbey Road, London, NW8 0JT, United Kingdom
(020) 7624 9111/ (020) 7624 9112
studioavp@btconnect.com

Sutton Sound Ltd 26 Cleveland Square, London, W2 6DD, United Kingdom
(020) 7262 9066/(07956) 910464 (020) 7262 6141
marktssutton@lineone.net

The Sound House Post Production 10th Floor, Astley House, Quay Street, Manchester, M3 4AE, United Kingdom
0161-832 7299/ 0161-832 7266
mail@thesoundhouse.tv
www.thesoundhouse.tv

The Soundhouse Ltd Unit 11, Goldhawk Industrial Estate, Vinery Way, off Brackenbury Road, London, W6 0BA, United Kingdom
(020) 8743 2677/ (020) 8740 9122
thesoundhouse@btconnect.com
www.thesoundhousestudios.co.uk

The Square Recording Studio Unit 1A, 113-115 Codicote Road, Welwyn, Herts, AL6 9TY,
07810 410892/
squarerecording@hotmail.com
www.thesquarerecordingstudio.co.uk

The Tape Gallery 28 Lexington Street, London, W1F 0LF, United Kingdom
(020) 7439 3325/ (020) 7734 9417
info@tape-gallery.co.uk
www.tape-gallery.co.uk

The Works Recording Studio 59 George Lane, Bredbury, Stockport, Cheshire, SK6 1AT, United Kingdom
0161-430 2928/ 0161-430 2928
theworksstudio@mac.com
theworksstudio.co.uk

Tim Stone 13 Clapton Common, Hackney, London, E5 9AA, United Kingdom
(020) 8806 6037/(07855) 370471/
stone.music@virgin.net
www.audiostone.co.uk

Opening doors to the world

Subtitling

Lip-sync dubbing

Translation, transcription

Foreign-language voice-overs

Complete in-house post-production and sound facilities

VSI

+44 (0)20 7692 7700

info@vsi.tv   www.vsi.tv

Up The Lane Recordings Cockshoot Ash, Upper Redbrook, Monmouth, Gwent, NP25 4LU, United Kingdom
(01600) 715339/
info@upthelane.org.uk
www.upthelane.org.uk

Uptown Studios 22 Denmark Street, London, WC2H 8NG, United Kingdom
(020) 7379 0003/(07951) 712480
info@uptownstudios.co.uk
www.uptownstudios.co.uk

Videosonics Ltd 13 Hawley Crescent, London, NW1 8NP, United Kingdom
(020) 7209 0209/ (020) 7419 4460
info@videosonics.com
www.videosonics.com

VirusAudio Ltd 8-10 Stanley Street, Liverpool, L1 6AF, United Kingdom
0151-227 2345/ 0151-227 3456
mail@virusaudio.com
www.virusaudio.com

Voltage Studios St. Stephens Mill, Ripley Street, Bradford, West Yorkshire, BD5 7JW, United Kingdom
(01274) 393998/
info@voltagestudios.com
www.voltagestudios.com

VSI Aradco House, 132 Cleveland Street, London, W1T 6AB, United Kingdom
(020) 7692 7700/ (020) 7692 7711
info@vsi.tv
www.vsi.tv

Whitfield Street Studios 31-37 Whitfield Street, London, W1T 2SF, United Kingdom
/ (020) 7580 2219
info@whitfield-street.com
www.whitfield-street.com

Wild Tracks Audio Studios Ltd 2nd Floor, 55 Greek Street, London, W1D 3DT, United Kingdom
(020) 7734 6331/ (020) 7734 6195
bookings@wildtracks.co.uk
www.wildtracks.co.uk

Zig Zag Music Productions Croeso Church Lane, Hilton, Huntingdon, Cambridgeshire, PE28 9NH, United Kingdom
(01480) 830073/ (01480) 830073
info@zigzagmusic.com
www.zigzagmusic.com

Zoo Studios 145 Wardour Street, London, W1F 8WB, United Kingdom
(020) 7734 2000/ (020) 7734 2200
mail@zoostudios.co.uk
www.soho-studios.co.uk

TRANSLATION

1-2 Translate 30 Counting House Lane, Dunmow, Essex, CM6 1BX, United Kingdom
(01371) 876588
jonathan.spooner@academy-life.com
www.12translate.co.uk

1st Applied Translations Ltd 107-111 Fleet Street, London, EC4A 2AB, United Kingdom
(020) 7248 7711/ (020) 7248 7722
translate@1stapplied.co.uk
www.1stapplied.co.uk

1st Temple Translations Ltd 197 Temple Chambers, Temple Avenue, London, EC4Y 0DT, United Kingdom
(020) 7842 0171/ (020) 7842 0172
enquiry@templetranslations.com
www.templetranslations.com

1st Transnational 211-212 Piccadilly, London, W1J 9HF, United Kingdom
(020) 7629 2787/ (020) 7629 2797
voices@1sttransnational.com
www.1sttransnational.com

A G E T Ltd 195 Kenton Road, Kenton, Harrow, Middlesex, HA3 0HD, United Kingdom
(020) 8907 0104/ (020) 8907 8785
info@aget.co.uk
www.aget.net

A S T Language Services Ltd Unit 8, Ayr Street Workshops, Ayr Street, Nottingham, NG7 4FX, United Kingdom
0115-970 5633/ 0115-978 0130
office@astls.co.uk
www.astls.co.uk

Accent Multilingual Services 9-11 Mansell Street, St. Peter Port, Guernsey, GY1 1HP, United Kingdom
(01481) 714909/ (01481) 715880
accent@guernsey.net
www.accent.guernsey.net

Accurate Translations Ltd Scotland Lane, Haslemere, Surrey, GU27 3AW, United Kingdom
(01428) 654013/ (01428) 651401
ceedassociation@aol.com

Akerbeltz Translations 1/2 47 Wilton Street, Glasgow, G20 6RT, United Kingdom
0141-946 4437/ 0141-945 2701
fios@akerbeltz.org
www.akerbeltz.com

Alchemy Translations 17 Sunnybank Road, Oldbury, West Midlands, B68 0DB, United Kingdom
01214 221414/ 01214 218117
info@alchemy-translations.co.uk
www.alchemy-translations.co.uk

Alden Group Ltd Osney Mead, Oxford, OX2 0EF, United Kingdom
(01865) 253200/ (01865) 249070
info@alden.co.uk
www.alden.co.uk

All Languages Ltd Nelson House, 362-364 Old Street, London, EC1V 9LT, United Kingdom
(020) 7739 6641/ (020) 7739 6542
info@alllanguages.co.uk
www.alllanguages.co.uk

Andiamo! Language Services Ltd Swan Yard, West Market Place, Cirencester, Gloucestershire, GL7 2NH, United Kingdom
(01285) 659100/ (01285) 659369
info@andiamo.co.uk
www.andiamo.co.uk

Anglia Translations Ltd Montagu House, 81 High Street, Huntingdon, Cambridgeshire, PE29 3NY, United Kingdom
(01480) 411514/ (01480) 434665
sales@anglia-translations.co.uk
www.anglia-translations.co.uk

APT Transtelex Ltd Unit F, The Mews, 6 Putney Common, London, SW15 1HL, United Kingdom
(020) 8246 4050/ (020) 8246 4059
marketing@aptplc.net
www.aptplc.net

Aquent Multilingual Communications 60 Parker Street, London, WC2B 5PZ, United Kingdom
(020) 7404 0077/ (020) 7404 0055
translation@aquent.com
www.mlc.aquent.com

Assoc of Translation Companies 5th Floor, Greener House, 66-68 Haymarket, London, SW1Y 4RF, United Kingdom
(020) 7930 2200/ (020) 7451 7051
info@atc.org.uk
www.atc.org.uk

Atlas Translations Ltd 14a Goodwins Court, Covent Garden, London, WC2N 4LL, United Kingdom
(020) 7240 6666/ (020) 7240 6996
london@atlas-translations.co.uk
www.atlas-translations.co.uk

Baytu Enterprises 29c Keyes Road, London, NW2 3XB, United Kingdom
(07717) 830809
bbaytu@baytu.com
www.baytu.com

BBC Languages Ltd Balfour House, 39 Brooklands Road, Weybridge, Surrey, KT13 0RU, United Kingdom
(01932) 348800/ (01932) 351400
jeyne@bbclanguages.prestel.co.uk
www.bbclang.co.uk

Bigmouth Translations 24-26 Broad Street, Staple Hill, Bristol, BS16 5NU, United Kingdom
(0845) 1304547/ (0870) 0114547
sales@bigmts.com
www.bigmts.com

Bilinguagroup 4th Floor East, 79-80 Margaret Street, London, W1W 8TA, United Kingdom
(020) 7580 4441/ (020) 7580 1909
info@bilinguagroup.com
www.bilinguagroup.com

Bond Street Translators Ltd 1 Hay Hill, Berkeley Square, London, W1J 6DH, United Kingdom
(020) 7493 2418/ (020) 7491 7971
info@bond-st-translators.co.uk
www.bond-st-translators.co.uk

Bridge Translation & Publishing 3 Albert Chambers, Canal Street, Congleton, Cheshire, CW12 4AA, United Kingdom
(01260) 299148/ (01260) 299352
martin@bridgetrans.co.uk
www.bridgetrans.co.uk

Brightlines Translation Ltd Freestone House, Box Hill, Corsham, Wiltshire, SN13 8HN, United Kingdom
(01225) 740011/ (01225) 744099
info@brightlines.co.uk
www.brightlines.co.uk

Business Language Services Ltd Westgate House, 2 Union Road East, Abergavenny, Monmouthshire, NP7 5UW, United Kingdom
☎ (01873) 856762/✆ (01873) 855006
✉ info@businesslanguageservices.co.uk
🖥 www.businesslanguageservices.co.uk

Central Translations Ltd 21 Woodstock Street, Mayfair, London, W1C 2AP, United Kingdom
☎ (020) 7493 5511/✆ (020) 7409 2774
✉ info@centraltranslations.co.uk
🖥 www.centraltranslations.co.uk

Chinese Marketing & Communications 4th Floor, 16 Nicholas Street, Manchester, M1 4EJ, United Kingdom
☎ /7971888080 ✆ 0161-228 3739
✉ simon.jones@sino-be.com
🖥 www.china-britain.org

Cicero Translations 5 Clanricarde Gardens, Tunbridge Wells, Kent, TN1 1PE, United Kingdom
☎ (01892) 676655/✆ (01892) 515514
✉ enquiries@cicerotranslations.co.uk
🖥 www.cicerotranslations.co.uk

Comtec Translations 168 The Parade, Leamington Spa, Warwickshire, CV32 4AF, United Kingdom
☎ (01926) 335681/✆ (01926) 833619
✉ info@comtectranslations.com
🖥 www.comtectranslations.com

D Q A Ltd Suite 300, 18-20 Barter Street, London, WC1A 2AH, United Kingdom
☎ (07041) 450220
✉ pottinger@datafileportugal.com
🖥 www.worthywords-translations.com

Dixon Associates The Creative Industry Centre, Wolverhampton Science Park, Wolverhampton, WV10 9TG, United Kingdom
☎ (0845) 6124888/✆ (01902) 312188
✉ info@dixon-associates.co.uk
🖥 www.dixon-associates.co.uk

E L S International 16 Church Road, Webheath, Redditch, Worcestershire, B97 5PG, United Kingdom
☎ (01527) 541725/✆ (08707) 059654
✉ mail@els-int.co.uk
🖥 www.els-int.co.uk

Eclipse Translations Ltd European Translation Centre, Lionheart Enterprise Park, Alnwick, Northumberland, NE66 2HT, United Kingdom
☎ (01665) 511000/✆ (01665) 511058
✉ info@eclipse-translation.co.uk
🖥 www.eclipse-translation.co.uk

Engineering Languages Ltd 6 West Cromwell Road, London, SW5 9QJ, United Kingdom
☎ (020) 7370 2728/✆ (020) 7373 3012
✉
🖥

English into Polish Translation Flat 906, Cascades Tower, 4 Westferry Road, London, E14 8JN, United Kingdom
☎ (020) 7515 6381/✆ (0870) 0516763
✉ monika@wheelerfamily.ws
🖥 monika.wheelerfamily.ws

Etymax Ltd 6 Bickels Yard, 151-153 Bermondsey Street, London, SE1 3HA, United Kingdom
☎ (020) 7089 9098/✆ (020) 7089 9099
✉ info@etymax.com
🖥 www.etymax.com

Europa Technical Translators Dunlewey House, 134 Greenfield Road, Birmingham, B17 0EG, United Kingdom
☎ 0121-427 2555/✆ 0121-427 1055
✉ info@europatrans.co.uk
🖥 www.europatechtrans.co.uk

Eurotransnet Ltd Chesham House, 150 Regents Street, London, W1R 5FA, United Kingdom
☎ (020) 7636 1881/✆ (020) 7636 1396
✉ translation@eurotransnet.co.uk
🖥 www.eurotransnet.co.uk

Foreign Legion 1 Kendal Road, London, NW10 1JH, United Kingdom
☎ (020) 8450 4451
✉ voices@foreignlegion.co.uk
🖥 www.foreignlegion.co.uk

Foreign Versions Ltd 60 Blandford Street, London, W1U 7JD, United Kingdom
☎ (020) 7935 0993/✆ (020) 7935 0507
✉ info@foreignversions.co.uk
🖥 www.foreignversions.co.uk

G L S Language Services 250 Crow Road, Glasgow, G11 7LA, United Kingdom
☎ 0141-357 6611/✆ 0141-357 6605
✉ info@glslanguages.demon.co.uk
🖥 www.glslanguageservices.co.uk

Gala Publishing and Copestone Copy Writers The Write House, 6 Park Meadow, Hatfield, Hertfordshire, AL9 5HA, United Kingdom
☎ (01707) 890118/✆ (01707) 895587
✉ mail@galapublishing.com
🖥 www.galapublishing.com

GoUK.com Translations , Petersfield, Hampshire, GU32 2FA, United Kingdom
☎ (01730) 263006
✉ translations@gouk.com
🖥 www.gouk.com/translations

Inter-Com (Foreign Voices) Hurlingham Studios, Ranelagh Gardens, London, SW6 3PA, United Kingdom
☎ (020) 7731 8000/✆ (0870) 0941954
✉ mail@intercom-translations.co.uk
🖥 www.intercom-translations.co.uk

International Translations Ltd 9 Queensway, Heswall, Wirral, Merseyside, CH60 3SL, United Kingdom
☎ 0151-342 7044/✆ 0151-342 9407
✉ admin@itltranslations.com
🖥 www.itltranslations.com

Italian Translations - Words You Can Rely On Billingsley Farm, Holme Lacy, Hereford, HR2 6PH, United Kingdom
☎ (01432) 870661
✉ lorenz@claranet.co.uk
🖥 www.martinelli.co.uk

J R Translations 2 Delft Close, Locks Heath, Southampton, SO31 7TQ, United Kingdom
☎ (01489) 576415/✆ (01489) 576541
✉ jrtranslation@ntlworld.com
🖥

K International Carina Building East, Sunrise Parkway, Linford Wood, Milton Keynes, MK14 6PW, United Kingdom
☎ (01908) 670399/✆ (01908) 670170
✉ info@k-international.com
🖥 www.k-international.com

Key Language Services Linford Forum, 32 Rockingham Drive, Milton Keynes, MK14 6LY, United Kingdom
☎ (01908) 232101/✆ (01908) 232815
✉ sales@keylanguageservices.co.uk
🖥 www.keylanguageservices.co.uk

Kunze London 12 Byron Road, Mill Hill, London, NW7 4AD, United Kingdom
☎ (020) 8959 2513/✆ (020) 8959 7626
✉ info@kunzelondon.com
🖥 www.kunzelondon.com

Language Bureau Ltd 77-79 Lee Lane, Horwich, Bolton, BL6 7AU, United Kingdom
☎ (01204) 669622/✆ (01204) 698192
✉ enquiries@languagebureau.co.uk
🖥 www.languagebureau.co.uk

Leagal & Technical Translations Ltd 16 Old Market Place, Altrincham, Cheshire, WA14 4DF, United Kingdom
☎ 0161-941 2024/✆ 0161-927 7024
✉ enquiries@itsgroup.co.uk
🖥 www.itsgroup.co.uk

Legal & Technical Translation Services 13 Earl Street, Maidstone, Kent, ME14 1PL, United Kingdom
☎ (01622) 751537/✆ (01622) 754431
✉ translations.ltts@virgin.net
🖥 www.ltts.co.uk

Lifeline Language Services Premier House, Church Street, Preston, PR1 3BQ, United Kingdom
☎ (01772) 558858/✆ (01772) 558878
✉ info@lifelinelanguageservices.co.uk
🖥 www.lifelinelanguageservices.co.uk

Linguaset Sunderland House, Sunderland Street, Macclesfield, Cheshire, SK11 6JF, United Kingdom
☎ (01625) 617174/✆ (0871) 2510455
✉ info@linguaset.co.uk
🖥 www.linguaset.co.uk

Linguatext (Scotland) 8 Randolph Place, Edinburgh, EH3 7TE, United Kingdom
☎ 0131-624 2091/✆ 0131-624 1220
✉ sylvia@linguatext.com
🖥 www.linguatext.com

Liquid Translations 1 Devonshire Terrace, Glasgow, G12 0XE, United Kingdom
☎ 0141-334 9031/✆ 0141-334 9031
✉ info@liquid-translations.com
🖥 www.liquid-translations.com

Lloyd International Translation Ltd Birch Heath Road, Tarporley, Cheshire, CW6 9UR, United Kingdom
☎ (01829) 730050/✆ (01829) 730060
✉ mail@lloyd.co.uk
🖥 www.lloyd.co.uk

Monde Media 4 Ransomes Dock, Park Gate Road, London, SW11 4NP, United Kingdom
☎ (020) 7924 6299/✆ (020) 7924 6301
✉ info@monde.net
🖥 www.monde.net

Newcom Language Services Ltd Newcom House, 125 Poplar High Street, London, E14 0AE, United Kingdom
☎ (020) 7517 1270/✆ (020) 7517 1271
✉ newcom@newcomgroup.com
🖥 www.newcomgroup.com

P B S S Translations PO Box 371, Pembury, Tunbridge Wells, Kent, TN2 4XE, United Kingdom
☎ (01892) 824833/✆ (01892) 825134
✉ partners@pbss-uk.com
🖥 www.pbss-uk.com

PASSWORD Ltd 118 Chevening Road, London, NW6 6TP, United Kingdom
☎ (020) 8723 8841
✉ info@password-eu.net
🖥 www.password-eu.net

Peak Translations Shepherd's Bank, Kettleshume, High Peak, Derbyshire, SK23 7QU, United Kingdom
☎ (01663) 732074/✆ (01663) 735499
✉ info@peak-translations.co.uk
🖥 www.peak-translations.co.uk

Planet Languages Ltd 1 St. George's Yard, Castle Street, Farnham, Surrey, GU9 7LW, United Kingdom
☎ (01252) 713444/✆ (01252) 713445
✉ post@planetlanguages.com
🖥 www.planetlanguages.com

R F Translations Office 410, 98 Woodlands Road, Glasgow, G3 6HB, United Kingdom
☎ (07005) 900919/✆ (07092) 810417
✉ info@rf-translations.com
🖥 www.rf-translatins.com

Reach Marketing & Communications 3 Harrow Drive, Sale, Cheshire, M33 3TB, United Kingdom
☎ 0161-969 4515
✉ leoaspden@reach-mc.co.uk
🖥 ww.reach-mc.co.uk

Roevin Translations Concorde House, Trinity Park, Birmingham, B37 7UQ, United Kingdom
☎ 0121-635 5060/✆ 0121-635 5061
✉ birmingham.translation@roevin.co.uk
🖥 www.roevin.co.uk/translations

Rovin Computype Ltd Park Road Estate, Park Road, Timperley, Altrincham, Cheshire, WA14 5QH, United Kingdom
☎ 0161-935 2000/✆ 0161-973 5682
✉ manchester.translation@rovin.co.uk
🖥 www.rovin.co.uk/translation

Russia House 61a Queen Mary Road, Sheffield, S2 1HQ, United Kingdom
☎ (07814) 920071/✆ 0114-283 5973
✉ anna@russia-house.co.uk
🖥 www.russia-house.co.uk

Salford Translations Ltd 66 Lower Hillgate, Stockport, Cheshire, SK1 3AL, United Kingdom
☎ 0161-968 7100/✆ 0161-968 7109
✉ info@salftrans.co.uk
🖥 www.salftrans.co.uk

Star UK 15-17 Bridge Street, Leatherhead, Surrey, KT22 8BL, United Kingdom
☎ (01372) 377300/✆ (01372) 373355
✉ info@star-uk.co.uk
🖥 www.star-group.net

Thames Translations International Old Batsord Mill, Lower Luton Road, Harpenden, Hertfordshire, AL5 5BZ, United Kingdom
☎ (0870) 0111130/✆ (0870) 0111140
✉ info@thames.net
🖥 www.thames-translations.com

The Ask Group Ltd Ask House, 2 Northgate Avenue, Bury St. Edmunds, Suffolk, IP32 6BB, United Kingdom
☎ (01284) 768278/✆ (01284) 764025
✉ help@translate.co.uk
🖥 www.translate.co.uk

The Big Word 59 Charlotte Street, London, W1T 4PE, United Kingdom
☎ (0870) 748 8000/✆ (0870) 748 8001
✉ email@thebigword.com
🖥 www.thebigword.com

Tongue Tied (East Anglia) Ltd 23 Impington Lane, Impington, Cambridge, CB4 9LT, United Kingdom
📞 (01223) 479391/📠 (01223) 504985
✉ sales@tonguetiedeastanglia.co.uk
🖥 www.tonguetiedeastanglia.co.uk

Total Translation Co. Ltd 75 Railway Street, Hertford, SG14 1RP, United Kingdom
📞 (01284) 768278/📠 (01992) 532799
✉ vacancies@totaltranslations.com
🖥 www.totaltranslations.com

Tramont Translation Management 57 Upper Park Road, London, NW3 2UL, United Kingdom
📞 (0845) 6448254/📠 (0845) 6448259
✉ tramont@globalnet.co.uk
🖥 www.tramont.co.uk

Transaction Translators Ltd Redlands, Tapton House Road, Sheffield, S10 5BY, United Kingdom
📞 0114-266 1103/📠 0114-263 1959
✉ transaction@transaction.co.uk
🖥 www.transaction.co.uk

Transworld Linguist Services 38-40 Broad Green Avenue, Croydon, CR0 2ST, United Kingdom
📞 (020) 8683 4031/📠 (020) 8689 6015
✉ mail@transworld.co.uk
🖥 www.transworld.co.uk

TTC Creative Ltd Creative House, 20 St. Marys Road, London, W5 5ES, United Kingdom
📞 (020) 8567 5902/📠 (020) 8840 7349
✉ info@ttcweb.com
🖥 www.ttcweb.com

U P S Translations 111 Baker Street, London, W1U 6RR, United Kingdom
📞 (020) 7224 1220/📠 (020) 7486 3272
✉ info@upstranslations.com
🖥 www.upstranslations.com

Voice Squad Ltd 1 Kendal Road, London, NW10 1JH, United Kingdom
📞 (020) 8450 4451
✉ voices@voicesquad.com
🖥 www.voicesquad.com

VSI Aradco House, 132 Cleveland Street, London, W1T 6AB, United Kingdom
📞 (020) 7692 7700/📠 (020) 7692 7711
✉ info@vsi.tv
🖥 www.vsi.tv

Wessex Translations Unit A1, The Premier Centre, Abbey Park Industrial Estate, Romsey, Hampshire, SO51 9DG, United Kingdom
📞 (0870) 166 9300/📠 (0870) 166 9299
✉ sales@wt-lm.com
🖥 www.wt-lm.com

World Writers 29 Clerkenwell Road, London, EC1M 5TA, United Kingdom
📞 (020) 7287 4877/📠 (020) 7287 6159
✉ info@worldwriters.com
🖥 www.worldwriters.com

WorldAccent 30-31 Great Sutton Street, London, EC1V 0NA, United Kingdom
📞 (020) 7865 8300/📠 (020) 7865 8400
✉ sales@worldaccent.com
🖥 www.worldaccent.com

Events

PEEPSHOW.ORG.UK

CENTURY

Situated over four floors on Shaftesbury Avenue overlooking the greenery and foliage
of St. Anne's Church, Century is the Private Members club in Soho.
We can accommodate events for 25-300 guests, whether its private dining,
champagne & canapé receptions, meetings or product launches.

For further details please contact Ashley in the events team for further details.

events@centuryclub.co.uk

Century Club, 61-63 Shaftesbury Avenue, London W1D 6LG
020 7534 3080
www.centuryclub.co.uk
Nearest tube is Piccadilly Circus

3D IMAGING

0141 Design 38 Carmunnock Road, Glasgow, G44 4UE, United Kingdom
- 0141 4407241
- imariusz@0141design.co.uk
- www.0141design.co.uk

24/7 Visuals Foxcroft, Hoyland, Barnsley, South Yorkshire, S74 9DE, United Kingdom
- (01226) 749240/ (01226) 749240
- john@247visuals.com
- www.247visuals.com

3-D Images Ltd 31 The Chine, Grange Park, London, N21 2EA, United Kingdom
- (020) 8364 0022/ (020) 8364 1828
- burder3d@aol.com
- www.3dimages.co.uk

3D Pixel Perfect Visualisation Services The White House, Copse Road, Haslemere, Surrey, GU27 3QQ, United Kingdom
- (01428) 643500
- info@pixelperfect.co.uk
- www.pixelperfect.co.uk

3D4D.com 46 Calthorpe Street, London, WC1X 0JZ, United Kingdom
- (0500) 555245/(07973) 737891
- ch@3d4d.com
- www.3d4d.com

3DA Ltd 16 Bond Close, Tadley, Hampshire, RG26 4EW, United Kingdom
- 0118-981 6328/(07810) 008671/ 0118-981 9320
- damian@3-da.com
- www.3-da.com

3di Unit C, Dragon House, Back off Dragon Road, Harrogate, North Yorkshire, HG1 5DB, United Kingdom
- (0845) 4582898/ (0871) 2220189
- paul@threedi.net
- www.threedi.net

4 Reel Design 9 Ixworth Close, Northampton, NN3 8TW, United Kingdom
- (07940) 125004
- johnl@4reel.biz
- www.4reel.biz

ALL3D 21/4 Orwell Place, Edinburgh, EH11 2AD, United Kingdom
- 0131-337 1611/ 0131-466 4636
- lmaguire@all3d.co.uk
- www.all3d.co.uk

Another-Fine-Mesh.com 33a Fossgate, York, YO1 9TA, United Kingdom
- (01904) 630721
- 3d@another-fine-mesh.com
- www.another-fine-mesh.com

Arcmedia Ltd 5 Hardhorn Road, Poulton-le-Fylde, Lancashire, FY6 7SR, United Kingdom
- (01253) 896616/ (01253) 896996
- info@arc-media.org
- www.arc-media.org

ArtemDigital Unit 4 Perivale Park, Horsenden Lane ... uth, Perivale, Greenford, Middlesex, UB6 7RL, United ...ngdom
- (020) 8991 6060/ (020) 8997 1557
- info@artemdigital.com
- ...w.artemdigital.com

Artistan Studio 6, 8 Clissold Road, London, N16 9EU, United Kingdom
- (020) 7249 5398/ (020) 7503 0465
- one@artistan.net
- www.artistan.net

Baker Comarsh 9 Jacey Road, Birmingham, B16 0LL, United Kingdom
- 0121-454 0078
- dean@bakercomarsh.co.uk
- www.bakercomarsh.co.uk

Bridge Creative Ltd The Coach House Studio, 40 Higher Lane, Upholland, Lancashire, WN8 0NL,
- 01695 624966
- bridget@bridgecreative.co.uk
- www.bridgecreative.co.uk

Brightworks Product Design Mendip House, Silver Street, Cheddar, Somerset, BS27 3LE, United Kingdom
- (01934) 744956/ (01934) 744986
- graeme@brightworks.co.uk
- www.brightworks.co.uk

Built from scratch design New Plot, 1-2 Ivy cottages, Chapmans Lane, St Pauls Cray, Orpington, Kent, BR5 3JA, United Kingdom
- 01689 897740/ 01689 897740
- Info@builtfromscratch-design.co.uk
- www.builtfromscratch-design.co.uk

C G House bvl.Vasil levski 13b, Sofia, 1000, Bulgaria
- 00 359 029 813 263
- cghouse.abv.bg
- www.cghouse.bg

C M D 1 Ancre Hill Studio, Ancre Hill Lane, Monmouth, Gwent, NP25 5SS, United Kingdom
- (01600) 712998/ (0870) 0630170
- chris@cmdigital-design.co.uk
- www.cmdigital-design.co.uk

C R W Concept Design Ltd The Birches, Halfway Lane, Dunchurch, Rugby, Warwickshire, CV22 6RD, United Kingdom
- (01788) 816402
- info@crwconceptdesign.com
- www.crwconceptdesign.com

Candy Lab Ltd 130 Shaftesbury Avenue, London, W1D 5EU, United Kingdom
- (020) 7166 5353/ (020) 7031 4302
- info@candylab.co.uk
- www.candylab.co.uk

Catalyst Pictures Ltd 34 Chester Square, Ashton-under-Lyne, Lancashire, OL6 7TW, United Kingdom
- 0161-339 3353/ 0161-339 2914
- nik@catalystpics.co.uk
- www.catalystpics.co.uk

Cinedrome Studios 240 St 54, I8/3, Islamabad, 44000, Pakistan
- 51 443 5217/ 51 443 5218
- info@cinedromestudios.com
- www.cinedromestudios.com

Continuum St. Edmunds House, Margaret Street, York, YO10 4UX, United Kingdom
- (01904) 527700/ (01904) 527701
- rbriggs@continuum-group.com
- www.continuum-group.com

D V A Ltd (IVCA) 7 Campbell Court, Bramley, Tadley, Hampshire, RG26 5EG, United Kingdom
- (01256) 882032/ (01256) 882024
- barrieg@dva.co.uk
- www.dvafacilities.co.uk

Dano Battista 3D Ltd 9-10 Charlotte Mews, London, W1T 4EF, United Kingdom
- (07958) 735069/ (020) 7636 2455
- enquiries@danobattista.com
- www.danobattista.com

Dark Horse Graphics Yorkshire TV, Kirkstall Road, Leeds, LS3 1JS, United Kingdom
- 0113-222 8390/(07831) 729670/ 0113-222 8391
- chaz@darkhorsegraphics.co.uk
- www.darkhorsegraphics.co.uk

darkwater Apartment 10, Truman House, 22-28 Park Row, Nottingham, NG1 6GX, United Kingdom
- 0115-958 4458
- studio@darkwaterdesign.com
- www.darkwaterdesign.com

Dave Edwards GFX, London, United Kingdom
- (07855) 495135
- info@daveedwards.co.uk
- www.daveedwards.co.uk

David Pugh 10 Gadlys Terrace, Aberdare, Mid Glamorgan, CF44 8AN, United Kingdom
- (01685) 884108
- lastplanet@boltblue.com

Design 47a Springfield Road, Harrow, Middlesex, HA1 1QF, United Kingdom
- (020) 8427 9747/ (020) 8427 9747
- patrick@patrickhimbleby.com
- www.patrickhimbleby.com

Docmate Services Ltd 15 Millside Road, Peterculter, Aberdeen, AB14 0WE, United Kingdom
- (01224) 732780/ (01224) 732780
- info@docmates.co.uk
- www.docmates.co.uk

Dogfish Internet Ltd 26 Messenger Close, Bungay, Suffolk, NR35 1PW, United Kingdom
- (01986) 892965/ (01986) 892965
- pete@dogfish.co.uk
- www.dogfish.co.uk

Dragonfly Media 3 Berkeley Crescent, Clifton, Bristol, Avon, BS8 1HA,
- 0845 6520 888/ 0845 6520 808
- jon@dragonfly-media.co.uk
- www.dragonfly-media.co.uk

Falter Magazine 14 Furnival Mansions, Wells Street, London, W1T 3PL,
- 4.42076E+11
- info@faltermagazine.com
- www.faltermagazine.com

Flying Mouse 68 Rennets, Wood Road, London, SE9 2NH, United Kingdom
- (07780) 707092/ (020) 8850 1294
- digital@rtwork.co.uk

Fury X Ltd 17 Ensign House, Admirals Way, Canary Wharf, London, E14 9XQ, United Kingdom
- (020) 7863 2481/ (020) 7863 7510
- adrian.lemans@fury-x.com
- www.fury-x.com

Geoff Powell Photos 1 Flete Close, Newton Abbot, Devon, TQ12 4EZ, United Kingdom
- (01626) 332317
- geoffpowell@blueyonder.co.uk
- www.geoffpowellphotos.co.uk

Glowfrog Studios Unit 7G, Clapham North Arts Centre, 26 - 32 Voltaire Road, London, SW4 6DH, United Kingdom
- (020) 7652 5749/ (020) 7627 4705
- studio@glowfrog.com
- www.glowfrog.com

Golem Productions Ltd 31 Queens Walk, Ruislip, Middlesex, HA4 0LX, United Kingdom
- (07733) 003873/ (020) 8845 8289
- richard@golemproductions.co.uk
- www.golemproductions.co.uk

Greensplash Ltd Paddock View, 308 Chester Road, Hartford, Northwich, Cheshire, CW8 2AB, United Kingdom
- (01606) 884123/ (01606) 884212
- siu.wan@greensplash.com
- www.greensplash.com

Hive Associates Bewlay House, 2 Swallow Place, London, W1B 2AE, United Kingdom
- (020) 7664 0480/ (020) 7664 0481
- consult@hiveassociates.co.uk
- www.hiveassociates.co.uk

Iain Denby Ltd 46 West End Lane, Horsforth, Leeds, LS18 5JP, United Kingdom
- 0113-258 5585
- id@idenby.co.uk
- www.idenby.co.uk

Ian Rossenrode Silk Mill Road, Redbourn, St. Albans, Hertfordshire, AL3 7GE, United Kingdom
- (01582) 792046
- rossenrode@btinternet.com
- www.rossenrode-art.co.uk

if3d Mortimer House, Holmer Road, Hereford, HR4 9TA, United Kingdom
- (01432) 360 711/(07798) 876699
- studio@if3d.com
- www.if3d.com

Image Foundry Studios Foundry House, 9 Riverview, The Embankment Business Park, Heaton Mersey, Stockport, Cheshire, SK4 3GN, United Kingdom
- 0161-975 0909/ 0161-975 0908
- info@imagefoundry.co.uk
- www.imagefoundry.co.uk

Image Quest Marine The Moos, Poffley End, Witney, Oxfordshire, OX29 9UW, United Kingdom
- (01993) 704050/ (01993) 779203
- info@imagequestmarine.com
- www.imagequestmarine.com

Imigea Ltd 27 Lauriston Street, Edinburgh, EH3 9DQ, United Kingdom
- 0131-659 5239
- pete@imigea.com
- www.imigea.com

Ink & Colors Ltd 27 Old Gloucester Street, London, WC1N 3XX, United Kingdom
- (020) 7558 8374
- info@inkandcolors.com
- www.inkandcolors.com

iProduct 23 Alva Street, Edinburgh, EH2 4PS, United Kingdom
- (0131) 225 6292
- andrew@iproduct.co.uk
- www.iproduct.co.uk

Jannuzzi Smith 29 Queen Elizabeth Street, London, SE1 2LP, United Kingdom
☎ (020) 7234 0557
✉ email@jannuzzismith.com
🖥 www.jannuzzismith.com

Julian Tewkesbury 1 Britten Drive, Barnstaple, Devon, EX32 8AQ, United Kingdom
☎ (01271) 343507
✉ julian@juliantewkesbury.com
🖥 www.juliantewkesbury.com

Knock Knock S L Calle Paris 175, entresuelo 2B, Barcelona, 8036, Spain
☎ 00 34 93 5321625

Kokoro Design 80 Warwick Road, Solihull, West Midlands, B92 7JJ, United Kingdom
☎ 0121-707 8635
✉ botmatt@yahoo.co.uk

Larry Wooden 93 Lethe Grove, Colchester, CO2 8RH, United Kingdom
☎ (01206) 572287
✉ 3dcreations@ukcompanies.org
🖥 www.3dcreations.ukcompanies.org

LegendaryFX 34 Princelet Street, London, UK, E1 5LP, United Kingdom
☎ (0700) 7000 337
✉ list@legendaryfx.com
🖥 www.legendaryfx.com

Lionhouse 11 Bloomfield Road, Bath, BA2 2AD, United Kingdom
☎ (01225) 445427/✆ (01225) 422999
✉ les@lionhousecreative.com
🖥 www.lionhousecreative.com

LittleBigMachine Ridderstraat 10, Gent, 9000, Belgium
☎ 0032 495 89 30 14
✉ karim@littlebigmachine.com
🖥 www.littlebigmachine.com

Longneck Afgan Road 27, Battersea, London, SW11 2QD, United Kingdom
☎ 7506018062
✉ vlad@longneck.ro
🖥 www.longneck.ro

Mark Lawrence Croft House, The Street, All Cannings, Devizes, Wiltshire, SN10 3PA, United Kingdom
☎ (01380) 860 339
✉ studio@aurastudios.co.uk
🖥 www.aurastudios.co.uk

Mark Woollard 79 Trevelyan, Tawfield Copse, Bracknell, Berkshire, RG12 8YD, United Kingdom
☎ (01344) 429275/(07973) 256057/✆ (01344) 429275
✉ mark.woolard@ntlworld.com

Mindfizz Ltd 11 Barton Road, Eastleigh, Hampshire, SO50 6RN, United Kingdom
☎ (023) 8061 4649
✉ clare@mindfizz.com
🖥 www.mindfizz.com

Mindorchard Ltd 11 Jew Street, Brighton, BN1 1UT, United Kingdom
☎ (08700) 847441/✆ (08702) 862605
✉ info@mindorchard.com
🖥 www.mindorchard.com

Mokko Blue 21 Arncott Hall, 13 Poole Road, Bournemouth, BH2 5QR, United Kingdom
☎ 01202 269 257/✆ 01202 269 257
✉ info@mokko-blue.com
🖥 www.mokko-blue.com

Mr Creighton Global Enterprises 54/2 Willowbrae Road, Edinburgh, EH8 7HA, United Kingdom
☎ (07786) 478866
✉ mrcreighton@mrcreighton.com
🖥 www.mrcreighton.com

Nasdesigns, Romford, Essex, United Kingdom
☎ (07900) 612864
✉ nasibamoola@gmail.com

oddpixel.com Unit 13, 58 Dalston Lane, London, E8 2NG, United Kingdom
☎ (07891) 777374
✉ info@oddpixel.com
🖥 www.oddpixel.com

Olive Interactive Limited Suite16, The Coda Centre, Munster Road, Fulham, London, SW6 6AW, United Kingdom
☎ (08707) 605801/✆ (08707) 605802
✉ peter@oliveinteractive.com
🖥 www.oliveinteractive.com

Paul Beattie 3 Bacons Lane, Pinchbeck, Spalding, Lincolnshire, PE11 3XS, United Kingdom
☎ (01775) 680193
✉ paul@beattiep68.freeserve.co.uk

Pict 8 7 Lyndedoch Crescent, Glasgow, G3 6DZ, United Kingdom
☎ 0141-332 3815/✆ 0141-332 5295
✉ al@pict8.com
🖥 www.pict8.com

Pictures on the Wall Studio 14, 74-76 Firhill Road, Glasgow, G20 7BA, United Kingdom
☎ 0141-576 0117/✆ 0141-946 0001
✉ animation@potw.co.uk
🖥 www.potw.co.uk

Pinsharp 3D Graphics 29 Darby Road, Liverpool, L19 9BP, United Kingdom
☎ 0151-494 2928/(07719) 730847/✆ 0151-494 3829
✉ info@pinsharp3d.co.uk
🖥 www.pinsharp3d.co.uk

Piranha Media 10 Barley Mow Passage, London, W4 4PH, United Kingdom
☎ (020) 8997 8569
✉ info@piranha-media.com
🖥 www.piranha-media.com

Pixel DNA Ltd Hydra Clarkson House, PO Box 37, Sheffield, S6 3AH, United Kingdom
☎ 0114-224 6145
✉ marc@pixel-dna.com
🖥 www.pixel-dna.com

Pixogenic Dean Clough Industrial Park, Halifax, West Yorkshire, HX3 5WG, United Kingdom
☎ (01422) 322100/✆ (01422) 322200
✉ mike@pixogenic.com
🖥 www.pixogenic.com

planetnewmedia Unit 226, Great Guildford Business Square, 30 Great Guildford Street, London, SE1 0HS, United Kingdom
☎ (020) 7620 6060/✆ (020) 7620 6050
✉ create@planetnewmedia.com
🖥 www.planetnewmedia.com

Procreation UK Ltd Teddington Studios, Broom Road, Teddington, Middlesex, TW11 9NT, United Kingdom
☎ (020) 8977 5361/✆ (020) 8977 5361
✉ matt@procreationgroup.com
🖥 www.procreationgroup.com

Product Innovation Partners Ltd Studio 1D-1F Leroy House, 436 Essex Road, London, N1 3QP, United Kingdom
☎ (020) 7354 8677/✆ (020) 7354 5684
✉ lynne@pip-design.com
🖥 www.pip-design.com

Raymond Ore 9 Jesmond Road, Croydon, CR0 6JR, United Kingdom
☎ (020) 8654 2014/(07941) 692235 ✆ (020) 8654 2014
✉ rore@raymation.co.uk
🖥 www.raymation.co.uk

Richard Klein 61 Cleveden Drive, Glasgow, G12 0NX, United Kingdom
☎ 0141-337 2203
✉ rkderj@yahoo.com
🖥 www.rkderj.com

Riot of Colour 6-7 Anchorage Point, Anchor & Hope Lane, London, SE7 7RY, United Kingdom
☎ (020) 8853 1111/✆ (020) 8853 4888
✉ a.roblett@riot.lineuk.co.uk
🖥 www.riotofcolour.co.uk

Ripe Design (UK) Ltd Clarence House, 48 Black Bull Street, Leeds, LS10 1HW, United Kingdom
☎ 0113-204 2800/✆ 0113-204 2801
✉ info@ripe.co.uk
🖥 www.ripe.co.uk

Rockwood Flat 40, 216 Kennington Road, London, SE11 6HR, United Kingdom
☎ (020) 7582 9308
✉ richardrockwood@mac.com

Rogue Rocket Ltd 13 Upper Crescent, Belfast, BT7 1NT, United Kingdom
☎ (02890) 331600
✉ info@roguerocket.com
🖥 www.roguerocket.com

Rushes Post Production Ltd (APPC) 66 Old Compton Street, London, W1D 4UH, United Kingdom
☎ (020) 7437 8676/✆ (020) 7734 2519
✉ info@rushes.co.uk
🖥 www.rushes.co.uk

Sam Baguley Design 3 the hangar, perseverance works, 38 kingsland road, London, E2 8DD, United Kingdom
☎ (07903) 944242
✉ mail@sambaguley.com
🖥 www.sambaguley.com

Sandstorm 12 Oxford Road, Newbury, Berkshire, RG14 1PA, United Kingdom
☎ (020) 7379 5432
✉ tom@sandstormmedia.co.uk
🖥 www.sandstormmedia.co.uk

Schafline 29 Darby Road, Liverpool, L19 9BP, United Kingdom
☎ 0151-494 2928/✆ 0151-494 3829
✉ jbs@pinsharp3d.co.uk
🖥 www.pinsharp3d.co.uk

Set the Scene Home-Field-House, Burcott, Nr. Wing, Leighton Buzzard, Bedfordshire, LU7 0JW, United Kingdom
☎ (01296) 682344/(07970) 753142/✆ (01296) 682197
✉ shargreaves@btinternet.com

Shepdesign 7 Devon Way, Banbury, Oxfordshire, OX16 1UJ, United Kingdom
☎ 01295 252399/✆ 01295 252399
✉ info@shepdesign.net
🖥 www.shepdesign.net

Simon Knowles Illustration Studio 10, 21 Berry Close, London, N21 2RY, United Kingdom
☎ (020) 8292 5126/✆ (020) 8292 5126
✉ simon@skillustration.co.uk
🖥 www.skillustration.co.uk

Sliced Bread Animation 15 King Street, Covent Garden, London, WC2E 8HN, United Kingdom
☎ (020) 7379 7873/✆ (0870) 7620852
✉ info@sbanimation.com
🖥 www.thebestthingsince.com

Smoothe 1st Floor, 1 Portland Street, Manchester, M1 3BE, United Kingdom
☎ (0870) 890 9836
✉ samcrothers@smoothe.com
🖥 www.smoothe.com

Social Fabric UK Ltd William Blake House, 8 Marshall Street, London, W1F 7EJ, United Kingdom
☎ (020) 7788 7876
✉ us@thesocialfabric.com
🖥 www.thesocialfabric.com

Sparx 34 rue du Sentier, Paris, 75002, France
☎ 00 33 1 44 34 29 29/✆ 00 33 1 55 73 17 07
✉ contact@sparx.com
🖥 www.sparx.com

Start Creative 2 Sheraton Street, Soho, London, W1F 8BH, United Kingdom
☎ (020) 7269 0101/✆ (020) 7269 0102
✉ jen@startcreative.co.uk
🖥 www.startcreative.co.uk

T A G Creative, Adplates Group 29 Clerkenwell Road, London, EC1M 5TA, United Kingdom
☎ (020) 7251 4571/✆ (020) 7253 5355
✉ info@tagmedia.co.uk
🖥 www.tagmedia.co.uk

The Juice Group Ltd President Way, Sheffield, S4 7UR, United Kingdom
☎ 0114-275 5858/✆ 0114-275 5888
✉ designed@thejuice.co.uk
🖥 www.thejuice.co.uk

Three Blind Mice 9-10 Charlotte Mews, London, W1T 4EF, United Kingdom
☎ (020) 7636 2502/✆ (020) 7636 2455
✉ andy@three-blind-mice.co.uk
🖥 www.three-blind-mice.co.uk

Threerooms Ltd 13 Mayfield Drive, Stapleford, Nottingham, NG9 8JF, United Kingdom
☎ 0115-877 9429
✉ info@threerooms.com
🖥 www.threerooms.com

Touchpoint 14th Floor, Oakland House, Talbot Road, Manchester, M16 0PQ, United Kingdom
☎ (0161) 888 5747/✆ (0161) 888 5741
✉ info@touchpointuk.com
🖥 www.touchpointuk.com

Uniform 200Vanilla Factory, 39 Fleet Street, Liverpool, L1 4AR, United Kingdom
☎ 0151-709 9055/✆ 0151-709 9950
✉ info@uniform.net
🖥 www.uniform.net

V-real Ltd 3 Sylvan Avenue, London, N22 5HX, United Kingdom
☎ (020) 8881 0777/✆ (020) 8889 3124
✉ info@v-real.co.uk
🖥 www.v-real.co.uk

Vineyard C G 17 Lyndhurst Road, Exeter, EX2 4PA, United Kingdom
☎ (01392) 430316
✉ james@vineyardcg.com
🖥 www.vineyardcg.com

Visual Eyes Media 117-121 Curtain Road, London, EC2A 3AD, United Kingdom
☎ (020) 7613 1777
✉ info@visual-eyes-media.co.uk
🖥 www.visual-eyes-media.co.uk

VISUALS 3D 26 School Brow, Romiley, Stockport, Cheshire, SK6 3AT, United Kingdom
☎ 0161-430 2623
✉ info@visuals-3d.co.uk
🖥 www.visuals-3d.co.uk

Vivid Carlton Mills, Pickering Street, Leeds, LS12 2QG, United Kingdom
☎ 0113-224 4800/ 📠 0113-224 4801
✉ lindsay.kemp@logistik.co.uk
🖥 www.logistik-vivid.co.uk

Voila Image Unit 5, 139A Stroud Green Road, London, N4 3PX, United Kingdom
☎ (020) 7263 4445/ 📠 (020) 7281 2681
✉ info@voilaimage.com
🖥 www.voilaimage.com

W W A V Rapp Collins 1 Riverside, Manbre Road, London, W6 9WA, United Kingdom
☎ (020) 8735 8000/ 📠 (020) 8735 8005
🖥 www.wwavrc.co.uk

W.C.J. Burrows The Burrows Building, 5 Fayleigh Road, Brentwood, Essex, CM13 1AB, United Kingdom
☎ (01277) 246666/ 📠 (01277) 246777
✉ darrel_wright@burrows.yr.com
🖥 www.burrows.yr.com

CORPORATE VIDEO

1871 Productions Windsor House, 40-41 Great Castle Street, London, W1W 8LU, United Kingdom
☎ (020) 7631 4500/(07768) 918398
✉ info@1871productions.co.uk

A V T Ltd AVT House, Stone Street, Brighton, BN1 2HB, United Kingdom
☎ (01273) 299 001/ 📠 (01273) 299 002
✉ steve@avtgroup.com
🖥 www.avtgroup.com

Action Conference Team Ltd 44 Wellington Road, Sandhurst, Berkshire, GU47 9AY, United Kingdom
☎ (01344) 780242/ 📠 (01344) 777760
✉ conference@dial.pipex.com
🖥 www.procom.uk.com

Alternative Focus Media 4 Horseshoe Cottages, Station Road, Collingham, Newark, Nottinghamshire, NG23 7SA, United Kingdom
☎ (01636) 706106/ 📠 (01636) 893997
✉ mike@alternativefocusmedia.com
🖥 www.alternativefocusmedia.com

Arc Production Windsor House, Greville Road, Bristol, BS3 1LL, United Kingdom
☎ 0117-902 8353
✉ info@arcproduction.co.uk
🖥 www.arcproduction.co.uk

Aspect Ltd Solar House, 915 High Road, North Finchley, London, N12 8QJ, United Kingdom
☎ (020) 8282 7575/ 📠 (020) 8282 7576
✉ team@aspect.ltd.uk
🖥 www.aspect.ltd.uk

Audiostella 49-51 York Road, Brentford, Middlesex, TW8 0QP, United Kingdom
☎ (0700) 7664518/ 📠 (020) 8568 4151
✉ nick@audiostella.com
🖥 www.audiostella.com

Barford Productions 35 Bedfordbury, Covent Garden, London, WC2N 4DU, United Kingdom
☎ (020) 7240 4188/ 📠 (020) 7379 5210
✉ info@barford.co.uk
🖥 www.barford.co.uk

Benson Thomas 1 Swinleys Hey, Great Boughton, Chester, CH3 5XL, United Kingdom
☎ (01244) 345370/ 📠 (01244) 344511
✉ anthony@bensonthomas.co.uk
🖥 www.bensonthomas.co.uk

Blue Tuna Ltd 19 Fitzjohn Avenue, Barnet, Hertfordshire, EN5 2HH, United Kingdom
☎ (020) 8275 8780/(07785) 325806 📠 (020) 8275 8781
✉ jon@bluetuna.tv
🖥 www.bluetuna.tv

Buckmark Productions (IVCA) Commer House, Station Road, Tadcaster, North Yorkshire, LS24 9JF, United Kingdom
☎ (01937) 835900/ 📠 (01937) 835901
✉ info@buckmark.com
🖥 www.buckmark.com

C O Plus 2nd Floor, Millers House, Roydon Road, Stanstead Abbotts, Ware, Hertfordshire, SG12 8HN, United Kingdom
☎ (01920) 873000/ 📠 (01920) 873001
✉ info@coplus.co.uk
🖥 www.coplus.co.uk

Cambridge Film & Television Productions (IVCA) Building 7200, Cambridge Research Park, Beach Drive, Waterbeach, Cambridge, CB25 9TL, United Kingdom
☎ (01223) 236007/(07967) 727087
✉ contact@cftp.co.uk
🖥 www.cftp.co.uk

Cantab Films Ltd St Johns Innovation Centre, Cowley Road, Cambridge, CB4 0WS, United Kingdom
☎ (01223) 212014/ 📠 (01223) 212015
✉ info@cantabfilms.com
🖥 www.cantabfilms.com

Capricorn Productions 3rd Floor, 23-29 Albion Place, Maidstone, Kent, ME14 5DY, United Kingdom
☎ (01622) 766998/(07979) 412224 📠 (01622) 673787
✉ info@capricornproductions.co.uk
🖥 www.capricornproductions.co.uk

Catwalk Creations 63, March Court, Warwick Drive, London, SW15 6LE, United Kingdom
☎ (07834) 470117
✉ nicola@catwalkcreations.com
🖥 www.catwalkcreations.com

Centre for Media Arts & Performance Priory Street, Coventry, CV1 5FB, United Kingdom
☎ (024) 7688 7462

Centre Screen Productions Ltd (IVCA) Eastgate, Castle Street, Manchester, M3 4LZ, United Kingdom
☎ 0161-832 7151/ 📠 0161-832 8934
✉ info@centrescreen.co.uk
🖥 www.centrescreen.co.uk

Chase Production Management Unit 31, Waylett Hse, London, SE11 5PZ, United Kingdom
☎ (020) 8265 4701
✉ mail@chasingit.com
🖥 www.chasingit.com

Cheerful Scout P.L.C. 25-27 Riding House Street, London, W1W 7DU, United Kingdom
☎ (020) 7291 0444/ 📠 (020) 7291 0445
✉ info@cheerfulscout.com
🖥 www.cheerfulscout.com

Chris Chadwick Associates Unit 5 The Quadrangle, 49 Atalanta Street, London, SW6 6TU, United Kingdom
☎ (020) 7386 0254/ 📠 (020) 7381 0773
✉ chris@chadwickassociates.co.uk
🖥 www.chadwickassociates.co.uk

Chris Trengove 30 Sunderland Avenue, North Oxford, Oxford, OX2 8DX, United Kingdom
☎ (01865) 516004/(07866) 605281 📠 (01865) 513461
✉ chris.trengrove@ntlworld.com

Clearview Film Productions 10 Bracken Way, Shirebrook Park, Glossop, Derbyshire, SK13 8SY, UK
☎ (01457) 869566
✉ info@clearviewfilms.co.uk
🖥 www.clearviewfilms.co.uk

Clockhouse (IVCA) 34 Hanway Street, London, W1T 1UW, United Kingdom
☎ (020) 7436 7702/ 📠 (020) 7436 7679
✉ edit@clockhouse.co.uk
🖥 www.clockhouse.co.uk

Commercials Unlimited Garden Studios, 11-15 Betterton Street, London, WC2H 9BP, United Kingdom
☎ (020) 7470 8791/(07836) 523604 📠 (020) 7470 8792
✉ mail@commercialsunlimited.net
🖥 www.commercialsunlimited.net

Communicator Ltd (IVCA) 199 Upper Street, London, N1 1RQ, United Kingdom
☎ (020) 7704 8333/(07798) 525872 📠 (020) 7704 8444
✉ info@communicator.ltd.uk
🖥 www.communicator.ltd.uk

Contact 2 Unit 1, Piano Works, 113-117 Farringdon Road, London, EC1R 3BX, UK
☎ (020) 7833 3800
🖥 www.contact-2.com

Continuum St. Edmunds House, Margaret Street, York, YO10 4UX, United Kingdom
☎ (01904) 527700/ 📠 (01904) 527701
✉ rbriggs@continuum-group.com
🖥 www.continuum-group.com

Corporate Televison Networks (CTN) (IVCA) 114 St Martins Lane, London, WC2N 4BE, United Kingdom
☎ (020) 7395 4460
✉ info@ctn.co.uk
🖥 www.ctn.co.uk

Countrywise Communication 103 Main Road, Wilby, Wellingborough, Northamptonshire, NN8 2UB, United Kingdom
☎ (01933) 272400
✉ media@countrywise.com
🖥 www.countrywise.com

Create Media Partners 39 Telegraph Lane, Four Marks, Alton, Hampshire, GU34 5AX, United Kingdom
☎ (01420) 561144/(07939) 040720 📠 (01420) 560020
✉ info@create-media.co.uk
🖥 www.create-media.co.uk

Creative Channel (IVCA) La Pouquelaye, The Television Centre, St. Helier, Jersey, JE1 3ZD, United Kingdom
☎ (01534) 816873/ 📠 (01534) 816889
✉ david.evans@channeltv.co.uk
🖥 www.channelonline.tv

Creative Directions 1 Hinchley Way, Hinchley Wood, Esher, Surrey, KT10 0BD, United Kingdom
☎ (020) 8398 1253/ 📠 (020) 8224 9176
🖥 www.creativedirections.org.uk

Cypher Media Salters House, St. Andrews Square, Droitwich, Worcestershire, WR9 8HE, United Kingdom
☎ (01905) 827772/ 📠 (01905) 774114
✉ name@cyphermedia.co.uk
🖥 www.cyphermedia.co.uk

David Andrew 10 Bracken Way, Shirebrook Park, Glossop, Derbyshire, SK13 8SY, United Kingdom
☎ (01457) 869566
🖥 www.clearviewfilms.co.uk

Dusk Films 2/2 Maddock Street, Windsor, 3181 VIC, Australia
☎ 00 61 3 9521 1080/ 📠 00 61 3 9521 1080
✉ luke@duskfilms.com.au
🖥 www.duskfilms.com.au

Edge Picture Co. (IVCA) 7 Langley Street, London, WC2H 9JA, United Kingdom
☎ (020) 7836 6262/ 📠 (020) 7836 6949
✉ ask.us@edgepicture.com
🖥 www.edgepicture.com

Elevator Digital Unit 3.2, Waulk Mill, 51 Bengal Street, Manchester, M4 6LN, United Kingdom
☎ 0161-244 5544/ 📠 0161-244 5533
✉ c.jordan@elevatordigital.co.uk
🖥 www.elevatordigital.co.uk

Emerald Music 120A Coach Road, Templepatrick, Ballyclare, County Antrim, BT39 0HA, United Kingdom
☎ (028) 9443 2619/ 📠 (028) 9443 2162
✉ info@emeraldmusic.co.uk
🖥 www.emeraldmusiconline.com

Fastline Photographic Station Rise, York, YO1 6HT, United Kingdom
☎ (01904) 522 575/ 📠 (01904) 522 575
✉ seamus@fastlinephotographic.com
🖥 www.fastlinephotographic.com

Firehouse Productions (IVCA) 42 Glasshouse Street, London, W1B 5DW, United Kingdom
☎ (020) 7439 2220/ 📠 (020) 7439 2210
✉ postie@firehouse.biz
🖥 www.firehouse.biz

First Field (IVCA) Unit B5, 3 Bradbury Street, London, N16 8JN, United Kingdom
☎ (020) 7690 4990
✉ firstfield@clara.co.uk
🖥 www.firstfield.co.uk

Flaxman Wilkie Reed Hall, Ipswich Road, Holbrook, Ipswich, IP9 2QR, United Kingdom
☎ (01473) 326999/ 📠 (01473) 328422
✉ mike@flaxmanwilkie.com
🖥 www.flaxmanwilkie.com

Fliptop Films 22 Cheal Close, Brighton, BN43 5RQ, United Kingdom
☎ (07973) 428510
✉ charlie@fliptopfilms.com
🖥 www.fliptopfilms.com

Furious Photography 42-44 Surrey Road, Cliftonville, Margate, Kent, CT9 2LA, United Kingdom
☎ (01843) 209 514
✎ steventrevellion@gmail.com
🖥 www.furiousphotography.com

Gemini Productions 14 Morris Place, Finsbury Park Trading Estate, London, N4 3JG, United Kingdom
☎ (020) 7263 6336/ (020) 7263 8995
✎ events@gemprod.co.uk
🖥 www.gemprod.co.uk

Green Earth Production Inc Redondo Beach, Los Angeles, 90278, United States of America
☎ 00 1 310 318 9675/ 00 1 310 318 9995
✎ info@greenearthproductions.com
🖥 www.greenearthproductions.com

H M X Corporate Communication (IVCA) The Pigsty, Rectory Farm Barns, Buckingham Road, Weedon, Aylesbury, Buckinghamshire, HP22 4DR, United Kingdom
☎ (01296) 642070/ (01296) 640227
✎ timhorrox@hmx.cc
🖥 www.hmx.cc

H2 Business Communication Ltd (IVCA) Shepperton Studios, Studios Road, Shepperton, Middlesex, TW17 0QD, United Kingdom
☎ (01932) 593717/ (01932) 593718
✎ mail@h2bc.co.uk
🖥 www.h2bc.co.uk

Happy Hour Productions Ltd The Picture House, 4 Lower Park Road, Bristol, BS1 5BJ, United Kingdom
☎ 0117-929 9797/ 0117-923 0862
✎ info@hhour.co.uk
🖥 www.happyhourproductions.co.uk

Hawkshead (IVCA) Shepards Building Central, Charecroft Way, London, W14 0EE, United Kingdom
☎ (020) 8222 4408/ (020) 8222 4401
✎ info@hawksheadtv.com
🖥 www.hawksheadtv.com

Heavy Entertainment Ltd 111 Wardour Street, London, W1F 0UH, United Kingdom
☎ (020) 7494 1000/ (020) 7494 1100
✎ david@heavy-entertainment.com
🖥 www.heavy-entertainment.com

Hesketh Crean Consultants Ltd (IVCA) Flat 1, 8 Shepherd Market, London, W1J 7QE, United Kingdom
☎ (020) 7495 7222/ (020) 7399 9977
✎ n.crean@heskethcrean.com
🖥 www.heskethcrean.com

Holly Benson Communications House, Garsington Road, Cowley, Oxford, OX4 2NG, United Kingdom
☎ (01865) 383073
✎ mb@hollybenson.co.uk
🖥 www.hollybenson.co.uk

Hub Media 28 Rosslyn Hill, London, NW3 1NH, United Kingdom
☎ (020) 7435 3315/ (020) 7435 5385
✎ lynn@hub-media.com
🖥 www.hub-media.com

I B C Video 5 Barns Place, Hale Barns, Altrincham, Cheshire, WA15 0HP, United Kingdom
☎ (07976) 566701
✎ ibcvideo@aol.com
🖥 www.ibcvideo.com

I D 2 Media Ltd 19 Moody Terrace, Congleton, Cheshire, CW12 4AN, United Kingdom
☎ (01260) 299024/ (01260) 299059
✎ enquiries@id2.co.uk
🖥 www.id2.co.uk

Inside-out Branding (IVCA) Upper Woodhead, Krumlin, Barkisland, Halifax, West Yorkshire, HX4 0EQ, United Kingdom
☎ (01422) 825222/ (01422) 824433
✎ info@inside-outbranding.com
🖥 www.inside-outbranding.com

IQ Media The Coach House, Sundial House, Altringham Road, Styal, Near Wilmslow, Cheshire, SK9 4JE, United Kingdom
☎ (01625) 418666/ (01625) 522253
✎ info@iqmedia-uk.com
🖥 www.iqmedia-uk.com

Jacaranda Productions Ltd (IVCA) 6 Studland Street, London, W6 0JS, United Kingdom
☎ (020) 8741 9088/ (020) 8748 5670
✎ creative@jacaranda.co.uk
🖥 www.jacaranda.co.uk

Jack Morton Worldwide (IVCA) 16-18 Acton Park Estate, Stanley Gardens, London, W3 7QE, United Kingdom
☎ (020) 8735 2000/ (020) 8735 2020
✎ Adam_Norris@jackmorton.co.uk
🖥 www.jackmorton.com

James Willis 3 Old Garden House, The Lanterns, London, SW11 3AD, United Kingdom
☎ (020) 7801 3176/078 36 226597
✎ info@willismck.com

JiB Productions Royal Docks Business Centre Ltd, University of East London, 4-6 University Way, London, E16 2RD, United Kingdom
☎ (07811) 988 108
✎ info@jibproductions.co.uk
🖥 www.jibproductions.co.uk

Jim Watters 4 Brook Street, Twyford, Reading, RG10 9NX, United Kingdom
☎ 0118-934 2797/07702) 433847 0118-934 2797
✎ jimwatters@macunlimited.net
🖥 www.redstart.net/jameswatters/index.html

Line Communications Group Ltd (IVCA) 6th Floor, 14-16 Westbourne Grove, London, W2 5RH, United Kingdom
☎ (020) 7243 7181/ (020) 7243 9080
✎ info@line.co.uk
🖥 www.line.co.uk

Line Up Communications Ltd 6 Castle Row, Horticultural Place, London, W4 4JQ, United Kingdom
☎ (020) 8747 2200/ (020) 8747 2222
✎ info@lineup.uk.com
🖥 www.lineup.uk.com

Lonestar Ltd The Old Dance Hall, 338 London Road, Portsmouth, PO2 9JY, United Kingdom
☎ (023) 9265 1657/ (023) 9265 1658
✎ info@lonestar.co.uk
🖥 www.lonestar.co.uk

Maritz Communications Ltd (IVCA) Alexander House, 3rd Avenue, Marlow, Buckinghamshire, SL7 1YW, United Kingdom
☎ (01628) 486011/ (01628) 475737
✎ info@maritz.co.uk
🖥 www.maritz.co.uk

Medialink International 52-58 Shorts Gardens, London, WC2H 9AN, United Kingdom
☎ (020) 7845 7300/ (020) 7845 7310
✎ office@europe.medialink.com
🖥 www.europe.medialink.com

Metro 53 Great Suffolk Street, London, SE1 0DB, United Kingdom
☎ (020) 7202 2000/ (020) 7202 2007
✎ info@metrobroadcast.com
🖥 www.metrobroadcast.com

Mills Media Ltd 2 Morpeth Wharf, 12 Quays, Wirral, Merseyside, CH41 1LF, United Kingdom
☎ 0151-649 3600/ 0151-649 3700
✎ sales@millsmediagroup.com
🖥 www.millsmediagroup.com

Moving Media Marketing Ltd Round Foundry Media Centre, Foundry Street, Leeds, LS11 5QP, United Kingdom
☎ (0870) 4202430/ (0870) 4202400
✎ info@movingmedia.co.uk
🖥 www.movingmedia.co.uk

On Screen Productions Ltd (IVCA) Ashbourne House, 33 Bridge Street, Chepstow, Monmouth, NP16 5GA, United Kingdom
☎ (01291) 636300/ (01291) 636301
✎ action@onscreenproductions.com
🖥 www.onscreenproductions.com

Opex Creative 4th Floor, Room 475, Exhibition Centre, Warwick Road, London, SW5 9TA, United Kingdom
☎ (020) 7370 8145/ (020) 7370 8377
✎ ashrita.seshadri@opex.co.uk
🖥 www.opex.co.uk

Oriel Communications (IVCA) 4 Baron's Gate, Rothschild Road, London, W4 5HT, United Kingdom
☎ (020) 8995 3445/ (020) 8742 7578
✎ oriel@cix.co.uk
🖥 www.orielcommunications.com

Original Film & Video Productions Ltd (IVCA) 84 St Dionis Road, London, SW6 4TU, United Kingdom
☎ (020) 7731 0012/(07850) 780370
✎ original.films@btinternet.com
🖥 www.originalproductions.co.uk

Outrageous 57 Hatherley Road, Winchester, Hampshire, SO22 6RR, United Kingdom
☎ (01962) 859 055/ (01962) 859 033
✎ info@outrageous.co.uk
🖥 www.outrageous.co.uk

Ovation Productions (IVCA) Upstairs at the Gatehouse, Highgate Village, London, London, N6 4BD, United Kingdom
☎ (020) 8340 4256/ (020) 8340 3466
✎ events@ovationproductions.com
🖥 www.ovationproductions.com

Paper Moon Productions Wychwood House, Burchetts Green Lane, Maidenhead, Berkshire, SL6 3QW, United Kingdom
☎ (01628) 829819/(07836) 240815 (01628) 829819
✎ info@paper-moon.co.uk
🖥 www.paper-moon.co.uk

Paydirt Productions Ltd 34 Headlands, Kettering, Northamptonshire, NN15 7HP, United Kingdom
☎ (01536) 415347/ (01536) 312535
✎ info@paydirtproductions.tv
🖥 www.paydirtproductions.tv

PCI Fitch G4 Harbour Yard, Chelsea Harbour, London, SW10 0XD, United Kingdom
☎ (020) 7544 7500/ (020) 7352 7906
🖥 www.pcifitch.com

Peninsula Films 9 Saxon Road, Cambridge, CB5 8HS, United Kingdom
☎ (01223) 460459
✎ taplin@peninsulafilms.com
🖥 www.peninsulafilms.com

Peter Meech 9 Beech Avenue, High Wycombe, Buckinghamshire, HP14 3EQ, United Kingdom
☎ (01494) 883334/(07721) 444497
✎ peter@petermeech.co.uk
🖥 www.petermeech.co.uk

Picardy Media & Communication 1 Park Circus, Glasgow, G3 6AX, United Kingdom
☎ 0141-333 5555/ 0141-332 6002
✎ info@picardy.co.uk
🖥 www.picardy.co.uk

Plus Two Ltd Medius House, 2 Sheridan Street, Soho, London, W1F 8BH, United Kingdom
☎ (0870) 366 5270/ (0870) 132 0116
✎ info@plus-two.com
🖥 www.plus-two.com

Presentation Matters Ltd Linear House, Peyton Place, London, SE10 8RS, United Kingdom
☎ (020) 8858 8351/ (020) 8305 0268
✎ tony@othens.co.uk
🖥 www.presentation-matters.co.uk

Procreation UK Ltd Teddington Studios, Broom Road, Teddington, Middlesex, TW11 9NT, United Kingdom
☎ (020) 8977 5361/ (020) 8977 5361
✎ matt@procreationgroup.com
🖥 www.procreationgroup.com

Pump House Productions International Ltd (IVCA) Heath House, Princes Mews, Royston, Hertfordshire, SG8 9RT, United Kingdom
☎ (0870) 240 5553/ (0870) 240 5556
✎ mail@pumphouse.co.uk
🖥 www.pumphouse.co.uk

Razor Productions (IVCA) Westpoint, 39-40 Wharple Way, London, W3 0RG, United Kingdom
☎ (020) 8746 0708
✎ gary@razor-uk.com
🖥 www.razor-uk.com

Real To Reel Productions Ltd (IVCA) 61-63 Churchfield Road, London, W3 6AY, United Kingdom
☎ (020) 8993 6000/ (020) 8993 6006
✎ office@realtoreel.co.uk
🖥 www.realtoreel.co.uk

Rob Harris Productions The Studio, 310 King Street, Hammersmith, London, W6 0RR, United Kingdom
☎ (020) 8748 2430/(07860) 798450
✎ rob@robharrisproductions.com
🖥 www.robharrisproductions.com

S L V 70-74 Stewarts Road, London, SW8 4DE, United Kingdom
☎ (020) 7720 6464/ (020) 7622 3666
✎ shoot@slvision.co.uk
🖥 www.slvision.co.uk

Shelton Fleming Associates Ltd (IVCA) 14 Baden Place, Crosby Row, Borough, London, SE1 1YW, UK
☎ (020) 7378 7021/ (020) 7357 9009
✎ ideasintoexperiences@sheltonfleming.co.uk
🖥 www.sheltonfleming.co.uk

Six Digital 130 Mount Street, London, W1K 3NY, United Kingdom
☎ (020) 7409 0711
✎ jeremy@six-digital.com
🖥 www.six-digital.com

Sledge The Millhouse, Millers Way, London, W6 7NH, United Kingdom
- (020) 8743 3232/ (020) 8743 5062
- ian.irving@sledge.co.uk
- www.sledge.co.uk

Sound & Picture House The Coach House, 29 Woodburn Road, Edgbaston, Birmingham, B17 8BY, United Kingdom
- 0121-429 5462/ 0121-429 6952
- sph@sph.uk.com
- www.soundandpicturehouse.com

Spiral Communications Pte Ltd 28 Maxwell Road, 02-15A, Red Dot Traffic Building, Singapore,
- +65 65347184/ +65 63278902
- enquiry@spiralcomms.com
- www.spiralcomms.com

Spirit Media P.L.C. (IVCA) Canalot Studios, 222 Kensal Rd, London, W10 5BN, United Kingdom
- (020) 8960 0108/ (020) 8960 1227
- enquiries@spiritmedia.co.uk
- www.spiritmedia.co.uk

Straker Films 3 St Marks Place, London, SW19 7ND, United Kingdom
- (020) 8605 2012/ (020) 8605 2121
- nick@strakerfilms.com
- www.strakerfilms.com

Stream UK Media Services Ltd Studio 522, 53-79 Highgate Road, London, NW5 1TL, United Kingdom
- (020) 7387 6090/ (020) 7419 1819
- jessica@streamuk.com
- www.streamuk.com

T C Group 1A Poland Street, London, W1F 8PR, United Kingdom
- (020) 7851 9180/ (020) 7287 5323
- info@tcvideo.co.uk
- www.tcsoho.co.uk

Table Twelve Media 30 Citygate, 1 Blantyre Street, Manchester, M15 4JT, United Kingdom
- 0161-819 1084/ 0181-819 1084
- nick@tabltwelvemedia.com
- www.tabletwelvemedia.com

Take 3 Video & Film Production Ltd (IVCA) 72-73 Margaret Street, London, W1W 8ST, United Kingdom
- (020) 7637 2694/ (020) 7637 4678
- mail@take3.co.uk
- www.take3.co.uk

Target Communications Ltd 52 Elmwood Road, London, W4 3DZ, United Kingdom
- (020) 8995 9652/(07785) 250550/ (020) 8994 3164
- lamprod@compuserve.com
- www.lamproductions.co.uk

Taylor Made Broadcast Unit 3B, Marston House, Cromwell Park, Chipping Norton, Oxfordshire, OX7 5SR, United Kingdom
- (01608) 646444/ (01608) 646461
- post@tmtv.co.uk

The 5YLAC Group 26 York Street, London, W1U 6PZ, United Kingdom
- (0845) 3104314/ (0870) 7623212
- info56@5ylac.biz
- www.5ylac.biz

The Loop Communication Agency 5th Floor, Hanover House, Queen Charlotte Street, Bristol, BS1 4EX, United Kingdom
- 0117-311 2040/ 0117-311 2041
- info@theloopagency.com
- www.theloopagency.com

Those Media Guys Ltd 3rd Floor, 13 James Court, Edinburgh, EH1 2PB, United Kingdom
- 0131-466 2639
- info@thosemediaguys.com
- www.thosemediaguys.com

Tiger Vision 27 Maiden Lane, Covent Garden, London, WC2E 7JS, United Kingdom
- (020) 7438 9960/ (020) 7438 9980
- production@tigervision.com
- www.tigervision.com

Tomorrow London 222 Kingsland Road, London, E2 8DG, United Kingdom
- (020) 7739 0911
- contact@tomorrowlondon.com
- www.tomorrowlondon.com

Totem Event Ltd (IVCA) Penrith Lge, 61 Canbury Pk Rd, Kingston upon Thames, Surrey, KT2 6LQ, United Kingdom
- (020) 8133 3051
- neil@totemevent.co.uk
- www.totemevent.co.uk

Uden Associates Ltd (IVCA, PACT) Unit 37, Chelsea Wharf, 15 Lots Road, Chelsea, London, SW10 0QJ, United Kingdom
- (020) 7351 1255/ (020) 7376 3937
- www.simonharries.com/miscproductions/udenassociates.htm

V B M Productions Oak Cottage, Wonersh Common, Wonersh, Guildford, Surrey, GU5 0PP, United Kingdom
- (0845) 226 1336
- info@vbmproductions.co.uk
- www.vbmproductions.co.uk/

Video Image Productions The Cottage Newlands School, Seaford, East Sussex, BN25 4NP, United Kingdom
- (01323) 873513
- sales@videoimageprod.co.uk
- www.videoimageprod.co.uk

Video Monkeys LLP PO Box 285, Burgess Hill, West Sussex, RH15 0WN, United Kingdom
- (0845) 094 1179/ (0871) 733 3988
- info@videomonkeys.com
- www.videomonkeys.com

Visual Link (IVCA) Kingstown Broadway, Carlisle, CA3 0HA, United Kingdom
- (01228) 403900/ (01228) 511267
- info@tvl.co.uk
- www.tvl.co.uk

VT Group P.L.C. Portland Gate, Portland Square, Bristol, BS2 8SJ, United Kingdom
- 0117-987 7711/ 0117-987 7721
- sales@vt.tv
- www.vt.tv

Waterfall Multimedia Ltd 2 Silver Road, Wood Lane, London, W12 7SG, United Kingdom
- (020) 8746 2000/ (020) 8746 0180
- info@waterfall-studios.com
- www.waterfall-studios.com

A spark of an idea
is all it takes...

Whatever your film and
video needs:

Sales & Marketing
PR & Corporate Communications
Employee Engagement
Events & Promotions

strakerfilms

3 St Mark's Place, London,
SW19 7ND
Tel: +44 (0)208 605 2012
email: info@strakerfilms.com
web: www.strakerfilms.com

Wide Angle 10-Nov, 254-256 Belfize Road, London, Greater London, NW6 4BT, United Kingdom
- (020) 7916 3790/ (020) 7916 3799
- info@wideangle.co.uk
- www.wideangle.co.uk

WiseGuy Pictures Ltd Studio 54, Soho Wharf, Clink Street, London, SE1 9DG, United Kingdom
- (020) 7407 2007
- mail@wiseguy.co.uk
- www.wiseguy.co.uk

Wordley Production Partners (PACT) The Warehouse, 1 High Street, Penarth, Cardiff, CF64 1EY, United Kingdom
- (029) 2070 0590/ (029) 2070 0550
- info@wordleyproduction.com
- www.wordleyproduction.com

World Productions Ltd (IVCA) 16 Dufours Place, London, W1F 7SP, United Kingdom
- (020) 7734 3536/ (020) 7758 7000
- info@world-productions.com
- www.world-productions.com

World Wide Pictures (IVCA, PACT) 21-25 St Annes Court, London, W1F 0BJ, United Kingdom
- (020) 7434 1121/ (020) 7734 0619
- reception@worldwidegroup.ltd.uk
- www.worldwidegroup.ltd.uk

Write Angle Creative Services Ltd 29 London Road, Cheltenham, Gloucestershire, GL52 6EY, United Kingdom
- (01242) 241315
- info@writeanglegroup.co.uk
- www.writeanglegroup.co.uk

EXHIBITION DISPLAY SERVICES

422 Manchester Ltd 4th Floor, South Central, 11 Peter Street, Manchester, M2 5QR, United Kingdom
- 0161-839 6080/ 0161-839 6081
- richard@422.tv
- www.422.tv

7eq Studios The Seed Warehouse, The Wash, Hertford, SG14 1PX, United Kingdom
- (07790) 035484
- mrbasslo@yahoo.com
- www.dawgrecords.co.uk

A & C Audio Visual Ltd 98 Goremire Road, Carluke, Lanarkshire, ML8 4PF, United Kingdom
- (01555) 772648/ (01555) 752060
- alistair@aandcaudio.co.uk
- www.aandcaudio.co.uk

A P M Products Ltd Unit 2, Delta Way Business Centre, Longford Road, Bridgetown, Cannock, Staffordshire, WS11 3BE, United Kingdom
- (01543) 466868/ (01543) 466149
- mail@courprod.co.uk

Above Art Gallery 15 Fulham High Street, London, SW6 3JH, United Kingdom
- (020) 7371 7584/ (020) 7736 3033

Absolute Software Ltd Unit 11, Bosleake Rural Workshops, Redruth, Cornwall, TR15 3YG, United Kingdom
- (01209) 712444
- enquiries@absolute-software.co.uk
- www.absolute-software.co.uk

At www.designweek.co.uk there's more than you might think.

You'll find over 20 stories a week that aren't in the magazine, the latest jobs, a 15 year archive and our events diary to plan your design year by.

So why not pay us a visit today, at www.designweek.co.uk

design WEEK.co.uk

Accura Imaging Ltd Harvest House, Cranborne Road, Potters Bar, Hertfordshire, EN6 3JF, United Kingdom
(01707) 660055/ (01707) 660052
sales@accuraimaging.co.uk
www.accuraimaging.co.uk

Acre Jean Ltd Unit 7 The Kimber Centre, 54 Kimber Road, London, SW18 4PP,
020 8877 3211/ 020 8877 3213
dan.hill@acrejean.com
www.acrejean.com

Alpha 4 Ltd 24 Brunel Road, St. Leonards-on-Sea, East Sussex, TN38 9RT, United Kingdom
(01424) 854485/ (01424) 854402
info@alpha-4.co.uk
www.alpha-4.co.uk

Anderson Lambert 2 Kensworth Gate, High Street South, Dunstable, Bedfordshire, LU6 3HS, United Kingdom
(01582) 754000/ (01582) 706420
info@andersonlambert.com
www.andersonlambert.com

Arbiter Group Ltd 2nd Floor, Atlantic House, Stirling Way, Borehamwood, London, Hertfordshire, WD6 2BT, United Kingdom
(020) 8207 7860/ (020) 8953 6221
sales@arbitergroup.com
www.arbitergroup.com

Arcsound 443 New Cross Road, London, SE14 6TA, United Kingdom
(020) 8691 8161/ (020) 8691 8161
info@arcsound.co.uk
www.arcsound.co.uk

Artisan Glass Products Ltd Unit 2 Graylaw Trading Estate, Wareing Road, Aintree, Liverpool, L9 7AU, United Kingdom
(0151) 525 0220/ (0151) 524 2152
sue@artisanglassproducts.co.uk
www.artisanglassproducts.co.uk

Artisan Services (NW) Ltd Unit 2 Graylaw Trading Estate, Wareing Road, Aintree, LIVERPOOL, L9 7AU, United Kingdom
0151 524 2124/ 0151 524 2152
sue@artisanservices.co.uk
www.artisanservices.co.uk

Ashton Studios Ltd The Glasgow Media Park, Craigmont Street, Glasgow, G20 9BT, United Kingdom
0141-945 5858/ 0141-945 5511
info@ashtonstudios.co.uk
www.ashtonstudios.co.uk

Aspect Exihibitions Unit 1, Ashton Lodge Farm, Hartwell Road, Ashton, Northampton, NN7 2JT, United Kingdom
(01604) 864999/ (01604) 864888
paul@aspectexihibitions.co.uk
www.aspectexihibitions.co.uk

Audio Workshop 217 Askew Road, London, W12 9AZ, United Kingdom
(020) 8742 9242/ (020) 8743 4231
info@theaudioworkshop.co.uk
www.theaudioworkshop.co.uk

AV Matrix Ltd, Harrogate, North Yorkshire, HG3 2GR, United Kingdom
(01423) 521011/(07790) 496655 (01423) 521011
info@av-matrix.com
www.av-matrix.com

Avoncolour Ltd 131 Duckmoor Road, Ashton Gate, Bristol, BS3 2BJ, United Kingdom
0117-963 3456/ 0117-966 3456
info@avoncolour.co.uk
www.avoncolour.co.uk

B & S Graphics City Link Central, 145 Helen Street, Glasgow, G51 3HD, United Kingdom
0141-425 2300/ 0141-445 4619
enq@b-s.co.uk
www.b-s.co.uk

Backdrops 4 Bayer House, Golden Lane, London, EC1Y 0RN, United Kingdom
(020) 7490 2635

Bellard Electronics Ltd Bellard Court, Platts Lane, Tarporley, Cheshire, CW6 0EU, United Kingdom
(01829) 740740/ (01829) 740777
info@bellard.co.uk
www.bellard.co.uk

Better Sound Ltd 31 Cathcart Street, London, NW5 3BJ, United Kingdom
(020) 7482 0177/ (020) 7482 2677
hire@bettersound.co.uk
www.bettersound.co.uk

Betty Marsden 81 Casterbridge, Abbey Road, London, NW6 4DR, United Kingdom
(020) 7624 9478

BigStuff Ltd, Southampton, United Kingdom
(023) 8033 4332/ (023) 8033 4330
info@bigstuff.org.uk
www.bigstuff.org.uk

Black Dog Events 202 Balvernie Grove, London, SW18 5RW, United Kingdom
(020) 8870 7923/(07930) 682612 (020) 8516 8972
robinr@blackdogevents.com
www.blackdogevents.com

Blaze Neon Ltd Patricia Way, Pysons Road, Broadstairs, Kent, CT10 2XZ, United Kingdom
(01843) 601075/ (01843) 867924
chrisa@blazeneon.com
www.blazeneon.com

Blitz Communication Ltd 100 Centennial Avenue, Elstree, Hertfordshire, WD6 3SA, United Kingdom
(0870) 1621010/ (0870) 1621111
enquiries@blitzvision.com
www.blitzvision.com

Blitz Vision 7-8 Piccadilly Trading Estate, Giddings Road, Manchester, M1 2NP, United Kingdom
(0870) 1623300/ (0870) 1623333
man@blitzvision.com
www.blitzvision.com

Boiler Room London 31 Wardour Street, London, W1D 6PT, United Kingdom
(020) 7434 2256
jan@boiler-music.com
www.boiler-music.com

Brian Bennett Music 333 Washington Boulevard Suite 243, Marina Del Rey, 90292, United States of America
00 1 310 895 5635
brian.scott.bennett@lycos.co.uk

Buccaneer Films 5 Rainbow Court, Watford, WD19 4RP, United Kingdom
(01923) 254000

Bull Signs International Ltd Bayhorne Lane, Horley, Surrey, RH6 9ES, United Kingdom
(01293) 821313/ (01293) 821414
sales@bullsigns.com
www.bullsigns.com

Cafe Music 18 Ordell Road, London, E3 2DS, United Kingdom
(020) 8981 2588
info@cafestudio.co.uk
www.cafestudio.co.uk

Calavera Records Flat 29, 2 Martello Street, Hackney, London, E8 3PF, United Kingdom
(020) 7812 9881
mcbigbadal@btopenworld.com
www.johnwaynearmy.co.uk

Chameleon Pro Audio & Lighting Ltd Unit 10, Orton Industrial Estate, London Road, Coalville, Leicestershire, LE67 3JA, United Kingdom
(01530) 831337/ (01530) 838319
info@chameleon-pa.co.uk
www.chameleon-pa.co.uk

Chromatics 79-80 Western Road, Hove, East Sussex, BN3 2JQ, United Kingdom
(01273) 722242/ (01273) 739588
sales@chromatics.ltd.co.uk
www.chromatics.ltd.co.uk

Circa Group Imperial House, 15-19 Kingsway, London, WC2B 6UN, United Kingdom
(020) 7836 1600/ (020) 7420 1777
info@circagroup.co.uk
www.circagroup.co.uk

Clip Ltd Athena, 210 Bristol Business Park, The Close, Bristol, BS16 1FJ, United Kingdom
0117-937 5700/ 0117-931 4561
info@clipdisplay.com
www.clipdisplay.com

Colossal Solutions Little Brittin House, Alna Road, Chesham, Buckinghamshire, HP5 3HB, United Kingdom
(01494) 793700/ (01494) 773594
graham@colossal.co.uk
www.colossal.co.uk

Coloursonic 40 Chippenham Mews, Maida Vale, London, W9 2AW, United Kingdom
(020) 7286 4766/ (020) 7286 1139
info@coloursonic.co.uk
www.coloursonic.co.uk

Comtec Ltd Unit 19, Tait Road, Croydon, CR0 2DP, United Kingdom
(020) 8684 6615/ (020) 8684 6947
info@comtecav.co.uk
www.comtecav.co.uk

Concept Partners 5 Park View Mansions, Highgate High Street, London, N6 5JJ, United Kingdom
(020) 8348 6136/ (020) 8340 9717
bjbamsimon@yahoo.co.uk

Covent Garden Laminates Ltd 13 Macklin Street, Covent Garden, London, WC2B 5NH, United Kingdom
(020) 7242 1960/ (020) 7242 1001
info@cgluk.net
www.cgluk.net

Creation Design Consultancy 20 Meridian Place, Bristol, BS8 1JL, United Kingdom
0117-310 1212/(07706) 687199 0117-946 4723
nick@creationdesign.co.uk
www.creationdesign.co.uk

Creative Edge Design & Advertising 1st Floor Donald Hendry Building, Auchincruive, Ayr, KA6 5HW, United Kingdom
- (01292) 521404/ (01292) 521693
- paul@cedge.co.uk
- www.cedge.co.uk

Creative Services Displays & Exhibitions 14B Johnsons Way, Coronation Road, London, NW10 7PF, United Kingdom
- (020) 8453 0165/ (020) 8961 3804
- creati@creative-services.co.uk
- www.creative-services.co.uk

D B L Cromwell House, 68 Calvin Road, Bournemouth, BH9 1LN, United Kingdom
- (01202) 532366/ (01202) 535650
- info@dbl-imaging.co.uk
- www.dbl-imaging.co.uk

D Line Signs 6 High Street, Haddenham, Buckinghamshire, HP17 8ER, United Kingdom
- (01844) 299305/ (01844) 299310
- signs@dlinesigns.com
- www.dlinesigns.com

Dan Display & Imaging Ltd Harlequin House, Coedcad Lane, Pontyclun, Mid Glamorgan, CF72 9EW, United Kingdom
- (01443) 225656/ (01443) 226544
- info@dandisplay.co.uk
- www.dandisplay.co.uk

Dave Dixon 5 Gilpin Avenue, London, SW14 8QX, United Kingdom
- (020) 8876 8391/ (020) 8876 8391
- ddixn@supanet.com

David Andrew 10 Bracken Way, Shirebrook Park, Glossop, Derbyshire, SK13 8SY, United Kingdom
- (01457) 869566
- www.clearviewfilms.co.uk

Dead Clever Sound Studios Ltd 1 Bolton Road, Southbourne, Bournemouth, BH6 3DZ, United Kingdom
- (01202) 423372
- heather@deadcleversounds.co.uk
- www.deadcleversounds.co.uk

Design Distillery Ltd 12 Northgate, Chichester, West Sussex, PO19 1BA, United Kingdom
- (01243) 537837/ (01243) 839448
- guy@design-distillery.co.uk
- www.design-distillery.co.uk

Design Point Associates Old Barn Studios, Hereford Gardens, Pinner, Middlesex, HA5 5JR, United Kingdom
- (020) 8866 5660/ (020) 8866 6040
- sales@dpa-creative.com
- www.dpa-creative.com

Designcrew Creative Media Centre, 45 Robertson Street, Hastings, East Sussex, TN34 1HL,
- 01424 205 499/01424 205 499
- danny@designcrew.co.uk
- www.designcrew.co.uk

Designshop 34 Chester Square, Ashton-under-Lyne, Lancashire, OL6 7TW, United Kingdom
- 0161-330 3399
- mail@designshopltd.com
- www.designshopltd.com

Digital Disc Duplication Ltd 25 Huntingfield Road, Bury St. Edmunds, Suffolk, IP33 2JA, United Kingdom
- (01284) 700773
- info@digitaldiscduplication.com
- www.digitaldiscduplication.com

Digital Imaging Services Ltd Unit A1, Hilton Trading Est, Hilton Road, Lanesfield, Wolverhampton, WV4 6DW, United Kingdom
- (01902) 406000/ (01902) 406001
- sales@digital-is.co.uk
- www.digital-is.co.uk

Digital Print Factory Ltd 12-12A Rosebery Avenue, London, EC1R 4TD, United Kingdom
- (020) 7837 8666/ (020) 7404 4762
- t.harding@colyer.co.uk
- www.colyer.co.uk

Dijon Designs Unit 1, Castle Farm, Clifton Road, Deddington, Banbury, Oxfordshire, OX15 0TP, United Kingdom
- (01869) 337311/ (01869) 337322
- information@dijondesigns.com
- www.dijondesigns.com

Dijon Exhibition Designs Suite 1 Field Barns, Castle Farm, Clifton Road, Deddington, Banbury, Oxfordshire, OX15 0TP, United Kingdom
- (01869) 337311/ (01869) 337322
- information@dijondesigns.com
- www.dijondesigns.com

Dimension Group Ltd 4 Repton Court, Repton Close, Basildon, Essex, SS13 1LN, United Kingdom
- (01268) 285361/ (01268) 532474
- a.pritchard@dimensiongroup.co.uk
- www.dimensiongroup.co.uk

Dimensions Displays Ltd Unit 21, The Arches, Hartland Road, London, NW1 8HR, United Kingdom
- (020) 7485 8400/ (020) 7284 3064
- info@d4display.com
- www.d4display.com

Dir Design 195 Darlington Street East, Wigan, Lancashire, WN1 3EA, United Kingdom
- (07814) 961719
- christian@dirdesign.net
- www.dirdesign.net

Disc Wizards 3 Oakleigh Court, Edgware, Middlesex, HA8 5JB, United Kingdom
- (020) 8931 0001/ (020) 8931 0001
- info@discwizards.com
- www.discwizards.com

Dischromtics Ltd Unit 20, Prince of Wales Industrial Estate, Abercarn, Newport, Gwent, NP11 5AR, United Kingdom
- (01495) 243222/ (01495) 243777
- stewart@dischro.co.uk
- www.dischromatics.co.uk

Display Matrix 196 Broom Hill Road, Brislington, Bristol, BS4 5RA, United Kingdom
- 0117-977 2278/ 0117-977 2457
- info@displaymatrix.co.uk
- www.displaymatrix.co.uk

Displays 2 Go Unit 7, Leeway Court, Leeway Industrial Estate, Newport, Gwent, NP19 4SJ, United Kingdom
- (01633) 283838
- carl@displays2go.co.uk
- www.displays2go.co.uk

Displayways 16 Groton Road, Earlsfield, London, SW18 4EP, United Kingdom
- (020) 8877 6700/ (020) 8870 8706
- sales@displayways.co.uk
- www.displayways.co.uk

Dubmaster Studios 62 Ashdell Road, Alton, Hampshire, GU34 2TA, United Kingdom
- (01420) 82822
- info@dubmaster.com
- www.dubmaster.com

E V C Events 134 Queens Park Road, Brighton, BN2 0GG, United Kingdom
- (01273) 696006/(07970) 519932 (01273) 700734
- james.design@virgin.net

Eastern 108 Market Street, Musselburgh, Midlothian, EH21 6QA, United Kingdom
- 0131-653 5700/ 0131-665 5335
- sales@eastern-info.co.uk
- www.eastern-info.co.uk

Eclipse Design & Advertising Ltd Eclipse House, 2 North West Business Park, Leeds, LS6 2QH, United Kingdom
- 0113-244 3733/ 0113-244 3833
- andrewp@eclipsedesign.uk.com
- www.eclipsedesign.uk.com

Edric Audio Visual Ltd (IVCA) 34-36 Oak End Way, Gerrards Cross, Buckinghamshire, SL9 8BR, United Kingdom
- (01753) 481400/ (01753) 887163
- info@edric-av.co.uk
- www.edric-av.co.uk

EFG - Expo Flora Ltd The Tree House, Charlecote, Warwick, CV35 9GZ, United Kingdom
- (01789) 470847/ (01789) 470897
- sales@efg-europe.com
- www.efg-europe.com

Electro Signs Ltd 97 Vallentin Road, London, E17 3JJ, United Kingdom
- (020) 8521 8066/ (020) 8520 8127
- info@electrosigns.co.uk
- www.electrosigns.co.uk

Electro-Tech Colour Ltd Image House, 1 Blenheim Court, 62 Brewery Road, London, N7 9NY, United Kingdom
- (020) 7636 6677/ (020) 7636 5566
- info@etcltd.co.uk
- www.etcltd.co.uk

Emma Wood 24 St. Lawrence Terrace, London, W10 5SX, United Kingdom
- (020) 8960 1977/(07918) 112048

Equation Productions Ltd 14 Dovercourt Road, Bulidge, London, SE22 8ST, United Kingdom
- (020) 8692 2700/ (0870) 0521397
- info@equation-productions.com
- www.equation-productions.com

Eurostand Display Ltd The Barn, Coptfold Hall Farm, Writtle Road, Margaretting, Ingatestone, Essex, CM4 0EL, United Kingdom
- (01277) 350925/ (01277) 356732
- sales@eurostanddisplay.com
- www.eurostanddisplay.com

Exhibition Services Ltd Unit 6, 271 Merton Road, London, SW18 5JS, United Kingdom
- (020) 8874 1787/ (020) 8874 1587
- info@exhibitionservices.com
- www.exhibitionservices.com

Dubmaster Studios — see above

Frame Work Displayed Ltd Ltd 21 Ullswater Crescent, Ullswater Business Park, Coulsdon, Surrey, CR5 2HR, United Kingdom
- (020) 8655 6100/ (020) 8655 6101
- sales@premierportable.co.uk
- www.premiershowroom.net

Frontier Post 67 Wells Street, London, W1T 3PZ, United Kingdom
- (020) 7291 9191/ (020) 7291 9199
- info@frontierpost.co.uk
- www.frontierpost.co.uk

FT Audio Visual Ltd Unit 16, Valley House, Horn Beam Park, Hookstone Road, Harrogate, North Yorkshire, HG2 8QT, United Kingdom
- (01423) 810052/ (01423) 810053
- info@ftav.co.uk
- www.ftav.co.uk

Funky Concepts 5 Lansdowne Close, Coseley, Bilston, West Midlands, WV14 9TR, United Kingdom
- (01902) 651239/ (01902) 651239
- info@funkyconcepts.co.uk
- www.funkyconcepts.co.uk

G G S Photo Graphics Ltd 1 White Lodge Business Park, Hall Road, Norwich, NR4 6DG, United Kingdom
- (01603) 622500/ (01603) 633876
- enquir@ggs.co.uk
- www.ggs.co.uk

Generika.com 3 Norfolk Street, Northampton, NN2 6HR, United Kingdom
- (01604) 474944
- info@generika.com
- www.generika.com

Glidden Design Ltd 2 Braidburn Terrace, Edinburgh, EH10 6ES, United Kingdom
- 0131-447 3399/(07973) 432572 0131-447 3399
- andy@gliddendesign.com
- www.gliddendesign.com

GMID Design for Business Prospect House, 3 Prospect Place, Swansea, SA1 1QP, United Kingdom
- (01792) 641350/ (01792) 301548
- studio@gmid.net
- www.gmid.net

Gordon Audio Visual Ltd St. Leonards Road, London, NW10 6ST, United Kingdom
- (020) 7387 3399/ (020) 7387 3399
- sales@gav.co.uk
- www.bigtelly.com

Graphix Imaging Ltd Unit 5, Barrat Industrial Park, Gillender Street, London, E3 3JX, United Kingdom
- (0870) 600 9994/ (020) 7987 8601
- sales@graphiximaging.co.uk
- www.graphiximaging.co.uk

Green Ltd 11 Tor Crescent, Plymouth, PL3 5TW, United Kingdom
- (07977) 091440
- rdg@green.ltd.uk
- www.green.ltd.uk

Hammonds A V S Ltd 34 -36 Oak End Way, Gerrards Cross, Buckinghamshire, SL9 8BR, United Kingdom
- (01923) 239733/ (01753) 887163
- info@hammonds-avs.co.uk
- www.hammonds-avs.co.uk

Hawthorn Theatrical Ltd Crown Business Park, Old Dalby, Melton Mowbray, Leicestershire, LE14 3NQ, UK
📞 (01664) 821111/📠 (01664) 821119
✉ info@hawthorns.uk.com
🖥 www.hawthorns.uk.com

Headjog 5b Church Street, Carleton, Skipton, North Yorkshire, BD23 3HA, United Kingdom
📞 (07985) 433090/📠 (01756) 795966
✉ j.richard@headjog.co.uk
🖥 www.headjog.net

Heavy Entertainment Ltd 111 Wardour Street, London, W1F 0UH, United Kingdom
📞 (020) 7494 1000/📠 (020) 7494 1100
✉ david@heavy-entertainment.com
🖥 www.heavy-entertainment.com

Hocken Audio Visual Ltd 5 Waterhouse Lane, Kingswood, Tadworth, Surrey, KT20 6EB, United Kingdom
📞 (01737) 370371/📠 (01737) 370372
✉ info@hockenav.co.uk
🖥 www.hockenav.co.uk

Home Counties Colour Services Ltd Suite 1, Ground Floor, Chaucer House, Biscot Road, Luton, LU3 1AX, United Kingdom
📞 (01582) 816001/📠 (01582) 402410
✉ sales@hccs.co.uk
🖥 www.hccs.co.uk

Hypermania Design Forum House, Stirling Road, Chichester, West Sussex, PO19 7DN, United Kingdom
📞 (01243) 785678/📠 (01243) 785678
✉ sean@hypermania.com
🖥 www.hypermania.com

Inside Aluminium 8 Hangleton Lane, Hove, East Sussex, BN3 8AH, United Kingdom
📞 (01273) 220090/📠 (01273) 207993
✉ enquiries@inside-aluminium.co.uk
🖥 www.inside-aluminium.co.uk

Inspire Carlton Mills, Pickering Street, Leeds, LS12 2QG, United Kingdom
📞 0113-224 4800/📠 0113-224 4801
✉ lindsay.kemp@logistik.co.uk
🖥 www.logistik-inspire.co.uk

J P Temple Ltd 16A Chalwyn Industrial Estate, St Clements Road, Poole, Dorset, BH12 4PE, United Kingdom
📞 (01202) 715722/📠 (01202) 747811
✉ contactus@jptemple.com
🖥 www.jptemple.com

Joe Williams Music 4 Darnley Road, Leeds, LS16 5JF, United Kingdom
📞 0113-295 6111/(07760) 375712
✉ joe@joewilliams.co.uk
🖥 www.joewilliams.co.uk

Jupiter Display Ltd City Pavlion, 33 Britain Street, London, EC1M 5UG, United Kingdom
📞 (0870) 7509200/📠 (0870) 7509250
✉ robert.ward@jupiterdisplay.com
🖥 www.jupiterdisplay.com

K & S Digital Imaging Ltd Freemens Common, 90 Commercial Square, Leicester, LE2 7SR, United Kingdom
📞 0116-247 0270/📠 0116-247 1026
✉ sales@kands.co.uk
🖥 www.kands.co.uk

K 2 Unit 6 Haslemere Industrial Estate, Pig Lane, Bishop's Stortford, Hertfordshire, CM23 3HG, United Kingdom
📞 (01279) 508305/📠 (01279) 755530
✉ ken.day@k2a.co.uk
🖥 www.k2a.co.uk

K B S Signs 41 Marsh Green Road, Marsh Barton, Exeter, EX2 8PN, United Kingdom
📞 (01392) 208208/📠 (01392) 208200
✉ info@kbs-group.com
🖥 www.kbs-group.com

K P M Music House 127 Charing Cross Road, London, WC2H 0QY, United Kingdom
📞 (020) 7412 9111/📠 (020) 7413 0061
✉ info@kpmmusichouse.com
🖥 www.kpmmusichouse.com

KamPra Productions 2-10 Calypso Crescent, London, SE15 6GE, United Kingdom
📞 (020) 7708 1354
✉ kamal@kampra.com
🖥 www.kampra.com

Katherine Howard Public Relations Eastwick, Clay Lane, Stoke Ash, Eye, Suffolk, IP23 7DZ, United Kingdom
📞 (01379) 678811
✉ info@katherinehoward.co.uk
🖥 www.katherinehoward.co.uk

Ken Richman Voiceovers 1d Mount Road, Wimbledon Park, London, SW19 8ES, United Kingdom
📞 (07957) 487027/📠 (0870) 4583686
✉ ken@kenrichman.co.uk
🖥 www.kenrichman.co.uk

L A M Productions 52 Elmwood Road, Chiswick, London, W4 3DZ, United Kingdom
📞 (020) 8995 9652/(07785) 250550 📠 (020) 8994 3164
✉ larry@lamproductions.co.uk
🖥 www.lamproductions.co.uk

Lee Grainge, London, United Kingdom
📞 (07791) 043526
✉ info@leegrainge.com
🖥 www.leegrainge.com

Leightons of Leeds Ltd Webster Row, Wortley Moor Road, Leeds, LS12 4JF, United Kingdom
📞 0113-279 5755/📠 0113-279 5719
✉ leightonsofleeds@aol.com
🖥 www.leightonsofleeds.co.uk

Leitner 4 Monkspond Street, Northampton, NN1 2LF, United Kingdom
📞 (01604) 230445/📠 (01604) 231389
✉ sales@leitner.co.uk
🖥 www.leitner.co.uk

Limelight Design Limited 27 Bolingbroke Grove, London, SW11 6EJ,
📞 7946582074
✉ tom@limelight-design.co.uk
🖥 www.limelight-design.co.uk

Linden Studio Music Composition & Production & Recording Studio, High Bankhill Farmhouse, Kirkoswald, Penrith, Cumbria, CA10 1EZ, United Kingdom
📞 (01768) 870353
✉ guy@lindenstudio.co.uk
🖥 www.lindenstudio.co.uk

Lo-Tek Studios Friars Gate Farm, Mardens Hill, Crowborough, East Sussex, TN6 1XH, United Kingdom
📞 (01892) 610010
✉ studio@lo-tek.co.uk
🖥 www.lo-tekstudios.co.uk

Loungecore 63 Albert Street, Camden, London, NW1 7LX, United Kingdom
📞 (020) 7388 2605
✉ olly@loungecore.co.uk
🖥 www.loungecore.co.uk

M C L Birmingham 69 Dartmouth Middleway, Birmingham, B7 4UA, United Kingdom
📞 0121-333 3333/📠 0121-333 3347
✉ hire@mcl-birmingham.com
🖥 www.mclav.com

M W R 107 High Street, Winchester, Hampshire, SO23 9AH, United Kingdom
📞 (01962) 891160/📠 (01962) 891110
✉ pam.iannotti@mwr.biz
🖥 www.mwr.biz

Mardell-Pick Design Ltd 19 Ledbury Place, Croydon, CR0 1ET, United Kingdom
📞 (020) 8680 2646/📠 (020) 8680 0323
✉ info@mardell-pickdesign.com
🖥 www.mardell-pickdesign.com

Maria Chryssikos, London, United Kingdom
📞 (020) 8579 5121/07817 739614 📠 (08700) 517452
✉ maria@productiondesign.demon.co.uk

Marler Haley Expo Systems Ltd Hawley Road, Hinckley, Leicestershire, LE10 0PR, United Kingdom
📞 (01455) 896400/📠 (01455) 614056
✉ info@marlerhaley.co.uk
🖥 www.marlerhaley.co.uk

Masters Exhibitions & Shows Pilgrims Way, Dunton Green, Sevenoaks, Kent, TN13 2TL, United Kingdom
📞 (01732) 740370/📠 (01732) 462854
✉ sales@mastersexhibtions.co.uk
🖥 www.mastersexhibtions.co.uk

Maximus Operandi Unit 3B, Sanders Lodge Industrial Estate, Rushden, Northamptonshire, NN10 6BQ, United Kingdom
📞 (01933) 413113/📠 (01933) 413114
✉ info@maximusuk.com
🖥 www.maximusuk.com

McKenzie Clark Ltd 14-22 Ossory Road, London, SE1 5AN, United Kingdom
📞 (020) 7231 6070/📠 (020) 7232 1843
✉ sales@mckenzieclark.co.uk
🖥 www.mckenzieclark.co.uk

Mercury Conference AV Ltd 4 Shakespeare Avenue, London, N11 1AY, United Kingdom
📞 (0870) 2000805/📠 (0870) 2000815
🖥 www.mercury-av.com

Metro 53 Great Suffolk Street, London, SE1 0DB, United Kingdom
📞 (020) 7202 2000/📠 (020) 7202 2007
✉ info@metrobroadcast.com
🖥 www.metrobroadcast.com

Metrobroadcast Ltd 53 Great Suffolk Street, London, SE1 0DB, United Kingdom
📞 (020) 7202 2000/📠 (020) 7202 2007
✉ info@metrobroadcast.com
🖥 www.metrobroadcast.com

Midland Audio Visual Ltd Rear of 186-210 New Road, Rubery, Birmingham, B45 9JA, United Kingdom
📞 0121-453 3141/📠 0121-453 4626
✉ hire@midlandaudiovisual.co.uk
🖥 www.midlandaudiovisual.co.uk

Mills & MacCarthy Exhibitions Windsor Court, East Grinstead House, East Grinstead, West Sussex, RH19 1XA, United Kingdom
📞 /📠 (01342) 336113
✉ phewson@reedinfo.co.uk

Motivation Sound Studios Ltd 35A Broadhurst Gardens, London, NW6 3QT, United Kingdom
📞 (020) 7328 8305/📠 (020) 7624 4879
✉ info@motivationsound.com
🖥 www.motivationsound.co.uk

Multicord Audio Visual Services Hilltop Cottage, Coatham Mundeville, Darlington, County Durham, DL1 3NJ, United Kingdom
📞 (0845) 6060545/(07736) 808411
✉ info@multicord.co.uk
🖥 www.multicord.co.uk

Murricane & Murricane Kensington House, 227 Sauchiehall Street, Glasgow, G2 3EX, United Kingdom
📞 0141-332 7282/📠 0141-332 6517
✉ dawn@murricanes.co.uk
🖥 www.murricanes.co.uk

Myriad 106 Hampstead Road, London, NW1 2LS, United Kingdom
📞 (020) 7380 0191/📠 (020) 7388 9225
✉ sales@myriad-av.co.uk
🖥 www.myriad-av.com

Newangle Productions Ltd 102 Harmood Street, London, NW1 8DS, United Kingdom
📞 (020) 7916 0106/📠 (020) 7916 0107
✉ bev@newangle.co.uk
🖥 www.newangle.co.uk

Newland Corporate Communications Arrow Business Park, Arrow Close, Killingworth, Newcastle Upon Tyne, NE12 6QN, United Kingdom
📞 0191-256 6000/📠 0191-256 6056
✉ hire@newlandcc.co.uk
🖥 www.newlandcc.co.uk

Nimlok Ltd Nimlok House, Blooth Drive, Park Farm, Wellingborough, Northamptonshire, NN8 6NL, United Kingdom
📞 (01933) 409409/📠 (01933) 409451
✉ info@nimlok.co.uk
🖥 www.nimlok.co.uk

Objective The Court Yard, 17 West Street, Farnham, Surrey, GU9 7DR, United Kingdom
📞 (01252) 718400
✉ carl.groth@objectivestudio.com
🖥 www.objectivestudio.com

Octanorm Ltd 10 Lyon Road, Merton, London, London, SW19 2RL, United Kingdom
📞 (020) 8545 2945/📠 (020) 8545 2955
✉ sales@octanorm.co.uk
🖥 www.octanorm.co.uk

Octograph Unit B3, Manor Way Business Park, Manor Way, Swanscombe, Kent, DA10 0PP, UK
📞 (01322) 518 479
✉ sales@octograph.uk.com
🖥 www.octograph.uk.com

Opti Ltd 38 Cromwell Road, Luton, LU1 1DN, United Kingdom
📞 (01582) 411413/📠 (01582) 400613
✉ optiuk@optikinetics.com
🖥 www.optikinetics.com

Opto International Ltd Bayley Street, Stalybridge, Cheshire, SK15 1QQ, United Kingdom
☏ 0161-330 9136/ 0161-343 7332
✉ d.ramsdale@optoint.co.uk
🖥 www.optoint.co.uk

Opus Productions Ltd 9A Coverdale Road, Shepherds Bush, London, W12 8JJ, United Kingdom
☏ (020) 8743 3910/ (020) 8749 4537
✉ info@opusproductions.com
🖥 www.opusproductions.com

P F L Pro Audio & Lighting Tweedside Trading Estate, Tweedmouth, Berwick-upon-Tweed, TD15 2XF, UK
☏ (01289) 308030/ (01289) 308030
✉ info@pflaudio.co.uk
🖥 www.pflaudio.co.uk

Pannell Signs Ltd Chelsea House, Chelsea Street, Nottingham, NG7 7HN, United Kingdom
☏ 0115-970 0371/ 0115-942 2452
✉ sales@pannellsigns.co.uk
🖥 www.pannellsigns.co.uk

Paul Hyatt 406 Ware Road, Hertford, SG13 7EW, United Kingdom
☏ (07951) 015272
✉ www.paulhyatt80@hotmail.com

Pearce Signs Margate Road, Broadgate, Broadstairs, Kent, CT10 2PU, United Kingdom
☏ (01843) 863471/ (01843) 868340
✉ signs@pearcegroup.com
🖥 www.pearcegroup.com

Peel Partnership Unit 1, Edolph Farm, Norwood Hill Road, Charlwood, Horley, Surrey, RH6 0EB, United Kingdom
☏ (01293) 865018/ (01293) 863971
✉ sales@peelpartnership.co.uk
🖥 www.peelpartnership.co.uk

Peerless Designs Ltd Unit 9, Brunswick Way, London, N11 1JL, United Kingdom
☏ (020) 8362 8500/ (020) 8362 8525
✉ enquiries@peerlessdesigns.com
🖥 www.peerlessdesigns.com

Phil Kashdan Design, Print & Display Ltd The Studio, 47 Povey Cross Road, Horley, Surrey, RH6 0AG,
☏ 01293 773129/ 01293 773129
✉ phil@pk-design.com

Planetx 96 Carthew Road, London, W6 0DX, United Kingdom
☏ (020) 8748 3665/ (020) 8748 5281
✉ reception@planetx.co.uk
🖥 www.planetx.co.uk

Pro-ex Group Ltd Hamilton House, Rackery Lane, Wrexham, Clwyd, LL12 0PB, United Kingdom
☏ (01978) 855622/ (01978) 855151
✉ info@peg.uk.com
🖥 www.peg.uk.com

Pro2col Imaging Ltd Unit 4, Great Jackson Street, Manchester, M15 4NP, United Kingdom
☏ 0161-228 0303/ 0161-236 9149
✉ sales@pro2col-imaging.co.uk
🖥 www.pro2col-imaging.co.uk

Progressive Modelmakers Ltd The Croft, Montague Road, Berkhamsted, Hertfordshire, HP4 3DZ, United Kingdom
☏ (01442) 866866/ (01442) 865655

Protean International Ltd The Bell Tower, 12 High Street, Brackley, Northamptonshire, NN13 7DT, United Kingdom
☏ (01280) 706060/ (01280) 706565
✉ andy@protean.uk.com
🖥 www.protean.uk.com

Q Sound Design 2 Princes Buildings, George Street, Bath, BA1 2ED, United Kingdom
☏ (07977) 553975
✉ mail@qsounddesign.com
🖥 www.qsounddesign.com

R A L Display & Marketing Ltd 2 Cranmer Street, Leicester, LE3 0QA, United Kingdom
☏ 0116-255 4640/ 0116-255 0572
✉ sales@ral-display.co.uk
🖥 www.ral-display.co.uk

R.G. Jones Sound Engineering Ltd 16 Endeavour Way, Wimbledon, London, SW19 8UH, United Kingdom
☏ (020) 8971 3100/ (020) 8971 3101
✉ info@rgjones.co.uk
🖥 www.rgjones.co.uk

Radclyffe Associates 2 Berry Field Park, Amersham, Buckinghamshire, HP6 5QN, United Kingdom
☏ (01494) 434163/ (01494) 434164
✉ radders@dircon.co.uk

Rhubarb Voice-Overs 1st Floor, 1a Devonshire Road, Chiswick, London, W4 2EU, United Kingdom
☏ (020) 8742 8683/ (020) 8742 8693
✉ enquiries@rhubarbvoices.co.uk
🖥 www.rhubarbvoices.co.uk

Riverfront Media 28 Plum Lane, London, SE18 3AE, United Kingdom
☏ (020) 8854 7563
✉ info@riverfrontmedia.co.uk
🖥 www.riverfrontmedia.co.uk

Rivermeave Signs Roslin Road, South Acton Industrial Estate, London, W3 8BW, United Kingdom
☏ (020) 8992 7083/ (020) 8752 1691
✉ sales@rivermeade.com
🖥 www.rivermeade.com

Roche Audio Visual Ainleys Industrial Estate, Elland, West Yorkshire, HX5 9JP, United Kingdom
☏ (01422) 310193/ (01422) 310220
✉ information@rochev.co.uk
🖥 www.rochev.co.uk

RoSPA Head Office 353 Bristol Road, Edgbaston, Birmingham, B5 7ST, United Kingdom
☏ 0121-248 2000/ 0121-248 2001
✉ help@rospa.com
🖥 www.rospa.com

S D Displays Ltd Lancaster Road, Cressex Business Park, High Wycombe, Buckinghamshire, HP12 3PY, United Kingdom
☏ (0800) 289036/ (01494) 465145
✉ sales@sd-displays.co.uk
🖥 www.sd-displays.co.uk

Sarosa Dansa Highland Dance Company 1 Canmore Drive, Stenhousemuir, Larbert, Stirlingshire, FK5 4LA, United Kingdom
☏ (01324) 871921/ (01324) 554462
✉ gillian@whitelaw-dancing.demon.co.uk

Saville Audio Visual Ltd Unit 2, Blenheim Court, Welwyn Garden City, Hertfordshire, AL7 1AD, United Kingdom
☏ (01707) 378770/ (01707) 378771
✉ head.office@saville.co.uk
🖥 www.saville-av.com

Saville Group Ltd Millfield Lane, Nether Poppleton, York, YO26 6PQ, United Kingdom
☏ (01904) 782782/ (01904) 782700
✉ headoffice@saville.co.uk
🖥 www.saville.co.uk

Savin Productions 19 Woodlea Drive, Shirley, Solihull, West Midlands, B91 1PG, United Kingdom
☏ 0121-240 1100/ 0121-240 4042
✉ sales@savinproductions.com

Saw See Ltd Unit 28 1st Floor, 34 Bowater Road, London, SE18 5TF, United Kingdom
☏ (08701) 997726
✉ info@sawsee.net
🖥 www.sawsee.net

Scootman Music & Sound Design 2021 21st Avenue South, Suite C-100, Nashville, 37212, United States of America
☏ 615 319 9556/615 319 9556 ✆ 615 777 2122
✉ scott@scootmanmusic.com
🖥 www.scootmanmusic.com

Service Graphics Ltd, 3 Osiers Road, London, SW18 1NL, United Kingdom
☏ (020) 8874 4152/ (020) 8871 3521
✉ newenquiries@servicegraphics.co.uk
🖥 www.servicegraphics.co.uk

Shimmersigns Rear of 47-49 High Street, Ruislip, Middlesex, HA4 7BD, United Kingdom
☏ (01895) 638945/(07944) 274489 ✆ (01895) 672968
✉ sales@brendangraphics.co.uk
🖥 www.shimmersigns.co.uk

Shopkit Designs Ltd Units B & C, 100 Cecil Street, Watford, WD24 5AD, United Kingdom
☏ (01923) 818282/ (01923) 818280
✉ sales@shopkit.com
🖥 www.shopkit.com

Show Presentation Services Ltd Unit 6, North Holt Trading Estate, Belview Road, Northolt, Middlesex, UB5 5PR, United Kingdom
☏ (0870) 2400904/ (0870) 2400905
✉ sps@showpres.co.uk
🖥 www.showpres.com

Sign Co. Ltd Clench, Marlborough, Wiltshire, SN8 4NT, United Kingdom
☏ (0800) 3288099/ (01672) 810450
✉ info@thesignco.co.uk
🖥 www.thesignco.co.uk

Signbox Ltd Unit 3, Egham Business Village, Crabtree Road, Egham, Surrey, TW20 8RB, United Kingdom
☏ (01784) 438688/ (01784) 471694
✉ enquiries@signbox.co.uk
🖥 www.signbox.co.uk

Silverglade Associates Ltd 11A Enterprise House, 1-2 Hatfields, London, SE1 9PG, United Kingdom
☏ (020) 7827 9510/ (020) 7827 9511
✉ info@silverglade.com
🖥 www.silverglade.com

Sonica Studios SW4 17 Welmar Mews, 154 Clapham Park Road, London, SW4 7DD, United Kingdom
☏ (020) 7498 2990
✉ info@sonicamusic.co.uk
🖥 www.sonicamusic.co.uk

Sonique Ltd Burnhill Business Centre, 50 Burnhill Road, Beckenham, Kent, BR3 3LA, United Kingdom
☏ 020 8249 6007
✉ natalie.griffiths@soniqueltd.com
🖥 www.soniqueltd.com

Sound Marketing 6 Europa Way, Martineau Lane, Norwich, NR1 2EN, United Kingdom
☏ (01603) 667725/ (01603) 761577
✉ kevin@sound-marketing.co.uk

South West Colour Labs 1 Aspen Way, Yalberton Industrial Estate, Paignton, Devon, TQ4 7QR, United Kingdom
☏ (01803) 666640/ (01803) 409797
✉ sales@swcl.co.uk
🖥 www.swcl.co.uk

Stage Electrics Third Way, Avonmouth, Bristol, BS11 9YL, United Kingdom
☏ 0117-938 4000/ 0117-916 2828
✉ sales@stage-electrics.co.uk
🖥 www.stage-electrics.co.uk

Star Events Group Ltd Milton Road, Thurleigh, Bedford, MK44 2DF, United Kingdom
☏ (01234) 772233/ (01234) 772272
✉ sales@stareventsgroup.com
🖥 www.stareventsgroup.com

Steljes Ltd Bagshot Manor, Green Lane, Bagshot, Surrey, GU19 5NL, United Kingdom
☏ (0845) 0758758/ (0845) 0261500
🖥 www.steljes.co.uk

Strategies 37 Belmont Road, Beckenham, Kent, BR3 4HW, United Kingdom
☏ (020) 8658 0247/(07785) 361546 ✆ (020) 8658 0247
✉ martynjrose@btinternet.com
🖥 www.xpertuniverse.com

Stratos Design Ltd 365 High Street North, London, E12 6PG, United Kingdom
☏ (07834) 318208
✉ bala@onestratos.com
🖥 www.onestratos.co.uk

Studiohire (London) Ltd, London, United Kingdom
☏ (020) 7431 0212/ (020) 7431 1134
✉ mail@studiohire.net
🖥 www.studiohire.net

Stylo Graphics 132 St Albans Road, Hille Business Centre, Watford, WD24 4AJ, United Kingdom
☏ (01923) 800666/ (01923) 800777
✉ mail@stylographics.co.uk
🖥 www.stylographics.co.uk

Supalite Displays Ltd Sovereign Hse, 10 Lancaster Pk, Needwood, Burton-on-trent, Staffordshire, DE13 9PD, United Kingdom
☏ (01283) 575860/ 575734
✉ enquiry@supalite.com
🖥 www.supalite.com

Synergy Communications Ltd 250-252 Goswell Road, London, EC1V 7EB, United Kingdom
☏ (020) 7251 0303/ (020) 7251 0323
✉ info@synergy-communications.co.uk
🖥 www.synergy-communications.co.uk

T M C Ltd Hillam Road, Bradford, West Yorkshire, BD2 1QN, United Kingdom
✆ (01274) 370966/ (01274) 308706
✉ sales@tmc.ltd.uk
🖥 www.tmc.ltd.uk

T P S Visual Communications Ltd Warner House, Jubilee Business Park, Letchworth Garden City, Hertfordshire, SG6 1SP, United Kingdom
✆ (01462) 650700/ (01462) 650707
✉ sales@tpsdisplay.com
🖥 www.tpsvisual.com

Talk Events (UK) Ltd Unit 6, 229 Torrington Avenue, Coventry, CV4 9HN, United Kingdom
✆ (0845) 6126012/ (0845) 6126013
✉ info@talkevents.com
🖥 www.talkevents.com

Terminal Studios 4-10 Lamb Walk, Bermondsey, London, SE1 3TT, United Kingdom
✆ (020) 7403 3050/ (020) 7407 6123
✉ info@terminal.co.uk
🖥 www.terminal.co.uk

The 3D Centre London House, 100 New Kings Road, Fulham, London, SW6 4LX, United Kingdom
✆ (0870) 242 0638/ (0870) 242 0639
✉ trb@3dcentre.com
🖥 www.3dcentre.com

The 5YLAC Group 26 York Street, London, W1U 6PZ, United Kingdom
✆ (0845) 3104314/ (0870) 7623212
✉ info56@5ylac.biz
🖥 www.5ylac.biz

The Audio Visual Co Ltd 6 Oakleigh Gardens, Orpington, Kent, BR6 9PL, United Kingdom
✆ (01689) 858 767/ (01689) 862 764
✉ paul@theav.co.uk
🖥 www.theav.co.uk

The Gate Marketing & Design Ltd Murlain Business Centre, Union Street, Chester, CH1 1QP, United Kingdom
✆ (01244) 357242/ (01244) 357215
✉ info@thegatemarketing.com
🖥 www.thegatemarketing.com

The Little Bazaar Marlborough House, 159 High Street, Wealdstone, Harrow, Middlesex, HA3 5DX, United Kingdom
✆ (020) 7370 7850
✉ info@littlebazaar.co.uk
🖥 www.littlebazaar.co.uk

The Sound House Post Production Ltd 10th Astley House, 23 Quay Street, Manchester, M3 4AE, United Kingdom
✆ 0161-832 7299/ 0161-832 7266
✉ suekeane@thesoundhouse.tv
🖥 www.thesoundhouse.tv

The Voice and Music Company 8A Shelton Street, Covent Garden, London, WC2H 9JP, United Kingdom
✆ (020) 7240 7755/ (020) 7240 7752
✉ info@thevoiceandmusiccompany.com
🖥 www.thevoiceandmusiccompany.com

Thomas Fattorini Ltd Regent Street Works, Birmingham, B1 3HQ, United Kingdom
✆ 0121-236 1307/ 0121-200 1568
✉ sales@fattorini.co.uk
🖥 www.fattorini.co.uk

Tickle Music Hire Ltd The Old Dairy, 133-137 Kilburn Lane, London, W10 4AN, United Kingdom
✆ (020) 8964 3399/ (020) 8964 0343
✉ hire@ticklemusichire.com
🖥 www.ticklemusichire.com

Toby Wood Audio 42 Rosebank Road, London, W7 2EN, United Kingdom
✆ (07092) 055232/ (07092) 055232
✉ toby@lucidmusic.co.uk

Tye Phillips Associates The Barn, Almners Farm House, Chertsey, Surrey, KT16 0BH, United Kingdom
✆ (01932) 560101/ (01932) 562647
✉ info@tyephillips.com

Univibe Audio 20 Pool Street, Walsall, WS1 2EN, United Kingdom
✆ (07734) 151589
✉ info@univibeaudio.co.uk
🖥 www.univibeaudio.co.uk

V P TV Oddfellows Hall, London Road, Chipping Norton, Oxfordshire, OX7 5AR, United Kingdom
✆ (01608) 641592/ (01608) 641969
✉ info@vptv.com
🖥 www.vptv.com

W B P Visual Solutions Ltd 6 Progess Works, Heathmill Lane, Birmingham, B9 4DY, United Kingdom
✆ 0121-224 8333
✉ birmingham@wbp.co.uk
🖥 www.wbp.co.uk

Wall Candi High Street, Lane End, High Wycombe, Buckinghamshire, HP14 3JG, United Kingdom
✆ (01494) 883250/ (01494) 881826
✉ info@wallcandi.com
🖥 www.wallcandi.com

Walnut Media Communications Ltd 4 Sadler Close, Leeds, LS16 8NN, United Kingdom
✆ 0113-285 7906/(07850) 935541
✉ gary@walnutmedia.com
🖥 www.walnutmedia.com

Warrens Display Ltd 359 Burley Road, Leeds, LS4 2PX, United Kingdom
✆ 0113-278 3614/ 0113-274 4300
✉ sales@warrens.co.uk
🖥 www.warrens.co.uk

Westwood Sound Productions Flat 4, The Castle, Castle Street, Stroud, Gloucestershire, GL5 2HR, United Kingdom
✆ (01453) 751155/(07900) 690433
✉ mike.westwoodsound@tiscali.co.uk

Widescreen Centre 47 Dorset Street, London, W1U 7ND, United Kingdom
✆ (020) 7935 2580/ (020) 7486 1272
✉ call@widescreen-centre.co.uk
🖥 www.widescreen-centre.co.uk

Wise Buddah Ltd 74 Great Titchfield Street, London, W1W 7QP, United Kingdom
✆ (020) 7307 1600/ (020) 7307 1601
✉ becky.maxted@wisebuddah.com
🖥 www.wisebuddah.com

Wonderfuel 118 Hatherley Gardens, London, E6 3HQ, United Kingdom
✆ 020 8548 1358
✉ info@wonderfuel.co.uk
🖥 www.wonderfuel.co.uk

Wyatt International Wyatt House, 72 Francis Road, Birmingham, B16 8SP, United Kingdom
✆ 0121-454 8181/ 0121-455 9785
✉ info@wyattinternational.com
🖥 www.wyattinternational.com

VENUES

Acre Jean Ltd Unit 7 The Kimber Centre, 54 Kimber Rd, London, SW18 4PP,
✆ 020 8877 3211/ 020 8877 3213
✉ dan.hill@acrejean.com
🖥 www.acrejean.com

Alexandra Palace Alexandra Palace Way, Wood Green, London, N22 7AY, United Kingdom
✆ (020) 8365 2121/ (020) 8883 3999
✉ info@alexandrapalace.com
🖥 www.alexandrapalace.com

BAC Venues Lavender Hill, Battersea, London, SW11 5TN, United Kingdom
✆ (020) 7326 8211/ (020) 7585 0704
✉ venues@bac.org.uk
🖥 www.bacvenues.org.uk

BAFTA 195 Piccadilly, London, W1J 9LN, United Kingdom
✆ (020) 7292 5816/ (020) 7292 5869
✉ membership@bafta.org
🖥 www.bafta.org

Barbican Centre Silk Street, London, EC2Y 8DS, United Kingdom
✆ (020) 7638 4141/ (020) 7382 7250
✉ careers@barbican.org.uk
🖥 www.barbican.org.uk

Birbeck University of London Malet St, Bloomsbury, London, WC1E 7HX, United Kingdom
✆ (020) 7079 0736
✉ m.hoek@bbk.ac.uk
🖥 www.bbk.ac.uk

Bournemouth International Centre Exeter Road, Bournemouth, BH2 5BH, United Kingdom
✆ (01202) 456400/ (01202) 456500
✉ conference.bic@bournemouth.gov.uk
🖥 www.bic.co.uk

Bretby Conference Centre Ashby Road, Bretby, Burton-on-Trent, Staffordshire, DE15 0YZ, United Kingdom
✆ (01283) 553440/ (01283) 553448
✉ enquiries@bretbycc.co.uk
🖥 www.bretbycc.co.uk

Business Design Centre 52 Upper Street, Islington, London, N1 0QH, United Kingdom
✆ (020) 7359 3535/ (020) 7226 0590
✉ bdc@businessdesigncentre.co.uk
🖥 www.businessdesigncentre.co.uk

Cardiff International Arena Mary Ann Street, Cardiff, CF10 2EQ, United Kingdom
✆ (029) 2023 4500/ (0870) 7490607
✉ cia.sales@livenation.co.uk
🖥 www.livenation.co.uk/cardiff

Chateau Impney Hotel & Impney Regent Centre Chateau Hotel, Droitwich Spar, Droitwich, Worcestershire, WR9 0BN, United Kingdom
✆ (01905) 774411/ (01905) 772371
✉ enquiries@chateau-impney.com
🖥 www.chateau-impney.com

CRx - Digital Audio Productions 1 Kimble Court, Marsh Road, Little Kimble, Aylesbury, Buckinghamshire, HP22 5XS, United Kingdom
✆ (07841) 115338
✉ cerrie1@hotmail.com
🖥 djcrx.0catch.com

Doncaster Exhibition Centre Leger Way, Doncaster, South Yorkshire, DN2 6BB, United Kingdom
✆ (01302) 304200/ (01302) 323271
✉ jo.mapletoft@doncasterracing.co.uk
🖥 www.doncaster-racecourse.com

Earls Court & Olympia Ltd Earls Court Exhibition Centre, London, SW5 9TA, United Kingdom
✆ (020) 7385 1200/ (020) 7370 8144
✉ marketing@eco.co.uk
🖥 www.eco.co.uk

Edinburgh International Conference Centre Ltd The Exchange, 150 Morrison Street, Edinburgh, EH3 8EE, United Kingdom
✆ 0131-300 3000/ 0131-300 3030
✉ sales@eicc.co.uk
🖥 www.eicc.co.uk

Excel 1 Western Gateway, London, E16 1XL, United Kingdom
✆ (020) 7476 0101/ (020) 7069 5000
✉ info@excel-london.co.uk
🖥 www.excel-london.co.uk

G-MEX Seminar Centre Windmill Street, Manchester, M2 3GX, United Kingdom
✆ 0161-834 2700/ 0161-833 3168
✉ email@manchestercentral.co.uk
🖥 www.manchestercentral.co.uk

Harrogate International Centre Kings Road, Harrogate, North Yorkshire, HG1 5LA, United Kingdom
✆ (01423) 500500/ (01423) 537210
✉ sales@harrogateinternationalcentre.co.uk
🖥 www.harrogateinternationalcentre.co.uk

Hensol Castle Conference Centre Miskin, Hensol, Pontyclun, Mid Glamorgan, CF72 8YS, United Kingdom
✆ (01443) 224064/ (01443) 226559
✉ sales@hensol.co.uk
🖥 www.hensol.co.uk

Holborn Studios 49-50 Eagle Wharf Road, London, N1 7ED, United Kingdom
✆ (020) 7490 4099/ (020) 7253 8120
✉ reception@holborn-studios.co.uk
🖥 www.holbornstudios.com

Hull Conference Bureau 79 Ferensway, Hull, HU2 8LE, United Kingdom
✆ (01482) 615725/ (01482) 615699
✉ conference.bureau@hullcc.gov.uk
🖥 www.hullcc.gov.uk/hcb

Isle of Man Conference Bureau St Andrew's House, Finch Road, Douglas, Isle of Man, IM1 2PX, United Kingdom
✆ (01624) 686888/ (01624) 686860
✉ conferences@gov.im
🖥 www.visitisleofman.com

Lee Valley Regional Park Authority Myddelton House, Bulls Cross, Enfield, Middlesex, EN2 9HG, United Kingdom
✆ (01992) 709831/ (01992) 709922
✉ events@leevalleypark.org.uk
🖥 www.leevalleypark.org.uk

Longleat Estate Office, Longleat, Warminster, Wiltshire, BA12 7NW, United Kingdom
📞 (01985) 844400/📠 (01985) 844885
✉ enquiries@longleat.co.uk
🖥 www.longleat.co.uk

Manchester Conference Centre Sackvell Street, Manchester, M1 3BB, United Kingdom
📞 0161-955 8000/📠 0161-955 8050
✉ mcc@manchester.ac.uk
🖥 www.meeting.co.uk

Manchester Evening News Arena Victoria Station, Manchester, M3 1AR, United Kingdom
📞 0161-950 5000/📠 0161-950 6000
✉ sarah.hodson@men-arena.com
🖥 www.men-arena.com

Manchester Velodrome Stuart Street, Manchester, M11 4DQ, United Kingdom
📞 0161-223 2244/📠 0161-230 2309
✉ admin@manchestervelodrome.com
🖥 www.manchestervelodrome.com

Mid Wales Conference Bureau The Pavillion, Spa Road, Llandrindod Wells, Powys, LD1 5EY, United Kingdom
📞 (01597) 823421/079 70 723714
✉ mwcb@powys.gov.uk
🖥 www.midwalesconferences.co.uk

National Exhibition Centre NEC Group, Birmingham, B40 1NT, United Kingdom
📞 0121-780 4141/📠 0121-767 3510
✉ exhibition@necgroup.co.uk
🖥 www.necgroup.co.uk

National Museum of Photography Film & Television Pictureville, Bradford, West Yorkshire, BD1 1NQ, United Kingdom
📞 (0870) 7010200/📠 (01274) 723155
✉ talk.nmpft@nmsi.ac.uk
🖥 www.nmpft.org.uk

New Connaught Rooms 61-65 Great Queen Street, London, WC2B 5DA, United Kingdom
📞 (020) 7405 7811/📠 (020) 7831 1851
✉ events@newconnaughtrooms.co.uk
🖥 www.newconnaughtrooms.co.uk

Oxford University Begbroke Science Park Oxford University Begbroke Science Park, Sandy Lane, Yarnton, Kidlington, Oxfordshire, OX5 1PF, United Kingdom
📞 (01865) 283700/📠 (01865) 374992
✉ enquiries@begbroke.ox.ac.uk
🖥 www.begbroke.ox.ac.uk

Portsmouth Conference Office Portsmouth City Council Civic Offices, Guildhall Square, Portsmouth, PO1 2AD, United Kingdom
📞 (023) 9283 4727/📠 (023) 9283 4159
✉ conferences@portsmouthcc.gov.uk
🖥 www.visitportsmouth.co.uk

Royal Horticultural Halls & Conference Centre 80 Vincent Square, London, SW1P 2PE, United Kingdom
📞 (08453) 704 606/📠 (020) 7834 2072
✉ horthalls@rhs.org.uk
🖥 www.horticultural-halls.co.uk

S E C Ltd Finnieston, Glasgow, G3 8YW, United Kingdom
📞 0141-248 3000/📠 0141-226 3423
✉ info@secc.co.uk
🖥 www.secc.co.uk

Saint Georges Hall William Brown Street, Liverpool, L1 1JJ, United Kingdom
📞 0151-225 4457/📠 0151-709 2252
✉ steve.neill@liverpool.gov.uk
🖥 www.stgeorgeshall.com

Space-2 Battersea Studios, 80 Silverthorne Road, London, SW8 3HE, United Kingdom
📞 (07922) 224216
✉ mark@space2online.com
🖥 www.space2online.com

Staffordshire Showground The Pavillion Complex, Western Road, Stafford, ST18 0BD, United Kingdom
📞 (01785) 258060/📠 (01785) 246458
✉ enquiries@staffscountyshowground.co.uk
🖥 www.staffscountyshowground.co.uk

Staffordshire Stoke-on-Trent Conference Bureau Floor 1, Civic Centre, Glebe Street, Stoke-on-Trent, ST4 1WR, United Kingdom
📞 (01782) 232076/📠 (01782) 865007
✉ info@conferencestaffordshire.co.uk
🖥 www.conferencestaffordshire.co.uk

Stoke on Trent City Council Trentham Business Centre Trentham Lakes South, Trentham, Stoke-on-Trent, ST4 8HH, United Kingdom
📞 01782 865000/📠 01782 865010
✉ sitechinfo@stoke.gov.uk
🖥 www.stoke.gov.uk

The Brewery Chiswell Street, London, EC1Y 4SD, United Kingdom
📞 (020) 7638 8811
✉ info@thebrewery.co.uk
🖥 www.thebrewery.co.uk

Tredegar House & Park Tredegar House, Newport, Gwent, NP10 8YW, United Kingdom
📞 (01633) 815880/📠 (01633) 815895
✉ tredegar.house@newport.gov.uk
🖥 www.newport.gov.uk

Windermere Steamboat Museum Rayrigg Road, Windermere, Cumbria, LA23 1BN, United Kingdom
📞 (01539) 445565/📠 (01539) 448769
✉ post@steamboat.co.uk
🖥 www.steamboat.co.uk

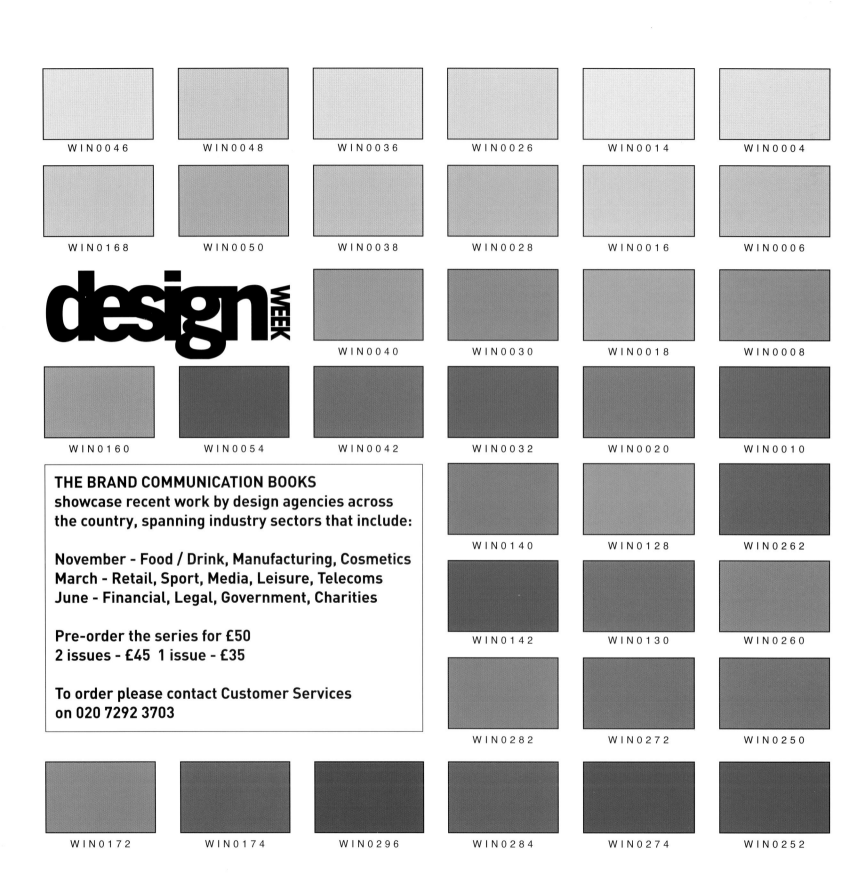

WIN0046 WIN0048 WIN0036 WIN0026 WIN0014 WIN0004

WIN0168 WIN0050 WIN0038 WIN0028 WIN0016 WIN0006

WIN0040 WIN0030 WIN0018 WIN0008

WIN0160 WIN0054 WIN0042 WIN0032 WIN0020 WIN0010

THE BRAND COMMUNICATION BOOKS
showcase recent work by design agencies across
the country, spanning industry sectors that include:

November - Food / Drink, Manufacturing, Cosmetics
March - Retail, Sport, Media, Leisure, Telecoms
June - Financial, Legal, Government, Charities

Pre-order the series for £50
2 issues - £45 1 issue - £35

To order please contact Customer Services
on 020 7292 3703

WIN0140 WIN0128 WIN0262

WIN0142 WIN0130 WIN0260

WIN0282 WIN0272 WIN0250

WIN0172 WIN0174 WIN0296 WIN0284 WIN0274 WIN0252

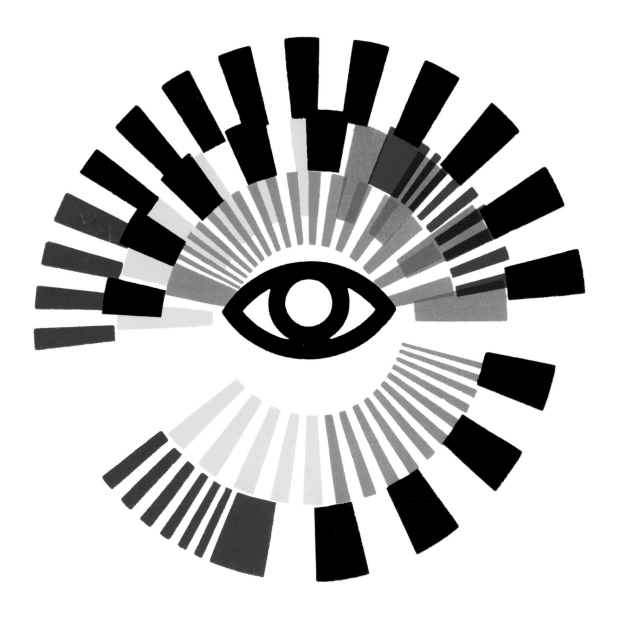

PEEPSHOW.ORG.UK

Design &
Advertising
Contacts

Masterfile
Rights-Managed and Royalty-Free

700-00507144 © Gary Conner / masterfile.com

Get your pictures here!

Masterfile.com

Train. Car. Coffee shop. Agency desk. His "office" may change,
but his photo source is always masterfile.com.

masterfile.com: the right images for every kind
of project from £39 to exclusive.

Advertising showcase:
Design & Advertising contacts
10.

Services

Fattorini

edsonwilliams

Absolute Zero Degrees

Bureau for Visual Affairs

Recruitment consultants

Gabriele Skelton

Source

With Us

Major Players

Fattorini

Artists-craftsmen
Since 1827

YELL GOLD AWARD

FOR BUSINESS EXCELLENCE

www.fattorini.co.uk
sales@fattorini.co.uk

For six generations the expert gold and silversmiths at Thomas Fattorini have been designing and manufacturing unique articles from intricate cufflinks to bespoke presentation pieces.

The company also specialises in badge design, producing the widest range of plastic badges in the UK.

Head office
Regent Street Works
Birmingham B1 3HQ
T: 0121 236 1307
F: 0121 200 1568

150 Minories
London
EC3N 1LS
T: 020 7264 2171
F: 020 7264 2172

Westbourne Road Works
Urmston
Manchester M41 0TR
T: 0161 748 0441
F: 0161 755 3258

Tree tent

Heineken HQ Lobby

Print campagne

bugaboo

Print campagne

Nike Park 2000
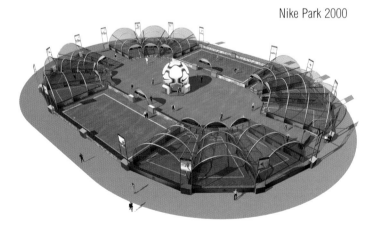

Heineken visibility items

alrik koudenburg   design director

www.edsonwilliams.com

info@edsonwilliams.com

+44(0)2073752077

ANOTHERCOMPANY

joachim baan   graphic designer

www.edsonwilliams.com   info@edsonwilliams.com   +44(0)2073752077

absolutezero°

IDENTITY
PRINT
PACKAGING
PRODUCT
SURFACE PATTERN
WRITING
PUBLICATIONS

UNIT 10
EMPRESS MEWS
LONDON SE5 9BT

TEL: +44 (0)20 77376767

www.absolutezerodegrees.com
info@absolutezerodegrees.com

Bureau for Visual Affairs

Visit www.bureau-va.com and drop us a line and
we'll send you one of our Daylight Calendars for London.
(as long as supplies last)

01
JANUARY

02
FEBRUARY

03
MARCH

04
APRIL

05
MAY

06
JUNE

07
JULY

08
AUGUST

09
SEPTEMBER

10
OCTOBER

11
NOVEMBER

12
DECEMBER

Websites

conception, design and technology

Brand

naming, creation and development

Print

design and production for print
application

Viral marketing

conception, design and technology
for viral and email marketing

Bureau for Visual Affairs
The Hop Exchange
24 Southwark Street
London SE1 1TY
United Kingdom

www.bureau-va.com
+44 (0)20 7407 2582

tarzan +june

(chemistry is everything)

Recruitment for
design + digital +
account + project management +
strategy + planning +
creative services

The recruiter of choice for the design + digital industry.
If you want to work with the best, work with us...

gabrieleskelton
gabrieleskelton.com
T 020 7580 0666

**We know how important
it is to be flexible**
Whatever you need, we'll jump to it.

www.sourcepersonnel.co.uk

(with us)

Dedicated Creative Recruiters

Chesterfield House, 385 Euston Road, London NW1 3AU
(Call)+44 (0)20 7391 5111 (Fax)+44 (0)20 7391 5112
(Mail) info@withus-recruit.com
www.withus-recruit.com

OUT THERE

Creative Recruitment Specialists
Account Handlers
Artworkers
Brand Consultants
Creative Directors
Designers
Freelancers
New Business Finders
Planners
Traffickers

Telephone 020 7836 4041
www.majorplayers.co.uk

MajorPlayers...

www.studiothomson.com

DESIGN CONSULTANCIES–GENERAL

032 Design The Manor, Main Street, Tur Langton, Leicester, Leicestershire, LE8 0PJ,
United Kingdom
☏ 01858 545147

10 Associates Ltd 6a Cartwright Court, Bradley Business Park, Dyson Wood Way, Huddersfield, West Yorkshire, HD2 1GN,
United Kingdom
☏ 01484 541827

11th Hour Ltd The Bakery Building, 3-4 Sundridge Place, Croydon, Surrey, CR0 6RL,
United Kingdom
☏ 020 86550111

2 Heads Global Design Kit Land, Chekendon, Berkshire, RG8 0TY,
United Kingdom
☏ 01491 681061

20/20 20-23 Mandela Street, London, NW1 0DU,
United Kingdom
☏ 020 73837071

2B Creative 12 Longstone St, Lisburn, BT28 1ER,
United Kingdom
☏ 028 92669888

2creation.com Ltd Old Coach House, Alston Works, Alston Road, Barnet, Hertfordshire, EN5 4EL,
United Kingdom
☏ 020 84497600

2nd Byte Ltd Network House, Lower South Street, Godalming, Surrey, GU7 1BZ,
United Kingdom
☏ 01483 424242

300 Million 1 Rosoman Place, Exmouth Market, London, EC1R 0JY,
United Kingdom
☏ 020 78333838

3D Labs Thorpe Lea Road, Egham, Surrey, TW20 8HE,
United Kingdom
☏ 01784 470555

3T Creative Ltd Suite C, Stephen House, 23a Bargates, Christchurch, Dorset, BH23 1QD,
United Kingdom
☏ 01202 470170

442 Design Ltd 40 Maritime Street, Edinburgh, Mid Lothian, EH6 6SA,
United Kingdom
☏ 0131 5381442

48 Fitzroy Ltd St Andrews Lane, Lewes, East Sussex, BN7 1UW,
United Kingdom
☏ 01273 402640

4C Design Ltd Unit 13 Borron Street, Port Dundas Business Park, Glasgow, Lanarkshire, G4 9XG,
United Kingdom
☏ 0141 3535490

85four 85 Clerkenwell Road, London, EC1R 5AR,
United Kingdom
☏ 020 74004700

999 Design Group Eastgate, Castle Street, Manchester, Lancashire, M3 4LZ,
United Kingdom
☏ 0161 8285900

A Plus 7 Melbray Mews, Hurlingham Road, London, SW6 3NS,
United Kingdom
☏ 020 77368793

A& NG Communications 18 Cleveland Street, London, W1T 4HZ,
United Kingdom
☏ 020 73231002

A& NG Creative Communications Unit G5 Chorlton Mill, 3 Cambridge Street, Manchester, Lancashire, M1 5BY,
United Kingdom
☏ 0161 2365506

A2 Creative Ltd 304 Parkway House, Sheen Lane, 123 Morte Lake High Street, London, SW14 8LS,
United Kingdom
☏ 020 84878995

AB Design Group 9 Richmond Road, Exeter, Devon, EX4 4JA,
United Kingdom
☏ 01392 211765

Able Creative Ltd Somerset House, London Road, Ascot, Berkshire, SL5 7EN,
United Kingdom
☏ 01344 885518

About Turn Creative Ltd Someford Business Court, Holmes Chapel Road, Somerford, Congleton, Cheshire, CW12 4SN,
United Kingdom
☏ 01260 281431

Above Line Design Wiftaston Road Business Centre, Wiftaston Road Crew, Cheshire, CW2 7RP,
United Kingdom
☏ 01270 848650

Absolute Action Ltd Focus House, No.6 Tonbridge Road, Maidstone, Kent, ME16 8RP,
United Kingdom
☏ 01622 351000

Absolute Product Design Ittc Tamar Science Park, Tamar Science Park, Derriford, Plymouth, Devon, PL6 8BX,
United Kingdom
☏ 01752 766166

Acid P O 5078, Pendock Road, Redmarley, Gloucester, Gloucestershire, GL19 3YB,
United Kingdom
☏ 01452 840853

Acrobat Design The Old Church, Albert Hill Street, Didsbury, Manchester, Lancashire, M20 6RF,
United Kingdom
☏ 0161 4458887

Acrylicize Second Floor, 116 College Road, Harrow, Middlesex, HA1 1BQ,
United Kingdom
☏ 020 88616640

Actis Group 3 Queen Victoria Street, 3 Minerva Court, Chester West Business Park, Chester, Cheshire, CH1 4QL,
United Kingdom
☏ 01244 398444

AD Creative Consultants Royal Victoria Building, Trinity Road, London, SW18 3SX,
United Kingdom
☏ 020 88708743

Adams Trainor Ltd 199 King'S Cross Road, London, WC1X 9DB,
United Kingdom
☏ 020 72785711

ADC Blueprint Verney House, 1b Hollywood Road, London, SW10 9HS,
United Kingdom
☏ 020 73496280

Adcock Clayton Ltd Unit 27, Waterside, 44-48 Wharf Road, London, N1 7UX,
United Kingdom
☏ 020 72513366

Addison 2 Cathedral Street, London, SE1 9DE,
United Kingdom
☏ 020 79404500

ADELPHI COMMUNICATIONS Adelphi Mill, Bollington, Macclesfield, Cheshire, SK10 5JB,
United Kingdom
☏ 01625 575500

Adjective Anchor Mill, Mill Lane, Chelmondiston, Ipswich, IP9 1DR,
United Kingdom
☏ 01473 781919

Advance Consultancy St Mary's House, Church Street, Uttoxeter, Staffordshire, ST14 8AG,
United Kingdom
☏ 01889 561510

Adventis Group plc 93-95 Wigmore Street, London, W1U 1HH,
United Kingdom
☏ 020 70344700

Adworks Design The Workhouse, 35 Ridgemont Road, St Albans, Hertfordshire, AL1 3AH,
United Kingdom
☏ 01727 810333

Ag/Cad Ltd Barlow Drive, Woodford Park Industrial Estat, Winsford, Cheshire, CW7 2JZ,
United Kingdom
☏ 01606 863344

Agenda Design Associates 108 Point Pleasant, London, SW18 1PP,
United Kingdom
☏ 020 88701847

Agog Ltd 66-68 King Street, Newcastle-under-Lyme, Staffordshire, ST5 1JB,
United Kingdom
☏ 01782 753470

Agwebdata-Design 13 South Suffolk Business Centre, Alexandra Road, Sudbury, Suffolk, CO10 2ZX,
United Kingdom
☏ 01787 371331

Air Creative Marketing Shire House, Waltham Road, Overton, Hampshire, RG25 3NJ,
United Kingdom
☏ 01256 772770

Aldine Design Services Ltd Arundell House, 50 High Street, Southam, Warwickshire, CV47 0EP,
United Kingdom
☏ 01926 816500

Allen Group Equi Point, Coventrey Road, Yardley, West Midlands, B25 8AD,
United Kingdom
☏ 0121 7652900

ALLEN INTERNATIONAL Berghem Mews, Blythe Road, Hammersmith, London, W14 0HN,
United Kingdom
☏ 020 73712447

Alu UK Ltd 1 Sycamore Street, London, EC1Y 0SF,
United Kingdom
☏ 020 72500466

Ambient Creative Services Ltd 43 Swinburne Road, Darlington, County Durham, DL3 7TD,
United Kingdom
☏ 01325 364144

Ame Momentum House, Carrera Court, Church Lane, Dinnington, South Yorkshire, S25 2RG,
United Kingdom
☏ 01909 550368

Aminto Ltd Express Networks, George Leigh Street, Manchester, Lancashire, M4 5DL,
United Kingdom
☏ 0161 2283762

Ammunition Creative Ltd Studio 1, 96 Debeauvior Road, London, N1 4EL,
United Kingdom
☏ 020 72412233

Anderson Retail Consultants 62 Glendhu Manor, Belfast, BT4 2RJ,
United Kingdom
☏ 028 90760700

Andrew Younger & Associates 30 The Avenue, Bedford Park, London, W4 1HT,
United Kingdom
☏ 020 89958787

Andy Woolnough Design 77a Windsor Road, Gravesend, Kent, DA12 5BW,
United Kingdom
☏ 01474 355769

Apex Co UK Exhibition House, London Road, Macclesfield, Cheshire, SK11 7QX,
United Kingdom
☏ 01625 429370

Appetite 4th Floor, Tennyson House, 159-165 Great Portland Street, London, W1W 5PA,
United Kingdom
☏ 020 76367800

Apple Juice The Grove, Wacton Road, Forncett St. Peter, Norwich, Norfolk, NR16 1JD,
United Kingdom
☏ 01508 532514

Arcmedia Ltd 5 Hardhorn Road, Poulton-Le-Fylde, Lancashire, FY6 7SR,
United Kingdom
☏ 01253 896616

Armstrong Design Aston Court, Marlborough Park, Southdown Road, Harpenden, Hertfordshire, AL5 1NL,
United Kingdom
☏ 01582 465100

Arnold Jones Associates Somerleigh Gate, Somerleigh Road, Dorchester, Dorset, DT1 1TL,
United Kingdom
☏ 01305 260606

Arra Design 5 Catherine Road, Newbury, Berkshire, RG14 7NA, United Kingdom
✆ 01635 41370

Arris Ltd Manor Farm, Hunsingore, Wetherby, LS22 5HY, United Kingdom
✆ 01423 358881

Art Works Parker Court, Knapp Lane, Cheltenham, Gloucestershire, GL50 3QJ, United Kingdom
✆ 01242 572559

Artech 11b Don Terrace, Aberdeen, Aberdeenshire, AB24 2UH, United Kingdom
✆ 01224 495010

Arthaus Design 32 Villiers Street, Leamington Spa, Warwickshire, CV32 5YF, United Kingdom
✆ 01926 313076

Arthouse Ltd St James Church, Bacup Road, Waterfoot, Rossendale, Lancashire, BB4 7JU, United Kingdom
✆ 01706 230077

artisan creative.co.uk The Long Barn, Southview Business Park, Tinwell Road, Stamford, Lincolnshire, PE9 2JL, United Kingdom
✆ 01780 484450

Arts Interactive Ltd First Floor, 1-5 Church Street, Douglas, Isle Of Man, IM1 2AG, United Kingdom
✆ 01624 668360

Arup Vehicle Design Group The Arup Campus Blythe Gate, Shirley, Solihull, West Midlands, B90 8AE, United Kingdom
✆ 0121 2133000

Ashleigh Signs Ashleigh House, Marsh Street, Rothwell, Leeds, West Yorkshire, LS26 0AG, United Kingdom
✆ 0845 6007446

Aspect Design & Marketing 22 Victoria Ave, Harrogate, North Yorkshire, HG1 5PR, United Kingdom
✆ 01423 501161

Astound Jessica House, Red Lion Square, 191 Wandsworth High Street, London, SW18 4LS, United Kingdom
✆ 020 88719066

Asylum Models 20 Thornsett Road, Earlsfield, London, SW18 4EF, United Kingdom
✆ 020 88712988

Atkinson Associates 3 Alice Court, Putney Bridge Road, London, SW15 2NQ, United Kingdom
✆ 020 88708220

Attik Ltd 1 Saw Mill Street, Holbeck, Leeds, West Yorkshire, LS11 5WE, United Kingdom
✆ 0113 2021530

Aukett Brockliss Guy 6 The Warehouse, Anchor Quay, Henryn, Falmouth, Cornwall, TR10 8GZ, United Kingdom
✆ 01326 376560

Avvio Design Associates Ltd The Quadrant, Upper Culham Farm, Cockpole Green, Berkshire, RG10 8NR, United Kingdom
✆ 01491 842270

Axiom Design Resource Unit 22 Cottage Lane, Cottage Lane Industrial Estate, Broughton Astley, Leicestershire, LE9 6TU, United Kingdom
✆ 01455 286767

B&W Studio Castleton Mill, Castleton Close, Armley Road, Leeds, West Yorkshire, LS12 2DS, United Kingdom
✆ 0113 2454300

B1 Creative Studio C, Garratt Court, Furmage Street, London, SW18 4DF, United Kingdom
✆ 020 88771137

Babel Media Ltd CMT 11-12, Hove Business Centre, Fonthill Road, Hove, East Sussex, BN3 6HA, United Kingdom
✆ 01273 764100

Bagshots Ltd The Clock Tower, Dover Marina, Kent, CT17 9TF, United Kingdom
✆ 01304 226621

Baigent Ltd 48 Church Street, Chesham, Buckinghamshire, HP5 1HY, United Kingdom
✆ 01494 770120

Bamboo Design Ltd Rowlandson House, Ballards Lane, London, N12 8NP, United Kingdom
✆ 020 84462800

Bang Marketing Fairway Lodge, 16a Kings Mill Lane, Huddersfield, West Yorkshire, HD1 3AW, United Kingdom
✆ 01484 540412

Barber Jackson 3 Park Farm, Inworth, Colchester, Essex, CO5 9SH, United Kingdom
✆ 01376 572465

BB/Saunders 2nd Floor, 7 Plough Yard, London, EC2A 3LP, United Kingdom
✆ 020 74229181

Bbm Carlson 220 Park Avenue, Aztec West, Almondsbury, Bristol, Avon, BS32 4SY, United Kingdom
✆ 01454 618811

Bdp Design 16 Brewhouse Road, London, EC1V 4LJ, United Kingdom
✆ 020 78128000

Be Creative 74 Preston Drove, Brighton, East Sussex, BN1 9SB, United Kingdom
✆ 01273 852440

Beacon Graphics The Mews, Brook Street, Mitchelldean, Gloucestershire, GL17 0SL, United Kingdom
✆ 01594 542888

Beck Interiors Victory House, Cox Lane, Chessington, Surrey, KT9 1SG, United Kingdom
✆ 020 89740500

Bell Design & Commns Ltd 77-78 St Martins Lane, London, WC2N 4AA, United Kingdom
✆ 020 73959740

Benoy Architects Handley House, 7 North Gate, Newark, Nottinghamshire, NG24 1EH, United Kingdom
✆ 01636 672356

Benoy Ltd 210 High Holborn, London, WC1V 7DL, United Kingdom
✆ 020 72425512

Bentley Holland & Partners Ltd Unit C21 Poplar Business Park, 10 Preston Road, London, E14 9RL, United Kingdom
✆ 020 75377575

Bernard Engle Archtcts & Plnrs 65 Kings Cross Road, London, WC1X 9LW, United Kingdom
✆ 020 78416464

Berry Place Models 1a Berry Place, London, EC1V 0JD, United Kingdom
✆ 020 74908222

Bespoke Designs 45 Nork Way, Banstead, Surrey, SM7 1PB, United Kingdom
✆ 01737 363438

Big Fish Design & Advertising 2 Atlantic Quay, 100-114 Strand Road, Londonderry, County Londonderry, BT48 7NR, United Kingdom
✆ 028 71362845

Big Green Door 15 Hatton Street, London, NW8 8PL, United Kingdom
✆ 020 77241434

Bionicmedia 23 St Georges Mews, Brighton, East Sussex, BN1 4EU, United Kingdom
✆ 01273 699864

Birchcourt Design Ltd 43 Church Lane, Pudsey, West Yorkshire, LS28 7RR, United Kingdom
✆ 0113 2047111

Bisset Adams 22 St James Walk, London, EC1R 0AP, United Kingdom
✆ 020 72533037

Black Dog Design CU Phosco Lighting, Lower Rd, Great Amwell, Ware, SG12 9TA, United Kingdom
✆ 01920 466775

Black Eye Design Henrietta House, 47 London Road, Turnbridge Wells, Kent, TN1 1DT, United Kingdom
✆ 01892 510888

Black Pig Design Co 48A Kneesworth St, Royston, SG8 5AH, United Kingdom
✆ 01763 222333

Black Sheep 103 Bute Street, Cardiff Bay, Cardiff, South Glamorgan, CF10 5AD, United Kingdom
✆ 029 20490722

Blaze Cdn Ltd Castle House, 27 London Road, Tunbridge Wells, Kent, TN1 1DB, United Kingdom
✆ 01892 516262

Blitz Charter Group 100 Centennial Avenue, Centennial Park, Elstree, Hertfordshire, WD6 3SA, United Kingdom
✆ 020 83271000

Bloc Media Ltd 61 Charlotte Road, London, EC2A 3QT, United Kingdom
✆ 020 77391718

Bloom 25 The Village, 101 Amies Street, London, SW11 2JW, United Kingdom
✆ 020 79244533

Blue 2 Charlton House, Old Estate Yard, East Hendridge, Wantage, Oxfordshire, OX12 8LL, United Kingdom
✆ 01235 862587

Blue Chilli Studio Ltd 7 Lonsdale Road, Birmingham, West Midlands, B17 9RA, United Kingdom
✆ 0121 4284200

Blue Design & Marketing Ltd Kingsway House, 134-140 Church Road, Hove, BN3 2QW, United Kingdom
✆ 01273 220054

Blue Frog Design 21 St Margarets Street, Leicester, Leicestershire, LE1 3EB, United Kingdom
✆ 0116 2530612

Blue Fruit Design 120 Western Road, Hove, East Sussex, BN3 1DB, United Kingdom
✆ 01273 820120

Blue Gem Eyewear Ltd 3 Sunbeam Road, Park Royal, London, NW10 6JP, United Kingdom
✆ 020 89655768

Blue Goose Design The Power House, West Street, Harrow On The Hill, Middlesex, HA1 3EL, United Kingdom
✆ 020 88698500

Blue River The Foundry, Forth Banks, Newcastle Upon Tyne, Tyne & Wear, NE1 3PA, United Kingdom
✆ 0191 2610000

Blue Stone Design Tamar Science Park, Derriford Road, Derriford, Plymouth, PL6 8BQ, United Kingdom
✆ 01752 700777

Bluelime 677 Princes Road, Dartford, Kent, DA2 6EF, United Kingdom
✆ 01322 285734

Blueprint Design Co Ltd Martins Barn, Birdham Road, Chichester, West Sussex, PO20 7BX,
United Kingdom
✆ 01243 512106

Blueprint Interior Design 3a Dinsdale Place, Sandyford, Newcastle Upon Tyne, Tyne & Wear, NE2 1BD,
United Kingdom
✆ 0191 2305540

Bluestone Design Group Bridge Road, Boston Spa, Wetherby, West Yorkshire, LS23 6HD,
United Kingdom
✆ 01937 849666

Bluflame The Limes, 5 Birmingham Road, Walsall, West Midlands, WS1 2LT,
United Kingdom
✆ 01922 645656

Bogacki Project Ltd 1st Floor, Duncley House, Albert Street, West Yorkshire, HX7 8AX,
United Kingdom
✆ 01422 847949

Bonfire Design Ltd 3a Woburn Street, Ampthill, Bedfordshire, MK45 2HP,
United Kingdom
✆ 01525 841079

Boss Design Ltd Boss Drive, Dudley, West Midlands, DY2 8SZ,
United Kingdom
✆ 01384 455570

Bossco 118 Gatley Road, Gatley, SK8 4AD,
United Kingdom
✆ 0161 2820011

Bovis Hornes Ltd Cleeve Hall, Cheltenham Road, Bishops Cleeve, Cheltenham, Gloucestershire, GL52 8ZD,
United Kingdom
✆ 01242 662400

Bradbury Graphics Ltd Equality House, 6-14 Donegall Pass, Belfast, County Antrim, BT7 1BS,
United Kingdom
✆ 028 90233535

Brand Design 73 High Street, Newport Pagnell, Buckinghamshire, MK16 8AD,
United Kingdom
✆ 01908 610768

Brandhouse Wts 10a Frederick Close, London, W2 2HD,
United Kingdom
✆ 020 72989606

Briggs Hillier Design Ltd Alma House, Wibtoft, Watling Street, Lutterworth, Leicestershire, LE17 5BE,
United Kingdom
✆ 01455 221919

Brilliant Ltd Duckling Lane, 2 Ducking Lane, Sawbridgeworth, Hertfordshire, CM21 9QA,
United Kingdom
✆ 01279 725358

Brinkworth Design Ltd 6 Ellsworth Street, London, E2 0AX,
United Kingdom
✆ 020 76135341

British School of Osteopathy 275 Borough High St, Southwark, London, SE1 1JE,
United Kingdom
✆ 020 74070222

Broome Jenkins Ltd Clifton House, 9 Clifton Street, Lytham St Annes, Lancashire, FY8 1HZ,
United Kingdom
✆ 01253 737054

Brownjohn Design Consultants 44 Carnaby Street, London, W1F 9PP,
United Kingdom
✆ 020 74949494

Bruce Dunlop & Associates 1-6 Falconberg Court, London, W1D 3AB,
United Kingdom
✆ 020 74401070

Bubble Media 51 Turner Street, Manchester, Lancashire, M4 1DN,
United Kingdom
✆ 0161 8393444

Building Design Partnership Sunlight House, PO Box 85, Quay Street, Manchester, Lancashire, M60 3JA,
United Kingdom
✆ 0161 8348441

Bulletlondon 47 Queens Road, Weybridge, Surrey, KT13 9UH,
United Kingdom
✆ 01932 885885

Bureaux Saxon House, 56 Commercial Street, Spitalfields, London, E1 6LT,
United Kingdom
✆ 020 73776261

Burleigh One Harbourmead, Harbour Road, Portishead, Bristol, Avon, BS20 7AY,
United Kingdom
✆ 01275 841280

Burnt Ltd Mill Street, 1st Floor, Wantage, Oxfordshire, OX12 9AB,
United Kingdom
✆ 01235 771770

Burrows Jonathan Scott Hall, Thorpe Road, Norwich, Norfolk, NR1 1UH,
United Kingdom
✆ 01603 767663

Burst Ltd 15 Wilbury Crescent, Hove, East Sussex, BN3 6FL,
United Kingdom
✆ 01273 731110

Butcher & Gundersen Ltd 3 Castle Row, Horticultural Place, Chiswick, London, W4 4JQ,
United Kingdom
✆ 020 89879926

Cactus Events Heliport Industrial Estate, 40 Lombard Road, London, SW11 3SS,
United Kingdom
✆ 020 79243002

Cada Design Group Suite4, 155 Bermondsey Street, London, SE1 3UY,
United Kingdom
✆ 020 72349700

Calcium 1a Elm Avenue, Longeaton, Nottingham, Nottinghamshire, NG10 4LR,
United Kingdom
✆ 0115 9728685

Cameron Design & Marketing Ltd Maria House, Camel Road, Littleport, Ely, Cambridgeshire, CB6 1PU,
United Kingdom
✆ 01353 860006

Cameron Robb Ltd 48 -52 Lombard Street, Birmingham, West Midlands, B12 0QN,
United Kingdom
✆ 0121 7728311

Candy & Candy Ltd 100 Brompton Road, Knightsbridge, London, SW3 1ER,
United Kingdom
✆ 020 75944300

Cardinus Ltd Glenister House, 14-16 King Street, East Grinstead, West Sussex, RH19 3DJ,
United Kingdom
✆ 01342 301639

Caro Communications 19-20 Great Sutton St, 1st Floor, London, EC1V 0DR,
United Kingdom
✆ 020 73368488

Carolyn Trayler Agency 70 Evelyn Gdns, London, SW7 3BQ,
United Kingdom
✆ 020 73700712

Carter Wong Tomlin 29 Brook Mews North, London, W2 3BW,
United Kingdom
✆ 020 75690000

Catch Graphics Woolhampton Design Centre, Station Road, Woolhampton, Reading, Berkshire, RG7 5SE,
United Kingdom
✆ 0118 9712324

Caulder Moore The Coach House, 273a Sandycombe Road, Richmond, Surrey, TW9 3LU,
United Kingdom
✆ 020 83320393

CD Partnership 22 Shad Thames, London, SE1 2YU,
United Kingdom
✆ 020 74038899

CDA Design 52 Maypole Green Road, Colchester, Essex, CO2 9QW,
United Kingdom
✆ 01206 575336

CDS 7 Eastgate, Leeds, West Yorkshire, LS2 7LY,
United Kingdom
✆ 0113 3994000

CDT Design Ltd 21 Brownlow Mews, London, WC1N 2LG,
United Kingdom
✆ 020 72420992

Central London Partnership 29 Heddon Street, London, W1B 4BL,
United Kingdom
✆ 020 74788460

Centre Design Tynecastle House, Low Prudhoe, Prudhoe, Northumberland, NE42 6NP,
United Kingdom
✆ 01661 836282

Centreline Design Hex Greive Hall, Hex Grieve, Farnsfield, Nottingham, Nottinghamshire, NG22 8LS,
United Kingdom
✆ 01623 884300

Centremark Design Ltd 143 New London Road, Chelmsford, Essex, CM2 0QT,
United Kingdom
✆ 01245 345143

Certikin International Witan Park, Avenue 2, Station Lane Industrial Estate, Oxon, Oxfordshire, OX28 4FJ,
United Kingdom
✆ 01993 778855

Cfh Creative Commns Ltd The Portal, Bridgewater Close, Bently Wood, Burnley, Lancashire, BB11 5TT,
United Kingdom
✆ 01282 839901

CGA Creative Ltd The Bothy, Albury Park, Albury, Guildford, Surrey, GU5 9BH,
United Kingdom
✆ 01483 202275

CGP Design Tun Yard, 7 Pearton Street, London, SW8 3HT,
United Kingdom
✆ 020 31771170

Chameleon Creative 16-18 Canon Harnett Court, Warren Farm, Milton Keynes, Buckinghamshire, MK12 5NF,
United Kingdom
✆ 01908 222255

Chaos Design Ltd 32 High Street, Guildford, Surrey, GU1 3EL,
United Kingdom
✆ 01483 557800

Character Graphics 56-58 Station Road, Taunton, Somerset, TA1 1NS,
United Kingdom
✆ 01823 279008

Chase Design Mill Lane Studio, Mill Lane, Godalming, Surrey, GU7 1EY,
United Kingdom
✆ 01483 424777

Cheeky Monkey Creative Ltd Unit 14 Royal Stuart Workshops, Adelaide Place, Cardiff, South Glamorgan, CF10 5BR,
United Kingdom
✆ 029 20491000

Chen Tsoi Design 87 Arlington Road, London, NW1 7ES,
United Kingdom
✆ 020 73830185

Chimera Design 2 Harlequin Avenue, Brentford, Middlesex, TW8 9EW,
United Kingdom
✆ 020 85698994

Christopher Lewis Associates 41 Charterhouse Square, London, EC1M 6EA,
United Kingdom
✆ 020 76000123

Chubb Fire Ltd Chubb House, Staines Road West, Sunbury On Thames, Middlesex, TW16 7AR,
United Kingdom
✆ 01932 785588

Circle Design 75 Holywood Road, Belfast, County Antrim, BT4 3BA,
United Kingdom
✆ 028 90473747

CIRCLE DESIGN CONSULTANTS 5-23 Old Street, Morelands Buildings, London, EC1V 9HL, United Kingdom
✆ 020 72514687

Classic Lines Design Ltd The Coach horse, Old Burcot Lane, Bromsgrove, Worcestershire, B60 1PH, United Kingdom
✆ 01527 882999

Clear 20 Orange Street, London, WC2H 7EF, United Kingdom
✆ 020 73890853

CLEAR GRAPHICS Ltd 26 Wadham Road, Putney, London, SW15 2LR, United Kingdom
✆ 020 88772662

Clement Clarke Intl Ltd Edinburgh Way, Harlow, Essex, CM20 2TT, United Kingdom
✆ 01279 414969

Clever4 Web Design 5 Priory Tec Park, Saxon Way, Hessle, North Humberside, HU13 9PB, United Kingdom
✆ 01482 640730

Clicks Digital Solutions Ltd 10 Bakers Yard, Bakers Row, London, EC1R 3DD, United Kingdom
✆ 020 72782300

Clik Design 43 Water Street, St Pauls, Birmingham, West Midlands, B3 1HP, United Kingdom
✆ 0121 2121612

Clipper Broadwinsor Road Ind Est, Broadwindsor Road, Beaminster, Dorset, DT8 3PR, United Kingdom
✆ 01308 863344

Cochrane McGregor Ltd 136 Tooley Street, London, SE1 2TU, United Kingdom
✆ 020 73781828

Coley Porter Bell 18 Grosvenor Gardens, Victoria, London, SW1W 0DH, United Kingdom
✆ 020 78247700

Colin Hargrave Associates 13 University Road, Leicester, Leicestershire, LE1 7RA, United Kingdom
✆ 0116 2552474

Collective Creative Ltd Engravers House, 35 Wick Road, Teddington, Middlesex, TW11 9DN, United Kingdom
✆ 020 89439492

Colne Vcs 9/12 Eastman Way, Hemel Hempstead, Hertfordshire, HP2 5RB, United Kingdom
✆ 01442 212922

Colourgraphic Arts 43 Woolmer Way, Bordon, Hampshire, GU35 9QE, United Kingdom
✆ 01420 474000

Communication by Design 6 The Courthouse, 38 Kingsland Road, London, E2 8DD, United Kingdom
✆ 020 77294000

Community Internet Windsor House, 12 High Street, Kidlington, Oxfordshire, OX5 2PJ, United Kingdom
✆ 01865 856000

Completely Digital Design Studio One, Rushington Court, Chapel Lane, Southampton, Hampshire, SO40 9NA, United Kingdom
✆ 023 80661868

Concept Associates Ltd Concept House, 271 High Street, Berkhampsted, Hertfordshire, HP4 1AA, United Kingdom
✆ 01442 385000

Connections in Design Ltd 27-29 Sovereign Road, Kings Norton Business Centre, Kings Norton, Birmingham, West Midlands, B30 3HN, United Kingdom
✆ 0121 4511201

Conrad Design Studio 14 Green Box, Westonhall Road, Stoke Prior, Bromsgrove, Worcestershire, B60 4AL, United Kingdom
✆ 01527 878773

Conran & Partners 22 Shad Thames, London, SE1 2YU, United Kingdom
✆ 020 73781161

Contagious The Bond Building, 33 Breadalbane, Edinburgh, Mid Lothian, EH6 5GW, United Kingdom
✆ 0131 5535545

Contra Integrated CRTV Servs 22 Ganton Street, London, W1F 7BY, United Kingdom
✆ 020 72923939

Cooksley Malem Ltd The Gatehouse, 10 Cheyne Walk, Northampton, Northamptonshire, NN1 5PT, United Kingdom
✆ 01604 630055

Cool Blue Communications 144-146 Borough Road, Garland House, Middlesbrough, Cleveland, TS1 2EP, United Kingdom
✆ 01642 351011

Corizon Ltd 119-121 Middlesex Street, London, E1 7JF, United Kingdom
✆ 020 75396800

Courts Design Whiteoak, London Road, Hartley Wintney, Hook, RG27 8RN, United Kingdom
✆ 01252 842350

Coutts Retail Communications Golden House, 28-31 Great Pulteney Street, London, W1F 9NN, United Kingdom
✆ 020 75348800

Cowan London 161 Rosebery Avenue, London, EC1R 4QX, United Kingdom
✆ 020 78374961

CP Hart Newnham Terrace, Hercules Road, London, SE1 7DR, United Kingdom
✆ 020 79021000

Crafts Council 44a Pentonville Road, Islington, London, N1 9BY, United Kingdom
✆ 020 72787700

Creactive Design Francis Court, High Ditch Road, Fen Ditton, Cambridge, Cambridgeshire, CB5 8TE, United Kingdom
✆ 01223 295959

Creation Agency Ltd 3 Walker Avenue, Wolverton Mill, Milton Keynes, Buckinghamshire, MK12 5TW, United Kingdom
✆ 0870 8502274

Creative Action Design Long Mire House, London Road, St Albans, Hertfordshire, AL1 1NG, United Kingdom
✆ 01727 799999

Creative Change 367 Chiswick High Road, The Swan Centre, London, W4 4AG, United Kingdom
✆ 020 84002490

Creative Edge Design 19 Seymour Terrace, Seymout Street, Liverpool, Merseyside, L3 5PE, United Kingdom
✆ 0151 7086660

Creative IDA Ltd 218 London Road, Leicester, Leicestershire, LE2 1NE, United Kingdom
✆ 0116 2552299

Creative Industry Ltd Chapel Beck Mill, Howgill, Sedburgh, Cumbria, LA10 5JD, United Kingdom
✆ 015396 21965

Creative Instore Activity 16 Cleveleys Road, Penketh Business Park, Great Sankey, Warrington, Cheshire, WA5 2TJ, United Kingdom
✆ 01925 416796

Creative Juice 4 Moorfield Mills, Moorfield Crescent, Yeadon, Leeds, West Yorkshire, LS19 7EA, United Kingdom
✆ 0113 2505540

Creative Touch Design Ltd 32 High Street, Henley-In-Arden, B95 5AN, United Kingdom
✆ 01564 797580

Creator Communications Ltd 4 Grafton Mews, London, W1T 5JE, United Kingdom
✆ 020 73915120

Creed Design Associates Ltd The Old Bank, 2 Cross Street, Enderby, Leicester, Leicestershire, LE19 4NJ, United Kingdom
✆ 0116 2752456

CREOGRAPHICS Haydons Road, London, SW19 8TY, United Kingdom
✆ 020 85405959

Crescent Lodge Design Ltd Foundation House, Perseverance Works, 38 Kingsland Road, London, E2 8DD, United Kingdom
✆ 020 76130613

Cristel Graphics Ltd Dunkirk Mills, Dunkirk Street, Halifax, West Yorkshire, HX1 3TB, United Kingdom
✆ 01422 331033

Crown Mortgage Services Crown House, Crown Street, Ipswich, Suffolk, IP1 3HS, United Kingdom
✆ 01473 283800

Crumpled Dog Design 18 Phipp Street, London, EC2A 4NU, United Kingdom
✆ 020 77395553

Cscape Ltd 4 Pear Tree Court, Clerkenwell, London, EC1R 0DS, United Kingdom
✆ 020 76898800

Cube 3 Media Ltd 4 6 Breightmet Street, Bolton, Lancashire, BL2 1BR, United Kingdom
✆ 01204 391707

Cube Group The Albany Boathouse, Lower Ham Road, Kingston Upon Thames, Surrey, KT2 5BB, United Kingdom
✆ 020 85471543

Cube Studios The Vale Industrial Centre, Southern Road, Aylesbury, Buckinghamshire, HP19 9EW, United Kingdom
✆ 01296 339200

Cunningham Design 38 High Street West, Uppingham, Rutland, Leicestershire, LE15 9QD, United Kingdom
✆ 01572 822599

Curious Group 10 Lynedoch Pl, Glasgow, G3 6AB, United Kingdom
✆ 0141 3312120

Cypher Digital Imaging Ltd Bridge End House, Park Road, Milthorpe, Preston, Cumbria, LA7 7AD, United Kingdom
✆ 015395 63433

Czech & Speake 244-254 Cambridge Heath Road, London, E2 9DA, United Kingdom
✆ 020 89837400

Dalton Maag Ltd Unit M2, 245a Coldharbour Lane, London, SW9 8RR, United Kingdom
✆ 020 79240633

Dalziel & Pow 5-8 Hardwick Street, London, EC1R 4RG, United Kingdom
✆ 020 78377117

David Aldridge Animations Ltd Hybris Business Park, Warmwell Road, Crossways, Dorchester, Dorset, DT2 8BF, United Kingdom
✆ 01305 854864

DAVID CHARLES & Co The Barn, Lantern Courtyard, The Street Bramley, Tadley, Hampshire, RG26 5DE, United Kingdom
✆ 01256 883712

David Morgan Associates 10 Broadbent Close, 20-22 Highgate High Street, London, N6 5JW, United Kingdom
✆ 020 83404009

David Richards Ltd 1 Deacon Trading Estate, Cabinet Way, North Circular Road, London, E4 8QF, United Kingdom
✆ 020 85232051

DCA Design 19 Church St, Warwick, Warwickshire, CV34 4AB, United Kingdom
☎ 01926 499461

Dcg Media Ltd 147 London Road, Kingston Upon Thames, Surrey, KT2 6NH, United Kingdom
☎ 020 85410800

Deep Creativity 4 Vernon Street, Derby, Derbyshire, DE1 1FR, United Kingdom
☎ 01332 208992

DEGW Ltd Porters North, 8 Crinan Street, London, N1 9SQ, United Kingdom
☎ 020 72397777

Deltalight UK Ltd 40 Rivington Street, London, EC2A 3LX, United Kingdom
☎ 020 77291977

Denovo Design 22-26 Clarendon Street, Nottingham, Nottinghamshire, NG1 5HQ, United Kingdom
☎ 0115 8415015

Design Activity Ltd Beech House, 6 St Pauls Road, Clifton, Bristol, Avon, BS8 1LT, United Kingdom
☎ 0117 9339400

Design Alliance 2 Allington Close, Wimbledon Village, London, SW19 5AP, United Kingdom
☎ 020 89441992

Design Central The Mill House, Greenway Farm, Bath Road, Bristol, Avon, BS30 5RL, United Kingdom
☎ 0117 9371360

Design Centre Ltd Number One, Heath Mill Road, Wombourne, Wolverhampton, West Midlands, WV5 8AP, United Kingdom
☎ 01902 324490

Design Directions Ltd Flagstaff House, 12 High Street, Twyford, Berkshire, RG10 9AE, United Kingdom
☎ 0118 9344477

Design Group Quay House, The Quay, Poole, Dorset, BH15 1HA, United Kingdom
☎ 01202 669090

Design House 4 Duke Street, Richmond, Surrey, TW9 1HP, United Kingdom
☎ 020 84399360

Design Links 89 Giles Street, Leith, Edinburgh, Mid Lothian, EH6 6BZ, United Kingdom
☎ 0131 5542807

Design LSM 58 Livingstone Road, Hove, East Sussex, BN3 3WL, United Kingdom
☎ 01273 820033

Design Matters 2 Capelrig Lane, Newton Mearns, Glasgow, Lanarkshire, G77 6XZ, United Kingdom
☎ 0141 6163152

Design Ministry Ltd 28 Bradmore Park Road, Hammersmith, London, W6 0DT, United Kingdom
☎ 020 87480055

Design One Malt House Barns, Grove Lane, Lapworth, Solihull, West Midlands, B94 6AR, United Kingdom
☎ 01564 786800

Design Point Associates Old Barn Studios, Hereford Gardens, Pinner, Middlesex, HA5 5JR, United Kingdom
☎ 020 88665660

Design Religion Hampton Court, Rainbow Hill, Worcestershire, WR3 8NF, United Kingdom
☎ 01905 724707

Design Stage Ltd 21 West Bute Street, Cardiff, South Glamorgan, CF10 5EP, United Kingdom
☎ 029 20465366

Design Stream Studio 106, Westbourne Studios, 242 Acklam Road, London, W10 5JJ, United Kingdom
☎ 020 75753246

Design Unique Ltd Top Floor 11, Duncan Close, Moulton Park, Northampton, Northamptonshire, NN3 6WL, United Kingdom
☎ 01604 671167

Design Wall Ltd 16 Woodland View, Wroughton, Wiltshire, SN4 9AB, United Kingdom
☎ 01793 812199

Design Works Unit 2 The Business Centre, Vansitart Est, Windsor, Berkshire, SL4 1SP, United Kingdom
☎ 01753 842404

Design4retail Ltd 2-3 Bitteswell Business Park, Lutterworth, Leicestershire, LE17 4LR, United Kingdom
☎ 01455 203352

Designease Unit 7, Stonehouse Commercial Centre, Bristol Road, Stonehouse, Gloucestershire, GL10 3RD, United Kingdom
☎ 01453 821990

Designleads 1 Pym Court, Pym Street, Off South Accomadation Road, Leeds, West Yorkshire, LS10 1PG, United Kingdom
☎ 0113 2420065

Deyton Bell Ltd Newton Hall, Town Street, Newton, Cambridge, Cambridgeshire, CB22 7ZE, United Kingdom
☎ 01223 873033

Digital Portfolios 52 Upper Street, Islington, London, N1 0QH, United Kingdom
☎ 020 72881188

Dimension Group 4 Repton Court, Repton Close, Basildon, Essex, SS13 1LN, United Kingdom
☎ 01268 285361

Dirty Design 61 Park Street, Bristol, Avon, BS1 5NU, United Kingdom
☎ 0117 9273344

Display Creatives UK Ltd The Byre, Furtho Manor Farm, Old Stratford, Milton Keynes, Buckinghamshire, MK19 6NR, United Kingdom
☎ 01908 543844

DJH DESIGN The Hayloft, Pury Hill Business Park, Alderton Road, Towcester, Northamptonshire, NN12 7LS, United Kingdom
☎ 01327 811881

DJPA Partnership 88 90 Grays Inn Road, London, WC1X 8AA, United Kingdom
☎ 020 70253850

Dkpm Ltd 15 Paternoster Row, Sheffield, South Yorkshire, S1 2BX, United Kingdom
☎ 0114 2210256

DMS Design Ltd 20 Lansdowne Terrace, Gosforth, Newcastle Upon Tyne, NE3 1HP, United Kingdom
☎ 0191 2849222

Doctor Direct Ruskin Court, Drury Lane, Knutsford, Cheshire, WA16 6HA, United Kingdom
☎ 01565 759500

Door 22 Design Collective 158b Church Road, Hove, East Sussex, BN3 2DL, United Kingdom
☎ 01273 711600

Dragon Brand Consulting Ltd 1 Craven Hill, London, W2 3EN, United Kingdom
☎ 020 72624488

Drinkworks 3 South Black Lion Lane, Hammersmith, London, W6 9TJ, United Kingdom
☎ 020 87426622

Dudson Ltd 200 Scotin Rd, Tunstall, Stoke On Trent, Staffordshire, ST6 4JD, United Kingdom
☎ 01782 819337

Dunning Design Ltd 90, Mitchell Street, Glasgow, Lanarkshire, G1 3NQ, United Kingdom
☎ 0141 2488627

Dunning Eley Jones 31 Oval Road, London, NW1 7EA, United Kingdom
☎ 020 74289491

Duo Consultants Ltd 9 Southwick Mews, London, W2 1JG, United Kingdom
☎ 020 77249500

Dusted Design Partners Studio 1A, 151 Tower Bridge Road, London, SE1 3LW, United Kingdom
☎ 020 74037776

Dyson Design Ltd 55 Regent Road, Leicester, Leicestershire, LE1 6YF, United Kingdom
☎ 0116 2855725

Dzd 145 Tottenham Court Road, London, W1T 7NE, United Kingdom
☎ 020 73887488

EC Design & Marketing 17 Corn Markets, Wimborne, Dorset, BH21 1JL, United Kingdom
☎ 01202 842725

Echo Studios The Pavillions, East Road, Wimbledon, London, SW19 1AH, United Kingdom
☎ 020 82543434

Eclipse Creative Unit F Linford Lane, Linsford Business Park, Mytchett, Surrey, GU16 6DL, United Kingdom
☎ 01252 378431

Eclipse Creative Ltd Pascoe House, 54 Bute Street, Cardiff, South Glamorgan, CF10 5AF, United Kingdom
☎ 029 20470070

Edge Exhibition Design Ltd 3 Brook Street, Chipping Sudbrey, Bristol, Avon, BS37 6AZ, United Kingdom
☎ 01454 319081

EDL Design House, Hills Meadows, Douglas, Isle Of Man, IM1 5EB, United Kingdom
☎ 01624 628292

edsonwilliams Creative Consultancy 52 Brushfield Street, London, E1 6AG
☎ **020 7375 2077/020 7375 3077** ✉ **info@edsonwilliams.com**
✍ **www.edsonwilliams.com**
See ad in showcase

Effective Marketing Solutions 114 Bath Road, Cheltenham, Gloucestershire, GL53 7JX, United Kingdom
☎ 01242 578888

EGG DESIGN MARKETING 5-6 Crescent Stables, 139 Upper Richmond Road, London, SW15 2TN, United Kingdom
☎ 020 87802299

Ego Creative Ltd The Wheat House, 98 High Street, Odiham, Hampshire, RG29 1LP, United Kingdom
☎ 01256 709910

Elan Creative Marketing The Barn, Bently Manor, Church Road, Little Bentley, Essex, CO7 8SC, United Kingdom
☎ 01206 252378

Electric Lemon Design The Manor House, 126 High Street, Solihull, West Midlands, B91 3SX, United Kingdom
☎ 0121 7040820

Elevator 35 West Bute Street, Cardiff Bay, Cardiff, South Glamorgan, CF10 5LH, United Kingdom
☎ 029 20491105

Elmwood Design Ltd 40-44 Thistle Street, Edinburgh, Mid Lothian, EH2 1EN, United Kingdom
📞 0131 2251181

Elmwood Studios Ltd Elmwood, Ghyll Royd, Leeds, West Yorkshire, LS20 9LT, United Kingdom
📞 01943 870229

Emerald Design 1 Universal Square, Devonshire Street, Manchester, Lancashire, M12 6JH, United Kingdom
📞 0161 2744007

Emperor Design Consultants Zetland House, 5-25 Scruton Street, London, EC2A 4HJ, United Kingdom
📞 020 77299090

Emperor Design Consultants 32 Castle Street, Edinburgh, Mid Lothian, EH2 3HT, United Kingdom
📞 0131 2207990

Emphasis Design Peel Mills Business Centre, Commercial Street, Morley, Leeds, LS27 7UY, United Kingdom
📞 0113 2524400

Empire Design Co Ltd 29 Queen Anne Street, London, W1G 9HU, United Kingdom
📞 020 74362202

Endpoint 2 Newhams Row, London, SE1 3UZ, United Kingdom
📞 020 70892670

Engine 6a New Concordia Wharf, Mill Street, London, SE1 2BB, United Kingdom
📞 020 72373756

Enterprise IG 11-33 St John Street, London, EC1M 4PJ, United Kingdom
📞 020 75597000

EON Productions Ltd Eon House, 138 Piccadilly, London, W1J 7NR, United Kingdom
📞 020 74937953

Epigram Commns & Design Barclay House, 35 Whitworth Street West, Manchester, Lancashire, M1 5NG, United Kingdom
📞 0161 2379660

Epitype 24 Bulwer Street, London, W12 8AR, United Kingdom
📞 020 87439282

Epoch Design Ltd 54 Queen Square, Bristol, Avon, BS1 4LH, United Kingdom
📞 0117 9258790

EQ Design 292 Rose Mount Place, Aberdeen, Aberdeenshire, AB25 2YA, United Kingdom
📞 01224 622277

EQtwo 45-49 Leather Lane, London, EC1N 7TJ, United Kingdom
📞 020 76819222

Equinox Design Ltd Equinox Park, 100 Jack Lane, Leeds, West Yorkshire, LS10 1BW, United Kingdom
📞 0113 2441300

Ergo Identity Consultants Ltd 34 Oppidans Road, London, NW3 3AG, United Kingdom
📞 020 77225500

Esterson Associates The Lux Building, Studio 6, 2-4 Hoxton Square, London, N1 6NU, United Kingdom
📞 020 76846500

Etal Design Ltd 32 East Street, Osney Island, Oxford, Oxfordshire, OX2 0AU, United Kingdom
📞 01865 243343

Event Communications Ltd 3rd Floor, India House, 45 Curlew Street, London, SE1 2ND, United Kingdom
📞 020 73789900

Evoke in Store Suite F9, Oaklands Office Park, Hooton, Cheshire, Merseyside, CH66 7NZ, United Kingdom
📞 0151 3280850

Evolve NPD Ltd 55 Bondway, London, SW8 1S7, United Kingdom
📞 020 75825149

Exposure Insight 22 23 Little Portland Street, London, W1W 8BU, United Kingdom
📞 020 79077130

Eyelevel Design Consultants Stane Street Nurseries, Stane Street, Codmore Hill, Pulborough, West Sussex, RH20 2BW, United Kingdom
📞 01798 875525

F8 Design Associates The White House, Wildpool Park, Greenalls Avenue, Warrington, Cheshire, WA4 6HL, United Kingdom
📞 01925 438058

Face Edge Ltd Fletcher Indust Est Clovelly Rd, Bideford, EX39 3EU, United Kingdom
📞 01237 424282

Facer Design Ltd The Studio, 8 Ronneby Close, Weybridge, Surrey, KT13 9SB, United Kingdom
📞 01932 222100

Factory Design 318 King Street, London, W6 0RR, United Kingdom
📞 020 87487007

Farrows Ltd Lion House, Muspole Street, Norwich, Norfolk, NR3 1DJ, United Kingdom
📞 01603 620735

Fastrak Calamine Street, Macclesfield, Cheshire, SK11 7HU, United Kingdom
📞 01625 439966

Fathom Creative The Stables, Paradise Wharf, Ducie Street, Manchester, M1 2JN, United Kingdom
📞 0161 2743407

Felton Communication 2 Bleeding Heart Yard, Greville Street, London, EC1N 8SJ, United Kingdom
📞 020 74050900

Fernleigh Design Ltd Unit 5 Park Ty Glas, Llanushen, Cardiff, South Glamorgan, CF14 5DU, United Kingdom
📞 029 20763524

Fibre Ltd 8 Play House Court, 62 Southwark Bridge Road, London, SE1 0AT, United Kingdom
📞 020 74018477

Field Group plc Unit 14 Colthrop Business Park, Colthrop Lane, Thatcham, Newbury, Berkshire, RG19 4NB, United Kingdom
📞 01635 864444

Fielding Design 11 Princeton Court, 55 Felsham Road, Putney, London, SW15 1AZ, United Kingdom
📞 020 87801309

Figtree Creative Services 54a Linhope Street, London, NW1 6HL, United Kingdom
📞 020 75358500

File FX 7 Shepperton House, 83-93 Shepperton Road, London, N1 3DF, United Kingdom
📞 020 72266646

Fin International 90-92 St John Street, London, EC1M 4EH, United Kingdom
📞 020 72532828

Finch Partnership 5 Covent Garden, Liverpool, Merseyside, L2 8UD, United Kingdom
📞 0151 2362885

Finishing Post Design Langham Court, Langham Hall, Bury St Edmunds, Suffolk, IP31 3EE, United Kingdom
📞 01359 259050

Fired Up Marketing Ltd The Boulevard, 77 The Boulevard, Stoke-On-Trent, Staffordshire, ST6 6BD, United Kingdom
📞 01782 824762

Firedog Design Ltd 43-44 Hoxton Square, London, N1 6PB, United Kingdom
📞 020 77394991

First Partnership Ltd The Old School House, 66 Leonard Street, London, EC2A 4LW, United Kingdom
📞 020 76134114

Fishbone Design Port View Trade Centre, B1.10, 310 Newtownards Road, Belfast, County Antrim, BT4 1HE, United Kingdom
📞 028 90459444

Fluid 12 Tenby Street, Birmingham, West Midlands, B1 3AJ, United Kingdom
📞 0121 2120121

Fluid Design Solutions Ltd Lofts 3 & 4 Bealim House, 17-25 Gallowgate, Newcastle City, Tyne & Wear, NE1 4SG, United Kingdom
📞 0191 2616404

Fluid Strategic Designers Ltd 59 Friar Gate, Derby, Derbyshire, DE1 1DF, United Kingdom
📞 01332 201743

Flyingfish Desn Cons Ltd The Hemmel, Blagdon Lane, Plessey North Moor, Cramlington, Northumberland, NE23 8AU, United Kingdom
📞 01670 591960

Focal Design Ltd Ensor House, Ensor Way, New Mills, High Peak, Derbyshire, SK22 4NQ, United Kingdom
📞 01663 746100

Focus Design 34 David Place, Channel Islands, Jersey, JE2 4TE, United Kingdom
📞 01534 887200

Foil 1a stamford Street, Leicester, Leicestershire, LE1 6NL, United Kingdom
📞 0116 2333413

Fore Point Ltd Mill House, 8 Mill Street, London, SE1 2BA, United Kingdom
📞 020 72373380

Forward Thinking Inc Indigo House, Holbrooke Place, Richmond, Surrey, TW10 6UD, United Kingdom
📞 020 89482503

Found Associates 14-16 Great Pulteney Street, London, W1F 9ND, United Kingdom
📞 020 77348400

Four 23 2nd Floor, 8 Hewitt Street, Manchester, Lancashire, M15 4GB, United Kingdom
📞 0161 8339929

Fourth Dimension Morrell House, 98 Curtain Road, London, EC2A 3AF, United Kingdom
📞 020 76135530

Fox & Hoyle 33 Wootton Street, Cosham, Hampshire, PO6 3AP, United Kingdom
📞 023 92385715

FPP Design 43 Eagle Street, London, WC1R 4AT, United Kingdom
📞 020 78316041

Frank The Barn, Craigmarloch, Port Glasgow Road, Kilmacolm, Renfrewshire, PA13 4SG, United Kingdom
📞 01505 872946

Fraser Randell 228 Long Lane, London, SE1 4QB, United Kingdom
📞 020 74036403

Frazer Designers Ltd. 224 Iverson Rd, London, NW6 2HL, United Kingdom
📞 020 76246011

Front Page Ltd 26 Woodside Place, Glasgow, Lanarkshire, G3 7QL, United Kingdom
☎ 0141 3331808

Frontier Plastics Ltd Newbridge Road Indus, Pontllanfraith, Blackwood, Gwent, NP12 2YN, United Kingdom
☎ 01495 235800

Frontline Display Intl 8-9 Avon Buildings, Lower Bristol Road, Bath, Avon, BA2 1ES, United Kingdom
☎ 01225 321900

FSG Design Bowden Inn Farm, Bowden Business Village, Market Harborough, Leicestershire, LE16 7SA, United Kingdom
☎ 01858 545488

Fudge Studios 41 Mawdsley Street, Bolton, Lancashire, BL1 1LN, United Kingdom
☎ 01204 366668

Full Stop Creative 3 Mount Pleasant Road, Caterham, Surrey, CR3 6LP, United Kingdom
☎ 01883 330335

Fuse 8 Online Ltd Wandsworth Business Centre, Broomhill Road, Wandsworth, London, SW18 4JQ, United Kingdom
☎ 020 88744456

Fusion Garstang Road, Fulwood, Preston, Lancashire, PR2 9AB, United Kingdom
☎ 01772 712555

Fusion Creative Ltd Old Anglo House, Mitton Street, Stourport On Severn, Worcestershire, DY13 9AQ, United Kingdom
☎ 01299 829613

Fusion Design 4 Risborough Street, London, SE1 0HE, United Kingdom
☎ 020 79289982

Gainford Design Associates The Gymnasium, Hindley Hall, Stocksfield, Northumberland, NE43 7RY, United Kingdom
☎ 01661 844777

Gardiner & Theobald LLP 32 Bedford Square, London, WC1B 3JT, United Kingdom
☎ 020 76372468

Gardiner Richardson Generator Studios, Trafalgar Street, Newcastle Upon Tyne, Tyne & Wear, NE1 2LA, United Kingdom
☎ 0191 2614250

Gargoyle Graphics 1 Bake House Mews, Aldershot, Hampshire, GU11 1BX, United Kingdom
☎ 01252 325256

Gavin Willis Art Direction 79 Sheep Street, Northampton, Northamptonshire, NN1 2NE, United Kingdom
☎ 01604 638200

GB Posters 1 Russell Street, Sheffield, South Yorkshire, S3 8RW, United Kingdom
☎ 0114 2767454

GDR Creative Intelligence Dilke House, 1 Malet Street, London, WC1E 7JN, United Kingdom
☎ 020 75805589

Gecko Direct Ltd Wharfebank House, Wharfebank Business Park, Ilkley Road, Otley, West Yorkshire, LS21 3JP, United Kingdom
☎ 01943 854848

Gem Creative 12 Lord Street, Wigan, Lancashire, WN1 2BN, United Kingdom
☎ 01942 739383

Genesis The Barn, Ipsden, Wallingford, Oxfordshire, OX10 6AS, United Kingdom
☎ 01491 682277

Genus Cotswold Business Park, Millfield Lane, Caddington, Luton, Bedfordshire, LU1 4AJ, United Kingdom
☎ 01582 840484

Geometry Wells Point, 79 Wells Street, London, W1T 3QN, United Kingdom
☎ 020 74535300

GGH Marketing 1 West Street, Titchfield, Fareham, Hampshire, PO14 4DH, United Kingdom
☎ 01329 511882

Ghost Creations 25 The Bridge, Burton Upon Trent, Staffordshire, DE14 1SY, United Kingdom
☎ 01283 510000

Giddings Design 1 Park Lane, Cheam, Surrey, SM3 8BN, United Kingdom
☎ 020 86437534

GJ Design Holyoake House, Hanover Street, Manchester, M60 0AS, United Kingdom
☎ 0161 8346626

Glazier Design 28 Heddon St, London, W1B 4BH, United Kingdom
☎ 020 77345211

Glorious Creative 10A Stevenson Square, Northern Quater, Manchester Cdo, Lancashire, M1 1FB, United Kingdom
☎ 0161 2373575

Glover & Co Suite 1, Heathcote Buildings, 4-6 Heathcote Street, Nottingham, Nottinghamshire, NG1 3AA, United Kingdom
☎ 0115 9101420

Glowcroft Ltd Williamsport Way, Lion Barn Industrial Estate, Needham Market, Suffolk, IP6 8RW, United Kingdom
☎ 01449 723330

GLS Design Roundel House, 16 Firgrove Hill, Farnham, Surrey, GU9 8LQ, United Kingdom
☎ 01252 739500

Go Cre8 Queens Dock Business Centre, 67-83 Norfolk Street, Liverpool, Merseyside, L1 0BG, United Kingdom
☎ 0151 7082617

Good Creative The Loft, 106 Hope Street, Glasgow, Lanarkshire, G2 6PH, United Kingdom
☎ 0141 2043090

Good Impressions Suite 12 Ensign House, Admirals Way, South Keath, London, E14 9XQ, United Kingdom
☎ 020 75170390

Goodall Design Jubilee Lodge, Jubilee Terrace, Dorking, Surrey, RH4 1JR, United Kingdom
☎ 01306 741553

Goodwin Product Design Barn House, Home Farm Warren Lane, Pyrford, Woking, Surrey, GU22 8XD, United Kingdom
☎ 01483 722686

Gorgeous Enterprises Gorgeous House, 11 Portland Mews, London, W1F 8JL, United Kingdom
☎ 020 72874060

Gosling Old Batford Mill, Lower Luton Road, Harpenden, Hertfordshire, AL5 5BZ, United Kingdom
☎ 01582 466477

Granite 50 Progress Road, Leigh-On-Sea, Essex, SS9 5PR, United Kingdom
☎ 01702 507900

Graphic Partners 179 Canongate, Gladstone Court, Edinburgh, Mid Lothian, EH8 8BN, United Kingdom
☎ 0131 5573558

Graphic Thought Facility 23-24 Easton Street, London, WC1X 0DS, United Kingdom
☎ 020 78372525

Graphic Traffic 1-3 Farman Street, Hove, East Sussex, BN3 1AL, United Kingdom
☎ 01273 321021

Graphical House Suite 1/1, 6 Dixon Street, Glasgow, Lanarkshire, G1 4AX, United Kingdom
☎ 0141 2483114

Gratterpalm Ltd Kirkstall Design Centre, Bridge Road, Kirkstall, Leeds, West Yorkshire, LS5 3BW, United Kingdom
☎ 0113 2759326

Graven Images 175 Albion St, Glasgow, G1 1LF, United Kingdom
☎ 0141 5526626

Green Room Retail Design Ltd The Penthouse Suite, Fournier House, 8 Tenby Street, Birmingham, West Midlands, B1 3AJ, United Kingdom
☎ 0121 2002828

Greencoat House Francis Street, London, SW1P 1DH, United Kingdom
☎ 020 75923800

Greene Design 17 Mentmore Terrace, London, E8 3PN, United Kingdom
☎ 020 85331303

Greenwich Design Associates David Mews, 11a Greenwich South Street, Greenwich, London, SE10 8NJ, United Kingdom
☎ 020 88533028

Groovy Gecko 1st Floor, 126 Long Acre, London, WC2E 9PE, United Kingdom
☎ 020 72400900

Grow Creative Ltd 135 The Parade, High Street, Watford, Hertfordshire, WD17 1NS, United Kingdom
☎ 01923 218700

Guerilla Communications Ltd 63 Westgate Road, Newcastle Upon Tyne, Tyne & Wear, NE1 1SG, United Kingdom
☎ 0191 2619799

GWD Ltd 12-13 Capital Place, Lovet Road, Pinnacles, Harlow, Essex, CM19 5AS, United Kingdom
☎ 01279 416093

H2 Product Development 53 St Pauls Square, Birmingham, West Midlands, B3 1QS, United Kingdom
☎ 0121 2366994

Haigh Thornley Design Ltd 132 Widney Lane, Solihull, West Midlands, B91 3LH, United Kingdom
☎ 0121 7114878

Haime & Bulter Designers 9 The Leathermarket, Weston Street, London, SE1 3ER, United Kingdom
☎ 020 74072141

Haley Sharpe Design Ltd 11-15 Guildhall Lane, Leicester, Leicestershire, LE1 5FQ, United Kingdom
☎ 0116 2518555

Hallmark Cards plc Hallmark House, Bingley Road, Heaton, Bradford, West Yorkshire, BD9 6SD, United Kingdom
☎ 01274 252000

Halo Designs Ltd The Pump House, 16 Queens Avenue, Christchurch, Dorset, BH23 1BZ, United Kingdom
☎ 01202 471177

Hamill Design 2B Heron Wharf, Heron Road, Belfast, County Antrim, BT3 9LE, United Kingdom
☎ 028 90228080

Hampton Associates 11 Victoria Street, Aberdeen, Aberdeenshire, AB10 1XB, United Kingdom
☎ 01224 620562

Hand Design The Edwin Suite, Bowden Business Village, Harborough Road, Market Harborough, LE16 7SA, United Kingdom
☎ 01858 540311

Harlequin Display Ltd 2nd Floor, 63 Charter House Street, London, EC1M 6HJ, United Kingdom
☎ 020 72536238

Harrimansteel 5 Bethnal Gn Rd, London, E1 6LA, United Kingdom
☎ 020 73247530

Hat Trick Design Consultants 4th Floor, 3 Morrocco Street, London, SE1 3HB, United Kingdom
✆ 020 74037875

Hbm Hb House, Chalfont Road, Seer Green, Beaconsfield, Buckinghamshire, HP9 2QP, United Kingdom
✆ 01494 671246

Head Creative Associates Ltd Allied House, 45 Hatton Gardens, London, EC1N 8EX, United Kingdom
✆ 020 74047810

Headland 11 Edison Village, Highfields Science Park, Nottingham, Nottinghamshire, NG7 2RF, United Kingdom
✆ 0115 9678111

Heard Design 4 Underwood Row, London, N1 7LQ, United Kingdom
✆ 020 72536688

Hemisphere 5 Devonhurst Place, Heathfield Terrace, London, W4 4JD, United Kingdom
✆ 020 87422533

Herfordshire Sports Village Hatfield Business Park, Mosquito Way, Hatfield, Hertfordshire, AL10 9AB, United Kingdom
✆ 01707 284466

Hessle Dock Livingstone Road, Hessle, North Humberside, HU13 0EG, United Kingdom
✆ 01482 642079

Hey Moscow Ltd Innovation Labs, Watford Road, Northwick Park, Harrow, Middlesex, HA1 3TP, United Kingdom
✆ 020 88691420

HGV Ltd 2-6 Northburgh Street, London, EC1V 0AY, United Kingdom
✆ 020 73366336

High Profile Ltd 56 Bath Street, Gravesend, Kent, DA11 0DF, United Kingdom
✆ 01474 533077

Hippo Creative Solutions Ltd 2 Carlton Court, 5th Avenue, Team Valley, Gateshead, Tyne & Wear, NE11 0AZ, United Kingdom
✆ 0191 4828830

Hi-Res! 8-9 Rivington Place, London, EC2A 3BA, United Kingdom
✆ 020 77293090

HOK International Ltd 216 Oxford Street, London, W1C 1DB, United Kingdom
✆ 020 76362006

Holmes & Marchant Group plc Marlow Place, Station Road, Marlow, Buckinghamshire, SL7 1NB, United Kingdom
✆ 01628 890890

Hotel Chocolat Ltd Mint House, Newark Close, Royston, Hertfordshire, SG8 5HL, United Kingdom
✆ 0870 4428282

Household 135 Curtain Rd, London, EC2A 3BX, United Kingdom
✆ 020 77396537

Howdy Unit 8s, Hewlett House, 5 Havelock Terrace, London, SW8 4AS, United Kingdom
✆ 020 77208111

Howe Design Ltd 54 Ashton Road, Droylsden, Manchester, Lancashire, M43 7BP, United Kingdom
✆ 0161 3707733

HPL Mount Nebo, Brickwall Farm, Sible Hedingham, Halstead, Essex, CO9 3RH, United Kingdom
✆ 01787 469911

HRG Bridgewater House, 4 Queensbridge, Northampton, Northamptonshire, NN4 7BF, United Kingdom
✆ 01604 609150

Hudson Fuggle 20 Gainsford St, London, SE1 2PG, United Kingdom
✆ 020 78150164

Hunter Design Hunter House, 30 Frances Road, Windsor, Berkshire, SL4 3AA, United Kingdom
✆ 01753 792999

Hurst Stores & Interiors Ltd Aynsley House, Common Road, Bradford, West Yorkshire, BD12 0UF, United Kingdom
✆ 01274 670077

IC Design Ltd 1 Galena Road, London, W6 0LT, United Kingdom
✆ 020 87482536

Icera 2520 The Quadrant, Aztec West, Bristol, Avon, BS32 4AQ, United Kingdom
✆ 01454 284800

Ico Design Ltd 75-77 Great Portland Street, London, W1W 7LR, United Kingdom
✆ 020 73231088

Icon Creative Design The Chapel, 91 Caerphilly Road, Bassaley, Newport, Gwent, NP10 8LJ, United Kingdom
✆ 01633 897086

IDA Creative Link Unit 8, Magna Road, South Wigston, Leicestershire, LE18 4ZH, United Kingdom
✆ 0116 2788822

Idea Ltd Roseanne House, Parkway, Welwyn Garden City, Hertfordshire, AL8 6JE, United Kingdom
✆ 01707 334332

Ideal Allied Sainif House, 412 Greenford Road, Greenford, Middlesex, UB6 9AH, United Kingdom
✆ 020 85785522

IE Creative Number One Holt Court, Aston Science Park, Birmingham, West Midlands, B7 4EJ, United Kingdom
✆ 0121 3337557

IE Design Consultancy 68 Middle St, Brighton, BN2 1LB, United Kingdom
✆ 01273 275511

IE Design Consultancy Ltd Aquinas House, 63 Warstone Road, Hockley, Birmingham, West Midlands, B18 6NG, United Kingdom
✆ 0121 6938700

Illustration Ltd 2 Brooks Court, Cringle Street, London, SW8 5BX, United Kingdom
✆ 020 77205202

Imagin' Promotions 3600 Parkway, Solent Business Park, Whiteley, Fareham, Hampshire, PO15 7AN, United Kingdom
✆ 0845 2308307

Imaginate Warwick Innovation Centre, Gallows Hill, Warwick, Warwickshire, CV34 6UW, United Kingdom
✆ 01926 495926

Imagination plc 25 Store Street, London, WC1E 7BL, United Kingdom
✆ 020 73233300

IMDA Ltd 17-21 Church Street, Darton, Barnsley, South Yorkshire, S75 5HF, United Kingdom
✆ 01226 388838

Impackt The Old Brewery, 22 Russell Street, Windsor, SL4 1HQ, United Kingdom
✆ 01753 853557

Impact Creative Partnership Stonecroft House, Ervington Court, Meridian Business Park, Leicester, Leicestershire, LE19 1WL, United Kingdom
✆ 0116 2893515

Impact Image Management Aspect House, Pattenden Lane, Marden, Kent, TN12 9QJ, United Kingdom
✆ 01622 833880

In 2 Marketing Thames House, Mere Park, Dedmere Road, Marlow, Buckinghamshire, SL7 1PB, United Kingdom
✆ 01628 899700

Inaria 10 Plato Place, 72-74 St Dionis Road, London, SW6 4TU, United Kingdom
✆ 020 73840900

Inca Creative 52 Grosvenor Gardens, Belgravia, London, SW1W 0AG, United Kingdom
✆ 020 77307941

Incepta Online Eldon House, 1 Dorset Street, London, W1U 4BB, United Kingdom
✆ 020 75359800

IncrediBull Design Ltd Incredibull Ideas Ltd, Unit 2-3, Bickels Yard,151-153 Bermondsey Street, London, SE1 3HA, United Kingdom
✆ 020 79403806

Independent Marketing 14-17 Wells Street, London, W1T 3PD, United Kingdom
✆ 020 76372614

Indigo Creative 49 Burney Street, Greenwich, London, SE10 8EX, United Kingdom
✆ 020 88585100

Infinite Design Consultants 56 Leazes Park Road, Newcastle Upon Tyne, Tyne & Wear, NE1 4PG, United Kingdom
✆ 0191 2611160

Initial Design 17 Church Lane, Selston, Nottinghamshire, NG16 6EX, United Kingdom
✆ 01773 811155

Innovia Design Ltd Marsh Wharf St., Marys Rd, Middlegreen, Slough, SL3 6DA, United Kingdom
✆ 01753 612040

Inside Information Design Ltd The Old Mill Studio, Cannich, Inverness-Shire, IV4 7LT, United Kingdom
✆ 01456 415484

Insight Ltd Kings House, 32-40 Widmore Road, Bromley, Kent, BR1 1RY, United Kingdom
✆ 020 84647808

INSYTE Ltd Victoria Avenue, Harrogate, North Yorkshire, HG1 1EQ, United Kingdom
✆ 01423 566855

Integrity Design Management Stella Web, Summerhill Road, Marden, Tonbridge, Kent, TN12 9DB, United Kingdom
✆ 01622 831238

Interbrand 85 Strand, London, WC2R 0DW, United Kingdom
✆ 020 75541000

International Decorative Surfaces, London Road, Chesterton, Newcastle, Staffordshire, ST5 7PY, United Kingdom
✆ 01782 717220

International Paper Road Three, Winsford Industrial Estate, Winsford, Cheshire, CW7 3RJ, United Kingdom
✆ 01606 562700

Interstate Associates 9 Ledbury Mews North, London, W11 2AF, United Kingdom
✆ 020 73137627

Invest NI Bedford Square, Bedford Street, Belfast, County Antrim, BT2 7EH, United Kingdom
✆ 028 90239090

Iris Associates 70-71 Cornish Place, Cornish Street, Sheffield, South Yorkshire, S6 3AF, United Kingdom
✆ 0114 2703500

ITE Group plc 105 Salusbury Road, London, NW6 6RG, United Kingdom
✆ 020 75965000

Ivor Heal Design Company 36a Cleveland Road, London, SW13 0AB, United Kingdom
✆ 020 88762569

J Marshall Partnership Ltd Brunel Drive, Northern Road Industrial Est, Newark, Nottinghamshire, NG24 2EG, United Kingdom
✆ 01636 705702

Jade Studio Unit 5, Edison Building, Electric Wharf, Coventry, West Midlands, CV1 4JA, United Kingdom
✆ 024 76228788

Jago Designs Ltd Larch Court, Royal Oak Yard, London, SE1 3GB, United Kingdom
✆ 020 73570690

James Park Associates Ltd 87a Worship Street, London, EC2A 2BE, United Kingdom
✆ 020 70837088

Janet Fitch 8 Newton Street, London, WC2B 5EG, United Kingdom
✆ 020 72091701

Jebens Design 32 Dale Street, London, W4 2BL, United Kingdom
✆ 020 89952929

Jedco Product Designers Ltd 9 Heath Road, Weybridge, Surrey, KT13 8SX, United Kingdom
✆ 01932 852497

Jefferson Sheard Architects The Hacienda, 21 Albion Street, Manchester, Lancashire, M1 5DA, United Kingdom
✆ 0161 2006370

Jennings Campbell Bibby 2 Wright Street, Southport, Merseyside, PR9 0TL, United Kingdom
✆ 01704 534653

JHP Design Block 2, 6 Erskine Road, Primrose Hill, London, NW3 3AJ, United Kingdom
✆ 020 77223932

John Sermon FCSD & Associates 24 Monks Walk, Evesham, Worcestershire, WR11 4SL, United Kingdom
✆ 01386 49967

John Watson & Co Ltd 35-47 Kyle Street, Glasgow, Lanarkshire, G4 0JQ, United Kingdom
✆ 0141 3328672

Jones Knowles Ritchie Ltd 128 Albert Street, London, NW1 7NE, United Kingdom
✆ 020 74288000

Jory & Co 22b Leathermarket Street, London, SE1 3HP, United Kingdom
✆ 020 74077819

Joules Clothing 53/55 High St, Market Harborough, LE16 7AF, United Kingdom
✆ 01858 462872

JP Creative 8d Brighton House, 9 Brighton Terrace, London, SW9 8DJ, United Kingdom
✆ 020 77338745

Judgegill 2 Fairfield St, Manchester, M1 3GF, United Kingdom
✆ 0161 2283066

Juice 45 The Broadway, Cheam, Sutton, Surrey, SM3 8BL, United Kingdom
✆ 020 87701058

Jump Media Ltd 3 Church Street, Penryn, Falmouth, Cornwall, TR10 8DA, United Kingdom
✆ 01326 375422

Junction Design Ltd Ormond Mansions, 17a Great Ormond Street, London, WC1N 3RA, United Kingdom
✆ 020 74046766

Junction Nine Dunstable Rd, Redbourn, St. Albans, AL3 7PR , United Kingdom
✆ 01582 793313

Jupiter Design Ruddington Manor, Ruddington, Nottingham, Nottinghamshire, NG11 6DS, United Kingdom
✆ 0115 9844200

K4 Creative Ltd 4 Portland Road, London, W11 4LA, United Kingdom
✆ 020 72213490

Kag Design Hazlehurst, 13 Chequers Road, Basingstoke, Hampshire, RG21 7PX, United Kingdom
✆ 01256 844566

Kamae Design Ltd The Old Barn, Worton Farm, Cassington, Witney, Oxfordshire, OX29 4AA, United Kingdom
✆ 01865 733240

Karma & Chips Ltd 5-9 Chartwell Drive, Wigston, Leicester, Leicestershire, LE18 2FL, United Kingdom
✆ 0116 2884560

Kcm Print & Design Unit 1/2, Trentside Business Park, Campbell Road, Stoke On Trent, Staffordshire, ST4 4EU, United Kingdom
✆ 01782 747471

Kdesigngroup 71 High St, Winchester, Hampshire, SO23 9DA, United Kingdom
✆ 01962 870269

Keeble & Hall 40 Iffley Road, London, W6 0PA, United Kingdom
✆ 020 87418959

Keenpac Ltd Centurion Way, Meridian Business Park, Leicester, Leicestershire, LE19 1WH, United Kingdom
✆ 0116 2890900

Kelvin Print Group East Tame Business Park, Rexcine Way, Millbrook, Hyde, Cheshire, SK14 4GX, United Kingdom
✆ 0845 6011007

Kerve Design Ltd, 35 Broad Street, Bath, Avon, BA1 5LP, United Kingdom
✆ 01225 787820

Killer Creative 19 Ship Street, Brighton, East Sussex, BN1 1AD, United Kingdom
✆ 01273 775733

Kinneir Dufort Design Ltd 5 Host Street, Bristol, Avon, BS1 5BU, United Kingdom
✆ 0117 9014000

Kinnersley Kent Design 5 Fitzroy Square, London, W1T 5HH, United Kingdom
✆ 020 76913131

KLC School of Design The Chambers, Chelsea Harbour, London, SW10 0XF, United Kingdom
✆ 020 73767400

Kneath Associates Ltd 53 Newton Road, Munbles, Swansea, West Glamorgan, SA3 4BD, United Kingdom
✆ 01792 522215

Kolakowski Design 115 George Street, Berkhamsted, Hertfordshire, HP4 2EJ, United Kingdom
✆ 01442 874570

Kraken Creative 8 Edison Buildings, Electric Wharf, Coventry, West Midlands, CV1 4JA, United Kingdom
✆ 024 76220801

Ksht 17 Hawarden Grove, London, SE24 9DQ, United Kingdom
✆ 020 86780713

Kubiak & Grange Design Assoc 86 King Street, Danley, Telford, Shropshire, TF4 2AH, United Kingdom
✆ 01952 501131

Kugel Ltd 55 Greek Street, London, W1D 3DT, United Kingdom
✆ 020 74788300

KWS Skyways House, Sywell Aerodrome, Northampton, Northamptonshire, NN6 0BT, United Kingdom
✆ 01604 491144

Kysen 16-18 Berners Street, London, W1T 3LN, United Kingdom
✆ 020 73233230

Laban Brown Design The Cart Lodge, 3 Oak Business Park, Wix Road, Beaumont, Essex, CO16 0AT, United Kingdom
✆ 01255 870600

Laing & Carroll 2a Lancaster Road, Wimbledon Village, London, SW19 5DD, United Kingdom
✆ 020 89467373

Lake Design Campaign House, 8 Cecil Road, Hale, Altrincham, Cheshire, WA15 9PA, United Kingdom
✆ 0161 9269898

Lambie-Nairn & Company Ltd Greencoat House, Francis Street, London, SW1P 1DH, United Kingdom
✆ 020 78025800

Land Design Studio 7d Blake Mws, Richmond, TW9 3GA, United Kingdom
✆ 020 83326699

Landau Reece Bull Inn Court, Maiden Lane, London, WC2E 7NA, United Kingdom
✆ 020 73951940

Landor Associates Klamath House, 18 Clerkenwell Green, London, EC1R 0QE, United Kingdom
✆ 020 78808000

Langsford Corporate Design Ltd 6-8 Cole Street, London, SE1 4YH, United Kingdom
✆ 020 73781457

Lawn Communications Ltd 6th Floor, Gostin Building, 32-34 Hanover Street, Merseyside, L1 4LN, United Kingdom
✆ 0151 7089005

Leahy Brand Design Ltd Rosebery House, 70 Rosebery Avenue, London, EC1R 4RR, United Kingdom
✆ 020 77131337

Leisure Concepts Common Lane Industrial Estate, Kenilworth, Warwickshire, CV8 2EL, United Kingdom
✆ 01926 851454

Lemon Ltd 6 Weltech Centre, Ridgeway, Welwyn Garden City, Hertfordshire, AL7 2AA, United Kingdom
✆ 01707 330525

Lemon Studios 2nd Floor, 85 Clerkenwell Road, London, EC1R 5AR, United Kingdom
✆ 0845 2450005

Leyshon Ltd Canton Mews, Cleveland Reach, London Road, Bath, Avon, BA1 6AA, United Kingdom
✆ 01225 427500

Lfh 6a-10 Frederick Close, Stanhope Place, London, W2 2HD, United Kingdom
✆ 020 77068762

Light Projects Ltd 23 Jacob Street, London, SE1 2BG, United Kingdom
✆ 020 72318282

Lightzone Ltd Kent House, Romley Place, Maidstone, Kent, ME15 6LH, United Kingdom
✆ 01622 682583

LILLINGTON.GREEN Kingfisher House, Headley Road East, Woodley, Reading, Berkshire, RG5 4SG, United Kingdom
✆ 0118 9272474

Lime Marketing Lime House, 17 Queens Road, Brighton, East Sussex, BN1 3WA, United Kingdom
✆ 01273 202022

Lime Razors 82b St Marys Street, Ely, Cambridgeshire, CB7 4HH,
United Kingdom
✆ 01353 616034

LimeHouse Software Ltd 1 London Bridge, 4th Floor Downstream, London, SE1 9BG,
United Kingdom
✆ 020 74036830

Linney Design Adamsway, Mansfield, Nottinghamshire, NG18 4FW,
United Kingdom
✆ 01623 450450

Lionheart Marketing Comms Ltd Little Bdge Busness Park, Clyst St Mary, Exeter, EX5 1AU,
United Kingdom
✆ 01392 876222

Lionhouse Haycombe Farm Barn, Haycombe Lane, Englishcombe, Bath, Avon, BA2 9DN,
United Kingdom
✆ 01225 445427

Lisa TSE Ltd Gresham House, 24 Holborn Viaduct, London, EC1A 2BN,
United Kingdom
✆ 020 72489248

Live 85 Strand, London, WC2R 0DW,
United Kingdom
✆ 020 75541111

Livewire Design Ltd 50 Greek Street, London, W1D 4EQ,
United Kingdom
✆ 020 74343330

Lloyd Design PO Box 252, Peterborough, Cambridgeshire, PE3 6NQ,
United Kingdom
✆ 01733 553456

Loaf Creative Whitemoss Business Park, Skelmersdale, WN8 9TG ,
United Kingdom
✆ 01695 555037

Locofoco 40 Speirs Wharf, Port Dundas, Glasgow, G4 9TH,
United Kingdom
✆ 0141 3413302

London Associates 105 High Street, Berkhamsted, Hertfordshire, HP4 2DG,
United Kingdom
✆ 01442 862631

Love Creative 65 High Street, Manchester, Lancashire, M4 1FS,
United Kingdom
✆ 0161 8396001

Lsa International Ltd Unit E Windmill Road, The Dolphin Estate, Windmill Road, Sunbury-On-Thames, Middlesex, TW16 7HE,
United Kingdom
✆ 01932 789721

Luck Old Hall Quarters, 48 Hall Lane, Willington, Derby, Derbyshire, DE65 6DR,
United Kingdom
✆ 01283 703704

Lucy Bye Design 44 Addison Close, Exeter, Devon, EX4 1SL,
United Kingdom
✆ 01392 411503

Luke Hughes & Co Ltd 182 Drury Lane, London, WC2B 5PP,
United Kingdom
✆ 020 74045995

Lussh Creative 358a Chatsworth Road, Chesterfield, Derbyshire, S40 2BY,
United Kingdom
✆ 01246 550000

M Moser Associates Ltd 6th Floor, Melbourne House, 46 Aldwych, London, WC2B 4LL,
United Kingdom
✆ 020 72578550

M4 Design Pound Court, Pound Street, Newbury, Berkshire, RG14 6AA,
United Kingdom
✆ 01635 524055

Mad About Design 32 Queensway, 32 Queens Way, London, W2 3RX,
United Kingdom
✆ 020 72435728

Maddison Ltd Walnut Tree Yard, Lower Street, Fittleworth, West Sussex, RH20 1JE,
United Kingdom
✆ 01798 865711

Magee & Co 7 Cinnamon Row, Plantation Wharf, Battersea, London, SW11 3TW,
United Kingdom
✆ 020 79243244

Magister Consultanting The Old Rectory, St. Mary's Road, Stone, Dartford, Kent, DA9 9AS,
United Kingdom
✆ 01332 201743

Majestic Design & Branding Majestic House, 29 Green Street, Huddersfield, West Yorkshire, HD1 5DQ,
United Kingdom
✆ 01484 427383

Manor Creative Ltd Units 7 & 8, Edison Road, Eastbourne, East Sussex, BN23 6PT,
United Kingdom
✆ 01323 514400

Marc & Anna Creative Ltd Studio 46, Regent Studios, 8 Andrews Road, London, E8 4QN,
United Kingdom
✆ 020 72496111

Marcus Smith Ind Designer 126 Milton Road, Cambridge, Cambridgeshire, CB4 1LD,
United Kingdom
✆ 01223 360788

Maris Interiors 11th Floor, The Tower Building, 11 York Road, London, SE1 7NX,
United Kingdom
✆ 020 79604900

Mark Turner Creative Regal House, 55b Bancroft, Hitchin, Hertfordshire, SG5 1LL,
United Kingdom
✆ 01462 455555

Marketsquare Creative Mktg Leicester Road, Market Harborough, LE16 7FB,
United Kingdom
✆ 01858 546800

Martin Dawe Design plc 347 Edinburgh Avenue, Slough, Berkshire, SL1 4TU,
United Kingdom
✆ 01753 828828

Martyn Cornwall Design 14 Boston Close, Eastbourne, East Sussex, BN23 5RA,
United Kingdom
✆ 01323 470146

Mask Event Design & Production Studio 302 Lana House, 118 Commercial Street, London, E1 6NF,
United Kingdom
✆ 020 73778001

Mather & Co 17 Manchester Road, Wilmslow, Cheshire, SK9 1BQ,
United Kingdom
✆ 01625 521128

Maximuscle 40 Caxton Way, Watford Business Park, Watford, Hertfordshire, WD18 8JZ,
United Kingdom
✆ 01923 650600

Maxx Design NorthBrook Court, Park Street, Newbury, Berkshire, RG14 1EA,
United Kingdom
✆ 01635 550007

Maze Communications Watermill House Chevening Road, Chipstead, Sevenoaks, Kent, TN13 2RY,
United Kingdom
✆ 01732 741800

Mazorca Project Ground Floor Rear, Shoreditch Stables, 138 Kingsland Road, London, E2 8DY,
United Kingdom
✆ 020 77293301

Mbi & Partners UK Ltd 78/80 Wigmore Street, London, W1U 2SJ,
United Kingdom
✆ 020 79355859

McDaniel Woolf Lakefield Studios, 32 Larkfield Road, Richmond, Surrey, TW9 2PF,
United Kingdom
✆ 020 83321981

MDUK Media Ltd 65A Grosvenor Road, London, W7 1HR,
United Kingdom
✆ 020 88400020

Media Design Partnership Ltd Enterprise House, Peel Hall Business Park, Peel Road, Blackpool, Lancashire, FY4 5JX,
United Kingdom
✆ 01253 796977

Melon Design & Marketing 6-7 Brittens Court, Clifton Reynes, Olney, Buckinghamshire, MK46 5LG,
United Kingdom
✆ 01234 714931

Mercator uNIT 5, 127-129 Great Suffolk Street, London, SE1 1PP,
United Kingdom
✆ 020 73786918

Merchant Desn Intl Ltd Saxon House, Saxon Wharf, Southampton, Hampshire, SO14 5QF,
United Kingdom
✆ 023 80225478

Met Studio Design Ltd 5 Maidstone Buildings Mews, 72-76 Borough High Street, London, SE1 1GN,
United Kingdom
✆ 020 73579634

Metier Design Consultants Smokehouse Yard, 44/46 St Johns Street, London, EC1M 4DF,
United Kingdom
✆ 020 76083366

MGA Design Ltd 22 Home Farm, Loseley Park, Guildford, Surrey, GU3 1HS,
United Kingdom
✆ 01483 440244

Michael Bell Ltd St Anne's House, 111 High Street, Lewes, East Sussex, BN7 1XY,
United Kingdom
✆ 01273 478822

Michael John Design Ltd Signal House, Station Road, Uppingham, Leicestershire, LE15 9TX,
United Kingdom
✆ 01572 822138

Michael Nash Associates 42-44 Newman Street, London, W1T 1QD,
United Kingdom
✆ 020 76313370

Michael R Dalby Ltd Mulberry Business Centre, Quebecway, London, SE16 7LB,
United Kingdom
✆ 020 73941112

Michael Sheridan & Co Riverside, Market Harborough, Leicestershire, LE16 7PT,
United Kingdom
✆ 01858 468000

Milestone Strategic Design Ltd 1 The Highway, Beaconsfield, Buckinghamshire, HP9 1QD,
United Kingdom
✆ 01494 676436

Mills Pitt Associates Unit 8 Princeton Mews, 167-169 London Road, Kingston Upon Thames, Surrey, KT2 6PT,
United Kingdom
✆ 020 85473838

Minale Tattersfield & Partners The Poppy Factory, 20 Petersham Road, Richmond, Surrey, TW10 6UR,
United Kingdom
✆ 020 89487999

Mintsalad Design Widgenton Old Stables, Oxford Road, Beaconsfield, Buckinghamshire, HP9 1XA,
United Kingdom
✆ 01494 681892

Mission Control Efx 28 Lexington Street, London, W1F 0LF,
United Kingdom
✆ 020 72926260

MJ Associates 364 Regents Park Road, London, N3 2LJ,
United Kingdom
✆ 020 83432021

Model Solutions 72X Clarence Road, London, N22 8PW,
United Kingdom
✆ 020 88812333

Modulex Systems Ltd North Portway Close, Round Spinney, Northampton, Northamptonshire, NN3 8RQ, United Kingdom
℡ 01604 672100

Monddi Dimond Press Well Hill, Pembroke, Dyfed, SA71 4DH, United Kingdom
℡ 01646 682424

Montpellier Lower Ground Floor, 11 Montpellier Terrace, Glendale House, Cheltenham, Gloucestershire, GL50 1UX, United Kingdom
℡ 01242 530999

Mooli Ltd Mountfields House, Off Squirrel Way, Epinal Way, Loughborough, Leicestershire, LE11 3GE, United Kingdom
℡ 01509 240040

Moore Wilson Design 19 Garrick Street, Covent Garden, London, WC2E 9AX, United Kingdom
℡ 020 73793300

Moore Wilson New Media Portway Centre, Spitfire Road, Old Sarum, Salisbury, Wiltshire, SP4 6EB, United Kingdom
℡ 01722 341642

Moot Studio 8C, Limehouse Cut, 46 Morris Road, London, E14 6NQ, United Kingdom
℡ 020 70680055

Morgan Lovell 16 Noel Street, London, W1F 8DA, United Kingdom
℡ 020 77344466

Morton Ward Ltd 12A Timber Bush, Edingburgh, Mid Lothian, EH6 6QH, United Kingdom
℡ 0131 5553553

Mount Design Ltd Postley Road, Woburn Road Industrial Estate, Bedford, Bedfordshire, MK42 7BU, United Kingdom
℡ 01234 852448

MPL Business Images Ltd 54 Church Road, Ashford, Middlesex, TW15 2TS, United Kingdom
℡ 01784 257676

Mr Designs Unit 6 Lower Farm, High Street, Irchester, Wellingborough, Northamptonshire, NN29 7AB, United Kingdom
℡ 01933 410016

M-Square The Point, Granite Way, Mountsorrel, Loughborough, Leicestershire, LE12 7TZ, United Kingdom
℡ 01509 620300

Muraspec 74-78 Wood Lane End, Hemel Hempstead, Hertfordshire, HP2 4RF, United Kingdom
℡ 01442 268890

Mystery Design 79 Parkway, London, NW1 7PP, United Kingdom
℡ 020 74241900

Mytton Williams 15 St James's Parade, Bath, Avon, BA1 1UL, United Kingdom
℡ 01225 332273

Naked Ideas Ltd 105 Ladbroke Grove, London, W11 1PG, United Kingdom
℡ 020 76168412

Nathaniel Lichfield & Partners 14 Regents Wharf, All Saints Street, London, N1 9RL, United Kingdom
℡ 020 78374477

National Council for Voluntary 8 Regents Wharf, All Saints Street, London, N1 9RL, United Kingdom
℡ 020 77136161

NB Design Channel View, Llangenith, Gower, Swansey, West Glamorgan, SA3 1JE, United Kingdom
℡ 01792 386340

NB Studio 4 - 8 Emerson Street, London, SE1 9DU, United Kingdom
℡ 020 76339046

New Look Retailers Ltd 7th Floor, Portman Road, Portman House, London, W1H 6DU, United Kingdom
℡ 020 76595900

Nexus Retail Interiors Ltd 53-59 New Tythe Street, Long Eaton, Nottinghamshire, NG10 2DL, United Kingdom
℡ 0115 9463222

Nicholas & Knight 1 The Willows, Watermill Estate, Aspenden Road, Buntingford, Hertfordshire, SG9 9JS, United Kingdom
℡ 01763 272118

Nim Design The Old Bank, 92 High Street, Harrow On The Hill, Harrow, Middlesex, HA1 3LP, United Kingdom
℡ 020 84266888

Ninety Degrees 30 King Street, Manchester, Lancashire, M2 6AZ, United Kingdom
℡ 0161 8331890

Nixon Design White's Warehouse, Foundry Square, Hayle, Cornwall, TR27 4HH, United Kingdom
℡ 01736 758600

Nolka Design 48 Dunboyne Park, Eglinton, Londonderry, County Londonderry, BT47 3YJ, United Kingdom
℡ 028 71813753

Northbank Design 16 Gay Street, Bath, Avon, BA1 2PH, United Kingdom
℡ 01225 332703

Northedge Design 158 Queens Drive, Glasgow, Lanarkshire, G42 8QN, United Kingdom
℡ 0141 4243133

Northern Technologies Netherfield Road, Nelson, Lancashire, BB9 9AR, United Kingdom
℡ 01282 724200

Not to Scale 48 Dean Street, London, W1D 5BF, United Kingdom
℡ 020 77344575

NUDE BRAND CREATION 2-4 Old Street, London, EC1V 9AA, United Kingdom
℡ 020 72532003

Nude Design Ltd 3 Mill Hill, Royston, Hertfordshire, SG8 9UD, United Kingdom
℡ 01763 244210

Oak Creative Royal Oak Building, Newingreen, Hythe, CT21 4JA, United Kingdom
℡ 01303 812848

OB Design no 1 Greenhill, Wirksworth, Matlock, Derbyshire, DE4 4EN, United Kingdom
℡ 01629 826284

Ocean Blue Design Consultants Nelson House, 19 West Street, Carshalton, Surrey, SM5 2PT, United Kingdom
℡ 020 87730433

Offshore Design Ltd Buchanan House, 63 Summer Street, Aberdeen, Aberdeenshire, AB10 1SJ, United Kingdom
℡ 01224 628000

Oliis 14a-15a The Arches, Goswell Hill, Windsor, Berkshire, SL4 1RH, United Kingdom
℡ 01753 857575

OLIVER & GRAIMES 63 Portland Road, Hove, East Sussex, BN3 5DQ, United Kingdom
℡ 01273 748884

OMK Design Stephen Building, 30 Stephen Street, London, W1T 1QY, United Kingdom
℡ 020 76311335

One Exception Ltd The Old Fire Station, 54 Head Street, Halstead, Essex, CO9 2BT, United Kingdom
℡ 01787 473635

One SPARE CHAIR Dock Road, Unit F11 Dock Road, London, E16 1AH, United Kingdom
℡ 020 74766644

One Strategic Communication 2 Abbey Court, Fraser Road, Priory Business Park, Bedford, Bedfordshire, MK44 3WH, United Kingdom
℡ 01234 831118

Onebestway Design Studios 1&5 Maling Studios, Hoults Estate Walker Road, Newcastle, NE6 2HL, United Kingdom
℡ 0191 2764777

Ontrac Communication 46 Mochdre Enterprise Park, Newtown, Powys, SY16 4LE, United Kingdom
℡ 01686 620400

Optima 12 West Parade, Lincoln, Lincolnshire, LN1 1JT, United Kingdom
℡ 01522 522773

Optimism Design The Mission Hall, Walker Place, London, SW15 1PP, United Kingdom
℡ 020 87888700

Osborne & Little plc Riverside House, 26 Osiers Road, London, SW18 1NH, United Kingdom
℡ 020 88123000

Osborne Pike Ltd 22 Circus Mws, Bath, BA1 2PW, United Kingdom
℡ 01225 489260

Owen & Avery 16 Bluelion Pl, London, SE1 4PU, United Kingdom
℡ 020 73576622

Pacific Interior Ltd 5th Floor, Thavis Inn House, 3-4 Holborn Circus, London, EC1N 2HA, United Kingdom
℡ 020 78221150

Page Setup Glendinning House, 6 Murray Street, Belfast, County Antrim, BT1 6DN, United Kingdom
℡ 028 90326200

Pama & Co Ltd Alvanley Indust Est, Bredbury, Stockport, SK6 2DJ, United Kingdom
℡ 0161 4944200

Papa Architects 222 Archway Road, Archway, London, N6 5AX, United Kingdom
℡ 020 83488411

Paper Scissor Stone 1 Thames Place, Putney, SW15 1HF, United Kingdom
℡ 020 87859588

Paperjam Design Ltd Cotton Court, 30-42 Waring Street, Belfast, County Antrim, BT1 2ED, United Kingdom
℡ 028 90310003

Paprika Design Associates 192 Warwick Road, Kenilworth, Warwickshire, CV8 1HU, United Kingdom
℡ 01926 511540

Paragon Interiors Paragon House, Orchard Place, Nottingham Business Park, Nottingham, Nottinghamshire, NG8 6PX, United Kingdom
℡ 0115 9795920

Parent Design Ltd Bristol and West House, Post Office Road, Bournemouth, Dorset, BH1 1BL, United Kingdom
℡ 01202 311711

Parenthesis Design Mktg Ltd 15-19 Canal Warehouse, Leicester Row, Coventry, West Midlands, CV1 4LH, United Kingdom
℡ 024 76229658

Park Corner Design Ltd 13 Southgate Street, Winchester, Hampshire, SO23 9DZ, United Kingdom
℡ 01962 866222

Parker Williams Design Voysey House, Barley Mow Passage, London, W4 4PT, United Kingdom
℡ 020 89955815

Path 2 Northfields Prospect, Putney Bridge Road, London, SW18 1PE,
United Kingdom
☎ 020 88719690

Paul Smith Ltd Riverside Building, Riverside Way, Nottingham, Nottinghamshire, NG2 1DP,
United Kingdom
☎ 0115 9868877

Pauley Design Ltd Broughton Manor, Broughton, Milton Keynes, Buckinghamshire, MK10 9AA,
United Kingdom
☎ 01908 678459

Pearce Goodwin Design Consultants Ltd Maybrook House, 97 Godstone Road, Caterham, Surrey, CR3 6RE,
United Kingdom
☎ 01883 34268

Pearson Matthews Design 9 Princess Mews, Horace Road, Kingston Upon Thames, Surrey, KT1 2SZ,
United Kingdom
☎ 020 85470470

Pedigree Dolls & Toys Beech Hill House, Walnut Gardens, Exeter, Devon, EX4 4DH,
United Kingdom
☎ 01392 427799

Pelican Buying Southern House, Flambard Way, Godalming, Surrey, GU7 1HH,
United Kingdom
☎ 01483 239100

Pemberton & Whitefoord 21 Ivor Place, Marylebone, London, NW1 6EU,
United Kingdom
☎ 020 77238899

Pentacor plc 4 Park House Business Centre, Desborough Park Road, High Wycombe, Buckinghamshire, HP12 3DJ,
United Kingdom
☎ 01494 898300

Pentagram Design 11 Needham Road, London, W11 2RP,
United Kingdom
☎ 020 73168000

People 8 Tideway Yard, Mortlake High Street, London, SW14 8SN,
United Kingdom
☎ 020 84871010

Perception Design Consultants Office Suit, 3 Green Lodge Barn, Nobottle, Northampton, Northamptonshire, NN7 4HD,
United Kingdom
☎ 01604 684860

Perfect Day 14-15 D'Arblay Street, London, W1F 8DZ,
United Kingdom
☎ 020 77344385

Peter Poland Design Ltd Centre Space, 6 Leonard Lane, Bristol, Avon, BS1 1EA,
United Kingdom
☎ 0117 9290077

Petersen New Media Western House Saddlers Lane, Tivoli Walk, Cheltenham, Gloucestershire, GL50 2UX,
United Kingdom
☎ 01242 573311

Philosophy 91 Paul Street, London, EC2A 4NY,
United Kingdom
☎ 020 72512233

Phoebus Associates 13 Harley Street, London, W1G 9QG,
United Kingdom
☎ 020 74367123

Photolink Creative Group Unit 2 Downing Street Industrial Estate, Charlton Place, Ardwick, Manchester, M12 6HH,
United Kingdom
☎ 0161 2759780

PI Global 1 Colville Mews, Lonsdale Road, London, W11 2AR,
United Kingdom
☎ 020 79080808

Picador Design 9 Unity Stree, Bristol, Avon, BS1 5HH,
United Kingdom
☎ 0117 9292969

Pierrot Print & Design Birtley Courtyard, Birtley Road, Bramley, Guildford, Surrey, GU5 0LA,
United Kingdom
☎ 01483 899000

Pinewood Media Merlin Centre, Lancaster Road, Cressex Business Park, High Wycombe, Buckinghamshire, HP12 3QH,
United Kingdom
☎ 01494 561700

Pinsharp 3D Graphics 29 Darby Road, Liverpool, Merseyside, L19 9BP,
United Kingdom
☎ 0151 4942928

Pixel Fountain Bowden Hall, Bowden Lane, Marple, Stockport, Cheshire, SK6 6ND,
United Kingdom
☎ 0161 4278684

Pixel Scene Ltd Pixel House, Church Street, Odiham, Hook, Hampshire, RG29 1LU,
United Kingdom
☎ 01256 703041

Planarama Ltd 26-32 Voltaire Road, Clapham North Art Centre, London, SW4 6DH,
United Kingdom
☎ 020 77202221

Planglow Ltd Kings House, Bond Street, Bristol, Avon, BS1 3AE,
United Kingdom
☎ 0117 3178600

Pleydell Smithyman 20a Wharfage, Ironbridge, Telford, Shropshire, TF8 7NH,
United Kingdom
☎ 01952 433211

Plus One Design 5 Dartmouth Road, London, NW2 4ET,
United Kingdom
☎ 020 89302266

Pmedia 2 Princes Bldgs, Bath, BA1 2ED,
United Kingdom
☎ 01225 337170

Pndesign F5 Barton Ho High Rd, Beeston, Nottingham, NG9 2JP,
United Kingdom
☎ 0115 9220017

Pod Creative 17 Willow Street, London, EC2A 4BH,
United Kingdom
☎ 020 77292817

Pod1 223 Westbourne Studios, 242 Acklam Road, London, W10 5JJ,
United Kingdom
☎ 0870 2462066

Point 6 Design The Linen House, Kilburn Lane, London, W10 4BQ,
United Kingdom
☎ 020 89625880

Point2creative First Floor, Millfields House, Huddersfield Road, Holmfirth, West Yorkshire, HD9 3JT,
United Kingdom
☎ 01484 686700

Poochie Amour 108 Great Portland Street, London, W1W 6PG,
United Kingdom
☎ 020 72997940

Positive Design Consultants 9 Donegall Street Place, Belfast, County Antrim, BT1 2FN,
United Kingdom
☎ 028 90313800

Precedent The Courtyard Building, 11 Curtain Road, London, EC2A 3LT,
United Kingdom
☎ 020 74268900

Premier Design Ltd 123 Newland Street, Witham, Essex, CM8 1BE,
United Kingdom
☎ 01376 513777

Premm Design Ltd The Studio, Unit 2, 1 Pooley Drive, London, SW14 8LU,
United Kingdom
☎ 020 88787772

Prescript Communications Old School, Church Street, Biggleswade, Bedfordshire, SG18 0JS,
United Kingdom
☎ 01767 600794

Preview Cromatic Ltd Suite 2 Building 2, St Cross Chambers, Upper Marsh Lane, Hoddesdon, Hertfordshire, EN11 8LQ,
United Kingdom
☎ 01992 479745

Preview Graphics Ltd 105 High Street, Hurstpierpoint, West Sussex, BN6 9AB,
United Kingdom
☎ 01273 834434

Priestman Goode 110 Crawford Street, London, W1H 2JD,
United Kingdom
☎ 020 79356665

Prime Creative Ltd Buckley Farm, Buckley Lane, Halifax, West Yorkshire, HX2 0RQ,
United Kingdom
☎ 01422 340220

Principal Image Ltd 4 Cherry Tree Farm, Cherry Tree Lane, Rostherne, Nr Knutsford, Cheshire, WA14 3RZ,
United Kingdom
☎ 01565 830213

Pritchards Creative Comms Ltd Gratton House, Gratton Street, Cheltenham, Gloucestershire, GL50 2AS,
United Kingdom
☎ 01242 226316

Product Partners Ltd The Old Warehouse, Church Street, Biggleswade, Bedfordshire, SG18 0JS,
United Kingdom
☎ 01767 600456

Production Point 4 Wells St, Chelmsford, CM1 1HZ,
United Kingdom
☎ 01245 344227

Profile 22 Systems Ltd Stafford Park 6, Telford, Shropshire, TF3 3AT,
United Kingdom
☎ 01952 290910

Progression Design Concept House, The Street, Capel, Dorking, Surrey, RH5 5EN,
United Kingdom
☎ 01306 712500

Project 1 Design Cowley Road, Oxford, Oxfordshire, OX4 1XG,
United Kingdom
☎ 01865 204417

Projector Brand Comms 65 Westgate Road, Sunniside, Newcastle Upon Tyne, Tyne & Wear, NE1 1SG,
United Kingdom
☎ 0191 2305003

Propeller Design 19 Princes Street, Ipswich, Suffolk, IP1 1PH,
United Kingdom
☎ 01473 287485

Propeller Graphics The Boat House, Navigation Way, Preston, Lancashire, PR2 2YP,
United Kingdom
☎ 01772 732244

Protean Design Ltd The Bell Tower, 12 High Street, Brackley, Northamptonshire, NN13 7DT,
United Kingdom
☎ 01280 706060

Psychographics Ltd Meridian House, Artist St, Leeds, West Yorkshire, LS12 2EW,
United Kingdom
☎ 0113 2460610

Public United House, North Road, London, N7 9DP,
United Kingdom
☎ 020 76075500

Publicscreen & Light Systm Ltd First Floor Offices, Bridewell Lane, Bury St Edmunds, Suffolk, IP33 1RE,
United Kingdom
☎ 01284 749809

Pufferfish Design & Marketing 27 Fiddlers Drive, Armthorpe, Doncaster, South Yorkshire, DN3 3TS,
United Kingdom
☎ 01302 300545

Purple Consultancy 52 Upper St, London, N1 0QH,
United Kingdom
☎ 020 72886700

Purple Creative Consultancy Unit 6 Third Floor, The Piano Works, 117 Farringdon Road, London, EC1R 3BX,
United Kingdom
☎ 020 77136569

Purple Frog The Byre, Manor Courtyard, Aston Sandford, Aylesbury (Rurals), Buckinghamshire, HP17 8LP,
United Kingdom
☎ 01844 295170

Purpose 14a Shouldham Street, London, W1H 5FG, United Kingdom
☎ 020 77245890

Pyramid The Works, Park Road, Blaby, Leicester, Leicestershire, LE8 4EF, United Kingdom
☎ 0116 2642642

Quadrant Communications Ltd 54 High Street, Eton, Windsor, Berkshire, SL4 6BL, United Kingdom
☎ 01753 483250

Quadrant Consultants Ltd 35 Endell Street, London, WC2H 9BA, United Kingdom
☎ 020 72407200

Quadrant Design 3 London Court, The Mews East Street, Reading, Berkshire, RG1 4QL, United Kingdom
☎ 0118 9591581

Quaike Design & Communication The Studio, Fernlea Gardens, Ferndown, Dorset, BH22 9HQ, United Kingdom
☎ 01202 870910

Quantrelle Newswell House, 21 Locksfield, Enfield, Middlesex, EN3 7PG, United Kingdom
☎ 020 88043222

Quantum 4 Ltd 14 The Point, Rockingham Road, Market Harborough, Leicestershire, LE16 7QU, United Kingdom
☎ 01858 410007

Quarry Fold Studio Billinge End Road, Pleasington, Blackburn, Lancashire, BB2 6OY, United Kingdom
☎ 01254 207620

Qube Design 82 Hotwell Road, Bristol, Avon, BS8 4UB, United Kingdom
☎ 0117 9297483

Quest E-Design Ltd Barnett House, 53 Fountain Street, Manchester, Lancashire, M2 2AN, United Kingdom
☎ 0161 2478470

Quiet Storm Productions Ltd 15-16 Margaret Street, London, W1W 8RW, United Kingdom
☎ 020 79071140

Quigley Design Westgate House, Hills Lane, Shrewsbury, Shropshire, SY1 1QU, United Kingdom
☎ 0174 3231661

Radford Wallis 3rd Floor, 27 Charlotte Road, London, EC2A 3PB, United Kingdom
☎ 020 70339595

Radio The Dispensary, 8 Cleveland Place East, Bath, Somerset, BA1 5DJ, United Kingdom
☎ 01225 337473

Radius Design Consultants Park Lane, Richmond, Surrey, TW9 2RA, United Kingdom
☎ 020 82876616

Radley Yeldar 24 Charlotte Road, London, EC2A 3PB, United Kingdom
☎ 020 70330700

Randak Design Consultants Gordon Chambers, 90 Mitchell Street, Glasgow, Lanarkshire, G1 3NQ, United Kingdom
☎ 0141 2217432

Rapport Design BIC 1, Units 10 & 12, 1 Kinetic Way, Enfield, EN3 7XU, United Kingdom
☎ 020 83448600

Rare Creative Group Arlewood's Mill, Nursery Street, Sheffield, South Yorkshire, S3 8GG, United Kingdom
☎ 0114 2823331

Ratcliffe Fowler Design Ltd 2 Chancery Place, Millstone Lane, Leicester, Leicestershire, LE1 5JN, United Kingdom
☎ 0116 2420200

Rawls & Co The Studio, 41 High Street, Barnes, London, SW13 9LN, United Kingdom
☎ 020 84875678

Razor Design Ltd Haywood House, 40 New Road, Stourbridge, West Midlands, DY8 3PA, United Kingdom
☎ 01384 372928

Rdc Foley Cooke Ltd 20-21 Northfields Prospect, Putney Bridge Road, London, SW18 1PE, United Kingdom
☎ 020 88744566

RDM 19 Margaret Street, London, W1W 8RS, United Kingdom
☎ 020 76377776

Reach Ltd Hope Chapel, Battle Lane, Chew Magna, Bristol, Avon, BS40 8PS, United Kingdom
☎ 01275 332296

Reading Room 65-66 Frith Street, Soho, London, W1D 3JR, United Kingdom
☎ 020 74326000

Real 451 102 Dean Street, London, W1D 3TQ, United Kingdom
☎ 020 78511390

Real Point Design The Cottage, 91 Main Road, Meriden, West Midlands, CV7 7NL, United Kingdom
☎ 01676 521444

Red 2 Design Ltd Hot House, Webberley Lane, Stoke On Trent, ST3 1RJ, United Kingdom
☎ 01782 313812

Red Door Ltd 103 Farringdon Road, London, EC1R 3BS, United Kingdom
☎ 020 75207570

Red Letter Design 133 Great Suffolk Street, London, SE1 1PP, United Kingdom
☎ 020 72074227

Redback Design Studio 39, Broyle road, Chichester, West Sussex, PO19 6BA, United Kingdom
☎ 01243 774755

Redesign 53 Jute Lane, Enfield, EN3 7JL, United Kingdom
☎ 020 88059585

Redpath Design 5 Gayfield Square, Edinburgh, Mid Lothian, EH1 3NW, United Kingdom
☎ 0131 5569115

Reef The Barns, Bakersgater Courtyard, Bullswater Common Road, Woking, Surrey, GU24 0NT, United Kingdom
☎ 01483 238900

Reef Design Management Ltd 14a Shouldham Street, London, W1H 5FG, United Kingdom
☎ 020 77243535

Reform Creative Ltd 12 Tariff Street, Manchester, Lancashire, M1 2FF, United Kingdom
☎ 0161 2360054

Reich & Petch Design Intl 209 B Latchmere Road, Battersea Bridge, London, SW11 2LA, United Kingdom
☎ 020 72288668

Relay 9 Holyrood Street, London, SE1 2EL, United Kingdom
☎ 020 73975400

Renfrew Creative Rocket Studios, Abbey Meadow, Leicester, Leicestershire, LE4 5DF, United Kingdom
☎ 0116 2531961

Resolution 58 Northgate St, Devizes, SN10 1JJ, United Kingdom
☎ 01380 728898

Resolution Interiors Lufton 2000, George Smith Way, Yeovil, Somerset, BA22 8QR, United Kingdom
☎ 01935 422700

Result Marketing Watermark Way, Foxholes Business Park, Hertford, Buckinghamshire, SG13 7TZ, United Kingdom
☎ 01992 514760

RF Design UK Ltd 5b Hillgate Place, Balham Hill, London, SW12 9ER, United Kingdom
☎ 020 87729905

Rhino Design 75 Oswin Road, Leicester, Leicestershire, LE3 1HR, United Kingdom
☎ 0116 2756111

Rhodes Design 7 Greenland Street, London, NW1 0ND, United Kingdom
☎ 020 74824101

Richmond International 9 Dallington Street, London, EC1V 0BQ, United Kingdom
☎ 020 74901901

Riverhorse Design Consultants Merchants House, 5-7 Southwark Street, London, SE1 1RQ, United Kingdom
☎ 020 73787844

Riverside Design & Marketing 108 Fulham Palace Road, 1 Playfair Street, London, W6 9PL, United Kingdom
☎ 020 87487499

RJ DESIGN STUDIO Derby Road, Risley, Derby, Derbyshire, DE72 3SS, United Kingdom
☎ 0115 9390666

Robert Welch Mill Sheep Street, Cotterels Alley, Chipping Camden, GL55 6DU, United Kingdom
☎ 01386 840522

Rocket Graphics 1 Woodshots Meadow, Croxley Business Park, Watford, WD18 8YS, United Kingdom
☎ 01923 230430

Rocket Science 3 Startforth Road, Riverside Park, Middlesbrough, Cleveland, TS2 1PJ, United Kingdom
☎ 01642 808888

Rocktime Ltd 94 High Street, Poole, Dorset, BH15 1DB, United Kingdom
☎ 01202 678777

Rodd Industrial Design Chart House, Sandy Lane, Lyndhurst, Hampshire, SO43 7DN, United Kingdom
☎ 023 80282456

Roger Lieberg 112 Hastings Road, Bromley, Kent, BR2 8NJ, United Kingdom
☎ 020 84627438

Romanski Ltd no 4, 2 Archie Street, London, SE1 3JT, United Kingdom
☎ 020 74074044

Room 2 Design Ltd The Bow House, Mill Lane Gaston Green, Lt Hallingbury, Bishops Stortford, Hertfordshire, CM22 7QT, United Kingdom
☎ 01279 722597

Root Ground Floor, Ravey Street, London, EC2A 4QP, United Kingdom
☎ 020 77392277

Rose Design Associates Ltd The old School, 70 St Marychuch Street, London, SE16 4HZ, United Kingdom
☎ 020 73942800

Roundel Design Group 7 Rosehart Mews, Westbourne Grove, London, W11 3TY, United Kingdom
☎ 020 72211951

Rowland Design Consultancy 197 High St, London, W3 9DD, United Kingdom
☎ 020 89932120

Royal Doulton UK Ltd Nile Street, Burslem, Staffordshire, ST6 2AJ, United Kingdom
☎ 01782 292406

Royds Raphael 35 Soho Square, London, W1D 3QX, United Kingdom
☎ 020 72872050

RT Facts Ltd 109 High Street, Hemel Hempstead, Hertfordshire, HP1 3AH, United Kingdom
☎ 01442 266590

RT Media Ltd Allen House, East Borough, Wimborne, Dorset, BH21 1PF, United Kingdom
☎ 01202 888192

RTC Europe Castle Road, Sittingbourne, Kent, ME10 3RN, United Kingdom
☎ 01795 412795

Rtc North Ltd 1 Hylton Park, Wessington Way, Sunderland, Tyne & Wear, SR5 3HD, United Kingdom
☎ 0191 5164400

RTKL 22 Torrington Place, London, WC1E 7HP, United Kingdom
☎ 020 73060404

Rubbaglove The Studio, Third Floor, 17 Blossom Street, London, E1 6PL, United Kingdom
☎ 020 72478300

Rufus Leonard The Drill Hall, 57a Farringdon Road, London, EC1M 3JB, United Kingdom
☎ 020 74044490

Rumba Graphic Design Ltd 2nd Floor, 24 Park Street, Bristol, Avon, BS1 5JA, United Kingdom
☎ 0117 9075323

Rumblefish Brackenhill, The Spinney, Rawdon, Leeds, West Yorkshire, LS19 6LH, United Kingdom
☎ 0113 2391523

S8080 Ltd Technium 2, Kings Road, Sa1 Swansea Waterfront, Swansea, West Glamorgan, SA1 8PJ, United Kingdom
☎ 01792 480807

Saatchi & Saatchi 82 Whitfield Street, London, W1T 4HG, United Kingdom
☎ 020 74366636

Sambrook Research 30 Station Road, Newport, Shropshire, TF10 7EN, United Kingdom
☎ 01952 825444

Sams Design The Granary, Mill Lane, Stotfold, Bedfordshire, Hertfordshire, SG5 4NU, United Kingdom
☎ 01462 734734

Sanders Design Associates Unit 8 Pacific Business Park, Pacific Road, Cardiff, CF24 5HJ, United Kingdom
☎ 029 20464661

SAS 6 Salem Road, London, W2 4BU, United Kingdom
☎ 020 72433232

Satherley Design Park Farm Stables, Woodstock Hill, East Grinstead, West Sussex, RH19 2RB, United Kingdom
☎ 01342 326060

Savva Design 10 Alma Road, Roath, Cardiff, South Glamorgan, CF23 5BD, United Kingdom
☎ 029 20404686

SCA Packaging Alexandra Docks, Newport, Gwent, NP20 2WE, United Kingdom
☎ 01633 776000

Schermuly Design Company St Mary Brookfield Hall, York Rise, London, NW5 1SB, United Kingdom
☎ 020 72840459

ScottKirkby Design Associates Trenance Farm, Withiel, Bodmin, Cornwall, PL30 5HN, United Kingdom
☎ 01208 832190

SCP Ltd 135-136 Curtain Rd, London, EC2A 3BX, United Kingdom
☎ 020 77391869

Screenbase Ltd Reith Way, West Portway Industrial Estate, Andover, Hampshire, SP10 3TY, United Kingdom
☎ 01264 332166

SDA Victoria Foundry, Marshall Street, Leeds, West Yorkshire, LS11 9EH, United Kingdom
☎ 0113 2881000

Sea Design 70 St John Street, London, EC1M 4DT, United Kingdom
☎ 020 75663100

Sears Davies Ltd Unit A, 25 Copperfield Street, London, SE1 0EN, United Kingdom
☎ 020 76330939

Second2 Ltd 104 High Street, Thame, Oxfordshire, OX9 3DZ, United Kingdom
☎ 01844 260055

SectorLight Sutton Young 1 James Street, London, W1U 1DR, United Kingdom
☎ 020 74992333

Sedley Place Ltd 68 Venn Street, London, SW4 0AX, United Kingdom
☎ 020 76275777

Seed Consultancy Ltd 125 Goldhurst Terrace, London, NW6 3EX, United Kingdom
☎ 020 74197115

Senator International Ltd Sykeside Drive, Altham Business Park, Altham, Accrington, Lancashire, BB5 5YE, United Kingdom
☎ 01282 725000

Seren c/o Renaisi, 21 Garden Walk, London, EC2A 3EQ, United Kingdom
☎ 020 76130040

Seymour Powell 327 Lillie Road, Fulham, London, SW6 7NR, United Kingdom
☎ 020 73816433

Shaun Power Associates 7 Bancroft Road, Hitchin, Hertfordshire, SG5 1JQ, United Kingdom
☎ 01462 453705

Shaw Marketing & Design Ltd 18 Albany Street, Edinburgh, Mid Lothian, EH1 3QB, United Kingdom
☎ 0131 5571545

Sheard & Hudson 11 West Street, Lacock, Chippenham, Wiltshire, SN15 2LH, United Kingdom
☎ 01249 730100

SHH 1 Vencourt Place, Ravenscourt Park, Hammersmith, London, W6 9NU, United Kingdom
☎ 020 86004171

Shoot The Moon 613 Highgate Studios, 53-59 Highgate Road, London, NW5 1TL, United Kingdom
☎ 020 74285680

Shopworks Ltd The Old Barn, Rossway Farm, Berkhamsted, Hertfordshire, HP4 3TZ, United Kingdom
☎ 01442 875666

Shore Design 46 Shore, Waterside House, Leith, Edinburgh, Mid Lothian, EH6 6QU, United Kingdom
☎ 0131 5542626

Shout Creative Ltd 107 Rangefield Court, Farnham Trading Estate, Farnham, Surrey, GU9 9NP, United Kingdom
☎ 01252 821015

Showcard Display Lacerta Court, Works Road, Letchworth, Hertfordshire, SG6 1FD, United Kingdom
☎ 01462 677254

Siebert Head Ltd 80 Goswell Road, London, EC1V 7DB, United Kingdom
☎ 020 76899090

Sign 2000 Ltd Leys Industrial Park, Maidstone Road, Paddock Wood, Kent, TN12 6QJ, United Kingdom
☎ 01892 834383

Silver & Co 5 Dryden Street, Covent Garden, London, WC2E 9NU, United Kingdom
☎ 020 78298464

Simmer Ltd 38-39 The Hop Exchange, 24 Southwark Street, London, SE1 1TY, United Kingdom
☎ 020 73576952

Simons Design Ltd 991 Doddington Road, Lincoln, Lincolnshire, LN6 3AA, United Kingdom
☎ 0808 2023991

Simply DNA Ltd 35-37 Parkgate Road, 31 Ransomes Dock, Battersea, London, SW11 4NP, United Kingdom
☎ 020 79242888

Sixfive Design Ltd Unit 1 8, Paintworks, Bath Road, Bristol, Avon, BS4 3EH, United Kingdom
☎ 0117 3005200

Skopos Design Ltd Prodidence Mills, Syke Lane, Earlsheaton, Dewsbury, West Yorkshire, WF12 8HT, United Kingdom
☎ 01924 465191

Slater Design 9 Church View, Holywood, County Down, BT18 9DP, United Kingdom
☎ 028 90421122

Slater Printing Ltd 9 Atlas Way, Carlisle Street, Sheffield, South Yorkshire, S4 7QQ, United Kingdom
☎ 0114 2493000

Slice Design Ltd 28 Bradmore Park Road, Hammersmith, London, W6 0DT, United Kingdom
☎ 020 87418828

Smadar Strategies Meadowcroft Farm, Gretton Fields, Cheltenham, Gloucestershire, GL54 5HJ, United Kingdom
☎ 01242 620403

Small Unit 9, Zeus House, 16-30 Provost Street, London, N1 7NG, United Kingdom
☎ 020 74901049

Smallfry School Street, Wolston, Coventry, West Midlands, CV8 3HG, United Kingdom
☎ 024 76545678

Smart Decision Dot Net Ltd 7 Marine Walk St, Hythe, CT21 5NW, United Kingdom
☎ 01303 237325

Smart Works The Barn, Kings Lane, Snitterfield, Stratford Upon Avon, CV37 0LZ, United Kingdom
☎ 01789 731367

Smith & Gilmour The Penthouse, West Point, 39-40 Warple Way, London, W3 0RG, United Kingdom
☎ 020 87435005

Smith & Milton The Boatmans Institution, 27 Junction Mews, London, W2 1PN, United Kingdom
☎ 020 72985500

Smosarski Design Ltd 117 Shaftesbury Avenue, London, WC2H 8AD, United Kingdom
☎ 020 72402777

Snakeye Creative Design Studio 192 Bedminster Down Road, Bristol, Avon, BS13 7NL, United Kingdom
☎ 0117 9638955

Soup Ltd St James Mill, Whitefriars, Norwich, Norfolk, NR3 1TN, United Kingdom
☎ 01603 751310

Special EFX Ltd 3 Ettington Park Business Ctr, Alderminster, Stratford Upon Avon, Warwickshire, CV37 8BT,
United Kingdom
✆ 01789 450005

Specs Studio Ltd Eastgate House, Town Quay, Southampton, Hampshire, SO14 2NY,
United Kingdom
✆ 023 80227440

Sphere Design 27 Mathew Street, Liverpool, Merseyside, L2 6RE,
United Kingdom
✆ 0151 2360233

Spin Communications Ltd Unit 2 and 4, 33 Stannary Street, London, SE11 4AA,
United Kingdom
✆ 020 77939555

Splash of Paint Larch House, Sulhamstead nr Theale, Sulhamstead, Reading, Berkshire, RG7 4BB,
United Kingdom
✆ 0118 9323566

Springetts 13 Salisbury Place, London, W1H 1FJ,
United Kingdom
✆ 020 79354211

Square Design Ltd Suite 6, 62 Bell Road, Sittingbourne, Kent, ME10 4HE,
United Kingdom
✆ 01795 477374

St Clair Mortgage & Insurance 114 St Clair Street, Kirkcaldy, Fife, KY1 2BZ,
United Kingdom
✆ 01592 655659

St Cross Design 87 Great North Road, Hatfield, Hertfordshire, AL9 5DA,
United Kingdom
✆ 01707 260044

St Ives Graphic Media Battye Street, Laisterdyke, Bradford, West Yorkshire, BD4 8AG,
United Kingdom
✆ 01274 269300

Standout 139 Queens Road, Leicester, Leicestershire, LE2 3FL,
United Kingdom
✆ 0116 2448222

Starfish Creative Design 6 St Georges Business Cntr, St Georges Square, Portsmouth, Hampshire, PO1 3EY,
United Kingdom
✆ 023 92428176

Steve Edge Design 1st Floor, 29 Charlotte Road, London, EC2A 3PB,
United Kingdom
✆ 020 76135100

Steve Turner Design Ltd 26 Main Street, Muston, Nottinghamshire, NG13 0FB,
United Kingdom
✆ 01949 842399

Steve Wilsher Creative Effects 30 Church Road, Teddington, Middlesex, TW11 8PB,
United Kingdom
✆ 020 89431066

Stills Design The Old Church, 76 Wells Street, Cardiff, South Glamorgan, CF11 6DY,
United Kingdom
✆ 029 20353940

Stocks Taylor Benson Ltd 1 Grove Court, Grove Park, Leicester, Leicestershire, LE19 1SA,
United Kingdom
✆ 0116 2405600

Stone The Crows Boot Hill, Callywhite Lane, Dronfield, Sheffield, South Yorkshire, S18 2XR,
United Kingdom
✆ 01246 299800

Store Display Developments Ltd 1-3 Fowke Street, Rothley, Leicester, Leicestershire, LE7 7PJ,
United Kingdom
✆ 0116 2301305

Storm Brand Design Consultants Marshall Hall Mills, Elland Lane, Elland, West Yorkshire, HX5 9DU,
United Kingdom
✆ 01422 371144

Storm Design Ltd 38 Cliftown Parade, Southend on Sea, Essex, SS1 1DL,
United Kingdom
✆ 01702 348484

Stride Treglown Promenade House, The Promenade, Clifton Down, Bristol, Avon, BS8 3NE,
United Kingdom
✆ 0117 9743271

Studio 6 12 Whiteladies road, Clifton Down, Bristol, Avon, BS8 1PD,
United Kingdom
✆ 0117 9745091

Studio Six Pannell House, 6/7 Litfield Place, Clifton Down, Bristol, Avon, BS8 3LX,
United Kingdom
✆ 0117 9089907

Stylographics Ltd Hille Business Centre, 132 St Albans Road, Watford, Hertfordshire, WD24 4AJ,
United Kingdom
✆ 01923 800666

Sumo 71 Westgate Road, Newcastle Upon Tyne, Tyne & Wear, NE1 1SG,
United Kingdom
✆ 0191 2619894

Suna Interior Design Ltd 15 York Road, London, SW19 8TP,
United Kingdom
✆ 020 85440429

Susan Rentoul Design 98 Ribblesdale Road, London, SW16 6SR,
United Kingdom
✆ 020 86775504

Swan Design 81 Leigh Road, Leigh On Sea, Essex, SS9 1JN,
United Kingdom
✆ 01702 471015

Switch The Chapel, 9 Sovereiegn Court, Graham Street, Birmingham, West Midlands, B1 3JR,
United Kingdom
✆ 0121 2332727

Synergy Creative Design 97-99 Chorley Street, Bl1 4al, Bolton, Lancashire, BL1 4AL,
United Kingdom
✆ 01204 559903

Systems by Design The Coterie, Preston Bagot, Solihull, West Midlands, B95 5DZ,
United Kingdom
✆ 01926 844100

Sytner Group Ltd Penman Way, Grove Park, Enderby, Leicester, LE19 1ST,
United Kingdom
✆ 0116 2821000

Talbot Designs Ltd 225 Long Lane, London, N3 2RL,
United Kingdom
✆ 020 83468515

Talisman Marketing Services Court 1, Bedfont Lakes Industrial Park, Challenge Road, Ashford, Middlesex, TW15 1AX,
United Kingdom
✆ 01784 423224

Tandem Design Twisel River Studios, 18 High Street, Holywood, County Down, BT18 9AD,
United Kingdom
✆ 028 90425590

Tangible Branding 93a Peascod Street, Windsor, Berkshire, SL4 1DH,
United Kingdom
✆ 01753 623523

Targetti UK 11-29 Fashion Street, Unit 1 4, London, E1 6PX,
United Kingdom
✆ 020 73772005

Tattersall Hammarling & Silk L Berkeley House, 163 Tottenham Lane, London, N8 9BT,
United Kingdom
✆ 020 83408320

Taxi Studio Ltd 93 Princess Victoria Street, Clifton, Bristol, Avon, BS8 4DD,
United Kingdom
✆ 0117 9735151

Tayburn 15 Kittle Yards, Causewayside, Edinburgh, Mid Lothian, EH9 1PJ,
United Kingdom
✆ 0131 6620662

TDG Creative 2nd Floor, Brambletye House, Brighton Road, Crawley, West Sussex, RH10 6AE,
United Kingdom
✆ 01293 619544

Team A go go 69a Bold Street, Liverpool, Merseyside, L1 4EZ,
United Kingdom
✆ 0151 7098499

Team Brand Communication Cons 11 Southwark Street, London, SE1 1RQ,
United Kingdom
✆ 020 70895800

Team Norden Mermaid House, 1 Mermaid Court, London, SE1 1HR,
United Kingdom
✆ 020 73788375

Techniquest Stuart Street, Cardiff, South Glamorgan, CF10 5BW,
United Kingdom
✆ 029 20475475

Tecknowledge UK 17c South Lane, Cowplain, Waterlooville, Hampshire, PO8 9RE,
United Kingdom
✆ 023 92570757

Telecity Redbus 6-7 Harbor Exchange Square, London, E14 9GE,
United Kingdom
✆ 020 75100400

Telescope Studios Ltd Axis Court, Nepshaw Lane South, Gildersome, Leeds, West Yorkshire, LS27 7UY,
United Kingdom
✆ 0113 2383066

Templar Downie 37 Floral Street, Covent Garden, London, WC2E 9DJ,
United Kingdom
✆ 020 72404020

Template Mktg & Desn Ltd 43 Main Street, Swannington, Coalville, Leicestershire, LE67 8QJ,
United Kingdom
✆ 01530 510800

Terence O'Rourke Everdene House, Wessex Fields, Deansleigh Road, Bournemouth, Dorset, BH7 7DU,
United Kingdom
✆ 01202 421142

Teviot Design 7 Dublin Street Lane South, Edinburgh, Mid Lothian, EH1 3PX,
United Kingdom
✆ 0131 5388300

The Barton Willmore Ptnrsp Beansheaf Farmhouse, Bourne Close, Calcot, Reading, Berkshire, RG31 7BW,
United Kingdom
✆ 0118 9430000

The Brewery 18 Petersham Road, Richmond, Surrey, TW10 6UW,
United Kingdom
✆ 020 84398400

The Bright Partnership President Buildings, Savile Street East, Sheffield, South Yorkshire, S4 7UQ,
United Kingdom
✆ 0114 2499178

The Carnyx Group 4th Floor, The Mereat Building, 26 Gallowgate, Glasgow, Lanarkshire, G1 5AB,
United Kingdom
✆ 0141 5525858

The Chase 1 North Parade, Parsonage Gardens, Manchester, Lancashire, M3 2NH,
United Kingdom
✆ 0161 8325575

The Clarion Portfolio Ltd 2 Great George Street, Godalming, Surrey, GU7 1EE,
United Kingdom
✆ 01483 414123

The Click Design 19 Muspole Street, Norwich, Norfolk, NR3 1DJ,
United Kingdom
✆ 01603 626249

The Consultancy The Innovation Centre, Venture Court, Queens Meadow Business Park, Hartlepool, Cleveland, TS25 5TG,
United Kingdom
☎ 01429 872633

The Core 90 Lots Rd, London, SW10 0QD,
United Kingdom
☎ 020 73512563

The Creative Clinic Ltd 139a The Broadway, Mill Hill, London, NW7 4RN,
United Kingdom
☎ 020 82011848

The Creative Village Ltd Bass Hill Farmhouse, Whaddon Road, Nash, Buckinghamshire, MK17 0ER,
United Kingdom
☎ 01908 520281

The Crocodile The Lux Building, 2-4 Hoxton Square, London, N1 6NU,
United Kingdom
☎ 020 77494400

The Design Base Ltd Northside, Wells Road, Chilcompton, Bath, Avon, BA3 4ET,
United Kingdom
☎ 01761 233443

The Design Board Worleigh House, 12 Green Leighs, Sedgley, Dudley, West Midlands, DY3 3RZ,
United Kingdom
☎ 01902 665333

The Design Dell Ltd 54 New Barns Rd, Ely, CB7 4PW,
United Kingdom
☎ 01353 659911

The Design Group Mill House, Haddricks Mill Road, Gosforth, Newcastle Upon Tyne, Tyne & Wear, NE3 1QL,
United Kingdom
☎ 0191 2845334

The Design Room Room 3, Bon Accord House, Riverside Drive, Aberdeen, Aberdeenshire, AB11 7SL,
United Kingdom
☎ 01224 589618

The Design Solution 5th Floor, King Court, 2-16 Dooge St, London, W1T 2QA,
United Kingdom
☎ 020 79085200

The Designers Republic Paternoster Row, Unit 415, 15 Paternoster Row, Sheffield, South Yorkshire, S1 2BX,
United Kingdom
☎ 0114 2754982

The Engine Room Royal Colonnade, 16 Great George Street, Bristol, Avon, BS1 5RH,
United Kingdom
☎ 0117 9294141

The Escape Design Co Unit E, Loddon Business Centre, Roentgen Road, Basingstoke, Hampshire, RG24 8NG,
United Kingdom
☎ 01256 334567

The Extension Little Critt, Cranbrook Road, Cranbrook, Kent, TN17 4EU,
United Kingdom
☎ 01580 241931

The Farm 59 Barnet Road, 59 Barnet Grove, London, E2 7BH,
United Kingdom
☎ 020 76136490

The Formation Charlotte Road, London, EC2A 3QW,
United Kingdom
☎ 020 77398198

The Future Laboratory Studio 2, 181 Cannon Street Road, London, E1 2LX,
United Kingdom
☎ 020 77912020

The Gate Films Ltd 213 The Box Works, Castlefield, Manchester, Lancashire, M15 4LD,
United Kingdom
☎ 0161 8324888

The Global Group The Studio, 76 Shelly Road East, Bournemouth, Dorset, BH7 6HB,
United Kingdom
☎ 01202 399990

The Good News Design Group Hallsford Bridge Ind Estste, Ongar, Essex, CM5 9RX,
United Kingdom
☎ 01277 367700

The Graphic Alliance 9 King Street, Covent Garden, London, WC2E 8HN,
United Kingdom
☎ 020 72401823

The Graphics Workshop 11 Bugle Street, Southampton, Hampshire, SO14 2AL,
United Kingdom
☎ 023 80335221

The Hub The Watermark, Ribbleton Lane, Preston, Lancashire, PR1 5EZ,
United Kingdom
☎ 01772 252377

The Hub Agency The Wheatsheaf Building, Speirs Wharf, Port Dudas, Glasgow, Lanarkshire, G4 9TJ,
United Kingdom
☎ 0141 3330313

The Identica Partnership Newcombe House, 45 Notting Hill Gate, London, W11 3LQ,
United Kingdom
☎ 020 75695600

The Ingram Partnership Ltd 7 - 10 Beaumont Mews, London, W1G 6EB,
United Kingdom
☎ 020 73172900

The Juice Design President Way, Sheffield, South Yorkshire, S4 7UR,
United Kingdom
☎ 0114 2755858

The Leadership Factor Taylor Hill Mill, Huddersfield, West Yorkshire, HD4 6JA,
United Kingdom
☎ 01484 517575

The Main Street Projects Co The Chapel, 1 Main Street, Humberstone, Leicester, Leicestershire, LE5 1AE,
United Kingdom
☎ 0116 2764222

The Maxim Creative Group Ltd Osborne Mill, Osborne Street, Oldham, Lancashire, OL9 6QQ,
United Kingdom
☎ 0161 6787776

The Nest 20 Flaxman Terrace, London, WC1H 9AT,
United Kingdom
☎ 020 76898344

The Partners Albion Court Yard, Green Hill Rents, Smithfield, London, EC1M 6PQ,
United Kingdom
☎ 020 76080051

The Pixel Factory Unit 5, Dungannon Enterprise Centre, Dungannon, County Tyrone, BT71 6JT,
United Kingdom
☎ 028 87726963

The Planet Group UK Ltd Bay Hall, Willow Lane, Birkby, Huddersfield, West Yorkshire, HD1 5EN,
United Kingdom
☎ 01484 321000

The Regency Group Regency House, 37-40 Alexandra Parade, Weston-Super-Mare, Somerset, BS23 1QZ,
United Kingdom
☎ 01934 637123

The Roundhouse Time Square, Newcastle Upon Tyne, Tyne & Wear, NE1 4EP,
United Kingdom
☎ 0191 2221144

The Russell Organisation Ltd Burton Road Business Park, Burton Road, Norwich, Norfolk, NR6 6AS,
United Kingdom
☎ 01603 787787

The Sloane Group 2-20 Booth Drive, Park Farm Industrial Estate, Wellingbororugh, Northamptonshire, NN8 6GR,
United Kingdom
☎ 01933 401555

The Small Back Room 5 Wootten Street, London, SE1 8TG,
United Kingdom
☎ 020 79027600

The TEAM 11 Southwark Street, London, SE1 1RQ,
United Kingdom
☎ 020 70895800

The Technology Partnership Ltd Melbourne Science Park, Cambridge Road, Melbourn, Royston, Hertfordshire, SG8 6EE,
United Kingdom
☎ 01763 212220

The White Room 2a Frant Road, Tunbridge Wells, Kent, TN2 5SE,
United Kingdom
☎ 01892 511867

The Workshop Ltd 15 Napier Street, Sheffield, South Yorkshire, S11 8HA,
United Kingdom
☎ 0114 2283500

Think! Design Victoria House, Victoria Street, Taunton, Somerset, TA1 3FA,
United Kingdom
☎ 01823 423212

Thirteen 9-10 King Street, Bristol, Avon, BS1 4EQ,
United Kingdom
☎ 0117 9081313

Three Blind Mice 9-10 Charlotte Mews, London, W1T 4EF,
United Kingdom
☎ 020 76362502

Threefold Communications Ltd 33 Manor Row, Bradford, West Yorkshire, BD1 4PS,
United Kingdom
☎ 01274 737373

Thru The Line 21 Holly Park Mills, Woodhall, Calverley, Pudsey, West Yorkshire, LS28 5QS,
United Kingdom
☎ 0113 2577999

Thunder Design East Tithe, Pury Hill, Alderton, Hampshire, NN12 7TB,
United Kingdom
☎ 01327 811056

Tictoc Design Consultants Ltd 14 Newton Terrace, Glasgow, Lanarkshire, G3 7PJ,
United Kingdom
☎ 0141 5642020

Tilney Shane 5 Heathmans Road, London, SW6 4TJ,
United Kingdom
☎ 020 77316946

Tin Fish Creative Ltd Terracotta Barn, Barton Road, Wisbech, Cambridgeshire, PE13 4TG,
United Kingdom
☎ 01945 580017

Tin Horse Design Ltd Pelham House, Pelham Court, London Road, Marlborough, Wiltshire, SN8 2AG,
United Kingdom
☎ 01672 519999

Together Design 106 Cleveland Street, London, W1T 6NX,
United Kingdom
☎ 020 73877755

Total Design 1 Bedford Road, London, N2 9DB,
United Kingdom
☎ 020 84447144

TPW Design Consultants Ltd 305 India Mill Business Centre, Darwen, Lancashire, BB3 1AE,
United Kingdom
☎ 01254 777111

Tree House Studios Ltd 53b Fernhead Road, Maida Vale, London, W9 3EY,
United Kingdom
☎ 020 89608222

Triad Design The Stables, Holdenby House, Holdenby, Northamptonshire, NN6 8DJ,
United Kingdom
☎ 01604 771100

Triangle Design Riverside House, Quarry Road, Chipping Sodbury, Bristol, Avon, BS37 6AX,
United Kingdom
☎ 01454 311220

Trinity Design Consultants Ltd Woodgate Stables, Crawley Lane, King Bromley, Burton on trent, Staffordshire, DE13 7JF,
United Kingdom
☎ 01543 473777

Triplicate Design Floor 5, 22 Adelaide Street, Belfast, County Antrim, BT2 8GD,
United Kingdom
☎ 028 90233296

True North 4th Floor, Fourways House, 57 Hilton Street, Manchester, Lancashire, M1 2EJ,
United Kingdom
☎ 0161 9095444

Tsl Design 17 Bond St, St Helier, Jersey, JE2 3NP,
United Kingdom
📞 01534 732203

Tuch Design Dock House, 79 High Street, Brentford,
Middlesex, TW8 8AE,
United Kingdom
📞 020 87581758

TUI Interactive Media 47 Greek Street, Soho, London,
W1D 4EE,
United Kingdom
📞 020 77347757

Turnbull Ripley Design First Floor, Monmouth House,
87-93 Westbourne Grove, London, W2 4UL,
United Kingdom
📞 020 72210110

Turnpike Press Ltd Unit A1, Valleylink Estate, Meridian
Way, Enfield, Middlesex, EN3 4TU,
United Kingdom
📞 020 88058850

Turquoise Brand Ltd Suite G / 1st Floor, Holborn Hall,
193-197 High Holborn, London, WC1V 7BD,
United Kingdom
📞 020 78312803

Tuscan Design Ltd Buckingham House, Wellington
Street, Cheltenham, Gloucestershire, GL50 1XY,
United Kingdom
📞 01242 236136

Two by Two Design Goswell Road, London, EC1V 7LQ,
United Kingdom
📞 020 72530081

Tynan D'Arcy Alexandra Court, St Leonards Road,
Windsor, Buckinghamshire, SL4 3BP,
United Kingdom
📞 01753 833550

Uffindell West 24 St John Street, London, EC1M 4AY,
United Kingdom
📞 020 76890000

UK Flyers Suite 210, Victory House, Somers Road North,
Portsmouth, Hampshire, PO1 1PJ,
United Kingdom
📞 023 92293050

Umbrella Design Ltd PO Box 904, 335 City Road,
London, EC1V 1LS,
United Kingdom
📞 020 78334032

UN Titled Factory 21, Wellington Street, Leicester,
Leicestershire, LE1 6HH,
United Kingdom
📞 0116 2554341

Underbrand Sectrum House, Bromell'S Road, London,
SW4 0BN,
United Kingdom
📞 020 76274291

United Biscuits Lane End Road, Sands, High Wycombe,
Buckinghamshire, HP12 4JX,
United Kingdom
📞 01494 615200

Universal Design Studio Ground Floor, 35/42 Charlotte
Road, London, EC2A 3PG,
United Kingdom
📞 020 70333881

Universal Showcards 23 Stonefield Way, Ruislip,
Middlesex, HA4 0YF,
United Kingdom
📞 020 88414551

Urbis Lighting Ltd Telford Road, Houndmills,
Basingstoke, Hampshire, RG21 6YW,
United Kingdom
📞 01256 354446

Valeria Design & Distribution 326 Kensal Road, Saga
Centre, 326 Kensal Rd, London, W10 5BZ,
United Kingdom
📞 020 89699880

Vario 167 Oakhill Road, The Laundry, London, SW15
2QW,
United Kingdom
📞 020 88756990

Vertigo Design 13 Beare Green Cottages, Beare Green,
Dorking, Surrey, RH5 4PE,
United Kingdom
📞 01306 711739

Vested Interest Design The Loft, 15a Watt Street,
Greenock, Renfrewshire, PA16 8JN,
United Kingdom
📞 01475 734066

Vibrandt The Old Brewery, Russell Street, Windsor,
Berkshire, SL4 1HQ,
United Kingdom
📞 01753 624242

Vicinity Marketing Ltd 78 Cannon Street, London,
EC4N 6HH,
United Kingdom
📞 020 79295677

Virtuality The Pump House, Victoria Road, Southborough,
Tunbridge Wells, Kent, TN4 0LX,
United Kingdom
📞 01892 515255

Visuality Design Ltd 31 The Calls, Leeds, West
Yorkshire, LS2 7EY,
United Kingdom
📞 0113 2470909

Vitamin V Ltd Millars Three, Southmill Road, Bishop'S
Stortford, Hertfordshire, CM23 3DH,
United Kingdom
📞 01279 654671

VIVID BRAND Ltd 26-34 Emerald Street, London,
WC1N 3QA,
United Kingdom
📞 020 74211750

Voltage Voltage Creative, 4 Lynedoch Place, Glasgow,
Lanarkshire, G3 6AB,
United Kingdom
📞 0141 3312120

Voyage Graphics Ltd Glendale House, Reading Road,
Burghfield Common, Reading, Berkshire, RG7 3BL,
United Kingdom
📞 0118 9835510

Wallace Print Group Ltd Unit 7 Ballard Business Park,
Ballard Business Park, Cuxton Road, Rochester, Kent, ME2
2NY,
United Kingdom
📞 01634 724772

Walter Brian Mktg Servs Unit 1, 407-409 Hornsey
Road, London, N19 4DX,
United Kingdom
📞 020 72630979

Warwick Dipple Design 6 Somers Road, Rugby,
Warwickshire, CV22 7DE,
United Kingdom
📞 01788 535105

Warwicks 45 Blondvil Street, Coventry, West Midlands,
CV3 5QX,
United Kingdom
📞 024 76505339

Wash Design Ltd The Watermark, Ribbleton Lane,
Preston, Lancashire, PR1 5EZ,
United Kingdom
📞 01772 880000

Washington Design Consultants 1-3 The Washington,
Stanwell Road, Penarth, South Glamorgan, CF64 2AD,
United Kingdom
📞 029 20711911

Waste Creative Studio 11, 6 Brewer Street, London,
W1F 0SD,
United Kingdom
📞 020 74370001

Watershed Design 31 Freegrove Road, Islington,
London, N7 9RG,
United Kingdom
📞 020 77001759

Watson Design 54 Mitchell Street, Kettering,
Northamptonshire, NN16 9HA,
United Kingdom
📞 01536 417839

Wave Creative Communications 28b Priestgate,
Peterborough, Peterborough Rurals, Cambridgeshire, PE1
1JA,
United Kingdom
📞 01733 558718

Webb Scarlett Devlam 12 Junction Mews, London, W2
1PN,
United Kingdom
📞 020 77063883

Westbrook Design 1 Skipton Road, Ilkley, West
Yorkshire, LS29 9EH,
United Kingdom
📞 01943 604100

WH Good (Systems) Ltd Carrs Industrial Estate,
Haslingden, Rossendale, Lancashire, BB4 5JT,
United Kingdom
📞 01706 211416

Whatever Design Ltd Unit 73 Eurolink Business Centre,
49 Effra Road, Brixton, London, SW2 1BZ,
United Kingdom
📞 020 72746763

Wheel House Creative 2 Albion Place, Hammersmith,
London, W6 0QT,
United Kingdom
📞 020 87484466

Wheeler & Porter 26 Marlborough Road, Banbury,
Oxfordshire, OX16 5DQ,
United Kingdom
📞 01295 258488

White Design High Wold Gate, Station Road,
Woldingham, Surrey, CR3 7DA,
United Kingdom
📞 0845 0611711

Whitehouse Mainwaring 3-6 The Old Fire Station, 68
Albion Street, Hockley, Birmingham, West Midlands, B1
3EA,
United Kingdom
📞 0121 2334845

Whiteknight 360 Ltd Applescan House, Latimer Road,
Luton, Bedfordshire, LU1 3XE,
United Kingdom
📞 01582 487580

Whitenoise Visual Co Teal Pavilion, Postside Business
Park, Airport Road West, Belfast, County Antrim, BT3
9ED,
United Kingdom
📞 028 90730999

Wida Group Ltd Brookside Road, Ruddington,
Nottingham, Nottinghamshire, NG11 6AT,
United Kingdom
📞 0115 9214797

Widdup Amer 91 Bancroft, Hitchin, SG5 1NQ,
United Kingdom
📞 01462 437777

Wild Dog Design Media Centre, 9-12 Middle Street,
Brighton, East Sussex, BN1 1AL,
United Kingdom
📞 01273 278766

Williams Lea Clifton House, Worship St, London, EC2A
2EJ,
United Kingdom
📞 020 77724400

Willow Group The Old Station Master'S House, Skipton
Station, Broughton Road, Skipton, North Yorkshire, BD23
1RT,
United Kingdom
📞 01756 797775

Wilson Design Metro House, Northgate, Chichester, West
Sussex, PO19 1BE,
United Kingdom
📞 01243 787100

Wire Design Unit 2.5, 11-29 Fashion Street, London, E1
6PX,
United Kingdom
📞 020 74221770

WLG Design Molewood Lodge, Molewood Road,
Hertford, Hertfordshire, SG14 3LT,
United Kingdom
📞 01992 504545

WMO Creative Worth Farm, Worth Lane, Little Horsted,
West Sussex, TN22 5TT,
United Kingdom
📞 01825 750699

Wolff Olins Ltd 10 Regents Wharf, All Saints Street,
London, N1 9RL,
United Kingdom
📞 020 77137733

Wolffe & Co Lochend Studio, 262 King Street, Castle
Douglas, Kirkcudbrightshire, DG7 1HA,
United Kingdom
📞 01556 505379

Woodmansterne Publications Ltd 1 The Boulevard, Blackmoor Lane, Watford, Hertfordshire, WD18 8UW, United Kingdom
✆ 01923 200600

Woods Creative Marketing Ltd 48 Town Road, Croston, Nr, Preston, Lancashire, PR26 9RB, United Kingdom
✆ 01772 602950

Worthington Brown Design 24 Huddersfield Road, Holmfirth, Huddersfield, West Yorkshire, HD9 2JS, United Kingdom
✆ 01484 689988

Wow Creative Services Unit 2, The Newburn Centre, Dean Street, Swindon, Wiltshire, SN1 5EW, United Kingdom
✆ 01793 719033

WPA Pinfold Nineveh Road, Leeds, West Yorkshire, LS11 9QG, United Kingdom
✆ 0113 2448549

Writers Ltd 9/10 King Street, Bristol, Avon, BS1 4EQ, United Kingdom
✆ 0117 9544700

Wylie Design Co Lark Cottage Studios, Mill Lane, Sherfield English, Romsey, Hampshire, SO51 6FN, United Kingdom
✆ 01794 323431

Wyndham Leigh Ltd The Courtyard, Bodymoor Green Farm, Coventry Road, Kingsbury, Warwickshire, B78 2DZ, United Kingdom
✆ 01827 875700

Yellobelly Brand Design Old Hall House, 133 The Street, Framsden, Stowmarket, Suffolk, IP14 6HF, United Kingdom
✆ 01473 892175

Yellow Door Creative Marketing 22-24 Torrington Place, London, WC1E 7HJ, United Kingdom
✆ 020 72900500

Yellow Triangle The Studio, 5 Stoneyfields, Farnham, Surrey, GU9 8DX, United Kingdom
✆ 01252 738950

Yellowdot Design 5 Bushy Park Mews, High Street, Hampton Hill, Middlesex, TW12 1ND, United Kingdom
✆ 020 89418484

Yogi Creative 3 Burt Street, Cardiff, South Glamorgan, CF10 5FZ, United Kingdom
✆ 029 20492679

Z& Co Design Ltd 2-6 North Burgh Street, London, EC1V 0AY, United Kingdom
✆ 020 73367808

Zakee Shariff Ltd 40-41 Great Western Studios, Great Westen Road, London, W9 3NY, United Kingdom
✆ 020 72665694

Zapf Creations UK Ltd 21 Chesnut Hse, Blenheim Pk, Medlicott, Corby, Northamptonshire, NN18 9NF, United Kingdom
✆ 01536 462800

Zerofifyone Media Ltd Compass House, 250a South Coast Road, Peacehaven, East Sussex, BN10 7NP, United Kingdom
✆ 01273 587446

Ziggurat 8-14 Vine Hill, London, EC1R 5DX , United Kingdom
✆ 020 77132900

Zone Creations Unit 1, Chelsea Fields, 278 Western Road, London, SW19 2QA, United Kingdom
✆ 020 86872450

Zulver & Co 183 Bermondsay Street, London, SE1 3UW, United Kingdom
✆ 020 79393939

Zumtobel Unit 5 The Argent Centre, Pump Lane, Hayes, Middlesex, UB3 3BL, United Kingdom
✆ 020 85891800

Zynk Design Consultants 11 The Chandlery, 50 Westminster Bridge Road, London, SE1 7QY, United Kingdom
✆ 020 77217444

PACKAGING DESIGN

A. Miah Prototype Packaging 98 Heath Road, Twickenham, TW1 4BW, United Kingdom
✆ (07090) 740500/✆ (07090) 740501
✉ amiah@mac.com
⌨ www.amiah.co.uk

Acrobat Creative Consultants The Old Church, Albert Hill Street, Didsbury, Manchester, M20 6RF, United Kingdom
✆ 0161-445 8887/✆ 0161-445 0900
✉ acrobat@btclick.com
⌨ www.acrobatdesign.co.uk

Allen International Berghem Mews, Blythe Road, London, W14 0HN, United Kingdom
✆ (020) 7371 2447/✆ (020) 7371 2448
✉ all@allen-international.com
⌨ www.allen-international.com

Aloof Design Ltd 5 Fisher Street, Lewes, East Sussex, BN7 2DG, United Kingdom
✆ (01273) 470887
✉ michellekostyrka@aloofdesign.com
⌨ www.aloofdesign.com

AND Creative Communications Ltd Whittaker House, Whittaker Avenue, Richmond, Surrey, TW9 1EH, United Kingdom
✆ (020) 8822 6720/✆ (020) 8822 6721
✉ jane@andccl.com
⌨ www.andccl.com

Appareo C/Zaragoza 1-3, No. 115, Castelldefels, Barcelona, 8860, Spain
✆ 00 34 93 636 6375/✆ 00 34 93 633 6854
✉ kevin@appareoconsulting.com
⌨ www.appareo.info

B D Network/Scotland Cochrane House, 29 Cochrane Street, Glasgow, G1 1HL, United Kingdom
✆ 0141-567 8037/✆ 0141-567 8001
⌨ www.bd-ntwk.com

B&G 40 Whellock Road, London, W4 1DZ, United Kingdom
✆ (07702) 813080
✉ m.girard@bandg.fr
⌨ www.bandg.fr

Beasley & Christopher 21 Castle Street, Brighton, BN1 2HD, United Kingdom
✆ (01273) 206997/✆ (01273) 206973
✉ beasley@pavillion.co.uk

Bleach 5 Hoxton Square, London, N1 6NU, United Kingdom
✆ (020) 7012 1211
✉ info@bleach-london.co.uk
⌨ www.bleach-london.co.uk

Blue Marlin Page Barn, Newbury, Frome, Somerset, BA11 3RG, United Kingdom
✆ (01373) 800010/✆ (01373) 814665
✉ larat@bluemarlinbd.com
⌨ www.bluemarlinbd.com

Bluestone Design Tamar Science Park, Derriford, Plymouth, PL6 8BT, United Kingdom
✆ (01752) 700777/✆ (01752) 752330
✉ design@bluestone.co.uk
⌨ www.bluestone.co.uk

Bow House Ltd 116 Long Street, Easingwold, York, YO61 3JA, United Kingdom
✆ (01347) 821928/✆ (01347) 822943
✉ admin@bowhouse.co.uk
⌨ www.bowhouse.co.uk

Brandhouse W T S 10A Frederick Close, London, W2 2HD, United Kingdom
✆ (020) 7262 1707/✆ (020) 7262 1512
✉ email@brandhousewts.com
⌨ www.brandhousewts.com

Burgopak Ltd 64 Great Suffolk Street, London, SE1 0BL, United Kingdom
✆ (020) 7593 1444/✆ (020) 7593 1414
✉ info@burgopak.com
⌨ www.burgopak.com

C V I Calendar Box (UK) Ltd Marwain Hse, Clarke Rd, Bletchley, Milton Keynes, MK1 1LG, United Kingdom
✆ (0870) 200 7001/✆ (0870) 2004001
✉ sales@cviuk.com
⌨ www.calendarbox.com

Campbell Aylin Design Copscap Barn, Eastgate, Hornton, Banbury, Oxfordshire, OX15 6BT, United Kingdom
✆ (01295) 678041/✆ (01295) 678079
✉ freddie@campbellaylin.com
⌨ www.campbellaylin.com

Clear View Ltd Unit 7, High Cross Centre, Fountayne Road, Tottenham, London, N15 4QN, UK
✆ (020) 8801 0020/✆ (020) 8801 0021
✉ sales@clearview.ltd.uk
⌨ www.clearview.ltd.uk

Clever4 Network Priory Tec Park, Saxon Way, Priory Park, Hessle, North Humberside, HU13 9PB, United Kingdom
✆ (01482) 640730/✆ (01483) 642408
✉ development@clever4.net
⌨ www.clever4.net

Cloud 9 Digital Design Ltd 2 Dairy Barns, Nuthurst Grange Lane, Hockley Heath, Solihull, West Midlands, B94 5NL, United Kingdom
✆ (01564) 785799
✉ mike@c9dd.com
⌨ www.c9dd.com

Conran Design Group 14 St Johns Square, London, EC1M 4NL, United Kingdom
✆ (020) 7566 4566/✆ (020) 7566 4555
✉ cdg@conrandesigngroup.com
⌨ www.conrandesigngroup.com

Corniche Fine Arts Ltd Lancaster Rd, Carnaby Ind Est, Bridlington, East Yorkshire, YO15 3QY, United Kingdom
✆ (0845) 230 6565/✆ (01262) 606724
✉ info@corniche.co.uk
⌨ www.corniche.co.uk

Corporate Edge Ltd Lyric House, 149 Hammersmith Rd, London, W14 0QL, United Kingdom
✆ (020) 7855 5888/✆ (020) 7855 5750
⌨ www.corporateedge.com

Creative Artworker & Packaging Designer Flat 3, Europa House, 11 Marsham Way, Gerrards Cross, Buckinghamshire, SL9 8BQ, United Kingdom
✆ (01753) 899352
✉ pm.day@vigin.net
⌨ www.foliofinder.com

Creative Edge Design & Advertising 1st Floor Donald Hendry Building, Auchincruive, Ayr, KA6 5HW, United Kingdom
✆ (01292) 521404/✆ (01292) 521693
✉ paul@cedge.co.uk
⌨ www.cedge.co.uk

D J P A Partnership 88 Gray's Inn Road, London, WC1X 8AA, United Kingdom
✆ (020) 7025 3850/✆ (020) 7025 3851
✉ info@djpa.com
⌨ www.djpa.com

D N A Creative 52 New Street, Pudsey, West Yorkshire, LS28 8PE, United Kingdom
✆ (07760) 252890
✉ noonan.hq@ntlworld.com
⌨ www.dnacreative.co.uk

DataCAM Models 18 Hewett Street, London, EC2A 3NN, United Kingdom
✆ (020) 7655 4822
✉ ashley@datacam.co.uk
⌨ www.datacam.co.uk

Design Activity Ltd Beech House, 6 St Paul's Road, Clifton, Bristol, BS8 1LT, United Kingdom
✆ 0117-933 9400/✆ 0117-923 9989
✉ info@design-activity.co.uk
⌨ www.design-activity.co.uk

Design Alliance Limited 2 Allington Close, Wimbledon Village, London, SW19 5AP, United Kingdom
✆ (020) 8944 1992/✆ (020) 8944 6392
✉ studio@designalliance.co.uk
⌨ www.designalliance.co.uk

Design Bridge Ltd 18 Clerkenwell Close, London, EC1R 0QN, United Kingdom
✆ (020) 7814 9922/✆ (020) 7814 9024
✉ enquiries@designbridge.co.uk
⌨ www.designbridge.co.uk

Design Forte Harewood Cottage, Main Street, Weeton, Leeds, LS17 0AY, United Kingdom
- (01423) 734856
- chris@designforte.co.uk
- www.designforte.co.uk

Design Group 111 Charterhouse Street, London, EC1M 6AW, United Kingdom
- (020) 7608 1144/ (020) 7253 7658
- www.the-design-group.co.uk

Design Matters Ltd 33 Cambridge Gardens, Hastings, East Sussex, TN34 1EN,
- 01424 722311/ 01424 722310
- paul@design-matters.co.uk
- www.design-matters.co.uk

Design Study Ltd East Hall Barn, Crown Road, Mundford, Thetford, Norfolk, IP26 5HQ, United Kingdom
- (01842) 877007/ (01842) 877008
- pip@designstudy.co.uk
- www.designstudy.co.uk

design@djhunter 133 Ravensbourne Avenue, Bromley, BR2 0AZ, United Kingdom
- (020) 8466 7196/ (020) 8466 7196
- design@djhunter.co.uk

Designcrew Creative Media Centre, 45 Robertson Street, Hastings, East Sussex, TN34 1HL,
- 01424 205 499/01424 205 499
- danny@designcrew.co.uk
- www.designcrew.co.uk

Designease Ltd Unit 7, Stonehouse Commercial Centre, Bristol Road, Stonehouse, Gloucestershire, GL10 3RD, United Kingdom
- (01453) 821990/ (01453) 821993
- sales@designease.co.uk
- www.designease.co.uk

DL Design Associates Limited 38a Duke Street, Chelmsford, CM1 1HY,
- 01245 299047/ 01245 299047
- darren@dl-design.co.uk
- www.dl-design.co.uk

Dohm 2 Blake Mews, Kew, Richmond, Surrey, TW9 3QA, United Kingdom
- (020) 8439 9070/ (020) 8439 9080
- design@dohm.net
- www.dohm.net

Duncan Print & Packaging Broadwater House, Mundells, Welwyn Garden City, Hertfordshire, AL7 1EU, United Kingdom
- (01707) 336271/ (01707) 338731
- sales@duncanprint.co.uk
- www.duncanprint.co.uk

E X X Projects 72 Rivington Street, London, EC2A 3AY, United Kingdom
- 0845-630 1262/ 0845-630 1282
- exx@plax.co.uk
- www.plax.co.uk

Ed Turnbull Design Associates 3a Clovelly View, Turnchapel, Plymouth, PL9 9SY, United Kingdom
- (01752) 482185/ (01752) 482185
- edturnbull@btinternet.com
- www.turnbullgallery.co.uk

Ergo Id Ltd 34 Oppidans Road, Primrose Hill, London, NW3 3AG, United Kingdom
- (020) 7722 5500/ (020) 7722 6900
- potential@ergo-id.com
- www.ergo-id.com

Ethos Brand Design 8a Wendell Road, London, W12 9RT, United Kingdom
- (020) 8735 5880/ (020) 8735 5888
- info@ethos-brandesign.com
- www.ethos-brandesign.com

Exposed, London, NW4 4UH, United Kingdom
- (020) 8202 5964/ (0870) 1259115
- davidc@exposed.co.uk
- www.exposed.co.uk

F L B Ltd De la Bere House, Bayshill Road, Cheltenham, Gloucestershire, GL50 3AW, United Kingdom
- (01242) 245851/ (01242) 519984
- fistname@flb.co.uk
- www.flb.co.uk

Finish Creative Services Ltd 37-42 Compton Street, London, EC1V 0AP, United Kingdom
- (020) 7251 2122/ (020) 7251 3221
- enquiries@finish-creative.com
- www.finish-creative.com

Firedog Design Ltd 43/44 Hoxton Square, London, N1 9PB, United Kingdom
- (020) 7739 1112/ (020) 7729 1002
- info@firedog-design.co.uk
- www.firedog-design.co.uk

Futurebrand Fox Court, 14 Gray's Inn Road, London, WC1X 8WS, United Kingdom
- (020) 7067 0010/ (0870) 9905467
- contact-london@futurebrand.com
- www.futurebrand.com

GMID Design for Business Prospect House, 3 Prospect Place, Swansea, SA1 1QP, United Kingdom
- (01792) 641350/ (01792) 301548
- studio@gmid.net
- www.gmid.net

Golden Section 1 Water Lane, Little Plumpstead, Norwich, NR13 5EX, United Kingdom
- (01603) 716699
- golden.section@virgin.net
- www.golden-section.co.uk

Graham Naylor Flat 7, Albany, 20 St. John's Avenue, London, SW15 2AA, United Kingdom
- (07789) 488956
- info@grahamnaylor.co.uk
- www.grahamnaylor.co.uk

Grays Packaging Ltd 68 Kent Road, Grays, Essex, RM17 6DF, United Kingdom
- 01375 399128
- sales1@grays-packaging.co.uk
- www.grayspackaging.co.uk

Halo Design Associates Ltd The Pump House, 16 Queens Avenue, Christchurch, Dorset, BH23 1BZ, United Kingdom
- (01202) 471177/ (01202) 488448
- andrew@haloassociates.co.uk
- www.haloassociates.co.uk

Heretakis@hotmail.com 54 Sina Street, Athens, Greece
- 00 30 694 2250 836/ 00 30 210 33615 055
- heretakis@hotmail.com
- www.heretakis.com

Hobb Plus Minerva House, 1-4 North Crescent, London, WC1E 7ER, United Kingdom
- (020) 7631 2800/ (020) 7631 9660
- info@hobbplus.com
- www.hobbplus.com

Ideas Start Here Ltd 452 Roundhay Road, Oakwood, Leeds, LS8 2HU, United Kingdom
- 0113-240 9822/ 0113-248 8468
- info@ideasstarthere.com
- www.ideasstarthere.com

Jim Stanton Plum Studio, 12 Ravensbury Terrace, London, SW18 4RL, United Kingdom
- (020) 8946 2456/(07951) 580207 / (020) 8946 2494

Jimmy Yang Associates 25 Chelsham Road, London, SW4 6NR, United Kingdom
- (020) 7622 5788/ (020) 7622 5788
- created@y-associates.com
- www.y-associates.com

John Brown Design 1 Arundel Gardens, Rayleigh, Essex, SS6 9GS, United Kingdom
- (01268) 786442/ (0870) 1166144
- studio@johnbrowndesign.com
- www.johnbrowndesign.co.uk

John Govett 66 Woodrow, London, SE18 5DH, United Kingdom
- (020) 8836 9113/ (0871) 242 2811
- johngovett.addesign@virgin.net
- www.contact-me.net/johngovett

Jolanta Damski Freelance Design Flat 1, 40 Ewelme Road, London, SE23 3BH, United Kingdom
- (020) 8291 6023
- jolantadamski@btinternet.com
- www.jolantadamski.co.uk

Jones Garrard Ltd 116 Regent Road, Leicester, LE1 7LT, United Kingdom
- 0116-254 2390/ 0116-255 6658
- design@jones-garrard.co.uk
- www.jones-garrard.co.uk

Jones Knowles Ritchie 128 Albert Street, London, NW1 7NE, United Kingdom
- (020) 7428 8000/ (020) 7428 8080
- info@jkr.co.uk
- www.jkr.co.uk

Juniper Design Ltd 117 Westbourne Grove, London, W2 4UP, United Kingdom
- (020) 7229 7332
- mail@juniperdesign.co.uk
- www.juniperdesign.co.uk

K G B 111-113 Great Portland Street, London, W1W 6QQ, United Kingdom
- (020) 7631 4082/ (020) 7631 3102
- alastair@kgb.uk.com
- www.kgb.uk.com

Ken Reilly Design Associates 11 Chiswick Staithe, Hartington Road, Grove Park, London, W4 3TP, United Kingdom
- (020) 8994 2228/ (020) 8994 2238
- ken.reilly@btconnect.com
- www.kenreilly.co.uk

Letterbox Communications Baird House, 15-17 St Cross Street, London, EC1N 8UN, United Kingdom
- (020) 7430 8203/ (020) 7430 8205
- production@domarn.com
- www.domarn.com

Lewis Moberly Ltd 33 Gresse Street, London, W1T 1QU, United Kingdom
- (020) 7580 9252/ (020) 7255 1671
- hallo@lewismoberly.com
- www.lewismoberly.com

Like A River 14-32 Hewitt Street, Manchester, M15 4GB, United Kingdom
- 0161-236 1552/ 0161-236 1553
- info@likeariver.co.uk
- www.likeariver.com

Lippa Pearce 11 Need Hand Road, Twickenham, TW1 2RP, United Kingdom
- (020) 7229 3477/ (020) 7727 9932
- email@pentagram.co.uk
- www.pentagram.co.uk

Lloyd Ferguson Hawkins Unit 6A-10 Frederick Close, Stenhope Place, London, W2 2HD, United Kingdom
- (020) 7706 8762/ (020) 7706 8763
- reception@lfh.co.uk
- www.lfh.co.uk

Longneck Afgan Road 27, Battersea, London, SW11 2QD,
- 7506018062
- vlad@longneck.ro
- www.longneck.ro

Lucian Marin, Bucharest, 61079, Romania
- 721 230 631
- lucian.marin@gmail.com
- www.lucianmarin.ro

Make Me Ltd 11 Plough Yard, London, EC2A 3LP, United Kingdom
- (020) 7392 8880
- info@makeme.biz
- www.makeme.biz

Mark Wolstencroft - Design & Strategic Brand Consulting The City Arc, 7 Curtain Road, London, EC2A 3LT, United Kingdom
- (020) 7917 2957
- mark@mark-wolstencroft.com
- www.mark-wolstencroft.com

Mash Media UK Ltd 62 Hatton Garden, London, EC1N 8LR, United Kingdom
- (020) 7242 1272
- info@mash-media.com
- www.mash-media.com

Mass Technology (UK) Ltd 36b Evington Road, Leicester, Leicestershire, LE2 1HG,
- 0116 25 44 171
- masstechnology@hotmail.com
- www.masstechnologyonline.com

Mastrom Ltd Park Road, Alrewas, Burton-on-Trent, Staffordshire, DE13 7AG, United Kingdom
- (01283) 790030/ (01283) 791068
- sales@mastrom.co.uk
- www.mastrom.co.uk

Millini Creative Services 81 Barwell Business Park, Leatherhead Road, Chessington, Surrey, KT9 2NY, United Kingdom
- (020) 8974 2242/ (020) 8974 3344
- enquiries@millini.com
- www.millini.com

Mountain Creative Design Consultancy 1 Park Terrace, Glasgow, G3 6BY, United Kingdom
- 0141-332 8007/ 0141-332 8822
- info@mountaincdc.com
- www.mountaincdc.com

Mytton Williams 15 St. James' Parade, Bath, BA1 1UL, United Kingdom
- (01225) 442634/ (01225) 442639
- design@myttonwilliams.co.uk
- www.myttonwilliams.co.uk

Nicholas Grimshaw & Partners 7 Clerkenwell, London, EC1M 5NG, United Kingdom
(020) 7291 4141/ (020) 7291 4194
info@grimshaw-architects.com
www.grimshaw-architects.com

Nicola L Robinson Mynachdy, Cardiff, Glamorgan, CF14 3AG, United Kingdom
nlrobinson@thesurrealdemon.co.uk
www.thesurrealdemon.co.uk

Nilorn Calmon Beckside House, Pitt Street, Keighley, West Yorkshire, BD21 4PF, United Kingdom
(01535) 673534/ (01535) 673519
chris.wildman@calmon.nilorn.com
www.nilorn.co.uk

P S D Fitch Ltd 121-141 Westbourne Terrace, London, W2 6JR, United Kingdom
(020) 7479 0900/ (020) 7479 0600
info@psd-fitch.com
www.fitchww.com

Parker Williams Design 1st Floor, Voysey House, Barley Mow Passage, London, W4 4PT, United Kingdom
(020) 8995 6411/ (020) 8995 6632
design@parkerwilliams.co.uk
www.parkerwilliamsdesign.co.uk

Partners in Communication 10 Whytecliffe Rd South, Purley, Surrey, CR8 2AU, United Kingdom
(020) 8763 1323/ (020) 8763 1322
creative@picom.co.uk
www.picom.co.uk

Paul Martin Design Co. 32 Dragon Street, Petersfield, Hampshire, GU31 4JJ, United Kingdom
(01730) 265814/ (01730) 263014
marketing@pmdc.co.uk
www.pmdc.co.uk

Point 6 Design Ltd 5 The Linen House, 253 Kilburn Ln, London, W10 4BQ, United Kingdom
(020) 8962 5880/ (020) 8962 5898
design@point6.co.uk
www.point6.co.uk

Postal Packaging Ltd K7 Cherrycourt Way, Stanbridge Road, Leighton Buzzard, Bedfordshire, LU7 4UH, United Kingdom
(01525) 382580/ (01525) 851465
info@postal-packaging.co.uk
www.postal-packaging.co.uk

Prima (Yorkshire) Ltd 31 Mortimer Street, Bradford, West Yorkshire, BD8 9RL, United Kingdom
(01274) 481222/ (01274) 482111
mail@primayorks.co.uk
www.primayorks.co.uk

Progress Packaging Ltd The Mill, 150 Penistone Road, Huddersfield, HD8 8JQ, United Kingdom
(01484) 608600/ (01484) 608550
sales@progresspkg.co.uk
www.progresspkg.co.uk

Ptarmigan Design 9 Gainsborough Drive, Adel, Leeds, LS16 7PF, United Kingdom
0113-261 3172/ 0113-293 9576
info@ptarmigan-design.co.uk
www.ptarmigan.co.uk

Pure Equator 4 The Heritage Centre, High Pavement, Nottingham, NG1 1HN, United Kingdom
0115-947 6555/(07989) 322304
david.rogers@pure-equator.com
www.pure-equator.com
See ad in showcase

Purple Circle Design Ltd Global Headquarters, 1 Howard Street, Nottingham, NG1 3LT, United Kingdom
0115-955 0005/ 0115-955 0006
info@purplecircle.co.uk
www.purplecircle.co.uk

R Design 420 Highgate Studios, 53-79 Highgate Road, London, NW5 1TL, United Kingdom
(020) 7284 5840/ (020) 7284 5849
info@r-email.co.uk
www.r-website.co.uk

Randak Grand Management Gordon Chambers, 90 Mitchell Street, Glasgow, G1 3NQ, United Kingdom
0141-221 2142/ 0141-226 5096
info@randakdesign.com
www.randakdesign.com

Reach Hope Chapel, Battle Lane, Bristol, BS40 8PS, United Kingdom
(01275) 332296/ (01275) 331399
richard@reachdesign.co.uk
www.reachdesign.co.uk

Redpath 5 Gayfield Square, Edinburgh, EH1 3NW, United Kingdom
0131-556 9115/ 0131-556 9116
redpath@redpath.co.uk
www.redpath.co.uk

Redrova Ltd The Big Barn, Red House Farm, Woodwalton, Huntingdon, Cambridgeshire, PE28 5YL, United Kingdom
(01487) 773679/ (01487) 773659
zoe@redrova.co.uk
www.redrova.co.uk

Rhubarb Associates Ltd Flat A, 349 Hale Road, Hale Barns, Altrincham, Cheshire, WA15 8SX, United Kingdom
(07887) 640584
matt@rhubarbcreative.com
www.rhubarbcreative.com

Rodney Simmonds Newbury House, Aston, Bampton, Oxfordshire, OX18 2DQ, United Kingdom
(01993) 850483/(07769) 978929 (01993) 851803
SimmondsR@aol.com

Sage Visual Solutions A4 13 Sisters Avenue, London, SW11 5SP, United Kingdom
(020) 7223 4700
damian@sagevisualsolutions.com

Sca Design 215 Woodhall Way, Beverley, North Humberside, HU17 7JX, United Kingdom
(01482) 863035
steve@scadesign.co.uk
www.scadesign.co.uk

Scarlet Creative Solutions Ltd 3 Yew Walk, Hoddesdon, Hertfordshire, EN11 8BB, United Kingdom
(0845) 4085402
solutions@scarletcreative.co.uk
www.scarletcreative.co.uk

Screenprint Doncaster Shaw Lane Industrial Estate, Ogden Road, Doncaster, South Yorkshire, DN2 4SE, United Kingdom
(01302) 322556
sales@screenprintdoncaster.co.uk
www.screenprintdoncaster.co.uk

Skirt Ltd 27 Cranbrook Road, Bristol, BS6 7BL, United Kingdom
0117-377 4079/ (07951) 289 668

Smith & Milton Boatmens Institution, 27 Junction Mews, London, W2 1PN, United Kingdom
(020) 7298 5500/ (020) 7262 6987
info@smith-milton.co.uk
www.smith-milton.co.uk

Spheredesign Mathew Court, 27 Mathew Street, Liverpool, L2 6RE, United Kingdom
0151-236 5755/ 0151-236 4322
nik@spheredesign.co.uk

Spiral Communications Pte Ltd 28 Maxwell Road, 02-15A, Red Dot Traffic Building, Singapore,
+65 65347184/ +65 63278902
enquiry@spiralcomms.com
www.spiralcomms.com

Stairway Communications Baird House, 15-17 St Cross Street, London, EC1N 8UN, United Kingdom
(020) 7430 8201/ (020) 7430 8205
design@domarn.co.uk
www.domarn.co.uk

Start Creative 2 Sheraton Street, Soho, London, W1F 8BH, United Kingdom
(020) 7269 0101/ (020) 7269 0102
jen@startcreative.co.uk
www.startcreative.co.uk

Storm Brand Design Marshall Hall Mills, Elland Lane, Elland, West Yorkshire, HX5 9DU, United Kingdom
(01422) 371144/ (01422) 371188
bruce@stormbranddesign.co.uk
www.stormbranddesign.co.uk

Studio SDA Unit 8, Pacific Business Park, Pacific Road, Cardiff, CF24 5HJ, United Kingdom
(029) 2046 4661/ (029) 2046 4981
lianne@studiosda.com
www.studiosda.com

Sutherland-Hawes McLean Design Consultants, 40 Ravenscourt Gardens, London, W6 0TU, United Kingdom
(020) 8141 9806/ (020) 8563 9975
shm@sutherlandhawes.co.uk
www.sutherlandhawes.co.uk

TAG Brand The Barn, 13-17 Margett Street, Cottenham, CB24 8QY, United Kingdom
(01954) 250100/ (01954) 250200
info@tagbrand.co.uk
www.tagbrand.co.uk

Tango Design Newcombe House, 45 Notting Hill Gate, London, W11 3LQ, United Kingdom
(020) 7569 5757/ (020) 7569 5656
tango@tangodesign.com
www.tangodesign.com

Tayburn Ltd 15 Kittle Yards, Causewayside, Edinburgh, EH9 1PJ, United Kingdom
0131-662 0662/ 0131-662 0606
simon.farrell@tayburn.co.uk
www.tayburn.co.uk

Taylor McCann 14th Floor, Oakland House, Old Trafford, Manchester, M16 0PQ, United Kingdom
0161-888 5700/ 0161-888 5741
email@taylormccann.com
www.taylormccann.com

The Core 152 High Street, Hull, HU1 1PS, United Kingdom
(01482) 581654/ (01482) 601176
design@coredesign.co.uk

The Design Fulcrum Ltd Thames House, Swan Street, Old Isleworth, Isleworth, Middlesex, TW7 6RS, United Kingdom
(020) 8568 7700
lever@thefulcrum.co.uk
www.thefulcrum.co.uk

The Design Inn 28 Upper Hamilton Road, Brighton, BN1 5DF, United Kingdom
(07903) 389990
liavittone@yahoo.co.uk

Tin Horse Design Ltd Pelham House, Pelham Court, London Road, Marlborough, Wiltshire, SN8 2AG, UK
(01672) 519999/ (01672) 511811
www.tinhorse.co.uk

Total Design Elland House, 2 John Charles Way, Leeds, LS12 6LY, United Kingdom
0113-263 7755/ 0113-387 4109
dianneb@goodd.co.uk

Total Spectrum Ltd 11 Intec 2, Wade Road, Basingstoke, Hampshire, RG24 8NE, United Kingdom
(01256) 814114/ (01256) 814115
sales@totalspectrum.co.uk
www.totalspectrum.co.uk

Typearea Ltd 13-14 Dean Street, Soho, London, W1D 3RS, United Kingdom
(020) 7439 3770/ (020) 7287 6101
info@typearea.com
www.typearea.com

Vibrandt Ltd Old Brewery, Russell Street, Windsor, Berkshire, SL4 1HQ, United Kingdom
(01753) 624242/ (01753) 857971
ideas@vibrandt.co.uk
www.vibrandt.co.uk

Vineyard Design Ltd No.3 The Hydra Building, 10 Hardwick Street, London, EC1R 4UG, United Kingdom
(020) 7833 5956/ (020) 7278 3549
info@vineyarddesign.com
www.vineyarddesign.com

W F C A Integrated Cobden House, 25 London Road, Tunbridge Wells, Kent, TN1 1DA, United Kingdom
(01892) 511085/ (01892) 512180
info@wfca.co.uk
www.wfca.co.uk

Ward Hayes Partnership 15 Bedford Street, Woburn, Milton Keynes, MK17 9QB, United Kingdom
(01525) 290696/ (01525) 290697
creative@wardhayes.co.uk
www.wardhayes.co.uk

Watt UK Ltd Albian Road, Greengates, Bradford, West Yorkshire, BD10 9TQ, United Kingdom
(01274) 200700/ (01274) 202425
info@wattswatt.co.uk
www.wattswatt.co.uk

Wickstead Design 128 Southwark Street, London, SE1 0SW, United Kingdom
020 7803 4910/ 020 7803 4915
design@wickstead.com
www.wickstead.co.uk

Wingnut Designs Waterfront Farm, Biddisham Lane, Biddisham, Axbridge, Somerset, BS26 2RS, United Kingdom
(01934) 750827
chris@wingnutdesigns.co.uk
www.wingnutdesigns.co.uk

Winter & Co. UK Ltd Stonehill, Stukeley Meadows Industrial Estate, Huntingdon, Cambridgeshire, PE29 6ED, United Kingdom
(01480) 377177/ (01480) 377166
sales@winteruk.com
www.winter-company.com

Wonderfuel 118 Hatherley Gardens, London, E6 3HQ, United Kingdom
020 8548 1358
info@wonderfuel.co.uk
www.wonderfuel.co.uk

Wren & Rowe 4 Denbigh Mews, London, SW1V 2HQ, United Kingdom
(020) 7828 5333/ (020) 7828 5444
mail@wrenrowe.co.uk
www.wrenrowe.com

Y R G Manchester Ltd Trafford Plaza, Seymour Grove, Manchester, M16 0LD, United Kingdom
0161-872 3735/ 0161-877 7531
yrgmanchester@aol.com

Z+Co. 2-6 Northburgh St, London, EC1V 0AY, UK
(020) 7336 7808/ (020) 7336 7828
design@z-and-co.com
www.z-and-co.com

Zenith Print & Packaging Ltd Gellihirion Ind Est, Treforest, Pontypridd, Mid Glamorgan, CF37 5SX, UK
(01443) 841166/ (01443) 841327
zenith@zenpak.co.uk
www.zenpak.co.uk

Ziggurat 8-14 Vine Hill, Clerkenwell, London, EC1R 5DX, United Kingdom
(020) 7969 7777/ (020) 7969 7788
info@zigguratbrands.com
www.zigguratbrands.com

Ziggy Zdziebko Creative Old Barn, Front Street, Ringwould, Deal, Kent, CT14 8HP, United Kingdom
(01304) 367 585/(07769) 781041
ziggy.zdz@btconnect.com
www.dezzign.co.uk

MULTIMEDIA DESIGN

0103media Web Design London 386a St. John Street, London, EC1V 4NN, United Kingdom
(07929) 836554
info@0103media.co.uk
www.0103media.co.uk

2CS Communications (IVCA) 5 St. Johns Lane, London, EC1M 4BH, United Kingdom
(020) 7250 4724/ (020) 7336 8589
mail@2cs.co.uk
www.2cs.com

3 T Productions Ltd Pennine House, Carrs Road, Cheadle, Cheshire, SK8 2BL, United Kingdom
0161-492 1400/ 0161-492 1401
queries@3t.co.uk
www.3t.co.uk

64 K Web Agency 14-15 Newbury Street, London, EC1A 7HU, United Kingdom
(020) 7796 0064/ (020) 7397 3939
info@64k.com
www.64k.com

A B A Design The Summit, 2 Castle Hill Terrace, Maidenhead, Berkshire, SL6 4JP, United Kingdom
(01628) 645000/ (01628) 783389
enquiries@aba-design.co.uk
www.aba-design.co.uk

A K Q A 1 St John's Lane, London, EC1M 4AR, United Kingdom
(020) 7780 4786
info@akqa.com
www.akqa.com

A T V Training 5 Eton Gardens, Bournemouth, BH4 9LN, United Kingdom
(01202) 751178/(07831) 137308
sales@atv.co.uk
www.atv.co.uk

A V T Ltd AVT House, Stone Street, Brighton, BN1 2HB, United Kingdom
(01273) 299 001/ (01273) 299 002
steve@avtgroup.com
www.avtgroup.com

Aardvark Media 2 Fulham Business Centre, The Boulevard, Imperial Wharf, London, SW6 2TL, United Kingdom
(020) 7582 7711/ (020) 7099 8641
enquiries@aardvarkmedia.co.uk
www.aardvarkmedia.co.uk

Abbey Road Interactive 3 Abbey Road, St John's Wood, London, NW8 9AY, United Kingdom
(020) 7266 7282/ (020) 7266 7250
interactive@abbeyroad.com
www.abbeyroad.com

Abrey-Nicholas Tower House, 139A Chinnor Road, Thame, Oxfordshire, OX9 3LS, United Kingdom
(01844) 261133
nicholas@nick-abrey.co.uk
www.nick-abrey.co.uk

Accent Integrated Media 51 Kingsway Place, Sans Walk, London, EC1R 0LU, United Kingdom
(020) 7251 4411/ (020) 7251 3311
enquiries@accent.co.uk
www.accent.co.uk

Act-Two Design Ltd 346 Old Street, London, EC1V 9RB, United Kingdom
(020) 7684 4000/ (020) 7613 3371
info@act-two.com
www.act-two.com

Action Conference Team Ltd 44 Wellington Road, Sandhurst, Berkshire, GU47 9AY, United Kingdom
(01344) 780242/ (01344) 777760
conference@dial.pipex.com
www.procom.uk.com

Ad Art Design 1 Brewery Court, North Street, Ashton, Bristol, BS3 1JS, United Kingdom
0117-963 7799/ 0117-963 7755
info@adartdesign.co.uk
www.adartdesign.co.uk

Adelphi Group Adelphi Mill, Grimshaw Lane, Bollington, Macclesfield, Cheshire, SK10 5JB, United Kingdom
(01625) 577200/ (01625) 575853
www.adelphigroup.com

Aid Visual 3 Goodrich Road, London, SE22 9EH, United Kingdom
(020) 8693 9334
laurence@visualaid.co.uk
www.visualaid.co.uk

Alex Black 51 Park Avenue, Egham, Surrey, TW20 8HN, United Kingdom
(07986) 659939
blaldesign@yahoo.co.uk

Alice Palace 35 Briar Close, Evesham, Worcestershire, WR11 4JJ, United Kingdom
(01386) 48363/(07990) 687670
alice@alicepalace.co.uk
www.alicepalace.co.uk

Amstore CD Duplication Tower Bridge Business Complex, 100 Clements Road, London, SE16 4DG, United Kingdom
(020) 7232 2779/ (020) 7237 6097
james@amstore.co.uk
www.amstore.co.uk

Antics Workshop 42 Champion Hill, Camberwell, London, SE5 8BS, United Kingdom
(01283) 701441/ (020) 7274 0135
info@antics1.demon.co.uk
www.antics1.demon.co.uk

Arc Intercreative Warwick Building, Kensington Village, Avonmorre, London, W14 8HQ, United Kingdom
(020) 7751 1663/ (020) 7348 3859
firstname.surname@artww.com
www.arcinteractive.co.uk

Artishock 33 Charlwood Road, London, SW15 1QA, United Kingdom
(020) 8785 1403/ (020) 8788 9828
contact@artishock.net
www.artishock.net

Assembly 3rd Floor, 38 Turner Street, London, E1 2AS, United Kingdom
(020) 7265 8856
www.assemblylondon.com

Atreum Cotswold Innovation Centre, Rissington Business Park, Upper Rissington, Cheltenham, Gloucestershire, GL54 2QB, United Kingdom
(01451) 812955/ (01451) 812216
becky@atreum.com
www.atreum.co.uk

Autonomy Multimedia Ltd 1 Spring Lane, Olney, Buckinghamshire, MK46 5BN, United Kingdom
(01234) 240552/ (01234) 240530
production@autonomy-multimedia.com
www.autonomy-multimedia.com

B M N Ltd Unit 6 Windmill Business Village, Brooklands Close, Sunbury-on-Thames, Middlesex, TW11 8EB, United Kingdom
(01932) 733100/ (01932) 733133
www.bmn-systems.com

B S G BSG House, 226-236 City Road, London, EC1V 2TT, United Kingdom
(020) 7880 8888/ (020) 7390 8500
info@bsg.co.uk
www.bsg.co.uk

beBRAND 12-16 Clerkenwell Road, London, EC1M 5PQ, United Kingdom
(020) 7324 6110/ (020) 7324 6001
james@bebrand.net
www.bebrand.net

Bennett & Co. Aireview Court, Low Green, Rawdon, Leeds, LS19 6HB, United Kingdom
0113-250 6533/ 0113-250 6534
sales@bennettandco.co.uk
www.bennettandco.co.uk

Binary Vision 104 St John Street, Clerkenwell, London, EC1M 4EH, United Kingdom
(020) 7490 1010/ (020) 7490 1020
pnorris@binaryvision.com
www.binaryvision.com

Bit2Flash Unit 30, Broughton Grounds, Broughton, Newport Pagnell, Buckinghamshire, MK16 0HZ, United Kingdom
(07793) 417159
liz@bit2flash.co.uk
www.bit2flash.co.uk

Black & Ginger 14 Colquitt Street, Liverpool, L1 4DE, United Kingdom
(07782) 201620
alex@blackandginger.com
www.blackandginger.com

Blank Canvass Media 20 Fearnley Street, Watford, WD18 0RD, United Kingdom
(01923) 223034
bendibble@aol.com
www.blankcanvassmedia.co.uk

Blitz the Net 10 Argyle Street, Bath, BA2 4BQ, United Kingdom
(01225) 422333
garry@blitzthenet.com
www.blitzthenet.com

Blue Sphere Audio Visual 58 Old Gransha Road, Bangor, County Down, BT19 7HA, United Kingdom
(028) 9127 0775/(07803) 580557 (028) 9146 5795
info@bluesphere.tv
www.bluesphere.tv

Bold Endeavours Ltd 7 Manor Park, Staines, Middlesex, TW18 4XE,
01784 460 064
derek@boldendeavours.com
www.big-easy-footage-library-software.co.uk

Boxnewmedia 6 Hoxton Square, London, N1 6NU, United Kingdom
(020) 7739 0021/ (020) 7739 0081
info@boxnewmedia.co.uk
www.boxnewmedia.co.uk

Brainstorm Interactive, London, NW5, United Kingdom
(020) 7485 9585
carl@newmedia.demon.co.uk
www.newmedia.demon.co.uk

Brever Web Design Edinburgh 60a Craigour Drive, Edinburgh, EH17 7NT, United Kingdom
(0845) 129 8534
info@breverwebdesign.com
www.breverwebdesign.com

Business and Decision The Innovation Centre, Kingston Bagpuize, Abingdon, Oxfordshire, OX13 5AP, UK
(01865) 821821/ (01865) 821881
info@businessdecision.co.uk
www.businessdecision.co.uk

C C G X M 121-141 Westbourne Terrace, London, W2 6JR, United Kingdom
(020) 7724 7228/ (020) 7479 0876
firstinitiallastname@xmlondon.com
www.xmlondon.com

C S I Media Waterside House, Waterside, Macclesfield, Cheshire, SK11 7HG, United Kingdom
(01625) 611229/ (0870) 1268255
richard@csimedia.co.uk
www.csimedia.net

C Scape Ltd 4 Pear Tree Court, London, EC1R 0DS, United Kingdom
(020) 7689 8800/ (020) 7689 8801
cscape@cscape.com
www.cscape.com

C V I Calendar Box (UK) Ltd Marwain Hse, Clarke Rd, Bletchley, Milton Keynes, MK1 1LG, United Kingdom
(0870) 200 7001/ (0870) 2004001
sales@cviuk.com
www.calendarbox.com

Cameron Design Group 20 Baltic Place, London, N1 5AQ, United Kingdom
(020) 7241 2388/ (020) 7241 2389
john@cameron-dg.com
www.cameron-dg.com

Capricorn Digital 41b Montagu Road, London, Greater London, NW4 3ER, United Kingdom
(020) 8202 9594/ (0870) 7623203
info@capricorn-digital.com
www.capricorn-digital.com

Carat Ltd Parker Tower, 43-49 Parker Street, London, WC2B 5PS, United Kingdom
(020) 7430 6320/ (020) 7430 6299
www.carat.com

Carl Sanders Photography Tower Studios, London, NW5 4PU, United Kingdom
(020) 7485 9585
carl@newmedia.demon.co.uk
www.newmedia.demon.co.uk

Carolan Media The Coach House, Adjacent Ealing Film Studios, Ealing, London, W5 5ER, United Kingdom
(020) 8566 1900/ (020) 8566 1900
info@carolanmedia.com
www.carolanmedia.com

Channel 20/20 Ltd 20/20 House, 26-28 Talbot Lane, Leicester, LE1 4LR, United Kingdom
0116-233 2220/ 0116-222 1113
info@channel2020.co.uk
www.channel2020.co.uk

Chord 9 Beckside House, Tunstall, Richmond, North Yorkshire, DL10 7QN, United Kingdom
(01748) 810180
contact@chord9.co.uk
www.chord9.co.uk

Cimex Inc. Ltd 53-55 Scrutton Street, London, EC2A 4PJ, United Kingdom
(020) 7324 7780/ (020) 7324 7781
sales@cimex.com
www.cimex.com

Clever Ltd. Milldown, Kingston Road, Lewes, East Sussex, BN7 3NB, United Kingdom
(01273) 487744
mikeb@cleverworks.co.uk
www.cleverworks.co.uk

Clicks Group Ltd 10 Baker's Yard, Baker's Row, London, EC1R 3DD, United Kingdom
(020) 7278 2300/ (020) 7278 1550
info@clicks.co.uk
www.clicks-ds.co.uk

Cogent Media Ltd Flat 8, Cedars House, 48-50 Acre Lane, London, SW2 5SP, United Kingdom
(020) 7737 4939/ (020) 7737 4939
simon.west@cogentmedia.co.uk
www.cogentmedia.co.uk

Cognitive Applications Lees House, 21-23 Dyke Road, Brighton, BN1 3FE, United Kingdom
(01273) 821600/ (01273) 728866
office@cogapp.com
www.cogapp.com

Comfy Sofa St Georges House, 14-17 Wells Street, London, W1T 3PD, United Kingdom
(020) 7636 1501/078 11 163703/ (020) 7636 1502
share-inspiration@comfysofa.co.uk
www.comfysofa.co.uk

Communique 360 Ltd 26 Dunstable Road, Richmond, Surrey, TW9 1UH, United Kingdom
(020) 8940 4444/ (020) 8408 7848
reception@communique360.co.uk
www.communique360.co.uk

Concise Ltd 5 The Quadrant Centre, 135 Salisbury Road, London, NW6 6RJ, United Kingdom
(020) 7644 6444/ (020) 7644 6445
mail@concisegroup.com
www.concisegroup.com

Connection Group Ltd Tectonic Place, Holyport Road, Maidenhead, Berkshire, SL6 2YE, United Kingdom
(01628) 634480/ (01628) 634482
info@theconnectiongroup.co.uk
www.theconnectiongroup.co.uk

Conrad Davies Design The Mistal, 3 Farnley Park, Otley, West Yorkshire, LS21 2QF, United Kingdom
(01943) 850088
conrad@conraddavies.com
www.conraddavies.com

Contact 2 Unit 1, Piano Works, 113-117 Farringdon Road, London, EC1R 3BX, UK
(020) 7833 3800
www.contact-2.com

Cottier & Sidaway Lloyds Bank Chamber, 7-8 Market Square, Potton, Sandy, Bedfordshire, SG19 2NP, United Kingdom
(01767) 262858/ (01767) 261599
sara@cottierandsidawaydesign.co.uk
www.cottiersidawaydesign.co.uk

Crawfords Designs 170 Toms Lane, Kings Langley, Hertfordshire, WD4 8NZ, United Kingdom
(01923) 261266/ (01923) 261267
info@crawforddesigns.co.uk
www.crawforddesigns.co.uk

Create One Media Solutions 48 Trinity Hall Close, Watford, WD24 4GN, United Kingdom
(08708) 791181/ (08701) 276922
info@creteone.biz
www.createone.biz

Creative Core Ltd Suite 4A Riverside Business Centre, North Esplanade West, Aberdeen, AB11 5RJ, United Kingdom
(01224) 577130/ (01224) 577139
info@creativecore.net
www.creativecore.net

Creative Edge Design & Advertising 1st Floor Donald Hendry Building, Auchincruive, Ayr, KA6 5HW, United Kingdom
(01292) 521404/ (01292) 521693
paul@cedge.co.uk
www.cedge.co.uk

Creative Pulse 16 West Barnes Lane, Raines Park, London, SW20 0BU, United Kingdom
(020) 8947 7789/ (020) 8947 6678
info@thecreativepulse.com
www.thecreativepulse.com

Creative Solutions Ltd Suite 7, Maritime House, Southwell Business Park, Portland, Dorset, DT5 2NA, United Kingdom
(01305) 824900/ (01305) 820012
roy@creativesolutions-uk.com
www.creativesolutions-uk.com

CST Group Ltd Lower Ground Floor, 94 Lewes Road, Brighton, BN2 3QA, United Kingdom
(01273) 621393/ (01273) 621390
info@cst-group.com
www.cst-group.com

Cyber 42 Ltd MTL Centre, Tranmere Avenue, Middlesbrough, Cleveland, TS3 8PB, United Kingdom
(01642) 247345/ (01642) 249345
enquiries@cyber42.co.uk
www.cyber42.co.uk

Cypher Media Salters House, St. Andrews Square, Droitwich, Worcestershire, WR9 8HE, United Kingdom
(01905) 827772/ (01905) 774114
name@cyphermedia.co.uk
www.cyphermedia.co.uk

D P A Corporate Communications The Granary, Abbey Mill Business Park, Lower Eashing, Godalming, Surrey, GU7 2QP, United Kingdom
(01483) 414000/ (01483) 414414
dpa@dpacoms.com
www.dpacoms.com

D W A Ltd 41 Great Guildford Street, SE1 0ES, United Kingdom
(020) 7928 5888/ (020) 7928 8593
design-studio@dwa.uk.com
www.dwa.uk.com

D Z Studios Studio I, Trinity Buoy Wharf, Docklands, London, E14 0JY, United Kingdom
(0844) 8404 130/ (0871) 242 1685
mardi@d-z.co.uk
www.d-z.co.uk

D8 93 Hope Street, Glasgow, G2 6LD, United Kingdom
0141-572 0810/ 0141-572 0811
info@d8web.co.uk
www.d8web.co.uk

DA Group plc The Lighthouse, 70 Mitchel Street, Glasgow, G1 3LX, United Kingdom
0141 582 0600/ 0141 582 0699
enquiries@dagroupplc.com
www.dagroupplc.com

Daniel West & Associates 41 Great Guilford Street, London, SE1 0ES, United Kingdom
(020) 7928 5888/ (020) 7928 8593
info@dwa.uk.com
www.dwa.uk.com

David K Wells 6d The Avenue, Cirencester, Gloucestershire, GL7 1EH, United Kingdom
(01285) 642916
wells@dazzle1.demon.co.uk
www.dazzle1.demon.co.uk

Deep LLP 12a Imperial Studios, 3-11 Imperial Road, London, SW6 2AG, United Kingdom
(020) 7751 0824/ (020) 7751 0823
dom@deep.co.uk
www.deep.co.uk

Delve Unit 450, Highgate Studios, London, NW5 1TL, United Kingdom
(020) 7267 7200
info@delve.net
www.delve.net

Denaploy Internet 8 The Lawn, St. Leonards-on-Sea, East Sussex, TN38 0HH, UK
(01424) 442400/ (01424) 430414
info@denaploy.co.uk
www.denaploy.co.uk

Dennis Interactive 30 Cleveland Street, London, W1P 5FF, United Kingdom
(020) 7907 6840/ (020) 7907 6835
info@dennisinter.com
www.dennisinteractive.com

Design Portfolio London Ltd
7 Ensign House, Admiral Way, London, E14 9XQ, United Kingdom
(020) 7536 2000/ (020) 7536 2001
production@design-portfolio.co.uk
www.design-portfolio.com

Design UK 12-14 Denman Street, Piccadily, London, W1D 7HJ, United Kingdom
(020) 7292 2700/(07968) 838611/ (020) 7292 2710
mail@designuk.com
www.designuk.com

design@djhunter 133 Ravensbourne Avenue, Bromley, BR2 0AZ, United Kingdom
(020) 8466 7196/ (020) 8466 7196
design@djhunter.co.uk

DesignGeist Ltd 1341 High Road, Whetstone, London, N20 9HR, United Kingdom
(020) 8441 7252/(07831) 201534/ (020) 8441 7252
info@designgeist.co.uk
www.designgeist.co.uk

Devote Design Studio 23 Swallow Mill, Swallow Street, Stockport, Cheshire, SK1 3HJ, United Kingdom
0161-480 5010/ 0161-480 5010
info@devotedesign.co.uk
www.devotedesign.co.uk

Digital Disc Duplication Ltd 25 Huntingfield Road, Bury St. Edmunds, Suffolk, IP33 2JA, United Kingdom
(01284) 700773
info@digitaldiscduplication.com
www.digitaldiscduplication.com

Digital Marmalade 186a High Street, Beckenham, Kent, BR3 1EN, United Kingdom
(020) 8249 5655/ (020) 8650 4949
info@digitalmarmalade.co.uk
www.digitalmarmalade.co.uk

Digital Portfolios Business Design Centre, 52 Upper St, London, N1 0QH, United Kingdom
(020) 7288 1188/ (020) 7288 1818
info@digitalportfolios.com
www.digitalportfolios.com

Dijit New Media 72 Charlotte Street, London, W1T 4QQ, United Kingdom
(020) 7436 5222
studio@dijit.net
www.dijit.net

Dimension Data Holdings P.L.C. Fleet Place House, 2 Fleet Place, London, EC4M 7RT, United Kingdom
(020) 7651 7000/ (020) 7651 7001
www.uk.didata.com

Direct Design 2 Furlongs, Portsmouth Road, Esher, Surrey, KT10 9AA, United Kingdom
☎ (01372) 466666/✆ (01372) 460250
✉ info@dda.co.uk
🖥 www.dda.co.uk

Dizine Studioz 34 Chiddlingford Court, Somerset Avenue, Blackpool, FY1 5RE, United Kingdom
☎ (07709) 129586
✉ craig@dizinestudioz.co.uk
🖥 www.dizinestudioz.co.uk

DNA Consulting Ltd 1-2 Berners Street, London, W1T 3LA, United Kingdom
☎ (020) 7907 4545/✆ (020) 7907 4546
✉ enquiries@dna.co.uk
🖥 www.dna.co.uk

Dog Digital Ltd 48 West George Street, Glasgow, G2 1BP, United Kingdom
☎ 0141-572 0730/✆ 0141-572 0735
✉ hello@dogdigital.co.uk
🖥 www.dogdigital.co.uk

Dragonfly Media 3 Berkeley Crescent, Clifton, Bristol, Avon, BS8 1HA,
☎ 0845 6520 888/✆ 0845 6520 808
✉ jon@dragonfly-media.co.uk
🖥 www.dragonfly-media.co.uk

Dreamteam Design Ltd Regent House, Hove Street, Hove, East Sussex, BN3 2DW, United Kingdom
☎ (01273) 204206/✆ (01273) 204201
✉ info@dreamteam.co.uk
🖥 www.dreamteam.co.uk

Drystone Design Ltd Unit 4, The Pinnacle Centre, Stockport, Cheshire, SK4 1RQ, United Kingdom
☎ 0161-477 5533/✆ 0161-477 6633
✉ info@drystonedesign.com
🖥 www.drystonedesign.com

E O S Media Astley House, Quay Street, Manchester, M3 4AE, United Kingdom
☎ 0161-906 4930/✆ 0161-906 4931
✉ info@eosmedia.co.uk
🖥 www.eosmedia.co.uk

E-Z Media Ltd 10 Montrave Road, London, London, SE20 7BS, United Kingdom
☎ (07899) 904508
✉ sales@ezme.com
🖥 www.ezme.com

E:Bloc Interactive 14 Church Road, Hove, East Sussex, BN3 2FL, United Kingdom
☎ (01273) 763500/✆ (01273) 763525
✉ info@e-bloc.co.uk
🖥 www.e-bloc.co.uk

Electrixity 16 Constantine Road, London, NW3 2NG, United Kingdom
☎ (07803) 299522
✉ jakob@electrixity.co.uk
🖥 www.electrixity.co.uk

Elevator Digital Unit 3.2, Waulk Mill, 51 Bengal Street, Manchester, M4 6LN, United Kingdom
☎ 0161-244 5544/✆ 0161-244 5533
✉ c.jordan@elevatordigital.co.uk
🖥 www.elevatordigital.co.uk

Ember Design 88a Thicket Road, London, SE20 8DR, United Kingdom
☎ (020) 8659 9560
✉ info@emberdesign.net
🖥 www.emberdesign.net

Enlightenment Productions East End House, 24 Ennerdale, Skelmersdale, Lancashire, WN8 6AJ, United Kingdom
☎ (01695) 727555
✉ mail@trainingmultimedia.co.uk
🖥 www.trainingmultimedia.co.uk

Eyedea Ltd Invicta House, Atkinson Street, Manchester, M3 3HH, United Kingdom
☎ 0161-833 2555/✆ 0161-833 2666
✉ enquiries@eyedea.co.uk
🖥 www.eyedea.co.uk

FandH Multimedia Solutions 28 Imperial Park, Rawreth Lane, Rayleigh, Essex, SS6 9RS, United Kingdom
☎ (07759) 230697
✉ info@fandhmultimedia.co.uk
🖥 www.fandhmultimedia.co.uk

Feref Associates Ltd 17-18 Great Pulteney Street, London, W1F 9NE, United Kingdom
☎ (020) 7292 6300/✆ (020) 7292 6301
🖥 www.feref.com

Firebomb 55 Hampden Close, North Weald, Epping, Essex, CM16 6JX, United Kingdom
☎ (01992) 524816
✉ watts@firebomb.com
🖥 www.firebomb.com

Firedog Design Ltd 43/44 Hoxton Square, London, N1 9PB, United Kingdom
☎ (020) 7739 1112/✆ (020) 7729 1002
✉ info@firedog-design.co.uk
🖥 www.firedog-design.co.uk

Firstline Interactive Systems Ltd Albert House, Rothbury, Morpeth, Northumberland, NE65 7SR, United Kingdom
☎ (01669) 621800
✉ gary@firstlineinteractive.co.uk
🖥 www.firstlineinteractive.co.uk

Fortune Cookie (UK) Ltd The Lightwell, 12-16 Laystall Street, London, EC1R 4PF, United Kingdom
☎ (0870) 7361000/✆ (0870) 7365000
✉ hello@fortunecookie.co.uk
🖥 www.fortune-cookie.uk

Fraserdesign The Barns, London Road, Bourne End, Hemel Hempstead, Hertfordshire, HP1 2RH, United Kingdom
☎ (01442) 200400/✆ (01442) 200401
✉ craig@fraserdesign.com
🖥 www.fraserdesign.com

Fresh Web Services Ltd 52 Craighill Road, Leicester, LE2 3FB, United Kingdom
☎ 0116-270 4887
✉ kellys@freshwebservices.com
🖥 www.freshwebservices.com

Frontrow Multimedia 233A Seaside, Eastbourne, East Sussex, BN22 7NR, United Kingdom
☎ (01323) 732786/✆ (01323) 725394
✉ info@frontrowmultimedia.co.uk
🖥 www.frontrowmultimedia.co.uk

Future PLC Beaufort Court, 30 Monmouth Street, Bath, BA1 2BW, United Kingdom
☎ (01225) 442244/✆ (01225) 446019
🖥 www.futureplc.co.uk

G H A Group 1 Great Chapel Street, London, W1F 8FA, United Kingdom
☎ (020) 7439 8705/✆ (020) 7437 5880
✉ sales@ghagroup.co.uk
🖥 www.ghagroup.co.uk

G P S Visual Communications Ltd Willow House, 47 West Street, Sutton, Surrey, SM1 1SJ, United Kingdom
☎ (020) 8661 4100/✆ (020) 8661 4118
✉ enquiries@gpsvis.com
🖥 www.gpsvis.com

G2G3 Media Ltd Panama House, 14 The High Street, Lasswade, Edinburgh, EH18 1ND, United Kingdom
☎ 0131-202 2000/✆ 0131-663 8194
✉ media@g2g3.com
🖥 www.g2g3.com

Genetics Ltd The Old Pump House, Cleedownton, Ludlow, Shropshire, SY8 3EG, United Kingdom
☎ (0870) 7492201/✆ (0870) 7492202
✉ enquiries@genetics.uk.com
🖥 www.genetics.uk.com

Global Beach Group (IVCA) 522 Fulham Road, London, SW6 5NR, United Kingdom
☎ (020) 7384 1188/✆ (020) 7384 8599
✉ info@globalbeach.com
🖥 www.globalbeach.com

Glocal Media 26-27 Southampton Street, London, WC2E 7RS, United Kingdom
☎ (020) 7717 8406
✉ steve.clayton@glocalmedia.com
🖥 www.glocalmedia.com

GMID Design for Business Prospect House, 3 Prospect Place, Swansea, SA1 1QP, United Kingdom
☎ (01792) 641350/✆ (01792) 301548
✉ studio@gmid.net
🖥 www.gmid.net

Goldmoor Television Ltd 30 Granby Court, Milton Keynes, MK1 1NE, United Kingdom
☎ (01908) 370516
✉ crewhire@goldmoor.co.uk
🖥 www.goldmoor.co.uk

Good Technology Ltd 15-19 Great Titchfield Street, London, W1W 8AZ, United Kingdom
☎ (020) 7299 7000/✆ (020) 7299 7070
✉ info@goodtechnology.com
🖥 www.goodtechnology.com

Greensplash Ltd Paddock View, 308 Chester Road, Hartford, Northwich, Cheshire, CW8 2AB, United Kingdom
☎ (01606) 884123/✆ (01606) 884212
✉ siu.wan@greensplash.com
🖥 www.greensplash.com

Hildebrand Interactive The Mall, Camden Passage, 93 Islington High Street, London, N1 0PD, United Kingdom
☎ (020) 7354 8858/✆ (020) 7704 2722
✉ design@interactive.co.uk
🖥 www.hildebrandinteractive.com

Hot Knife Digital Media Ltd 1 First Avenue, Nottingham, NG7 6JL, United Kingdom
☎ 0115-969 3600/✆ 0151-969 1800
✉ hot@hotknife.co.uk
🖥 www.hotknife.co.uk

Hub Communications Co. Ltd The Powerhouse, 1 Linkfield Road, Isleworth, Middlesex, TW7 6QG, United Kingdom
☎ (020) 8560 9222/✆ (020) 8560 9333
✉ enquiry@thehub.co.uk
🖥 www.thehub.co.uk

I M D C The Innovation Centre, 173 Curie Avenue, Didcot, Oxfordshire, OX11 0QG, United Kingdom
☎ (01235) 838626/✆ (01235) 838627
✉ design@imdc.co.uk
🖥 www.imdc.co.uk

I S Solutions P.L.C. Windmill House, 91-93 Windmill Road, Sunbury-on-Thames, Middlesex, TW16 7EF, United Kingdom
☎ (01932) 893333/✆ (01932) 893433
✉ moreinfo@issolutions.co.uk
🖥 www.issolutions.co.uk

I T Y Consultants 14 Oakfield Road, Stourbridge, West Midlands, DY8 5XS, United Kingdom
☎ (01384) 834966/079 73 706201 ✆ (01384) 834966
✉ ity@compuserve.com
🖥 www.i-t-y.demon.co.uk

I-D Media London Ltd Zetland House, 5-25 Scrutton Street, London, EC2A 4HJ, United Kingdom
☎ (020) 7749 5400/✆ (020) 7749 5401
✉ contact-london@idmedia.com
🖥 www.i-dmedialondon.com

Id Net Spirella Buildings, Bridge Road, Letchworth Garden City, Hertfordshire, SG6 4ET, United Kingdom
☎ (01462) 476555/✆ (01462) 476566
✉ contact@idnet.net.uk
🖥 www.idnet.net.uk

Idea The Mill, Longnor, Shrewsbury, SY5 7PZ, United Kingdom
☎ (01743) 719070/✆ (01743) 719060
✉ info@thinkidea.co.uk
🖥 www.thinkidea.co.uk

Imano Plc 198 High Holborn, London, WC1V 7BD, United Kingdom
☎ (020) 7632 6930/✆ (020) 7566 1740
✉ experts@imano.com
🖥 www.imano.com

Impartad Ltd Impartad House, Millstone Lane, Leicester, LE1 5JN, United Kingdom
☎ 0116-253 9212/✆ 0116-253 6381
✉ bill@impartad.co.uk

Indez International 6/6a Skypark, 8 Elliot Place, Glasgow, G3 8EP, United Kingdom
☎ 0870 873 4379/✆ 0141-204 5292
✉ info@indez..com
🖥 www.indez.com

Infinite Eye 2 Claremont Gardens, Glasgow, G3 7LW, United Kingdom
☎ 0141 - 5507 509
✉ hello@infinite-eye.com
🖥 www.infinite-eye.com

Influence Design Group Ducie House, Ducie Street, Manchester, M1 2JW, United Kingdom
☎ (0870) 2282272/✆ (0870) 2282202
✉ indulge@influencedesign.com
🖥 www.influencedesign.com

Interactive Dimension 4-6 Clifton Fields, Lythan Road, Preston, PR4 0XG, United Kingdom
☎ (01772) 632800/✆ (01772) 632900
✉ sales@interactivedimension.com
🖥 www.interactivedimension.com

Interactive Pages Ltd Eastern Court, 182-190 Newmarket Road, Cambridge, CB5 8HE, United Kingdom
☎ (01223) 502080
✉ dr.cb@interactivepages.co.uk
🖥 www.interactive-pages.co.uk

Intercea Ltd 1 Transcentral, Bennett Road, Reading, RG2 0QX, United Kingdom
- 0118-916 9900/ 0118-916 9901
- info@intercea.co.uk
- www.intercea.co.uk

Interface New Media 20A Brownlow Mews, London, WC1N 2LA, United Kingdom
- (020) 7416 0702/ (020) 7416 0700
- info@interface-newmedia.com
- www.interface-newmedia.com

Internet Vision 98 Curtain Road, London, EC2A 3AF, United Kingdom
- (0870) 7563500
- www.ivision.co.uk

Intro (AFVPA) 42 St John's Street, London, EC1M 4DL, United Kingdom
- (020) 7324 3244/ (020) 7324 3245
- intro@intro-uk.com
- www.introwebsite.com

Irebel 12 Printers Land, Clarkston, Glasgow, G76 8HP, United Kingdom
- 0141-644 5703
- info@irebel.co.uk
- www.irebel.co.uk

IUVO Design 93 Rivington Street, Elektra House, London, EC2A 3AY, United Kingdom
- (020) 7729 2006/ (07092) 872999
- studio@iuvodesign.co.uk
- www.iuvodesign.com

J B Communications Ltd 15 Brackenbury Road, London, W6 0BE, United Kingdom
- (020) 8749 6036/ (020) 8749 9676
- inspire@jbcommunications.co.uk
- www.jbcommunications.co.uk

J D Associates Ltd The Courtyard, 60 Station Road, Marlow, Buckinghamshire, SL7 1NX, United Kingdom
- (01628) 890015/ (01628) 890361
- enquiries@jda-multimedia.co.uk
- www.jda-mulitmedia.co.uk

Jigsaw7 Ltd The Coach House, 8A Fore Street, Trowbridge, Bath, BA14 88D, United Kingdom
- (01225) 710770/ (01225) 762526
- info.collinge@jigsaw7.com
- www.jigsaw7.com

Joan Blencowe Imaging The Lodge, 155 Lascelles Hall Rd, Huddersfield, HD5 0BE, United Kingdom
- (01484) 513363
- imaging@frogs-eye.com
- www.frogs-eye.com

John Henry Productions Ltd 8 Lonsdale Rd, Queens Pk, London, NW6 6RD, United Kingdom
- (020) 7372 7708
- lewis@johnhenry.net
- www.johnhenry.net

Joshua G2 Ltd Wells Point, 79 Wells Street, London, W1T 3QN, United Kingdom
- (020) 7453 8320/ (020) 7453 7934
- info@joshua-g2.co.uk
- www.joshua-g2.co.uk

Junkyard Puppy 94 Brondesbury Road, Queens Park, London, NW6 6RX, United Kingdom
- (020) 7604 3467
- woof@junkyardpuppy.com
- www.junkyardpuppy.com

JWD Graphic 139 Winkworth Road, Banstead, Surrey, SM7 2JW, United Kingdom
- (01737) 353013/07973 520292
- jwmail@btinternet.com

K M P Associates Kingfisher Court, Yew Street, Stockport, Cheshire, SK4 2HG, United Kingdom
- (0870) 868 8900/ (0870) 868 8890
- info@kmp.co.uk
- www.kmp.co.uk

Ketchum PR Folgate Street, London, E1 6BX, United Kingdom
- (020) 7611 3500/ (020) 7611 3501
- www.ketchum.com

Keyframe Computer Graphics Ltd 431 Meanwood Road, Unity Court, Leeds, LS7 2LL, United Kingdom
- 0113-246 5913/ 0113-234 0038
- info@keyframe.co.uk
- www.keyframe.co.uk

Kino Creative Holy Jesus Hospital, City Road, Newcastle Upon Tyne, Tyne & Wear, NE1 2AS,
- 0191 2333 880
- seth@kinocreative.co.uk
- www.kinocreative.co.uk

Kugel 55 Greek Street, London, W1D 3DT, United Kingdom
- (020) 7478 8300/ (020) 7478 8311
- nick.hughes@kugel.co.uk
- www.kugel.co.uk

La Camorra C/ Olivar 17 1∞ 1, Madrid, 28011, Spain
- 00 34 90 6869966
- lacamorra@ouchzine.com

Large Design Ltd 36-42 New Inn Yard, London, EC2A 3EY, United Kingdom
- (020) 7729 2040
- large@largedesign.com
- www.largedesign.com

Lateral Net Charlotte House, 47-49 Charlotte Road, London, EC2A 3QT, United Kingdom
- (020) 7613 4449/ (020) 7613 4645
- newbiz@lateral.net
- www.lateral.net

LBI Beaumont House, Kensington Village, Avonmore Road, London, W14 8TS, United Kingdom
- (020) 7348 1000/ (020) 7348 1111
- info.uk@lbi.co.uk
- www.lbigroup.com

LC1 Ltd 55 Merthyr Terrace, Barnes, London, SW13 8DL, United Kingdom
- (020) 8741 5747/ (020) 8748 9879
- contact@lci-uk.com
- www.lci-uk.com

Lewis Creative Consultants 6 Quayside Mills, Leith, Edinburgh, EH6 6EX, United Kingdom
- 0131-554 1286/ 0131-555 2600
- postman@lewis.co.uk
- www.lewis.co.uk

Limehouse Group Ltd 4th Floor, 1 London Bridge, London, SE1 9BG, United Kingdom
- (020) 7939 7100/ (020) 7939 7101
- stephenb@limehouse.co.uk
- www.limehouse.co.uk

Liquid Light 22A Dukes Lane, Brighton, BN1 1BG, United Kingdom
- (0845) 6588835/ (0845) 6584435
- info@liquidlight.co.uk
- www.liquidlight.co.uk

Littleloud 1 Sidney Street, Brighton, BN1 4EN, United Kingdom
- (01273) 625066
- david@littleloud.com
- www.littleloud.com

Locofoco Ltd 40 Spiers Wharf, Port Dundas, Glasgow, G4 9TH, United Kingdom
- (0845) 2722840/ (0845) 2722841
- info@locofoco.co.uk
- www.locofoco.co.uk

Lonedog Multimedia 5 Cove Hollow, Groomsport, Bangor, County Down, BT19 6HT, United Kingdom
- (028) 9146 8224
- aoife@lonedog.co.uk
- www.lonedog.co.uk

Longneck Afgan Road 27, Battersea, London, SW11 2QD, United Kingdom
- 7506018062
- vlad@longneck.ro
- www.longneck.ro

Lost In Space, London, United Kingdom
- (0870) 1371356/(07092) 112619 (0870) 1371356
- info@lostinspace.com
- www.lostinspace.com

Lowe Plus 60 Sloane Avenue, London, SW3 3XB, United Kingdom
- (020) 7894 5030/ (020) 7589 0637
- www.draftlondon.com

LShift Hoxton Point, 1st Floor, 6 Rufus Street, London, N1 6PE, United Kingdom
- (020) 7729 7060/ (020) 7729 7005
- query@lshift.net
- www.lshift.net

Lucian Marin, Bucharest, 61079, Romania
- 721 230 631
- lucian.marin@gmail.com
- www.lucianmarin.ro

M & H 36 Lexington Street, London, W1F 0LJ, United Kingdom
- (020) 7412 2121/ (020) 7412 2122
- info@mandh.co.uk
- www.mandh.co.uk

M W R 107 High Street, Winchester, Hampshire, SO23 9AH, United Kingdom
- (01962) 891160/ (01962) 891110
- pam.iannotti@mwr.biz
- www.mwr.biz

Mac 4 105 Great Portland Street, London, W1W 6QF, United Kingdom
- (020) 7637 9000/ (020) 7637 9001
- production@mac4.com
- www.mac4.com

Magnetic North 101 Princes Street, Manchester, M1 6DD, United Kingdom
- 0161-228 7171/ 0161-228 7755
- hello@magneticn.co.uk
- www.magneticn.co.uk

MarketingNet Ltd Waterloo House, Bath Place, Leamington Spa, Warwickshire, CV31 3RJ, United Kingdom
- (01926) 832123/ (01926) 452579
- enquiries@marketingnet.com
- www.marketing.com

Marsteller 24-28 Bloomsbury Way, London, WC1A 2PX, United Kingdom
- (020) 7300 6301/ (020) 7340 1033
- martin_hey@uk.bm.com
- www.bm.co.uk

Media House 166-168 High Street, Margate, Kent, CT9 1LA, United Kingdom
- (01843) 229111/ (01843) 229222
- ap@wpd.co.uk
- www.wpd.co.uk

Mediatel Interactive 84-86 Regent Street, London, W1B 5AJ, United Kingdom
- (020) 7439 7575/ (020) 7734 0940
- nicolam@mediatelgroup.co.uk
- www.mediatel.co.uk

Melissa Allen Design 48 Llyswen Road, Cardiff, CF23 6PP, United Kingdom
- (029) 2075 6239
- mel@melissaallendesign.com
- www.melissaallendesign.com

Melissa Evans Illustration Ltd 2b St. Johns Crescent, Canton, Cardiff, CF5 1NX, United Kingdom
- (07780) 987540
- melissajevans@hotmail.com

Mike Diver, United Kingdom
- (020) 7706 8833/ (020) 7706 8833
- mike@mikediver.com
- www.mikediver.com

Milestone Strategic Design Ltd 1 The Highway, Beaconsfield, Buckinghamshire, HP9 1QD, United Kingdom
- (01494) 676436/ (01494) 676438
- info@milestonedesign.co.uk
- www.milestonedesign.co.uk

Modem Media UK 183 Eversholt Street, London, NW1 1BU, United Kingdom
- (020) 7874 9400/ (020) 7874 9555
- admin@modemmedia.com
- www.modemmedia.com

Mokko Blue 21 Arncott Hall, 13 Poole Road, Bournemouth, BH2 5QR, United Kingdom
- 01202 269 257/ 01202 269 257
- info@mokko-blue.com
- www.mokko-blue.com

Mondo Ltd, London, N8 9XB, United Kingdom
- (020) 8292 1064
- info@mondo.co.uk
- www.mondo.co.uk

Monitor Media 120 South Street, Dorking, Surrey, RH4 2EU, United Kingdom
- (01306) 743838/ (01306) 743737
- enquiries@monitormedia.co.uk
- www.monitormedia.co.uk

Moonfish 43 Hulme Street, Manchester, M15 6AW, United Kingdom
- (0870) 0704321/ (0870) 7418931
- fish.market@moonfish.com
- www.moonfish.com

Mosquitomedia 3 Thurleigh Road, London, SW12 8UB, United Kingdom
- (020) 8673 4489/(07951) 828981
- mail@mosquitomedia.co.uk
- www.mosquitomedia.co.uk

Motion Blur Ltd Bryn Hyfryd, Bryncroes, Pwllheli, Gwynedd, LL53 8ET, United Kingdom
- (01758) 730777
- pix@motionblur.tv
- www.motionblur.tv

Motion Pixels 15 Nevill Street, Abergavenny, Monmouthshire, NP7 5AA, United Kingdom
- (0845) 6002515
- paul@motionpixels.com
- www.motionpixels.com

Movingtarget 26 Outram Place, London, N1 0UX, United Kingdom
- (020) 7837 5280
- max.howell@mac.com
- www.movingtarget.co.uk

MusicWing 69 Riley Road, Brighton, BN2 4AG, United Kingdom
- (01273) 699768
- andy@musicwing.co.uk
- www.musicwing.co.uk

MyTinCan Interactive Multimedia 1 Kirkland Way, Mile Oak, Tamworth, Staffordshire, B78 3PL, UK
- (01827) 260971/ (07966) 139265
- tomcoffee@mytincan.net
- www.mytincan.net

Nap Media 2 Peacock Yard, Kennington, London, SE17 3LH, United Kingdom
- (020) 7701 2422
- post@nap-media.com
- www.nap-media.com

NBS Studio 12 Kempson Drive, Great Cornard, Sudbury, Suffolk, CO10 0ND, United Kingdom
- (01787) 376763
- info@nbs-studio.com
- www.nbs-studio.com

Net Creative 24 Modwen Road, Waters Edge Business Park, Salford, Manchester, M5 3EZ, United Kingdom
- (0870) 7530900/ (0870) 7530901
- mail@netservicesplc.com
- www.netservicesplc.com

Net-Workers Organisation Ltd Thornleigh, 197 Dialstone Lane, Stockport, Cheshire, SK2 7LF, United Kingdom
- 0161-456 9020/ 0161-355 1176
- info@net-workers.org
- www.net-workers.co.uk

Netatomix Ltd Suite 5, Butlers Wharf, 36 Shad Thames, London, SE1 2YE, United Kingdom
- (020) 7378 9600/ (020) 7357 9700
- pgatward@netatomix.com
- www.netatomix.com

NetFusion 111 Ross Walk, Leicester, LE4 5HH, United Kingdom
- 0116-266 8134
- info@netfusion.co.uk
- www.netfusion.co.uk

Netstep The Spire, Leeds Road, Halifax, West Yorkshire, HX3 8NU, United Kingdom
- (01422) 200308/ (01422) 200306
- info@netstep.co.uk
- www.netstep.co.uk

Network Maintenance Unit 4, Snowhill Business Centre, Copthorne, West Sussex, RH10 3EZ, United Kingdom
- (0870) 7557616/ (0870) 7557626
- info@network-group.com
- www.nml-net.com

New Media Collective 46 The Calls, Leeds, LS2 7EY, United Kingdom
- 0113-202 1400/ 0113-3010 223
- dave@newmediacollective.com
- www.newmediacollective.com

Nicky Scott Francis DiGiTAL DESiGNS & ANiMATiON 4th Floor, 2-4 Whitfield Street, London, W1T 2RB, United Kingdom
- (020) 7636 3915

Oceanic Design Highview, Little Staughton, Bedford, MK44 2BH, United Kingdom
- (01234) 378171/ (07092) 023480
- phil@oceanicdesign.com
- www.oceanicdesign.com

Officina Design Via Fara, 8, Milano, 21204, Italy
- 00 39 02 667 1065/ 00 39 02 6693904
- info@officinadesign.it
- www.officinadesign.it

Olive 8 78 Bromyard Road, Worcester, WR2 5DA, United Kingdom
- (07980) 595767
- caroline.walker@olive8.co.uk
- www.olive8.co.uk

Onnpoint Design 1-5 Jeffries Passage, Guildford, Surrey, GU1 4AP, United Kingdom
- (01483) 510515/ (01483) 510519
- info@onnpoint.co.uk
- www.onnpoint.co.uk

Opex Creative 4th Floor, Room 475, Exhibition Centre, Warwick Road, London, SW5 9TA, United Kingdom
- (020) 7370 8145/ (020) 7370 8377
- ashrita.seshadri@opex.co.uk
- www.opex.co.uk

Out of the Blue (UK) Ltd 308 Highfields Park Drive, Broadway, Derby, DE22 1JX, United Kingdom
- (01332) 552331/(07960) 959856
- andy@outoftheblue.net
- www.outoftheblue.net

Outside Line 177-178 Tottenham Court Road, London, W1T 7NY, United Kingdom
- (020) 7636 5511/ (020) 7636 1155
- admin@outsideline.co.uk
- www.outsideline.co.uk

OWMM Design Ltd The Watchoak, Chain Lane, Battle, East Sussex, TN33 0YD, United Kingdom
- (01424) 777192/ (01424) 773333
- enquiries@owmmdesign.com
- www.owmmdesign.com

Owtanet 16-18 Whiteladies Road, Clifton, Bristol, BS8 2LG, United Kingdom
- 0117-980 9400/ 0117-980 9401
- info@owta.net
- www.owta.net

Oxygen 12A Churchyard, Hitchin, Hertfordshire, SG5 1HR, United Kingdom
- (01462) 636800/ (01462) 636900
- geoff.ide@oxygenate.net
- www.oxygenate.net

Pacer Graphics 28 Berechurch Road, Colchester, CO2 7QH, United Kingdom
- (01206) 760760/ (01206) 762626
- adam@wordtech.co.uk

Phoebus Associates 13 Harley Street, London, W1G 9QG, United Kingdom
- (020) 7436 7123/ (020) 7436 5991
- sam@phoebusassociates.com
- www.phoebusassociates.com

Piranha Media 10 Barley Mow Passage, London, W4 4PH, United Kingdom
- (020) 8997 8569
- info@piranha-media.com
- www.piranha-media.com

Pixel Co. The Coach House, adjacent Ealing Film Studios, Ealing Green, London, W5 5ER, United Kingdom
- (020) 8579 8585/ (020) 8579 2090
- admin@solachannel.tv
- www.solachannel.tv

Pixel Pressure 42 Schoolbell Mews, London, E3 5BZ, United Kingdom
- (020) 8980 4939
- jinks.tek@btinternet.com
- www.pixelpressure.com

Plus Two Ltd Medius House, 2 Sheridan Street, Soho, London, W1F 8BH, United Kingdom
- (0870) 366 5270/ (0870) 132 0116
- info@plus-two.com
- www.plus-two.com

Polestar Whitefriars Ltd 3rd Floor, Northgate Place, Tunbridge Wells, Kent, TN1 2AX, United Kingdom
- (01892) 544366/ (01892) 543464
- paul.seaborn@polestar-group.com
- www.polestar-group.com

Printing.com @ Fluidmedia 56-58 Bolton Street, Bury, Lancashire, BL9 0LL, United Kingdom
- 0161-764 6464/ 0161-761 0408
- bury@printing.com
- www.buryprinting.com

Pro Creative Talbot House, 204-206 Imperial Drive, Harrow, Middlesex, HA2 7HH, United Kingdom
- (0845) 3003753/ (0845) 3003754
- design@procreative.co.uk
- www.procreative.co.uk

Punch NMC Fern House, 53 Padbrook, Limpsfield, Surrey, RH8 0DZ,
- 01883 730073
- andrew.richardson@thinkpunch.co.uk
- www.thinkpunch.co.uk

Pure Design Consultants Ltd 8 Randolph Crescent, Edinburgh, EH3 7TH, United Kingdom
- 0131-220 5522/ 0131-220 5533
- john@puredesign.co.uk
- www.puredesign.co.uk

QiQ Ltd Studio 3, Home Farm, Cottesbrooke, Northampton, NN6 8PH, United Kingdom
- (07092) 115100
- info@qiq.co.uk
- www.qiq.co.uk

Qudos Design Ltd Queen Anne House, 15 Thames St, Hampton, Middlesex, TW12 2EW, United Kingdom
- (020) 8979 8880/ (020) 8979 9881
- mark.p@qudosdesign.com
- www.qudosdesign.com

Razzdesign.com 108 / 3F2, Edinburgh, EH3 9HX, United Kingdom
- (07792) 161591
- steve@razzdesign.com
- www.stephenrasmussen.com

Re:Media Plc Media House, Buckston Road, Bakewell, Derbyshire, DE45 1GT, United Kingdom
- (01629) 813961/ (01629) 813349
- enquiries@re-m.com
- www.re-m.com

Reading Room 77 Deans Street, Soho, London, W1D 3SH, United Kingdom
- (020) 7025 1800/ (020) 7439 4190
- info@readingroom.com
- www.readingroom.com

Realise Ltd Quay House, 142 Commercial Street, Edinburgh, EH6 6LB, United Kingdom
- 0131-476 6000/ 0131-476 6061
- info@realise.com
- www.realise.com

Red Snapper Ltd 20 Mortlake High Street, London, SW14 8JN, United Kingdom
- (020) 8487 8640/ (020) 8487 8641
- contact@redsnapper.net
- www.redsnapper.net

Redweb Quay House, The Quay, Poole, Dorset, BH15 1HA, United Kingdom
- (0845) 1303010/ (01202) 773643
- sales@redweb.co.uk
- www.redweb.co.uk

Remedica Commonwealth House, 1 New Oxford Street, London, WC1A 1NU, United Kingdom
- (020) 7759 2929/ (020) 7759 2951
- info@remedica.com
- www.remedica.com

Ripe Design (UK) Ltd Clarence House, 48 Black Bull Street, Leeds, LS10 1HW, United Kingdom
- 0113-204 2800/ 0113-204 2801
- info@ripe.co.uk
- www.ripe.co.uk

Rob Harris Productions The Studio, 310 King Street, Hammersmith, London, W6 0RR, United Kingdom
- (020) 8748 2430/(07860) 798450
- rob@robharrisproductions.com
- www.robharrisproductions.com

Robert Hinton & Partners 1st Floor, 101 Goswell Road, London, EC1V 7RU, United Kingdom
- (020) 7490 5871/ (020) 7490 5873
- info@rhp.co.uk
- www.rhp.co.uk

Rocket Visuals The Matrix, 62-66 New Haven Road, Edinburgh, EH6 5QB, United Kingdom
- 0131-467 7740/ 0131-467 7741
- enquiries@rocket.co.uk
- www.rocket.co.uk

S B I Framfab Ltd 5th Floor, Elizabeth House, 39 York Road, London, SE1 7NQ, United Kingdom
- (020) 7071 6300/ (020) 7071 6666
- www.sbiframfab.com

S8080 Ltd Technium 2, Kings Road, SA1 Swansea Waterfront, Swansea, SA1 8PJ, UK
- (01792) 485566/ (01792) 485577
- sales@s8080.com
- www.s8080.com

Scotland on Line Gateway House, Lunar Place, Dundee Technology Park, Dundee, DD2 1TP, UK
℡ (01382) 429000/ (01382) 429001
✉ admin@scotlandonline.co.uk
🖳 www.scotlandonline.co.uk

Serco Usability Services 22 Hand Court, London, WC1V 6JF, United Kingdom
℡ (020) 7421 6499/ (020) 7421 6477
✉ usability@serco.com
🖳 www.serco.com/usability

Seven Communications 10 Canal Street, Stockport, Cheshire, SK1 3BZ, United Kingdom
℡ 0161-429 5700/ 0161-429 5705
✉ mail@7comms.co.uk
🖳 www.7comms.co.uk

Seventy One Creative Media 71 Granley Road, Cheltenham, Gloucestershire, GL51 6LJ, United Kingdom
℡ (01242) 523742
✉ info@seventy-one.co.uk
🖳 www.seventy-one.co.uk

Sharpturn Productions, London, United Kingdom
℡ (020) 7733 0055
✉ info@sharpturn.co.uk
🖳 www.sharpturn.co.uk

Shiel Humphrey Design 5 Grosvenor Gardens, London, SW14 8BY, United Kingdom
℡ (020) 8876 5466
✉ info@sheilhumphreydesign.com
🖳 www.shdesign.co.uk

Simon Morris Associates Unit 5, Ravensquay Business Centre, Cray Avenue, Orpington, Kent, BR5 4BQ, United Kingdom
℡ (0845) 612 1831/ (0845) 612 1832
✉ info@madesignstudios.com
🖳 www.madesignstudios.com

Skakel & Skakel Design Ltd 18 Shore Place, Edinburgh, EH6 6SW, United Kingdom
℡ 0131-554 0404/ 0131-554 0400
✉ skakel@skakel.co.uk
🖳 www.skakel.co.uk

Sliced Bread Animation 15 King Street, Covent Garden, London, WC2E 8HN, United Kingdom
℡ (020) 7379 7873/ (0870) 7620852
✉ info@sbanimation.com
🖳 www.thebestthingsince.com

Smartways Technology 8-9 Westleigh Office Park, 29 Scirocco Close, Moulton Park, Northampton, NN3 6BW, United Kingdom
℡ (01604) 670500/ (01604) 670567
✉ info@smartways.net
🖳 www.smartways.net

Smooth Design Walden Lodge, Walden Street, Aylesbury, Buckinghamshire, HP21 7QY, United Kingdom
℡ (01296) 393977
✉ info@smoothdesign.com
🖳 www.smoothdesign.com

Sonopress UK Ltd Wedenesbury One, Black Country New Road, Wednesbury, West Midlands, WS10 7NY, United Kingdom
℡ 0121-502 7800/ 0121-502 7811
✉ info@sonopress.co.uk
🖳 www.sonopress.co.uk

Spark & Zoom Productions The Stables, Luttrell House, Brockencote, Chaddesley Corbett, Kidderminster, Worcestershire, DY10 4PZ, United Kingdom
℡ (01562) 777424
✉ mail@sparkandzoom.com
🖳 www.sparkandzoom.com

Spark of Genius Ltd 35 Moss Street, Paisley, Renfrewshire, PA1 1DL, United Kingdom
℡ 0141-587 2710/ 0141-587 2711
✉ admin@sparkofgenius.co.uk
🖳 www.sparkofgenius.co.uk

Specialmoves 3rd Floor, Northburgh House, London, EC1V 0AT, United Kingdom
℡ (020) 7253 3399
✉ info@specialmoves.com
🖳 www.specialmoves.com

Spiral Productions Ltd Aberdeen Studios, 22 Highbury Grove, London, N5 2EA, United Kingdom
℡ (020) 7354 5492/ (020) 7359 6123
✉ info@spiralproductions.co.uk
🖳 www.spiralproductions.co.uk

Spoken Image Ltd 8 Hewitt Street, Knottmill, Manchester, M15 4GB, United Kingdom
℡ 0161-236 7522/ 0161-236 0020
✉ multimedia@spoken-image.com
🖳 www.spoken-image.com

Spotless Design 39 Atalanta Street, Fulham, London, SW6 6TU, United Kingdom
℡ (020) 7168 7526/(07971) 002292 / (020) 7681 4375
✉ info@spotlessdesign.com
🖳 www.spotlessdesign.com

Start Creative 2 Sheraton Street, Soho, London, W1F 8BH, United Kingdom
℡ (020) 7269 0101/ (020) 7269 0102
✉ jen@startcreative.co.uk
🖳 www.startcreative.co.uk

Static 2358 Ltd Ground Floor, 5 Old Street, London, EC1V 9HL, United Kingdom
℡ (020) 7250 1244/ (020) 7251 0263
✉ reception3@static2358.com
🖳 www.static2358.com

Storm Recording Studio Unit 10, Globe Works, Bromley Street, Lye, Stourbridge, West Midlands, DY9 8HU, United Kingdom
℡ (07811) 291913
✉ stormrecordingstudio@hotmail.com
🖳 www.stormrecordingstudio.co.uk

Stylorouge 57-60 Charlotte Road, London, EC2A 3QT, United Kingdom
℡ (020) 7729 1005/ (020) 7739 7124
✉ mail@stylorouge.co.uk
🖳 www.stylorouge.co.uk

Syzygy Elsley House, 24-30 Great Titchfield Street, London, W1W 8BF, United Kingdom
℡ (020) 7460 4080/ (020) 7460 4081
✉ studio@syzygy.net
🖳 www.syzygy.net

T A G Worldwide, Adplates Group The Smokery, 2 Green Hill Rents, London, EC1M 6BN, United Kingdom
℡ (020) 7336 6316
🖳 www.tagworldwide.com

T M C Unit 7 Forest Hill Business Centre, 2 Clyde Vale, Forest Hill, London, SE23 3JF, United Kingdom
℡ (0870) 4441184/ (0870) 4441181
✉ info@tmc-group.co.uk
🖳 www.tmc-group.co.uk

T M S Internet Faraday Drive, Bridgnorth, Shropshire, WV15 5BA, United Kingdom
℡ (01746) 766860/ (01746) 764543
✉ sales@tmsnet.co.uk
🖳 www.tmsinternet.co.uk

Taglab Power Road Studios, 114 Power Road, London, W4 5PY, United Kingdom
℡ (020) 7183 3600/ (020) 7183 3639
✉ sarah.wales@taglab.com
🖳 www.taglab.com

Tandem Consultancy Ltd 55 West Street, Chichester, West Sussex, PO19 1RU, United Kingdom
℡ (01243) 778822/ (01243) 779951
✉ creating.biz@tandem.uk.com
🖳 www.tandem.uk.com

Target Communications Ltd 52 Elmwood Road, London, W4 3DZ, United Kingdom
℡ (020) 8995 9652/(07785) 250550 / (020) 8994 3164
✉ lamprod@compuserve.com
🖳 www.lamproductions.co.uk

The Communications Group Graffix House, Newtown Road, Henley-on-Thames, Oxfordshire, RG9 1HG, United Kingdom
℡ (020) 7381 6000
✉ info@thecommunicationsgroup.com
🖳 www.thecommunicationsgroup.com

The Constructive 141a Constantine Road, London, NW3 2LR, United Kingdom
℡ (020) 7871 7618
✉ info@theconstructive.co.uk
🖳 www.theconstructive.co.uk

The Gate Marketing & Design Ltd Murlain Business Centre, Union Street, Chester, CH1 1QP, United Kingdom
℡ (01244) 357242/ (01244) 357215
✉ info@thegatemarketing.com
🖳 www.thegatemarketing.com

The Studio 2 Johnston Park, Inverkeithing, Fife, KY11 1BT, United Kingdom
℡ (01383) 415690/(07932) 642884
✉ keith@studioscotland.co.uk
🖳 www.studioscotland.co.uk

The Unit Unit 5, Level 5 South, New England House, New England Street, Brighton, BN1 4GH, United Kingdom
℡ (01273) 686713
✉ studio@theunit.co.uk
🖳 www.theunit.co.uk

The Zen Agency Gordon Chambers, 3/4. 82 Mitchell St, Glasgow, G1 3NA, United Kingdom
℡ 0141-229 1333/ 0141-226 3456
✉ enquiries@thezenagency.com
🖳 www.thezenagency.com

the061 38 Bankfield Cottages, Wall Hill Road, Dobcross, Oldham, OL3 5BH, United Kingdom
℡ (01457) 870360
✉ andy@the061.co.uk
🖳 www.the061.co.uk

Think Pod A1 Riverside, Metropolitan Wharf, London, E1W 3SS, United Kingdom
℡ (020) 7709 7883/ (020) 7709 7884
✉ think@thinkpod.co.uk
🖳 www.thinkpod.co.uk

Thinking Fish Trafalgar House, Grenville Place, London, NW7 3SA, United Kingdom
℡ (0845) 4588211/ (0845) 588688
✉ jonathan.kirsten@thinkingfish.com
🖳 www.thinkingfish.com

This Way Up Design Ltd 59 Compton Road, Islington, London, N1 2PB, United Kingdom
℡ (020) 7688 8800/ (020) 7688 8801
✉ mail@thiswayupdesign.com
🖳 www.thiswayupdesign.co.uk

Three Design 6 Stuart Road, London, W3 6DG, United Kingdom
℡ (020) 8992 0572
✉ studio@threedesign.co.uk
🖳 www.threedesign.co.uk

Tickle Group The Gate House, Summerseat, Bury, Lancashire, BL9 5PE, United Kingdom
℡ (01706) 823456
✉ tony@tickle.co.uk
🖳 www.tickle.co.uk

Tijuana Design 26 Stokes Croft, Bristol, BS1 3QD, United Kingdom
℡ 0117-909 6609
✉ tony@tijuanadesign.com
🖳 www.tijuanadesign.com

Tomato Interactive 3rd Floor, 14 Baltic Street East, London, EC1Y 0UJ, United Kingdom
℡ (020) 7033 0455/ (020) 7033 0456
✉ liz@tomato.co.uk
🖳 www.tomato.co.uk

Tonic Design 141-143 Shoreditch High Street, London, E1 6JE, United Kingdom
℡ (020) 7033 0660/ (020) 7691 2228
✉ design@tonic.co.uk
🖳 www.tonic.co.uk

Traveltainment (UK) Ltd 1-4 Afton Business Park, Shrewsbury Avenue, Peterborough, PE2 7BX, United Kingdom
℡ (01733) 361345/ (01733) 394313
✉ sales@traveltainment.co.uk
🖳 www.traveltainment.co.uk

Trilby Multimedia Ltd 47-49 Loveday Street, Birmingham, B4 6NR, United Kingdom
℡ 0121-333 6860/ 0121-359 8989
✉ team@trilby.co.uk
🖳 www.trilby.co.uk

Trinity Heriot 11 Canon Street, Canonmills, Edinburgh, EH3 5HE, United Kingdom
℡ (0131) 558 8663
✉ info@trinityheriot.co.uk
🖳 www.trinityheriot.co.uk

Trizeps Photography & Mediadesign Langoth & Fallnhauser GnbR, Zollergasse 13, Wien, 1070, Austria
℡ 00 33 1 526 3393/ 00 33 1 526 6020
✉ studio@trizeps.com

Twentyfirst Century Communications 27-31 Clerkenwell Close, 101 PM Building, London, EC1R 08T, United Kingdom
℡ (020) 7612 1021/ (020) 7612 1010
✉ theatre@twentyfirst.com
🖳 www.twentyfirst.com

twentysix London Eldon House, 1 Dorset Street, London, W1U 4EE, United Kingdom
℡ (020) 7535 9800/ (020) 7535 9801
✉ info@twentysixlondon.com
🖳 www.twentysixlondon.com

Unit 9 Ltd 2-4 Hoxton Square, London, N1 6NU, United Kingdom
℡ (020) 7613 3330
✉ info@unit9.com
🖳 www.unit9.com

Venus Internet Ltd 24 Denmark Street, London, WC2H 8NJ, United Kingdom
✆ (020) 7240 5858/✆ (020) 7240 5859
✉ sales@venus.co.uk
🖳 www.venus.co.uk

Vested Interest Design The Loft, 15A Watt Street, Greenock, Renfrewshire, PA16 8JN, United Kingdom
✆ (01475) 721042/✆ (01475) 721103
✉ info@vested-interest.com
🖳 www.vested-interest.com

View The Penthouse, Long Island House, 1-4 Warple Way, London, W3 0RG, United Kingdom
✆ (020) 8740 9751/✆ (020) 8740 9857
✉ bguly@view.uk.com
🖳 www.view.uk.com

VisionTribe 8 Parade Court, Marlow Road, Bourne End, Buckinghamshire, SL8 5SF, United Kingdom
✆ (01628) 810788/✆ (01628) 527118
✉ amanda.foister@visiontribe.co.uk
🖳 www.visiontribe.co.uk

Visual Communications 8 Manor Road, Chigwell, Essex, IG7 5PD, United Kingdom
✆ (020) 8504 9009/✆ (020) 8504 9030
✉ viscom2@aol.com
🖳 www.viscom-design.co.uk

Visual Source The Barn, Bottom Road, West Wycombe, High Wycombe, Buckinghamshire, HP14 4BS, United Kingdom
✆ (01494) 481482
✉ info@visualsource.co.uk
🖳 www.visualsource.co.uk

Viva Presentations Ltd 4 Spectrum House, 32-34 Gordon House Road, London, NW5 1LP, United Kingdom
✆ (020) 7267 8668/✆ (020) 7267 4007
✉ studio@vivapres.com
🖳 www.vivapres.com

Vivum Intelligent Media Ltd 17 Scawfell Street, London, E2 8NG, United Kingdom
✆ (020) 7729 2749/(07971) 543703 ✆ (020) 7684 8128
✉ livewire@vivum.net
🖳 www.vivum.net

Vpress Ltd Church Mews, Church Street, Cheltenham, Gloucestershire, GL50 3HA, United Kingdom
✆ (0870) 2005858
✉ info@vpress.co.uk
🖳 www.vpress.co.uk

W P P Group P.L.C. 27 Farm Street, London, W1J 5RJ, United Kingdom
✆ (020) 7408 2204/✆ (020) 7493 6819
✉ vedwards@wpp.com
🖳 www.wpp.com

W.C.J. Burrows The Burrows Building, 5 Fayleigh Road, Brentwood, Essex, CM13 1AB, United Kingdom
✆ (01277) 246666/✆ (01277) 246777
✉ darrel_wright@burrows.yr.com
🖳 www.burrows.yr.com

Wax New Media Agency 22 Stephenson Way, London, NW1 2HE, United Kingdom
✆ (020) 7388 7766/✆ (020) 7388 7766
✉ agency@wax.co.uk
🖳 www.wax.co.uk

Web 3D Studio 55 Grove Street, Edinburgh, EH3 8AB, United Kingdom
✆ 0131 228 9722
✉ bill.tseng@web3d.co.uk
🖳 www.web3d.co.uk

Web Technology Group 90 Longacre, London, WC2E 9RA, United Kingdom
✆ (020) 7339 8600/✆ (020) 7339 8601
✉ emma.hardman@webtechnologygroup.co.uk
🖳 www.webtechnologygroup.co.uk

Whitespace 7/8 Randolph Place, Edinburgh, EH3 7TE, United Kingdom
✆ 0131-625 5500/✆ 0131-625 5501
✉ jim@whitespacers.com
🖳 www.whitespacers.com

Wickedweb Ltd Eden House, Enterprise Way, Edenbridge, Kent, TN8 6HF, United Kingdom
✆ (01732) 863300/✆ (01732) 863747
✉ info@wickedweb.co.uk
🖳 www.wickedweb.co.uk

Willsons Group Services Strand Street, Grimsby, North East Lincolnshire, DN32 7BE, UK
✆ (01472) 268643/✆ (01472) 240292
✉ dave@willson.com
🖳 www.willsons.com

Wolff Olins 10 Regents Wharf, All Saints Street, London, N1 9RL, United Kingdom
✆ (020) 7713 7733/✆ (020) 7713 0217
✉ info@wolff-olins.com
🖳 www.wolff-olins.com

Wonderfuel 118 Hatherley Gardens, London, E6 3HQ, United Kingdom
✆ 020 8548 1358
✉ info@wonderfuel.co.uk
🖳 www.wonderfuel.co.uk

www.oceanbutterflies.net 49 Ronalds Road, London, N5 1XF, United Kingdom
✆ (07906) 223318
✉ mich@oceanbutterflies.net
🖳 www.oceanbutterflies.net

Xube Ltd Unit 4, 51 Derbyshire Street, London, E2 6JQ, United Kingdom
✆ (020) 7739 5811/✆ 020 7900 6867
✉ info@xube.co.uk
🖳 www.xube.co.uk

Zentropy Partners Lynton House, 7-12 Tavistock Square, London, WC1H 9LT, United Kingdom
✆ (020) 7554 0500/✆ (020) 7554 0555
🖳 www.zentropypartners.com

Zig Zag Advertsing 48-50 Birmingham Street, Oldbury, West Midlands, B69 4DZ, United Kingdom
✆ 0121-552 9929/✆ 0121-552 3241
✉ mike@zigzagadvertising.co.uk
🖳 www.zigzagadvertising.co.uk

PRODUCT DESIGN

Absolute Software Ltd Unit 11, Bosleake Rural Workshops, Redruth, Cornwall, TR15 3YG, UK
✆ (01209) 712444
✉ enquiries@absolute-software.co.uk
🖳 www.absolute-software.co.uk

Acumen Design Associates Ltd 1 Sekforde Street, London, EC1R 0BE, United Kingdom
✆ (020) 7107 2900/✆ (020) 7107 2901
✉ john@acumen-da.com
🖳 www.acumen-da.com

AND Creative Communications Ltd Whittaker House, Whittaker Avenue, Richmond, Surrey, TW9 1EH, United Kingdom
✆ (020) 8822 6720/✆ (020) 8822 6721
✉ jane@andccl.com
🖳 www.andccl.com

Artseens Images The Hub, 123 Star Lane, London, E16 4PZ, United Kingdom
✆ (020) 7055 0005/✆ (020) 7055 0005
✉ info@artseens.com
🖳 www.artseens.com

B I B Design 10 Wood Street, New Bradwell, Milton Keynes, MK13 0AU, United Kingdom
✆ (01908) 313292
✉ design@bibdesign.com
🖳 www.bibdesign.com

Browndesign 4 Smalley Close, Stoke Newington, London, N16 7LE, United Kingdom
✆ (020) 7254 2690
✉ design@browndesign.co.uk
🖳 www.browndesign.co.uk

Cambridge Consultants Ltd Science Park, Milton Road, Cambridge, CB4 0DW, United Kingdom
✆ (01223) 420024/✆ (01223) 423373
✉ info@cambridgeconsultants.com
🖳 www.cambridgeconsultants.com

Centrum Design Ltd 31 Clarence Road, Walton-on-Thames, Surrey, KT12 5JY, United Kingdom
✆ (01932) 248585/✆ (01932) 241869
✉ enquiries@centrumdesign.com

Conran & Partners 22 Shad Thames, London, SE1 2YU, United Kingdom
✆ (020) 7403 8899/✆ (020) 7407 5502
🖳 www.conran.com

Creactive Design Ltd 22 New Street, Leamington Spa, Warwickshire, CV31 1HP, United Kingdom
✆ (01926) 833113/✆ (01926) 832788
✉ creactive@creactive-design.co.uk
🖳 www.creactive-design.co.uk

Dano Battista 3D Ltd 9-10 Charlotte Mews, London, W1T 4EF, United Kingdom
✆ (07958) 735069/✆ (020) 7636 2455
✉ enquiries@danobattista.com
🖳 www.danobattista.com

DataCAM Models 18 Hewett Street, London, EC2A 3NN, United Kingdom
✆ (020) 7655 4822
✉ ashley@datacam.co.uk
🖳 www.datacam.co.uk

David Fox Design Briars Lane, Stainforth, Doncaster, South Yorkshire, DN7 5AZ, United Kingdom
✆ (01302) 849299/✆ (01302) 849299
✉ info@davidfoxdesign.com
🖳 www.davidfoxdesign.com

Deco Chic Boutique Waterfront Farm, Biddisham Lane, Biddisham, Axbridge, Somerset, BS26 2RS, United Kingdom
✆ (01934) 750827
✉ alexi@decochicboutique.com
🖳 www.decochicboutique.com

Design Stream Ltd Studio 106, Westbourne Studios, 242 Acklam Road, London, W10 5JJ, United Kingdom
✆ (020) 7575 3246/(07931) 361709 ✆ (020) 7575 3250
✉ enquiries@designstream.co.uk
🖳 www.designstream.co.uk

Design Technology International P.L.C. 14 High Street, Hadleigh, IP7 5AP, United Kingdom
✆ (01473) 823637/✆ (01473) 827389
✉ sales@design-technology.co.uk
🖳 www.design-technology.co.uk

design@djhunter 133 Ravensbourne Avenue, Bromley, BR2 0AZ, United Kingdom
✆ (020) 8466 7196/✆ (020) 8466 7196
✉ design@djhunter.co.uk

Dew Gibbons 49 Tabernacle Street, London, EC2A 4AA, United Kingdom
✆ (020) 7689 8999/✆ (020) 7689 9377
✉ itsgreat@dewgibbons.com
🖳 www.dewgibbons.com

Digital Fabric Innovations Olympic Court, Third Avenue, Trafford Park Village, Lancs, M17 1AP,
✆ 0161 8775000
✉ ann.marie@digitalfabrics.co.uk
🖳 www.digitalfabrics.co.uk

Dragonfly Media 3 Berkeley Crescent, Clifton, Bristol, Avon, BS8 1HA,
✆ 0845 6520 888/✆ 0845 6520 808
✉ jon@dragonfly-media.co.uk
🖳 www.dragonfly-media.co.uk

E R A 22 Butlers & Colonial Wharf, Shad Thames, London, SE1 2PX, United Kingdom
✆ (020) 7403 3311/✆ (020) 7403 1100
✉ design@erastudio.com
🖳 www.erastudio.com

E X X Projects 72 Rivington Street, London, EC2A 3AY, United Kingdom
✆ 0845-630 1262/✆ 0845-630 1282
✉ exx@plax.co.uk
🖳 www.plax.co.uk

Evoke Creative Ltd Suite F9, Oaklands Office Park, Hooton Road, Hooton, Ellesmere Port, CH66 7NZ, United Kingdom
✆ 0151-328 1617
✉ info@evoke-creative.co.uk
🖳 www.evoke-creative.co.uk

Exentric Holdings Ltd 63 Webber Street, London, SE1 0QW, United Kingdom
✆ (020) 7902 8282/✆ (020) 7902 8283
✉ mail@exentricthinking.com
🖳 www.exentricthinking.com

Factory Design Ltd 318 King Street, Hammersmith, London, W6 0RR, United Kingdom
✆ (020) 8748 7007/✆ (020) 8748 8808
✉ mail@factorydesign.co.uk
🖳 www.factorydesign.co.uk

Form Fittings Ltd Sycamore Road, Eastwood Trading Estate, Rotherham, South Yorkshire, S65 1EN, United Kingdom
✆ (01709) 829511/✆ (01709) 378380
✉ brucecantrell@formfittings.com
🖳 www.formfittings.com

Frazer Designers Ltd 6 Hampstead West, 224 Iverson Road, London, NW6 2HL, United Kingdom
✆ (020) 7624 6011/✆ (020) 7328 6085
✉ stephen@frazerdesigners.com
🖳 www.frazerdesigners.com

G S B Designers 18 Airthrie Road, Ilford, Essex, IG3 9QU, United Kingdom
✆ (07930) 918071
✉ dons55@hotmail.com

glassdomain ltd Sherwood Road, Aston Fierlds, Bromsgrove, Worcestershire, B60 3DR, United Kingdom
✆ (01527) 577446/ ✆ (01527) 579148
✉ info@glassdomain..co.uk
🖳 www.glassdomain.co.uk

Graham Lincoln & Partners The Courtyard, Loddington Hall, Loddington, Kettering, Northamptonshire, NN14 1LA, United Kingdom
✆ (01536) 418255/ ✆ (01536) 418256

Greaves Best Design 26 Home Farm Business Park, East Tytherley Road, Lockerley, Romsey, Hampshire, S051 0JT, United Kingdom
✆ (01794) 342341/ ✆ (01794) 342349
✉ design@greavesbest.com
🖳 www.greavesbest.com

Identica Partnership Newcombe Hse, 45 Notting Hill Gate, London, W11 3LQ, United Kingdom
✆ (020) 7569 5600/ ✆ (020) 7569 5656
✉ info@identica.com
🖳 www.identica.com

Info Group The Village Studio, Heol-y-Coed, Cardiff, CF14 6HP, United Kingdom
✆ (029) 2069 4040/ ✆ (029) 2069 4141
✉ info@the-info-group.co.uk
🖳 www.the-info-group.co.uk

John Ewans Design Capital House, Westbourne Street, High Wycombe, Buckinghamshire, HP11 2PZ, UK
✆ (01494) 473441/ ✆ (01494) 473442
✉ office@john-ewans-design.co.uk
🖳 www.john-ewans-design.co.uk

Jones Garrard Ltd 116 Regent Road, Leicester, LE1 7LT, United Kingdom
✆ 0116-254 2390/ ✆ 0116-255 6658
✉ design@jones-garrard.co.uk
🖳 www.jones-garrard.co.uk

K D Models 5 Host Street, Bristol, BS1 5BU, United Kingdom
✆ 0117-901 4040/ ✆ 0117-901 4001
✉ ian.hollister@kinneirdufort.com
🖳 www.kinneirdufort.com

Kinneir Dufort Design Ltd 5 Host Street, Bristol, BS1 5BU, United Kingdom
✆ 0117-901 4000/ ✆ 0117-901 4001
✉ design@kinneirdufort.com
🖳 www.kinneirdufort.com

Leming Design Studio, Kharkiv, 61000, Ukraine
✆ 00 380 50 2240450
✉ admin@lemingdesign.com
🖳 lemingdesign.com

Lokinlado Design 117 Eton Rise, Eton College Road, London, NW3 2DD, United Kingdom
✆ (020) 7483 2425
✉ lokinlado@gmail.com
🖳 www.lokinlado.com

London Associates 105 High Street, Berkhamsted, Hertfordshire, HP4 2DG, United Kingdom
✆ (01442) 862631/ ✆ (01442) 874354
✉ info@la-design.co.uk
🖳 www.la-design.co.uk

Lucian Marin, Bucharest, 61079, Romania
✆ 721 230 631
✉ lucian.marin@gmail.com
🖳 www.lucianmarin.ro

Maddison Ltd Walnut Tree Yard, Lower Street, Fittleworth, Pulborough, West Sussex, RH20 1JE, United Kingdom
✆ (01798) 865711/ ✆ (01798) 865742
✉ info@maddison.co.uk
🖳 www.maddison.co.uk

Mass Technology (UK) Ltd 36b Evington Road, Leicester, Leicestershire, LE2 1HG,
✆ 0116 25 44 171
✉ masstechnology@hotmail.com
🖳 www.masstechnologyonline.com

McComb Developments Estate Yard, Eridge Road, Eridge Green, Tunbridge Wells, Kent, TN3 9JR, UK
✆ (01892) 752060/ ✆ (01892) 752161
✉ info@teleseal.co.uk
🖳 www.teleseal.co.uk

Mokko Blue 21 Arncott Hall, 13 Poole Road, Bournemouth, BH2 5QR, United Kingdom
✆ 01202 269 257/ ✆ 01202 269 257
✉ info@mokko-blue.com
🖳 www.mokko-blue.com

Nicola L Robinson Mynachdy, Cardiff, Glamorgan, CF14 3AG,
✉ nlrobinson@thesurrealdemon.co.uk
🖳 www.thesurrealdemon.co.uk

one-or-more.com 1 Longley Road, London, SW17 9LA, United Kingdom
✆ (020) 8767 3376/ ✆ (020) 8767 3424
✉ info@one-or-more.com
🖳 www.one-or-more.com

Opius Ltd 74-77 White Lion Street, London, N1 9PF, United Kingdom
✆ (020) 7427 2100/ ✆ (020) 7833 9444
✉ russell@opius.co.uk
🖳 www.opius.co.uk

Ozturk & Robotica 17-23 Park Terrace Lane, Glasgow, G3 6BQ, United Kingdom
✆ 0141-353 2261/ ✆ 0141-353 2614
✉ models@ozturk.co.uk
🖳 www.ozturk.co.uk

P A B Concepts 16 Bloomfield Road, Bromley, BR2 9RZ, United Kingdom
✆ (07879) 811659
✉ info@pab-concepts.com
🖳 www.pab-concepts.com

P D U (Product Design Understood) Ltd Holdsworth Mill Business & Arts Centre, Reddish, Stockport, Cheshire, SK5 6DA, United Kingdom
✆ 0161-975 6086/ ✆ 0161-975 6087
✉ info@pd-u.com
🖳 www.pd-u.com

P M W Design Ltd 57 Cowbridge Road East, Cardiff, CF11 9AE, United Kingdom
✆ (02920) 399772/ ✆ (02920) 237112
✉ studio@pmwdesign.co.uk
🖳 www.pmwdesign.co.uk

Paul Usher Design 91 Luton Road, Harpenden, Hertfordshire, AL5 3BA, United Kingdom
✆ (01582) 766449/ ✆ (01582) 765619
✉ usherdesign@btinternet.com

Peebles Media Group 20 Clifton Street, Glasgow, G3 7LA, United Kingdom
✆ 0141-567 6000/ ✆ 0141-331 1395
✉ enquiries@peeblesmedia.com
🖳 www.peeblesmedia.com

Pentagram Design Ltd 11 Needham Road, London, W11 2RP, United Kingdom
✆ (020) 7229 3477/ ✆ (020) 7727 9932
✉ email@pentagram.co.uk
🖳 www.pentagram.com

Philip Watts Design Unit 11, Fire & industrial Estate, Brook field Road, Nottingham, NG5 7ER, United Kingdom
✆ 0115-947 4809/ ✆ 0115-9205 395
✉ sales@philipwattsdesign.com
🖳 www.philipwattsdesign.com

Priestman Goode Ltd 110 Crawford Street, London, W1H 2JD, United Kingdom
✆ (020) 7935 6665/ ✆ (020) 7935 0668
✉ studio@priestmangoode.com
🖳 www.priestmangoode.com

Product Innovation Partners Ltd Studio 1D-1F Leroy House, 436 Essex Road, London, N1 3QP, United Kingdom
✆ (020) 7354 8677/ ✆ (020) 7354 5684
✉ lynne@pip-design.com
🖳 www.pip-design.com

Product Partners Ltd The Old Warehouse, Church St, Biggleswade, Bedfordshire, SG18 0JS, United Kingdom
✆ (01767) 600456/ ✆ (01767) 600155
✉ steveg@productpartners.co.uk
🖳 www.productpartners.co.uk

Quadro Consulting Ltd The Cow Shed, Hyde Hall Farm, Buckland, Sandon, Buntingford, Hertfordshire, SG9 0RU, United Kingdom
✆ (01763) 275847/ ✆ (01763) 275840
✉ info@quadro-consult.com
🖳 www.quadro-consult.com

Ratio Design Associates Ltd 47-49 High Street, Kingston upon Thames, Surrey, KT1 1LQ, United Kingdom
✆ (020) 8392 0099/ ✆ (020) 8392 0066
✉ simon@ratiodesignassociates.com
🖳 www.ratiodesignassociates.com

Redrova Ltd The Big Barn, Red House Farm, Woodwalton, Huntingdon, Cambridgeshire, PE28 5YL, United Kingdom
✆ (01487) 773679/ ✆ (01487) 773659
✉ zoe@redrova.co.uk
🖳 www.redrova.co.uk

Renfrew Creative Rocket Studios, Abbey Meadow, Leicester, LE4 5DF, United Kingdom
✆ 0116-253 1961/ ✆ 0116-253 9827
✉ design@rg3.com
🖳 www.renfrewgroup.com

Showcard Group Display Division Inches Court, Works Road, Letchworth Garden City, Hertfordshire, SG6 1FD, United Kingdom
✆ (01462) 677254/ ✆ (01462) 675565
✉ sales@showcard.com
🖳 www.showcard-display.com

Smith of Derby Ltd 112 Alfreton Road, Derby, DE21 4AU, United Kingdom
✆ (01332) 345569/ ✆ (01332) 290642
✉ sales@smithofderby.com
🖳 www.smithofderby.com

Studio SDA Unit 8, Pacific Business Park, Pacific Road, Cardiff, CF24 5HJ, United Kingdom
✆ (029) 2046 4661/ ✆ (029) 2046 4981
✉ lianne@studiosda.com
🖳 www.studiosda.com

Tangerine Product Direction & Design Unit 9, Blue Lion Place, 237 Long Lane, London, SE1 4PU, United Kingdom
✆ (020) 7357 0966/ ✆ (020) 7357 0784
✉ martin@tangerine.net
🖳 www.tangerine.net

Team Creatif 89 Rue de Miromesnil, Paris, 75008, France
✆ 00 33 1 42 89 90 00/ ✆ 00 33 1 42 89 90 01
✉ team@team-creatif.com

TECAtech Production Design 6 The Corniche, Sandgate, Folkestone, Kent, CT20 3TA, United Kingdom
✆ (07747) 747681/ ✆ (01303) 266120
✉ info@tecatech.com
🖳 www.tecatech.com

The Division No 4, 15-17 Stratheden Road, London, SE3 7TH, United Kingdom
✆ (020) 8465 5396
✉ info@the-division.com
🖳 www.the-division.com

The Food Business Ground Floor, St Georges House, 50 Adelaide Street, St. Albans, Hertfordshire, AL3 5BG, United Kingdom
✆ (01727) 832834/(07989) 304850 / ✆ (01727) 832836
✉ sally@thefoodbusiness.co.uk

The Gate Marketing & Design Ltd Murlain Business Centre, Union Street, Chester, CH1 1QP, United Kingdom
✆ (01244) 357242/ ✆ (01244) 357215
✉ info@thegatemarketing.com
🖳 www.thegatemarketing.com

Therefore Ltd 2 Huntsworth Mews, London, NW1 6DD, United Kingdom
✆ (020) 7723 8322/ ✆ (020) 7723 8644
✉ jf@therefore.co.uk
🖳 www.therefore.com

Thomas Fattorini Ltd 150 Minories, London, EC3N 1LS, United Kingdom
✆ **(020) 7264 2171**/ ✆ **(020) 7264 2172**
✉ **sales@fattorini.co.uk**
🖳 **www.fattorini.com**
See ad in showcase

Travers GFX 44 Raynham Street, Hertford, SG13 7DE, United Kingdom
✆ (07766) 825632
✉ rupert@traversgfx.com
🖳 www.traversgfx.com

Tutssels Enterprise I G 11-33 St. John's Street, London, EC1M 4PJ, United Kingdom
✆ (020) 7559 7526/(07850) 482805
✉ glenn.tutssel@enterpriseig.com
🖳 www.tutssels.com

Vernon Wood 5 Wharfedale Crescent, Garforth, Leeds, LS25 1LD, United Kingdom
✆ 0113-286 2560/ ✆ 0113-286 2560
✉ vernwood@supernet.com

Wingnut Designs Waterfront Farm, Biddisham Lane, Biddisham, Axbridge, Somerset, BS26 2RS, United Kingdom
✆ (01934) 750827
✉ chris@wingnutdesigns.co.uk
🖳 www.wingnutdesigns.co.uk

www.danielknappert.com Flat 49, 16 UMBERSTON, London, E1 1PY, United Kingdom
✆ (07720) 397417
✉ daniel@danielknappert.com
🖳 www.danielknappert.com

Xor Software Ltd Valley Road, Wotton-Under-Edge, Gloucestershire, GL12 7NP, United Kingdom
- (01453) 843033
- ask@xorsoftware.co.uk
- www.xorsoftware.co.uk

GRAPHIC DESIGN

273K 6 Rangers Square, London, SE10 8HR, United Kingdom
- (020) 7240 6692
- paul@273k.co.uk
- www.273k.co.uk

3sixtymedia The Manchester Studio, Quay Street, Manchester, M60 9EA, United Kingdom
- 0161-839 0360/ 0161-827 2360
- enquiry@3sixtymedia.com
- www.the-manchester-studios.tv

549design 549 Rayners Lane, Pinner, Middlesex, HA5 5HU, United Kingdom
- (020) 8429 4801
- vince@549design.co.uk
- www.549design.co.uk

Absolute Zero Degrees Unit 10. Empress Mews, London, SE5 9BT, United Kingdom
- **(020) 7737 6767**
- **info@absolutezerodegrees.com**
- **www.absolutezerodegrees.com**
See ad in showcase

Agent-Art Department Studio 5, 4 Clarendon Avenue, Altrincham, Cheshire, WA15 8HD, United Kingdom
- (07811) 352322
- paul@karalius.co.uk
- www.karalius.co.uk

Aktiviti Design 672 Greenwich Street, San Francisco, 94133, United States of America
- 00 1 818 486 1677
- tomi@theouterone.com
- www.theouterone.com

Anarkitty 18c Englefield Road, London, N1 4JU, United Kingdom
- (07736) 301 006
- thekitties@anarkitty.co.uk
- www.anarkitty.co.uk

Art Edit 16 Lake Street, Oxford, OX1 4RN, United Kingdom
- (07813) 183482/ (0870) 1694700
- pierre@artedit.co.uk
- www.artedit.co.uk

Artdesign 52 Salmons Lane, Whyteleafe, Surrey, CR3 0AN, United Kingdom
- (020) 8660 3552
- vanessajacynth@aol.com
- www.artdesign-vjwagstaff.com

Artext 28 Sedley Rise, Loughton, Essex, IG10 1LT, United Kingdom
- (020) 8508 1328
- simon@artext.co.uk

Artseens Images The Hub, 123 Star Lane, London, E16 4PZ, United Kingdom
- (020) 7055 0005/ (020) 7055 0005
- info@artseens.com
- www.artseens.com

Artshole.co.uk Studio 10, 64 Weston Street, London, SE1 3QJ, United Kingdom
- (020) 7378 0876/(07879) 648898
- tony@artshole.co.uk
- www.artshole.co.uk

Ashdown Imaging Ltd Pippingford Manor, Pippingford Park, Nutley, Uckfield, East Sussex, TN22 3HW, United Kingdom
- (0800) 58747400
- info@ashdownimaging.co.uk
- www.ashdownimaging.co.uk

Ask Seven Studio 276, 17 Holywell Hill, St. Albans, Hertfordshire, AL1 1DT, United Kingdom
- 0845-686 1236
- info@askseven.co.uk
- www.askseven.co.uk

Assembly 3rd Floor, 38 Turner Street, London, E1 2AS, United Kingdom
- (020) 7265 8856
- www.assemblylondon.com

B E D A Design Solutions 21 Irvine Road, Colchester, CO3 3TS, United Kingdom
- (01206) 501868/ (01206) 501914
- studio@beda.co.uk
- www.beda.co.uk

Barcod Design 51a Torquay Road, Paignton, Devon, TQ3 3DT, United Kingdom
- (07833) 705460
- barcod@fsmail.net

beeuneek The Graphic Village, Cornwall Road, Hatch End, Pinner, Middlesex, HA5 4JR, United Kingdom
- (020) 8421 2102/ (020) 8421 2103
- studio@beeuneek.co.uk
- www.beeuneek.co.uk

Beirutlove 9 Rue St. Didier, Paris, 75016, France
- 00 33 66 555 8488
- tinko@beirutlove.com
- www.beirutlove.com

Ben Branagan Assembly Studio, 38 Turner Street, London, E1 2AS, United Kingdom
- 07867 806 865
- ben@assemblelondon.com
- www.benbranagan.co.uk

Benji Creates The Studio, 9 Lightfoot Street, Hoole, Chester, CH2 3AH, United Kingdom
- (07776) 055465
- bholroyd1@orange.net

Benoit Soucaret Centr Point House, London, WC2 H8LW, United Kingdom
- (07780) 594558
- whatld@hotmail.com

Benson Thomas 1 Swinleys Hey, Great Boughton, Chester, CH3 5XL, United Kingdom
- (01244) 345370/ (01244) 344511
- anthony@bensonthomas.co.uk
- www.bensonthomas.co.uk

Beyond Design Consultancy 68 Beulah Hill, London, SE19 3EW, United Kingdom
- (020) 8771 8596/ (020) 8626 9015
- info@bdc-limited.com
- www.bdc-limited.com

Big Blue Banana 346 Crofton Road, Orpington, Kent, BR6 8NN, United Kingdom
- (01689) 882038/ (01689) 882048
- info@bigbluebanana.co.uk

Black & Ginger 14 Colquitt Street, Liverpool, L1 4DE, United Kingdom
- (07782) 201620
- alex@blackandginger.com
- www.blackandginger.com

Blaze Creative Ltd 77 East Road, London, N1 6AH, United Kingdom
- (020) 7253 0099/ (020) 7253 4358
- mail@blaze-creative.co.uk
- www.blaze-creative.co.uk

Bleach 5 Hoxton Square, London, N1 6NU, United Kingdom
- (020) 7012 1211
- info@bleach-london.co.uk
- www.bleach-london.co.uk

Blink Studio Limited, United Kingdom
- (0845) 009 7997/ (0845) 009 7998
- matthew@blink.biz
- www.blink.biz

Bloodybigspider 4 Renmuir Street, London, SW17 9SS, United Kingdom
- (020) 8772 4549
- info@bloodybigspider.com
- www.bloodybigspider.com

Blue Skies Graphic Design Ltd 37 Oldfield Road, London Colney, St. Albans, Hertfordshire, AL2 1HZ, United Kingdom
- (01727) 822633
- peterch@blueskiesdes.plus.net

BN1 Communications, Brighton, BN1 2AQ, United Kingdom
- 01273 823085
- info@bn1com.com
- www.bn1com.com

Brace 209 High Street South, Dunstable, Bedfordshire, LU6 3HY, United Kingdom
- (0845) 0094500/ (0845) 0094501
- enquiries@bracedesign.co.uk
- www.bracedesign.co.uk

Brandfish The Barn, Tye Green, Elsenham, Bishop's Stortford, Hertfordshire, CM22 6DY, United Kingdom
- (01279) 817878/ (01279) 817740
- graham@brandfish.co.uk
- www.brandfish.co.uk

Brever Web Design Edinburgh 60a Craigour Drive, Edinburgh, EH17 7NT, United Kingdom
- (0845) 129 8534
- info@breverwebdesign.com
- www.breverwebdesign.com

Bridge Creative Ltd The Coach House Studio, 40 Higher Lane, Upholland, Lancashire, WN8 0NL,
- 01695 624966
- bridget@bridgecreative.co.uk
- www.bridgecreative.co.uk

Bronze Design 21 Tudor Avenue, Hampton, Middlesex, TW12 2ND, United Kingdom
- (020) 8979 8525
- bronya@bronze-design.com
- www.bronze-design.com

Brown Dog Creative The Barn, Main Street, Wartnaby, Melton Mowbray, Leicestershire, LE14 3HY, United Kingdom
- (01664) 823920/ (01664) 823518
- mandeep@browndogcreative.co.uk
- www.browndogcreative.co.uk

Browndog Design 3a Cartwright Court, Bradley Business Park, Dyson Wood Way, Huddersfield, HD2 1GN, United Kingdom
- (01484) 453131/ (01484) 540893
- info@browndog-design.com
- www.browndog-design.com

Bubble Media 51 Turner Street, Manchester, M4 1DN, United Kingdom
- 0161-839 3444
- liz@thebubblesite.co.uk
- www.thebubblesite.co.uk

Build 114 Diana Road, London, E17 5LF, United Kingdom
- (020) 8503 2752
- informyou@designbybuild.com
- www.designbybuild.com

Bulletproof 1103 Argyle Street, Glasgow, G3 8ND, United Kingdom
- 0141-222 2079/ 0141-222 2082
- info@bulletproofid.com
- www.bulletproofid.com

Byboth Ltd 145 Marlborough Road, London, N19 4AN, United Kingdom
- (020) 7281 1109
- us@byboth.com
- www.byboth.com

C A S Graphics Back Building, 150 Curtain Road, London, EC2A 3AR, United Kingdom
- (020) 7613 2510/ (020) 7613 2512
- mail@casgraphics.co.uk
- www.casgraphics.co.uk

C T D 65 Marlborough Road, Falmouth, Cornwall, TR11 3LL, United Kingdom
- (01326) 315551/ (01326) 315232
- chris@ctd-studio.co.uk
- www.ctd-studio.co.uk

C'est Bon Sign 10 Rue Jean Sign, Grenoble, 38000, France
- 00 33 611 73 99 33
- gregory.thouvenin@cestbonsign.com
- www.cestbonsign.com

C&C Design Ltd The Basement, 26 Old Church Street, London, SW3 5BY,
- 020 7351 4157/ 020 7351 3363
- oonagh@candc-design.com
- www.candc-design.com

Calverts 9-10 The Oval, London, E2 9DT, United Kingdom
- (020) 7739 1474/ (020) 7739 0881
- info@calverts.coop
- www.calverts.coop

Caron Stace Freelance Designer, London, N1 7RD, United Kingdom
- (07910) 072627
- caron@caronstace.co.uk
- www.caronstace.co.uk

CGI London Limited Cupola House, 15 Alfred Place, London, WC1E 7EB, United Kingdom
- (020) 7467 9300/ (020) 7467 9301
- louise.h@cgi-london.com
- www.cgi-london.com

Chameleon Graphics Ltd 2b Gypsy Lane, Great Amwell, Ware, Hertfordshire, SG12 9RN, United Kingdom
- (01920) 877206
- andrew@chameleon-graphics.co.uk
- www.chameleon-graphics.co.uk

Cherry Creative 99 Shalmsford Street, Chartham, Canterbury, Kent, CT4 7RQ, United Kingdom
- (07775) 745424
- carolyn.cherry@cherrycreative.co.uk
- www.cherrycreative.co.uk

Cite - The Internet Agency 42 Duke Street, Leicester, LE1 6WA, United Kingdom
- 0116-254 9888
- daf@cite.co.uk
- www.cite.co.uk

Clausen Design Limited 3 Park Road, Teddington, Middlesex, TW11 0AP, United Kingdom
- (020) 8943 9141/ (020) 8943 3141
- gavin@clausendesign.biz
- www.clausendesign.biz

Clement Graphics 21 John Tofts House, Leicester Row, Coventry, CV1 4LY, United Kingdom
- (07958) 009133
- jeanette@clementgraphics.com
- www.clementgraphics.com

Clockwise Design Ltd 1 Ridgeway Road, Redhill, RH1 6PQ, United Kingdom
- (01737) 767922/ (020) 8541 4616
- simon@clockwise.co.uk
- www.clockwise.co.uk

Cogmedia Ltd 180 West Regent Street, Glasgow, G2 4RW, United Kingdom
- 0141-248 6030
- richard@cogmedia.net
- www.cogmedia.net

Collective Engravers House, 35 Wick Road, Teddington, Middlesex, TW11 9DN, United Kingdom
- (020) 8943 9492/ (020) 8943 4359
- robin@collectivecreative.com
- www.collectivecreative.com

Constanza Natalino Flat 2, Chandos Court, 61 Haverstock Hill, London, NW3 4SN, United Kingdom
- (07783) 389580
- connie@constanzanatalino.com
- www.constanzanatalino.com

Copywrite Corporation 12 The Inner Silk Mill, Malmesbury, Wiltshire, SN16 9LP, United Kingdom
- (01666) 824130/ (01666) 825397
- lee@faberfaber.com
- www.faberfaber.com

Covent Garden Designs Parallel House, 32-34 London Road, Guildford, Surrey, GU1 2AB, United Kingdom
- (01483) 562224/ (01483) 457567
- www.coventgardendesign.co.uk

Creative Consortium Ltd 326 Upper Richmond Road West, East Sheen, London, SW14 7JN, United Kingdom
- (020) 8392 5050/ (020) 8392 5060
- peter@creative.uk.com
- www.creative.uk.com

Creative Edge Design & Advertising 1st Floor Donald Hendry Building, Auchincruive, Ayr, KA6 5HW, United Kingdom
- (01292) 521404/ (01292) 521693
- paul@cedge.co.uk
- www.cedge.co.uk

D C M graphics 6 Shirley Close, Otley, West Yorkshire, LS21 1HF, United Kingdom
- (01943) 466365
- info@dcm-graphics.com
- www.dcm-graphics.com

Dave Hills Art 28 Deanstone Walk, Coatbridge, Lanarkshire, ML5 4AZ, United Kingdom
- (01236) 436467
- dave@davehillsart.co.uk
- www.davehillsart.co.uk

David Hardy 66B Haydn Park Road, London, W12, United Kingdom
- /07887 572 580
- contactme@davidhardy.co.uk
- www.davidhardy.co.uk

Decode Design 9a Beech Road, Bounds Green, Middlesex, London, N11 2DA, United Kingdom
- (07812) 744915
- sheran@decodedesign.com
- www.decodedesign.com

Deep LLP 12a Imperial Studios, 3-11 Imperial Road, London, SW6 2AG, United Kingdom
- (020) 7751 0824/ (020) 7751 0823
- dom@deep.co.uk
- www.deep.co.uk

Design & Software Solutions, Birkenhead, Merseyside, CH42 0WA, United Kingdom
- (07985) 165646
- info@dassol.co.uk
- www.dassol.co.uk

Design Matters Ltd 33 Cambridge Gardens, Hastings, East Sussex, TN34 1EN, United Kingdom
- 01424 722311/ 01424 722310
- paul@design-matters.co.uk
- www.design-matters.co.uk

Design Typography 1 Sans Walk, Clerkenwell, London, EC1R 0LT, United Kingdom
- (020) 7251 6430/(07944) 519 784
- studio@designtypography.com
- www.designtypography.com

design@djhunter 133 Ravensbourne Avenue, Bromley, BR2 0AZ, United Kingdom
- (020) 8466 7196/ (020) 8466 7196
- design@djhunter.co.uk

Design73 26 Kingswear Road, Ruislip, Middlesex, HA4 6AY, United Kingdom
- (01895) 460942/ (01895) 460942
- martin@design73.co.uk
- www.design73.co.uk

Designcrew Creative Media Centre, 45 Robertson Street, Hastings, East Sussex, TN34 1HL, United Kingdom
- 01424 205 499/01424 205 499
- danny@designcrew.co.uk
- www.designcrew.co.uk

Dijon Designs Unit 1, Castle Farm, Clifton Road, Deddington, Banbury, Oxfordshire, OX15 0TP, United Kingdom
- (01869) 337311/ (01869) 337322
- information@dijondesigns.com
- www.dijondesigns.com

Dijon Exhibition Designs Suite 1 Field Barns, Castle Farm, Clifton Road, Deddington, Banbury, Oxfordshire, OX15 0TP, United Kingdom
- (01869) 337311/ (01869) 337322
- information@dijondesigns.com
- www.dijondesigns.com

Dir Design 195 Darlington Street East, Wigan, Lancashire, WN1 3EA, United Kingdom
- (07814) 961719
- christian@dirdesign.net
- www.dirdesign.net

DL Design Associates Limited 38a Duke Street, Chelmsford, CM1 1HY,
- 01245 299047/ 01245 299047
- darren@dl-design.co.uk
- www.dl-design.co.uk

Duncan Print & Packaging Broadwater House, Mundells, Welwyn Garden City, Hertfordshire, AL7 1EU, United Kingdom
- (01707) 336271/ (01707) 338731
- sales@duncanprint.co.uk
- www.duncanprint.co.uk

Dunning Design 90 Mitchell Street, Glasgow, G1 3NQ, United Kingdom
- (0845) 0551350/ (0845) 0551352
- claire@dunningdesign.com
- www.dunningdesign.com

Ecce Media Ltd Crossways Business Centre, 101 Cray Avenue, Orpington, Kent, BR5 4AA, United Kingdom
- (01959) 522210/ (01959) 524025
- info@eccemedia.com
- www.eccemedia.com

Egelnick and Webb 23 Charlotte Road, London, EC2A 3PB, United Kingdom
- (020) 7739 3339/ (020) 7739 3799
- mail@egelnickandwebb.com
- www.egelnickandwebb.com

Emak Mafu First Floor, 388 Old Street, London, EC1V 9LT, United Kingdom
- (020) 7168 8241
- studio@emakmafu.com
- www.emakmafu.com

Ember Design 88a Thicket Road, London, SE20 8DR, United Kingdom
- (020) 8659 9560
- info@emberdesign.net
- www.emberdesign.net

Estelle Baylis, London, United Kingdom
- (07958) 562239
- estellebaylis@homechoice.co.uk
- www.estellebaylis.homechoice.co.uk

FaberFaber Partnership 12 The Inner Silk Mill, Malmesbury, Wiltshire, SN16 9LP, United Kingdom
- (01666) 824130/ (01666) 825397
- lee@faberfaber.com
- www.faberfaber.com

Fiona Hamilton Clifton Arcade, Boyces Avenue, Bristol, BS8 4AA, United Kingdom
- (0117) 973 9838
- fiona@fiona-hamilton.co.uk
- www.fiona-hamilton.co.uk

Fire & Ice Creative The Old Stable, Moor Lane, East Coker, Yeovil, Somerset, BA22 9JR, United Kingdom
- (01935) 864588/ (01935) 864588
- chantelle@fireandicecreative.com
- www.fireandicecreative.com

Firespit 45 Myrtle Avenue, Bingly, BD16 1EW,
- 7968505946
- firespitdesign@yahoo.com

Fold Design Flat 27, Chadworth House, Lever Street, London, EC1V 3RB, United Kingdom
- (020) 7336 6693
- lmg@fold.it
- www.fold.it

Funky Concepts 5 Lansdowne Close, Coseley, Bilston, West Midlands, WV14 9TR, United Kingdom
- (01902) 651239/ (01902) 651239
- info@funkyconecpts.co.uk
- www.funkyconcepts.co.uk

Gaffa Ltd 60 Downham Road, London, N1 5AY, United Kingdom
- (07932) 008917
- info@dreibholz.com
- www.driebholz.com

Gener8 Digital, London, United Kingdom
- (020) 8866 9638
- www.gener8digital.com

Geoff Strange 99 Whitstable Road, Canterbury, Kent, CT2 8EE, United Kingdom
- (01227) 457292/ (01227) 457292
- zen12582@zen.co.uk
- www.geoffstrange.co.uk

GMID Design for Business Prospect House, 3 Prospect Place, Swansea, SA1 1QP, United Kingdom
- (01792) 641350/ (01792) 301548
- studio@gmid.net
- www.gmid.net

Graphics & Co. 87 Melrose Road, Galashiels, Selkirkshire, TD1 2BX, United Kingdom
- (01896) 668694/ (01896) 668694
- steve.whelan@graphicsandco.co.uk
- www.graphicsandco.co.uk

Greensplash Ltd Paddock View, 308 Chester Road, Hartford, Northwich, Cheshire, CW8 2AB, United Kingdom
- (01606) 884123/ (01606) 884212
- siu.wan@greensplash.com
- www.greensplash.com

Hannah Goudge 4 Mordaunt House, Albion Avenue, London, SW8 2AL,
- 7736944860
- hannahthestar@hotmail.com

Hazelwood Design Studios Catherine House, Suite D2, Harborough Road, Brixworth, Northampton, NN6 9BX, United Kingdom
- (01604) 882600/ (01604) 882023
- hds@hazelwooddesign.com
- www.hazelwooddesign.com

Heretakis@hotmail.com 54 Sina Street, Athens, Greece
- 00 30 694 2250 836/ 00 30 210 33615 055
- heretakis@hotmail.com
- www.heretakis.com

High Pitch Graphics 1st Floor, 51 Prestonville Road, Brighton, BN1 3TJ, United Kingdom
- (01273) 710466
- info@high-pitch.co.uk
- www.high-pitch.co.uk

Hot Frog Graphics Stanmore, 4 Moorland Avenue, Barnsley, South Yorkshire, S70 6PQ, United Kingdom
- (01226) 242777/ (01226) 242777
- hotfroggraphics@blueyonder.co.uk
- www.hotfroggraphics.com

Hudge Design Studios Ltd 4 North Field Road, Ealing, London, W13 9XR, United Kingdom
- (020) 8840 1914
- info@hudge.co.uk
- www.hudge.co.uk

Illustration Reps Inc 1234 SilverLake, SilverLake, Hollywood, Los Angeles, 90039, United States of America
☎ 323 667 1234
✉ illustrationreps@hotmail.com
🖥 www.illustrationreps.com

In Unison Design Consultants 2nd Floor, 20 Lincoln's Inn Fields, London, WC2A 3ED, United Kingdom
☎ (020) 7396 7405/✆ (020) 7831 4044
✉ mgore@inunison.co.uk
🖥 www.inunison.co.uk

Incito Design Unit 5, First Floor, 170 Corporation Street, Preston, PR1 2UQ, United Kingdom
☎ (01772) 880840
✉ richard.sullivan@incitodesign.com
🖥 www.incitodesign.com

Independent Freelance Creative Calico House, Levenshulme Trading Estate, Printworks Lane, Manchester, M19 3JP, United Kingdom
☎ (0870) 4445586/✆ (0870) 4445510
✉ phil@4design-uk.com
🖥 www.4design-uk.com

Ink & Colors Ltd 27 Old Gloucester Street, London, WC1N 3XX, United Kingdom
☎ (020) 7558 8374
✉ info@inkandcolors.com
🖥 www.inkandcolors.com

Itonic Design Ltd 38 Coombe Lea, Grand Avenue, Hove, East Sussex, BN3 2ND, United Kingdom
☎ (01273) 720608
✉ mail@itonicdesign.com
🖥 www.itonicdesign.com

J T Creative 3 Fieldhouse Road, London, SW12 0HL, United Kingdom
☎ (020) 8673 0641
✉ james@jtcreative.co.uk
🖥 www.jtcreative.co.uk

James Cartledge Graphic Design 16 Fairfax Road, Teddington, Middlesex, TW11 9DH, United Kingdom
☎ (07971) 544712/✆ (020) 8977 7828
✉ james@jamescartledge.co.uk
🖥 www.jamescartledge.co.uk

James Lambertus Design 106 Eureka St, No. 5, San Francisco, USA, 94114,
☎ 415.948.5506
✉ jameslambertus@earthlink.net
🖥 www.creativehotlist.com/jlambertus

Jawa and Midwich 45 - 46 Charlotte Road, London, EC2A 3PD, United Kingdom
☎ (07790) 517006
✉ jawa@jawa-midwich.com
🖥 www.jawa-midwich.com

Jawabrand 45-46 Charlotte Road, London, EC2A 3PD, United Kingdom
☎ (07790) 527006
✉ nils@jawabrand.co.uk
🖥 www.jawabrand.co.uk

Johanna Gale 15 New Close, Feltham, Middlesex, TW13 6TH, United Kingdom
☎ (020) 8893 3958
✉ jo@johannagale.plus.com

Jones Garrard Ltd 116 Regent Road, Leicester, LE1 7LT, United Kingdom
☎ 0116-254 2390/✆ 0116-255 6658
✉ design@jones-garrard.co.uk
🖥 www.jones-garrard.co.uk

Jorvik Design 7 Heath Ride, Strensall, York, YO32 5YW, United Kingdom
☎ (01904) 499377/✆ (01904) 499377
✉ studio@jorvik-design.co.uk
🖥 www.jorvik-design.co.uk

Julian Nix, London, United Kingdom
☎ (07932) 599346
✉ julian.nix@btopenworld.com

Justine Capelle Art Director Leighcliff Road, Leigh-on-Sea, Essex, SS9, United Kingdom
☎ (07973) 323709
✉ justine.capelle@infamie.com
🖥 www.justinecapelle.com

K G B 111-113 Great Portland Street, London, W1W 6QQ, United Kingdom
☎ (020) 7631 4082/✆ (020) 7631 3102
✉ alastair@kgb.uk.com
🖥 www.kgb.uk.com

Kalligraphic Design Ltd 11 Gatwick Metro Centre, Balcombe Road, Horley, Surrey, RH6 9GA, United Kingdom
☎ (01293) 776468/✆ (01293) 776491
✉ admin@kalligraphic-design.co.uk
🖥 www.kalligraphic-design.co.uk

Karen Spinks 63 Alberta Road, Enfield, Middlesex, EN1 1JA, United Kingdom
☎ (07881) 884740
✉ karencrowley@blueyonder.co.uk
🖥 www.advertisingontap.co.uk

Kashdan Design Consultants The Studio EBM House, Sandy Lane, Crawley Down, West Sussex, RH10 4HS, United Kingdom
☎ (01342) 714744/✆ (01342) 719414
✉ steve@kashdandesign.com
🖥 www.kashdandesign.com

Kiosk Design & Print No 2, 43 High Street, Leamington Spa, Warwickshire, CV31 1NL, United Kingdom
☎ (01926) 776282/✆ (01926) 776282
✉ info@kioskgraphics.co.uk
🖥 www.kioskgraphics.co.uk

Korelogic Westbourne House, 60 Bagley Lane, Farsley, Pudsey, West Yorkshire, LS28 5LY, United Kingdom
☎ (08707) 507497
✉ info@korelogic.coi.uk
🖥 www.korelogic.com

L D A 1 Lake End Court, Taplow Road, Maidenhead, Berkshire, SL6 0JQ, United Kingdom
☎ (01628) 668966/✆ (01628) 668977
✉ design@lda-uk.com
🖥 www.lda-uk.com

Laurel Studio 12 Aberdeen Terrace, Northampton, NN5 7AD, United Kingdom
☎ (01604) 456197
✉ info@laurelstudio.com
🖥 www.laurelstudio.com

Leming Design Studio, Kharkiv, 61000, Ukraine
☎ 00 380 50 2240450
✉ admin@lemingdesign.com
🖥 lemingdesign.com

Longneck Afgan Road 27, Battersea, London, SW11 2QD,
☎ 7506018062
✉ vlad@longneck.ro
🖥 www.longneck.ro

Lucian Marin, Bucharest, 61079, Romania
☎ 721 230 631
✉ lucian.marin@gmail.com
🖥 www.lucianmarin.ro

M&M Creative High Trees, Bishops Down Park Road, Tunbridge Wells, Kent, TN4 8XU,
☎ 01892 533103
✉ mike@mandmcreative.co.uk
🖥 www.mandmcreative.co.uk

Mandarin 17 Cowley Mill Road, Uxbridge, Middlesex, UB8 2QB, United Kingdom
☎ (01895) 253297
✉ info@mandarindesign.biz

MAP 72 Rochester Place, London, NW1 9JX, United Kingdom
☎ (020) 7424 9144/✆ (020) 7284 3274
✉ info@mapltd.com
🖥 www.mapltd.com

Marc & Anna 71 Regent Studios, 8 Andrews Road, London, E8 4QN, United Kingdom
☎ (020) 7249 6111
✉ hello@marcandanna.co.uk
🖥 www.marcandanna.co.uk

Mark McGrath Design & Art Direction 3 Ravenoak Road, Cheadle Hulme, Cheadle, Cheshire, SK8 7DL, United Kingdom
☎ (07962) 233564

Mark Richardson 91b Ermine Road, Ladywell, London, SE13 7JJ, United Kingdom
☎ (07855) 358023
✉ mail@mark-richardson.com
🖥 www.mark-richardson.com

Mark Russell 16 Porpen Road, London, SW2 5RT, United Kingdom
☎ (07881) 904476
✉ open@resaturate.com
🖥 www.resaturate.com

Mark Wolstencroft - Design & Strategic Brand Consulting The City Arc, 7 Curtain Road, London, EC2A 3LT, United Kingdom
☎ (020) 7917 2957
✉ mark@mark-wolstencroft.com
🖥 www.mark-wolstencroft.com

Marmalade 59 Lateward Road, Brentford, Middlesex, TW8 0PL, United Kingdom
☎ (020) 8400 5932
✉ ruth@marmalade.eu.com
🖥 www.marmalade.eu.com

Martin Hopkins Partnership The Maltings Easttyndall Street, Cardif Bay, Cardiff, CF24 5EA, United Kingdom
☎ (029) 2046 1233/✆ (029) 2049 7208
✉ info@martinhopkins.co.uk
🖥 www.martinhopkins.co.uk

Martin Rosten Design 1 Bramble Way, Wymondham, Norfolk, NR18 0UN, United Kingdom
☎ (07985) 333044
✉ martin@martinrostendesign.co.uk
🖥 www.martinrostendesign.co.uk

Mass Technology (UK) Ltd 36b Evington Road, Leicester, Leicestershire, LE2 1HG,
☎ 0116 25 44 171
✉ masstechnology@hotmail.com
🖥 www.masstechnologyonline.com

MCC Creative 4, Park Farm, Chichester Road, Arundel, West Sussex, BN18 0AG,
☎ 01903 885 235
✉ dan@m-c-c.biz
🖥 www.mcccreative.co.uk

Metalhouse UK Ltd 35 Byfeld Gardens, London, SW13 9HP, United Kingdom
☎ (020) 8563 1436
✉ gillianbrett@f2s.com

Milk it Design 111b Sunnyhill Road, London, SW16 2UW, United Kingdom
☎ (07899) 871498
✉ zac@milkitdesign.co.uk
🖥 www.milkitdesign.co.uk

Mind's Eye Design Ltd Carn Brea, Shutta Road, Looe, Cornwall, PL13 1HW, United Kingdom
☎ (01503) 264422/✆ (01503) 264422
🖥 www.mindseyedesign.co.uk

Mint 192 Clapham High Street, London, SW4 7UD, United Kingdom
☎ (020) 7627 0066/✆ (020) 7627 0676
✉ scott@mint-design.co.uk
🖥 www.mint-design.co.uk

Modus Media Ltd 18 Iliffe Yard, London, SE17 3QA, United Kingdom
☎ 0207 77406045
✉ info@modus-media.com
🖥 www.modus-media.com

Mokko Blue 21 Arncott Hall, 13 Poole Road, Bournemouth, BH2 5QR, United Kingdom
☎ 01202 269 257/✆ 01202 269 257
✉ info@mokko-blue.com
🖥 www.mokko-blue.com

Movingtarget 26 Outram Place, London, N1 0UX, United Kingdom
☎ (020) 7837 5280
✉ max.howell@mac.com
🖥 www.movingtarget.co.uk

My Mate Dave Designs 5 Buchanan Court, Buchanan Drive, Luton, Beds, LU2 0SA,
☎ 7736939770
✉ d.sweeney@ntlworld.com
🖥 www.mymatedaves.com

Mystery Design 79 Parkway, London, NW1 7PP, United Kingdom
☎ (020) 7424 1900/✆ (020) 7267 0191
✉ design@mystery.co.uk
🖥 www.mystery.co.uk

N G Studio 58 Hazel Avenue, Guildford, Surrey, GU1 1NT, United Kingdom
☎ (01483) 833118
🖥 www.ngstudio.co.uk

Net Efekt 17 Littleworth Road, Wheatley, Oxford, OX33 1NW, United Kingdom
☎ (01865) 873487
✉ studio@efekt.net
🖥 www.efekt.net

Niche Consultants 1 Hanover Yard, Noel Road, London, N1 8YA, United Kingdom
☎ (020) 7692 7001/✆ (020) 7692 7002
✉ chris@nicheconsultants.co.uk
🖥 www.nicheconsultants.co.uk

Nicholas J Jones Graphics Hillside House, Pitchcombe, Stroud, Gloucestershire, GL6 6LN, United Kingdom
☏ (01452) 812550/☏ (01452) 812690
✉ studio@nicholasjjonesgraphics.co.uk
🖳 www.nicholasjjonesgraphics.co.uk

Nick Jesse 21 Dunsfold Rise, Coulsdon, Surrey, CR5 2ED, United Kingdom
☏ (020) 8660 0120/(07763) 229339 ☏ (020) 8660 0120
✉ nick.jesse@virginr.net
🖳 www.nickjesse.pwp.blueyonder.co.uk

Nick Plant 26 Queenston Road, Manchester, M20 2NX, United Kingdom
☏ 0161-4380 052
✉ post@thisisnickplant.co.uk
🖳 www.thisisnickplant.co.uk

Nicola L Robinson Mynachdy, Cardiff, Glamorgan, CF14 3AG, United Kingdom
✉ nlrobinson@thesurrealdemon.co.uk
🖳 www.thesurrealdemon.co.uk

Nigel Partridge Design Ltd Beechurst, Woodway, Princes Risborough, Buckinghamshire, HP27 0NS, United Kingdom
☏ (01844) 343602/☏ (01844) 274158
✉ beechursh@btconnect.com

Nineteen to the Dozen Ltd Evesham House Business Centre, 48-52 Silver Street, Dursley, Gloucestershire, GL11 4ND, United Kingdom
☏ (0845) 0701925/☏ (0845) 0701926
✉ info@2gui4u.com
🖳 www.2gui4u.com

Ninety Degrees Design and Marketing Ltd 30 King Street, Manchester, M2 6AZ, United Kingdom
☏ 0161-833 1890/☏ 0161-833 1690
✉ jules@90degrees.com
🖳 www.90degrees.com

Ninteencreative 19 Sadlers Ride, Hurst Park, West Molesey, Surrey, KT8 1SU, United Kingdom
☏ (07950) 449004
✉ m.fidler@nineteencreative.co.uk
🖳 www.nineteencreative.co.uk

Objective The Court Yard, 17 West Street, Farnham, Surrey, GU9 7DR, United Kingdom
☏ (01252) 718400
✉ carl.groth@objectivestudio.com
🖳 www.objectivestudio.com

Oct-21 1st Floor, 140 High Street, Egham, Surrey, TW20 9HL, United Kingdom
☏ (0870) 8965521
✉ charlotte@october21.co.uk
🖳 www.october21.co.uk

on-IDLE Ltd Lincoln House, 75 Brokesley Street, London, E3 4QJ, United Kingdom
☏ (020) 8980 8960/☏ (020) 7841 7482
✉ create@on-idle.com
🖳 www.on-idle.com

Panther Advertising Unit 24, Business Centre West, Avenue One, Letchworth Garden City, Hertfordshire, SG6 2HB, United Kingdom
☏ (01462) 483122/☏ (01462) 483129
✉ mail@pantherinternational.co.uk
🖳 www.pantherinternational.co.uk

Panther Interactive Marketing The Innovation Centre, Epinal Way, Loughborough, Leicestershire, LE11 3EH, United Kingdom
☏ (07041) 471146/☏ (07041) 471246
✉ peter@panther.org.uk
🖳 www.panther.org.uk

Patrick Budge 53 Marlborough Road, Oxford, OX1 4LW, United Kingdom
☏ (01865) 452778/(07946) 640409
✉ patrickbudge@ntlworld.com
🖳 www.patrickbudge.com

Patrick O'Callaghan Design 10 Barley Mow Passage, London, W4 4PH, United Kingdom
☏ (020) 8994 6477/☏ (020) 8400 6162
✉ pat.design@vylan.com
🖳 www.pat.design.com

Paul Antonio Scribe Studio 6c, Clapham North Art Centre, 26-32 Voltaire Road, London, SW4 6DH, UK
☏ 020 7720 8883
✉ paulantonioscribe@yahoo.co.uk
🖳 www.paulantonioscribe.com

Pene Parker Design 9 Albert Road, Hampton Hill, Middlesex, TW12 1LB, United Kingdom
☏ 0771 2556243
✉ pene@peneparker.com
🖳 www.peneparker.com

Peppermint 39 Coach Road, Baildon, Shipley, West Yorkshire, BD17 5JE, United Kingdom
☏ (01274) 424221
✉ sadie@peppermint.org.uk
🖳 www.peppermint.org.uk

Pete Corcoran Design Services, Altrincham, Cheshire, WA15 6AA, United Kingdom
☏ (07968) 368092
✉ pete@petecorcoran.com
🖳 www.petecorcoran.com

Peter Ward Design 7 Stanford Way, Broadbridge Heath, Horsham, West Sussex, RH12 3LH, United Kingdom
☏ (01403) 276570
✉ peter@wardacolour.fsnet.co.uk (pw@peterward.info)
🖳 www.peterward.info

Pink Star Design Flat 4, 4 Medina Terrace, Hove, East Sussex, BN3 2WL, United Kingdom
☏ (01273) 326538
✉ clare@pinkstardesign.co.uk
🖳 www.pinkstardesign.co.uk

Piranha Design Ltd 117 Salisbury Avenue, Barking, Essex, IG11 9XP, United Kingdom
☏ (020) 8591 7664/(07885) 958953 ☏ (020) 8591 8664
✉ chris@piranha.co.uk
🖳 www.piranha.co.uk

Platinum Graphics Ltd 3 jJonhs Place, Edinburgh, EH6 7EL, United Kingdom
☏ (0845) 1235525/☏ (0845) 1235525
✉ stuart@platinumgraphics.co.uk
🖳 www.platinumgraphics.co.uk

Pressing Buttons 22 Chapel Street, Greasbrough, Rotherham, South Yorkshire, S61 4EN, United Kingdom
☏ (01709) 559045
✉ info@pressingbuttons.co.uk
🖳 www.pressingbuttons.co.uk

Produkt 189 Saint Asaph Road, Flat 5, Holcombe, London, SE4 2DY, United Kingdom
☏ (07970) 975993
✉ sass@produkt.co.uk
🖳 www.produkt.co.uk

Propeller Graphics Navigation Way, Ashton-on-Ribble, Preston, PR2 2YP, United Kingdom
☏ (01772) 732244
✉ info@propellergraphics.co.uk
🖳 www.propellergraphics.co.uk

Quirst 2 Brunswick Terrace, #2A, Hove, East Sussex, BN3 1HN, United Kingdom
☏ (01273) 202760
✉ sheila@quirst.com
🖳 www.quirst.com

R Design & Communications Ltd Heathercroft, Bagshot Road, Woking, Surrey, GU21 2SF, United Kingdom
☏ (01483) 481282/(07775) 761146
✉ info@r-mail.co.uk
🖳 www.r-web.co.uk

R Morris Assoc Batch Cottage, North Road, Charlton Horethorne, Sherborne, Somerset, DT9 4NS,
☏ 01963 220719
✉ morrione@btconnect.com
🖳 www.rmorrisdesign.co.uk

Ram Design 110 Birchover Way, Allestree, Derby, DE22 2DA, United Kingdom
☏ (07958) 062312
🖳 www.ram-design.co.uk

Ravenscourt Design LLP 41 Wavendon Avenue, Chiswick, London, W4 4NT, United Kingdom
☏ (020) 8995 2255
✉ design@ravenscourt.com

Redrova Ltd The Big Barn, Red House Farm, Woodwalton, Huntingdon, Cambridgeshire, PE28 5YL, United Kingdom
☏ (01487) 773679/☏ (01487) 773659
✉ zoe@redrova.co.uk
🖳 www.redrova.com

Rhubarb Associates Ltd Flat A, 349 Hale Road, Hale Barns, Altrincham, Cheshire, WA15 8SX, United Kingdom
☏ (07887) 678604
✉ matt@rhubarbcreative.com
🖳 www.rhubarbcreative.com

Riorici Design 6 Granary Mansions, Erebus Drive, London, SE28 0GH, United Kingdom
☏ (07941) 117150
✉ ricorici@hotmail.com
🖳 www.riorici.com

Rockwood Flat 40, 216 Kennington Road, London, SE11 6HR, United Kingdom
☏ (020) 7582 9308
✉ richardrockwood@mac.com

Rubberband Graphic Design 156A Haxby Road, York, YO31 8JP, United Kingdom
☏ (01904) 633800/☏ (01904) 633201
✉ peter@rubberbandisthe.biz
🖳 www.rubberbandisthe.biz

S B Design 20b Castle Hill Drive, Brockworth, Gloucester, GL3 4PQ, United Kingdom
☏ (01452) 862966
✉ steve@sb-design.co.uk

S C W Design & Publishing Ltd Unit 3, Enterprise Centre, Chapman Way, Tunbridge Wells, Kent, TN2 3EF, United Kingdom
☏ (01892) 509273/☏ (01892) 512232
✉ lee.smith@scw.uk.com
🖳 www.scw.uk.com

S H A Design Perspective Ltd Oakwood Park, Near East Ashling, Chichester, West Sussex, PO18 9AL, United Kingdom
☏ (01243) 779927/☏ (01243) 775089
✉ sarah.harvey@sha-design.co.uk

Safety First Design 3 Gibson Green, Witham St Hughs, Lincoln, LN6 9GA, United Kingdom
☏ (07753) 740589
✉ enquiries@safetyfirstdesign.co.uk
🖳 www.safetyfirstdesign.co.uk

Sage Visual Solutions A4 13 Sisters Avenue, London, SW11 5SP, United Kingdom
☏ (020) 7223 4700
✉ damian@sagevisualsolutions.com

Sands Thomas Design Ltd 3 Alwyne Villas, London, N1 2HG, United Kingdom
☏ (020) 7226 9526/☏ (0870) 0515792
✉ design@sandsthomas.com

Sarah Roe 32 Granville Road, Poole, Dorset, BH12 3BG, United Kingdom
☏ (01202) 731793/(07815) 076693
✉ sarah9000@ntlworld.com
🖳 www.sarahroe.co.uk

Sauce Creative Unit 3, Tring Business Park, Icknield Way, Tring, Hertfordshire, HP23 4JX, United Kingdom
☏ (01442) 892090/☏ (01442) 892091
✉ helen.sauce@btinternet.com
🖳 www.fetch-the-sauce.co.uk

Saw See Ltd Unit 28 1st Floor, 34 Bowater Road, London, SE18 5TF, United Kingdom
☏ (08701) 997726
✉ info@sawsee.net
🖳 www.sawsee.net

Scarlet Creative Solutions Ltd 3 Yew Walk, Hoddesdon, Hertfordshire, EN11 8BB, United Kingdom
☏ (0845) 4085402
✉ solutions@scarletcreative.co.uk
🖳 www.scarletcreative.co.uk

Screenworx 856a Green Lanes, Winchmore Hill, London, N21 2RS, United Kingdom
☏ (020) 8373 8126
✉ screenworx@blueyonder.co.uk
🖳 www.screenworx.pwp.blueyonder.co.uk

Seer Design Services Ltd 4 Waun Hir, Efail Isaf, Pontypridd, Mid Glamorgan, CF38 1AX, United Kingdom
☏ (01443) 209731
✉ info@seerdesign.co.uk
🖳 www.seerdesign.co.uk

Severin Furneaux Flat 1, 13 New King Street, Bath, BA1 2BL, United Kingdom
☏ 07929 156270
✉ contact@severinfurneaux.co.uk
🖳 www.severinfurneaux.co.uk

Shark Attack Suite 24, Stirling House, 9 Burroughs Gardens, London, NW4 4AU, United Kingdom
☏ (020) 8359 1202
✉ info@sharkattack.co.uk
🖳 www.sharkattack.co.uk

Shoot The Moon Design Concept House, Naval Street, Manchester, M4 6AX, United Kingdom
☏ 0161-205 3311/☏ 0161-205 3355
✉ info@shoot-the-moon.co.uk
🖳 www.shoot-the-moon.co.uk

Silverwell Creative 4 Cambridge Place, Falmouth, Cornwall, TR11 4QR, United Kingdom
(01326) 315277/(07763) 458972
info@silverwellcreative.co.uk
www.silverwellcreative.co.uk

Simon Isaacs 7 Lymore Terrace, Oldfield Park, Bath, BA2 2JL, United Kingdom
(01225) 335228/(07976) 758430
design@simonisaacs.co.uk
www.simonisaacs.co.uk

Slave to Design Unit 12, Joiners Square Industrial Estate, Hampton Street, Hanley, Stoke-on-Trent, ST1 3EX, United Kingdom
(01782) 221130/ (01782) 221131
info@slavetodesign.com
www.slavetodesign.com

Sliwa Creative 66 Lower Street, Stansted, Essex, CM24 8LR, United Kingdom
(0845) 2260995
info@sliwacreative.com
www.sliwacreative.com

Smutt Magazine 41 Kensington Road, Chichester, West Sussex, PO19 7XS,
70926368776
lou.marshall@hotmail.com
www.smuttmagazine.com

Sol Art Limited 46 Great Eastern Street, London, EC2A 3EP, United Kingdom
(020) 7613 3600/ (020) 7613 2203
lambert@sol.uk.com
www.sol.uk.com

Spiral Communications Pte Ltd 28 Maxwell Road, 02-15A, Red Dot Traffic Building, Singapore,
+65 65347184/ +65 63278902
enquiry@spiralcomms.com
www.spiralcomms.com

Sq. Circle 22 Claremont Road, Queens Park, London, W9 3DZ, United Kingdom
(020) 8968 2251
sqcircle@hotmail.co.uk

St. Cross 87 Great North Road, Hatfield, Hertfordshire, AL9 5DA, United Kingdom
(01707) 260044/ (01707) 262999
info@st-x.co.uk
www.st-x.co.uk

Stewart Sutters Design 3 Belton Corner, Marine Parade, Leigh-on-Sea, Essex, SS9 2HP, United Kingdom
(01702) 719595/07811 929205 (01702) 719596
info@stewartsuttersdesign.com
www.stewartsuttersdesign.com

Sticky Creation 27 Hoxton Street, London, N1 6NH, United Kingdom
(020) 7729 5480/ (020) 7739 2513
info@stickycreation.co.uk
www.stickycreation.co.uk

Storm Creative Ltd 7B Boyces Avenue, Clifton, Bristol, BS8 4AA, United Kingdom
0117-915 9692/ 0117-915 9692
charles@stormcreative.gb.com
www.stormcreative.gb.com

Studio SDA Unit 8, Pacific Business Park, Pacific Road, Cardiff, CF24 5HJ, United Kingdom
(029) 2046 4661/ (029) 2046 4981
lianne@studiosda.com
www.studiosda.com

Substance Design Ltd The Business Village, 3-9 Broomhill Road, London, SW18 4JQ, United Kingdom
(020) 8871 5230
glan@gotsubstance.co.uk
www.substance-design.com

Sue Rogers 7a Kestrel Avenue, London, SE24 0ED, United Kingdom
(020) 8762 7276
mail@suerogers.co.uk
www.suerogers.co.uk

Sutherland-Hawes McLean Design Consultants, 40 Ravenscourt Gardens, London, W6 0TU, United Kingdom
(020) 8141 9806/ (020) 8563 9975
shm@sutherlandhawes.co.uk
www.sutherlandhawes.co.uk

Swantje Jackel 55 Poppy Road, Southampton, SO16 3LA, United Kingdom
(07743) 957574
swantjejackel@hotmail.com

Synergy Communications Ltd 250-252 Goswell Road, London, EC1V 7EB, United Kingdom
(020) 7251 0303/ (020) 7251 0323
info@synergy-communications.co.uk
www.synergy-communications.co.uk

Tag Design Albert Road, Romford, RM1 2PP, United Kingdom
(01708) 784732/(07793) 556557
tim@tagdesignuk.com
www.tagdesignuk.com

Tempo Graphic Design Ltd 14-22 Ossory Road, London, SE1 5AN, United Kingdom
(020) 7231 5160/ (020) 7231 6631
studio@tempo-gdl.co.uk
www.tempo-gdl.co.uk

The Brand Doctor 23 Harrow Road, Worthing, West Sussex, BN11 4RB, United Kingdom
(01903) 824229/ (01903) 824230
design@vaughanographic.co.uk
www.vaughanographic.co.uk

The Constructive 141a Constantine Road, London, NW3 2LR, United Kingdom
(020) 7871 7618
info@theconstructive.co.uk
www.theconstructive.co.uk

The Creative Pulse 16 West Barnes Lane, London, SW20 0BU, United Kingdom
(020) 8947 7789/ (020) 8947 6678
peter@thecreativepulse.com
www.thecreativepulse.com

The Gate Marketing & Design Ltd Murlain Business Centre, Union Street, Chester, CH1 1QP, United Kingdom
(01244) 357242/ (01244) 357215
info@thegatemarketing.com
www.thegatemarketing.com

The Loft Room 30 Riland Road, Sutton Coldfield, West Midlands, B75 7AT, United Kingdom
0121-329 3197
info@theloftroom.co.uk
www.theloftroom.co.uk

The Mad Agency Mad House, Horton, Wimborne, Dorset, BH21 7JH, United Kingdom
01258 840841/ 01258 840849
lisa@themadagency.com
www.themadagency.com

The Metal Dog 155 Green Lanes, London, N16 9DB, United Kingdom
(07952) 921 505
jhadame@servidor.unam.mx

The No Nonsense Group River Studios, 84 Bendemeer Road, London, SW15 1JU, United Kingdom
(020) 8789 7123/ (07092) 277278
claire@tnng.co.uk
www.tnng.co.uk

The Print Studio 38 Regents Park Road, London, NW1 7SX, United Kingdom
(020) 7722 3362
dennis@atlas.co.uk

The Touch Agency 4 Stafford Street, Edinburgh, EH3 7AU, United Kingdom
0131-220 4545
martin@thetouchagency.co.uk
www.thetouchagency.co.uk

The Well Graphic Design Ltd Studio 5B, Holbury Business Complex, Manor Road, Horbury, Wakefield, West Yorkshire, WF4 6HH, United Kingdom
(01924) 266133/ (01924) 266144
studio@welldesigned.co.uk
www.welldesigned.uk.com

The Yellow Yoyo Co. Ltd The Studio, Barn Cottage, Brownlow Avenue, Edlesborough, Dunstable, Bedfordshire, LU6 2JE, United Kingdom
(01525) 229177/(07956) 366053 (01525) 221335
amanda@yoyo.co.uk
www.yoyo.co.uk

Thought by Design 47 Greys Road, Henley-on-Thames, Oxfordshire, RG9 1SB, United Kingdom
(01491) 411439/(07967) 729085 (01491) 411439
info@thoughtbydesign.co.uk
www.thoughtbydesign.co.uk

Thought By Design Ltd 47 Greys Road, Henley-on-Thames, Oxfordshire, RG9 1SB, United Kingdom
(07967) 729085/ (01491) 411439
simon@thoughtbydesign.co.uk
www.thoughtbydesign.co.uk

Three Circles Publication Chy-an-Pandora, 1 Eastcliff Avenue, Porthtowan, Truro, Cornwall, TR4 8AL, United Kingdom
(01209) 891471
stephanie@threecirclespublication.com

Tonic Fusion 4C Parkway, Porters Wood, St. Albans, Hertfordshire, AL3 6AA, United Kingdom
(01727) 810254/ (01727) 810257
info@tonicfusion.com
www.tonicfusion.com

Touchmedia Ltd 3 Imperial Square, Cheltenham, Gloucestershire, GL50 1QB, United Kingdom
(01242) 519914/ (01242) 226397
design@touchmedia.uk.net
www.touchmedia.uk.net

Tracey Knight 56 Thackeray Road, Bradford, West Yorkshire, BD10 0JR, United Kingdom
(01274) 410743/ (01274) 410743
tracey@misato.co.uk
www.traceyknight.com

True i.d. Designs 351 Fishguard Way, Galleons Lock, London, E16 2RZ, United Kingdom
(07971) 077751/ (020) 7511 2971
info@trueiddesigns.com
www.trueiddesigns.com

Urbansoul Design Kingfisher Centre, Futures Park, Bacup, Lancashire, OL13 0BB, United Kingdom
(01706) 877899/(07967) 968893 (01706) 877899
dave@urbansouldesign.co.uk
www.urbansouldesign.com

Vanessa Warren, London, United Kingdom
(07708) 111027
vanessa@vanessawarren.com
www.vanessawarren.com

Verso Communications Limited DesignRooms, The Mews, St. Marys Place, Stafford, ST16 2AP, United Kingdom
01785 272932/ 01785 661501
design@versocommmunications.co.uk
www.versocommunications.co.uk

Vicky Newman Illustrations 34 Mill Court, Ashford, Kent, TN24 8DN, United Kingdom
(07989) 449835
v_newman@yahoo.com
www.vickynewman.com

Village Design Ltd St Thomas Court, Thomas Lane, Bristol, BS1 6JG, United Kingdom
0117-910 6050/ 0117-910 6051
info@village-design.co.uk
www.villagedesign.co.uk

Vinney White Design 83 Connaught Avenue, Shoreham-by-Sea, West Sussex, BN43 5WL, United Kingdom
(01273) 887452
vinney@vinneywhite.co.uk
www.vinneywhite.co.uk

Wallcandy 295 View 146 Conway Street, Liverpool, L5 3BB, United Kingdom
0151-207 4531
sales@wallcandyuk.com
www.wallcandyuk.com

Warm Red Design The Old House, 36 Southend Road, Beckenham, Kent, BR3 5AA, United Kingdom
(0845) 9001291
info@warmred.com
www.warmred.com

Whitewater Design 37 Valley Road, Henley-on-Thames, Oxfordshire, RG9 1RL, United Kingdom
(01491) 576883
sales@whitewaterdesign.co.uk
www.whitewaterdesign.co.uk

Wickstead Design 128 Southwark Street, London, SE1 0SW, United Kingdom
020 7803 4910/ 020 7803 4915
design@wickstead.com
www.wickstead.com

Willis Reddick Partnership 10 Ivanhoe Avenue, Carryduff, Belfast, BT8 8BN, United Kingdom
(028) 9081 5996/ (028) 9081 5996
info@willisreddick.com
www.willisreddick.com

Windpower Design Ltd, Beech Pike, Elkstone, Cheltenham, Gloucestershire, GL53 9PL, United Kingdom
(01285) 821345/ (01285) 821864
mail@windpower.uk.com
www.windpower.uk.com

Wingnut Designs Waterfront Farm, Biddisham Lane, Biddisham, Axbridge, Somerset, BS26 2RS, United Kingdom
(01934) 750827
chris@wingnutdesigns.co.uk
www.wingnutdesigns.co.uk

Wonderfuel 118 Hatherley Gardens, London, E6 3HQ, United Kingdom
☎ 020 8548 1358
✉ info@wonderfuel.co.uk
🖳 www.wonderfuel.co.uk

Writersworld Limited 9 Manor Close, Enstone, Chipping Norton, Oxfordshire, OX7 4LU, United Kingdom
☎ (01608) 677393
✉ enquiries@writersworld.co.uk
🖳 www.writersworld.co.uk

www.oceanbutterflies.net 49 Ronalds Road, London, N5 1XF, United Kingdom
☎ (07906) 223318
✉ mich@oceanbutterflies.net
🖳 www.oceanbutterflies.net

Zero-Five 49 Oxford Street, Leicester, LE1 5XY, United Kingdom
☎ 0116 257 7931
✉ info@zero-five.co.uk
🖳 www.zero-five.co.uk

CORPORATE IDENTITY

1st Creative Services 4th Floor, Lafore House, The Leathermarket, Weston Street, London, SE1 3ER, United Kingdom
☎ (0870) 7461381/ (0870) 120 9560
✉ phil@1stcreative.co.uk
🖳 www.1stcreative.co.uk

3 Media Solutions 251 Kingsway, Manchester, M19 1AL, United Kingdom
☎ (0870) 638370/ 0161-610 6018
✉ sales@3gmediasolutions.com
🖳 www.3gmediasolutions.com

7 Gods 126 Wightman Road, London, N4 1RL, United Kingdom
☎ (020) 8482 1572/ (020) 8482 1572
✉ hello@7gods.co.uk
🖳 www.7gods.co.uk

85 four 85 Clerkenwell Road, London, EC1R 5AR, United Kingdom
☎ (020) 7400 4700/ (020) 7242 3848
✉ info@85four.com
🖳 www.85four.com

999 Design Group Eastgate, Castle Street, Manchester, M3 4LZ, United Kingdom
☎ 0161-828 5900/ 0161-828 5901
✉ info@999design.com
🖳 www.999design.co.uk

Absolute Zero Degrees Unit 10. Empress Mews, London, SE5 9BT, United Kingdom
☎ (020) 7737 6767
✉ info@absolutezerodegrees.com
🖳 www.absolutezerodegrees.com

Abstracts 39 Doughty Street, London, WC1N 2LF, United Kingdom
☎ (020) 7490 7561/ (020) 7430 7711
✉ mail@abstracts.co.uk
🖳 www.abstracts.co.uk

ActiveM.co.uk 9 Piper Close, Wellingborough, Northamptonshire, NN8 4US, United Kingdom
☎ (01933) 678522/ (01933) 678522
✉ info@activem.co.uk
🖳 www.activem.co.uk

Adrian Singer Design Budock Water, Falmouth, Cornwall, TR11 5DS, United Kingdom
☎ (01326) 378100/ (01326) 378100
✉ asd1@btconnect.com

Aitch Em 1 Tyrell Close, Buckingham, Buckingham, MK18 1EJ, United Kingdom
☎ (01280) 822613
✉ contact@aitchem.co.uk

Alan Brannan Design Grange Farm, Wetherden, Stowmarket, Suffolk, IP14 3LW, United Kingdom
☎ (01359) 240202/ (01359) 241292
✉ info@alanbrannandesign.co.uk
🖳 www.alanbrannandesign.co.uk

Alan Clark 118 Goldhurst Terrace, London, NW6 3HR, United Kingdom
☎ 020-7624 6640/(07940) 598379
✉ alanclarkuk@aol.com

Alchemede Ltd 98 Sydney Place, Bath, BA2 6NE, United Kingdom
☎ (01225) 866623/ (01225) 444540
✉ admin@alchemede.co.uk

Alder Limited 5 Philpotts Yard, Beare Green, Dorking, Surrey, RH5 4QU, United Kingdom
☎ (0845) 6441870/ (0845) 6445870
✉ simon@thecreativeteam.co.uk
🖳 www.thecreativeteam.co.uk

Aliasdesign 246 The Avenue, Acocks Green, Birmingham, B27 6NU, United Kingdom
☎ 0121-449 2539/(07989) 508817
✉ tom@aliasdesign.co.uk
🖳 www.aliasdesign.co.uk

Allen Design Group 9 Clay Cliff Office Pk, Wayleigh Rd, Bark Green, Barnsley, South Yorkshire, S75 1HQ, United Kingdom
☎ (01226) 292921/ (01226) 329292
✉ ab@allendesigngroup.com
🖳 www.allendesigngroup.com

AllyAllez 23 Old Deer Park Gardens, Richmond, Surrey, TW9 2TN, United Kingdom
☎ (07745) 174378
✉ tom@allyallex.co.uk
🖳 www.allyallez.co.uk

Anderton Overton Design Windmill Studio, 74 Windmill Rise, Holgate, York, YO26 4TX, United Kingdom
☎ (01904) 798938/ (01904) 791529
✉ andertondesign@btconnect.com

Andrew Morgan Design Beechwood, Grinshill, Shrewsbury, SY4 3BT, United Kingdom
☎ (01939) 220776/ (01939) 220252
✉ amdwww@btinternet.com

Appareo C/Zaragoza 1-3, No. 115, Castelldefels, Barcelona, 8860, Spain
☎ 00 34 93 636 6375/ 00 34 93 633 6854
✉ kevin@appareoconsulting.com
🖳 www.appareo.info

Appetite Tennyson House, 159-165 Great Portland Street, London, W1W 5PA, United Kingdom
☎ (020) 7636 7800/ (020) 7580 6744
✉ laura.haynes@appetiteuk.com
🖳 www.appetiteuk.com

Appleby Bowers Bank House Studios, Warwick Street, Prestwich, Manchester, M25 3HN, United Kingdom
☎ 0161-773 5553/ 0161-798 5553
✉ sales@applebybowers.com
🖳 www.applebybowers.com

Aquarium Creative 26C Marmora Road, London, SE22 0RX, United Kingdom
☎ (020) 7253 2172/(078 80) 621306
✉ anna@aquariumcreative.com
🖳 www.aquariumcreative.com

Arc Worldwide Warwick Building, Kensington Village, Avonmore Road, London, W14 8HQ, United Kingdom
☎ (020) 7751 1662/ (020) 7348 3856
🖳 www.arcwww.co.uk

Archer Advertising Vision House, 56 Donegall Pass, Belfast, BT7 1BU, United Kingdom
☎ (028) 9043 4111/ (028) 9024 1777
✉ tony@archeradvertising.co.uk
🖳 www.archeradvertising.co.uk

Arena Advertising & Marketing Ltd Georgian House, Greenhill, Sherborne, Dorset, DT9 4EP, United Kingdom
☎ (01935) 813999/ (01935) 816565
✉ info@arenaadvertising.co.uk
🖳 www.arenaadvertising.co.uk

Ark Studios 201/2F The Big Peg, 120 Vyse Street, Birmingham, B18 6NF, United Kingdom
☎ 0121-246 4610/ 0121-246 4600
✉ info@arkstudios.co.uk
🖳 www.arkstudios.co.uk

Arnatt Abrey Bennett Design Studio 4, The Leathermarket, London, SE1 3HN, United Kingdom
☎ (020) 7407 2627/ (020) 7407 2606
✉ mail@aabdesign.co.uk
🖳 www.aabdesign.co.uk

Arthur Pottersman Flat D, Second Floor, 33 Redington Rd, Hampstead, London, NW3 7QY, UK
☎ **(020) 7431 7101/(07929) 011113**
✉ **mail@wfscreate.com**
🖳 **www.wfscreate.com**
See ad

Avocado Design Communications Ltd 1-3 Gravel Ln, Salford, Manchester, M3 7WQ, United Kingdom
☎ 0161-839 0242/ 0161-839 0233
✉ enquiries@avocado-design.com
🖳 www.avocado-design.com

Axis Marketing Communications Ltd 7 Dorcan Business Village, Murdock Road, Dorcan, Swindon, SN3 5HY, United Kingdom
☎ (01793) 693443/ (01793) 531910
✉ info@axisltd.uk.com
🖳 www.axisltd.uk.com

B D A Advertising & Design Consultants Pepperpot Studios, 46 Queens Park Terrace, Brighton, BN2 9YB, United Kingdom
☎ (01273) 685601
✉ info@bda-design.co.uk
🖳 www.bda-design.co.uk

B D Network/Scotland Cochrane Hse, 29 Cochrane St, Glasgow, G1 1HL, United Kingdom
☎ 0141-567 8037/ 0141-567 8001
🖳 www.bd-ntwk.com

Baines Design Barley House, Sopers Road, Potters Bar, Hertfordshire, EN6 4RY, United Kingdom
☎ (01707) 876555/ (01707) 872882
✉ info@bainesdesign.co.uk
🖳 www.bainesdesign.co.uk

Barker Brooks Media Ltd i2a Hornbeam Park Oval, Harrogate, North Yorkshire, HG2 8RB, United Kingdom
☎ (01423) 872828/ (01423) 872488
✉ lucinda@barkerbrooks.co.uk
🖳 www.barkerbrooks.co.uk

Bazzoo Limited 18 Church Street, Sutton-on-Trent, Newark, Nottinghamshire, NG23 6PD, United Kingdom
☎ (08458) 842200/ (0870) 762 5736
✉ info@bazzoo.com
🖳 www.bazzoo.com

bc-3, London, United Kingdom
☎ (07768) 502863
✉ mail@bc-3.com
🖳 www.bc-3.com

beBRAND 12-16 Clerkenwell Road, London, EC1M 5PQ, United Kingdom
☎ (020) 7324 6110/ (020) 7324 6001
✉ james@bebrand.net
🖳 www.bebrand.net

Beyond Design Consultancy 68 Beulah Hill, London, SE19 3EW, United Kingdom
☎ (020) 8771 8596/ (020) 8626 9015
✉ info@bdc-limited.com
🖳 www.bdc-limited.com

Big Blue Banana 346 Crofton Road, Orpington, Kent, BR6 8NN, United Kingdom
☎ (01689) 882038/ (01689) 882048
✉ info@bigbluebanana.com

Big Purple Box 13 Linden Terrace, Whitley Bay, Tyne and Wear, NE26 2AA, United Kingdom
☎ 0191-280 2023
✉ john@bigpurplebox.co.uk
🖳 www.bigpurplebox.co.uk

Binding Associates 66 Colston Street, Bristol, BS1 5AZ, United Kingdom
☎ 0117-929 0845
✉ info@binding-associates.com
🖳 www.binding-associates.com

Bisqit Design 20 Soho Square, London, W1A 1PR, United Kingdom
☎ (020) 7413 3739/ (020) 7413 3738
✉ info@bisqit.co.uk
🖳 www.bisqit.co.uk

Bite Ltd 11 Northburgh Street, London, EC1V 0AN, United Kingdom
☎ (020) 7253 2500/ (020) 7253 2600
✉ info@bite.ltd.uk
🖳 www.anotherbiteidea.com

Blaze Communications Sun House, 64 Abbey Road, Enfield, Middlesex, EN1 2QN, United Kingdom
☎ (020) 8360 8244/ (020) 8364 3966
✉ hot@blazegroup.co.uk
🖳 www.blazegroup.co.uk

Blue Goose The Power House, 87 West Street, Harrow, Middlesex, HA1 3EL, United Kingdom
☎ (020) 8869 8500/ (020) 8869 8501
✉ design@bluegoose.co.uk
🖳 www.bluegoose.co.uk

Blue Sky Media Ltd 19-21 Uplands Crescent, Uplands, Swansea, SA2 0NX, United Kingdom
☎ (01792) 473235/ (01792) 472303
✉ info@bluesky-media.net
🖳 www.bluesky-media.net

Blueprint Design Co Ltd Martins Barn, Birdham Road, Chichester, West Sussex, PO20 7BX, United Kingdom
☎ (01243) 512106/ (01243) 514829
✉ michael.hendry@blueprint-design.co.uk
🖳 www.blueprint-design.co.uk

Bobbett Creative Ltd Unit 10 Woodfalls Farm, Gravelly Ways, Laddingford, Maidstone, Kent, ME18 6DA, United Kingdom
☏ (01622) 873800/✆ (01622) 873341
✎ jonathan@bobbett.com
🖳 www.bobbett.com

Bostock & Pollitt Ltd 9-10 Floral Street, London, WC2E 9HW, United Kingdom
☏ (020) 7379 6709/✆ (020) 7497 2333
✎ info@bostockandpollitt.com
🖳 www.bostockandpollitt.com

Bowes Design 30 Easton House, Grosvenor Bridge Road, Bath, BA1 6BG, United Kingdom
☏ (01225) 482780
✎ info@bowesdesign.com
🖳 www.bowesdesign.com

BranchCom Limited Arbor House, 139 Chepstow Avenue, Sale, Cheshire, M33 4GP, United Kingdom
☏ (0870) 742 3985
✎ sales@avwork.co.uk
🖳 www.avwork.co.uk

Brand Experience Co. 34-40 King Street, Norwich, NR1 1PD, United Kingdom
☏ (01603) 612792/✆ (01603) 615268
✎ info@brandex.co.uk
🖳 www.brandex.co.uk

Brazil Design Ltd 53 The Parade, Cardiff, CF24 3AB, United Kingdom
☏ (029) 2045 2244/✆ (029) 2045 3738
✎ enquiries@brazildesign.co.uk
🖳 www.brazildesign.co.uk

Brett Mead Flat 51, 41 Provost Street, London, N1 7NB, United Kingdom
☏ (07784) 983782

Brever Web Design Edinburgh 60a Craigour Drive, Edinburgh, EH17 7NT, United Kingdom
☏ (0845) 129 8534
✎ info@breverwebdesign.com
🖳 www.breverwebdesign.com

Bridge & Co. 25 Holliwell Row, London, EC2A 4XE, United Kingdom
☏ (020) 7539 3486/(07775) 560270
✎ sales@bridgeandco.com
🖳 www.bridgeandco.com

Brightsky Castle Court, 41 London Road, Reigate, Surrey, RH2 9RJ,
☏ 01737 735049
✎ martin@brightsky.biz
🖳 www.brightsky.biz

Brittan Design Partnership 7 The Old Fire Station Annexe, Fairfield Road, Market Harborough, Leicestershire, LE16 9QJ, United Kingdom
☏ (01858) 466950/✆ (01858) 434632
✎ enquiry@goto-bdp.co.uk
🖳 www.goto-bdp.co.uk

Browndog Design 3a Cartwright Ct, Bradley Business Pk, Dyson Wood Way, Huddersfield, HD2 1GN, United Kingdom
☏ (01484) 453131/✆ (01484) 540893
✎ info@browndog-design.com
🖳 www.browndog-design.com

Browndog Retail The Media Centre, 7 Northumberland St, Huddersfield, HD1 1RL, United Kingdom
☏ (01484) 487933/✆ (01484) 487934
✎ dan@browndog-retail.com
🖳 www.browndog-retail.com

Butcher-Doulton Communications Ltd, Royston, Hertfordshire, SG8 7WD, United Kingdom
☏ (01763) 208426/✆ (01763) 208396

Butler Cornfield Dedman 50A Rosebery Avenue, London, EC1R 4RP, United Kingdom
☏ (020) 7278 3999/✆ (020) 7278 3039
✎ mail@bcdonline.co.uk
🖳 www.bcdonline.co.uk

C A D A Design Group Suite 4, 155 Bermondsey Street, London, SE1 3UY, United Kingdom
☏ (020) 7234 9700/✆ (020) 7403 5692
✎ design@cada.co.uk
🖳 www.cada.co.uk

C Eye James House, 22-24 Corsham Street, London, N1 6DR, United Kingdom
☏ (020) 7490 2393/✆ (020) 7490 2487
✎ info@c-eye.co.uk
🖳 www.c-eye.co.uk

C G I BrandSense 14 St John's Square, London, EC1M 4NL, United Kingdom
☏ (020) 7566 4600/✆ (020) 7566 4555
✎ info@cgibrandsense.com
🖳 www.cgibrandsense.com

C M W North 3 Sovereign Place, Leeds, LS1 4SP, United Kingdom
☏ 0113-234 2022/✆ 0113-247 0265
🖳 www.cmwnorth.com

C'est Bon Sign 10 Rue Jean Sign, Grenoble, 38000, France
☏ 00 33 611 73 99 33
✎ gregory.thouvenin@cestbonsign.com
🖳 www.cestbonsign.com

Campbell Lumgair 165 Battersea Rise, London, SW11 1HP, United Kingdom
☏ (020) 7924 3363/(07966) 242640
✎ pst@campbell-lumgair.com
🖳 www.campbell-lumgair.com

Carnegie Orr Clerkenwell Workshops, 31 Clerkenwell Close, London, EC1R 0AT, United Kingdom
☏ (020) 7610 6140/✆ (020) 7384 2118
✎ info@carnegieorr.co.uk
🖳 www.carnegieorr.com

Caryl Harris Associates 2A Clareville Grove, London, SW7 5AR, United Kingdom
☏ (020) 7370 0922/✆ (020) 7244 8230
✎ ci@creativeinterpartners.co.uk
🖳 www.creativeinterpartners.co.uk

Causeway Communications Ltd 81 Whitfield Street, London, W1T 4HG, United Kingdom
☏ (020) 7255 5265/(07802) 430932 ✆ (020) 7255 5262
✎ info@causewaycommunications.com
🖳 www.causewaycommunications.com

Cesar Sassoon 16 Ambrose Avenue, London, NW11 9AN, United Kingdom
☏ (07956) 444440

Chapter & Verse 20 York Street, Bedford, MK40 3RJ, United Kingdom
☏ (01234) 345161
✎ david@chapterandverse.co.uk
🖳 www.chapterandverse.co.uk

COPYWRITING **with DESIGN in mind**

To length, on time, to budget.

B2B & B2C know-how across Financial, Legal, FMCG, Automotive, Transport and Leisure sectors.
Special presentation and beauty parade rates – UK and worldwide.

Arthur Pottersman

T 020 7431 7101   **M** 07929 011 113
E arthurp@wfscreate.com

Flat D, Second Floor, 33 Redington Road, London NW3 7QY

Checkland Kindleysides Design Ltd Charnwood Edge, Syston Road, Cossington, Leicester, LE7 4UZ, United Kingdom
☏ 0116-264 4700/✆ 0116-264 4701
✎ info@checkind.com
🖳 www.checkind.com

Chris Mitchell Epic Icons, Long Reach, Down Street, West Ashling, Chichester, West Sussex, PO18 8DP, United Kingdom
☏ (01243) 572099/(07802) 874349 ✆ (01243) 572099
✎ chris@epicicons.com
🖳 www.epicicons.com

Circle Design Morelands Building, Block C, 4th Floor, 5-23 Old Street, London, EC1V 9HL, United Kingdom
☏ (020) 7251 4687/✆ (020) 7251 4689
✎ neil.giles@circle-design.co.uk
🖳 www.circle-design.co.uk

City Creative Ltd City House, Swallowdale Lane, Hemel Hempstead Industrial Estate, Hemel Hempstead, Hertfordshire, HP2 7EA, United Kingdom
☏ (01442) 419419/✆ (01442) 419451
✎ info@city-creative.co.uk
🖳 www.city-creative.co.uk

Clift Jones Associates 26 Millers Close, Bishop's Stortford, Hertfordshire, CM23 4FJ, United Kingdom
☏ (01279) 656036
✎ cliftjones@ntlworld.com
🖳 www.cliftjones.com

Clinton-Smith Ltd 84 Haverstock Hill, Hampstead, London, NW3 2BD, United Kingdom
☏ (020) 7267 7727/✆ (020) 7482 3862
✎ info@clintonsmith.co.uk
🖳 www.clintonsmith.co.uk

Clyde Internet Media Ltd The Hexagon, 674 Pollokshaws Road, Glasgow, G41 2QE, United Kingdom
☏ 0870 4121050/✆ 0870 4121060
✎ hello@clydeinternetmedia.co.uk
🖳 www.clydeinternetmedia.co.uk/

Co-ord.com 9 Tynwald Road, West Kirby, Wirral, Merseyside, CH48 4DA, United Kingdom
☏ 0151-625 1443
✎ info@co-ord.com
🖳 www.co-ord.com

Coley Porter & Bell Ltd 18 Grosvenor Gardens, London, SW1W 0DH, United Kingdom
☏ (020) 7824 7700/✆ (020) 7824 7701
🖳 www.cpb.co.uk

Colin M. Bennett Branding Suite 27, 26 Charing Cross Road, London, WC2H 0DG, United Kingdom
☏ (020) 7836 8743/✆ (020) 7836 8743

Colourtech Unit 2 Stafford Cse, Fairwood Industrial Est, Ashford, Kent, TN23 4TT, United Kingdom
☏ 01233 642020/✆ 01233 632040
✎ Sarah@colourtechgroup.com
🖳 www.colourtechgroup.com

Commedia Studio 11 Model House Craft & Design Centre, Bull Ring, Llantrisant, Pontyclun, Mid Glamorgan, CF72 8EB, United Kingdom
☏ (01443) 230758/✆ (01443) 230759
✎ mark@commediaonline.co.uk
🖳 www.commediaonline.co.uk

Commune The Studio, 5-6 Eton Garages, London, NW3 4PE, United Kingdom
☎ (020) 7794 5558/✆ (020) 7794 4651
✉ response@commune.co.uk
🖥 www.commune.co.uk

Communique Group Ltd Studio 360, 26 Dunstaboe Road, Richmond, Surrey, TW9 1UH, United Kingdom
☎ (020) 8940 4444/(07721) 610957 ✆ (020) 8408 7846
✉ enquiries@communique360.co.uk
🖥 www.enquirie@communique360.co.uk

Communisis PLC Manston Lane, Crossgates, Leeds, LS15 8AH, United Kingdom
☎ 0113-225 2555/✆ 0113-225 2525
✉ enquiries@communisis-one.co.uk
🖥 www.communisis-one.co.uk

Contra 22 Ganton Street, London, W1F 7BY, United Kingdom
☎ (020) 7292 3939/✆ (020) 7292 3940
✉ info@contra.net
🖥 www.contra.net

Cooper Designs Beech House, 12 The Street, Uley, Dursley, Gloucestershire, GL11 5TE, United Kingdom
☎ (01453) 860979
✉ cooperdesigns@btopenworld.com

Corporate Edge Ltd Lyric House, 149 Hammersmith Road, London, W14 0QL, United Kingdom
☎ (020) 7855 5888/✆ (020) 7855 5750
🖥 www.corporateedge.com

Corporation Pop Ltd 22 Lever Street, Manchester, M1 1EA, United Kingdom
☎ 0161-228 7772/✆ 0161-228 7776
✉ info@copop.co.uk
🖥 www.copop.co.uk

Countryscape 125 Ducie House, Ducie Street, Manchester, M1 2JW, United Kingdom
☎ 0161-236 3432/✆ (0870) 0523 270
✉ info@countryscape.org
🖥 www.countryscape.org

Create One Media Solutions 48 Trinity Hall Close, Watford, WD24 4GN, United Kingdom
☎ (08708) 791181/✆ (08701) 276922
✉ info@creteone.biz
🖥 www.createone.biz

Creative Core Ltd Suite 4A Riverside Business Centre, North Esplanade West, Aberdeen, AB11 5RJ, UK
☎ (01224) 577130/✆ (01224) 577139
✉ info@creativecore.net
🖥 www.creativecore.net

Creative Edge Design & Advertising 1st Floor Donald Hendry Building, Auchincruive, Ayr, KA6 5HW, United Kingdom
☎ (01292) 521404/✆ (01292) 521693
✉ paul@cedge.co.uk
🖥 www.cedge.co.uk

Creative Line Design Group Purley House, Todds Green, Stevenage, Hertfordshire, SG1 2JE, United Kingdom
☎ (01438) 352525
✉ creativeline@creativeline.co.uk
🖥 www.creativeline.co.uk

Creative Sponge 1 Netherconesford, King Street, Norwich, NR1 1PH, United Kingdom
☎ (01603) 622766/✆ (01603) 622347
✉ info@creativesponge.co.uk
🖥 www.creativesponge.co.uk

Crescent Lodge Foundation House, Perseverance Works, 38 Kingsland Road, London, E2 8DD, United Kingdom
☎ (020) 7613 0613/✆ (020) 7729 0500
✉ design@crescentlodge.co.uk
🖥 www.crescentlodge.co.uk

D F P Associates Ltd Burnhill Business Centre, 50 Burnhill Road, Beckenham, Kent, BR3 3LA, United Kingdom
☎ (020) 8290 6901
✉ design@zoo.co.uk
🖥 www.dfpassociates.co.uk

D S M Design Beta Centre, 262 Ringwood Road, Poole, Dorset, BH14 0RS, United Kingdom
☎ (01202) 746661/✆ (01202) 746662
✉ sales@dsm-design.co.uk
🖥 www.dsm-design.co.uk

D2L 4 Lapwing Lane, Manchester, M20 2WS, United Kingdom
☎ (0161) 4456814/✆ (0161) 4476081
✉ sion@design2last.com
🖥 www.design2last.com

D8 93 Hope Street, Glasgow, G2 6LD, United Kingdom
☎ 0141-572 0810/✆ 0141-572 0811
✉ info@d8web.co.uk
🖥 www.d8web.co.uk

Dalziel & Pow Ltd 5-8 Hardwick Street, London, EC1R 4RG, United Kingdom
☎ (020) 7837 7117/✆ (020) 7837 7137
✉ info@dalziel-pow.co.uk
🖥 www.dalziel-pow.co.uk

dare! 3 East Causeway Close, Leeds, LS16 8LN, United Kingdom
☎ 0113 281 7080/✆ 0113 281 7088
✉ dare.smt@virgin.net

David Higham 5-8 Lower John Street, Golden Square, London, W1F 9HA, United Kingdom
☎ (020) 7437 7888/✆ (020) 7437 1072
✉ carolinewalsh@davidhigham.co.uk
🖥 www.davidhigham.co.uk

David Will & Associates 24 Cauldstream Place, Glasgow, G62 7NL, United Kingdom
☎ 0141-955 0303/✆ 0141-955 0309
✉ davidwill@btconnect.com

Deep LLP 12a Imperial Studios, 3-11 Imperial Road, London, SW6 2AG, United Kingdom
☎ (020) 7751 0824/✆ (020) 7751 0823
✉ dom@deep.co.uk
🖥 www.deep.co.uk

design @ perfect Ridge House, Kemerton Road, Beckenham, Kent, BR3 6NJ, United Kingdom
☎ (020) 8663 1613/✆ (020) 8650 1033
✉ info@designatperfect.com
🖥 www.designatperfect.com

Design Board Worleigh House, 12 Greenleighs, Sedgley, Dudley, West Midlands, DY3 3RZ, United Kingdom
☎ (01902) 661199/✆ (01902) 665333
✉ info@designboard.co.uk
🖥 www.designboard.co.uk

Design Bridge Ltd 18 Clerkenwell Close, London, EC1R 0QN, United Kingdom
☎ (020) 7814 9922/✆ (020) 7814 9024
✉ enquiries@designbridge.co.uk
🖥 www.designbridge.co.uk

Design Directions Ltd Flagstaff House, 12 High Street, Twyford, RG10 9AE, United Kingdom
☎ 0118-934 4477/✆ 0118-932 1292
✉ info@designdirections.co.uk
🖥 www.designdirections.co.uk

Design Group 111 Charterhouse Street, London, EC1M 6AW, United Kingdom
☎ (020) 7608 1144/✆ (020) 7253 7658
🖥 www.the-design-group.co.uk

Design Identity 55 Cross Lane, Wakefield, West Yorkshire, WF2 8DA, United Kingdom
☎ (01924) 387684
✉ info@designidentity.co.uk
🖥 www.designidentity.co.uk

Design Intuition 25 Sandown Road, Brighton, BN2 3EH, United Kingdom
☎ (07981) 877055
✉ rachel.north@gmail.com
🖥 www.foxlorecards.com

Design Principles The Studio, 3 Bridge Street, Kineton, Warwick, CV35 0HP, United Kingdom
☎ (01926) 641614
✉ studio@designprinciples.co.uk
🖥 www.designprinciples.co.uk

Design Quorum 9-10 Oxford Road, Tatling End, Gerrards Cross, Buckinghamshire, SL9 7AY, United Kingdom
☎ (01753) 891707/✆ (01753) 891777
✉ mail@tdq.co.uk
🖥 www.thedesignquorum.co.uk

Design Resource Clematis Cottage, Shelton, Newark, Nottinghamshire, NG23 5JL, United Kingdom
☎ (01949) 850867/(07774) 900258 .
✉ designresource@ng23.co.uk

design@djhunter 133 Ravensbourne Avenue, Bromley, BR2 0AZ, United Kingdom
☎ (020) 8466 7196/✆ (020) 8466 7196
✉ design@djhunter.co.uk

Designcrew Creative Media Centre, 45 Robertson Street, Hastings, East Sussex, TN34 1HL,
☎ 01424 205 499/01424 205 499
✉ danny@designcrew.co.uk
🖥 www.designcrew.co.uk

Designers 26 Fitzroy Square, London, W1P 6BT, United Kingdom
☎ (020) 7388 9228/✆ (020) 7388 9228
✉ designers@atlas.co.uk
🖥 www.designers_london.com

Designhouse 4 Duke Street, Richmond, Surrey, TW9 1HP, United Kingdom
☎ (020) 8439 9360/✆ (020) 8439 9373
✉ info@designhouse.co.uk
🖥 www.designhouse.co.uk

Designworld 59 Cowbridge Road East, Canton, Cardiff, CF11 9AE, United Kingdom
☎ (029) 2038 9840/✆ (029) 2023 5334
✉ kwright@design-world.org.uk
🖥 www.design-world.org.uk

Direct Works Ltd Unit 1, Union Park, Bircholt Road, Maidstone, Kent, ME15 9XT, United Kingdom
☎ (01622) 757111/✆ (01622) 757222
✉ matt@direct-works.com
🖥 www.direct-works.com

Domain Creative Associates Unit 1.5, Paintworks, Colthurst Mews, Bristol, BS4 3EH, United Kingdom
☎ 0117-972 8700/✆ 0117-972 8820
✉ stephen.fenton@domain-uk.com
🖥 www.domain-uk.com

Donnellyfoote 43 Belmont Street, Brighton, BN1 4HN, United Kingdom
☎ (01273) 604055
✉ lucy@donnellyfoote.com
🖥 www.donnellyfoote.com

DOT 16 High Street, Lewes, East Sussex, BN7 2LN, United Kingdom
☎ (01273) 477700
✉ tellmemore@dotco.co.uk
🖥 www.dotco.co.uk

Dragon 1 Craven Hill, London, W2 3EN, United Kingdom
☎ (020) 7262 4488/✆ (020) 7262 6406
✉ deborah.carter@dragonbrands.com
🖥 www.dragonbrands.com

Dreamdebris.com 255 Bluewater House, Riverside West, Smugglers Way, London, SW18 1EA, United Kingdom
☎ (07989) 574112
✉ anees@dreamdebris.com
🖥 www.dreamdebris.com

Dreamscape Design Elliot Park Innovations Centre, Unit 1.7, Elliot Park, Barling Way, Nuneaton, Warwickshire, CV10 7RH, United Kingdom
☎ (0800) 0197034
✉ info@dreamscapedesign.co.uk
🖥 www.dreamscapedesign.co.uk

e-novations.co.uk Angel House, 225 Marsh Wall, Docklands, London, E14 9FW, United Kingdom
☎ (0870) 7605100/✆ (0870) 1319236
✉ manoj@e-novations.co.uk
🖥 www.e-novations.co.uk

Eden Co. 2nd Floor, Barratt House, 341-349 Oxford Street, London, W1C 2JE, United Kingdom
☎ (020) 7629 8177/✆ (020) 7495 5720
🖥 www.eden-co.co.uk

Egelnick and Webb 23 Charlotte Road, London, EC2A 3PB, United Kingdom
☎ (020) 7739 3339/✆ (020) 7739 3799
✉ mail@egelnickandwebb.com
🖥 www.egelnickandwebb.co.uk

Elements Creative 1 Fountain Hall Road, Edinburgh, EH9 2NL, United Kingdom
☎ 0131-667 2220/078 02818919 ✆ 0131-667 1022
✉ media@elementscreative.com

Elite Edge Marketing Consultants Ltd Technology House, Lissadel Street, Salford, M6 6AP, United Kingdom
☎ (0161) 278 2788/✆ (0161) 278 2789
✉ mmc@elite-edge.co.uk
🖥 www.elite-edge.co.uk

Elliott Young Ltd Millennium House, 7 High Street, Hampton, Middlesex, TW12 2SA, United Kingdom
☎ (0845) 0540070/✆ (0870) 7627106
✉ daniel@elliottyoung.com
🖥 www.elliottyoung.co.uk

Ellis James Creative Consultants 21 Barkers Mead, Brimsham Park, Yate, Bristol, BS37 7LF, United Kingdom
☎ (01454) 318572
✉ info@ellis-james.co.uk
🖥 www.ellis-james.co.uk

Emperor Design Consultants Zetland House, 5-25 Scrutton Street, London, EC2A 4HJ, United Kingdom
(020) 7729 9090
robert.b@emperordesign.co.uk
www.emperordesign.co.uk

English & Pockett Ltd 13-19 Vine Hill, London, EC1R 5DW, United Kingdom
(020) 7278 4272/ (020) 7278 8632
info@english-pockett.com
www.english-pockett.com

Enterprise IG Burgoine Quay, 8 Lower Teddington Road, Hampton Wick, Kingston upon Thames, Surrey, KT1 4ER, United Kingdom
(020) 8943 9555/ (020) 8943 9515
www.enterpriseig.com

Et al 32 East Street, Oxford, OX2 0AU, United Kingdom
(01865) 243343/ (01865) 248348
mail@etal-design.com
www.etal-design.com

Evans May Partnership 1 Waterloo Court, 10 Theed Street, London, SE1 8ST, United Kingdom
(020) 7928 5388
info@evansmay.co.uk
www.evansmay.co.uk

Evolution Design 29 Dundas Street, Edinburgh, EH3 6QQ, United Kingdom
0131-556 8562
neale@evolution-design.co.uk
www.evolution-design.co.uk

Eyelevel Design Consultants Stain Street Nursey, Codmore Hill, Pulborough, West Sussex, RH20 1BQ, United Kingdom
(01798) 875525
info@eyeleveldesign.co.uk
www.eyeleveldesign.co.uk

F B A Unit 4, Cefn Llan Science Park, Aberystwyth, Dyfed, SY23 3AH, United Kingdom
(01970) 636400/ (01970) 636414
engs@fbagroup.co.uk
www.fbagroup.co.uk

Fabric Brantridge Lane, Balcombe, Haywards Heath, West Sussex, RH17 6JR, United Kingdom
(01444) 400781/ (01444) 400781
info@fabric-design.co.uk
www.farbric-design.co.uk

Farrow Design 23-24 Great James Street, Bloomsbury, London, WC1N 3ES, United Kingdom
(020) 7404 4225/ (020) 7404 4223
studio@farrowdesign.com
www.farrowdesign.com

Fingo Marketing 1a Church Street, Epsom, Surrey, KT17 4PF, United Kingdom
(0870) 1993363/ (0870) 1991631
info@fingo.co.uk
www.fingomedia.co.uk

Fire & Ice Creative The Old Stable, Moor Lane, East Coker, Yeovil, Somerset, BA22 9JR, United Kingdom
(01935) 864588/ (01935) 864588
chantelle@fireandicecreative.com
www.fireandicecreative.com

Fire I M C 10 Dargan Crescent, Duncrue Road, Belfast, BT3 9JP, United Kingdom
(028) 9077 4388/ (028) 9077 6906
info@fireimc.com
www.fireimc.com

Firedog Design Ltd 43/44 Hoxton Square, London, N1 9PB, United Kingdom
(020) 7739 1112/ (020) 7729 1002
info@firedog-design.co.uk
www.firedog-design.co.uk

Fleet Design Consultants Upnor Road, Upnor, Rochester, Kent, ME2 4UP, United Kingdom
(01634) 294466/ (01634) 294466
chris@fleetdesign.com
www.fleetdesign.com

Fletcher Ward Design 27 Albemarle Street, London, W1S 4HZ, United Kingdom
(020) 7491 4399
fwd@fletcherwarddesign.co.uk
www.fletcherwarddesign.co.uk

Fluid Business Communications Unit 1, Europa Park, Croft Way, Witham, Essex, CM8 2FN, United Kingdom
(01376) 515573
john@fluid-communications.com
www.fluid-communications.com

Fly on the Wire Ltd 4th Floor Argyle House, Marketgait, Dundee, DD1 1QP, United Kingdom
(01382) 228947/ (0870) 1366817
anique@flyonthewire.com
www.flyonthewire.com

Foil Ltd The Warehouse, 1A Stamford Street, Leicester, LE1 6NL, United Kingdom
0116-233 3413/ 0116-233 3414
info@foildesign.com
www.foildesign.com

Format Design Ltd 25 St Andrews, Norwich, NR2 4TP, United Kingdom
(01603) 215115/ (01603) 215116
contact@format-design.co.uk
www.format-design.co.uk

Fox & Hoyle 33 Wootton Street, Cosham, Portsmouth, PO6 3AP, United Kingdom
(023) 9238 5715/ (023) 9221 0983
fox-hoyle@fox-hoyle.co.uk
www.fox-hoyle.co.uk

Fox Design Consultants The Studio, Broadmead House, Crockerton, Warminster, Wiltshire, BA12 8AQ, United Kingdom
(01985) 219133/ (01985) 219973
info@foxdc.co.uk
www.foxdc.co.uk

Frank! Communication Solutions 29 Channel View Road, Brighton, BN2 6DR, United Kingdom
(01273) 681117
jo@frankontheweb.com
www.frankontheweb.com

Freeway Media Ltd 20 Orange Street, London, WC2H 7EF, United Kingdom
(020) 7389 0800/ (020) 7839 6719
info@freewaymedia.com
www.freewaymedia.com

Frost Design London Ltd The Gymnasium, 56 Kingsway Place, Sands Walk, London, EC1R 0LU, United Kingdom
(020) 7490 7994/ (020) 7490 7995
info@frostdesign.co.uk
www.frostdesign.co.uk

Funky Concepts 5 Lansdowne Close, Coseley, Bilston, West Midlands, WV14 9TR, United Kingdom
(01902) 651239/ (01902) 651239
info@funkyconecpts.co.uk
www.funkyconcepts.co.uk

Fuze Design 25 Layters Avenue, Chalfont St. Peter, Gerrards Cross, Buckinghamshire, SL9 9HP, United Kingdom
(01753) 202555
claire@fuzedesign.co.uk
www.fuzedesign.co.uk

G M T Design Ltd 24-31 Greenwich Market, Greenwich, London, SE10 9HZ, United Kingdom
(020) 8858 6700/ (020) 8858 6111
info@gmtdesign.co.uk
www.gmtdesign.co.uk

G2G3 Media Ltd Panama House, 14 The High Street, Lasswade, Edinburgh, EH18 1ND, United Kingdom
0131-202 2000/ 0131-663 8194
media@g2g3.com
www.g2g3.com

Gamma Three 1 Bedford Street, Hitchin, Hertfordshire, SG5 2JG, United Kingdom
(01462) 457233/ (01462) 457232
studio@gammathree.com
www.gammathree.com

Gardiner Richardson Generator Studios, Trafalgar Street, Newcastle upon Tyne, NE1 2LA, United Kingdom
0191-261 4250/ 0191-261 4026
enquiries@gardiner-richardson.com
www.gardiner-richardson.com

George Robinson 36 Grove Street, Edinburgh, EH3 8AZ, United Kingdom
0131-229 1524
george.e.robinson@btinternet.com

Gilderson Print Ltd Ground Floor, 31-35 Pitfield Street, London, N1 6HB, United Kingdom
(020) 7324 0180/ (020) 7490 4333
studio@gildersons.co.uk
www.gildersons.co.uk

Giraffe Print, Epsom, Surrey, KT18 7WJ, United Kingdom
0800 328 4712
info@giraffeprint.com
www.giraffeprint.com

Glass 35 Kingsland Road, London, E2 8AA, United Kingdom
(020) 7613 7751
kevin.eade@glasspartnership.co.uk
www.glasspartnership.co.uk

Glazer Ltd The People's Hall, 2 Olaf Street, London, W11 4BD, United Kingdom
(020) 7221 2595/ (020) 7221 2667
ian@glazer.co.uk
www.glazer.co.uk

GMID Design for Business Prospect Hse, 3 Prospect Pl, Swansea, SA1 1QP, United Kingdom
(01792) 641350/ (01792) 301548
studio@gmid.net
www.gmid.net

Golden Section 1 Water Lane, Little Plumpstead, Norwich, NR13 5EX, United Kingdom
(01603) 716699
golden.section@virgin.net
www.golden-section.co.uk

Gorard Dean Coach House, 8 Over Hill, Warlingham, Surrey, CR6 9JR, United Kingdom
(020) 8543 9669/ (020) 8545 0355
stuart_duncan@gorarddean.com
www.gorarddean.com

Gosling Old Batford Mill, Lower Luton Road, Harpenden, Hertfordshire, AL5 5BZ, United Kingdom
(01582) 466477/ (01582) 466478
info@goslingdesign.com
www.goslingdesign.com

Gough Allen Stanley Advertising & Marketing Ltd Kembrey House, 5 Worcester Road, Bromsgrove, Worcestershire, B61 7DL, United Kingdom
(01527) 579555/ (01527) 579902
natalie@gough.co.uk
www.gough.co.uk

Graphic Ad Unit 1, Morfield Business Park, Yeadon, Yeadon, LS19 7BN, United Kingdom
0113-250 2188/ 0113-250 2189
studio@graphic-ad.com
www.graphic-ad.com

H Factor Design Ltd 56 Rowallan Road, London, SW6 6AG, United Kingdom
(07761) 341412
info@hfactordesign.com

H G V 2-6 Northburgh Street, London, EC1V 0AY, United Kingdom
(020) 7336 6336/ (020) 7336 6345
design@hgv.co.uk
www.hgv.co.uk

Harlequin Solutions 2 Exmoor Street, London, W10 6BD, United Kingdom
(020) 8960 9400/ (020) 8964 0447
info@solutions.co.uk
www.solutions.co.uk

Harper Partnership The Studio, Micklems Farmhouse, Reading, RG10 9YD, United Kingdom
(01628) 519110/ (01628) 825711
rosemary@theharperpartnership.com
www.theharperpartnership.com

Harrison & Co. Manor Farm Business Centre, Poynings Road, Poynings, Brighton, BN45 7AG, United Kingdom
(01273) 857463
info@harrisonandco.com
www.harrisonandco.com

Henrion, Ludlow & Schmidt Ltd 12 Hobart Place, London, SW1W 0HH, United Kingdom
(020) 7245 4600/ (020) 7245 4601
info@henrion.com
www.henrion.com

Heroes Design Ltd Tower House, 139A Chinnor Road, Thame, Oxfordshire, OX9 3LS, United Kingdom
(01844) 261133
design@nick-abrey.co.uk
www.nick-abrey.co.uk

Hieroglyphics Ltd 54 Ayres Street, London, SE1 1EU, United Kingdom
(020) 7887 3993/ (020) 7403 5768
sales@hiero-design.co.uk
www.hiero-design.co.uk

Hierographics Ltd Designer House, Sandford Lane Industrial Estate, Sandford Lane, Wareham, Dorset, BH20 4DY, United Kingdom
(01929) 554454/ (01929) 554460
info@hierographics.co.uk
www.hierographics.co.uk

Hilton Creative Ltd 37 Rosewood Way, Farnham Common, Slough, SL2 3QD, United Kingdom
(01753) 648149/ (01753) 648149
design@hiltoncreative.co.uk
www.hiltoncreative.co.uk

Hobb Plus Minerva House, 1-4 North Crescent, London, WC1E 7ER, United Kingdom
☎ (020) 7631 2800/✆ (020) 7631 9660
✉ info@hobbplus.com
🖥 www.hobbplus.com

Hookson Ltd 30 Annandale Street Lane, Edinburgh, EH7 4LS, United Kingdom
☎ 0131-524 7940/✆ 0131-524 7941
✉ creative@hookson.co
🖥 www.hookson.com

Horrex Davis Design Associates Ltd (HDDA) 29 Dorset Street, London, W1U 8AT, United Kingdom
☎ (020) 7486 8132/✆ (020) 7487 2936
✉ design@hdda.co.uk
🖥 www.hdda.co.uk

Hot Frog Graphics Stanmore, 4 Moorland Avenue, Barnsley, South Yorkshire, S70 6PQ, United Kingdom
☎ (01226) 242777/✆ (01226) 242777
✉ hotfroggraphics@blueyonder.co.uk
🖥 www.hotfroggraphics.com

HTDL The Courtyard, 132 Widney Lane, Solihull, West Midlands, B91 3LH, United Kingdom
☎ 0121-711 4878/✆ 0121-711 4767
✉ at@htdl.co.uk
🖥 www.htdl.co.uk

Iimage Marketing Ltd 22 Westbrook Road, Reading, RG30 1LB, United Kingdom
☎ 0118-956 9874
✉ pjtoner@iimage.co.uk
🖥 www.iimage.co.uk

Illustrated History Albion Wharf, 19 Albion Street, Manchester, M1 5LN, United Kingdom
☎ 0161 2346544/✆ 0161 2477959
✉ studio@illustrated-history.net
🖥 www.illustrated-history.net

In Unison Design Consultants 2nd Floor, 20 Lincoln's Inn Fields, London, WC2A 3ED, United Kingdom
☎ (020) 7396 7405/✆ (020) 7831 4044
✉ mgore@inunison.co.uk
🖥 www.inunison.co.uk

Incentive Solutions Incentive Hse, 115 Pilkington Ave, Sutton Coldfield, West Midlands, B72 1LQ, United Kingdom
☎ (0845) 4084783/✆ (0709) 2876085
✉ davidh@incentive-solutions.co.uk
🖥 www.incentive-solutions.co.uk

Intermarketing & Communications Ltd 3-5 Alma Road, Headingley, Leeds, LS6 2AH, United Kingdom
☎ 0113-275 3912/✆ 0113-275 3174
🖥 www.intermarketing.co.uk

Intuitive Marketing Communicat 120 Anyards Road, Cobham, Surrey, KT11 2LH, United Kingdom
☎ (01932) 864946/✆ (01932) 869513

Irebel 12 Printers Land, Clarkston, Glasgow, G76 8HP, United Kingdom
☎ 0141-644 5703
✉ info@irebel.co.uk
🖥 www.irebel.co.uk

Irrational Design 122 Hollydale Road, London, SE15 2TQ, United Kingdom
☎ (07956) 512509
✉ andy.knowles@irrational.info
🖥 www.irrational.info

Irwin Stuart Design 8 Sandyford Place, Glasgow, G3 7NB, United Kingdom
☎ 0141-572 9000/✆ 0141-572 9100
✉ irwin-stuart@btconnect.com
🖥 www.irwin-stuart.com

Itonic Design Ltd 38 Coombe Lea, Grand Avenue, Hove, East Sussex, BN3 2ND, United Kingdom
☎ (01273) 720608
✉ mail@itonicdesign.com
🖥 www.itonicdesign.com

IUVO Design 93 Rivington Street, Elektra House, London, EC2A 3AY, United Kingdom
☎ (020) 7729 2006/✆ (07092) 872999
✉ studio@iuvodesign.co.uk
🖥 www.iuvodesign.com

J D P S Third Floor, Redwither Tower, Wrexham, Clwyd, LL13 9XR, United Kingdom
☎ (01978) 664458
✉ studio@jpds.co.uk
🖥 www.jpds.co.uk

JacoByte Ltd 35 Dundonald Road, Dreghorn, Irvine, Ayrshire, KA11 4AN, United Kingdom
☎ (0845) 226 0084
✉ info@jacobyte.co.uk
🖥 www.jacobyte.co.uk

James Willis 3 Old Garden House, The Lanterns, London, SW11 3AD, United Kingdom
☎ (020) 7801 3176/078 36 226597
✉ info@willismck.com

Jannuzzi Smith 29 Queen Elizabeth Street, London, SE1 2LP, United Kingdom
☎ (020) 7234 0557
✉ email@jannuzzismith.com
🖥 www.jannuzzismith.com

JeremyGetsCash 505 Hackney Road, London, E2 9ED, United Kingdom
☎ (020) 8299 1737/(07944) 450422
✉ jeremy@jeremygetscash.com
🖥 www.jeremygetscash.com

John Brown Design 1 Arundel Gardens, Rayleigh, Essex, SS6 9GS, United Kingdom
☎ (01268) 786442/✆ (0870) 1166144
✉ studio@johnbrowndesign.co.uk
🖥 www.johnbrowndesign.co.uk

John Vernon Design The Studio, 24 Alric Avenue, New Malden, Surrey, KT3 4JN, United Kingdom
☎ (020) 8942 8273
✉ mail@johnvernon-design.co.uk
🖥 www.johnvernon-design.co.uk

Jolanta Damski Freelance Design Flat 1, 40 Ewelme Road, London, SE23 3BH, United Kingdom
☎ (020) 8291 6023
✉ jolantadamski@btinternet.com
🖥 www.jolantadamski.co.uk

Jordan Design 16 Berkeley Place, Wimbledon, London, SW19 4NN, United Kingdom
☎ (020) 8947 8540/✆ (020) 8296 9229
✉ juliet@jordan-design.co.uk
🖥 jordan-design.co.uk

Jory & Co. 22b Leathermarket Street, London, SE1 3HB, United Kingdom
☎ (020) 7407 7819/✆ (020) 7407 7887
🖥 www.jory.co.uk

K A G Design Ltd Hazelhurst, 13 Chequers Road, Basingstoke, Hampshire, RG21 7PX, United Kingdom
☎ (01256) 844566/✆ (01256) 460255
✉ email@kag-design.co.uk
🖥 www.kag-design.co.uk

Kopanska 13 Grosvenor Crescent, Glasgow, G12 9AF, United Kingdom
☎ 0141-342 4539
✉ info@kopanska.com
🖥 www.kopanska.com

Korysanders 20 Great Portland Street, London, W1W 8QR, United Kingdom
☎ (020) 7637 2960/✆ (020) 7637 2959
✉ design@korysanders.co.uk
🖥 www.korysanders.co.uk

LaGrafica 3 Ivor Park, Brynsadler, Pontyclun, Mid Glamorgan, CF72 9BF, United Kingdom
☎ (07782) 660 855/✆ (01443) 222 860
✉ dan@lagrafica.co.uk
🖥 www.lagrafica.co.uk

Lanecreative 54 Norwood Road, London, SE24 9BH, United Kingdom
☎ (07734) 200730/✆ (020) 7681 1157
✉ andy@lanecreative.co.uk
🖥 www.lanecreative.co.uk

Langsford Corporate Design Cole Street Studios, 6-8 Cole Street, London, SE1 4YH, United Kingdom
☎ (020) 7378 1457/✆ (020) 7403 9014
✉ p.langsford@langsford.co.uk
🖥 www.langsford.co.uk

Lateral Line Creative Services 27-29 Goosestep Lane, Glasgow, G1 5HT, United Kingdom
☎ 0141-226 3335/✆ 0141-226 3337
✉ enquiry@lateralline.co.uk
🖥 www.lateralline.co.uk

Lenco International Ltd Pembroke Hse, 53 George St, Grantham, Lincolnshire, NG31 6QL, United Kingdom
☎ 01476 590297/✆ 01476 591055
✉ marketing@lenco.co.uk
🖥 www.lenco.co.uk

Leodis Photography Ltd 11 St Annes Lane, Headingley, Leeds, LS4 2SE, United Kingdom
☎ 0113-278 9339/(07801) 913800 ✆ 0113-289 9908
✉ create@leodis.com
🖥 www.leodis.com

Lewis Moberly Ltd 33 Gresse Street, London, W1T 1QU, United Kingdom
☎ (020) 7580 9252/✆ (020) 7255 1671
✉ hallo@lewismoberly.com
🖥 www.lewismoberly.com

Lighthouse Belgrave House, 7 Belgrave Terrace, Aberdeen, AB25 2NR, United Kingdom
☎ (01224) 627396/✆ (01224) 621115
✉ info@lighthousethinking.com
🖥 www.lighthousethinking.com

Limehouse Group Ltd 4th Floor, 1 London Bridge, London, SE1 9BG, United Kingdom
☎ (020) 7939 7100/✆ (020) 7939 7101
✉ stephenb@limehouse.co.uk
🖥 www.limehouse.co.uk

Lippa Pearce 11 Need Hand Road, Twickenham, TW1 2RP, United Kingdom
☎ (020) 7229 3477/✆ (020) 7727 9932
✉ email@pentagram.co.uk
🖥 www.pentagram.co.uk

Llewelyn-Davies Brook House, 2-16 Torrington Place, London, WC1E 7HN, United Kingdom
☎ (020) 7637 0181/✆ (020) 7637 8740
✉ info@ldavies.com
🖥 www.ldavies.com

Lloyd Northover Kings Court, 2-16 Goodge Street, London, W1T 2QA, United Kingdom
☎ (020) 7420 4850/✆ (020) 7420 4858
🖥 www.lloydnorthover.com

Logo Design Ltd Engine House, The Flete Estate, Ivybridge, Devon, PL21 9NX, United Kingdom
☎ (01752) 830000/✆ (01752) 830529
✉ enquiries@logodesign.co.uk
🖥 www.logodesign.co.uk

Longneck Afgan Road 27, Battersea, London, SW11 2QD,
☎ 7506018062
✉ vlad@longneck.ro
🖥 www.longneck.ro

Lucian Marin, Bucharest, 61079, Romania
☎ 721 230 631
✉ lucian.marin@gmail.com
🖥 www.lucianmarin.ro

Luminous & Reputation Management Ltd 6A New Concordia Wharf, Mill Street, London, SE1 2BB, United Kingdom
☎ (020) 7394 2737/✆ (020) 7394 2731
✉ brightideas@luminous.co.uk
🖥 www.luminous.co.uk

Lumsden Design Partnership 1 Hanover Yard, Noel Road, London, N1 8YA, United Kingdom
☎ (020) 7288 4290/✆ (020) 7288 4291
✉ info@ldp.co.uk
🖥 www.ldp.co.uk

M 4 Design Co. Ltd Pound Court, Pound Street, Newbury, Berkshire, RG14 6AA, United Kingdom
☎ (01635) 524055/✆ (01635) 43275
✉ john@m4design.co.uk
🖥 www.m4design.co.uk

M H G Design The Old Kilim Warehouse, 28A Pickets Street, London, SW12 8QB, United Kingdom
☎ (020) 8675 6644/✆ (020) 8675 9944
✉ info@mhgdesign.co.uk
🖥 www.mhgdesign.co.uk

M W A Marketing & Creative Design 16 Coniscliffe Road, Darlington, County Durham, DL3 7RG, United Kingdom
☎ (01325) 369919/✆ (01325) 369919
✉ info@mwamarketing.com
🖥 www.mwamarketing.com

Magnetic Design 10 Millford Place, Kings Heath, Birmingham, B14 7LS, United Kingdom
☎ (07759) 057549
✉ info@magnetic-design.co.uk
🖥 www.magnetic-design.co.uk

Map Ref Ltd 5/1 53 Morrison Street, Glasgow, G5 8LB, United Kingdom
☎ 0141-429 7956
✉ contact@mapref.co.uk
🖥 www.mapref.co.uk

Mark Wolstencroft - Design & Strategic Brand Consulting The City Arc, 7 Curtain Road, London, EC2A 3LT, United Kingdom
☎ (020) 7917 2957
✉ mark@mark-wolstencroft.com
🖥 www.mark-wolstencroft.com

Marketplace Design Ltd, London, United Kingdom
(020) 7420 4850/ (01235) 532878
richardh@marketplace-design.co.uk
www.marketplace-design.co.uk

Marlin Design & Marketing Thomas Street, Stretford, Manchester, M32 0JT, United Kingdom
0161-864 1134/ 0161-864 5240
kj@marlindesign.co.uk
www.marlindesign.co.uk

Marsh & Malone Bower Cottage, High Street, Limpsfield, Oxted, Surrey, RH8 0DY, United Kingdom
(01883) 730610/ (01883) 370600
tony@marshandmalone.com
www.marshandmalone.co.uk

Martin Lock Associates Ltd 19 Inner Courtyard, Whiteway Farm, Cirencester, Gloucestershire, GL7 7BA, United Kingdom
(01285) 885803/ (01285) 640064
talkto@mla-design.co.uk
www.mla-design.co.uk

Maxim Design Group Ltd 6 Manor Park, Banbury, Oxfordshire, OX16 3TB, United Kingdom
(01295) 277200/ (01295) 275671
central@maximgroup.co.uk
www.maximgroup.co.uk

MCC Creative 4, Park Farm, Chichester Road, Arundel, West Sussex, BN18 0AG,
01903 885 235
dan@m-c-c.biz
www.mcccreative.co.uk

McCombie Skinner 1-5 Beehive Place, London, SW9 7QR, United Kingdom
(020) 7274 2244

Mercer Design & Photography Chapel Studio, Downhead, Shepton Mallet, Somerset, BA4 4LQ, United Kingdom
(01749) 880523/ (01749) 880690
tim@mercerdesign.co.uk
www.mercerdesign.co.uk

Met Studio 5 Maidstone Buildings Mews, 72-76 Borough High Street, London, SE1 1GN, United Kingdom
(020) 7378 7348/ (020) 7378 7330
reception@metstudio.com
www.metstudio.com

Milestone Strategic Design Ltd 1 The Highway, Beaconsfield, Buckinghamshire, HP9 1QD, United Kingdom
(01494) 676436/ (01494) 676438
info@milestonedesign.co.uk
www.milestonedesign.co.uk

Mind's Eye Design Ltd Carn Brea, Shutta Road, Looe, Cornwall, PL13 1HW, United Kingdom
(01503) 264422/ (01503) 264422
www.mindseyedesign.co.uk

Minx Creative 2 Old Library Court, 45 Gillender Street, London, E14 6RN, United Kingdom
(020) 7510 1005/ (020) 7510 1007
roz@minxcreative.com
www.minxcreative.com

Modus Media Ltd 18 Iliffe Yard, London, SE17 3QA, United Kingdom
0207 77406045
info@modus-media.com
www.modus-media.com

Monastery Design 2 Roseneath, Bramhall, Stockport, Cheshire, SK7 3LP, United Kingdom
0161-485 4777/ 0161-485 6444
mail@monasterydesign.co.uk
www.monasterydesign.co.uk

Mountain Creative Design Consultancy 1 Park Tce, Glasgow, G3 6BY, United Kingdom
0141-332 8007/ 0141-332 8822
info@mountaincdc.com
www.mountaincdc.com

Mpjdesign Ltd Wareton, Calcott Hill, Sturry, Canterbury, Kent, CT3 4ND, United Kingdom
(01227) 713181
martin@mpjdesign.ltd.uk
www.mpjdesign.ltd.uk

My Mate Dave Designs 5 Buchanan Court, Buchanan Drive, Luton, Beds, LU2 0SA,
7736939770
d.sweeney@ntlworld.com
www.mymatedaves.co.uk

N9 Design 33 Looe Street, Plymouth, PL4 0EA, United Kingdom
(0870) 2422928
nick@n9design.com
www.n9design.com

Natural Associates 55 Charterhouse Street, London, EC1M 6HA, United Kingdom
(020) 7490 4575/ (020) 7490 4307
linda.vaux@naturalassociates.com
www.naturalassociates.com

Navyblue Design 3rd Floor, 5-23 Old Street, London, EC1V 9HL, United Kingdom
(020) 7253 0316/ (020) 7553 9409
geoff.nicol@navyblue.com
www.navyblue.com

Neujuice Design 45 Gloucester Street, Brighton, BN1 4EW, United Kingdom
(01273) 688872/ (0870) 168 0590
info@neujuice.com
www.neujuice.com

New Moon Graphics 15A Main Street, Doagh, Ballyclare, County Antrim, BT39 0QL, United Kingdom
(028) 9334 2369/ (028) 9334 2990
navin@newmoongraphics.co.uk
www.newmoongraphics.co.uk

Newenglish Pilgrim House, 10 Bishop Street, Leicester, LE1 6AF, United Kingdom
0116-291 5375
design@newenglish.co.uk
www.newenglish.co.uk

Newton E H 6 13-15 Circus Lane, Edinburgh, EH3 6SU, United Kingdom
0131-220 4141/ 0131-220 4004
design@newtoneh6.com
www.newtoneh6.com

Nigel Abbey Design 1 Hayward Road, Thames Ditton, Surrey, KT7 0BF, United Kingdom
(020) 8947 9955/(07947) 684126 / (020) 8398 1491
info@nigelabbeydesign.com
www.nigelabbeydesign.com

Nim Design The Old Bank, 92 High Street, Harrow, Middlesex, HA1 3LP, United Kingdom
(020) 8426 6888/ (020) 8426 9888
info@nimdesign.com
www.nimdesign.com

Ninety Degrees Design and Marketing Ltd 30 King St, Manchester, M2 6AZ, United Kingdom
0161-833 1890/ 0161-833 1690
jules@90degrees.com
www.90degrees.com

Nomas Creative Ltd Widbury Farmhouse, Widbury Hill, Ware, Hertfordshire, SG12 7QE, United Kingdom
(01920) 462302
studio@nomascreative.com
www.nomascreative.com

North Unit G2, The Glasshouse, 3 Royal Oak Yard, Bermondsey Street, London, SE1 3GD, United Kingdom
(020) 7357 0071/ (020) 7490 4968
info@northdesign.co.uk
www.northdesign.co.uk

Northbank Design Ltd 16 Gay Street, Bath, BA1 2PH, United Kingdom
(01225) 332703/ (01225) 332802
studio@northbankdesign.co.uk
www.northbankdesign.co.uk

O'Zone Communications Ltd 4 Crown Street, Harrow, Middlesex, HA2 0HR, United Kingdom
(020) 8426 9999/ (020) 8426 4951
numerouno@o-zone.co.uk
www.o-zone.co.uk

Onepom 17 Spa Court, 79 Rouel Road, London, SE16 3SL, United Kingdom
(020) 7252 2205/ (020) 7761 6962
contact@onepom.com
www.onepom.com

Open Agency Mill House, 8 Mill Street, London, SE1 2BA, United Kingdom
(020) 7740 7000/ (020) 7740 7001
info@openagency.com
www.openagency.com

Optimism Design The Mission Hall, Walkers Place, London, SW15 1PP, United Kingdom
(020) 8788 8700/ (020) 8788 8702
info@optimism.co.uk
www.optimism.co.uk

Ottley Design Company Unit 3.02 The Tea Building, 56 Shoreditch High Street, London, E1 6JJ, United Kingdom
(020) 7060 1967/(07940) 0028736
chb@ottleydesign.co.uk
www.ottleydesign.co.uk

Parent Design Bristol & West House, Post Office Road, Bournemouth, BH1 1BL, United Kingdom
(01202) 311711/ (01202) 555 402
mail@parentdesign.co.uk
www.parentdesign.co.uk

Partners by Design Ltd Essex House, High Street, Dunmow, Essex, CM6 1AE, United Kingdom
(01371) 875057/ (01371) 875027
info@pbdltd.co.uk
www.pbdltd.co.uk

Patrick Budge 53 Marlborough Road, Oxford, OX1 4LW, United Kingdom
(01865) 452778/(07946) 640409
patrickbudge@ntlworld.com
www.patrickbudge.com

Penknife Ltd Column Building, 13 Mountstuart Square, Cardiff, CF10 5EE, United Kingdom
(029) 2046 1021/ (029) 2048 0426
creativ@penknife.co.uk
www.penknife.co.uk

Periscope 11 St. James Avenue West, Stanford-le-Hope, Essex, SS17 7BB, United Kingdom
(0845) 6446681
info@periscope.co.uk
www.periscope.co.uk

Peter Gill & Associates 256 Cowbridge Road East, Cardiff, CF5 1GZ, United Kingdom
(029) 2037 7312/ (029) 2039 8101
peter@petergill.com
www.petergill.com

Peter Grant & Partners 144 Gloucester Avenue, Regents Park, London, NW1 8JA, United Kingdom
(020) 7911 0044/ (020) 7911 0045
www.petergrant-ptrs.com

Peter Powell Design 2 Temple Gardens, Brighton, BN1 3AE, United Kingdom
(01273) 206406
peterpowell@ppdesign.co.uk
www.ppdesign.co.uk

Philosophy Design Ltd 91 Paul Street, London, EC2A 4NY, United Kingdom
(020) 7251 2233/ (020) 7251 8333
natasha@philosophydesign.com
www.philosophydesign.com

Pickton Design 42 Windsor Road, London, N13 5PR, United Kingdom
(020) 8882 0122
keith@picktondesign.co.uk
www.picktondesign.co.uk

Point Creative Design Studio 3, The Old Malt House, Little Ann Street, Bristol, BS2 9EB, United Kingdom
0117-904 2921
info@point-creative.com
www.point-creative.com

Pointsize Associates Ltd 60 Tradeston Street, Glasgow, G5 8BH, United Kingdom
0141-429 8222/ 0141-429 8803
info@pointsize.co.uk
www.pointsize.co.uk

Practice Design Consultants Ltd Eanam Wharf, Blackburn, BB1 5BL, United Kingdom
(01254) 266600/ (01254) 266601
work@practicedesign.co.uk
www.practicedesign.co.uk

Pre Consultants Ltd Bank Chambers, 64 High Street, Epsom, Surrey, KT19 8AJ, United Kingdom
(01372) 744220/ (01372) 740963
info@pre.co.uk
www.pre.co.uk

Precedent 109-123 Clifton Street, London, EC2A 4LD, United Kingdom
(020) 7216 1300/ (020) 7256 0323
info@precedent.co.uk
www.precedent.co.uk

Price Watkins Design 203A Upper Street, London, N1 1RQ, United Kingdom
(020) 7288 7288/ (020) 7226 2255
design@pricewatkins.co.uk
www.pricewatkins.co.uk

Pro Creative Talbot House, 204-206 Imperial Drive, Harrow, Middlesex, HA2 7HH, United Kingdom
(0845) 3003753/ (0845) 3003754
design@procreative.co.uk
www.procreative.co.uk

Product Solutions Ltd 6 Birchwood Close, Leicester Forest East, Leicester, LE3 3PU, UK
📞 0116-239 3330/ 0116-239 2163
✉ enquiries@pro-solutions.co.uk
🖥 www.pro-solutions.co.uk

Produkt 189 Saint Asaph Road, Flat 5, Holcombe, London, SE4 2DY, United Kingdom
📞 (07970) 975993
✉ sass@produkt.co.uk
🖥 www.produkt.co.uk

Project 1 Design 225 Cowley Road, Oxford, OX4 1XG, United Kingdom
📞 01865 204417
✉ info@p1d.co.uk
🖥 www.p1d.co.uk

Prontaprint Bristol Centre 70 Park Row, Bristol, BS1 5LE, United Kingdom
📞 (0117) 925 3868/ (0117) 9457722
✉ sales@bristolcentral.prontaprint.com
🖥 www.prontaprint.com

Proworx Media Ltd The Studio, Castle Works, Westgate Street, Lewes, East Sussex, BN7 1YR, United Kingdom
📞 (01273) 481001
✉ info@proworx.co.uk
🖥 www.proworx.co.uk

Ptarmigan Design 9 Gainsborough Drive, Adel, Leeds, LS16 7PF, United Kingdom
📞 0113-261 3172/ 0113-293 9576
✉ info@ptarmigan-design.co.uk
🖥 www.ptarmigan.co.uk

Publicity Project (Newbury) Ltd Liberty House, The Enterprise Centre, Newbury, Berkshire, RG19 6HW, United Kingdom
📞 (01635) 817311/ (01635) 817530
✉ design@publicityproject.co.uk
🖥 www.publicityproject.co.uk

Punch It Up Ltd 39 Defoe House, Barbican, London, EC2Y 8DN, United Kingdom
📞 (020) 7382 9497
✉ info@punchitup.co.uk
🖥 www.punchitup.co.uk

Punch NMC Fern House, 53 Padbrook, Limpsfield, Surrey, RH8 0DZ,
📞 01883 730073
✉ andrew.richardson@thinkpunch.co.uk
🖥 www.thinkpunch.co.uk

Pure Design Consultants Ltd 8 Randolph Crescent, Edinburgh, EH3 7TH, United Kingdom
📞 0131-220 5522/ 0131-220 5533
✉ john@puredesign.co.uk
🖥 www.puredesign.co.uk

Purple Circle Design Ltd Global Headquarters, 1 Howard Street, Nottingham, NG1 3LT, United Kingdom
📞 0115-955 0005/ 0115-955 0006
✉ info@purplecircle.co.uk
🖥 www.purplecircle.co.uk

Q E D Marketing Ltd 5 St. Matthews Business Centre, Gower Street, Leicester, LE1 3LJ, United Kingdom
📞 0116-262 1110/ 0116-262 1114
✉ info@qedmarketing.biz
🖥 www.qedmarketing.co.uk

Quirst 2 Brunswick Terrace, #2A, Hove, East Sussex, BN3 1HN, United Kingdom
📞 (01273) 202760
✉ sheila@quirst.com
🖥 www.quirst.com

R Design & Communications Ltd Heathercroft, Bagshot Road, Woking, Surrey, GU21 2SF, United Kingdom
📞 (01483) 481282/(07775) 761146
✉ info@r-mail.co.uk
🖥 www.r-web.co.uk

Radius Design The Granary, Walnut Tree Lane, Sudbury, Suffolk, C010 1BD, United Kingdom
📞 (01787) 373710/ (01787) 310033
✉ rd@radiusdesign.com
🖥 www.radiusdesign.com

Randak Grand Management Gordon Chambers, 90 Mitchell Street, Glasgow, G1 3NQ, United Kingdom
📞 0141-221 2142/ 0141-226 5096
✉ info@randakdesign.com
🖥 www.randakdesign.com

Rapture Design Ltd Shinfield Grange, Cutbush Lane, Reading, RG2 9AF, United Kingdom
📞 0118 9888001
✉ info@rapturedesign.co.uk
🖥 www.rapturedesign.co.uk

Red Central Ltd 18 Monmouth Place, Bath, BA1 2AY, United Kingdom
📞 (01225) 423344/ (01225) 427766
✉ info@redcentral.co.uk
🖥 www.redcentral.co.uk

Red Letter Design Ltd 133 Great Suffolk Street, London, SE1 1PP, United Kingdom
📞 (020) 7207 4226/ (020) 7787 5880
✉ info@redletterdesign.co.uk
🖥 www.redletterdesign.co.uk

Redpath 5 Gayfield Square, Edinburgh, EH1 3NW, United Kingdom
📞 0131-556 9115/ 0131-556 9116
✉ redpath@redpath.co.uk
🖥 www.redpath.co.uk

Remedica Commonwealth House, 1 New Oxford Street, London, WC1A 1NU, United Kingdom
📞 (020) 7759 2929/ (020) 7759 2951
✉ info@remedica.com
🖥 www.remedica.com

Resident 42b Wetherell Road, London, E9 7DB, United Kingdom
📞 (07976) 619658
✉ paul@resident.co.uk
🖥 www.resident.co.uk

Rhubarb Associates Ltd Flat A, 349 Hale Road, Hale Barns, Altrincham, Cheshire, WA15 8SX, United Kingdom
📞 (07887) 678604
✉ matt@rhubarbcreative.com
🖥 www.rhubarbcreative.com

Richard Harrison Flat 3, 30 Fonnereau Road, Ipswich, IP1 3JP, United Kingdom
📞 (01473) 251277/(07786) 930674
✉ richard@richardaharrison.com
🖥 www.richardaharrison.com

Rocket Creative Ltd Mobbs Miller House, 6 Christchurch Road, Northampton, NN1 5LL, United Kingdom
📞 (01604) 250900/ (01604) 602880
✉ sales@rocket-creative.com
🖥 www.rocket-creative.com

Room 58 16 Imperial Square, Cheltenham, Gloucestershire, GL50 1QZ, United Kingdom
📞 0870 2245858/ 0870 2245859
✉ joanna.jones@room58.com
🖥 www.room58.com

Rooster 26 Bloomsby Street, London, WC1B 3QJ, United Kingdom
📞 (020) 7691 3939/ (020) 7691 3929
✉ info@rooster.co.uk
🖥 www.rooster.co.uk

Roundel Design Group Ltd 7 Rosehart Mews, Westbourne Grove, London, W11 3TY, United Kingdom
📞 (020) 7221 1951/ (020) 7221 1843
✉ info@roundel.com
🖥 www.roundel.com

RRROAR 137 Nelson Road, Twickenham, TW2 7BB, United Kingdom
📞 (020) 8889 5510/(07770) 995096 (020) 8893 9674
✉ creative@rrroar.com
🖥 www.rrroar.com

Rufus Leonard The Drill Hall, 57A Farringdon Road, London, EC1M 3JB, United Kingdom
📞 (020) 7404 4490/ (020) 7404 4491
✉ enquiries@rufusleonard.com
🖥 www.rufusleonard.com

S G H Design 140 St John's Street, London, EC1V 4UA, United Kingdom
📞 (020) 7253 1436/ (020) 7253 5977
✉ info@sghdesign.co.uk
🖥 www.sghdesign.co.uk

S H O Design 57 Farringdon Road, London, EC1M 3JB, United Kingdom
📞 (020) 7993 5472
✉ adam@sho-mail.com
🖥 www.sho-studio.com

Saatchi & Saatchi Design 81 Whitfield Street, London, W1T 4HG, United Kingdom
📞 (020) 7307 5327/ (020) 7307 5328
✉ saatchi@saatchi-design.com
🖥 www.facilities.co.uk

Sage Visual Solutions A4 13 Sisters Avenue, London, SW11 5SP, United Kingdom
📞 (020) 7223 4700
✉ damian@sagevisualsolutions.com

Sanderson Art Services 78 Beech Lees, Farsley, Leeds, LS28 5JZ, United Kingdom
📞 0113-257 9444/ 0113-257 9444

Sandy Field 90 Alfriston Road, Battersea, London, SW11 6NW, United Kingdom
📞 (020) 7228 5263/ (020) 7228 5263

Sarah Fawkes Graphic Design 79 Grooms Lane, Silver End, Witham, Essex, CM8 3SH, United Kingdom
📞 (07759) 125598
✉ sarahfawkes@btinternet.com

Sarah Nuttall 11 Hambleton Terrace, Knaresborough, North Yorkshire, HG5 0DD, UK
📞 (01423) 541072
✉ sarah@sarahnuttall.com
🖥 www.sarahnuttall.com

Sauce Design Ltd 57 Farringdon Road, London, EC1M 3JB, United Kingdom
📞 (020) 7813 2098/ (020) 7813 2097
✉ info@saucedesign.co.uk
🖥 www.saucedesign.co.uk

Savvy Graphics 77 Park Street, Top Floor Flat, Bristol City Centre, Bristol, BS1 5PF, United Kingdom
📞 (07734) 823877
✉ mrdavidhampshire.@yahoo.com

Scarlet Creative Solutions Ltd 3 Yew Walk, Hoddesdon, Hertfordshire, EN11 8BB, United Kingdom
📞 (0845) 4085402
✉ solutions@scarletcreative.co.uk
🖥 www.scarletcreative.co.uk

Schmakk Ltd Harborne West, 326 High Street, Harborne, Birmingham, B17 9PU, United Kingdom
📞 0121-428 4545/ 0121-428 4190
✉ info@schmakk.com
🖥 www.schmakk.com

Scott Brown Rigg Ltd Tower House, 10 Southampton Street, London, WC2E 7HA, United Kingdom
📞 (020) 7240 7766/ (020) 7240 2454
✉ info@scottbrownrigg.com
🖥 www.scottbrownrigg.com

Sears Davies Ltd Unit A, 25 Copperfield Street, London, SE1 0EN, United Kingdom
📞 (020) 7633 0939/ (020) 7633 9953
✉ julian@searsdavies.com
🖥 www.searsdavies.com

Servicepoint UK 192-198 Vauxhall Bridge Road, London, SW1V 1DX, United Kingdom
📞 (020) 7931 0222
✉ mark.dobson@servicepointuk.com
🖥 www.servicepointuk.com

Shandwick Design 9 Lynedoch Crescent, Glasgow, G3 6EQ, United Kingdom
📞 0141-333 0445/ 0141-333 9909
✉ design@shandwick.com
🖥 www.shandwickdesign.com

Shaw Design Associates Ltd, London, EC1M 5RD, United Kingdom
📞 (020) 7250 3800
✉ studio@shaw-design.co.uk
🖥 www.shaw-design.co.uk

Simon Griffin Studio 416, Durrant Court, Brook Street, Chelmsford, CM1 1UE, United Kingdom
📞 (01245) 352258/(07776) 131519
✉ info@simongriffin.co.uk
🖥 www.simongriffin.com

Simon Morris Associates Unit 5, Ravensquay Business Centre, Cray Avenue, Orpington, Kent, BR5 4BQ, United Kingdom
📞 (0845) 612 1831/ (0845) 612 1832
✉ info@madesignstudios.com
🖥 www.madesignstudios.com

Slater Clark Associates Ltd New Street, Doncaster, South Yorkshire, DN1 3QU, United Kingdom
📞 (01302) 325306/ (01302) 368973
✉ mail@slaterclark.co.uk

sm creative ltd 8 Redwood Drive, Chorley, Lancashire, PR7 2BW, United Kingdom
📞 (01257) 232392/(07759) 235403 (01257) 232 392
✉ design@smcreative.co.uk
🖥 www.smcreative.co.uk/

Smith & Milton Boatmens Inst, 27 Junction Mews, London, W2 1PN, United Kingdom
📞 (020) 7298 5500/ (020) 7262 6987
✉ info@smith-milton.co.uk
🖥 www.smith-milton.co.uk

Social Fabric UK Ltd William Blake Hse, 8 Marshall St, London, W1F 7EJ, United Kingdom
(020) 7788 7876
us@thesocialfabric.com
www.thesocialfabric.com

Spencer Dubois 52-54 Rosebury Avenue, London, EC1R 4RP, United Kingdom
(020) 7843 0030/ (020) 7837 0785
design@spencerdubois.co.uk
www.spencerdubois.co.uk

Spiral Communications Pte Ltd 28 Maxwell Road, 02-15A, Red Dot Traffic Building, Singapore,
+65 65347184/ +65 63278902
enquiry@spiralcomms.com
www.spiralcomms.com

Splinter Maxwell Busines Park, Maxwell house, Liverpool, L7 9NJ, United Kingdom
0151-709 9066/ 0151-709 9077
design@splinter.co.uk
www.splinter.co.uk

Spring London 140-142 St John's Street, London, EC1V 4UA, United Kingdom
(020) 7253 1449/ (020) 7253 5977
info@springlondon.com
www.springlondon.com

Springetts 13 Salisbury Place, London, W1H 1FJ, United Kingdom
(020) 7486 7527/ (020) 7487 3033
all@springetts.co.uk
www.springetts.co.uk

Starling Design Barley Hill Farm, Combe St Nicholas, Chard, Somerset, TA20 3HJ, United Kingdom
(01460) 234384/ (01460) 234730
lora@lorastarling.co.uk

Start Creative 2 Sheraton Street, Soho, London, W1F 8BH, United Kingdom
(020) 7269 0101/ (020) 7269 0102
jen@startcreative.co.uk
www.startcreative.co.uk

Steel McNeil Rogers Ltd 78 Canon Street, London, EC4N 6NQ, United Kingdom
(020) 7618 8911
dsteel@dircon.co.uk
www.s-m-r.com

Stephanos Attalides The Drawing Room, Mount Pleasant, London, WC1X 0AP, United Kingdom
(020) 7482 7190/(07956) 293125

Stewart Sutters Design 3 Belton Corner, Marine Parade, Leigh-on-Sea, Essex, SS9 2HP, United Kingdom
(01702) 719595/07811 929205 (01702) 719596
info@stewartsuttersdesign.com
www.stewartsuttersdesign.com

Stillman Communications Ltd The Wharf, 843 Western Boulevard, Nottingham, NG8 5FG, United Kingdom
0115-942 0088/ 0115-942 0162
darrenleach@btconnect.com
www.stillman.co.uk

Stone Agency 12A Fitzroy Place, Glasgow, G3 7RW, United Kingdom
0141-221 5965/ 0141-221 0069
bill.imrie@stoneagency.co.uk
www.stoneagency.co.uk

Storm Design Ltd 38 Clifftown Parade, Southend-on-Sea, SS1 1DL, United Kingdom
(01702) 348484/ (01702) 393739
greg@storm-uk.net
www.storm-uk.net

Studio Hagger 3 Fersfield, Perrymead, Bath, BA2 5AR, United Kingdom
(01225) 837256/ (01225) 832607
all@studiohagger.com
www.studiohagger.com

Stylo Design Bedford Chambers, The Piazza, Covent Garden, London, WC2E 8HA, United Kingdom
(020) 7836 9474
ben@stylodesign.co.uk
www.stylodesign.co.uk

Sumo 71 Westgate Road, Newcastle upon Tyne, NE1 1SG, United Kingdom
0191-261 9894/ 0191-261 9010
info@sumodesign.co.uk
www.sumodesign.co.uk

Sutherland-Hawes McLean Design Consultants, 40 Ravenscourt Gardens, London, W6 0TU, United Kingdom
(020) 8141 9806/ (020) 8563 9975
shm@sutherlandhawes.co.uk
www.sutherlandhawes.co.uk

Sutton Cooper 7 King William IV Gardens, London, SE20 7EG, United Kingdom
(020) 8776 8101
rogercooper@suttoncooper.com

Synergy Communications Ltd 250-252 Goswell Road, London, EC1V 7EB, United Kingdom
(020) 7251 0303/ (020) 7251 0323
info@synergy-communications.co.uk
www.synergy-communications.co.uk

Tang Creative Marketing Communications Suite 319, Eagle Tower, Montpellier Drive, Cheltenham, Gloucestershire, GL50 1TA, United Kingdom
(0870) 0633663
studio@tangmedia.com
www.tangmedia.com

Tanka Creative Ltd Coppergate House, 16 Brune Street, London, E1 7NJ, United Kingdom
(020) 7953 7909/ (020) 7900 2733
jon@tanka.co.uk
www.tanka.co.uk

Tara Signs Ltd St. Peters Place, Western Road, Lancing, West Sussex, BN15 8SB, United Kingdom
(01903) 750710/ (01903) 754008
admin@tarasigns.com
www.tarasigns.com

Tayburn Ltd 15 Kittle Yards, Causewayside, Edinburgh, EH9 1PJ, United Kingdom
0131-662 0662/ 0131-662 0606
simon.farrell@tayburn.co.uk
www.tayburn.co.uk

Taylor McKenzie 59 Charlottes Road, London, EC2A 3QT, United Kingdom
(020) 7613 3130/ (020) 7613 5773
kate@taylor-mckenzie.co.uk
www.taylor-mckenzie.co.uk

The Ark C M Ltd 3 Ram Court, Wicklesham Lodge Farm, Faringdon, Oxfordshire, SN7 7PN, United Kingdom
(0870) 2352222/ (0870) 2350034
mark@arkcm.com
www.arkcm.com

The Cap Fits Ltd 1 helix gardens, London, SW2 2JH, United Kingdom
(020) 8674 1777
tim@thecapfits.co.uk
www.thecapfits.co.uk

The Chase 1 North Parade, Parsonage Garden, Manchester, M3 2NH, United Kingdom
0161-832 5575/ 0161-832 5576
simonf@thechase.co.uk
www.thechase.co.uk

The Constructive 141a Constantine Road, London, NW3 2LR, United Kingdom
(020) 7871 7618
info@theconstructive.co.uk
www.theconstructive.co.uk

The Creative Store Ltd Studio House, 142 Merton Hall Road, London, SW19 3PZ, United Kingdom
(020) 8543 3855
sales@thecreativestore.co.uk
www.thecreativestore.co.uk

The Crocodile The Lux Building, 2-4 Hoxton Square, London, N1 6NU, United Kingdom
(020) 7749 4400/ (020) 7739 4042
chris.tongeman@thecroc.com
www.thecroc.com

The Forster Co. 49 Southwark Street, London, SE1 1RU, United Kingdom
(020) 7403 2230/ (020) 7403 2240
reception@forster.co.uk
www.forster.co.uk

The Hamiltons 8 The Glass House, 3 Royal Oak Yard, London, SE1 3GE, United Kingdom
(020) 707 9500/(07989) 592874 0870 2851533
mjh@thehamiltons.co.uk
www.thehamiltons.co.uk

The Loop Design Studio 54, Smithbrook Kilns, Cranleigh, Surrey, GU6 8JJ, United Kingdom
(01483) 267532
loopme@theloopdesign.com
www.theloopdesign.com

The McAlpine Partnership 67 North Drive, Troon, Ayrshire, KA10 7DL, United Kingdom
(01292) 318028/ (01292) 318037
enquiries@mcalpinepartnership.co.uk
www.mcalpinepartnership.co.uk

The Partners Albion Courtyard, Greenhill Rents, London, EC1M 6PQ, United Kingdom
(020) 7608 0051/ (020) 7250 0473
info@thepartners.co.uk
www.thepartners.co.uk

The Tangent 1 Lilac Cottage, Northchapel, Petworth, West Sussex, GU28 9HL, United Kingdom
(01428) 707844/ (01428) 707845
david@thetangent.net
www.thetangent.co.uk

The Wax Mill Parternship The Raylor Ctre, James St, York, YO24 4BP, United Kingdom
(01904) 422114

Think Pod A1 Riverside, Metropolitan Wharf, London, E1W 3SS, United Kingdom
(020) 7709 7883/ (020) 7709 7884
think@thinkpod.co.uk
www.thinkpod.co.uk

Think Smart Marketing Unit B2, Arc Progress, Beckerings Park, Lidlington, Bedford, MK43 0RD, United Kingdom
(01525) 288828/ (01525) 288904
marka@thinksmartmarketing.co.uk
www.thinksmartmarketing.co.uk

Thinlayer Internet 16 Strathearn Avenue, Twickenham, TW2 6JU, United Kingdom
(0709) 2002425/ (0709) 2002425
info@thinlayer.co.uk
www.thinlayer.co.uk

Third Eye Design 23 Newton Place, Glasgow, G3 7PY, United Kingdom
0141-332 3335/(07903) 825157 0141-332 9253
stewart@thirdeyedesign.co.uk
www.thirdeyedesign.co.uk

Thirst Design & Marketing Broadwater Barn, Parts Lane, Reading, RG7 1RU, United Kingdom
0118-988 8826/ 0118-988 8827
info@thirstdesign.com
www.thirstdesign.com

Thomas Cochrane Associates 3/2 150 Butterbiggins Road, Glasgow, G42 7AF, United Kingdom
0141-585 8581
info@thomas-cochrane-associates.com
www.thomas-cochrane-associates.com

Thomas Fattorini Ltd Regent Street Works, Birmingham, B1 3HQ, United Kingdom
0121-236 1307/ 0121-200 1568
sales@fattorini.co.uk
www.fattorini.co.uk
See ad in showcase

Thompson Design Ltd The Old Stables, Springwood Gardens, Leeds, LS8 2QB, United Kingdom
0113-232 9222/ 0113-232 3775
info@thompsondesign.co.uk
www.thompsondesign.co.uk

Threerooms Ltd 13 Mayfield Drive, Stapleford, Nottingham, NG9 8JF, United Kingdom
0115-877 9429
info@threerooms.com
www.threerooms.com

Totem Design 33 Eastfield Road, Westbury-on-Trym, Bristol, BS9 4AE, United Kingdom
0117-962 5000/ 0117-962 5001
team@totem-design.co.uk
www.totem-design.co.uk

Trademark Graphics Graphic House, 35-41 Essex Road, Basingstoke, Hampshire, RG21 7TB, United Kingdom
(01256) 479774/ (01256) 840672
studio@tm-graphics.co.uk
www.tm-graphics.co.uk

Trevor Beynon 7 Jardine House, The Harrovian Business Village, Bessborough Road, Harrow, Middlesex, HA1 3EX, United Kingdom
(020) 8422 7099/ (020) 8422 4411
trevorbeynon@btconnect.com
www.trevorbeynon.co.uk

Turnbull Ripley 1st Floor, Monmouth House, 87-93 Westbourne Grove, London, W2 4UL, United Kingdom
(020) 7221 0110/ (020) 7243 3093
design@turnbullripley.co.uk
www.turnbullripley.co.uk

TWO:design 176 Finchley Road, London, NW3 6BT, United Kingdom
(020) 8275 8594
studio@twodesign.net
www.twodesign.net

Upper Room 4 Foxearth Spur, Selsdon, South Croydon, Surrey, CR2 8EP, United Kingdom
(020) 8406 1010
info@theupperroom.co.uk

Vested Interest Design The Loft, 15A Watt Street, Greenock, Renfrewshire, PA16 8JN, United Kingdom
(01475) 721042/ (01475) 721103
info@vested-interest.com
www.vested-interest.com

Village Design Ltd St Thomas Court, Thomas Lane, Bristol, BS1 6JG, United Kingdom
0117-910 6050/ 0117-910 6051
info@village-design.co.uk
www.villagedesign.co.uk

Visible Edge Ltd 7-10 Batemans Row, London, EC2A 3HH, United Kingdom
(020) 7739 1860/ (020) 7739 4091
design@vis-edge.co.uk
www.visible-edge.co.uk

Vision 120 Queens Road, Brighton, BN1 3WB, United Kingdom
(01273) 766300/ (01273) 766319
richard.maennling@visiondesign.co.uk
www.visiondesign.co.uk

Vivienne Rawnsley Design 60A High St, Boston Spa, Wetherby, West Yorkshire, LS23 6EA, United Kingdom
(01937) 842471
vivienne@rawnsleyscott.co.uk
www.viviennerawnsley.co.uk

Voltage 4 Lynedoch Place, Glasgow, G3 6AB, United Kingdom
0141-331 2120/ 0141-331 2110
info@powerfulstuff.co.uk
www.powerfulstuff.co.uk

W F C A Integrated Cobden House, 25 London Road, Tunbridge Wells, Kent, TN1 1DA, United Kingdom
(01892) 511085/ (01892) 512180
info@wfca.co.uk
www.wfca.co.uk

Warnes Design Id Co The Barn, Yew Trees, Broad Hinton, Swindon, SN4 9PN, United Kingdom
(01793) 731080/ (01793) 731856
info@warnesdesign.co.uk
www.warnesdesign.co.uk

Warwicks UK Ltd 45 Blondvil Street, Cheylesmore, Coventry, CV3 5QX, United Kingdom
(024) 7650 5339/ (024) 7650 3135
design@warwicks-uk.com
www.warwicks-uk.com

Watt UK Ltd Albian Road, Greengates, Bradford, West Yorkshire, BD10 9TQ, United Kingdom
(01274) 200700/ (01274) 202425
info@wattswatt.co.uk
www.wattswatt.co.uk

Weav Design Enterprise House, 5 Roundwood Lane, Harpenden, Hertfordshire, AL5 3BW, United Kingdom
(0845) 165 1677/ (0845) 165 1678
mail@weav.co.uk
www.weav.co.uk

Webb & Webb 16H Perseverance Works, 38 Kings Lynn Road, London, E2 8DD, United Kingdom
(020) 7739 7895
design@webbandwebb.co.uk
www.webbandwebb.co.uk

White Leaf Creative Media Centre, 45 Roberts Street, Hastings, East Sussex, TN34 1HL, United Kingdom
(01424) 205492/ (01424) 205401
info@whiteleafdesign.net
www.whiteleafdesign.net

White Total Design March House, 44 Leigh Road, Eastleigh, Hampshire, SO50 9DT, United Kingdom
(023) 8062 0088/ (023) 8062 0080
info@whitetotaldesign.co.uk
www.whitetotaldesign.co.uk

Whithot Creative Southgate House, St Georges Way, Stevenage, Hertfordshire, SG1 1HG, United Kingdom
(01438) 741666/ (01438) 741665

Wonderfuel 118 Hatherley Gardens, London, E6 3HQ, United Kingdom
020 8548 1358
info@wonderfuel.co.uk
www.wonderfuel.co.uk

Woods Creative Marketing Ltd 48 Town Road, Croston, Preston, PR26 9RB, United Kingdom
(01772) 602950/ (01772) 602951
us@woodscreative.co.uk

Words that Work 28 Lenton Road, The Park, Nottingham, NG7 1DT, United Kingdom
0115-9482 555
info@thewriteway.co.uk
www.document-doctor.co.uk

Wordsearch 5 Old Street, London, EC1V 9HL, United Kingdom
(020) 7549 5400/ (020) 7336 8660
cassius@wordsearch.co.uk
www.wordsearch.co.uk

Wordswork 58 Queens Road, Swanage, Dorset, BH19 2EU, United Kingdom
(01929) 427277/ (01929) 427277
mail@mikehadley.net
www.mikehadley.net

Wright Design & Advertising Ltd 83 West Regent Street, Glasgow, G2 2AX, United Kingdom
0141-331 2341/ 0141-331 1885
enquiries@wrightdesign.co.uk
www.wrightdesign.co.uk

Write Angle 29 London Road, Cheltenham, Gloucestershire, GL52 6EY, United Kingdom
(01242) 241315
info@writeanglegroup.com
www.writeanglegroup.com

Writing Machine 19 City Business Centre, Hyde Street, Winchester, Hampshire, SO23 7TA, United Kingdom
(01962) 841250/ (01962) 870558
info@writingmachine.com
www.writingmachine.com

X! Artwork Suite VP, PO Box 43128, London, E17 6WS, United Kingdom
(020) 8925 6542/ (020) 8925 6542
services@artwork.co.uk
www.xartwork.co.uk

XXVIII 28 Langdale Avenue, Croston, Leyland, PR26 9SE, United Kingdom
(01772) 603270/ (01772) 603270
david.price5@btconnect.com

Zulver & Co. The Vellum Building, 183-185 Bermondsey Street, London, SE1 3UW, United Kingdom
(020) 7939 3939/ (020) 7403 4906
andrew@zulver.com
www.zulver.com

AD AGENCIES

& ADVERTISING Ltd 143-145 Farringdon Road, London, EC1R 3AB, United Kingdom
0207 833 5955

& Partners Ltd Waulk Mill, Bengal Street, Manchester, Lancashire, M4 6LN, United Kingdom
0161 2371573

121 Media Golden Cross House, 8 Duncannon Street, London, WC2N 4JF, United Kingdom
0870 4057722

23red Elsley Court, 20-22 Great Titchfield Street, London, W1W 8BE, United Kingdom
020 73230313

2HEADS TV Kit Lane, Checkendon, Oxfordshire, RG8 0TY, United Kingdom
01491 681061

77Agency Ltd 29 Queen Elizabeth Street, London, SE1 2LP, United Kingdom
020 73787358

A&Ng G5 Chorlton Mill, 3 Cambridge Street, Manchester, Lancashire, M1 5BY, United Kingdom
0161 2365506

Abbott Barker Brooks Ltd Alexandra Barn, 1 Waverley Lane, Farnham, Surrey, GU9 8BB, United Kingdom
01252 737181

ABC Media Ltd 2 Exmoor Street, London, W10 6BD, United Kingdom
020 89622300

Accept Ltd 65 Curzon Street, Derby, Derbyshire, DE1 1LN, United Kingdom
01332 202777

Accord Holdings Ltd The Grange, 100 High St, London, N14 6BN, United Kingdom
020 89209020

AD 78 Ltd Netherton PArk, Stannington, Morpeth, Northumberland, NE61 6EF, United Kingdom
01670 789071

Ad2-one 32 Percy Street, London, W1T 2DE, United Kingdom
0207 2919930

Adam B Ltd 143 Whitfield Street, London, W1T 5EP, United Kingdom
0207 3880888

Adams Advertising & Design Ltd 2 Albion Place, Maidstone, Kent, ME14 5DY, United Kingdom
01622 687729

Adconnection 10 Beulah Road, Wimbledon, London, SW19 3SB, United Kingdom
020 85452150

Adlink Internet Media 4th Floor, New Penderell House, 283-288 High Holborn, London, WC1V 7HP, United Kingdom
0207 4009250

Admast Advertising Ltd 190 Portland Road, Jesmond, Newcastle Upon Tyne, Tyne & Wear, NE2 1DJ, United Kingdom
0191 2220916

Advertising International The Studio, 7 Bath Street, St Helier, Channel Isles, Jersey, JE2 4ST, United Kingdom
01534 730001

Advouch Ltd 28-42 Banner Street, London, EC1Y 8QE, United Kingdom
0207 6740300

Agency Inc 47-49 High Street, Kingston Upon Thames, Surrey, KT1 1LQ, United Kingdom
020 85464646

Ainsworth & Parkinson Northern Unit 14, Sceptre Court, Sceptre Way, Preston, Lancashire, PR5 6AW, United Kingdom
01772 770700

Aka 115 Shaftesbury Ave, Cambridge Circus, London, WC2H 8AF, United Kingdom
0207 8364747

Albion Brand Communication Tea Building, 56 Shoreditch Highstreet, London, E1 6JJ, United Kingdom
0207 0338900

Alcazar Ltd The Maling Pottery, Walker Road, Newcastle Upon Tyne, Tyne & Wear, NE6 2AB, United Kingdom
0191 2244000

Allison Mitchell Ltd Bucklersbury House, 11 Walbrook, London, EC4N 8EL, United Kingdom
020 72487200

Alternative 25 Great George Street, Bristol, Avon, BS1 5QT, United Kingdom
0117 9099900

Ambridge Harris Associates Ltd 20 Apex Court, Woodlands, Bristol, Avon, BS32 4JT, United Kingdom
01454 456300

Ambrose West Curtis Ltd The Old Rectory, Church Lane, Claydon, Ipswich, Suffolk, IP6 0EQ, United Kingdom
01473 831323

Ananova Ltd Marshall Mill, Marshall Street, Leeds, West Yorkshire, LS11 9YJ,
United Kingdom
☎ 0113 3674680

Anderson Burnbreck Ltd Burnbreck House, St James Square, Cheltenham, Gloucestershire, GL50 3QG,
United Kingdom
☎ 01242 518399

ANDERSON LAMBERT 2 Kensworth Gate, High Street South, Dunstable, Bedfordshire, LU6 3HS,
United Kingdom
☎ 01582 706440

AndersonSprattGroup Anderson House, Holywood Road, Belfast, County Antrim, BT4 2GU,
United Kingdom
☎ 028 90802020

Answer Marketing Ltd 18 Clarence Road, Horsforth, Leeds, West Yorkshire, LS18 4LB,
United Kingdom
☎ 0113 2581791

Aqueduct Des & Advertisement 85 Clerkenwell Road, London, EC1R 5AR,
United Kingdom
☎ 020 70718600

ARC London Warwick Building, Avonmore Road, London, W14 8HQ,
United Kingdom
☎ 020 77511663

Archibald Ingall Stretton Berners House, 47-48 Berners Street, London, W1T 3NF,
United Kingdom
☎ 020 74676100

Ardmore Advertising & Mktg Ardmore House, Pavilions Office Park, Kinnesar Drive, Belfast, County Down, BT18 9JQ,
United Kingdom
☎ 028 90425344

Arm Direct 1 Bentinck Mews, London, W1U 2AF,
United Kingdom
☎ 020 72243040

ARTAVIA ADVERTISING Portland Buildings, Portland Street, Manchester, Lancashire, M1 4PZ,
United Kingdom
☎ 0161 2363072

Artavia Advertising Renstade House, Bonham Road, Exeter City, Devon, EX4 3AY,
United Kingdom
☎ 01392 496629

Artavia Advertising Parkway House, 28 Avenue Road, Bournemouth, Dorset, BH2 5SL,
United Kingdom
☎ 01202 293999

Arthaus Visual Comms Ltd Old Trinity Church, Trinity Road, Marlow, Buckinghamshire, SL7 3AN,
United Kingdom
☎ 01628 487333

artisan creative 31 Roseburn Terrace, Edinburgh, EH12 5NQ,
United Kingdom
☎ 0131 3378363

Artisan Creative Agency Southview Business Park, Tinwell Road, Stamford, Lincolnshire, PE9 2JL,
United Kingdom
☎ 01780 484450

Atalanta Advertising & Design 33 Port Dundas Road, Cowcaddens, Glasgow, Lanarkshire, G4 0HF,
United Kingdom
☎ 0141 33244447

ATP Advtg & Marketing Ltd Elmete House, Elmete Lane, Leeds, West Yorkshire, LS8 2LJ,
United Kingdom
☎ 0113 2738555

Attinger Jack Advertising 2 Queen Square, Bath, Avon, BA1 2HD,
United Kingdom
☎ 01225 758222

AV Browne Advertising Ltd 46 Bedford Street, Belfast, County Antrim, BT2 7GH,
United Kingdom
☎ 028 90320663

Avlesworth Fleming Ltd Aardvark House, 24 Poole Hill, Bournemouth, Dorset, BH2 5PS,
United Kingdom
☎ 01202 295723

AWA Ltd 69 Dane Road, Sale, Cheshire, M33 7BP,
United Kingdom
☎ 0161 9686900

Ballyhoo Publicity Ltd Ballyhoo House, 81 High Street, Wallingford, Oxfordshire, OX10 0BX,
United Kingdom
☎ 01491 838666

Barkers Advertising 37 Queens Square, Bristol, Avon, BS1 4QS,
United Kingdom
☎ 0117 9252888

Barkers Advertising Regents House, 5 Queen Street, Leeds, West Yorkshire, LS1 2TW,
United Kingdom
☎ 0113 2431243

Barkers Human Resources Goose Gate, Nottingham, NG1 3AA,
United Kingdom
☎ 0115 9580010

Barkers Integrated 30 Farringdon Street, London, EC4A 4EA,
United Kingdom
☎ 020 76341200

Barkers Scotland 234 West George Street, Glasgow, Lanarkshire, G2 4QY,
United Kingdom
☎ 0141 2485030

Barneys Ltd 42 Baldwin Street, Bristol, Avon, BS1 1PN,
United Kingdom
☎ 0117 9214551

Barrett Howe plc Curfew Yard, Thames Street, Windsor, Berkshire, SL4 1SN,
United Kingdom
☎ 01753 869455

Barry Hook Associates 94 Churchgate, Stockport, Cheshire, SK1 1YJ,
United Kingdom
☎ 0161 4779854

Utopia.
Paradise.
Heaven.
Elysium
Shangri-la.
Nirvana.
Arcadia.
Found where you want to be yet?

Freelance and Permanent resourcing across Editorial, Communications & PR, Marketing, Events, Design, Advertising, Media and Digital

020 7025 4400
info@xchangeteam.com
www.xchangeteam.com

Xchangeteam has been established for eight years and consists of a team of passionate and knowledgeable ex-industry and recruitment professionals.

We work with the top design, advertising and integrated marketing agencies (on and off line) and corporate clients on both freelance and permanent requirements.

We have an in-depth understanding of the market and cover the entire spectrum of roles including: creative directors, creative teams, copywriters, creative services, art directors, designers, art workers, production, account handling, client services, project management and business development – at every level.

Whether a client or a candidate, we would love to work with you! So why not give us a call on 020 7025 4400.

the best people for your business
xchangeteam

Bartle Bogle Hegarty 60 Kingly Street, Soho, London, W1B 5DS,
United Kingdom
☎ 020 77341677

Barton Grange Advertising Ltd 9 Lynwood Grove, Sale, Cheshire, M33 2AN,
United Kingdom
☎ 0161 9051959

BBH 1-2 Manor Farm, Old Wolverton Road, Old Wolverton, Milton Keynes, Buckinghamshire, MK12 5NN,
United Kingdom
☎ 01908 221784

Bcmb Ltd 2 Brindley Road, Old Trafford, Manchester, Lancashire, M16 9HQ,
United Kingdom
☎ 0161 8770521

Bdh St. Pauls, 781 Wilslow Road, Manchester, M20 2RW, United Kingdom
☎ 0161 9088600

BDO Stoy Hayward Emerald House, East Street, Epsom, Surrey, KT17 1HS,
United Kingdom
☎ 01372 734300

Beechwood Creative Consultancy The Crows Nest, 2 Acre Road, Kingston Upon Thames, Surrey, KT2 6EF,
United Kingdom
☎ 0208 5473797

Beechwood Group Ltd Medius House, 2 Sheraton Street, London, W1F 8BH,
United Kingdom
☎ 0207 4394142

Bell Pottinger Corp./Financial Holborn Gate, 330 High Holborn, London, WC1V 7QD,
United Kingdom
☎ 0207 8613232

Bellman More House Business Centre, Haywards Heath, West Sussex, RH17 7RE,
United Kingdom
☎ 01444 471884

Bernard Hodes Advertising 3rd Floor, 10 Regents Wharf, All Saints Street, London, N1 9RL,
United Kingdom
☎ 020 75514794

Bernard Hodes Group Ltd Salisbury House, 1 Bluecoats Avenue, Hertford, Hertfordshire, SG14 1PU,
United Kingdom
☎ 01992 535455

Betley Whitehorne 55 Le Bordage, St Peterport, Channel Islands, Guernsey, GY1 1BP,
United Kingdom
☎ 01481 725115

Bias Tech 10 Denton Road, Wokingham, Berkshire, RG40 2DX,
United Kingdom
☎ 0118 9782272

Big COMMUNICATIONS Ltd 223 London Road, Leicester, Leicestershire, LE2 1ZE,
United Kingdom
☎ 0116 270869

Big Picture Interactive 9 Parade, Leamington Spa, Warwickshire, CV32 4DG,
United Kingdom
☎ 01927 422002

Bird & Moore Ltd The Old Vicarage, 26 Church Street, Uttoxeter, Staffordshire, ST14 8AA,
United Kingdom
☎ 01869 565111

Bite CP The Old Stables, Rectory Farm, Broadway Road, Lightwater, Surrey, GU18 5SH,
United Kingdom
☎ 01276 0450870

Bivouac King's House, 12 King Street, York Central, North Yorkshire, YO1 9WP,
United Kingdom
☎ 01904 679305

Blackbridge Communications Ltd 21-22 Great Sutton Street, London, EC1V 0DY,
United Kingdom
☎ 0207 6080668

Blackdog Desn & Production Ltd C U Phosco Lighting, Lower Rd, Great Amwell, Ware, SG12 9TA,
United Kingdom
☎ 01920 466775

Blackman AMD The Media Centre, Abbeywood Business Park, Bristol, Avon, BS34 7JU,
United Kingdom
☎ 0117 9799598

Blacksheep Advertising Ltd 67 Liverpool Road, Chester, Cheshire, CH2 1AP,
United Kingdom
☎ 01244 384384

Blah D Blah Ltd Brunswick House, Riverside Business Park, Benarth Road, Conwy, Gwynedd, LL32 8UB,
United Kingdom
☎ 01492 576969

BLM Quantum 50 Marshall Street, London, W1F 9BQ,
United Kingdom
☎ 0207 4340813

BLOWFISH ADVERTISING The Natraj Building, 55 The Tannery, Bermondsey Street, London, SE1 3XG,
United Kingdom
☎ 020 31170035

Blue Sky UK Ltd Castle Park Road, Whiddon Valley Ind Estate, Barnstaple, Devon, EX32 8PA,
United Kingdom
☎ 01271 3233213

Blue Tiger Marketing Ltd Chapel House, 52B High Street, Maldon, Essex, CM9 5PN,
United Kingdom
☎ 01621 1855717

BMP DDB Ltd 12 Bishops Bridge Road, London, W2 6AA,
United Kingdom
☎ 020 72583979

Bonnington Hotels 92 Southampton Row, London, WC1B 4BH,
United Kingdom
☎ 020 72422828

Bostock & Pollitt 9-10 Floral Street, London, WC2E 9HW,
United Kingdom
☎ 020 73796709

Boyden Carmichael Smith 88-90 North Sherwood Street, Nottingham, Nottinghamshire, NG1 4EE,
United Kingdom
☎ 01594 80900

BPH Ltd Manor House, Manor Lane, Halesowen, West Midlands, B62 8PU,
United Kingdom
☎ 0121 4238111

Bradley Dyer Group Liberty Court, Bell Street, Reigate, Surrey, RH2 7JB,
United Kingdom
☎ 01737 249479

Brahm Direct The Brahm Building, Alma Road, Headingley, Leeds, West Yorkshire, LS6 2AH,
United Kingdom
☎ 01132 304000

Branding Science Unit 9b Compass House, Smuggles Way, London, SW18 1DB,
United Kingdom
☎ 020 88773482

Breed Communications Ltd 67-69 Whitfield Street, London, W1T 4HF,
United Kingdom
☎ 020 74687888

Brise Publicity Ltd The Barn Tye Green, Bishops Stortford, Hertfordshire, CM22 6DY,
United Kingdom
☎ 01279 817878

Broadgate 15 Basinghall Street, London, EC2V 5BR,
United Kingdom
☎ 020 77266111

Bruce Davis Associates Meadow House, Ingon Lane, Snitterfield, Stratford Upon Avon, Warwickshire, CV37 0QF,
United Kingdom
☎ 01789 731007

Burkitt DDB 1 East Poultry Avenue, London, EC1A 9PT,
United Kingdom
☎ 020 73209300

Burrows The Burrows Building, 5 Rayleigh Road, Hutton, Brentwood, Essex, CM13 1AB,
United Kingdom
☎ 01272 46666

Business Link Ltd 26 Kings Hill Avenue, Kings Hill, West Malling, Kent, ME19 4AE,
United Kingdom
☎ 0845 226655

Butterfield Morris Bushell Bute Mills, Mill Yard, Guildford Street, Luton, Bedfordshire, LU1 2NH,
United Kingdom
☎ 01582 725454

Byron Design Ltd Byron House, Wallingford Road, Uxbridge, Middlesex, UB8 2RW,
United Kingdom
☎ 01895 252131

C-21 Advertising & Marketing Back Grafton Street, Altrincham, Cheshire, WA14 1DY,
United Kingdom
☎ 0161 9412331

Canna Kendall & Co 83 Charlotte Street, London, W1T 4PR,
United Kingdom
☎ 020 75803455

CANTOR HINDSON ASSOCIATES Ltd 600 Kingston Road, London, SW20 8DN,
United Kingdom
☎ 020 85450778

Carbon Marketing Ltd 134 Wigmore Street, London, W1U 3SD,
United Kingdom
☎ 020 74672300

Carlson Marketing Group 220 Park Avenue, Aztec West, Almondsbury, Bristol, Avon, BS32 4SY,
United Kingdom
☎ 01454 618811

Carlton Screen Advertising 12 Golden Square, London, W1F 9JE,
United Kingdom
☎ 020 75346363

Carrington Caunter Assocs Ltd The Saxon Centre, Bargates, Christchurch, Dorset, BH23 1PZ,
United Kingdom
☎ 01202 499612

Cartwright 2 The Byre Pump House Farm, Ongar Road, Kelvedon Hatch, Brentwood, Essex, CM15 0LA,
United Kingdom
☎ 01277 366900

Cartwright 10 Pilgrims Close, Pilgrims Hatch, Brentwood, Essex, CM15 9RQ,
United Kingdom
☎ 01277 366900

Cashcade 10 Valentine Place, London, SE1 8QH,
United Kingdom
☎ 0845 0502270

Cavendish Design & Advtg Ltd 118-120 Gt Titchfield Street, London, W1W 6SS,
United Kingdom
☎ 020 76362801

CDP Travis Sully 9 Lower John Street, London, W1F 9DZ,
United Kingdom
☎ 020 74374224

Chalk & Ward Advertising Kings Wharf, The Quay, Exeter, Devon, EX2 4AN,
United Kingdom
☎ 01392 666291

Chandler Chicco Agency 151 Shaftesbury Avenue, London, WC2H 8AL,
United Kingdom
☎ 020 76321800

Charles Advertising Ltd Hampshire House, High Street, Kingswinford, West Midlands, DY6 8AW,
United Kingdom
☎ 01384 401144

Charles Whalley Advertising Saxon House, Main Street, Southwick, Peterborough, Cambridgeshire, PE8 5BL,
United Kingdom
☎ 01832 273443

Cherry 42-44 Great Titchfield Street, London, W1W 7PY,
United Kingdom
☎ 020 75802455

CHILWORTH COMMUNICATIONS 106 Star Street, London, W2 1QF,
United Kingdom
☎ 020 77061014

Cib Ltd Bridge House, 27 Bridge Street, Leatherhead, Surrey, KT22 8DD,
United Kingdom
☎ 01372 371800

Cicero Mktg Comms Ltd 8 Exchange Quay, Manchester, Lancashire, M5 3EQ,
United Kingdom
☎ 0161 8765522

CLEAR COMMUNICATIONS Church Street, Tetbury, Gloucestershire, GL8 8JG,
United Kingdom
☎ 01666 501110

clear marketing communications 121 Palatine Road, Didsbury, Manchester, Lancashire, M20 3YA,
United Kingdom
☎ 0161 4488808

Cloth Court Communications 20 Britton Street, London, EC1M 5UA,
United Kingdom
☎ 020 72516400

CM3 COMMUNICATIONS Ltd Compton Way, Farnham, Surrey, GU10 1QZ,
United Kingdom
☎ 01252 781469

CMAS Ltd The Granary, Southill, Cornbury Park, Chipping Norton, Oxfordshire, OX7 3EW,
United Kingdom
☎ 01608 811228

Cogent Elliot Ltd Heath Farm, Hampton Lane, Meriden, Coventry, West Midlands, CV7 7LL,
United Kingdom
☎ 01676 522805

Cognition 4 Dormer Place, Leamington Spa, Warwickshire, CV32 5AE,
United Kingdom
☎ 01926 330800

Cognito Eagle House, 16 Procter Street, London, WC1V 6NX,
United Kingdom
☎ 020 74381100

Colbear Advertising Heather Wood House, Armthorpe Road, Doncaster, South Yorkshire, DN2 5PX,
United Kingdom
☎ 01302 360042

Commotion 99-101 Farringdon Road, London, EC1R 3BN,
United Kingdom
☎ 020 76899971

Communicator Ltd 199 Upper Street, London, N1 1RQ,
United Kingdom
☎ 020 77048333

Communique Advertising Ltd 74 Lairgate, Beverley, North Humberside, HU17 8EX,
United Kingdom
☎ 01482 863635

Connectpoint Advertising St Johns Court, 19b Quay Street, Manchester, Lancashire, M3 3HN,
United Kingdom
☎ 0161 8174200

Conrad Advertising The Grange, 100 High Street, London, N14 6EQ,
United Kingdom
☎ 0208 9209000

Cooney Bains Home Farm, Ardington, Wantage, Oxfordshire, OX12 8PN,
United Kingdom
✆ 01235 813110

Covey McCormick Bon Accord House, Riverside Drive, Aberdeen, Aberdeenshire, AB11 7SL,
United Kingdom
✆ 01224 581700

Cravens Advertising 42 Leazes Park Road, Newcastle Upon Tyne, Tyne & Wear, NE1 4PL,
United Kingdom
✆ 0191 2326683

Crayon Direct Advertising Ltd 26 Finsbury Square, London, N1 8LN,
United Kingdom
✆ 020 73546000

Crazyhorse Brand Warriors Birchlands Business Centre, Benhall Mill Road, Tunbridge Wells, Kent, TN2 5JH,
United Kingdom
✆ 01892 516116

Cre8 Results Ltd 8 Marshall Street, London, W1F 7EJ,
United Kingdom
✆ 020 77349199

Creative & Commercial 8-9 Pratt Mews, Camden, London, NW1 0AD,
United Kingdom
✆ 020 73874555

Creative Marketing Services Hollinthorpe Hall, Swillington Lane, Leeds, West Yorkshire, LS26 8BZ,
United Kingdom
✆ 0113 2877973

Creative Media Advertising Ltd Overton House, West Road, Congleton, Cheshire, CW12 1JY,
United Kingdom
✆ 01260 292600

Ctc 12 Whiteladies Road, Clifton, Bristol, Avon, BS8 1PD,
United Kingdom
✆ 0117 3119009

Cunning 192 St John Street, London, EC1V 4JY,
United Kingdom
✆ 020 75665300

Curtis Edington & Say Ltd 3 Lion Yard, Tremadoc Road, London, SW4 7NQ,
United Kingdom
✆ 020 76227474

CW Advertising Agency Saturn House, Mercury Rise, Altham Business Park, Altham, Lancashire, BB5 5YE,
United Kingdom
✆ 01282 858200

CWT Advertising Ltd 121 Becontree Avenue, Dagenham, Essex, RM8 2UJ,
United Kingdom
✆ 020 85900083

Dark Arts Marketing 54/56 Highpavement, The Lace Market, Nottingham, Nottinghamshire, NG1 1HW,
United Kingdom
✆ 0115 9472863

Dark Horse Agency Ltd The Steadings, Maisemore, Gloucester, Gloucestershire, GL2 8EY,
United Kingdom
✆ 01452 310567

Datadrum Ltd 1 Page Road, Sweet Briar Road Industrial Es, Norwich, Norfolk, NR3 2BX,
United Kingdom
✆ 01603 484484

Davies Media 146 Maryleborne Road, 146 Marylebone Road, London, NW1 5PH,
United Kingdom
✆ 020 74860660

Davmark Group 10 Willow Street, London, EC2A 4BH ,
United Kingdom
✆ 020 70333400

Deal Group Media plc Unit 800, Highgate Studios, 53-79 Highgate Road, London, NW5 1TL,
United Kingdom
✆ 020 76911880

DEFINITIVE CONSULTING INTIATIV Farnsby Street, Swindon, Wiltshire, SN1 5AH,
United Kingdom
✆ 01793 616159

Denfield Advtg & Mktg Trinity House Stables, Trinity Street, Leamington Spa, Warwickshire, CV32 5YN,
United Kingdom
✆ 01926 881178

Designate 4 St Georges Place, Brighton, East Sussex, BN1 4GA,
United Kingdom
✆ 01273 704040

Dewynters plc 48 Leicester Square, London, WC2H 7QD,
United Kingdom
✆ 020 73210488

Diablo Creative Marketing 2 Meridians Cross, Ocean Way, Ocean Village, Southampton, Hampshire, SO14 3TJ,
United Kingdom
✆ 023 80715585

Different Ltd 10 Summerhill Terrace, Summerhill Square, Newcastle Upon Tyne, Tyne & Wear, NE4 6EB,
United Kingdom
✆ 0191 2610111

Dig for Fire Players House, 300 Attercliffe Common, Sheffield, South Yorkshire, S9 2AG,
United Kingdom
✆ 0114 2560863

Digital Clarity Ltd 32 High Street, Guilford, Surrey, GU1 3EL,
United Kingdom
✆ 01483 577780

Digital View Ltd 6 Marylebone Pass, London, W1W 8EX,
United Kingdom
✆ 020 76312150

DKA 87 New Cavendish Street, London, W1W 6XD,
United Kingdom
✆ 020 76366992

DONER CARDWELL HAWKINS 26-34 Emerald Street, London, WC1N 3QA,
United Kingdom
✆ 020 74001230

Donkin Thompson Hood Ltd Devonshire House, Devonshire Avenue, Leeds, West Yorkshire, LS8 1AY,
United Kingdom
✆ 0113 2888522

Dorset Police Force Headquarters, Winfrith Newburgh, Dorchester, Dorset, DT2 8DZ,
United Kingdom
✆ 01202 222233

Dowell & Associates Advtg Ltd 10 The Causeway, Teddington, Middlesex, TW11 0HE,
United Kingdom
✆ 020 89439999

DRB Marketing 40 Great Lister Street, Birmingham, West Midlands, B7 4LF,
United Kingdom
✆ 0121 3333132

Drugstore The Tea Building, Studio G.01, 56 Shoreditch High Street, London, E1 6JJ,
United Kingdom
✆ 020 77296000

DTW Advertising & Marketing Bank Chambers, Market Place, Guisborough, Cleveland, TS14 6BN,
United Kingdom
✆ 01287 610404

Dunwoody Mktg Comms Ltd The Litten, Newtown Road, Newbury, Berkshire, RG14 7BB,
United Kingdom
✆ 01635 35599

DWS Advertising Ltd 141-143 Commercial Road, London, E1 1PX,
United Kingdom
✆ 020 72471303

Eastern Daily Press PO Box 28, Rouen Road, Norwich, Norfolk, NR1 1RE,
United Kingdom
✆ 01603 628311

Edson Williams 52 Brushfield Street, London, E1 6AG,
United Kingdom
✆ 2073753077

Ekay Advertising & Marketing The Maltings, 54 Bath Street, Gravesend, Kent, DA11 0DF,
United Kingdom
✆ 01474 334343

Eldridge Ranger Adv Ltd 30 Quay Street, Newport, Isle Of Wight, PO30 5BA,
United Kingdom
✆ 01983 532636

Electronic Solutions Minerva House, 1-4 North Crescent, London, WC1E 7ER,
United Kingdom
✆ 020 76319500

Elmscott Advertising Ltd Stag House, Old London Road, Hertford, Hertfordshire, SG13 7LA,
United Kingdom
✆ 01992 517517

EMAP Communications Group 41-47 Seabourne Road, Bournemouth, Dorset, BH5 2HU,
United Kingdom
✆ 01202 432121

EMAP Retail 33 Bowling Green Lane, London, EC1R 0DA,
United Kingdom
✆ 020 75058000

Emberton Dale Advertising 224 Upper Fifth Street, Milton Keynes, Buckinghamshire, MK9 2HR,
United Kingdom
✆ 0190 8668338

Equi Media Ltd 60-61 Cherry Orchid East, Kembrey Park, Swindon, Wiltshire, SN2 8UQ,
United Kingdom
✆ 01793 715440

Essence Media 3rd Floor, The Tower building, 11 York Road, London, SE1 7NX,
United Kingdom
✆ 020 76333850

Estates Gazette Group 1 Procter Street, London, WC1V 6EU,
United Kingdom
✆ 020 79111700

Euro RSCG Worldwide UK 15 17 Alfred Place, London, WC1E 7EB,
United Kingdom
✆ 020 72404111

EURO RSG KLP 109 Wardour Street, London, W1F 0UH,
United Kingdom
✆ 020 74781800

Exclaim Advertising Dukes House, 4 High Street, Newburn, Newcastle, Tyne & Wear, NE15 8LN,
United Kingdom
✆ 0191 2642371

Eye Candy Media Ltd 3 Wilkin Street, Kentish Town, London, NW5 3NL,
United Kingdom
✆ 020 74282300

Eyeblaster Baird House, 15-17 St Cross Street, London, EC1N 8UW,
United Kingdom
✆ 020 78319410

EYE-D CREATIVE 220 Tower Bridge Road, 1 Mill Street, London, SE1 2UP,
United Kingdom
✆ 020 74071440

Factor 3 Royal House, Parabola House, Cheltenham, Gloucestershire, GL50 3AH,
United Kingdom
✆ 01242 254242

Fallon London Ltd 67-69 Beak Street, London, W1F 9SW,
United Kingdom
✆ 020 74949120

Fantasia Advertising Unit G05 Courtenay House, 10 Courtenay Road, East Lane Business Park, Wembley, Middlesex, HA9 7ND,
United Kingdom
✆ 020 89080068

FERRIES TRAINES PLANES Ltd 10 Station Parade, High Street Wanstead, London, E11 1QF,
United Kingdom
✆ 020 89893437

Fifth Element 46 The Calls, Leeds, West Yorkshire, LS2 7EY,
United Kingdom
✆ 0113 2431645

Fire IMC Ltd 10 Dargan Crescent, Duncrue Road, Belfast, County Antrim, BT3 9JP,
United Kingdom
✆ 028 90774388

First City Advertising 22 Goodge Place, London, W1T 4SL,
United Kingdom
☏ 020 74367020

Fluid Design 59 Friar Gate, Derby, Derbyshire, DE1 1DF,
United Kingdom
☏ 01332 201743

Fmg Communications 175 Munster Road, London, SW6 6DA,
United Kingdom
☏ 020 77316461

Fold 7 47 Underwood Street, London, N1 7LG,
United Kingdom
☏ 020 72510101

Folio Creative Comm First Floor, Kingfisher House, 45 Market Place, Henley-On-Thames, Oxfordshire, RG9 2AA,
United Kingdom
☏ 01491 411311

Forum Advertising & Marketing 154- 156 London Road, Leicester, Leicestershire, LE2 1NN,
United Kingdom
☏ 0116 2744208

Four Communications The Communications Building, 48 Leicester Square, London, WC2H 7FG,
United Kingdom
☏ 0870 4203212

Four Ninety Ltd Nepshaw Lane South, Gildersome, Leeds, West Yorkshire, LS27 7JQ,
United Kingdom
☏ 0113 2382400

Fox Kalomaski 48 Fitzroy Street, London, W1T 5BS,
United Kingdom
☏ 020 76918090

Fox Murphy Ltd 17-19 St Georges Street, Norwich, Norfolk, NR3 1AB,
United Kingdom
☏ 01603 621587

Frank The Agency Camellia House, 76 Water Lane, Wilmslow, Cheshire, SK9 5BB,
United Kingdom
☏ 01625 521444

FREESTYLE MARKETING COMMS 3 Pelham Road, Nottingham, Nottinghamshire, NG5 1AP,
United Kingdom
☏ 0115 9856954

Fresh Media Group 58 White Lion St, London, N1 9PP,
United Kingdom
☏ 020 72391300

Fresh01 6 The Hangar, Perseverance Works, 38 Kingsland Road Shoreditch, London, E2 8DD,
United Kingdom
☏ 020 77391255

Front Door Marketing Unit 4 Phoenix Business Centre, Higham Road, Chesham, Buckinghamshire, HP5 2AF,
United Kingdom
☏ 01494 794111

Fsw Group Ltd Manor Farm Barns, Fox Road, Framingham Pigot, Norwich, Norfolk, NR14 7PZ,
United Kingdom
☏ 01408 491400

G2 International Marketing Cornelius House, 178 - 180 Church Road, Hove, East Sussex, BN3 2DJ,
United Kingdom
☏ 01273 202901

Gale Priggen & Co Lincoln'S Inn Fields, 52 Lincolns Inn Fields, London, WC2A 3LZ,
United Kingdom
☏ 020 74045043

GDA Creative Communications The Old Vicarage, Park Road, Barnsley, South Yorkshire, S70 6NA,
United Kingdom
☏ 01226 294014

Genesis Advertising 7 Crescent Gardens, Belfast, County Antrim, BT7 1NS,
United Kingdom
☏ 028 90313344

GGS 1 White Lodge Business Park, Hall Road, Norwich, Norfolk, NR4 6DG,
United Kingdom
☏ 01603 622500

glue London 31 Redchurch Street, London, E2 7DJ,
United Kingdom
☏ 020 77392345

Gluemedia 31-39 Redchurch Street, London, E2 7DJ,
United Kingdom
☏ 020 77392345

Golley Slater - Results Mktg Richmond House 5 8, Richmond Terrace, Guiseley, Leeds, West Yorkshire, LS20 8FP,
United Kingdom
☏ 01943 883520

Golley Slater & Partners 12 Margaret Street, London, W1W 8JQ,
United Kingdom
☏ 020 76375263

Golley Slater Contact Mgmt Wharton Place, 13 Wharton Street, Cardiff, South Glamorgan, CF10 1GS,
United Kingdom
☏ 029 20388621

Gough Allen Stanley Ltd Kembrey House, 5 Worcester Road, Bromsgrove, Worcestershire, B61 7DL,
United Kingdom
☏ 01527 579555

Grant Thornton House 204 Silbury Boulevard, Milton Keynes, Buckinghamshire, MK9 1LT,
United Kingdom
☏ 01908 660666

Gray Associates 10 Meadow Court, Amoss Road, Sheffield, South Yorkshire, S9 1BX,
United Kingdom
☏ 0114 2444110

Gray Matter Ltd 18 Davy Avenue, Knowl Hill, Milton Keynes, Buckinghamshire, MK5 8PL,
United Kingdom
☏ 01908 675444

Greenspottedgiraffe 16 Earls Court Sqaure, London, SW5 9DN,
United Kingdom
☏ 020 73410800

Grey Global Group Argosy House, 215 227 Great Portland Street, London, W1W 5PN,
United Kingdom
☏ 020 76363399

Group Impact The Old Granary Cotton End, Cotton End, Northampton, Northamptonshire, NN4 8HP,
United Kingdom
☏ 01604 825500

Group Nexus H Multimedia House, Hill Street, Tunbridge Wells, Kent, TN1 2BY,
United Kingdom
☏ 01892 517777

Grp 1 Eagle Street, Craighall Business Park, Glasgow, Lanarkshire, G4 9XA,
United Kingdom
☏ 0141 3412800

Gyro International Ltd 603 The Chambers, Chelsea Harbour, London, SW10 0XF,
United Kingdom
☏ 020 73511550

Halpern Cowan 172a Arlington Road, London, NW1 7HL,
United Kingdom
☏ 020 72849700

Hamptons International 168 Brompton Road, Knightsbridge, London, SW3 1HW,
United Kingdom
☏ 020 75842044

Hartley Stone Ltd Barry House, 20-22 Worple Road, London, SW19 4DH,
United Kingdom
☏ 020 86059990

Hay Smith Advertising 15 Mentone Gardens, Edinburgh, Mid Lothian, EH9 2DJ,
United Kingdom
☏ 0131 6233200

HBA Creative Ltd Mortimer House, 1 Birmingham Road, Kidderminster, Worcestershire, DY10 2BU,
United Kingdom
☏ 01562 822208

HDM Agency Ltd 1st Floor, Shaftesbury House, 151 Shaftesbury Avenue, London, WC2H 8LA,
United Kingdom
☏ 020 74208020

Heresy Group Scorpio House, 102 Sydney Street, London, SW3 6NJ,
United Kingdom
☏ 020 73767505

HH&S Regal Place, Maxwell Road, London, SW6 2HD,
United Kingdom
☏ 020 73715588

HHC Lewis 22-26 Commercial Road, Southampton, Hampshire, SO15 1GE,
United Kingdom
☏ 0238 0226361

Hippo Creative Solutions Ltd 2 Carlton Court, Fifth Avenue, Team Valley, Team Valley Trading Estate, Gateshead, NE11 0AZ ,
United Kingdom
☏ 0191 4828830

Hird Advertising Omega Court, 376 Cemetery Road, Sheffield, South Yorkshire, S11 8FT,
United Kingdom
☏ 0114 2665289

Hoffi Enterprise House, 127-129 Bute Street, Cardiff, South Glamorgan, CF10 5LE,
United Kingdom
☏ 029 20487941

Holler 13-19 Vine Hill, Clerkenwell, London, EC1R 5DW,
United Kingdom
☏ 020 77135178

Holman Advertising Holman House, 30 Maple Street, London, W1T 6HA,
United Kingdom
☏ 020 75807079

Home Marketing Ltd Hilton Court, 2 North Hill Road, Leeds, West Yorkshire, LS6 2EN,
United Kingdom
☏ 0113 2242662

Hoo HA Ltd 47 The Market, Covent Garden Plazza, Covent Garden, London, WC2E 8RF,
United Kingdom
☏ 020 72408932

Hooper Galton Ltd 39-43 Brewer Street, London, W1F 9UD,
United Kingdom
☏ 020 74946300

HOST UNIVERSAL Ltd 6-10 Lexington Street, Soho, London, W1F 0LB,
United Kingdom
☏ 020 78494500

HPS Group 34 Station Road, Marlow, Buckinghamshire, SL7 1ND,
United Kingdom
☏ 0121 4549707

HPS Group Ltd Parkhouse, Desborough Park Road, High Wycombe, Buckinghamshire, HP12 3DJ,
United Kingdom
☏ 0161 8353100

HROC Design Ltd 15 Highfield Road, Edgbaston, Birmingham, West Midlands, B15 3DU,
United Kingdom
☏ 020 72876404

IAS SMARTS 100 Ocean Drive, Leith Docks, Edinburgh, Mid Lothian, EH6 6JJ,
United Kingdom
☏ 0131 5550425

Ias Smarts plc Clarence Mill, Clarence Road, Bollington, Cheshire, SK10 5JZ,
United Kingdom
☏ 01625 578578

ICM CRTV Comms Ltd Granby House, 7 Otley Road, Headingley, Leeds, West Yorkshire, LS6 3AA,
United Kingdom
☏ 0113 2783070

Ideas London House, Great Eastern Wharf, Parkgate Road, London, SW11 4NQ,
United Kingdom
☏ 020 77381900

Ignis Ltd 525 Fulham Road, London, SW6 1HD,
United Kingdom
☏ 020 73856677

Illumination Design Ltd 11 Christchurch House, Beaufort Court, Rochester, Kent, ME2 4FX,
United Kingdom
☏ 01634 739117

Image Group 1 West Centre, Bath Street, St Helier, Channel Islands, Jersey, JE2 4ST,
United Kingdom
✆ 01534 734444

Image Group Ltd Caslon Court, Pitronnerie Road, St Peter Port, Channel Isles, Guernsey, GY1 3NE,
United Kingdom
✆ 01481 723456

Imagecreative The Bank - Four Lane Ends, 155 Victoria Road East, Thornton Cleveleys, Lancashire, FY5 5HH,
United Kingdom
✆ 01253 338260

Imex Group Ltd Unit 4 Ash Ct, Viking Wy, Winch Wen, Swansea, SA1 7DA ,
United Kingdom
✆ 01792 232630

Inkpressions 23 Campbell Court, Bramley, Tadley, Hampshire, RG26 5EG,
United Kingdom
✆ 01256 880070

Insight Advertising Leonardslee House, Brighton Road, Lower Beeding, Horsham, West Sussex, RH13 6PP,
United Kingdom
✆ 01403 892910

Inter Regional Group Hill House, Hill House Road, Norwich, NR1 4BE,
United Kingdom
✆ 01603 627294

International Co Production 33 Queen Anne Street, London, W1G 9HY,
United Kingdom
✆ 020 74364300

Isobel 91 New Cavendish Street, London, W1W 6XE,
United Kingdom
✆ 020 72085555

J WALTER THOMPSON 1 Knightsbridge Green, London, SW1X 7NW,
United Kingdom
✆ 020 76567000

J Walter Thompson Astley House, Quay Street, Manchester, Lancashire, M3 4AS,
United Kingdom
✆ 0161 8328884

Jacob Bailey Ltd Unit 1 01, Tea Building, 56 Shoreditch High Street, London, E1 6JJ,
United Kingdom
✆ 020 77290934

Jacob Bailey Ltd 1 Woodbridge Road, Ipswich, Suffolk, IP4 2EA,
United Kingdom
✆ 01473 215656

JDI Integrated Advertising 41 Overstone Road, Hammersmith, London, W6 0AD,
United Kingdom
✆ 020 85631414

Jelly Communications 21 Old Channel Road, Belfast, BT3 9DE ,
United Kingdom
✆ 0289 9453999

Jellybean Creative Solutions 4 Bridge Street, Leatherhead, Surrey, KT22 8BZ,
United Kingdom
✆ 01372 227950

JJ Group The Clock Barn, Little Baldon, Oxford, Oxfordshire, OX44 9PU,
United Kingdom
✆ 01865 343100

JK Advertising Ltd 730 Pershore Road, Selly Park, Birmingham, Selly-Park, West Midlands, B29 7NJ,
United Kingdom
✆ 0121 4721000

John Ryan International Inc Queens Wharf, Queen Caroline St, London, W6 9RQ ,
United Kingdom
✆ 020 86002640

Jordan Design 330 Princess House, 56-60 Eastcastle Street, London, W1W 8EA,
United Kingdom
✆ 020 76372947

Joshua Wells Point, 79 Wells Street, London, W1T 3QH,
United Kingdom
✆ 020 75807099

JPW Advertising Ltd 3 Maritime House, The Hart, Farnham, Surrey, GU9 7HW,
United Kingdom
✆ 01252 737707

Just Media First Floor, 4-8 Emerson Street, London, SE1 9DU,
United Kingdom
✆ 020 78034400

Jwl 27 Gorse Hill, Broad Oak, Heathfield, TN21 8TW,
United Kingdom
✆ 01435 866626

Kaleidoscope 78 Rodney Street, Liverpool, Merseyside, L1 9AL,
United Kingdom
✆ 0151 7072220

Kastner Partners in London Ltd 33-41 Dallington Street, London, EC1V 0BB,
United Kingdom
✆ 020 76896989

KBW Ltd 55 Riding House Street, London, W1W 7EE,
United Kingdom
✆ 020 76318430

Kent Lyons Unit 203-204, Great Guildford Business Sq, 30 Great Guildford Street, London, SE1 0HS,
United Kingdom
✆ 020 76330580

Key PARKER Ltd York House, Leicester Road, Lutterworth, Leicestershire, LE17 4HF,
United Kingdom
✆ 01455 552246

Keywest Design & Advertising Trinity House, 33 Lynedoch Street, Glasgow, Lanarkshire, G3 6AA,
United Kingdom
✆ 0141 3530032

Khemistry Ltd 14-16 Brewer Street, London, W1F 0SG,
United Kingdom
✆ 020 74374084

Kinesis Creative Ltd Station Wks, Bridgeside, Lytham St Annes, FY8 2SN,
United Kingdom
✆ 01253 402600

Kingadventures Ltd 13 Shepard Market, London, W1J 7PN,
United Kingdom
✆ 020 76299210

Kinghorn Davies Adog Ltd 35-39 Blandford Square, Newcastle Upon Tyne, Tyne & Wear, NE1 4HW,
United Kingdom
✆ 0191 2618666

KPMG LLP 8 Salisbury Square, London, EC4Y 8BB,
United Kingdom
✆ 020 73111000

LANGLAND 61 Thames Street, Windsor, Berkshire, SL4 1QW,
United Kingdom
✆ 01753 857140

Large Smith & Walford 4 Percy Street, London, W1T 1DF,
United Kingdom
✆ 020 76936150

Lateral Line The Town House, 163 Bath Street, Glasgow, Lanarkshire, G2 4SQ,
United Kingdom
✆ 0141 2263335

Lavery Rowe Advertising Ltd 69-71 Newington Causeway, London, SE1 6BD,
United Kingdom
✆ 020 73781780

Lavery Rowe Advertising Ltd Ludgate House, 28d Ludgate Hill, Birmingham, West Midlands, B3 1DX,
United Kingdom
✆ 0121 2122230

Lawrence & Pierce 3 Canalside, Canal Street, Nottingham, Nottinghamshire, NG1 7ET,
United Kingdom
✆ 0115 9506862

Lawton Media Communications 4 Grosvenor Square, Southampton, Hampshire, SO15 2BE,
United Kingdom
✆ 02380 639133

Leagas Delaney-London Ltd 1 Alfred Place, London, WC1E 7EB,
United Kingdom
✆ 020 77581758

Led Burnett Ltd Warwick Building, Kensington Village, Avonmore Road, London, W14 8HQ,
United Kingdom
✆ 020 77511800

Ledgard Jepson Ltd 1 Maple Park, Maple Road, Tankerfley, Sheffield, South Yorkshire, S75 3DP,
United Kingdom
✆ 01226 732100

Ledger Bennett plc Haywood House, Lake Street, Leighton Buzzard, Bedfordshire, LU7 1RS,
United Kingdom
✆ 01525 383883

Lee & Nightingale 1 Thursby Road, Croft Business Park, Bromborough, Merseyside, CH63 0NF,
United Kingdom
✆ 0151 3342987

Leo Burnett Warwick Building, Avonmore Rd, London, W14 8TS,
United Kingdom
✆ 020 77511800

Letterspace Origination St Peter's House, Mansfield Road, Derby, Derbyshire, DE1 3TP,
United Kingdom
✆ 01332 242042

Levy McCallum 22 Great Victoria Street, Belfast, County Antrim, BT2 7BA,
United Kingdom
✆ 02890 319220

Levy Mccallum Ltd 203 St Vincent Street, Glasgow, Lanarkshire, G2 5NH,
United Kingdom
✆ 0141 2487977

Levy McCallum Ltd 4 Newton Place, Glasgow, Lanarkshire, G3 7PR,
United Kingdom
✆ 0141 2487977

Lighthouse Adcomms LLP Merlin House, 606 Purley Way, Croydon, Surrey, CR0 4RF,
United Kingdom
✆ 020 86670175

LINDON PARRISS Ltd Jonathan Scott Hall, Thorpe Road, Norwich, Norfolk, NR1 1UH,
United Kingdom
✆ 01603 232222

Linnett Webb Jenkins 6 Highbury Corner, London, N5 1RD,
United Kingdom
✆ 020 76970077

Litmus Blue 10 Dallington Street, London, EC1V 0DB,
United Kingdom
✆ 020 75496549

Livesey Ltd 101 Longden Road, Shrewsbury, Shropshire, SY3 9EB,
United Kingdom
✆ 01743 235651

Loewy Group Ltd 147a Grosvenor Road, London, SW1V 3JY,
United Kingdom
✆ 020 76301795

Lowe & Partners Worldwide 60 Sloane Avenue, London, SW3 3XB,
United Kingdom
✆ 020 78945010

Luxmedia Ltd 15 Galston Road, Luton, Hertfordshire, LU3 3JZ,
United Kingdom
✆ 01582 2495016

Lyle Bailie International Ltd 31 Bruce Street, Great Victoria Street, Belfast, County Antrim, BT2 7JD,
United Kingdom
✆ 028 90331044

Marketing Team Direct Unit 2, Manor Farm Barns, Witney Road Finstock, Chipping Norton, Oxfordshire, OX7 3DG,
United Kingdom
✆ 01993 869330

Marriott Design 3 Lower St James Street, Newport, Isle Of Wight, PO30 5HE,
United Kingdom
✆ 01983 529039

Marriott Howard Publicity Ltd 630 Woodbridge Road, Ipswich, Suffolk, IP4 4PG,
United Kingdom
01473 715556

Martin Tait Redheads Buxton House, 1 Buxton Street, Newcastle Upon Tyne, Tyne & Wear, NE1 6NJ,
United Kingdom
0191 2321926

Martin Waxman & Associates 56 St Johns Street, London, EC1M 4HG,
United Kingdom
020 72535500

Matrix The Office Village, River Way, Uckfield, East Sussex, TN22 1SL,
United Kingdom
0870 1210201

Maverick Moray House, 23 31 Great Titchfield Street, London, W1W 7PA,
United Kingdom
020 72913450

Maxim Communications Maxim House, Kingsmill Park, London Road, High Wycombe, Buckinghamshire, HP10 9UB,
United Kingdom
01494 474444

MBA 82 Charing Cross Road, London, WC2H 0BA,
United Kingdom
020 73097201

McCann Erickson Highlands Road, Shirley, West Midlands, B90 4WE,
United Kingdom
0121 7133500

McCann Erickson Advertising Mccann Erickson House, 7-11 Herbrand Street, London, WC1N 1EX,
United Kingdom
020 78373737

McCann ERIKSON MANCHESTER Ltd Bonis Hall, Bonis Hall Lane, Macclesfield, Cheshire, SK10 4EF,
United Kingdom
01625 822200

Mcconnells Advertising 49 Uttoxeter New Road, Derby, Derbyshire, DE24 8QE,
United Kingdom
01332 222900

Mcconnells Advertising & PR 49 Uttoxeter New Road, Derby, Derbyshire, DE22 3NL,
United Kingdom
01332 222900

MDA Media Ltd Pepper Road, Hazel Grove, Stockport, Cheshire, SK7 5DP,
United Kingdom
0161 4871111

Media Contacts 15 Windsor Street, London, N1 8QG,
United Kingdom
020 73598244

Media Junction Advertising Ltd 40a Old Compton Street, Soho, London, W1D 4TU,
United Kingdom
020 74349919

Media Run Ltd 20 Conduit Street, London, W1S 2XW ,
United Kingdom
020 74911533

MEDIA WORKS Ltd 4-14 Fishponds Road, Eastville, Bristol, Avon, BS5 6SA,
United Kingdom
0117 9021212

MediaCom London 124 Theobald'S Road, London, WC1X 8RX,
United Kingdom
020 71585500

Mediawise 121 Queens Park Avenue, Bournemouth, Dorset, BH8 9HA,
United Kingdom
01202 399636

Merchant Group LLP 17 Lincolns Inn Fields, London, WC2A 3ED,
United Kingdom
020 72421336

Meviavest Manchester 117-119 Portland Street, Manchester, Lancashire, M1 6ED,
United Kingdom
0161 2283909

Mhm Grax 19 Garrick Street, London, WC2E 9AX,
United Kingdom
020 72407767

Michael K Howard Mulberry House, 750 Capability Green, Luton, Bedfordshire, LU1 3LU,
United Kingdom
01582 693000

Michaelides & Bednash Elsley Court, 20-22 Great Titchfield Street, London, W1W 8BE,
United Kingdom
020 74681168

Michon Design Co The Warehouse, Fleeman Grove, West Bridgford, Nottingham, Nottinghamshire, NG2 5BH,
United Kingdom
0115 9455434

Millennium Advertising Ltd Emerson House, 14-B Ballynahinch Road, Carryduff, Belfast, County Antrim, BT8 8DN,
United Kingdom
028 90815522

Minerva London Ltd Minerva House, Chenies St, London, WC1E 7LP,
United Kingdom
020 70793900

Mirabelle Communications Ltd Mirabelle House, 26 Barclay Road, Croydon, Surrey, CR0 1JN,
United Kingdom
020 86815799

Mirago plc Equinox House, Oriel Court, Omega Park, Alton, Hampshire, GU34 2YT,
United Kingdom
01420 82601

Mitham Bryant Smith Adv Ltd Old Station Works, Station Road, Shepreth, Royston, Hertfordshire, SG8 6PZ,
United Kingdom
01763 261385

MJL Ltd 2 Walsworth Road, Hitchin, Hertfordshire, SG4 9SP,
United Kingdom
01462 431477

Modem Media UK Ltd 183 Eversholt Street, London, NW1 1BU,
United Kingdom
020 78749400

Monitor Marketing Ltd 54 Oldfield Road, Salford, Manchester, Lancashire, M5 4LZ,
United Kingdom
0161 7430980

Moose Partnership The City Business Centre, Llanthony Road, Gloucester, Gloucestershire, GL2 5JH,
United Kingdom
01452 308781

Morgan Artwork & Design 19 Whitwell Close, Great Sankey, Warrington, Cheshire, WA5 3HW,
United Kingdom
0870 2418684

Mortimer Whitaker O'Sullivan The Carriage Hall, 29 Floral Street, London, WC2E 9TD,
United Kingdom
020 73798844

Mostly Media Ltd 27 Hendford, Yeovil, Somerset, BA20 1UN,
United Kingdom
01935 415100

MOTHER Biscuit Building, 10 Redchurch Street, London, E2 7DD,
United Kingdom
020 70121999

Motoring Oppourtunities 11 Cardale Court, Beckwith Head Road, Harrogate, North Yorkshire, HG3 1RY,
United Kingdom
01423 524300

Mr Lucky Bags Ltd Unit 6 Sneyd Bsns Pk, Stoke On Trent, ST6 2NP ,
United Kingdom
01782 284688

MRM Worldwide 11 Bywater Place, London, SE16 5ND,
United Kingdom
020 72783856

Mulberry Communications Ltd 97 High Street, Old Harlow, Essex, CM17 0DP,
United Kingdom
01279 416017

MURPHY VARLEY Ltd 4 Kensworth Gate, High Street South, Dunstable, Bedfordshire, LU6 3HS,
United Kingdom
01582 664045

Muse Advertising Ltd 64 Maltings Place, 169 Tower Bridge Road, London, SE1 3LJ,
United Kingdom
020 74039100

Mustoes 206-212b St John Street, Clerkenwell, London, EC1V 4PH,
United Kingdom
020 73241420

My Agency 88 Goswell Road, London, EC1V 7DB,
United Kingdom
020 73366691

Nation 1 Ltd 144 West Regent Street, Glasgow, Lanarkshire, G2 2RQ,
United Kingdom
0870 7568600

Native Manchester International, Office Centre, Styal Road, Manchester, Lancashire, M22 5WB,
United Kingdom
0161 4996650

Navigator Blue Ltd The Baths, 18 Ormeau Avenue, Belfast, County Antrim, BT2 8HS,
United Kingdom
028 90246722

NB Group Meridan House, Kingsway North Team Valley, Team Valley, Gateshead, Tyne & Wear, NE11 0JH,
United Kingdom
0191 4825305

New Image 90 Duncreggan Road, Derry City, County Londonderry, BT48 0AA,
United Kingdom
028 71261188

Next Level The Old School House, School Street, Cleckheaton, West Yorkshire, BD19 6AF,
United Kingdom
01274 851325

Nielsen Media Research Atrium Court, The Ring, Bracknell, Berkshire, RG12 1BZ,
United Kingdom
01344 469100

Nitro First Floor, 25 Bedford Street, London, WC2E 9ES,
United Kingdom
020 77595999

Norris Lincloln Adcom Ltd Dolphin Court, Great Turnstile 10-11, London, WC1V 7JU,
United Kingdom
020 72698880

O2 Creative Ltd 87 Yarmouth Road, Norwich, Norfolk, NR7 0HF,
United Kingdom
01603 708094

Oakbase plc Oakbase House, Trafford Street, Chester, Cheshire, CH1 3HP,
United Kingdom
01244 391391

OCW Advertising & Marketing 22-24 Northgate, Elland, Halifax, West Yorkshire, HX5 0RU,
United Kingdom
01422 377469

Oliver Taylor & Turner Ltd 7 River Close, East Farleigh, Maidstone, Kent, ME15 0JE,
United Kingdom
01622 728776

Omnia Advertising & Mktg Ltd Rectory House, Market Street, St Peter Port, GY1 1HB,
United Kingdom
01481 740666

One Advertising 26 Kings Road, Harrogate, North Yorkshire, HG1 5JW,
United Kingdom
01423 7011711

One O Clock Gun DC Ltd 18 Porphichen Street, Haymarket, Edinburgh, Mid Lothian, EH3 8JB,
United Kingdom
0131 5388886

Open Sky Ltd Aspect House, Herriard Business Park, Basingstoke, Hampshire, RG25 2PN,
United Kingdom
01256 385600

Orgill Advertising Ltd Grosvenor House, Belgrave La, Plymouth, PL4 7DA,
United Kingdom
📞 01752 201601

Otb (Outside The Box) Ltd Escher House, 116 Cardigan Road, Headingley, Leeds, West Yorkshire, LS6 3BJ,
United Kingdom
📞 0113 2162820

Oticon Ltd Cadzow Industrial Estate, Hamilton, Lanarkshire, ML3 7QE,
United Kingdom
📞 01698 283363

OTL Advertising Otl House, 8 Hill Street, St Helier, Jersey, JE2 4UA,
United Kingdom
📞 01534 724421

Outdoor Advertising Assoc Summit House, 27 Sale Place, London, W2 1YR,
United Kingdom
📞 020 79730315

Outrider 1 Paris Garden, London, SE1 8NU,
United Kingdom
📞 020 78032390

Palmer Hargreaves Wallis 18 - 20 Parade, Leamington Spa, Warwickshire, CV32 4DW,
United Kingdom
📞 01926 452525

Panlogic Ltd 3 Paradise Road, Richmond, Surrey, TW9 1RX,
United Kingdom
📞 020 89485511

Paver Downes Associates 2 Queen Square, Liverpool, Merseyside, L1 1RH,
United Kingdom
📞 0151 2930505

PEARL & DEAN 3 Waterhouse Square, 138-142 Holborn, London, EC1N 2NY,
United Kingdom
📞 020 78821100

Perception Advertising Ltd 101 Park Road, Brentwood, Essex, CM14 4TT,
United Kingdom
📞 01277 205728

Perspektiv Ltd 34 Stoney Street, The Lace Market, Nottingham, Nottinghamshire, NG1 1NB,
United Kingdom
📞 0115 9500510

Peter Bush Communications Stansted House, Shire Hill, Saffron Walden Essex, Essex, CB11 3AQ,
United Kingdom
📞 01799 420022

PH Media Victoria Square, Roche, St Austell, Cornwall, PL26 8LQ,
United Kingdom
📞 01726 891111

Phoenix plc The Chapel, Reigate Road, Leatherhead, Surrey, KT22 8RA,
United Kingdom
📞 01372 372372

Pjm Advertising & Marketing 28 Brindley Road, City Park Business Village, Cornbrook, Manchester, Lancashire, M16 9HQ,
United Kingdom
📞 0161 8778125

Pmn Marketing 34 West Street, Marlow, Buckinghamshire, SL7 2NB,
United Kingdom
📞 01628 481147

PMW Communications Stane Court, Stane Street, Billingshurst, West Sussex, RH14 9HP,
United Kingdom
📞 01403 783400

Pogo 34 Kemp Street, Brighton, East Sussex, BN1 4EF,
United Kingdom
📞 01273 523532

Positive Advertising Ltd Park House, Abbeyfore Gate, Shrewsbury, Shropshire, SY2 6BL,
United Kingdom
📞 01743 235770

Posterscope Cardinal Tower, 12 Farringdon Road, London, EC1M 3HS,
United Kingdom
📞 020 73366363

Poulsen Selleck The Manor House, 10 St Margarets Green, Ipswich, Suffolk, IP4 2BS,
United Kingdom
📞 01473 288700

Poulter Partners Rose Wharf, 78 East Street, Leeds, West Yorkshire, LS9 8EE,
United Kingdom
📞 0113 2856500

Principles Agency Devonshire Hall, Devonshire Avenue, Street Lane, Leeds, West Yorkshire, LS8 1AW,
United Kingdom
📞 0113 2262222

Promedia Advertising Ltd Kelvin House, Chestergate, Chester Street, Stockport, Cheshire, SK3 0BQ,
United Kingdom
📞 0161 4774447

Propaganda Agency Ltd Brookfield Court, Brookfield, Leeds, West Yorkshire, LS25 1NB,
United Kingdom
📞 0113 2876985

Proteus Marketing Comms 3-8 Redcliffe Parade West, Bristol, Avon, BS1 6SP,
United Kingdom
📞 0117 9858888

Proximity Worldwide 191 Old Marylebone Road, London, NW1 5DW,
United Kingdom
📞 020 72981000

PSI Advertising 20/22 Grosvenor Gardens Mews, London, SW1W 0JP,
United Kingdom
📞 020 78241700

PURE EQUATOR
DESIGN CONSULTANTS

"The PureEquator team were essential in the development of Cocoa Bay, creating a design route that surpasses any branded product Ashbury have ever done. We are all excited about this and are looking forward to working on more projects with the PureEquator team in the future."
– Head of Marketing, Ashbury Confectionery Ltd

T +44 (0)115 947 6444
www.pure-equator.com

COCOA BAY
FINE CHOCOLATE
INDULGENT TRUFFLE SELECTION

COCOA BAY
FINE CHOCOLATE
LUXURY MADAGASCAN CHOCOLATE
MARC DE CHAMPAGNE TRUFFLES

Ptarmigan Media Ltd Italian Building, 41-43 Dockhead, London, SE1 2BS, United Kingdom
✆ 020 72310014

Publicis 5 Countisbury Avenue, Bush Hill Park, Enfield, EN1 2NL, United Kingdom
✆ 020 78303688

Publicis Blueprint 83-89 Whitfield St, London, W1A 4XA, United Kingdom
✆ 020 74627777

Publicis London 82 Baker St, London, W1U 6AE, United Kingdom
✆ 020 79354426

Publicity Matters 2 Bellevue Road, Clevedon, BS21 7NR, United Kingdom
✆ 01275 342734

Pulse Pulse House, 1-3 Colebrooke Place, London, N1 8HZ, United Kingdom
✆ 020 72888000

Pure Automotive Westgate House, Hills Lane, Shrewsbury, Shropshire, SY1 1QU, United Kingdom
✆ 01743 289383

Purity Elme House, 133 Long Acre, Covent Garden, London, WC2E 9DT, United Kingdom
✆ 020 74207900

QD Ltd 93 Great Titchfield Street, London, W1W 6RP, United Kingdom
✆ 020 74621700

QPQ Ltd The Pillars, Park Green, Macclesfield, Cheshire, SK11 7NA, United Kingdom
✆ 01625 425670

Quayside Creative Ltd Basin End, Chester Road, Acton, Nantwich, Cheshire, CW5 8LB, United Kingdom
✆ 01270 610397

Quick-Thinking 2 Station Road West, Oxted, RH8 9EP, United Kingdom
✆ 01883 722278

R&G Advertising & Marketing 8 Bugle Street, Southampton, Hampshire, SO14 2AJ, United Kingdom
✆ 023 80228656

Radio Works Ltd 36-40 Maple Street, London, W1T 6HE, United Kingdom
✆ 020 7631 0939

Rainey Kelly Campbell Roalfe Greater London House, Hampstead Road, London, NW1 7QP, United Kingdom
✆ 020 7404 2700

RAINMAKER ADVERTISING 140-142 St Johns Street, London, EC1V 4UB, United Kingdom
✆ 020 7031 1141

Rapier The Network Building, 97 Tottenham Court Road, London, W1T 4TP, United Kingdom
✆ 020 73698000

Rave Communications 37 Parkfield Road, Coleshill, Birmingham, West Midlands, B46 3LD, United Kingdom
✆ 01675 467462

Real Creatures Ltd 13-14 Dean Street, London, W1D 3RS, United Kingdom
✆ 020 74374188

Real Media UK Ltd 19 Harcourt Street, London, W1H 4HF, United Kingdom
✆ 020 75633800

Red Cell Ltd 8 Minerva Way, Glasgow, Lanarkshire, G3 8AU, United Kingdom
✆ 0141 2216882

Red ROUTE 32 34 Great Marlborough Street, London, W1F 7JB, United Kingdom
✆ 020 72873557

Rees Bradley Hepburn Diddington Farm, Diddington Lane, Meriden, Coventry, West Midlands, CV7 7HQ, United Kingdom
✆ 01675 443939

Refinery Marketing Commns Ltd 10 Pittbrook Street, Manchester, Lancashire, M12 6JX, United Kingdom
✆ 016273 5511

Renishaw plc New Mills, Wotton-Under-Edge, Gloucestershire, GL12 8JR, United Kingdom
✆ 01453 524524

Retail & Detail Advertising The Vergery, Bromley Coll, Bromley, BR1 1PE, United Kingdom
✆ 0870 7873100

RH Advertising 7 Barnfield Crescent, Exeter, Devon, EX1 1QT, United Kingdom
✆ 01392 219797

Rhythm Communications Trelawney House, Surrey Street, Bristol, Avon, BS2 8PS, United Kingdom
✆ 0117 9429786

Riley Advertising Hanover House, Queen Charlotte Street, Bristol, Avon, BS1 4LG, United Kingdom
✆ 0117 9257777

Riley Advertising & Comms 33 Pilcher Gate, Nottingham, Nottinghamshire, NG1 1PX, United Kingdom
✆ 0115 9590006

Riley Advertising Ltd Trafford House, Chester Road, Manchester, Lancashire, M32 0RS, United Kingdom
✆ 0161 6102200

RLA Group 86 Lisburn Road, Belfast, BT9 6AF, United Kingdom
✆ 028 90664444

RLA Group Parley Court Farm, Parley Green Lane, Parley, Christchurch, Dorset, BH23 6BB, United Kingdom
✆ 0202 597140

ROBSON BROWN ADVERTISING Clavering House, Clavering Place, Newcastle Upon Tyne, Tyne & Wear, NE1 3UE, United Kingdom
✆ 0191 232 2443

Robson Brown Communications Clavering House, Clavering Place, Newcastle Upon Tyne, Tyne & Wear, NE1 3NG, United Kingdom
✆ 0191 2322443

Rock Kitchen Harris 31 Lower Brown Street, Leicester, Leicestershire, LE1 5TH, United Kingdom
✆ 0116 2337500

Rocket Creative Services Bridge Cottage, 489 Station Road, Aylesford, Kent, ME20 7QR, United Kingdom
✆ 01622 716305

Rod Fraser Associates Oxford Office Village, Langford Lane, Kidlington, OX5 1HT, United Kingdom
✆ 01865 840800

Rodber Thorneycroft Ltd Brompton House, 97-99 Kew Road, Richmond, Surrey, TW9 2PN, United Kingdom
✆ 020 83347870

Ross Levenson Harris Ltd 60-63 Victoria Road, Surbiton, Surrey, KT6 4NQ, United Kingdom
✆ 020 83904611

Round Peg Advertising Ltd 24 Talbot Lane, Leicester, Leicestershire, LE1 4LR, United Kingdom
✆ 0116 2539494

Rpm William Blake House, 8 Marshall Street, London, W1F 7EH, United Kingdom
✆ 020 77349041

Ryan EMO Advertising Ltd Ferry House, Canute Road, Ocean Village, Southampton, Hampshire, SO14 3FJ, United Kingdom
✆ 023 80230940

Rzed 75 Newman Street, London, W1T 3EN, United Kingdom
✆ 020 74368474

Saatchi & Saatchi 80 Charlotte Street, London, W1T 4QS, United Kingdom
✆ 020 76365060

SASS Brand Communications Ltd The Haybarn, Warrington Road, Mere Hall Estate, Knutsford, Cheshire, WA16 0PY, United Kingdom
✆ 01565 832832

Savage Design & Advertising The Top Floor, West Wing Ivor House, bridge Street, Cardiff, South Glamorgan, CF10 2EE, United Kingdom
✆ 02920 345533

Scott Dawson Advertising Dawson Court, Billington Road Ind Estate, Burnley, Lancashire, BB11 5BW, United Kingdom
✆ 01282 426846

Sellers & Rogers Price House, 37 Stoney Street, Nottingham, Nottinghamshire, NG1 1LS, United Kingdom
✆ 0115 9551159

Sequoia Marcher Court, Sealand Road, Sealand, Chester, Cheshire, CH1 6BS, United Kingdom
✆ 01244 377322

Seriously Bright 8 Marshall Street, London, W1F 7EJ, United Kingdom
✆ 020 74942677

Sheppard Day Associates 47 Francis Street, London, SW1P 1QR, United Kingdom
✆ 020 78212222

Smarter Communications 77-91 New Oxford Street, London, WC1A 1DG, United Kingdom
✆ 020 74205890

Smooth Creative Production The Workshop Cornwells Farm, Sheephurst Lane, Marden, Tonbridge, Kent, TN12 9NS, United Kingdom
✆ 01622 832300

Smurfit Display Sitwell Industrial Park, Heage Road Industrial Estate, Ripley, Derbyshire, DE5 3GH, United Kingdom
✆ 01773 513068

Social UK 35 Britannia Row, Islington, London, N1 8QH, United Kingdom
✆ 020 73544422

Solution 2 11 Brightmoor Street, The Lace Market, Nottingham, Nottinghamshire, NG1 1FD, United Kingdom
✆ 0114 9552902

Somethinkelse The Biscuit Factory, 16 Stoddart St, Newcastle Upon Tyne, Tyne & Wear, NE2 1AN, United Kingdom
✆ 0191 2619639

SPD 1st Floor, 21 Bateman Street, London, W1D 3AL, United Kingdom
✆ 020 77344955

SPIDERZONE Ltd Unit 2 Ridgacre Road, Ridgacre Road, West Bromwich, West Midlands, B71 1BB, United Kingdom
✆ 0121 4245808

Spring Associates Ltd 212 Century Buildings, Tower Street, Brunswick Businss Park, Liverpool, Merseyside, L3 4BJ, United Kingdom
✆ 0151 7096666

Spurgeon Walker Ltd 67 High Street, Sevenoaks, Kent, TN13 1JY, United Kingdom
✆ 01732 459821

Square One Advertising Ltd 134 Archer road, Sheffield, South Yorkshire, S8 0JZ, United Kingdom
✆ 0114 2557911

St Lukes Communications 22 Dukes Road,
London, WC1H 9PN,
United Kingdom
☎ 020 73808888

Starfish Advtng & Mktg Ltd Claremont House,
Claremont Bank, Essington, Shropshire, SY1 1RW,
United Kingdom
☎ 01902 732883

Stephen Talbot Advertising Ltd The Quadrangle, Crewe
Hall, Weston Road, Crewe, Cheshire, CW1 6UY,
United Kingdom
☎ 01270 252888

Sterling Brands 19a Floral Street, Covent Garden,
London, WC2E 9DS,
United Kingdom
☎ 020 74201280

Stills Marketing Ltd 6 George Street, Alderley Edge,
Cheshire, SK9 7EJ,
United Kingdom
☎ 01625 584959

Strange & Dawson Advertising Ninth Floor, Clifton
Heights, Triangle West, Bristol, Avon, BS8 1EJ,
United Kingdom
☎ 0117 9253830

Sudler & Hennessey 34 Cleveland St,
London, W1T 4JE ,
United Kingdom
☎ 020 73077801

Survey Force Ltd Algarve House, 140 Borden Lane,
Sittingbourne, Kent, ME9 8HW,
United Kingdom
☎ 01795 423778

Sutcliffe Reynolds Fitzgerald The Malthouse,
William Street, Leamington Spa, Warwickshire,
CV32 4HJ, United Kingdom
☎ 01926 311786

Suzanne Gillies Associates Ltd 25 South Street,
Reading, Berkshire, RG1 4QU,
United Kingdom
☎ 0118 9592059

Syzygy UK 2nd Floor The Johnson Buildin,
77 Hatton Garden, London, EC1N 8JS,
United Kingdom
☎ 020 82064000

Syzygy UK Ltd 8 Alexandra Mansions,
333 Kings Road, London, SW3 5ET,
United Kingdom
☎ 020 82064000

Tag 29 Clerkenwell Road, London, EC1M 5TA,
United Kingdom
☎ 020 72514571

Tango Marketing Communications
81 Hagley Court North, Waterfront East, Level Street,
Brierley Hill, West Midlands, DY5 1XF,
United Kingdom
☎ 0870 6091541

Tango Zebra Golden House, 30 Great Pulteney Street,
London, W1F 9NN,
United Kingdom
☎ 020 32301088

Target Marketing Comms Brandan House,
62 Painswick Road, Cheltenham,
Gloucestershire, GL50 2EU, United Kingdom
☎ 01242 584417

Tbg London Highgate Road, 53 59 Highgate Road,
London, NW5 1TL,
United Kingdom
☎ 020 74286650

TBWA LONDON 76-80 Whitfield Street,
London, W1T 4EZ,
United Kingdom
☎ 020 75736666

TC Communications plc Kings Ride Court, Kings Ride,
Ascot, Berkshire, SL5 7JR,
United Kingdom
☎ 01344 622280

TCS ADVERTISING Grove Chambers, 36 Green Lane,
Wilmslow, Cheshire, SK9 1LD,
United Kingdom
☎ 01625 525818

TDP Advertising 76 University Street, Belfast,
County Antrim, BT7 1HE,
United Kingdom
☎ 028 0322882

Tea - The Entertainment Agency Second Floor,
8-14 Vine Hill, London, EC1R 5DX,
United Kingdom
☎ 020 75201080

Technical Advertising 26-34 Liverpool Road, Luton,
Bedfordshire, LU1 1RS,
United Kingdom
☎ 01582 878878

Technique Studios Ltd Wildmere Industrial Estate,
Banbury, Oxfordshire, OX16 3TL,
United Kingdom
☎ 01295 709894

TEN ALPS MTD Ltd 14 Links Place, Edinburgh,
Mid Lothian, EH6 7EZ,
United Kingdom
☎ 0131 5539200

TFG Whitfield House, 81 Whitfield Street,
London, W1T 4HG,
United Kingdom
☎ 020 7255 5100

The Agency 27 Park Street, Macclesfield, Cheshire,
SK11 6SR,
United Kingdom
☎ 01625 428550

The Bank Orwell House, 16-18 Berners Street, London,
W1T 3LN,
United Kingdom
☎ 020 74368656

The Bio Agency 8-9 Carlisle Street, London, W1D 3BP,
United Kingdom
☎ 020 74943494

The Bridge Norhyrst House, 39 Park Hill, Carshalton,
Surrey, SM5 3SD,
United Kingdom
☎ 020 86699888

The Communications Unit 28 Britton Street,
Clerkenwell, London, EC1M 5UE,
United Kingdom
☎ 020 75660035

The Consultancy (Southern) Ltd 8 Leeson Road,
Bournemouth, Dorset, BH7 7AY,
United Kingdom
☎ 01202 720311

The Dairy Park Lane Business Centre, Park Lane,
Old Basford, Nottingham, Nottinghamshire, NG6 0DI,
United Kingdom
☎ 0115 9770221

The Drayton Bird Partnership 23 Gwydir Street,
Cambridge, CB1 2LG,
United Kingdom
☎ 01223 305600

The Gate Devon House, 58 St Katharines Way, London,
E1W 1LB,
United Kingdom
☎ 020 74234500

The Grass Roots Group plc Pennyroyal Court, Station
Road, Tring, Hertfordshire, HP23 5QZ,
United Kingdom
☎ 01442 829400

The Idea Works Ltd 29 Broad Street, St Helier, Channel
Isles, Jersey, JE2 3RR,
United Kingdom
☎ 01534 755400

The IF agency 25 Weldon Road, Broadheath,
Altrincham, Cheshire, WA14 4HP,
United Kingdom
☎ 0161 9263200

The Leaflet Company 1 Gunpowder Square,
Fleet Street, London, EC4A 3EP,
United Kingdom
☎ 020 75832010

The Leith Agency 37 The Shore, Leith, Edinburgh,
Mid Lothian, EH6 6QU,
United Kingdom
☎ 0131 5618600

The Marketing Machine 30 Marsh Wall,
London, E14 9FY,
United Kingdom
☎ 020 75123456

The One Off 55 Derby Road, Melbourne, Derby,
Derbyshire, DE73 8FE,
United Kingdom
☎ 01332 694555

The Open Agency 8 Shepherdess Walk, 8 Mill Street,
London, SE1 2BA,
United Kingdom
☎ 020 77407000

The Osmosis Agency Deanhurst Park, Gelderd Road,
Leeds, West Yorkshire, LS27 7LG,
United Kingdom
☎ 0113 2203040

The Point Marketing & Comms no 9 High Street,
Wells, Somerset, BA5 2AA,
United Kingdom
☎ 01749 685190

The PR Department 6 Saxonbury Avenue,
Sunbury On Thames, TW16 5HP ,
United Kingdom
☎ 01932 761889

The Price Jameson Group Price Jamieson House,
Oxford St, London, W1D 1LP,
United Kingdom
☎ 020 79178136

The Sonic Network 74 Great Eastern Street,
London, EC2A 3JL,
United Kingdom
☎ 020 76130555

The Square Frith Street, Soho Square,
London, W1D 3JL,
United Kingdom
☎ 020 74341273

The Union Advertising Agency Union House, 66 Street
Lane, Leeds, West Yorkshire, LS8 2DQ,
United Kingdom
☎ 0113 2666050

The Viral Factory 3rd Floor, 58-60 Rivington Street,
London, EC2A 3AU,
United Kingdom
☎ 020 76137300

The Whole Caboodle The Coach House, 184 Otley Road,
Leeds, West Yorkshire, LS16 5LW,
United Kingdom
☎ 0113 2036030

The Workhouse Advtg & Mktg Blackburn Road,
Ribchester, Preston, Lancashire, PR3 3ZQ,
United Kingdom
☎ 01254 878956

The WORKS 12 Thorpe Road, Norwich,
Norfolk, NR1 1RY,
United Kingdom
☎ 01603 761500

Them 107 Mortlake High Street, London, SW14 8HQ,
United Kingdom
☎ 020 88784491

Thenetworkone Ltd 41 Shelton Street,
London, WC2H 9HG,
United Kingdom
☎ 020 72407117

Threes Co Communications Ltd 6 Victoria Works,
Vitoria Street, Birmingham, West Midlands, B1 3PE,
United Kingdom
☎ 0121 2122363

Tiga Communications 49 Dartford Road, Sevenoaks,
Kent, TN13 3TE,
United Kingdom
☎ 01732 779222

Tiger Red Partnership Marble House, Britannia Road,
Patchway, Bristol, Avon, BS34 5TA,
United Kingdom
☎ 0117 9314379

TMA Marketing Group Five Horseshoes House,
Remenham Hill, Remenham, Henley-On-Thames,
Oxfordshire, RG9 3EP,
United Kingdom
☎ 01491 415500

TMCA 13 John Princes Street, London, W1G 0JR,
United Kingdom
☎ 020 74935480

TMP UK Ltd Chancery House, 53-64 Chancery Lane,
London, WC2A 1QS,
United Kingdom
☎ 020 74065000

TMP Worldwide 100 Queen Street, Glasgow, Lanarkshire, G1 3DN, United Kingdom
📞 0141 2437450

Together Communications Ltd 1 Sycamore Road, Amersham, Buckinghamshire, HP6 5EQ, United Kingdom
📞 01494 720310

Top Corner Advertising Canada House, 3 Chepstow Street, Manchester, Lancashire, M1 5FW, United Kingdom
📞 0161 2371881

Torch B2B Ltd 7 Doolittle Mill, Froghall Road, Ampthill, Bedford, Bedfordshire, MK45 2ND, United Kingdom
📞 01525 840830

Tradedoubler 52 Grosvenor Gardens, London, SW1W 0AU, United Kingdom
📞 020 78811400

Tregartha Dinnie 199 Silbury Boulevard, Milton Keynes, Buckinghamshire, MK9 1JL, United Kingdom
📞 01908 306500

Triang Marketing 86 Lisburn Road, Belfast, County Antrim, BT9 6AF, United Kingdom
📞 028 90660103

Tribal Advertising The Clove Building, 4 Maguire Street, Butlers Wharf, London, SE1 2NQ, United Kingdom
📞 020 73783030

Tribal Kingsway Advertising 4 McGuire Street, Butlers Wharf, London, SE1 2NB, United Kingdom
📞 020 73783030

Trigger 35 Atresian Road, London, W2 5DA, United Kingdom
📞 020 72293889

TW Research 5 Cowcross Street, London, EC1M 6DW, United Kingdom
📞 020 72349999

Uber Agency Ltd Royds Mills, Windsor Street, Sheffield, South Yorkshire, S4 7WB, United Kingdom
📞 0114 2787100

Unity 5-8 Hardwick Street, London, EC1R 3RH, United Kingdom
📞 020 74272194

UNIVERSAL McCann 42-47 St Johns Square, London, EC1M 4EA, United Kingdom
📞 020 78335858

Universal McCann Mccann Erickson Central Limited Mccann House Highlands Rd Shi, Highlands Road, Shirley, Birmingham, West Midlands, B90 4WE, United Kingdom
📞 0121 7133700

Universal McCann Europe 28 Manbey Street, Stratford, London, E15 1EU, United Kingdom
📞 020 78335858

Unsworth Sugden Advertising de Montfort House, 19b De Montfort Street, Leicester, Leicestershire, LE1 7GE, United Kingdom
📞 0116 2471777

USP Headline 83 Victoria Road, Chislehurst, Kent, BR7 6DE, United Kingdom
📞 020 84687045

Vccp 5th Floor, Greencoat House, Francis Street, London, SW1P 1DH, United Kingdom
📞 020 75929331

Vef(UK)Ltd City Reach, 5 Greenwich View Place, London, E14 9NN, United Kingdom
📞 020 75158660

Velocity Advertising Ltd 30 Gresse Street, London, W1T 1QR, United Kingdom
📞 020 74300204

WAA Wrens Court 58 Victoria Road, 58 Victoria Road, Sutton Coldfield, West Midlands, B46 2QL, United Kingdom
📞 0121 3211411

Walker Communications Ltd 43 High Street, Holywood, County Down, BT18 9AB, United Kingdom
📞 028 90425555

Wallace Barnaby 24 Hill Street, St Helier, Channel Islands, Jersey, JE2 4UA, United Kingdom
📞 01534 759807

Wallace Barnaby Advertising 11 Champ de L'Ouest, Le Vieux Mont Cochon, St Helier, Chanel Islands, Jersey, JE2 3UY, United Kingdom
📞 01534 759807

Wallace Barnaby Associates Sydney Vane House, Admiral Park, St Peter Port, Channel Islands, Guernsey, GY1 3YH, United Kingdom
📞 01534 759807

Walsh Trott Chick Smith Holden House, 57 Rathbone Place, London, W1T 1JU, United Kingdom
📞 020 79071200

Walters Associates The White Cottage, 1 School Lane, Aston, Stevenage, Hertfordshire, SG2 7HA, United Kingdom
📞 01438 880484

Warl Change Behavior Ltd 30-32 Gray'S Inn Road, London, WC1X 8HR, United Kingdom
📞 020 74000900

Web Diversity Ltd 20 Church Street, Twickenham, Middlesex, TW1 3NJ, United Kingdom
📞 020 88910299

Wentworth Communications Arden Hall, 66 Brooklands Road, Sale, Cheshire, M33 3SJ, United Kingdom
📞 0161 9736763

WFCA Integrated Leap House, Frog Lane, Tunbridge Wells, TN1 1YT, United Kingdom
📞 01892 510244

White Agency 61 North Bar Within, Beverley, North Humberside, HU17 8DG, United Kingdom
📞 01482 871878

White Space Communications Joseph Exley House, Dean Street, Barnsley, South Yorkshire, S70 6EX, United Kingdom
📞 01226 248000

Whitedoor Greener House, 66-68 Haymarket, London, SW1Y 4RF, United Kingdom
📞 020 74512999

Whiteworth-Smith 3 Brooklyn Cottages, Thurston Road, Great Barton, Bury St Edmunds, Suffolk, IP31 2PW, United Kingdom
📞 01359 232299

WHO Ltd Harris House, Moorbridge Rd, Bingham, Nottingham, NG13 8GG, United Kingdom
📞 01949 836468

Wieden & Kennedy UK Ltd 27 Wilkes Street, London, E1 6QF, United Kingdom
📞 020 71947000

Wild Wild West 5 Devonhurst Place, Heathfield Terrace, London, W4 4JD, United Kingdom
📞 020 87420855

William Murray PR Cygnet House, 12-14 Sidemham House, Croydon, Surrey, CR9 2ET, United Kingdom
📞 020 82561360

Williams Blake Reay Ltd 7/9 Lonsdale Gardens, Tunbridge Wells, Kent, TN1 1NU, United Kingdom
📞 01892 774200

Wolverhampton City Council Performance & Development, Civic Centre St Peters Square Wolverhampton, Wolverhampton, West Midlands, WV1 1SH, United Kingdom
📞 01902 556556

Wonderberry 41-43 Saffron Hill, London, EC1N 8FH, United Kingdom
📞 020 74049594

Woodreed Creative Consultancy 49 The Pantiles, Tunbridge Wells, Kent, TN2 5TE, United Kingdom
📞 01892 515025

Woolley Pau 36-37 Maiden Lane, Covent Garden, London, WC2E 7LJ, United Kingdom
📞 020 78361222

Workhead Ltd Queenhithe House, Kings Square, High Wycombe, Buckinghamshire, HP11 1RX, United Kingdom
📞 01494 444031

WPP Group plc Berger House, 36-38 Berkeley Square, London, W1J 5AJ, United Kingdom
📞 020 74082204

Wright Design & Advtg Ltd 83 West Regent Street, Glasgow, Lanarkshire, G2 2AX, United Kingdom
📞 0141 3312341

WWAV 1 Riverside, Manbre Road, London, W6 9WA, United Kingdom
📞 020 87358000

Wyatt International 72 Francis Road, Edgbaston, Birmingham, West Midlands, B16 8SP, United Kingdom
📞 0121 4548181

Yellow Pages Queens Walk, Reading, Berkshire, RG1 7PT, United Kingdom
📞 0800 605060

YOUNG PHILLIPS ADVERTISING Ltd Wellington Road, Bournemouth, Dorset, BH8 8JN, United Kingdom
📞 01202 298969

Zebra Crossing 23 Noel Street, London, W1F 8GT, United Kingdom
📞 020 72285500

Zenith Media Ltd 63-65 North Wharf Road, Paddington, London, W2 1LA, United Kingdom
📞 020 72984700

RECRUITMENT CONSULTANTS

Adrem 1-3 Dufferin Street, London, EC1Y 8NA, United Kingdom
📞 020 7562 8282/📠 020 7562 8283
✉ info@adrem.uk.com
🖳 www.adrem.uk.com

Agenda Recruitment 65 London Wall, London, United Kingdom EC2M 5TU,
📞 020 7496 9254
✉ info@agendarecruitment.co.uk
🖳 www.agendarecruitment.co.uk

Aquent, London, United Kingdom
📞 020 7404 0077/0161 237 3399/📠 020 7404 0088
🖳 www.aquent.co.uk

Artworkers Republic Unit 1.1, 11 Fashion Street, London, E1 6PX, United Kingdom
📞 020 7539 9400/📠 020 7539 9401
✉ info@artworkersrepublic.com
🖳 www.artworkersrepublic.com

Bespoke Studio 301, 24-28 Hatton Wall, Clerkenwell, London, EC1N 8JH, United Kingdom
✉ info@bespokecareers.com
🖳 www.bespokecareers.com

Blue Skies, London, United Kingdom
📞 020 8241 9070

Cream 14 Trinity Place, Windsor, Berkshire, SL4 3AS, United Kingdom
📞 01753 867856/📠 01753 865599
✉ info@the-creamery.co.uk
🖳 www.the-creamery.co.uk

Creative Career Partnership 5 Green Dragon Court,
London, SE1 9AW, United Kingdom
0870 901 7001/ 0870 901 7009
info@ccp.uk.com
www.ccp.uk.com

Creative People Barnett House, 53 Fountain Street,
Manchester, M2 2AN, United Kingdom
0161 235 6320/ 0161 235 6329
manchester@macpeople.co.uk
www.macpeople.co.uk

Creative Recruitment Ltd 17 Devonshire Square,
London, EC2M 4SQ, United Kingdom
020 7247 3458/ 020 7375 0096
perm@creativerecruitment.co.uk
www.creativerecruitment.co.uk

Design Studio People 37-38 Golden Square,
London, W1F 9LA, United Kingdom
020 7470 5555/ 0870 220 3874
jobs@designstudiopeople.com
www.designstudiopeople.com

Design Task Force 10 Denmark Street,
London, WC2H 8TD, United Kingdom
020 7240 0200/ 020 7240 9700
info@dtf.co.uk
www.dtf.co.uk

Devonshire, London, United Kingdom
020 7469 0800/ 020 7469 0801
creative@devonshire.co.uk
www.devonshire.co.uk

Fishtank Solutions Ltd 3rd Floor, 15 Colston Street,
Bristol, BS1 5AP, United Kingdom
0117 905 5160
www.fishtank.co.uk

Gabriele Skelton Ltd
146 New Cavendish Street,
London, W1W 6YQ, United Kingdom
020 7580 0666/ 020 7580 0660
info@gabrieleskelton.com
www.gabrieleskelton.com
See ad in showcase

Gallery Resources Limited Top Barn Offices,
Bownhill, Woodchester,
Gloucestershire, GL5 5PW, United Kingdom
0845 450 3200
info@galleryresources.co.uk
www.galleryresources.co.uk

Greythorn 21 Wilson Street,
London, EC2M 2SN, United Kingdom
020 7850 7446
creative@greythorn.co.uk
www.greythorn.com

Hudson York Farrell, 020 7638 0303/ 020 7638 4300
creativeservices@hyf.co.uk
www.hyf.co.uk

Mac People 80-81 St Martins Lane,
London, WC2N 4AA, United Kingdom
020 7240 0088/ 020 7240 0089
jobs@macpeople.co.uk
www.macpeople.co.uk

Major Players, 020 7836 4041/ 020 7836 4009
talk@majorplayers.co.uk
www.majorplayers.co.uk
See ad in showcase

Mustard Langdale House, 11 Marshalsea Road,
London, SE1 1EN, United Kingdom
020 7089 2625
jobs@mustardconsult.com
www.mustardconsult.com

Network 34 Mortimer Street, London, W1W 7JS,
United Kingdom
020 7580 5151/020 7580 6242
apply@network.cc
www.network.cc

Network - Scotland 21-23 Thistle Street,
Edinburgh, EH2 1DF, United Kingdom
0131 225 4111/ 0131 220 5633
apply@network.cc
www.network.cc

Periscope UK Ltd 6 Sherlock Mews,
London, W1U 6DW, United Kingdom
020 7563 9855
scope@periscopeuk.com
www.periscopeuk.com

Profiles Creative
08704 146 288
cr-recruit@profilescreative.com
www.profilescreative.com

Propel London 5th Floor,
23 Tavistock Street, Covent Garden,
London, WC2E 7NX, United Kingdom
020 7395 1300
design@propellondon.com
www.propellondon.com

Purple Business Design Centre, Islington,
London, N1 0QH, United Kingdom
020 7288 6700/ 020 7288 6730
purple@purple-consultancy.com
www.purple-consultancy.com

Recruit Media Regency House,
1-4 Warwick Street, W1R 5WB, United Kingdom
020 7758 4550
info@recruitmedia.co.uk
www.recruitmedia.co.uk

RP Cushing Elizabeth House, 39 York Road, Waterloo,
London, SE1 7NQ, United Kingdom
020 7401 6066/ 020 7401 8088
design@rpcushing.com
www.rpcushing.com

Source
The Penthouse, Colonial Buildings,
59-61 Hatton Garden, London,
EC1N 8LS, United Kingdom
020 3116 0000/020 3116 0011
info@sourcepersonnel.co.uk
www.sourcepersonnel.co.uk
See ad in showcase

The Book,
0113 218 3550
info@thebook.uk.com
www.thebook.uk.com

Third Edge 17a Ridinghouse Street, London, W1 7DS,
United Kingdom
020 7436 7930/ info@the3rdedge.com
www.the3rdedge.com
See ad in showcase

With Us Chesterfield House,
385 Euston Road, London, NW1 3AU,
United Kingdom
020 7391 5111/ 020 7391 5112
info@withus-recruit.com
www.withus-recruit.com

Workstation,
020 7371 7161
potential@workstation.co.uk
www.workstation.co.uk

Xchangeteam,
020 7025 4400/ 020 7925 4401
vgascoyne@xchangeteam.com
www.xchangeteam.com
See ad

FashShot.com is the UK's leading Ecommerce fashion photography provider, operating studios in London's Camden Town and across the country. A 12 strong full time photographer team guarantees quality creative performance on any size of project on the tightest of deadlines or when budgets are pressurised FashShot backs its Photographers with outstanding studio facilities, Europe's finest unmatched digital technology and shoot managers.

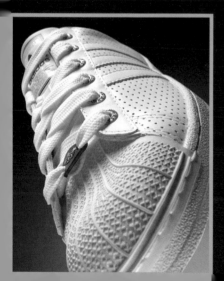